D1179709

LICENSED LAND SURVEYOR
TERRY FLETCHER
No. 5834
Exp.
STATE OF CALIFORNIA

SURVEYING

SURVEYING

fifth edition

By the late

HARRY BOUCHARD

*Professor of
Geodesy and Surveying
University of Michigan*

Revised by

FRANCIS H. MOFFITT

*Professor of
Civil Engineering
University of California*

INTERNATIONAL TEXTBOOK COMPANY

Scranton, Pennsylvania

INTERNATIONAL TEXTBOOKS IN CIVIL ENGINEERING

Consulting Editor

RUSSELL C. BRINKER

Professor of Civil Engineering
New Mexico State University

Fifth Printing, July 1968

Preface to Fifth Edition

Since the fourth edition of this book was published, new instrumentation has been developed to measure distances electronically. The material on this subject appearing in the fourth edition has been expanded and updated to incorporate these developments. Revisions and additions on electronic devices will be found particularly in Chapters 2 and 10. Chapter 10 has also been revised to include the latest classification for the accuracy of horizontal-control surveys, and to show triangulation computations performed by desk computers.

Sophisticated measuring systems that are now used in the fields of plane surveying, geodesy, and photogrammetry produce masses of data which must be reduced to reliable and useful form. As a result, the engineer and scientist must rely more heavily than heretofore on the methods of statistics and the adjustment of observations by the principles of least squares. Consequently, an introduction to these principles at an early stage in the career of the engineer is most desirable. The chapter on random errors has been expanded to establish the basis of least squares, and an appendix has been added to the book to show the development of the method of least squares in adjusting the more elementary surveying projects, namely, level and traverse nets and triangulation quadrilaterals. However, the principles developed in the book are not confined to surveying measurements. On the contrary, the engineer will find these principles applicable to any system of engineering measurement.

Control surveys of any extent should be tied to the state plane coordinate systems in order to upgrade the surveys and eliminate much duplicated effort on the part of agencies and individuals responsible for these surveys. With this objective in mind, and to encourage the use of the state coordinate systems, several examples have been included in Chapter 11. The refinement necessary for the conversion of grid and geodetic azimuths for long lines or for high-order surveys has also been introduced.

Some of the commonly used stereoscopic plotting instruments are described in the chapter on photogrammetry to present a general idea of the variation in the design and operation of these instruments. Measurements made with automatic devices to obtain earthwork data directly from stereoscopic models are discussed in Chapter 16.

The chapter on stadia measurements has been expanded to include optical distance-measuring devices other than the transit and the telescopic alidade. There are many possible applications of these instruments. However, the general unfamiliarity of the surveyor or engineer with their operation has caused a certain amount of indifference to their applications and use. This revision has been made to help rectify the situation.

New problems follow all but a few of the chapters. These problems should be solved by the student in order to increase his facility in the subject matter of the different chapters.

The revisor wishes to thank the instrument manufacturers and their representatives for kindly furnishing photographs for this revision.

Criticisms of portions of the fourth edition received from the teachers and students who have used the book, as well as from colleagues in the profession, have been extremely helpful in preparing this revision.

FRANCIS H. MOFFITT

Berkeley, California
June, 1965

Preface to Fourth Edition

The first edition of this book, written by the late Harry Bouchard, was published in 1935. It was revised by Professor Bouchard in 1940 and again in 1947. Each subsequent revision revealed the author's keen awareness of the changes taking place in the art and practice of surveying through the years in which the book enjoyed wide acceptance.

Professor Bouchard was in the process of revising the book at the time of his death in 1954. His untimely passing was indeed a great loss to the teaching profession, and especially to the teachers of surveying and mapping, who deeply respected his judgment and wisdom.

This fourth edition is a general revision of the previous edition. It includes several major changes in both presentation and subject matter.

A new chapter has been written on the basic principles of photogrammetry, a subject which has gained widespread interest and coverage in surveying curricula. This chapter includes the principles of a stereoscopic plotting instrument of simple design.

The use of accurate design topographic maps for determining earthwork quantities is explained in great detail. This addition is necessary to keep the student abreast of current methods in estimating volumes of cut and fill.

The chapter on state plane coordinate systems has been completely revised and expanded.

The uses of the subtense bar, the geodimeter, and the tellurometer have been introduced in the chapter on the measurement of horizontal distances. Numerous examples of the application of corrections for systematic errors in taping have also been included in this chapter.

A brief description of the automatic, or self-leveling, type of level has been included, and the use of the optical micrometer in leveling is explained. The adjustment of the tilting level has been added.

The chapter on random errors has been rewritten, and it now comes right after the chapters on the measurement of horizontal distances and leveling. It is located in this position because the nature of random errors presumably has been observed by the student in taping and leveling exercises. The chapter covers the nature and propagation of errors, weighted measurements, and the adjustment of simple measurements and weighted measurements.

The optical-reading repeating and direction theodolites are described in the chapter on the measurement of angles. Examples of various types of optical micrometers are given. Illustrations of several types of optical-reading instruments are shown.

The chapter on traverse computations has been extensively revised and has been expanded by the inclusion of several complete examples. Because of the development of the use of high-speed digital computers in surveying computations, the use of analytic geometry in the solution of surveying problems is discussed in detail.

The definition of the length of a circular curve has been restated to enable the student to better understand the computations involving deflection angles and chord lengths.

The determination of difference in elevation in stadia surveys is both explained and illustrated.

Triangulation computations have been expanded. The subject of trilateration and trilateration slope reductions is introduced in the chapter on triangulation.

The chapter on practical astronomy includes a procedure for observing the sun by bringing its image on a card and using the center-tangent method. This procedure is illustrated for additional clarity. Also the method of reducing the observations taken on the sun and plotting the results to verify their validity and eliminate mistakes is explained and amplified by illustration.

The only revisions in the chapter on U. S. Public Land Surveys are to note the latest manual and the current addresses of the repositories of field notes in the various states.

Sets of numerical problems follow all but a few of the chapters to enable the student to consolidate his understanding of the text material.

The revisor wishes to thank the instrument manufacturers and their representatives for so kindly furnishing photographs from which several of the illustrations were prepared.

FRANCIS H. MOFFITT

Berkeley, California
January, 1959

Contents

Measures of Precision. Propagation of Random Errors. Weighted Measurements. Simple Adjustment of Measurements. Adjustment of Weighted Measurements. Adjustment of a Level Circuit. Other Adjustments.

Astronomical Meridian. Magnetic Meridian. Assumed Meridian. Convergence of Meridians. Grid Meridian. Azimuth of a Line. Back Azimuth. Bearing of a Line. Back Bearing. Relation Between Azimuths and Bearings. The Magnetic Compass. Dip of the Compass Needle. Determining Directions with the Magnetic Compass. Magnetic Declination. Relation Between True and Magnetic Bearings and Azimuths.

Horizontal Angle. Measuring Angles by Tape. Laying off Angles with the Tape. Angles with Transit. Parts of the Transit. Transit Telescope. Rotation of Spindles. Horizontal Circle and Verniers. Vertical Circle and Vernier. Transit Stations. Setting up Transit. Measuring a Horizontal Angle. Double Centering. Angles by Repetition. Vertical Angle. Sighting with the Transit. Sources of Error in Transit Angles. Mistakes in Transit Angles. Repeating and Direction Instruments. Optical Reading Theodolites. Angles by Compass. Angles with the Plane Table. Description of Sextant. Measuring Angles with the Sextant. Precision of Sextant Angles. Accuracy Required in Measuring Angles. Precision of Angles Used in Trigonometric Computations.

Introduction. Measuring Interior Angles. Measuring Angles to the Right. Measuring Deflection Angles. Laying off Angles. Straight Line by Double Centering. Establishing Points on a Straight Line. Balancing-In. Random Lines. Intersection of Two Straight Lines. Obstacles on a Line. Parallel Lines. Location of a Point.

Traverse. Open Traverse. Closed Traverse. Interior-Angle Traverse. Deflection-Angle Traverse. Angle-to-the-Right Traverse. Traverse-by-Azimuth Method. Azimuth Traverse. Compass Traverse. Referencing a Traverse Station. Traverse Computation. Latitudes and Departures. Closure in Latitudes and Departures. Traverse Closure. Balancing a Traverse. Balancing by the Compass Rule. Balancing by Transit Rule. Least-Squares Adjustment. Remarks on Adjustments. Traverse Computation by Logarithms. Rectangular Coordinates. Adjustment of Traverse by Coordinate Adjustment. The Use of Rectangular Coordinates. Coordinates of Unoccupied Points. Location of a Line Based on Computations. Area from Rectangular Coordinates. Area from Latitudes and Double Meridian Distances. Areas from Maps. Area with One Curved Boundary. Errors in Areas. Significant Figures in Areas. Prob-

Use of Astronomy. Definitions. Time. Standard Time. Local
Time. Time by Radio. Observing the Sun with the Transit.
Observing a Star with the Transit. Time by Transit of the Sun.
Time by Altitude of the Sun. Time by Altitude of a Star.
Time by the Transit of a Star. Latitude. Latitude by Sun's
Altitude at Noon. Latitude by Observation on Circumpolar
Star. Latitude from Polaris at Any Hour Angle. Longitude.
Azimuth from Observations on Polaris at Elongation. Azimuth
from Observations on Polaris at Any Hour Angle. Solar Obser-
vation for Azimuth. Azimuth by Solar Attachment. Azimuth
by Equal Altitudes. Order of Making Observations.

Uses of Stadia. Principle of Transit Stadia Measurements.
Determination of Stadia Constant. Determination of Stadia
Interval Factor. Inclined Stadia Measurements. Beaman
Stadia Arc. Difference in Elevation Between Two Points.
Stadia Traverse. Details About a Point. Stadia Leveling.
Errors in Stadia Measurements. Errors in Stadia Elevations.
Telescopic Alidade. Self-Reducing Stadia Instruments. Dis-
tance Wedge. Reduction Tacheometer. Subtense Bar. Plane
Table. Plane-Table Traverse. Method of Radiation. Plane-
Table Leveling. Plane-Table Intersection. Plane-Table Resec-
tion. Three-Point Resection. Height of Instrument Following
Three-Point Resection. Errors in Plane-Table Surveys.

General Procedures. Scales and Accuracy. Methods of Representing Topography. Contour Lines. Field Methods. Cross-
Section Method. Methods of Interpolating. Contour Location
with Hand Level. Trace-Contour Method. Grid Method.
Controlling-Point Method.

Scope. Aerial Camera. Types of Aerial Photographs. Photo-
graphic Scale. Relief Displacement. Photograph Overlap.
Ground Control for Photographs. Mosaic. Radial-Line Plot.
Stereoscopy and Parallax. Stereoscopic Plotting Instruments.
Advantages and Disadvantages of Photogrammetric Mapping.

Remarks. Cross Sections. Preliminary Cross Sections. Final
Cross Sections. Cross-Sectioning with Slope Tape and Auto-
matic Leveling Rod. Distance Between Cross Sections. Calcu-
lation of Areas. Volume by Average End Areas. Volume by
Prismoidal Formula. Prismoidal Correction. Volumes from
Tables and Diagrams. Volume by Truncated Prisms. Volumes
from Topographic Maps. Earthwork Data from Photogram-
metric Model. Earthwork Quantities by Grading Contours.
Reservoir Volumes from Contour Maps. Mass Diagram.
Shrinkage. Computation of Mass Diagram. Calculation of
Overhaul. Economical Handling of Material.

1

Introduction

1-1. Surveying. The purpose of surveying is to locate the positions of points on or near the surface of the earth. Some surveys involve the measurement of distances and angles for the following reasons: 1) to determine horizontal positions of arbitrary points on the earth's surface; 2) to determine elevations of arbitrary points above or below a reference surface, such as mean sea level; 3) to determine the configuration of the ground; 4) to determine the directions of lines; 5) to determine the lengths of lines; 6) to determine the positions of boundary lines; and 7) to determine the areas of tracts bounded by given lines. Such measurements are data-gathering measurements.

In other surveys it is required to lay off distances and angles to locate construction lines for buildings, bridges, highways, and other engineering works, and to establish the positions of boundary lines on the ground.These distances and angles constitute layout measurements.

A survey made to establish the horizontal or vertical positions of arbitrary points is is known as a *control survey*. A survey made to determine the lengths and directions of boundary lines and the area of the tract bounded by these lines, or a survey made to establish the positions of boundary lines on the ground is termed a *cadastral, land, boundary,* or *property survey*. A survey conducted to determine the configuration of the ground is termed a *topographic survey*. The determination of the configuration of the bottom of a body of water is a *hydrographic survey*. Surveys executed to locate or lay out engineering works are known as *construction surveys*.

All surveys involve some computations, which may be made in the office or in the field or in both places.

Some types of surveys require very few computations, whereas others involve lengthy and tedious computations. In the study of surveying, therefore, the student not only must become familiar with the field operational techniques, but must also learn the mathematics applied in surveying computations.

1

1-2. Field Notes. When a survey is performed for the purpose of gathering data, then the field notes become the record of the survey. If the notes have been carelessly recorded and documented, falsified, lost, or made grossly incorrect in any way, the survey or a portion of the survey is rendered useless. Defective notes result in tremendous waste of both time and money. Furthermore, it will become obvious that, no matter how carefully the field measurements are made, the survey as a whole may be useless if some of those measurements are not recorded or if the meaning of any record is ambiguous.

The keeping of neat, accurate, complete field notes is one of the most exacting tasks. Although several systems of note-keeping are in general use, certain principles apply to all. The aim is to make the clearest possible notes with the least expenditure of time and effort. Detailed examples of forms of notes suited to the principal surveying operations will be given later.

All field notes should show when, where, for what purpose, and by whom the survey was made. The signature of the recorder should appear. Habits are formed by constant repetition. One of the best habits is to make each page of notes complete. The field notes of a surveyor or engineer are often presented as evidence in court cases, and such things as time and place and members of the field party may be of extreme importance.

A hard pencil—4H or harder—should be used to prevent smearing. The notebook should be of good quality, since it is subjected to hard usage. No erasures should be made, because such notes will be under suspicion of having been altered. If an error is made, a line should be drawn through the incorrect value and the new value should be inserted above. In some organizations the notes are kept in ink, but this is rather inadvisable unless a waterproof ink is used or unless there is no possible chance of the notes becoming wet.

Clear, plain figures should be used, and the notes should be lettered rather than written. The record should be made in the field book at the time the work is done, and not on scraps of paper to be copied into the book later. Copied notes are not original notes, and there are too many chances for making mistakes in copying or of losing some of the scraps. All field computations should appear in the book so that possible mistakes can be detected later.

It should always be remembered that the notes are frequently used by others than the person who makes them. For this reason, they should be so clear that there can be no possible chance of misinterpreting them.

If the numbers stamped on the field equipment are recorded, it may be possible to explain at some later date apparent discrepancies which were caused by some imperfection in the equipment. Thus, errors in linear measurements can sometimes be explained by a broken tape being improperly repaired.

1-3. Methods of Keeping Notes. There are four general methods of keeping notes: 1) by a written description of what has been done; 2) by means of a sketch on which all numerical values are shown; 3) by a tabulation of the numerical values; and 4) by a combination of these methods.

1) A detailed written description of what has been done is given in the notes for surveys made in connection with the subdivision of the public lands. However, for the usual surveys, such a description would likely be long and involved, and it would be difficult to pick out the numerical values that are to be used in the office computations. By means of sketches or by a proper tabulation of the field measurements, the notes are greatly simplified and yet the field operations will be perfectly apparent to one who has a knowledge of surveying.

2) In the case of a relatively simple survey, such as that of a piece of property with few sides, a sketch that is roughly to scale can be made, and all linear and angular values can be shown directly on the sketch.

3) Where many angles and distances are measured from the same point, as in the case of a topographic survey, a sketch showing all observed values would be hopelessly complicated. For this reason, the angles and distances are recorded in tabular form, care being taken to show clearly between what points the measurements are made. The notes for most leveling operations are recorded in tabular form.

4) On extensive surveys a combination of tabulated numerical values and sketches is used. Whenever there may be any doubt concerning field conditions, a sketch accompanies the numerical values. This sketch need not be drawn to scale; in fact, the doubt can usually be cleared up more easily by a distorted scale. The notes of most route surveys, as surveys for railroads, highways, canals, and transmission lines, are usually kept in this fashion. The numerical values are recorded on the left-hand page of the notebook, and the right-hand page is used for the sketch. If the notes start from the bottom of the page, and the various points and lines on the sketch are placed opposite the numerical values relating to them, the right-hand page will be a normally oriented map of what has been found on the ground.

1-4. Indexing of Notes. Since many isolated surveys may appear in the same notebook, an index in the front pages of the book will assist in locating any desired survey. Each notebook should bear a number. The owner's name and address should also appear to aid in its recovery in case of loss. Though desirable, it is not necessary that the notes for a given survey appear on consecutive pages. If separated, they should be cross-referenced. Some type of card index or loose-leaf index to all the books is extremely valuable. Property surveys should be indexed according to the name of the owner of the property and also according to the location of the property.

1-5. **Basic Definitions.** In order to gain a clear understanding of the procedures for making surveying measurements on the earth's surface, you must be familiar with the meanings of certain basic terms. The terms discussed here have reference to the actual figure of the earth.

A *spheroid* is an ellipse rotated on its shorter axis. The ideal figure of the earth is a spheroid having the actual axis of rotation as the shorter axis. Because of its relief, the earth's surface is not a true spheroid. However, an imaginary surface representing a mean sea level extending over its entire surface very nearly approximates a spheroid. This imaginary surface is used as the figure on which surveys of large extent are computed.

A *vertical line* at any point on the earth's surface is the line which follows the direction of gravity at that point. It is the direction which a string will assume if a weight is attached to the string and the string is suspended freely at the point. At a given point there is only one vertical line. The earth's center of gravity cannot be considered to be located at its geometric center, because vertical lines passing through several different points on the surface of the earth do not intersect in that point. In fact, all vertical lines do not intersect in any common point. A vertical line is not necessarily normal to the surface of the earth, nor even to the spheroid.

A *horizontal line* at a point is any line which is perpendicular to the vertical line at the point. At any point there are an unlimited number of horizontal lines.

A *horizontal plane* at a point is the plane which is perpendicular to the vertical line at the point. There is only one horizontal plane through a given point.

A *vertical plane* at a point is any plane which contains the vertical line at the point. There are an unlimited number of vertical planes at a given point.

A *level surface* is a continuous surface which is at all points perpendicular to the direction of gravity. It is exemplified by the surface of a large body of water at complete rest (unaffected by tidal action).

A *horizontal distance* between two given points is the distance between the points projected onto a horizontal plane. The horizontal plane, however, can be defined at only one point. For a survey the reference point may be taken as any one of the several points of the survey.

A *horizontal angle* is an angle measured in a horizontal plane between two vertical planes. In surveying this definition is effective only at the point at which the measurement is made or at any point vertically above or below it.

A *vertical angle* is an angle measured in a vertical plane.

The *elevation* of a point is its vertical distance above or below a given level surface.

The *difference in elevation* between two points is the vertical distance between two level surfaces containing the two points.

Plane surveying is that branch of surveying wherein all distances and horizontal angles are assumed to be projected onto one horizontal plane. A single reference plane may be selected for a survey where the survey is of limited extent. For the most part, this book deals with plane surveying.

Geodetic surveying is that branch of surveying wherein all distances and horizontal angles are projected onto the surface of the spheroid which represents mean sea level on the earth.

The surveying operation of leveling takes into account the curvature of the spheroidal surface in both plane and geodetic surveying. The leveling operation determines vertical distances and hence elevations and differences of elevation.

1-6. Units of Measurement. In English-speaking countries, the linear unit most commonly used is the foot, and the unit of area is the acre, which is 43,560 sq ft. In Europe and South America, distances are expressed in meters. This unit is also used by the United States Coast and Geodetic Survey, although the published results of leveling are expressed in feet.

On all United States government land surveys, the unit of length is the Gunter's chain, which is 66 ft long and is divided into 100 links, each of which is 0.66 ft or 7.92 in. long. A chain, therefore, equals ⅛₀ mile. This is a convenient unit where areas are to be expressed in acres, since 1 acre = 10 square chains. A distance of 2 chains 18 links can also be written as 2.18 chains. Any distance in chains can be readily converted into feet, if desired, by multiplying by 66.

In those portions of the United States that came under Spanish influences another unit, known as the vara, has been used. A vara is about 33 in. long. The exact length varies slightly in different sections of the Southwest, where the lengths of property boundaries are frequently expressed in this unit.

For purposes of computation and plotting, decimal subdivisions of linear units are the most convenient. Most linear distances are therefore expressed in feet and tenths, hundredths, and thousandths of a foot. The principal exception to this practice is in the layout work on a construction job, where the plans of the structures are dimensioned in feet and inches. Tapes are obtainable graduated either decimally or in feet and inches.

Volumes are expressed in either cubic feet or cubic yards.

Angles are measured in degrees ($°$), minutes ($'$), and seconds ($''$). One circumference $= 360°$; $1° = 60'$; $1' = 60''$. In astronomical work, some angles are expressed in hours (^{h}), minutes (^{m}), and seconds (^{s}). Since one circumference $= 24^h = 360°$, it follows that $1^h = 15°$ and $1° = \frac{1}{15}^h = 4^m$.

1-7. Metric Equivalents. The metric system, used extensively throughout the world, is finding a more widespread adoption in the English-speaking countries. This adoption has come about primarily to facilitate exchange of scientific and technical data with countries using the metric system.

The basis of distance measurement in the metric system is the meter, which is defined as 1,650,763.73 wavelengths of orange-red krypton gas with an atomic weight of 86 and at a specified energy level in the spectrum. This natural standard was adopted in lieu of a man-made physical standard, such as the International Prototype Meter Bar, because of the ever-present danger that the latter might be destroyed by accident or by a hostile act.

The meter is more commonly subdivided into the following units:

1 centimeter (cm)	$= 0.01$ meter
1 millimeter (mm)	$= 0.001$ meter
1 micron (μ)	$= 0.001$ mm $= 10^{-6}$ meter
1 millimicron (mμ)	$= 0.001\ \mu = 10^{-9}$ meter
1 Ångström (Å)	$= 0.1$ m$\mu = 10^{-10}$ meter

It was not until 1959 that the technical and scientific agencies of the United States and the United Kingdom adopted the following equivalence:

$$1\text{ U.S. inch} = 2.54\text{ cm}$$
$$1\text{ British inch} = 2.54\text{ cm}$$

The previous United States equivalent was 1 meter $= 39.37$ U.S. inches, or 1 U.S. inch $= 2.540005+$ cm. Since plane and geodetic surveys may involve very long distances, sometimes on the order of 200 miles, and since results of important nationwide surveys going back 40 years are still used, inconsistencies would be introduced if

the 1959 equivalence were adopted for surveying operations. Therefore, the previous equivalence of 1 meter = 39.37 U.S. inches is used
to define the *survey foot.*

1-8. Centesimal System. Many surveying and mapping instruments with angular scales are graduated in the centesimal system.
In this system, one circumference is divided into 400 grades$^{(g)}$. The
grade is divided into 100 centesimal minutes$^{(c)}$, and the minute is
subdivided into 100 centesimal seconds$^{(cc)}$. The degree value of the
grade is determined by the following equivalences:

$$400^g = 360°$$
$$1^g = 0.9°$$
$$0.01^g = 1^c = 0.009° = 0° \ 00' \ 32.4''$$
$$0.0001^g = 1^{cc} = 0.00009° = 0° \ 00' \ 0.32''$$

An angle expressed as 324.4625^g could also be expressed as 324^g 46^c
25^{cc}, but this latter notation would be much more awkward and
entirely unnecessary. If trigonometric tables based on centesimal
units are available, many computations are greatly simplified.

1-9. Errors and Mistakes. The value of a distance or an angle
obtained by field measurements is never exactly the true value, except
by chance. The measured value approaches the true value as the
number and size of errors in the measurements become increasingly
small. An error is the difference between the true value of a quantity
and the measured value of the same quantity. Errors result from
instrumental imperfections, personal limitations, and natural conditions affecting the measurements. Examples of instrumental errors
are: 1) a tape which is actually longer or shorter than its indicated
length; 2) errors in the graduations of the circles of an engineer's
transit; and 3) a defect in adjustment of a transit or level. Examples
of personal limitations are the observer's inability to bisect a target
or read a vernier exactly, his inability to maintain a steady tension
on the end of a tape, and his failure to keep a level bubble centered
at the instant at which a leveling observation is taken. Examples of
natural conditions affecting a measurement are temperature changes,
wind, refraction of a line of sight because of atmospheric conditions,
and magnetic attraction.

An error is either a *systematic error* or a *random error.* A systematic error is one the magnitude and algebraic sign of which can
theoretically be determined. If a tape is found to measure 99.94 ft
between the 0-ft mark and the 100-ft mark when compared with a
standard, then the full tape length introduces a systematic error of
+0.06 ft each time it is used to measure the distance between two

given points. If a tape is used at a temperature other than that at which it was compared with a standard, then the amount by which the nonstandard temperature increases or decreases the length of the tape can be computed from known characteristics of the material of which the tape is made.

A random error is one the magnitude and sign of which cannot be predicted. It can be plus or minus. Random errors tend to be small and tend to distribute themselves equally on both sides of zero. If an observer reads and records a value of, say, 6.242 ft when the better value is 6.243 ft, a random error of −0.001 ft has been introduced. When a man is holding a signal on which a transitman is sighting, his failure to hold the signal directly over the proper point will cause a random error of unknown size and algebraic sign in the measured angle. If, however, he *fixes* the signal eccentrically, the resultant error will be systematic.

A *mistake* is not an error, but is a blunder on the part of the observer. Examples of mistakes are failure to record each full 100 ft in taping, misreading a tape, interchanging figures, and forgetting to level an instrument before taking an observation. Mistakes are avoided by exercising care in making measurements, by checking readings, by making check measurements, and to a great extent by common sense and judgment. If, for example, a leveling rod is read and the reading is recorded as 7.13 ft, whereas the levelman knows that this is absurd since he is very nearly at the top of a 14-ft rod, then he is exercising common sense in suspecting a mistake.

The subject of random errors is considered in more detail in Chapter 4.

2

Measurement of
Horizontal Distances

2-1. Horizontal Distances. One of the basic operations of surveying is the determination of the distance between two points on the surface of the earth. In surveys of limited extent the distance between two points at different elevations is reduced to its equivalent horizontal distance either by the procedure used to make the measurement or by computing the horizontal distance from a measured slope distance. Distances are measured by scaling from a map, by pacing, by using an odometer, stadia, subtense, light waves, or radio waves, or by taping.

2-2. Pacing. Where approximate results are satisfactory, distances can be obtained by pacing. A person can best determine the length of his pace by walking over a line of known length several times, maintaining a natural walking stride. No particular advantage is obtained by developing a pace of, say, 3 ft. The natural stride is reproducible from day to day, whereas an artificial pace is not. The number of paces can be counted with a tally register or by the use of a pedometer, which is carried like a watch in a vertical position in the pocket.

2-3. Odometer. The odometer of a motor vehicle will give fairly reliable distances along highways, provided that the odometer is periodically checked against a known distance. This method can often be used to advantage on preliminary surveys where precise distances are not necessary. The odometer is used to obtain distances for writing descriptions of the locations of survey points and markers.

2-4. Stadia. The telescope of an engineer's transit usually contains three horizontal cross hairs. The top and bottom hairs are called stadia hairs. These are usually so spaced that each foot intercepted between them on a rod held vertically at a point some distance from the transit represents a distance of 100 ft from the transit. Most distances obtained in topographic surveys are determined by stadia measurements. Both horizontal and vertical distances can be obtained by means of stadia.

The self-reducing telemeter and the distance wedge, which are discussed in Chapter 13, are variations of the transit-stadia method for measuring horizontal distances.

The distance between two points can be determined by measuring the angle at one point between the two ends of a short base at the other point. The short base, consisting of either a graduated rod or a rod containing a target on each end, is oriented so that it is in a horizontal position and is also perpendicular to the line being measured. The rod is called a *subtense bar*. The distance is computed from the isosceles triangle formed by the known base on the rod and the sides of the opposite measured angle. The subtense bar is discussed in greater detail in Chapter 13.

2-5. Electronic Surveying. In recent years, several ingenious electronic systems have been developed for the express purpose of measuring distances in surveying with a high degree of accuracy. They are based on the invariant velocity of light or electromagnetic waves in a vacuum. It is of interest to note that the first of these instruments, which is called the geodimeter, was the outgrowth of instrumentation developed to determine an accurate value of the velocity of light. The value adopted by the International Union of Geodesy and Geophysics in 1957 is 299,792.5 kilometers per second, and it differs by only 0.4 kilometer from that determined by geodimeter instrumentation in 1951.

2-6. Geodimeter. The geodimeter, illustrated in Fig. 2-1, uses the length of a modulated wave or pulse of light as the unit of measurement to obtain the slope distance between the transmitting device and a reflecting mirror. The transmitter at one end of a line sends out modulated pulses of light at a carefully controlled frequency of approximately 30 megacycles. The reflecting mirror at the other end of the line reflects these pulses back to the transmitter. Circuitry in the transmitter then advances or delays the positions of the pulses, which vary in intensity from zero to a maximum, until a null point is reached between the outgoing and incoming pulses of light.

If the incoming pulse nullifies the outgoing pulse with no advance or delay, then the distance between the geodimeter and the mirror is an integral but unknown number of half wavelengths. The circuitry therefore measures the fractional part of the wavelength in

FIG. 2-1. The geodimeter. (Courtesy of
AGA Corp. of America.)

excess of a whole number required to cover the distance from the
transmitter to the mirror and back to the transmitter.

In Fig. 2-2, T is the transmitter, M is the mirror, D is the
intervening distance, L is the wavelength of the light pulse, and l is
the fractional part of a wavelength measured by the delay circuitry.
The number of whole wavelengths, however, is not known. Note that
if the mirror is moved away from or toward the transmitter by
exactly a half wavelength, or by any integral number of half wavelengths, the distance l will be the same in each case. By transmitting
a second set of pulses at a slightly different frequency and causing
the outgoing and incoming pulses to nullify one another, the number

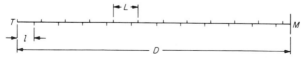

FIG. 2-2. Geodimeter principle.

of wavelengths and the fraction of a wavelength in the distance between the two points can again be determined. If the wavelength of each modulated wave is known, the distance between the transmitter and the reflector, in feet, can be determined. This distance can then be reduced to an equivalent horizontal or spheroidal distance by computation.

The geodimeter type of measuring device is used on long lines of control surveys. It is capable of limiting the error to 1 part in 100,000 or less. One serious drawback to the use of the instrument is its susceptibility to stray light from sources other than the reflector. The most successful geodimeter measurements are confined to night-time operations. Atmospheric conditions affect the accuracy of measurements to a slight degree and must be evaluated in order to eliminate errors from this source.

2-7. Micro-Wave Instrumentation. Whereas the geodimeter uses visible light waves for measurement, another type of electronic measuring device measures the transit time of micro waves traveling from a transmitter to a receiver and back to the transmitter. One such instrument is the tellurometer, shown in Fig. 2-3. Modulated micro waves are sent out from one end of the line to be measured on a carrier frequency of 3000 megacycles and at a modulated frequency

Fig. 2–3.   The tellurometer. (Courtesy of Tellurometer, Inc.)

of the order of 10 megacycles. A receiver at the other end of the line retransmits these waves back to the initial station. There being no measurable time loss during retransmission at the second station, the time lapse between initial transmission and final reception is that required for the waves to travel from one end of the line to the other and back. The incoming waves are out of phase with those being transmitted, unless the two stations are by chance separated by an exact number of half wavelengths. This phase shift is measured on an oscilloscope in the form of a circular trace, in which a small interruption is read against a circular scale. One full sweep represents approximately 15 meters. Thus, just as with the geodimeter, more than one modulated frequency must be used in order to determine the length of a line, since the length of the line is not usually known to the nearest 7½ meters ahead of time.

In order to eliminate the subjective method of determining the phase difference by interpreting the break in the circular sweep on the oscilloscope, the later models of the tellurometer incorporate a digital readout actuated by the control knob of the phase-comparison circuitry. Thus, the fractional part of a wavelength in the distance,

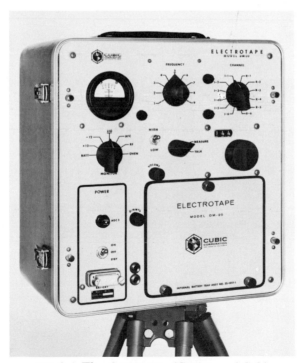

FIG. 2-4. The electrotape. (Courtesy of Cubic Corp.)

uncorrected for atmospheric conditions, is read directly on the digital display.

The electrotape, shown in Fig. 2-4, and the micro chain, shown in Fig. 2-5, operate on the same principle as the tellurometer, that is, by micro-wave phase comparison. Each of these devices also has a digital readout actuated by the control knob of the phase-comparison circuitry. All three instruments provide for radio communication between the operators at the two ends of the line. The transmitter operator can then let the receiver operator know which new frequency is being transmitted each time the frequency is changed.

A micro-wave instrument has an inherent error the magnitude of which is 1 inch or less plus or minus about one part per 250,000 of the measured length. Such an instrument has a distinct advantage in that the indicated distance is not affected by light of any kind. Since it uses a micro-wave radio system, it is operable either during

FIG. 2-5. The micro chain.
(Courtesy of Fairchild Camera and Instrument Corp.)

the day or at night, as well as under inclement weather conditions such as rain or fog. Atmospheric conditions, however, have a greater effect on a micro-wave system than they do on the geodimeter system. They must therefore be determined to a greater degree of accuracy when a micro-wave system is used.

One serious problem involved in the use of micro waves, which is not present when the geodimeter is used, is the error in the measured distance due to strong reflections of the waves off the intervening terrain. Such reflected waves can cause a faulty distance (l in Fig. 2-2) to be displayed. Since the displayed distance is the fractional part of a wavelength, then at different frequencies the displayed distance will be different for reflected waves than for direct rays in a cyclic manner. This cyclic variation at different frequencies is called *swing*. However, if enough different frequencies are used, say ten or more, taking the average of the resulting distance determinations should tend to eliminate the effect of swing.

Detailed descriptions of the electronic measuring systems, and the operational procedures involved in their use, are outside the scope of this book.

2-8. Chains. Two kinds of chains were formerly used in surveying, namely, the 100-ft engineer's chain and the 66-ft Gunter's chain. Each kind is divided into 100 links. A link of an engineer's chain is therefore 1 ft long, and a link of a Gunter's chain is only 0.66 ft or 7.92 in. long. Such chains are seldom, if ever, used at present. Although the 66-ft chain is still employed as a unit of length in the survey of the public lands and of some farm lands, the actual field measurements are made with steel tapes graduated in chains and links. If the distances recorded are in chains, a chain of 66 ft is implied.

2-9. Tapes. Steel tapes for most surveying operations are graduated in feet and decimal parts of a foot. Their lengths vary from 3 to 1000 ft, although 50 ft and 100 ft are the more common lengths. Lightweight tapes may be graduated to hundredths of a foot for the entire length. For moderate precision, a heavy band of steel with foot graduations throughout, and with only the two end feet further graduated to tenths or hundredths, may be used.

As most engineering and architectural plans show dimensions in feet and inches, a tape graduated in feet and inches is an advantage on construction work for layout purposes.

Tapes graduated in meters are used in most countries where English is not the official language. These tapes are also used on most geodetic work in English-speaking countries.

Tapes of cloth, or of cloth containing threads of bronze or brass, are sometimes used where low precision is permissible and where a steel tape might be broken, as in cross-sectioning for a railroad or a highway.

For extreme precision an invar tape, made of an alloy of steel and nickel, is used. The advantage of a tape of this material is that its coefficient of expansion is about one-thirtieth that of steel, and hence its length is not so seriously affected by temperature changes. However, since such a tape is expensive and must be handled very carefully to prevent kinking, invar tapes are not used for ordinary work.

2-10. **Equipment Used for Taping.** For the direct measurement of a line several hundred feet long, the equipment used consists of a 100-ft steel tape, two plumb bobs, one or more line rods, a set of taping pins, and, if the ground is hilly, a hand level. These items are shown in Fig. 2-6.

Line rods, also called range poles, are from ⅜ in. to more than 1 in. in diameter and from 6 to 8 ft long. They are pointed at one end and are painted with alternate foot-long bands of white and red. The rods are used to sight upon and thus keep the forward and rear ends of the tape on the line that is being measured.

Taping pins are used to mark the positions of the ends of the tape on the ground while a measurement is in progress. A taping pin may be a heavy spike, but is usually a piece of No. 10 wire that is

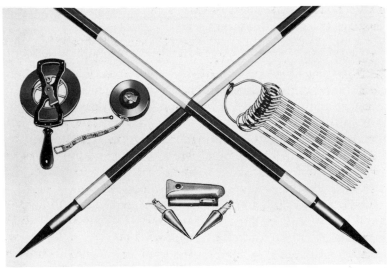

Fig. 2–6.   Equipment used for taping.
(Courtesy of W. & L. E. Gurley Co.)

10 to 18 in. long, is sharpened at one end, and is provided with an eye at the other end. Pieces of colored cloth can be tied to the eyes to make the pins more visible in tall grass or weeds.

The hand level is used to keep the two ends of the tape in the same horizontal plane when a measurement is made over rough or sloping ground.

The plumb bobs are used to project a point on the ground up to the tape, or to project a point on the tape down to the ground.

Some tapes are kept on reels when not in use. But a metal tape must be entirely removed from the reel when any length other than a few feet is to be measured. If such a tape is not supplied with thongs on both ends with which to hold the tape, a taping pin is slipped through the eye at the end of the tape and used as a handle. A tape which is thrown together in the form of a series of loops when not in use must be carefully unwrapped and checked for short kinks before it can be used for measurement. As long as a tape is stretched straight, it will stand any amount of tension that two men can apply. If kinked or looped, however, a very slight pull is sufficient to break it.

2-11. Measurements with Tape Horizontal. The horizontal distance between two points can be obtained with a tape either by keeping the tape horizontal or by measuring along the sloping ground and applying a correction to the measured length. For extreme precision, such as is required in the length of a base line in a triangulation system, the latter method is used. This method is also advantageous where steep slopes are encountered and it would be difficult to obtain the horizontal distance directly.

For moderate precision where the ground is level and fairly smooth, the tape can be stretched directly on the ground, and the ends of the tape lengths can be marked by taping pins or by scratches on a paved area. Where the ground is level but ground cover prevents laying the tape directly on the ground, both ends of the tape are held at the same distance above the ground by the forward tapeman and the rear tapeman. The tape is preferably held somewhere between knee height and waist height. The graduations on the tape are projected to the ground by means of the plumb bobs. The plumb-bob string is best held on the tape graduation by clamping it with the thumb, so that the length of the string can be altered easily if necessary. When a tape is supported throughout its length on the ground and subjected to a given tension, a different value for the length of a line will be obtained than when the tape is supported only at the two ends and subjected to the same tension. See Sec. 2-19. Where fairly high accuracy is to be obtained, the method of support must be recorded in the field notes, provided that both methods of support are used on one survey. Experienced tapemen should obtain as good results by plumbing the ends of the tape over the marks as they will obtain by having the tape supported on the ground.

When the ground is not level, either of two methods may be used. The first is to hold one end of the tape on the ground at the higher point, to raise the other end of the tape until it is level, either by estimation or with the aid of the hand level, and then to project the tape graduation over the lower point to the ground by means of a plumb bob. The other method is to measure directly on the slope as described in Sec. 2-13. These methods are shown in Fig. 2-7.

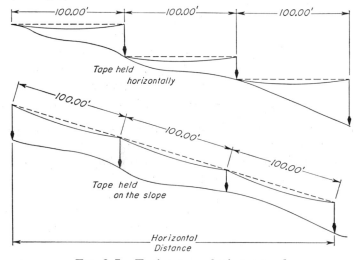

Fig. 2–7.   Taping over sloping ground.

For high precision, a taping tripod or taping buck must be used instead of a plumb bob. Such a tripod is shown in Fig. 2-8. Taping tripods are usually used in groups of three, the rear tripod then being carried to the forward position. A pencil mark is scribed at the forward tape graduation, and on the subsequent measurement the rear tape graduation is lined up with this mark in order to carry the measurement forward. Since taping is usually done on the slope when tripods are used, the elevations of the tops of the tripods must be determined at the same time the taping proceeds. The elevations, which are determined by leveling, give the data necessary to reduce the slope distances to horizontal distances as discussed in Sec. 2-13.

The head tapeman carries the zero end of the tape and proceeds toward the far end of the line, stopping at a point approximately 100 ft from the point of beginning. The rear tapeman lines in the for-

FIG. 2-8. Taping tripod.

ward end of the tape by sighting on the line rod at the far end of the line. Hand signals are used to bring the head tapeman on line. The rear tapeman takes a firm stance and holds the tape close to his body with one hand, either wrapping the thong around his hand or holding a taping pin which has been slipped through the eye of the tape. Standing to the side of the tape, he plumbs the 100-ft graduation over the point on the ground marking the start of the line. The tip of the plumb bob should be less than ⅛ in. above the ground point.

The head tapeman applies the tension to be used, either by estimation or by means of a spring balance fastened to the zero or forward end of the tape. At approximately the correct position on the ground, he clears a small area where the taping pin will be set. After again applying the tension, the head tapeman waits for a vocal signal from the rear tapeman indicating that the latter is on the rear point. When the plumb bob has steadied and its tip is less than ¼ in. from the ground, the head tapeman dips the end of the tape slightly so that the plumb bob touches the ground. He then sets a taping pin at the tip of the plumb bob to mark the end of the first full tape length. The pin is set at right angles to the line and inclined at an angle of about 45° with the ground away from the side on which the rear tapeman will stand for the next measurement. The tape is then stretched out again to check the position of the pin. The notekeeper records the distance, 100.00 ft, in the field notes. The tape is advanced another tape length, and the entire process is repeated.

If the taping advances generally downhill, the head tapeman checks to see that the tape is horizontal by means of the hand level. If the taping advances generally uphill, the rear tapeman checks for level.

When the end of the line is reached, the distance between the last pin and the point at the end of the line will usually be a fractional part of a tape length. The rear tapeman holds the particular full-foot graduation that will bring the subgraduations at the zero end of the tape over the point marking the end of the line. The head tapeman rolls the plumb-bob string along the subgraduations with his thumb until the tip of the plumb bob is directly over the ground point marking the end of the line.

Two types of end graduations are shown in Fig. 2-9. In view (a),

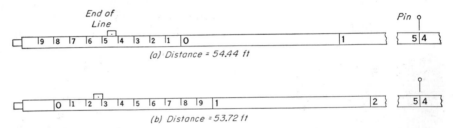

FIG. 2–9.   Graduations at end of tape.

the subgraduations are outside the zero mark, and the fractional part of a foot is added to the full number of feet. Hence, the distance is 54 + 0.44 = 54.44 ft. In view (b), the subgraduations are between the zero and the 1-ft graduation, and the fractional part of a foot must be subtracted from the full number of feet. So the distance is 54 − 0.28 = 53.72 ft. Because of the variation in the type of end graduations, the rear tapeman must call out the actual foot mark he holds, and both the head tapeman and the notekeeper must agree that the value recorded in the field notes is the correct value.

Where the slope is too steep to permit bringing the full 100-ft length of the tape horizontal, the distance must be measured in partial tape lengths, as shown in Fig. 2-10. It is then necessary to enter a series of distances in the field notes. Some or all of them will be less than 100 ft. For a partial tape length, the head tapeman holds the zero end and the rear tapeman holds a convenient whole foot mark which

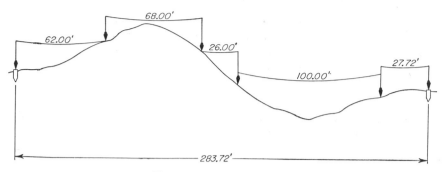

FIG. 2-10. Breaking tape.

will allow the selected length of tape to be horizontal. When the forward pin is set, this partial tape length is recorded in the field notes. The head tapeman then advances with the zero end of the tape, and the rear tapeman again picks up a convenient whole foot mark and plumbs it over the pin. Each partial tape length is recorded as it is measured, or as the forward pin is set. In Fig. 2-11 is illustrated the use of a device called a tape clamp for holding a tape at any place other than at an end.

All distances should be taped both forward and backward, to obtain a better value of the length of the line and to detect or avoid

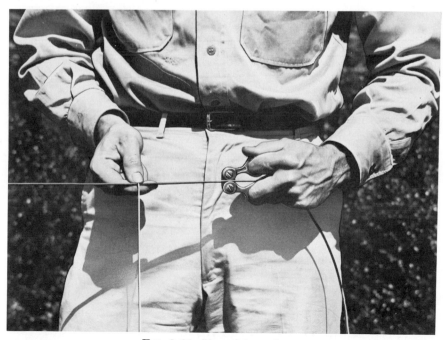

FIG. 2-11. Use of tape clamp.

mistakes. When the backward measurement is made, the new positions of the pins should be completely independent of their previous positions. This practice eliminates the chance of repeating a mistake.

2-12. Tension. Most steel tapes are correct in length at a temperature of 68 deg F when a tension of 10 to 12 lb is used and the tape is supported throughout the entire length. If this same tension is used when the tape is suspended from the two ends, the horizontal distance between the ends of the tape will be shorter than the nominal length. The amount of the shortening depends on the length and the weight of the tape. A light 100-ft tape weighs about 1 lb. Such a tape, when suspended from the two ends, would be shortened about 0.042 ft. A heavy 100-ft tape weighs about 3 lb and would be shortened about 0.375 ft. Some engineers attempt to eliminate this error by increasing the tension used. The tension for the light tape is then increased to about 18 lb. It is practically impossible to eliminate the error in the heavy tape by this method, as the tension would have to be increased to about 50 lb. Generally, less tension is used and a correction is applied to each measured length.

2-13. Slope Measurements. Where the slopes are considerable or where extreme accuracy is required, measurements are made directly along the slopes and corrections are applied to obtain the horizontal distances. For computing the correction, either the angle with the horizontal or the vertical distance between the two ends of the tape must be known. If the distance along the slope is s, and the slope makes an angle a with the horizontal, the corrected horizontal distance is

$$H = s \cos a \qquad (2\text{-}1)$$

If a table of natural versed sines is available, the horizontal distance can be obtained from the formula

$$H = s - s \text{ vers } a \qquad (2\text{-}2)$$

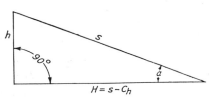

F ɪɢ. 2–12. Slope correction.

Where the vertical distance between the ends of an inclined measurement, as the height h in Fig. 2-12, is known, the horizontal distance may be readily found by subtracting a correction C_h from the inclined distance s. A formula for this correction may be derived as follows: In the right-angled triangle in the illustration, $s^2 = h^2 + (s - C_h)^2$; hence, $s^2 - h^2 = (s - C_h)^2$, and

$$C_h = s - (s^2 - h^2)^{1/2}$$

Since the quantity $(s^2 - h^2)^{1/2}$ may be expressed in the form $s - (h^2/2s) - (h^4/8s^3) \ldots$,

$$C_h = \frac{h^2}{2s} + \frac{h^4}{8s^3} + \cdots \tag{2-3}$$

For moderate slopes, the first term of this correction is sufficient. An inspection of the second term will show when it should be used. Thus, if the vertical distance is 10 ft in a 100-ft slope distance, the second term is $10^4/(8 \times 100^3) = 1/800$, or about 0.001 ft. When the vertical distance is 25 ft, the second term increases to $25/512 = 0.049$ ft.

2-14. Sources of Errors in Taped Measurements. The principal sources of error in linear measurements made with a tape are: 1) incorrect length of tape; 2) tape not horizontal; 3) changes in temperature; 4) incorrect tension; 5) sag; 6) incorrect alignment; 7) tape not straight; 8) mistakes; 9) random error.

2-15. Error from Incorrect Length. Under field conditions, the actual length of a tape is seldom exactly its designated length. The actual length can be determined by comparing it with a known distance, or by sending the tape to the Bureau of Standards at Washington, D. C. For a small fee, the Bureau will furnish its length at a known temperature and under any tension that may be specified, and also its coefficient of expansion. The given length will be for the tape supported throughout its entire length, suspended from the two ends, or supported at the two ends and the middle point, as specified.

It is obvious that every tape length measured with a tape of incorrect length will be in error and that the total error from this source will be in direct proportion to the number of tape lengths measured.

2-16. Tape not Horizontal. If the tape is assumed to be horizontal but actually is inclined, an error is introduced. The amount of this error C_h can be computed from Eq. 2-3 or may be taken as $h^2/2s$. If one end of a 100-ft tape is 1.41 ft higher or lower than the other, the error will amount to 0.01 ft. It should be noted that the error is proportional to the square of the vertical distance. When one end is 2.82 ft above or below the other, the error increases to 0.04 ft.

Errors from this source are cumulative and may be considerable when measuring over hilly ground. The error can be kept at a minimum by using a hand level to determine when the tape is horizontal.

2-17. **Changes in Temperature.** The coefficient of expansion of steel is about 0.0000065 per degree Fahrenheit. As a difference of 15 deg in temperature will cause a change in length of nearly 0.01 ft in a 100-ft tape, a measurement made with a tape on an extremely hot day in the summer cannot be expected to agree with one made during zero weather.

If the temperature remains constant and is different from that at which the tape was standardized, the resulting error will be cumulative and in direct proportion to the number of tape lengths measured. When the field temperature differs considerably from the standard, the temperature should be determined, and a correction should be applied to the measured length.

The amount of the correction for temperature is determined by the formula

$$C_t = L \, \alpha \, (T - T_s) \tag{2-4}$$

where C_t = correction to be applied, in feet;
L = length of the tape actually used, in feet;
α = coefficient of thermal expansion;
T = temperature at which the measurement is made;
T_s = temperature at which the tape was standardized.

Since the temperature of the tape may be considerably different from that of the surrounding air on a bright day, important measurements should be made on a cloudy day, early in the morning, or late in the afternoon.

2-18. **Incorrect Tension.** The error caused by applying incorrect tension to the tape is relatively unimportant. The correction to the measured length because of variation in tension can be computed from the following formula:

$$C_p = \frac{(P - P_s) \, L}{A E} \tag{2-5}$$

where C_p = correction per tape length, in feet;
P = tension applied, in pounds;
P_s = standard tension, in pounds;
L = length, in feet;
A = cross-sectional area, in square inches;
E = modulus of elasticity of the steel.

The modulus of elasticity of steel is about 28,000,000 to 30,000,000 psi (pounds per square inch).

A light tape, weighing about 1 lb, will have a cross-sectional area of about 0.0025 sq in. An increase of 10 lb in tension will stretch a

100-ft tape about 0.013 ft. The same increase with a heavy tape, weighing about 3 lb, will produce a change in length of but 0.003 ft.

On careful work, a spring balance is used for maintaining a constant tension. If the spring balance is not used, errors from incorrect tension will tend to be compensating, since the tensions applied to the tape may be either greater or less than the standard tension. The tendency is usually to underpull, rather than to exceed the standard tension.

2-19. Sag. If a tape has been standardized when supported throughout its entire length, a correction must be applied to every measurement that is made with the tape suspended from the two ends, or the tension must be increased. A tape suspended in this way will take the form of a catenary and the horizontal distance between the two ends will be less than when the tape is supported throughout its entire length. If the amount of the sag is such that the center of a 100-ft tape is about 7⅜ in. below the two ends, the measured distance has been shortened by 0.01 ft. The correction for sag is given by the formula

$$C_s = n \frac{w^2 l^3}{24 P^2} \tag{2-6}$$

where C_s = correction for sag, in feet;
n = number of unsupported lengths;
w = weight per foot of tape, in pounds;
l = unsupported length, in feet;
P = tension applied, in pounds.

When a tape is suspended from the two ends and subjected to the standardized tension for the tape supported throughout its length, the observed distance is always greater than the true distance, and the error due to sag is constant.

Error from sag can be eliminated by applying the necessary corrections to the observed distances or, in the case of a light tape, by increasing the tension sufficiently to compensate for the effect of sag. When a tape having a total weight of W pounds is supported at the two ends, this increased tension P_n, which is called the normal tension for the tape, may be found by either of the following formulas:

$$P_n = \frac{0.204 W \sqrt{AE}}{\sqrt{P_n - P_s}} \tag{2-7}$$

or

$$P_n = \sqrt[3]{\frac{AEW^2}{24}} \tag{2-8}$$

Equation 2-7 is more exact, but must be solved by trial.

For a light tape, the tension would be increased from 10 lb to about 18 lb. For a heavy tape, the normal tension would be about 50 lb, which would be difficult to apply in practice.

For extremely accurate work the tape is supported at enough points to render the error due to sag negligible. Or the tape is standardized when it is supported in the manner in which it is to be used in the field.

2-20. Incorrect Alignment. If a field measurement comprises more than one tape length and the points marking the ends of the various lengths are not along a straight line, the measured length will be too great. The amount of error for any given tape length may be computed from Eq. 2-3, where h is the amount one end of the tape is off line. To produce an error of 0.01 ft in a 100-ft measurement, one end of the tape would have to be 1.41 ft off line. Under normal circumstances the rear tapeman should be able to keep the forward tapeman much closer to the true line than this, and the error from this source should be practically negligible. For measurements of high precision the tapemen can be kept on line with a transit.

2-21. Tape not Straight. If the tape is not stretched straight, as when it is being bent either horizontally or vertically around trees or bushes, or is blown by a strong wind, the measured length will be too great. The error is the least when the obstruction is near the middle of the tape. If the middle point of a 100-ft tape is 0.71 ft or about 8½ in. off line, the resulting error in length is 0.01 ft. Errors from this source are cumulative.

2-22. Applying Corrections to Tape Measurements. In order to illustrate the application of corrections to tape measurements, the following examples are given. Notice that these corrections may be computed by slide rule.

EXAMPLE 2-1. A steel tape is standardized at 68 deg F under a tension of 15 lb when supported throughout its entire length, and the distance between the zero mark and the 100-ft mark is 99.98 ft. The tape weighs 0.013 lb/ft and has a cross-sectional area of 0.0030 sq in. In the field this tape is used under a 15-lb tension and is supported at the ends only, and the temperature of the tape is recorded as 88 deg F throughout the measurement. A series of distances are measured with the tape held horizontal, and the observed distances are recorded as 100.00, 100.00, 100.00, and 57.22 ft. What is the total actual or true distance after corrections for systematic errors have been applied?

Solution: The total observed distance is 357.22 ft. The errors for incorrect length, for temperature, and for incorrect tension are all in direct proportion to the length of the measurement. Therefore, the total correction for incorrect length is

$$-0.02 \times 3.57 = -0.071 \text{ ft}$$

and the total correction for temperature is

$$C_t = 357.22 \times 0.0000065 \times (88 - 68) = + 0.046 \text{ ft}$$

The correction for incorrect tension is zero, since the standard pull was used when the measurements were made.

For computing the correction for sag, the three 100-ft measurements are treated together and the 57-ft measurement is treated separately. For the three 100-ft measurements,

$$C_s = 3 \times \frac{0.013^2 \times 100^3}{24 \times 15^2} = -0.094 \text{ ft}$$

For the 57-ft measurement,

$$C_s = \frac{0.013^2 \times 57.2^3}{24 \times 15^2} = -0.006 \text{ ft}$$

The total sag correction is −0.100 ft.

The total correction to be applied to the measured distance is −0.071 + 0.046 −0.100 = −0.125 ft. To the nearest hundredth, it is −0.13 ft. So the corrected distance is 357.09 ft.

EXAMPLE 2-2. A steel tape is standardized at 68 deg F under a tension of 15 lb when supported at the two ends only, and the distance between the zero mark and the 100-ft mark is 99.972 ft. The total weight of the tape is 2.80 lb, and its cross-sectional area is 0.0065 sq. in. For steel E is assumed to be 30,000,000 psi. What is the distance between the zero and 100-ft marks when the tape is supported at the two ends only, the tension is 25 lb, and the standard temperature prevails?

Solution: First determine the distance when the tape is supported throughout and the tension is 15 lb. Then determine the distance for support throughout and a 25-lb pull. Finally determine the distance when the tape is supported only at the two ends under a 25-lb pull. When the tape is supported throughout under a 15-lb pull, the distance between the end graduations will be greater than that with the tape supported only at the ends by the following amount:

$$C_s = \frac{0.028^2 \times 100^3}{24 \times 15^2} = 0.145 \text{ ft}$$

The distance for support throughout and a 15-lb pull is

$$99.972 + 0.145 = 100.117 \text{ ft}$$

When the tension is increased to 25 lb with the tape supported throughout, the additional increase in length is

$$C_p = \frac{(25 - 15) \times 100}{0.0065 \times 30,000,000} = 0.005 \text{ ft}$$

The distance for support throughout and a 25-lb pull is 100.122 ft.

Finally, when the support is taken away and the tape is supported only at the ends under a 25-lb pull, the distance will be less than that for support throughout. The correction is

$$C_s = \frac{0.028^2 \times 100^3}{24 \times 25^2} = 0.052 \text{ ft}$$

The distance between end graduations when the tape is supported at the ends only under a tension of 25 lb is 100.070 ft.

EXAMPLE 2-3. A steel tape with a cross-sectional area of 0.004 sq in. and weighing 2.00 lb has a length of 100.03 ft between the zero and 100-ft marks when supported throughout at 68 deg F and subject to a tension of 12 lb. This tape is used to measure a distance along a uniform 4-per cent grade and is supported throughout during the measurement. The tension applied is 25 lb. The temperature of the tape is 36 deg F. The measured distance is recorded as 1252.44 ft. What is the corrected distance?

Solution: All errors affecting this measurement are in direct proportion to the distances considered. So the problem can be solved by determining the actual horizontal distance between the zero and 100-ft marks when the tape is being used and multiplying this distance by the ratio of 1252.44 to 100. The corrections per tape length are as follows:

$$C_h = \frac{4^2}{2 \times 100} = -0.080 \text{ ft}$$

$$C_t = 100 \times 0.0000065 \times (36 - 68) = -0.021 \text{ ft}$$

$$C_p = \frac{(25 - 12) \times 100}{0.004 \times 30,000,000} = +0.011 \text{ ft}$$

$$C_s = 0$$

The horizontal distance between the zero and 100-ft marks is, therefore,

$$100.03 - 0.080 - 0.021 + 0.011 = 99.940 \text{ ft}$$

The required distance is

$$99.940 \times \frac{1252.44}{100} = 1251.69 \text{ ft}$$

To permit the use of a slide rule, the total correction may be computed and applied to the measured distance. For every 100 ft of measured distance, the actual horizontal distance is only 99.940 ft. Therefore in 1252.44 ft of measured distance, a total of 12.52 × 0.060, or 0.75 ft, must be subtracted. So the result is 1251.69 ft as before.

This problem can also be solved by computing the individual corrections for the entire line rather than for each 100-ft measurement. The calculations, which may be performed with a slide rule, follow:

$$\text{Correction for incorrect length} = 12.52 \times 0.03 = +0.38 \text{ ft}$$

$$h = 4 \times 12.52 = 50.08 \text{ ft}$$

$$C_h = \frac{50.08^2}{2 \times 1252.44} = -1.00 \text{ ft}$$

$$C_t = 1252.44 \times 0.0000065 \times (36 - 68) = -0.26 \text{ ft}$$

$$C_p = \frac{(25 - 12) \times 1252.44}{0.004 \times 30,000,000} = +0.14 \text{ ft}$$

$$C_s = 0$$

Total correction $= + 0.38 - 1.00 - 0.26 + 0.14 = -0.74$ ft

Correct distance $= 1252.44 - 0.74 = 1251.70$ ft

The slight difference between this result and the first value is due to rounding off errors.

2-23. Random Taping Errors. Random errors are introduced into taping measurements from several causes. Some of these are the following: 1) error in determining temperature of tape; 2) failure to apply the proper tension; 3) wind deflecting the plumb bob; 4) taping pin not set exactly where the plumb bob touched the ground; 5) inability of the tapeman to steady the plumb bob; 6) inability of the observer to estimate the last place in reading between graduations. Random errors and their effects on measurements will be discussed more fully in Chapter 4.

2-24. Precision Required in Linear Measurements. The precision required in any particular case will depend entirely on the use to be made of the results. Thus, if the data are being secured for the preparation of a topographic map that is to be drawn to a scale of 1 in. $= 10,000$ ft, many of the shorter distances can be estimated, since distances on the map cannot be plotted much closer than to the nearest 0.02 in. This corresponds to 200 ft on the ground, and many distances can be estimated to within 50 ft, which is more than sufficiently accurate.

As another example, let it be supposed that the area of a rectangular piece of ground about 50 ft by 100 ft is required to be accurate to the nearest square foot. The approximate area will be 5000 sq ft, and the computed area will be expressed to four significant figures. Since the measured distances must be accurate to that many figures, the shorter lengths should probably be measured to 0.001 ft and the longer ones to 0.01 ft.

Linear measurements are frequently used with angular ones. When this is done, the precision should be such that the effect of errors in linear measurements will equal the effect of errors in the angular measurements. (See Sec. 6-26.) If the angles of the survey are not read by means of a vernier but are obtained by estimation, it would be a waste of effort to measure the distances to the nearest thousandth of a foot. If the angles are measured to seconds, the linear measurements must be correspondingly accurate, and stadia measurements would not be sufficiently precise.

2-25. Specifications for Linear Measurements. In the preceding articles the various sources of error in linear measurements have been discussed. The principal sources of error in any tape length are those due to the incorrect length of the tape, variations in temperature and tension, incorrect determination of slope, and inaccurate marking of the tape end. These errors may either increase or decrease the length of the measurement. The total random error in any tape length may be assumed equal to the square root of the sum of the squares of the maximum individual errors.

Specifications for any desired precision can be prepared from a knowledge of these errors. Thus, if the actual error is not to exceed 1/5000, the following limits for the various errors in 100 ft would suffice:

Length of tape to be known within 0.01 ft. Maximum error, ± 0.01 ft.

Temperature to be known within 10 deg F. Maximum error, ± 0.006 ft.

Tension to be known within 5 lb. Maximum error, ± 0.005 ft.

For slopes averaging 5 per cent, vertical distance to be known within 0.2 ft. Maximum error, ± 0.01 ft.

Tape lengths to be marked within 0.01 ft. Maximum error, ± 0.01 ft.

Alignment errors to be eliminated by keeping tape on line by transit.

Effect of sag to be eliminated by having tape standardized when suspended from the two ends.

PROBLEMS

2-1. The length of a line given on a map is 56 chains 42 links. What is the corresponding length in feet?

2-2. The length of a line is given as 56,545.28 meters. How many survey feet are contained in this line?

2-3. A distance is measured on a constant slope between two points. The difference in elevation between the points is 47.25 ft. The slope distance measures 848.64 ft. What is the horizontal distance between the two points?

2-4. Two points are to be set 2760.00 ft apart. If the tape to be used measures 100.034 ft between the zero and 100-ft marks under the conditions to be used in the field, what distance should be laid out?

2-5. A 100-ft tape weighing 1.45 lb measures 100.006 ft when supported throughout under a tension of 10 lb. When it is used to measure a line, it is supported at the two ends only. The recorded length is 700.00 ft. What is the actual length of the line?

2-6. What distance on a 7.5 percent grade should be laid out with a tape that is 0.03 ft too short, if the horizontal distance is to be 955.20 ft?

2-7. A certain line is measured with a 100-ft steel tape that is 99.986 ft long at a temperature of 68 deg F. A measurement of 2884.60 ft is obtained. The temperature of the tape was 30 deg F. What is the correct length of the line?

2-8. What error is produced when a 50-ft tape is held so that one end is out of line by 8 in.?

2-9. A line was measured along sloping ground with a 100-ft tape, and the following results were recorded:

Slope Distance (ft)	Difference in Elevation (ft)
100.00	9.01
100.00	3.45
100.00	5.06
100.00	4.55
63.22	5.91

What is the actual horizontal length of the line?

2-10. A steel tape standardized at 72 deg F under a tension of 12 lb measures 100.00 ft when supported throughout its length. When the tape was used in the field to measure a line, the tension was 28 lb and the tape was supported at the two ends only. The recorded length was 640.00 ft. The temperature throughout the measurement is assumed to have been 50 deg F. The tape weighs 2.06 lb and has a cross-sectional area of 0.0031 sq in. Assuming that E is 28,000,000 psi for steel, what is the actual length of the line?

2-11. What is the horizontal length of a line measured on a 6° 30' slope, if the slope distance is 1446.60 ft?

2-12. A 100-ft steel tape weighs 1.76 lb and has a cross-sectional area of 0.0026 sq in. The tape measures 100.00 ft when supported throughout and under a tension of 14.5 lb. Assume that $E = 30 \times 10^6$ psi. What tension, to the nearest ¼ pound, must be applied to overcome the effect of sag when the tape is supported at the 0-ft, 50-ft, and 100-ft marks?

3

Leveling

3-1. General. Leveling is the operation in surveying performed to determine and establish elevations of points, to determine differences in elevation between points, and to control grades in construction surveys. The basic instrument is a spirit level which establishes a horizontal line of sight by means of a telescope fitted with a set of cross hairs and a level bubble. The level is described in later sections of this chapter. Other instruments used for determining vertical distances are the engineer's transit, the aneroid barometer, the hand level and the telescopic alidade. The use of the engineer's transit and the telescopic alidade are explained in Chapters 6 and 13.

3-2. Curvature and Refraction. Where differences of elevation are determined trigonometrically or by using a level and a rod, the effects of curvature and refraction must be considered. This is particularly true when the horizontal distances are considerable, and also when a high degree of precision is required.

Let it be assumed that the two points A and B in Fig. 3-1 are 1 mile apart on a level surface. With respect to the horizontal line AC, the point B would apparently be lower than A by an amount CB, which is approximately equal to AD, whereas actually the two points are at the same elevation. The amount of this discrepancy due to

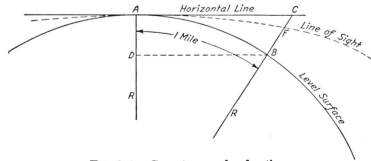

Fig. 3-1. Curvature and refraction.

32

curvature can be computed from Eq. 2-3, or $AD = \overline{BD^2}/(2R)$. If BD is assumed equal to AB, or 1 mile, and R is taken as the mean radius of the earth, or 3959 miles, $AD = 5280^2/(2 \times 3959 \times 5280)$ = 0.667 ft. It should be noted that the error due to curvature is proportional to the square of the horizontal distance. Thus, for a distance of 10 miles, the error increases to about 67 ft, whereas for 100 ft it diminishes to 0.00024 ft.

Rays of light passing through the earth's atmosphere in any direction other than vertical are refracted or bent from a straight path. This bending is toward the earth's surface and it tends to diminish the error in leveling caused by curvature. Thus, an apparently horizontal ray of light actually comes from F in Fig. 3-1 instead of C. The amount of this refraction depends on atmospheric conditions. It is usually assumed to diminish the error due to curvature by about one-seventh, and one correction is used to take care of both curvature and refraction.

The combined effect of curvature and refraction is computed from one of the following two formulas:

$$c + r = 0.574 \, K^2 \tag{3-1}$$

$$c + r = 0.021 \, M^2 \tag{3-2}$$

where $(c + r)$ = combined effect of curvature and refraction, in feet;
K = distance, in miles;
M = distance, in thousands of feet.

3-3. Trigonometric Leveling. The difference in elevation between two points can be determined by measuring the vertical angle of the line from one point to the other and then computing the difference in elevation from a knowledge of either the slope distance or the horizontal distance between the two points. In Fig. 3-2, DE is a horizontal line, and the vertical distance CE is $DC \sin \alpha$ or $DE \tan \alpha$. So the difference in elevation between A and B is $AD + CE - CB$, where

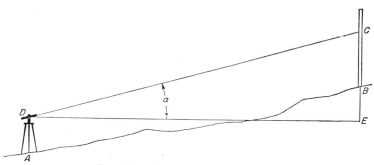

FIG. 3-2. Trigonometric leveling.

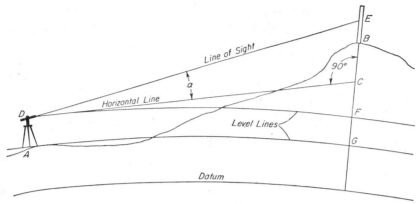

FIG. 3–3.   Curvature and refraction in trigonometric leveling.

AD is the height of the instrument above point *A*, and *CB* is the height of the the line of sight above point *B* measured with a leveling rod or with some other type of graduated rod. This method of determining difference in elevation is limited to horizontal distances less than 1000 ft when moderate precision is sufficient, and to proportionately shorter distances as higher precision is desired.

Beyond 1000 ft, the effect of curvature and refraction must be considered and applied. In Fig. 3-3 the vertical distance *CE* is *DC* tan α, but the vertical distance from a level line through *D* to point *E* is *FE*, which is *CE* + *CF*. It is seen that the effect of curvature and refraction is to make plus vertical angles too small and minus vertical angles too large. The difference in elevation between *A* and *B* is, therefore, $AD + DC \tan \alpha + 0.021 \ (DC/1000)^2 - EB$. Where sighting from both ends of the line is possible, the effect of curvature and refraction cancels, and the difference in elevation between the two points is the mean of the values computed from both ends without considering curvature and refraction.

3-4. Direct Differential Leveling. The purpose of differential leveling is to determine the difference of elevation between two points on the earth's surface. The most accurate method of determining differences of elevation is with the spirit level and a rod, in the manner

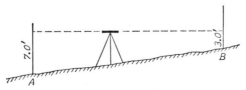

FIG. 3–4.   Direct differential leveling.

illustrated in Fig. 3-4. It is assumed that the elevation of point A is 976 ft and that it is desired to determine the elevation of point B. The level is set up, as described in Sec. 3-25, at some convenient point so that the plane of the instrument is higher than both A and B. A leveling rod is held vertically at the point A, which may be on the top of a stake or on some solid object, and the telescope is directed toward the rod. The vertical distance from A to a horizontal plane can be read on the rod where the horizontal cross hair of the telescope appears to coincide. If the rod reading is 7.0 ft, the plane of the telescope is 7.0 ft above the point A. The elevation of this horizontal plane is $976 + 7 = 983$ ft. The leveling rod is next held vertically at B and the telescope is directed toward the rod. The vertical distance from B to the same horizontal plane is given by the rod reading with which the horizontal cross hair appears to coincide. If the rod reading at B is 3.0 ft, the point B is 3.0 ft below this plane and the elevation of B is $983 - 3 = 980$ ft. The elevation of the ground at the point at which the level is set up need not be considered.

The same result may be obtained by noting that the difference in elevation between A and B is $7 - 3 = 4$ ft, and that B is higher than A. The elevation of B equals the elevation of A plus the difference of elevation between A and B, or $976 + 4 = 980$ ft.

3-5. Stadia Leveling. Stadia leveling combines features of trigonometric leveling with those of direct differential leveling. In stadia leveling, vertical angles are read by using the transit and horizontal distances are determined at the same time by means of the stadia hairs mentioned in Sec. 2-4. As in direct differential leveling, the elevation of the ground at the point at which the instrument is located is of no concern in the process. Stadia leveling is a rapid means of leveling where moderate precision is sufficient. It is described in detail in Sec. 13-10.

3-6. Leveling with Aneroid Barometer. The fact that atmospheric pressure, and hence the reading of a barometer, decreases as the altitude increases is utilized in determining differences of elevation. Because of transportation difficulties, the mercurial barometer is not used for survey purposes. Instead, the aneroid barometer or altimeter is used in surveys where errors of 5 to 10 ft are of no consequence. Altimeters vary in size from that of an ordinary watch to one that is 10 or 12 in. in diameter. The dials have two sets of graduations, namely, feet of elevation and inches of mercury. The smaller altimeters can be read by estimation to about 10 ft. A larger type, one of which is shown in Fig. 3-5, is much more sensitive, and differences of elevation of 2 or 3 ft can be detected.

FIG. 3-5. Precision altimeter.

An altimeter is, of course, subject to natural changes in atmospheric pressure due to weather, and it is also subject to effects of temperature and humidity. For this reason, altimeters should be used in groups of three or more.

In Fig. 3-6, an altimeter is maintained at L, which is a point of known elevation and is designated the low base. A second altimeter, whose reading has been compared with the one kept at the low base, is taken to H, which is a second point of known elevation and is

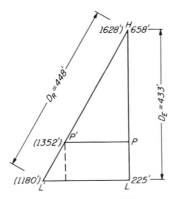

FIG. 3-6. Two-base altimetry.

designated the high base. At regular intervals, say every 5 minutes, the altimeters at the low and high bases are read. A third altimeter, which is referred to as the field altimeter or roving altimeter, is initially compared to the low-base altimeter and then taken to various points whose elevations are to be established. At each point, the reading of the roving altimeter and the time are recorded. The elevation of any point can be determined from the reading of the roving altimeter at the point and the readings of the altimeters at the high and low bases at that time. In order to maintain accuracy, limitations must be imposed on the elevation difference between the two bases, and on the area covered by the roving altimeter. These limitations tend to eliminate the effects of changing atmospheric pressure due to the weather, and also the effects of differences in temperature and humidity.

In the accompanying tabulation, the readings of the three altimeters indexed at the low base are shown. The high-base altimeter is taken to the high base, and the roving altimeter is taken to various field points. Three readings of the roving altimeter are shown in the tabulation.

TWO-BASE ALTIMETER READINGS

INDEXING ON LOW BASE

Low-base altimeter   1180
High-base altimeter   1189
Roving altimeter   1188

Time	Low-Base Reading (ft)	Low-Base Elevation (ft)	High-Base Reading (ft)	High-Base Elevation (ft)	Roving-Altimeter Reading (ft)
1:55 PM	1180	225	1637	658	1360
2:15 PM	1186	225	1650	658	1425
2:20 PM	1184	225	1646	658	1452

Before either the high-base readings or the roving-altimeter readings are used for computing elevations, they must be corrected for index error. Thus, the high-base readings must be reduced by 9 ft and the roving-altimeter readings by 8 ft. It is possible to make all three altimeters read the same at the time of indexing by physically adjusting the pointers, but this practice is not recommended. The corrected readings are shown here for convenience.

Time	Low-Base Reading (ft)	Corrected High-Base Reading (ft)	Corrected Roving-Altimeter Reading (ft)	Difference High − Low (ft)	Difference Roving − Low (ft)	Δh (ft)
1:55 PM	1180	1628	1352	448	172	166
2:15 PM	1186	1641	1417	455	231	220
2:20 PM	1184	1637	1444	453	260	249

The known difference in elevation between the high base and the low base is $658 - 225 = 433$ ft. This value is represented by the length of the vertical line LH in Fig. 3-6. At the time of the first field reading, the difference between the corrected readings at the high and low bases is 448 ft. This value is represented by the length of the sloped line $L'H$. Also, at the same time, the difference between the corrected readings at the field point and the low base is 172 ft, which is represented by the distance $L'P'$. Then, by proportion, the difference in elevation Δh between the low base and the field point, or the distance LP, is $(172)(433) / 448 = 166$ ft. Similarly, the differences in elevation between the low base and the other two points are, respectively, $(231)(433) / 455 = 220$ ft and $(260)(433) / 453 = 249$ ft.

3-7. Types of Levels. The instrument most extensively used in leveling is the engineer's level. It consists essentially of a telescope to which a very accurate spirit level is attached longitudinally. The telescope is supported at the ends of a straight bar that is firmly secured at the center to the perpendicular axis on which it revolves. The whole is supported on a tripod.

There are two general classes of engineer's levels. In the *wye level*, also written *Y level*, the telescope rests in Y-shaped supports from which it can be removed. In the *dumpy level*, the telescope is rigidly attached to its supports.

Formerly, most of the levels in use were of the wye type. This type was preferred because, unless the instrument is badly worn, it can be adjusted without the aid of a rodman. Most levels of the better grade, and practically all those intended for precise work, are of the dumpy type, which has fewer movable parts and remains in adjustment much longer than the wye level.

3-8. Description of Wye Level. An engineer's wye level is shown in Fig. 3-7. The telescope a, with the spirit level b attached, rests in the Y-shaped supports c. It is held in place by clips d, hinged at one end and secured at the other by small tapered pins. When these pins are removed and the clips are opened, the telescope either can be rotated in the wyes or can be entirely removed and turned end for end. This is done when the adjustment of the instrument is being tested.

The lower ends of the wyes are threaded and pass through holes in the cross bar e. They are held in place and adjusted vertically by the capstan-headed nuts f, which bear against the upper and lower surfaces of the bar. The bar e is attached rigidly to a center, or spindle, which turns in the socket g. The collar h, which is connected

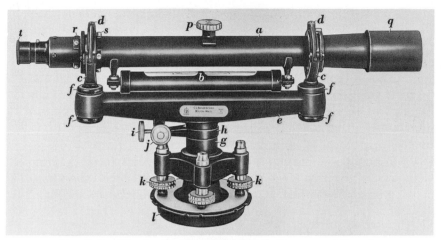

FIG. 3–7.   Wye level. (Courtesy of C. L. Berger and Sons.)

to the cross bar by means of a projection from the bar, revolves on the socket. When the clamp i is loose, the telescope can be rotated in a horizontal plane. The instrument is secured against rotation by tightening the clamp i, which then holds the collar fixed on the socket. After the clamp i has been tightened, the telescope can be revolved slowly through a small angle by means of the screw j, known as a *tangent screw* or *slow-motion screw*.

The inclination of the socket g is controlled by the four leveling screws k. The instrument is supported on a tripod, which consists of three legs shod with steel and connected by hinge joints to a metal tripod head. The tripod head is threaded and the plate l of the level is screwed on.

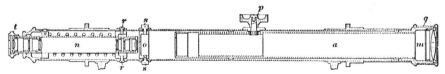

FIG. 3–8.   Longitudinal section of a telescope.

3-9. The Telescope.   A longitudinal section through the telescope a, Fig. 3-7, is shown in Fig. 3-8. The essential parts are the objective m, the eyepiece n, and the cross hairs attached to the reticule o.

The objective is a compound lens, made up of an outer double convex lens of crown glass and an inner concavo-convex lens of flint glass, the two being cemented together with balsam. The purpose of the objective is to bring to a focus in the plane of the cross hairs the rays of light that come from the object sighted upon. Focusing upon any desired object is accomplished by turning the milled wheel p, Figs. 3-7 and 3-8. The image is less subject to chromatic aberration if a compound lens, rather than a simple lens, is used. When the instrument is not in use, the objective is protected by the metal dust cap q. This is replaced by a thin metal tube, called a sunshade, when the instrument is being used. The sunshade shields the objective from the glare of the sun. It should always be used, even when the sun is not shining. Otherwise, the objective may not move horizontally when the focusing wheel is turned.

Most modern telescopes are designed so that focus is obtained by moving a negative lens located inside the telescope tube when the focusing knob is turned. This arrangement is shown in Fig. 3-9.

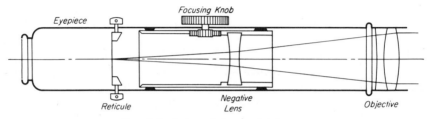

FIG. 3-9. Internal focus of telescope.

Since the objective need not move like that of the telescope shown in Fig. 3-8, the entire telescope can be made practically dust-free by eliminating the sliding objective tube. Also, since the negative lens is more nearly centered over the vertical axis of the instrument, moving it back and forth by the focusing knob does not shift the center of balance as would a movement of the objective. Although this shift is not serious in leveling for moderate precision, it would become so for precise leveling.

3-10. The Eyepiece. When an object is viewed through the telescope and the objective is focused properly, a small inverted image of the object is formed at the plane of the cross hairs by the objective. The purpose of the eyepiece is to magnify both this image and the cross hairs. Whether the object will appear erect or inverted, when viewed through the telescope, depends on the number of lenses in the eyepiece. Four lenses are necessary if the object is to appear erect, whereas only two lenses are required for an inverting eyepiece. An object will be more clearly defined if viewed through an inverting telescope than if an erecting one is used. For this reason, most precise instruments are of the inverting type. The screws r, shown in Figs. 3-7 and 3-8, are for centering the end of the longer erecting eyepiece.

3-11. The Cross Hairs. The cross hairs used in some surveying instruments are very fine threads, taken from the cocoon of a brown spider. Many instrument makers use finely-drawn platinum wires, some use fine glass threads, and others use a glass diaphragm on which lines have been etched. Levels intended for ordinary work have two cross hairs, one horizontal and one vertical. Those instruments which are intended for precise leveling have two additional horizontal hairs, one on either side of the usual horizontal cross hair. These additional hairs are called stadia hairs and are found in most transits.

The cross hairs are attached to a reticule, or cross-hair ring, *o*, Fig. 3-8. As shown in Fig. 3-10, this reticule is practically a heavy brass washer that is somewhat smaller in diameter than the inner surface of the telescope shell. It is thick enough to be tapped and threaded for the capstan-headed screws *s*, Figs. 3-7 and 3-8, by which it is held in place in the telescope tube. The holes through

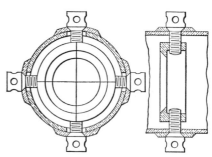

FIG. 3–10. Cross-hair reticule.

the telescope tube are large enough to permit the cross-hair ring to be rotated through a small angle, and are therefore covered by beveled washers. The ring can be moved vertically or horizontally by turning the proper capstan screws.

Focusing of the eyepiece is accomplished by changing the distance between it and the cross hairs. On most telescopes this is done by twisting the end *t* of the eyepiece. A second milled wheel is provided on some instruments for focusing the eyepiece. When both the eyepiece and the objective are properly focused, the cross hairs should be very distinct and should have no apparent motion as the eye is moved up and down. If there is any apparent motion, parallax is present and should be eliminated by refocusing the objective. See Sec. 3-35.

3-12. Level Tube. The spirit level *b*, Fig. 3-7, is the part of the instrument on which the accuracy chiefly depends. As indicated in Fig. 3-11, in plan in view (*a*) and in side elevation in view (*b*), it consists of a sealed glass tube nearly filled with alcohol or with a mixture of alcohol and ether. The upper surface of the tube, and sometimes also the lower surface, is ground to form a longitudinal circular curve. The sensitiveness of the bubble tube is dependent on the radius of this circular curve, and is usually expressed in terms of the angle

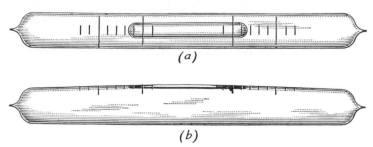

FIG. 3–11. Level tube.

through which the tube must be tilted to cause the bubble to move over one division of the scale etched on the glass. This angle may vary from 1 or 2 seconds, in the case of a precise level, up to 10 to 30 seconds on an engineer's level. The radius to which the tube for an engineer's level is ground is usually between 75 and 150 ft.

In a properly designed level, there should be a definite relation between the sensitiveness of the bubble and the magnifying power of the telescope. If, with the telescope focused on a distant object, the leveling screws are turned just enough to cause a barely perceptible movement of the horizontal cross hair, a corresponding displacement of the bubble should be apparent. Conversely, when the bubble is changed very slightly, a movement of the horizontal cross hair should be detected.

The angular value of one division of the level tube can be determined by turning the leveling screws so as to cause the bubble to move over several divisions and by observing the corresponding vertical distance the horizontal cross hair is raised or lowered on a leveling rod held at a known horizontal distance from the level. Thus, if the bubble is moved over five divisions and the vertical movement of the cross hair is 0.102 ft on a rod 300 ft from the level, the value of one division equals

$$\frac{0.102}{5 \times 300 \times \tan 1''} = \frac{0.102}{5 \times 300 \times 0.00000485} = 14 \text{ sec}$$

The metal case containing the level tube is adjustable vertically at one end and laterally at the other end, as indicated in Fig. 3-7.

3-13. The Dumpy Level. A dumpy level is shown in Fig. 3-12. Its general construction is similar to that of the wye level, but there are two important differences. First, in the dumpy level, the telescope a is rigidly attached to the cross bar b. Second, the level tube c is also attached to the cross bar and is adjustable in a vertical direction only.

FIG. 3–12. Dumpy level. (Courtesy of C. L. Berger and Sons.)

The telescope itself and other parts of the instrument are the same as in the wye level and require no special description. A sunshade is shown at *d*.

3-14. **Tilting Dumpy Level.** When a level is used, the level bubble must be centered at the instant of observation. Otherwise, serious random errors are introduced. If he is using a conventional wye or dumpy level, the observer must constantly check the level bubble and readjust the leveling screws. The tilting dumpy level, shown in Fig. 3-13, is brought to approximate level by means of a circular type, or bull's-eye, level. When a reading is to be taken, the observer rotates a tilting knob, which moves the telescope through a small vertical angle. With his head in the normal position for viewing the rod through the telescope, he can at the same time look through a window to the left of the eyepiece of the telescope and observe the more-sensitive, main-level bubble as two half-images of opposite ends of the bubble. These half-images are brought into superposition and made visible to the observer by a prismatic arrangement directly over the bubble. The observer then tilts the telescope until the two half-images are made to coincide, in which position the bubble is centered. The split bubble before and after coincidence is shown in Fig. 3-14. Note that the apparent discrepancy between the two half-images is actually twice the centering error. Because of the fine tilting adjust-

FIG. 3–13.   Tilting dumpy level. (Courtesy of Keuffel and Esser Co.)

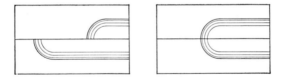

FIG. 3–14.   Coincidence bubble.

ment and the ability to view both ends of the bubble simultaneously, the observer can center the bubble to within 0.3 mm.

In Fig. 3-15 is shown a tilting level of European design. Its operation is identical with that of the level shown in Fig. 3-13. The eyepiece, however, does not erect the image of the level, and this difference accounts for the relatively shorter telescope. In this instrument, the image of the coincidence bubble appears directly in the field of view of the telescope, rather than through an adjacent eyepiece, and the observer may view the bubble, the cross hairs, and the image of the leveling rod with one eye and from one position.

3-15.   Self-Leveling Level.   The level shown in Fig. 3-16 is said to be self-leveling. When the bull's-eye bubble has been centered, a

FIG. 3–15. European tilting level. (Courtesy of Kern Instruments Inc.)

prism carried on a pendulum supported by two pairs of wires reflects the light rays entering the objective lens on back to the eyepiece end of the telescope. The lengths of the supporting wires and the positions of the points of suspension are so designed that the only rays of light reflected back to the intersection of the cross hairs by the swinging prism are the horizontal rays passing through the optical center of the objective lens. Hence, as long as the prism is free to swing, a horizontal line of sight is maintained, even though the telescope barrel itself is not horizontal. A damping device brings the pendulum to rest quite rapidly, so that the observer does not have to wait until it settles of its own accord. This type of level has the advantage of offering very rapid instrument set-ups and of eliminating random errors in centering the level bubble.

3-16. Geodetic Level. The geodetic level, used for extreme pre-

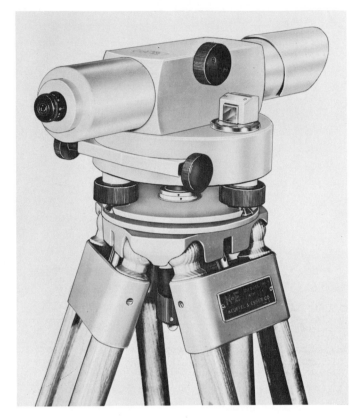

FIG. 3–16.   Self-leveling level. (Courtesy of Keuffel & Esser Co.)

cision required in first-order leveling conducted by the U. S. Coast
and Geodetic Survey, is a tilting level made of invar to lessen the
effect of temperature. The magnification of the objective-eyepiece
combination is about 42 diameters. The vial for the very sensitive
level bubble is recessed into the barrel of the telescope, and it contains
on one end a small chamber into or out of which there can be leaked
a small amount of the fluid from the main vial. This arrangement
allows the length of the level bubble to be kept fairly constant under
all temperature conditions and eliminates the possibility of error due
to any irregularity in the curvature of the inside surface of the level
vial. The geodetic level is equipped with stadia hairs for determining
three rod readings at one observation and for determining the lengths
of the sights. The tripod on which the geodetic level rests is of such
height that the observer may stand erect while observing. The unusu-
ally high tripod brings the line of sight somewhat farther from the
intervening ground than does the ordinary tripod, helping to lessen
differential refraction of the line of sight.

3-17. **Hand Level and Clinometer.** The hand level, shown in Fig. 3-17, is a brass tube with a small level tube mounted on the top. A 45° mirror on the inside of the main tube enables the user to tell when it is being held horizontally. As the rod viewed through the level is not magnified, the length of sight is limited by the visibility of rod readings with the naked eye.

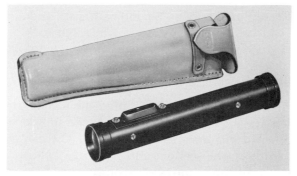

FIG. 3–17. Hand level. (Courtesy of Keuffel & Esser Co.)

The hand level is used on reconnaissance surveys where extreme accuracy is unnecessary, and in taping to determine when the tape is being held horizontally. It is also used to advantage for estimating how high or how low the engineer's level must be set in order to be able to read the leveling rod.

The clinometer, shown in Fig. 3-18, can be used in the same manner as the hand level. In addition, it can be employed for measuring vertical angles where approximate results are sufficient.

FIG. 3–18. Clinometer. (Courtesy of Keuffel & Esser Co.)

3-18. **Leveling Rods.** There are two general classes of leveling rods, namely, self-reading and target rods. A self-reading rod has painted graduations that can be read directly from the level. When a target rod is used, the target is set by the rodman as directed by the levelman, and the reading is then made by the rodman. Some types of rods can be used either as self-reading rods or as target rods.

The graduations on self-reading rods should appear sharp and distinct for the average length of sight. In the United States, the rods are ordinarily graduated so as to indicate feet and decimals, the smallest division usually being 0.01 ft. On some rods, intended for precise work, the divisions are decimals of the meter. For sights of considerable length, 0.01-ft graduations become very hazy and indistinct, and a rod with 0.10-ft graduations is better.

3-19. **Philadelphia Rod.** The Philadelphia rod, front and rear views of which are shown in Fig. 3-19, is made in two sections that are held together by the brass sleeves a and b. The rear section slides with respect to the front section, and it can be held in any desired position by means of the clamp screw c on the upper sleeve b. The rod is said to be a *short rod* when the rear portion is not extended, and a *long* or *high rod* when it is extended. The short rod is used for readings up to 7 ft. For readings between 7 and 13 ft, the long rod must be used. When the rod is fully extended, the graduations on the face are continuous.

As shown in Fig. 3-19, the rod is graduated to hundredths of a foot by alternate black and white spaces painted on the rod. Each fifth hundredth is indicated by a longer graduation mark, so that an acute angle is formed at one corner of the black space of which the graduation is a part. The tenths are marked by large black figures, half above and half below the graduation mark, and the feet are shown in a similar manner by red figures (shaded in the illustrations). The graduations can be seen distinctly through the telescope of a level at distances up to about 400 ft, and the rod can thus be used as a self-reading or speaking rod.

In case the graduations cannot be read directly from the telescope with sufficient accuracy, the target d is used. The target is a circular or elliptical metal plate divided into quadrants alternating red and white. There is an opening in the face of the target in order that the graduations on the face of the rod can be seen through it. One side of this opening is beveled to a thin edge, and a scale is marked along this edge so that it is close to the face of the rod. This scale is used for determining readings between graduation marks. One of its ends is exactly on the horizontal line dividing the colors on the target.

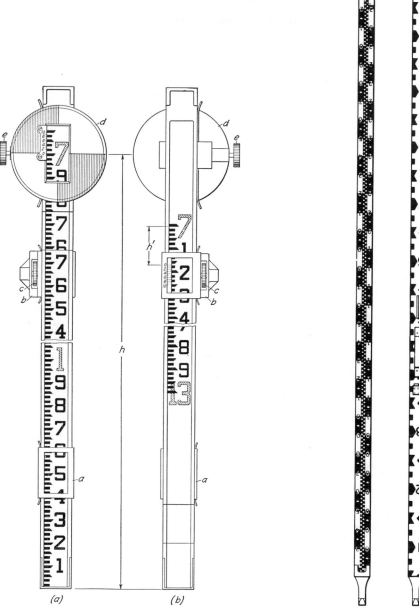

FIG. 3–19.   Philadelphia rod.

FIG. 3–20.   Precise
leveling rod.

When the clamp e is loose, the target can be moved over the face
of the rod until the line dividing the colors coincides with the horizontal cross hair of the level. The target can then be fixed in that position by tightening the clamp e.

When the target is used on a high rod, it is first set exactly at 7 ft on the extension part of the rod, as shown in Fig. 3-19 (a). The extension with the target is then raised until the line dividing the colors coincides with the horizontal cross hair of the telescope, and the rod is held in that position by tightening the clamp c. To determine the reading for a high rod, the graduations on the back of the sliding part and a scale on the back of the upper sleeve are used. As shown in view (b), these graduations begin at 7 ft at the top and increase downward to 13 ft.

The reading of a high rod is the distance from the base of the rod to the target. Thus, for the position shown in Fig. 3-19(b), the rod reading represents the distance h. When the target is set at 7 ft on the extension part of the rod while the rod is closed, the reading of the high rod is 7 ft, and the 7-ft graduation on the back of the rod is opposite the zero of the scale on the sleeve. As the rod is raised, the 7-ft mark moves upward, while the zero mark of the scale remains stationary since it is attached to the lower portion of the rod. The distance h' between these two marks, therefore, increases as the rod is extended further. Consequently, the distance h' is equal to the amount by which the target is raised above 7 ft, and for any high-rod reading the distance h is equal to 7 ft plus the distance h'. To obviate actual addition, the foot-graduations on the back of the rod are numbered downward from 7 to 13. Thus, when the rod is extended 1 ft, the reading on the back is $7 + 1 = 8$ ft, and so on. It is seen, therefore, that the numbers must increase downward in order that the rod readings may become greater as the target is raised.

If the rod has been damaged by allowing the upper portion to slide down with a bang, it is possible that the reading on the back of the rod will be less than 7 ft when the rear section is in the lowered position. In this case the target should be set at the corresponding reading on the face of the rod before extending the rod.

3-20. **Precise Leveling Rods.** A precise rod is graduated on an invar strip which is independent of the main body of the rod except at the shoe at the bottom of the rod. The graduations are in yards, in feet, or in meters, and the smallest graduations are 0.01 yd, 0.01 ft, and 1 cm, respectively. A yard rod or a meter rod is also graduated in feet on the back of the rod. These foot graduations are painted directly on the main body of the rod. They serve as a check on the more precise readings taken on the invar strip, and help to prevent mistakes in rod readings. The precise rod is equipped with either a bull's-eye level or a pair of level vials at right angles to each other to show when the rod is vertical, and also with a thermometer. Front and back views of a precise rod are shown in Fig. 3-20.

3-21. **Reading the Rod Directly.** If the target is not used, the reading of the rod is made directly from the telescope. The number of feet is given by the red figure just below the horizontal cross hair when the level has an erecting telescope, or just above the horizontal cross hair when it has an inverting telescope. The number of tenths is shown by the black figure just below or above the hair, the position depending on whether the telescope is erecting or inverting. If the reading is required to the nearest hundredth, the number of hundredths is found by counting the divisions between the last tenth and the graduation mark nearest to the hair. If thousandths of a foot are required, the number of hundredths is equal to the number of divisions between the last tenth and the graduation mark on the same side of the hair as that tenth, and the number of thousandths is obtained by estimation.

The readings on the rod for the positions x, y, and z in Fig. 3-21 are determined as follows: For x, the number of feet below the cross hair is 4, the number of tenths below is 1, and the cross hair coincides with the first graduation above the tenth-mark; consequently, the reading is 4.11 ft to the nearest hundredth, or 4.110 ft to the nearest thousandth. For y, the feet and tenths are again 4 and 1, respectively; also, the hair is just midway between the graduations indicating 4 and 5 hundredths, and therefore the reading to the nearest hundredth can be taken as either 4.14 or 4.15 ft. In determining the hundredths, it is convenient to observe that the hair is just below the acute-angle graduation denoting the fifth hundredth, and it is, therefore, unnecessary to count up from the tenth-graduation. If thousandths are required, the number of hundredths is the lower one, or 4; and, since the hair is midway between two graduation marks on the rod, and the distance between the graduations is 1 hundredth or 10 thousandths of a foot, the number of thousandths in the required reading is $\frac{1}{2} \times 10$, or 5.

FIG. 3-21. Direct reading of rod.

Hence, the reading to the nearest thousandth is 4.145 ft. For z, the reading to the nearest hundredth is 3.96 ft, and that to the nearest thousandth is 3.963 ft.

Direct long-rod readings are made with the rod fully extended, as the graduations on the face of the rod then appear continuous.

3-22. **Verniers.** The vernier is a device by means of which readings closer than the smallest division of a scale can be made with more certainty than they can be obtained by estimation. The verniers found

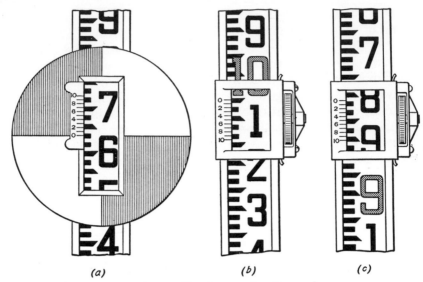

FIG. 3–22.   Verniers on leveling rod.

on a leveling rod are shown in Fig. 3-22. The front view in (*a*) shows
the target and vernier for a short rod, and the rear views in (*b*) and
(*c*) show the vernier on the back of the rod, which is employed in
making high-rod readings when the target is used.

The principle of the vernier is dependent on the fact that the
lengths of the divisions on the vernier are slightly less than the lengths
of the divisions on the scale. A vernier of the type found on leveling rods
is shown in Fig. 3-23. On this vernier a length corresponding to nine
of the smallest divisions on the scale, or 0.09 ft, is divided into ten
parts on the vernier. The length of one of these vernier divisions is
$\frac{1}{10} \times 0.09$ or 0.009 ft. The difference between the length of one division on the scale and one division on the vernier is equal to $0.01 -
0.009 = 0.001$ ft. Hence, if the vernier is shifted from the position
shown in Fig. 3-23 (*a*), where the zero of the vernier is coinciding with
the 0.3-ft mark, to the position shown in view (*b*), where the first
division on the vernier coincides with the 0.31-ft mark, the distance
the vernier has been moved must be the difference between the length
of a main-scale division and the length of a vernier division, or 0.001
ft. In Fig. 3-23 (*c*) the eighth division on the vernier is coinciding with
a mark on the main scale, and hence the vernier must have been
moved 0.008 ft from the original position in view (*a*). The number of
thousandths of a foot must always be the same numerically as the
number of the vernier graduation that coincides with a mark on the
main scale. The readings shown in the three positions in Fig. 3-23 are
0.300, 0.301, and 0.308 ft, respectively.

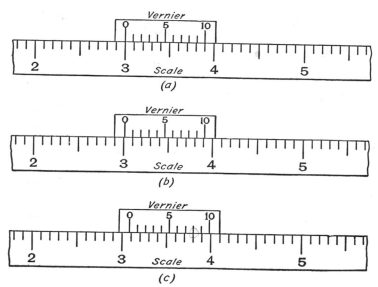

FIG. 3–23. Vernier.

In the following formulas, let l represent the least reading or least count of the vernier; d, the length of one division of the vernier; D, the length of one division of the scale; and n, the number of divisions on the vernier between two marks that coincide with two marks on the scale. Then, from the principles of the vernier,

$$nd = (n - 1) D \qquad (3\text{-}3)$$

and

$$d = \frac{(n - 1) D}{n} \qquad (3\text{-}4)$$

Also,

$$l = D - d \qquad (3\text{-}5)$$

or

$$l = D - \frac{(n - 1) D}{n} = \frac{D}{n} \qquad (3\text{-}6)$$

Although the least reading of a vernier can be obtained from either of the two latter formulas, the last one is the more convenient. The least count is thus determined by dividing the length of the smallest division on the scale by the number of divisions on the vernier between two marks that coincide with marks on the main scale. The least count of the vernier shown in Fig. 3-23 is $0.01/10 = 0.001$ ft.

The readings on the rods shown in Fig. 3-22 are as follows: (a) 0.635 ft, (b) 10.053 ft, (c) 8.807 ft. Mistakes can often be averted by first estimating the number of thousandths and then looking at that part of the vernier where the coincidence must occur.

3-23. Optical Micrometer. The optical micrometer, the principle of which is shown in Fig. 3-24, measures the vertical distance on the rod from the point at which a horizontal line of sight strikes the rod to the next lower graduation mark. It consists of a thick piece of optical glass, the front and rear surfaces of which are ground flat and parallel to one another, together with a micrometer drum graduated so as to indicate the amount by which the plano-parallel element raises or lowers the line of sight. The unit fits over the barrel of the telescope directly in front of the objective lens. A complete revolution of the drum, or that part of a revolution between the zero graduation

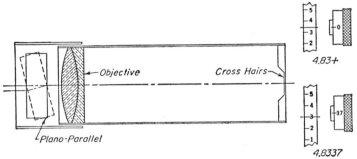

Fig. 3-24.   Optical micrometer principle.

and the last graduation, represents a fixed value, such as 0.01 ft, 1 cm, or 5 mm. The rod graduations must therefore correspond to the particular optical micrometer being used.

The micrometer eliminates the necessity for estimating between graduations, and it furthermore subdivides the distance between graduations very precisely into 50 or 100 parts. The position of the horizontal line of sight on the rod shown in Fig. 3-24(a) is between 4.83 and 4.84 ft, and the micrometer drum reads zero. Also the drum is divided into 100 parts. When the micrometer drum is turned and the plano-parallel element is rotated so that the line of sight is lowered to the 4.83-ft rod graduation, the micrometer drum reads 37. This reading means that the line of sight has been lowered 37/100 of 0.01 ft, or 0.0037 ft. The rod reading is therefore 4.8337 ft.

3-24. Bench Mark. A bench mark is a permanent or semipermanent physical mark of known elevation. A good bench mark is a bronze disk set either in the top of a concrete post or in the foundation wall of a structure. Other locations for bench marks are the top of a culvert headwall, the top of an anchor bolt, or the top of a spike driven into the base of a tree. The elevations of bench marks are determined to varying degrees of accuracy by the field operations to be described in the following sections.

3-25. **Setting up the Level.** The purpose of direct leveling, as explained in Sec. 3-4, is to determine the difference of elevation between two points by reading a rod held on the points. These rod readings can be made by the levelman without setting the target, or the target can be set as directed by the levelman and the actual reading made by the rodman. At the instant the readings are made, it is necessary that the line of sight determined by the intersection of the cross hairs and the optical center of the objective be horizontal. In a properly adjusted instrument this line will be horizontal only when the bubble is at the center of the bubble tube.

The first step in setting up the level is to spread the tripod legs so that the tripod head will be approximately horizontal. The legs should be far enough apart to prevent the instrument from being blown over by a gust of wind, and they should be pushed into the ground far enough to make the level stable. Repairs to a damaged instrument are always expensive. For this reason, neither a level nor a transit should be set up on a pavement or a sidewalk if such a set-up can possibly be avoided. When the instrument must be so set up, additional care should be exercised to protect it from possible mishaps.

If two adjacent leveling screws are loosened slightly, the leveling head can be turned in any direction. Where there are four leveling screws, it will be a convenience in the final leveling up if the line through one pair of opposite screws is placed as nearly as possible in the direction in which the first sight is to be taken. After this has been done, the telescope is turned over either pair of opposite leveling screws. The bubble is then brought nearly to the center of the tube by loosening one screw and tightening the opposite one at the same rate. It will be found that the bubble moves in the same direction as the left-hand thumb. No great care should be taken to bring the bubble exactly to the center the first time.

The next step is to turn the telescope over the other pair of screws and to bring the bubble exactly to the center of the tube by means of these screws. The telescope is now turned over the first pair of screws once more, and this time the bubble is centered accurately. The telescope is then turned over the second pair of screws and, if the bubble has moved away from the center of the tube, it is brought back to the center. When the instrument is finally leveled up, the bubble should be in the center of the tube when the telescope is turned over either pair of screws. If the instrument is in adjustment, the bubble should remain in the center as the telescope is turned in any direction.

The beginner will need considerable practice in leveling up the instrument. It is by practice alone that he is able to tell how much to turn the screws to bring the bubble to the center. The more sensitive the bubble, the more skill is required to center it exactly. For the final centering, when the bubble is to be moved only a part of a division, only one screw need be turned. The screw that has to be tightened should be turned if both are a little loose, and the one that has to be loosened should be turned when they are tight. When the telescope is finally leveled up, all four screws should be bearing firmly but should not be so tight as to put a strain in the leveling head. If the head of the tripod is badly out of horizontal, it may be found that the leveling screws turn very hard. The cause is the binding of the ball-and-socket joint at the bottom of the spindle. The tension may be relieved by loosening both screws of the other pair.

Many surveying instruments contain not four, but three, leveling screws. When a three-screw instrument is to be leveled, the level bubble is brought parallel with a line joining any two screws, such as a and b in Fig. 3-25(a). By rotating these two screws in opposite

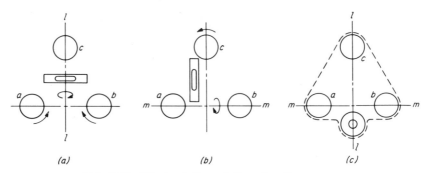

(a)   (b)   (c)

Fig. 3-25. Manipulation of three leveling screws.

directions, the instrument is tilted about the axis l–l, and the bubble can be brought to the center. The level bubble is now brought perpendicular to the line joining these first two screws, as shown in Fig. 3-25(b). Then only the third screw c is rotated to bring the bubble to the center. This operation tilts the instrument about the axis m–m. The procedure is then repeated to bring the bubble exactly to the center in both directions.

When leveling a three-screw tilting level or an automatic level equipped with a bull's-eye bubble, as shown in Fig. 3-25(c), opposite rotations of screws a and b cause the bubble to move in the direction of the axis m–m. Rotation of screw c only causes the bubble to move in the direction of the axis l–l.

In walking about the instrument, the levelman must be careful not to step near the tripod legs, particularly when the ground is soft.

Neither should any part of the level be touched as the readings are being made, because the bubble can be pulled off several divisions by resting the hand on the telescope or on a tripod leg. The bubble will not remain in the center of the tube for any appreciable length of time. The levelman should form the habit of always checking the centering of the bubble just before and just after making a reading. Only in this way can he be sure that the telescope was actually horizontal when the reading was made.

3-26. Signals. In running a line of levels, it is necessary for the levelman and the rodman to be in almost constant communication with each other. As a means of communication, certain convenient signals are employed. It is important that the levelman and the rodman understand these in order to avoid mistakes. When the target is used, it is set by the rodman according to signals given by the levelman. Raising the hand above the shoulder, so that the palm is visible, is the signal for raising the target; lowering the hand below the waist is the signal for lowering the target. The levelman, viewing the rod and the rodman through the telescope, should remember that he can see them much more distinctly than he can be seen by the rodman. Hence, his signals should be such that there is no possible chance of misunderstanding. A circle described by the hand is the signal for clamping the target, and a wave of both hands indicates that the target is properly set, or all right. The signal for plumbing the rod is to raise one arm above the head and then to lean the body in the direction in which the rod should be moved.

3-27. Running a Line of Levels. In the preliminary example of direct leveling, given in Sec. 3-4, it was assumed that the difference of elevation between the two points considered could be obtained by a single setting of the level. This will be the case only when the difference in elevation is small and when the points are relatively close together. In Fig. 3-26, rods at the points A and K cannot be seen from the same position of the level. If it is required to find the elevation of point K from that of A, it will be necessary to set up the level several times and to establish intermediate points such as C, E, and G. These are the conditions commonly encountered in the field and may serve as an illustration of the general methods of direct leveling.

Let the elevation of the bench mark, abbreviated B. M., at A be assumed as 820.00 ft. The level is set up at B, near the line between A and K, so that a rod held on the B. M. will be visible through the telescope; the reading on the rod is found to be 8.42 ft. The *height of instrument*, abbreviated H.I., is the vertical distance from the datum to the plane of sight. Numerically, the H. I. is found by adding the

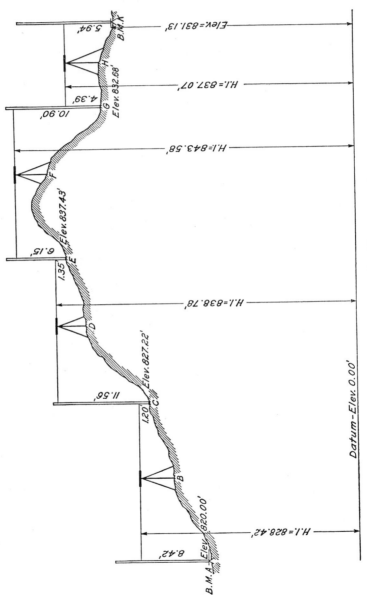

FIG. 3–26. Direct leveling.

rod reading taken on the bench mark to the elevation of the bench mark. Thus, the H. I. of the level at B is $820.00 + 8.42 = 828.42$ ft. The rod reading taken at A by directing the line of sight toward the start of the line is called a *backsight reading*, or simply a *backsight*, abbreviated B. S. The backsight is the rod reading that is taken on a point of known elevation to determine the height of instrument. Since a backsight is usually added to the elevation of the point on which the rod is held, it is also called a *plus sight*, written $+$ S.

After the reading has been taken on a rod at A, a point C is selected which is slightly below the line of sight, and the reading is taken on a rod held at C. If this reading is 1.20 ft, the point C is 1.20 ft below the line of sight, and the elevation of C is $828.42 - 1.20 = 827.22$ ft. The reading on C is called a *foresight reading*, or *foresight*, abbreviated F. S. It is taken on a point of unknown elevation in order to determine that elevation from the height of instrument. Since the reading on a foresight is usually subtracted from the height of instrument to obtain the elevation of the point, a foresight is also called a *minus sight* and is written $-$ S.

Occasionally successive foresights and backsights are taken on an overhead point such as on a point in the roof of a tunnel. The foresight taken on such a point is added to the H. I. to obtain the elevation of the point. The backsight taken on the point is subtracted from the elevation of the point to determine the H. I. Such readings must be carefully noted in the field notes.

While the rodman remains at C, the level is moved to D and set up as high as possible but not so high that the line of sight will be above the top of the rod when it is again held at C. The reading 11.56 ft is taken as a backsight or $+$ S reading. Hence, the H. I. at D is $827.22 + 11.56 = 838.78$ ft. When this reading is taken, it is important that the rod be held on exactly the same point which was used for a foresight when the level was at B. The point C should be some stable object, so that the rod can be removed and put back in the same place as many times as may be necessary. For this purpose, a sharp-pointed rock or a well-defined projection on some permanent object is preferable. If no such object is available, a stake or peg can be driven firmly into the ground and the rod held on top of it. Such a point as C, on which both a foresight $(-$ S) and a backsight $(+$ S) are taken, is called a *turning point*, abbreviated T. P.

After the backsight on C has been taken, another turning point E is chosen and a foresight of 1.35 ft is obtained. The elevation of E is $838.78 - 1.35 = 837.43$ ft. The level is then moved to F and the backsight of 6.15 ft taken on E. The new H. I. is $837.43 + 6.15 =$

843.58 ft. From this position of the level a foresight of 10.90 ft is taken on G, the elevation of which is $843.58 - 10.90 = 832.68$ ft. The level is then set up at H, from which position a $+ S$ reading of 4.39 ft is taken on G and a $- S$ reading of 5.94 ft is taken on the new B. M. at K. The final H. I. is $832.68 + 4.39 = 837.07$ ft, and the elevation of K is $837.07 - 5.94 = 831.13$ ft. As the starting elevation was 820.00 ft, the point K is 11.13 ft higher than A.

If the only purpose of the levels is to find the difference of elevation between A and K, it can be computed, without the use of the H. I.'s, by calculating the differences of elevation between each pair of turning points and then obtaining the algebraic sum of these differences. The first difference of elevation, between A and C, is $+ 8.42 - 1.20 = + 7.22$ ft. The difference between C and E is $+ 11.56 - 1.35 = + 10.21$ ft. The difference between E and G is $+ 6.15 - 10.90 = - 4.75$ ft. The final difference between G and K is $+ 4.39 - 5.94 = - 1.55$ ft. The total difference between A and K is $+ 7.22 + 10.21 - 4.75 - 1.55 = + 11.13$ ft, as before. The result can be checked by obtaining the difference between the sums of the $+ S$ and $- S$ readings.

3-28. Forms of Notes. There are two forms of field notes in common use for the type of leveling described in the preceding article. In one form the H. I.'s are calculated, and in the other form only differences of elevation are obtained. Samples of these two forms are shown in Figs. 3-27 and 3-28.

The student should carefully review the operations described in Sec. 3-27 and diagrammed in Fig. 3-26 while at the same time observ-

FORM A

Sta.	+s	H.I.	−s	Elev.	
1960 -4-10. Leveling, B.M.A. to B.M.K. *Washtenaw Ave. Sewer Project.* *Ann Arbor, Mich.*					*Level #4096. Level & Rec. J.Brown* *Rod #18.　　Rodman　　F. Smith*
B.M.A.	8.42	828.42		820.00	Top of iron pipe, S.E. cor. Washtenaw & Hill Sts.
T.P.	11.56	838.78	1.20	827.22	
T.P.	6.15	843.58	1.35	837.43	
T.P.	4.39	837.07	10.90	832.68	
B.M.K.	+30.52		5.94	831.13	Top of iron pipe, N.W. cor. Washtenaw & Oxford Rd.
	−19.39		19.39		
	+11.13				820.00 B.M.A. +11.13 Diff. Elev. 831.13 B.M.K. Check. J. Brown

Fig. 3–27.　Level notes.

FORM B

1960-4-10. Leveling B.M.A. to B.M.K. Washtenaw Ave. Sewer Project. Ann Arbor, Mich.					Level #4096. Level & Rec. J. Brown Rod #18. Rodman F. Smith

Sta.	+S	−S	Diff. Elev. +	Diff. Elev. −	
B.M.A.	8.42				Top of iron pipe, S.E. corner Washtenaw & Hill Sts.
T.P.	11.56	1.20	7.22		
T.P.	6.15	1.35	10.21		
T.P.	4.39	10.90		4.75	
B.M.K.	+30.52	5.94		1.55	Top of iron pipe, N.W. corner Washtenaw & Oxford Rd.
	−19.39	19.39	17.43	6.30	820.00 B.M.A.
	+11.13		−6.30		+11.13 Diff. Elev.
			+11.13		831.13 B.M.K.
					J. Brown

FIG. 3–28. Level notes.

ing the manner in which the notes were recorded and the arithmetic was performed.

3-29. Proof of Level Notes. To eliminate arithmetical mistakes in the reduction of field notes, the final elevation or difference of elevation on each page of notes should be calculated in two ways. This is called proving the notes. In Form A in Fig. 3-27, the elevation of B. M. *K* is obtained by using the heights of instrument and computing the elevation of each turning point. It is also obtained by calculating the difference of elevation between B. M. *A* and B. M. *K* by taking the difference between the sum of the plus sights and the sum of the minus sights, or + 11.13 ft, and adding this difference to the elevation of B. M. *A*.

In Form B in Fig. 3-28, the difference of elevation between B. M. *A* and B. M. *K* is obtained in two ways; namely, by finding the difference between the sum of the plus sights and the sum of the minus sights, and also by finding the difference of elevation at each set-up of the level and then calculating the algebraic sum of these differences. If the two final results are identical, it is reasonably certain that no arithmetical mistakes were made.

3-30. Check Levels. Although the arithmetic in the reduction of the field notes may have been verified, there is no guarantee that the difference of elevation is correct. The difference of elevation is dependent on the accuracy of each rod reading and on the manner in which the field work has been done. If there has been any mistake in reading the rod or in recording a reading, the difference of elevation is incorrect.

The only way in which the difference of elevation can be checked is by rerunning the levels, preferably in the reverse direction. If this is done, it should be found that the difference in elevation between B. M. *K* and B. M. *A* is − 11.13 ft. The two differences in elevation will be of opposite sign. The amount by which they vary numerically will be an indication of the errors that were made in the field work. If the notes are kept according to Form A in Fig. 3-27, the elevation of B. M. *A* in the check levels should be very close to the original elevation of 820.00 ft. Any considerable variation from this value indicates that a mistake was made.

3-31. Sources of Error in Leveling. The principal sources of error in leveling are instrumental defects, faulty manipulation of the level or rod, settling of the level or the rod, errors in sighting, mistakes in reading the rod or in recording or computing, errors due to natural sources, and personal errors.

3-32. Instrumental Errors. The most common instrumental error is caused by the level being out of adjustment. As has been previously stated, the line of sight of the telescope is horizontal when the bubble is in the center of the tube, provided the instrument is in perfect adjustment. When it is not in adjustment, the line of sight will be either elevated or depressed when the bubble is brought to the center of the tube. The various tests and adjustments of the level are given in Chapter 19.

Instrumental errors can be eliminated or kept at a minimum by testing the level frequently and adjusting it when necessary. Such errors can also be eliminated by keeping the lengths of the sights for the backsight and foresight readings nearly equal at each setting of the level. Since it is never known just when an instrument goes out of adjustment, this latter method is the more certain and should always be used for careful leveling.

In Fig. 3-29 the line of sight with the level at B should be in the horizontal line $EBGK$. If the line of sight is elevated as shown and a sight is taken on a rod at A, the reading is AF, instead of AE. This reading is in error by the amount of $EF = e_1$. When the telescope is directed toward a rod held at C or D, the line of sight will still be elevated through the same vertical angle, if it is assumed that the bubble remains in, or is brought to, the center of the tube. The rod reading taken on C will be CH, which is in error by an amount $GH = e_2$. If the horizontal distances BE and BG are equal, the errors e_1 and e_2 will be alike, and the difference between the two rod readings

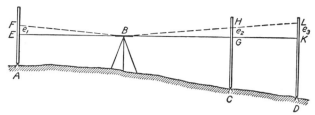

FIG. 3–29. Errors caused by imperfect adjustment of level.

AF and CH will be the true difference of elevation between A and C. A rod reading taken at D will be DL, with an error $KL = e_3$. Since BK is longer than BE, the difference in elevation between A and D will be in error by an amount equal to the difference between e_3 and e_1. Similar reasoning applies if the line of sight is depressed instead of elevated.

If the telescope is badly worn, the objective lens may move in an inclined direction instead of horizontally as it is moved in and out for focusing. For this reason, extremely short sights should be avoided whenever possible. If the rod is but 10 ft from the level, the focusing slide will be run out nearly its entire length. For sights greater than 100 ft, the position of the slide will be changed very slightly, and there will be little chance for error from faulty movement of the slide in the longer sights.

Extremely long sights should also be avoided. The further the rod is from the level, the greater will be the space covered on the rod by the cross hair and the more difficult it will be to determine the reading accurately. For accurate results, sights with the engineer's level should be limited to about 300 ft.

3-33. Errors Due to Manipulation. As has been previously stated, the careful levelman will form the habit of checking the position of the bubble just before and just after making each rod reading. This is the only way in which he can be certain that he is getting the proper reading.

The amount of the error due to the bubble being off center will depend on the sensitiveness of the bubble. A very convenient way to determine this error for any given bubble and for any given distance is to remember that an error of 1 minute in angle causes an error of about 1 in. or 0.08 ft at a distance of 300 ft. Thus, if a 30″ bubble is off 1 division at the instant the reading is made, the resulting error will be about 0.04 ft when the rod is 300 ft away.

A common mistake in handling the rod is in not being careful to see that the target is properly set before a high-rod reading is made with the target. Many rods have been damaged by allowing the upper portion to slide down rapidly enough to affect the blocks at the bottom of the lower section and the top of the upper section. If this has been done, it is probable that the reading on the back of a Philadelphia rod will not be exactly 7 ft when set as a low rod. In this case, the target should be set at that reading, rather than at exactly 7 ft, for a high-rod reading with the target. When a high rod is being read directly from the level, the rodman should make sure that the rod is properly extended and has not slipped down.

When the target is being used, the levelman should check its position after it has been clamped, in order to make sure that it has not slipped. The beginner will be astonished at the care that must be exercised in making the target coincide exactly with the horizontal cross hair. Readings taken on the same point about 300 ft from the level may vary by several hundredths of a foot if the bubble is not exactly centered and if the target is carelessly set.

3-34. Errors Due to Settlement. If any settlement of the level takes place in the interval between the reading of the backsight and the reading of the foresight, the resulting foresight will be too small, and all elevations beyond that point will be too high by the amount of the settlement. Also, if the turning point should settle while the level is being moved forward after the foresight has been taken, the backsight on the T. P. from the new position of the level will be too great and all elevations will be too high by the amount of the settlement.

Errors due to the settlement of the level can be avoided by keeping the level on firm ground. If this is impossible, stakes can be driven in the ground and the tripod legs can be set on these instead of directly on the ground. In precise leveling, two rods and two rodmen are used in order that the backsight and foresight readings from a set-up can be made more quickly. The error is still further diminished by taking the backsight first at one set-up of the level and the foresight first at the next set-up.

A proper choice of turning points should eliminate error from their settlement. If soft ground must be crossed, long stakes should be used as turning points.

3-35. Errors in Sighting. Parallax is the relative movement of the image of the leveling rod with respect to the cross hairs as the observer's eye is moved, and is caused by improper focusing of the objective lens. If the image formed by the lens lies either in front of or behind the plane of the cross hairs, as shown in Fig. 3-30(a) and (b), and the observer's eye is lowered and raised slightly, the cross hairs seem to move up and down on the rod. This movement is

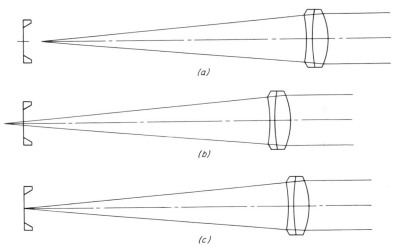

(a)

(b)

(c)

FIG. 3-30. Parallax.

corrected or eliminated by moving the objective lens in or out by means of the focusing knob until the cross hairs remain in one position on the rod as the position of the eye is changed. This position of the objective is shown in Fig. 3-30(c). If the cross hairs become slightly fuzzy, then the eyepiece needs adjusting. However, as long as no parallax exists between the cross hairs and the image of the rod, the only error introduced by lack of sharpness of the cross hairs will be that due to difficulty in reading the rod.

The rod should be plumb when the reading is made. The level-man can tell whether or not the rod is plumb in one direction by noting if it is parallel to the vertical cross hair. He cannot tell, however, if it is leaning toward or away from him. The leveling rods used on precise work are equipped with circular levels, so that the rodman can tell when he is holding the rod vertically. For less accurate work, the rodman can balance the rod between his fingers, if the wind is not blowing, or he can wave it slowly toward and then away from the level, as indicated in Fig. 3-31. The least reading obtainable is the proper one. If the target is being used, the line dividing the colors should just coincide with the cross hair, and then drop away from it. Errors from failure to hold the rod plumb will be much greater on

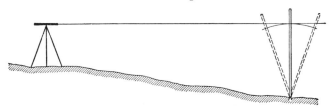

FIG. 3-31. Waving the rod.

readings near the top of the rod than for those near the bottom. For this reason more care should be exercised when making high-rod readings.

For careful work the lengths of the backsight and the foresight from the same set-up should be kept nearly equal. (See Sec. 3-32.) If, in ascending a steep hill, the level is always kept on the straight line between the turning points, the distance to the backsight will be about twice as great as the distance to the foresight, and considerable error may result if the instrument is not in good adjustment. If there are no obstructions, these two distances can be kept nearly equal by setting the level some distance away from the straight line between the turning points. By thus zigzagging with the level, this source of error can be eliminated.

3-36. Mistakes in Reading Rod, Recording, and Computing. A common mistake in reading the rod is to misread the number of feet or tenths. The careful levelman observes the foot and tenth marks both above and below the cross hair. On close sights, no foot mark may appear within the field of the telescope. In this case, the reading can be checked by directing the rodman to place his finger on the rod at the cross hair or, if the reading is a high one, by having him slowly raise the rod until a foot mark appears in the telescope. In case of doubt, the target can always be used.

Instruments for precise leveling are equipped with three horizontal cross hairs. All three hairs are read at each sighting. If the hairs are evenly spaced, the difference between the readings of the upper and the middle hairs should equal the difference between the readings of the middle and lower hairs. This comparison is always made before the rodman leaves a turning point.

Where readings to thousandths of a foot are being made with the target, a common mistake in recording is to omit one or more ciphers from such readings as 5.004, and to record instead 5.04 or 5.4. Such mistakes can be avoided by making sure that there are three decimal places for each reading. Thus, the second reading, if correct, should be recorded as 5.040, and the third as 5.400. If the values are not so recorded, the inference would be that the levelman was reading only to hundredths of a foot on the second reading and only to tenths on the third.

Other common mistakes of recording are the transposition of figures and the interchanging of backsight and foresight readings. If the levelman will keep the rodman at the point long enough to view the rod again after recording the reading, mistakes of the first type can often be detected. To prevent the interchange of readings, the beginner should remember that ordinarily the first reading taken from each position of the level is the backsight, or + S, reading and that only one + S reading is taken from any position of the level. Any other sights taken are foresight, or − S, readings.

Mistakes in computations, as far as they affect the elevations of turning points and bench marks, can be detected by proving the notes, as described in Sec. 3-29. This should be done as soon as the bottom of a page is reached, so that incorrect elevations will not be carried forward to a new page.

3-37. **Errors Due to Natural Sources.** One error due to natural sources is that caused by curvature and refraction, as described in Sec. 3-2. The error from this source amounts to but 0.0002 ft in a 100-ft sight, and to about 0.002 ft in a 300-ft sight. So, for ordinary leveling, it is a negligible quantity. It can be eliminated entirely by keeping the backsight and foresight distances from the same set-up equal. In precise leveling, if the sums of the backsight and foresight distances are not substantially equal, a correction is applied to the computed difference of elevation.

The familiar heat waves seen on a hot day are evidence of refraction and, when they are seen, refraction may be a fruitful source of error in leveling. When they are particularly intense, it may be impossible to read the rod unless the sights are much shorter than those usually taken. Refraction of this type is much worse close to the ground. For careful work, it may be necessary to discontinue the leveling for 2 or 3 hours during the middle of the day. It may be possible to keep the error from this source at a low figure by taking shorter sights and by so choosing the turning points that the line of sight will be at least 3 or 4 ft above the ground.

Better results will usually be obtained when it is possible to keep the level shaded. If the sun is shining on the instrument, it may cause an unequal expansion of the various parts of the instrument; or, if it heats one end of the bubble tube more than the other, the bubble will be drawn to the warmer end of the tube. For precise work, the level must be protected from the direct rays of the sun.

To guard against changes in the length of the leveling rod from variations in temperature, the graduations on rods used for precise leveling are placed on strips of invar, which has an extremely small coefficient of expansion. For ordinary leveling, errors from this source are negligible.

3-38. **Personal Errors.** Some levelmen consistently tend to read the rod too high or too low. This may be caused by defective vision, or by an inability to decide when the bubble is properly centered. In general, personal errors tend to be compensating, although some individuals may manipulate the level in such a way as to cause them to be cumulative. Such a tendency can be discovered by leveling over a line that has been previously checked by several different parties, or by running a number of circuits of levels each of which begins and ends on the same point.

3-39. **Limits of Error.** If care is used in leveling, most of the errors will tend to be random. For this reason, the error in any line can be expected to be proportional to the square root of the number of set-ups. See Sec. 4-7. Since the number of set-ups per mile of levels will be nearly constant, the error will also be proportional to the square root of the distance in miles. The precision that is being attained can be determined by comparing the two differences of elevation obtained by running levels in both directions over a line.

Since 1925, levels have been classified as first order, second order, third order, or fourth order, the class depending on the agreement between the results of leveling in both directions over a line. To be classed as first order, the difference, in feet, between the forward and backward measures should not be more than $0.017 \sqrt{M}$, where M is the length of the line in miles. For second-order precision, the coefficient of $\sqrt{M}$ is 0.035; and for third order it is increased to 0.05. If the error of closure is greater than this last limit, the levels are classed as fourth order.

3-40. **Reciprocal Leveling.** In leveling across a river or a deep valley, it is usually impossible to keep the lengths of the foresight and the backsight nearly equal. In such cases reciprocal leveling is used, except where approximate results are sufficient. The difference of elevation between points on the opposite sides of the river or valley is then obtained from two sets of observations.

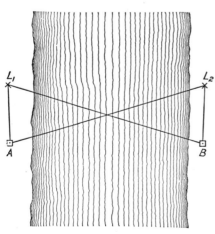

Fig. 3–32. Reciprocating leveling.

The method is illustrated by Fig. 3-32. The level is first set up at L_1 and rod readings are taken on the two points A and B. From these readings a difference of elevation is obtained. The level is then taken across the stream and set at such a position L_2 that $L_2B = L_1A$ and $L_2A = L_1B$. From this second position, readings are again taken on A and B, and a second difference of elevation is obtained. It is probable that these two differences will not agree. Both may be incorrect because of instrumental errors and curvature and refraction. However, the true difference of elevation should be very close to the mean of the two differences thus obtained.

The accuracy of this method will be increased if two leveling rods can be used, so that no appreciable time will elapse between the backsight and the foresight readings. It will be further increased by taking a number of rod readings on the more distant point, and using the average of these readings, rather than to depend on a single observation. If the distance AB is very great, it is important that the atmospheric conditions be the same for both positions of the level. Otherwise, a serious error may be introduced by a changed coefficient of refraction.

3-41. Double-Rodded Lines. When a line of levels must be run hastily and no time is available for regular check levels, double-rodded lines can be used to furnish a check on the elevation of a distant bench mark. The check is provided by using two sets of turning points. Readings on both sets are made from each position of the level. From these turning-point readings, two H. I.'s can be computed. Any considerable discrepancy between the two computed values indicates that a mistake has been made.

The two turning points may be very close together horizontally, but it will be advantageous if they have different elevations. Most specifications for accurate leveling forbid the use of double-rodded lines. The principal objection to them is the likelihood of repeating a mistake in the foot mark, unless the elevations of the two turning points differ by an appreciable amount.

An example of the form of notes kept on a short double-rodded line is shown in Fig. 3-33.

3-42. Three-Wire Leveling. Three-wire leveling, also referred to as precise leveling, is a process of direct leveling wherein three cross hairs, referred to as threads, are read and recorded rather than the single horizontal cross hair. The cross hairs are spaced so as to represent a horizontal distance of about 100 ft for every full foot intercepted on the rod between the upper and lower cross hairs. Any tilting level equipped with three horizontal cross hairs can be used for three-wire leveling.

In the geodetic level discussed in Sec. 3-16, the cross hairs are spaced so as to represent a horizontal distance of about 350 ft for every foot of rod interval. This spacing has the advantage in that, with greater magnification, long sights can be made, while at the same time all three hairs can be observed on the rod. Suppose, for example, that the sight length is 400 ft, the reading of the center cross hair is 1.500 ft, and the ratio of distance to rod intercept is 100 to 1. The upper cross hair would fall on the 3.500-ft mark, but

FORM C

1959-9-13. Survey for J.C.Harris. Levels from U.S.G.S. B.M. to Harris Property. Ann Arbor, Mich.				Level #4096. Level & Rec. J.Brown Rod #18. Rodman F. Smith	
+s	H.I.	-s	Elev.	Object	
4.18	880.60		876.42	U.S.G.S. B.M., S. side of U. of M. library	
4.18	880.60		876.42		
8.87	883.85	5.62	874.98	T.P. A-1	
9.48	883.84	6.24	874.36	T.P. B-1	+63.26
					−29.06
11.27	891.68	3.44	880.41	T.P. A-2	2)+34.20
10.50	891.67	2.67	881.17	T.P. B-2	+17.10
					876.42
7.77	897.87	1.58	890.10	T.P. A-3	893.52, check
7.01	897.85	0.83	890.84	T.P. B-3	
63.26					
		4.34	893.53	A. B.M. Top of iron pipe, S.E. corner	
		4.34	893.51	B. property of J.C.Harris, 843 Church	
		29.06	893.52	Mean	
				J. Brown	

Fig. 3–33.   Double-rodded level line.

the lower cross hair would fall 0.500 ft below the bottom of the rod. If the ratio is 350 to 1, the upper cross hair would fall on the 2.072-ft mark while the lower cross hair would fall on the 0.928-ft mark.

The rods used are graduated in feet, yards, or meters. Since three-wire leveling is used for great precision, the precise leveling rods described in Sec. 3-20 are preferred for use in leveling of this type. Furthermore, the rods are used in pairs.

The direction diagram and the form of notes for three-wire leveling are given in Figs. 3-34 and 3-35. The left-hand page is for the backsight readings, and the right-hand page is for the foresight readings.

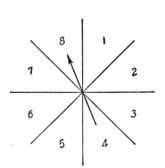

Fig. 3–34.   Direction diagram.

It is to be noted that a station refers to an instrument set-up, and not to a point on the ground. The procedure is explained with reference to the notes of Fig. 3-35. The levels are carried from B. M. 23 to B. M. 24 in the forward direction. The sun is shining from direction 5, and the wind is blowing from direction 2.

The forward rodman, carrying rod No. 4, selects a turning point, and the rear rodman is at the previous turning point. The level is now set up, and the observer backsights on the back turning point, reading 2487, 2416, and 2345 on the three cross hairs. He must take care that the level bubble is centered at each reading. These readings are made on a meter rod and are actually 2.487, 2.416, and 2.345 meters, respectively. The back of the rod is read by using only the middle cross hair, and the reading is 7.93 ft. The upper interval and the lower interval of 71 and 71 are computed and found to agree within 2 mm. So the mean of the three cross-hair readings is computed. This is compared with the equivalent reading in feet as a check against a mistake.

The observer then takes readings on rod No. 4 which is held on the forward turning point. The readings are 0519, 0444, and 0369 from the front of the rod and 1.46 ft from the back of the rod. The half-intervals are then computed for agreement, and the mean reading is computed and recorded. The total backsight interval of 142 mm, representing the backsight distance, differs from the total foresight interval of 150 mm, and the sum of the backsight intervals from the point of beginning (B. M. 23) is out of balance with the sum of the foresight intervals.

The back rodman advances to locate the next forward turning point. The next instrument set-up is at station 43. At this set-up, the foresight readings are taken before the backsight readings. Alternating the sequence of readings at each set-up tends to eliminate the effect of instrument settlement. Note that rod No. 7 will be sighted on first at each set-up. The accumulated sum of the backsight intervals is still out of balance with the sum of the foresight intervals, and the foresight distances must be made shorter. After station 46, the sums of intervals are out of balance by only 1 mm.

As a check on computing the mean readings, all the readings are added, the sum is divided by 3, and the result is compared with the sum of the means. This check is shown on the backsight page. A further check is made by adding the middle-thread readings in feet and converting the sum to meters as shown.

3-43. Collimation Correction. In the example of Sec. 3-42, the sum of the backsight intervals is 725 mm, and the sum of foresight intervals is 724 mm. If the distance-to-intercept ratio is assumed to be 350 to 1, the total of the backsight lengths is $725 \times 350 = 253750$ mm or about 254 meters. The total foresight length is 253 meters. This is a very close balance, requiring no measurable correction for the error discussed in Sec. 3-32 and shown in Fig. 3-29. Usually, however, such a close balance is not possible, and it becomes necessary to apply a collimation correction before the correct difference in elevation can be determined. This correction is commonly referred to as the C-factor correction, in which C represents the inclination of the line of sight when the level bubble is centered.

FORM D

THREE-WIRE LEVELING

DATE : 8-30-59   FORWARD – ~~BACKWARD~~

Sun : 5   (Strike out one word)

No. of Station	Thread Reading Back Sight	Mean	Middle Thread Reading Feet	Thread Interval	Sum of Intervals
	2487			71	
42	2416	2416.0	7.93	71	
	2345			142	142
	2800			83	
43	2717	2716.7	8.92	84	
	2633			167	309
	3242			61	
44	3181	3181.0	10.43	61	
	3120			122	431
	2744			72	
45	2672	2672.3	8.77	71	
	2601			143	574
	2602			75	
46	2527	2526.7	8.29	76	
	2451			151	725
	40538	13512.7	44.34		
	−10417	3472.3	11.40		
	3) 30121	+10040.4	+32.94 ft.	= + 10.04	meters
	+10040.3				

FIG. 3–35.

FORM D

THREE-WIRE LEVELING

From B.M.: 23   To B.M.: 24
Wind: 2   Time: 3⁴⁵

Rod and Temp.	Thread Reading Fore Sight	Mean	Middle Thread Reading Feet	Thread Interval	Sum of Intervals
4	0519			75	
22°C	0444	0444.0	1.46	75	
	0369			150	150
7	0748			82	
	0666	0665.3	2.19	84	
	0582			166	316
4	0663			57	
	0606	0606.3	1.99	56	
	0550			113	429
7	1066			74	
	0992	0991.7	3.25	75	
	0917			149	578
4	0838			73	
24°C	0765	0765.0	2.51	73	
	0692			146	724
	10417	3472.3	11.40		

Three-wire levels.

In Fig. 3-36, it is assumed that the level bubble is centered but the line of sight is inclined by the small angle α. The reading of a rod would be R, instead of R'. The error introduced is $R - R' = D \tan \alpha = D\alpha$, where α is a small angle expressed in radians. The

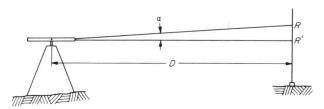

FIG. 3-36. Inclination of line of sight of level.

correction to R is then $-D\alpha = DC$, in which C is the value of the C-factor. Thus, $C = -\alpha$ and it follows that if C is positive, the line of sight is inclined downward.

In order to correct for an inclined line of sight when precise levels are run, the C-factor must be determined from time to time, perhaps as frequently as twice a day. It takes only a few minutes to determine C, and this factor should be evaluated not only for the tilting level but also for the self-leveling level, since the same type of error always exists in this type of instrument.

To compute C, two points at least 200 ft apart are chosen in fairly level terrain, and two independent differences of elevation between the points are determined from two set-ups. In Fig. 3-37(a), the instrument is set up about 20 ft from A. The distance to A is d_1, and the distance to B is D_1. These distances are measured. The rod reading at A is n_1, and that at B is N_1. The line of sight is shown sloping downward, or C is assumed to be positive. The difference in elevation found from this set-up is the corrected backsight at A minus the corrected foresight at B. Thus,

$$\text{D.E.}_{AB} = (n_1 + Cd_1) - (N_1 + CD_1) \tag{3-7}$$

The instrument is then set up about 20 ft from B, as indicated in Fig. 3-37(b). Rod readings N_2 and n_2 are taken at A and B, and the distances D_2 and d_2 from the instrument to the two rods are measured. The difference in elevation found from the second set-up is

$$\text{D.E.}_{AB} = (N_2 + CD_2) - (n_2 + Cd_2) \tag{3-8}$$

Equating the right-hand sides of Eq. 3-7 and Eq. 3-8 gives

$$(n_1 + Cd_1) - (N_1 + CD_1) = (N_2 + CD_2) - (n_2 + Cd_2)$$

The result obtained by solving for C is

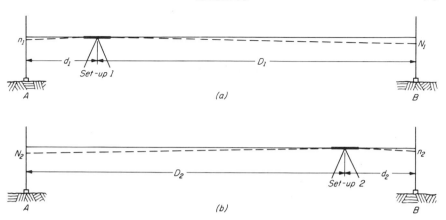

Fɪɢ. 3-37. Set-ups to determine C-factor.

$$C = \frac{(n_1 + n_2) - (N_1 + N_2)}{(D_1 + D_2) - (d_1 + d_2)} \qquad (3\text{-}9)$$

Since, as will be shown, corrections for collimation errors are computed from intervals rather than from distances, the two terms in the denominator are expressed in intervals. The quantity C is then expressed in feet per foot of interval or in millimeters per millimeter of interval.

Notes for the determination of C are shown in Fig. 3-38. The leveling rod was graduated in feet, and thread readings were recorded in feet. The conditions are represented in Fig. 3-37. When the instrument was set up near A, the readings of the three threads with the rod held at A were 4.600, 4.448, and 4.298, as shown in column 2 of Fig. 3-38. Their mean, which is shown in column 3, is 4.449 ft. This is n_1 in Fig. 3-37. The value of d_1 expressed as an interval is 0.302 ft, as shown in column 4 of Fig. 3-38 and again in column 5. The rod is now taken to B, and the three thread readings are 4.237, 3.515, and 2.790, as shown in column 6. The mean, which is 3.514, is shown in column 7. This is N_1 in Fig. 3-37. The value of D_1 expressed as an interval is 1.447, as shown in columns 8 and 9 of Fig. 3-38.

With the instrument set up near B in Fig. 3-37, the rod readings taken on B are recorded on the left-hand page of the notes in Fig. 3-38 in column 2. These rod readings give n_2 and d_2, as shown. In column 5, the quantity $(d_1 + d_2)$, or the sum of the intervals, is shown as 0.692 ft. From this set-up, the rod readings taken at A are recorded on the right-hand page in column 6. These readings give N_2 and D_2, as shown. In column 9, the quantity $(D_1 + D_2)$ is shown as 2.845. The sum of the two means in column 3 gives $(n_1 + n_2)$ in Eq. 3-9; the sum of the two means in column 7 gives $(N_1 + N_2)$. The

DETERMINATION OF C-FACTOR

No. of Station (1)	Thread Reading Feet (2)	Mean Feet (3)		Thread Interval Feet (4)	Sum of Intervals Feet (5)	Thread Reading Feet (6)	Mean Feet (7)		Thread Interval Feet (8)	Sum of Intervals Feet (9)
			BACKSIGHT					FORESIGHT		
	4.600			0.152		4.237			0.722	
1	4.448	4.449=n₁		0.150		3.515	3.514=N₁		0.725	
	4.298		d₁=	0.302	0.302=d₁	2.790		D₁=	1.447	1.447=D₁
	4.400			0.195		5.863			0.698	
2	4.205	4.205=n₂		0.195		5.165	5.164=N₂		0.700	
	4.010		d₂=	0.390	0.692=d₁+d₂	4.465		D₂=	1.398	2.845=D₁+D₂
		8.654 =n₁+n₂					8.678 =N₁+N₂			−0.692=d₁+d₂
		−8.678 =N₁+N₂							(D₁+D₂)−(d₁+d₂)	= 2.153
		−0.024 =(n₁+n₂)−(N₁+N₂)								
		$C = \frac{-0.024}{2.153} = -0.0112$ ft/ft of interval								

$$C = \frac{-0.024}{2.153} = -0.0112 \text{ ft/ft of interval}$$

FIG. 3-38. Notes for determining C-factor.

remaining computations needed to determine C are shown directly in the notes.

Assume that the results obtained when a line of levels was run between two points A and B in Fig. 3-39 are as follows: sum of backsight means, 31.422 ft; sum of foresight means, 12.556 ft; sum of backsight intervals, 22.464 ft; and sum of foresight intervals, 27.845 ft. The difference between ΣF.S. intervals and ΣB.S. intervals is $27.845 - 22.464 = 5.381$ ft. Therefore, the observed value of ΣF.S. means must be corrected by an amount equal to the C-factor times the difference between the intervals, that is, by $-0.0112 \times 5.381 = -0.060$ ft. The corrected value of ΣF.S. means is, thus, $12.556 -$

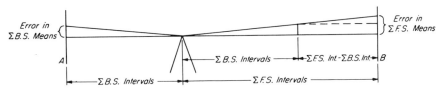

FIG. 3-39. Imbalance of sum of backsight and sum of foresight intervals.

0.060 = 12.496 ft. The corrected difference in elevation is then ΣB.S. means − ΣF.S. means = 31.422 − 12.496 = +18.926 ft.

3-44. Profile Levels. The purpose of profile leveling is to determine the elevations of the ground surface along some definite line. Before a railroad, highway, transmission line, sidewalk, canal, or sewer can be designed, a profile of the existing ground surface is necessary. The route along which the profile is run may be a single straight line, as in the case of a short sidewalk; a broken line, as in the case of a transmission line or sewer; or a series of straight lines connected by curves, as in the case of a railroad, highway, or canal. The data obtained in the field are usually employed in plotting the profile. This plotted profile is a graphical representation of the intersection of a vertical surface or a series of vertical surfaces with the surface of the earth, but it is generally drawn so that the vertical scale is much larger than the horizontal scale in order to accentuate the differences of elevation.

3-45. Stations. The line along which the profile is desired must be marked on the ground in some manner before the levels can be taken. The common practice is to set stakes at some regular interval— which may be 100, 50, or 25 ft, depending on the regularity of the ground surface and the accuracy required—and to determine the elevation of the ground surface at each of these points. The beginning point of the survey is designated as station 0. Points at multiples of 100 ft from this point are termed *full stations*. Horizontal distances along the line are most conveniently reckoned by the station method. Thus, points at distances of 100, 200, 300, and 1000 ft from the starting point of the survey are stations 1, 2, 3, and 10, respectively. Intermediate points are designated as *plusses*. A point that is 842.65 ft from the beginning point of the survey is station 8 + 42.65. If the plus sign is omitted, the resulting figure is the distance, in feet, from station 0.

When the stationing is carried continuously along a survey, the station of any point on the survey, at a known distance from any station or plus, can be calculated. Thus, a point that is 227.94 ft beyond station 8 + 42.65 is 842.65 + 227.94 = 1070.59 ft from station 0 or at station 10 + 70.59. The distance between station 38 + 66.77 and station 54 + 43.89 is 5443.89 − 3866.77 = 1577.12 ft.

In the case of a route survey, the stationing is carried continuously along the line to be constructed. Thus, if the survey is for a highway or a railroad, the stationing will be carried around the curves and will not be continuous along the straight lines which are eventually connected by curves. For the method of stationing that is used in surveys of this sort, see Chapter 9.

3-46. Field Routine of Profile Leveling. The principal difference between differential and profile leveling is in the number of foresights, or − S readings, taken from each setting of the level. In differential leveling only one such reading is taken, whereas in profile leveling any number can be taken. The theory is exactly the same for both types of leveling. A backsight, or + S reading, is taken on a bench mark or point of known elevation to determine the height of instrument. The rod is then held successively on as many points, whose elevations are desired, as can be seen from that position of the level, and rod readings (foresights, or − S readings) are taken. The elevations of these points are calculated by subtracting the corresponding rod readings from the H. I. When no more stations can be seen, a foresight is taken on a turning point, the level is moved forward, and the process is repeated.

The method of profile leveling is illustrated in Fig. 3-40. The level having been set up, a sight is taken on a bench mark, not shown in the sketch. Foresights are then taken on stations 0, 1, 2, 2 + 65, 3, and 4. The sight is taken at station 2 + 65 because there is a decided change in the ground slope at that point. The distance to this point from station 2 is obtained either by pacing or by taping, the better method depending on the precision required. To determine the elevation of the bottom of the brook between stations 4 and 5, the level is moved forward after a foresight reading has been taken on the turning point just beyond station 4. With the level in the new position, a backsight is taken on the turning point and foresights are taken on stations 4 + 55, 4 + 63, 4 + 75, 5, 5 + 70, 6, 6 + 25, and 7, and lastly on a turning point near station 7. From the third set-up, a backsight is taken on the turning point and foresights are taken on stations 8, 8 + 75, 9, 10, 10 + 40, and 11, and on a turning point near station 11. From the final set-up shown in the figure, a backsight is taken on this turning point and foresights are taken on stations 12 and 13, and on a bench mark not shown in the sketch.

Readings have thus been taken at the regular 100-ft stations and at intermediate points wherever there is a decided change in the slope. The level has not necessarily been set on the line between the stations. In fact, it is usually an advantage to have the level from 30 to 50 ft away from the line, particularly when readings must be taken on intermediate points. More of the rod will then be visible through the telescope and the reading can be made more easily and quickly.

If bench marks have not been established in advance, they should

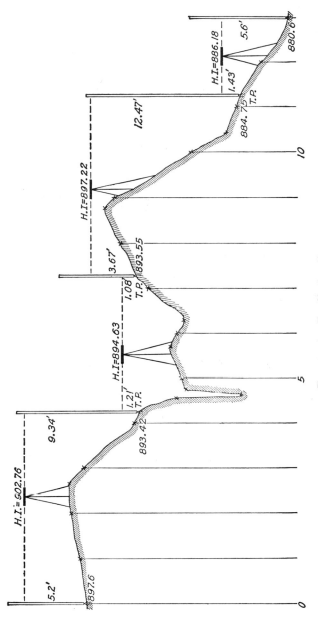

FIG. 3-40. Profile leveling.

be established as the work progresses. Bench marks may be from 10 to 20 stations apart when the differences of elevation are moderate, but the vertical intervals between bench marks should be about 20 ft where the differences of elevation are considerable. These bench marks should be so located that they will not be disturbed during any construction which may follow. Their elevations should be verified by running check levels.

FORM E

1960-3-1. Profile, Preliminary Location. Saline - Manchester, Highway. Washtenaw County, Mich. Location notes in field book 36, p.27.					Level #40.96. Level & Rec. J.Brown Rod #18. Rodman F.Smith	
Sta.	+s	H.I.	-s	Elev.		Remarks
B.M.	4.18	902.76		898.58		Spike in root of white-oak stump, 60' left of Sta. 0
0			5.2	897.6		
1			4.6	898.2		
2			3.9	898.9		
2+65			3.8	899.0		
3			4.9	897.9		
4			9.2	893.6		
T.P.	1.21	894.63	9.34	893.42		Top of stake, near Sta. 4.
4+55			4.4	890.2		S. bank Spring Brook
+63			9.9	884.7		℄ " "
+75			5.3	889.3		N. " " " Proof
5			5.0	889.6		898.58 9.34
5+70			3.9	890.7		4.18 1.08
6			4.5	890.1		1.21 12.47
6+25			5.4	889.2		3.67 7.47
7			2.2	892.4		1.43 878.71
T.P.	3.67	897.22	1.08	893.55		909.07 909.07 / On rock, near Sta. 7
8			2.4	894.8		
8+75			1.1	896.1		
9			1.9	895.3		
10			8.4	888.8		
10+40			11.3	885.9		
11			12.2	885.0		
T.P.	1.43	886.18	12.47	884.75		Top of stake, near Sta.11
12			3.4	882.8		
13			5.6	880.6		
B.M.			7.47	878.71		Spike in root of 14" maple, 50' right of Sta. 13+80
						J. Brown

FIG. 3-41. Profile level notes.

(**3-47.**) **Profile Level Notes.** Two different forms of profile level notes for the line of levels run over the route shown in Fig. 3-40 are given in Figs. 3-41 and 3-42. The principal difference between them is the manner in which the − S readings are recorded. In Form E, Fig. 3-41, all foresight readings are recorded in the same column, whereas in Form F, Fig. 3-42, two columns are provided, the − S readings taken on turning points and bench marks being kept in a

FORM F

Sta.	+S	H.I.	− S	Intermed. −S	Elev.	Remarks
						*1960-3-1. Profile, Preliminary Location. Saline – Manchester Highway. Washtenaw County, Mich. Location notes in field book 36, p.27.* / *Level #4096. Level & Rec. J. Brown* / *Rod #18. Rodman F. Smith*
B.M.	4.18	902.76			898.58	Spike in root of white-oak stump, 60' left of Sta. 0
0				5.2	897.6	
1				4.6	898.2	
2				3.9	898.9	
2+65				3.8	899.0	
3				4.9	897.9	
4				9.2	893.6	
T. P.	1.21	894.63	9.34		893.42	Top of stake, near Sta. 4
4+55				4.4	890.2	S. bank, Spring Brook
+63				9.9	884.7	¢ " "
+75				5.3	889.3	N. " " "
5				5.0	889.6	
5+70				3.9	890.7	
6				4.5	890.1	
6+25				5.4	889.2	
7				2.2	892.4	
T. P.	3.67	897.22	1.08		893.55	On rock, near Sta. 7
8				2.4	894.8	
8+75				1.1	896.1	*Proof*
9				1.9	895.3	898.58
10				8.4	888.8	−19.87
10+40				11.3	885.9	878.71 Check
11				12.2	885.0	
T. P.	1.43	886.18	12.47		884.75	Top of stake, near Sta.11
12	10.49			3.4	882.8	
13				5.6	880.6	
B.M.			7.47		878.71	Spike in root of 14" maple, 50' right of Sta. 13 + 80
			−30.36			
			+10.49			
			−19.87			J. Brown

FIG. 3–42.   Profile level notes.

separate column. This is a decided advantage in proving the notes, because the sums of the + S and − S columns can be obtained and the proof carried out in the same way as for differential levels, as shown in Form A, Fig. 3-27. In Form E the arithmetic is correct if the sum of the original B. M. elevation and all + S readings agrees with the sum of the − S readings, taken on turning points and bench marks, and the final elevation on the page.

It will be noticed that the readings on the ground surface are to tenths of a foot and those on bench marks and turning points are to hundredths. The ground surface is seldom regular enough to warrant readings closer than this. The closer readings on the B. M.'s and T. P.'s prevent the accumulation of error. Since the rod readings on the ground are to tenths, the corresponding ground-surface elevations are also to tenths.

3-48. Plotting the Profile. To facilitate the construction of profiles, paper prepared especially for the purpose is commonly used. This has horizontal and vertical lines in pale green, blue, or orange, so spaced as to represent certain distances to the horizontal and vertical scales. Such paper is called profile paper. If a single copy of the profile is sufficient, a heavy grade of paper is used. When reproductions are necessary, either a thin paper or tracing cloth is available. The common form of profile paper is divided into ¼-in. squares by fairly heavy lines. The space between each two such horizontal lines is divided into 5 equal parts by lighter horizontal lines, the distance between these light lines being ½₀ in. In order to accentuate the differences of elevation, the space between two horizontal lines can be considered as equivalent to 0.1, 0.2, or 1.0 ft, and the space between two vertical lines as 25, 50, or 100 ft, according to the total difference of elevation, the length of the line, and the requirements of the work.

To aid in estimating distances and elevations, each tenth vertical line and each fiftieth horizontal line is made extra heavy. A piece of profile paper showing the profile for the level notes given in Forms E and F is illustrated in Fig. 3-43. The elevation of some convenient extra-heavy horizontal line is assumed to be 900 ft and a heavy vertical line is taken as station 0. Each division between horizontal lines represents 1 ft and each division between vertical lines represents 100 ft, or 1 station. As the elevation or station of each printed line is known, the points on the ground surface can be plotted easily. When these points are connected with a smooth line, an accurate representation of that ground surface should result.

It is often a convenience to have several related profiles plotted on the same sheet. Thus, in designing a pavement for a city street, three profiles may appear, namely, those of the center line and of the

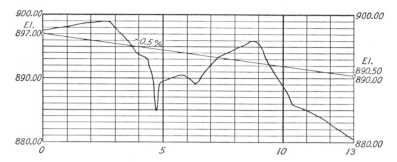

Preliminary Location
Saline-Manchester Highway
Washtenaw County, Mich.
Scales: Horiz. 1in.=400ft.
Vert. 1in. =15   "
Surveyed Sept.14,1959 by J.Brown
Platted   Sept. 28,1959 by A.Wishnefski

FIG. 3–43. Profile.

two curb lines. This is practically a necessity when there is any considerable difference in elevation between the two sides of the street. When only a single copy is being made, different colored inks can be used to distinguish one profile from another. When reproductions are to be made, different kinds of lines, such as different combinations of dots and dashes, are used.

As indicated in Sec. 16-13, it is possible to prepare a profile from a topographic map.

When it is desirable to have both the plan and the profile appear on the same sheet, paper which is half plain and half profile-ruled is used. Plans for highways and sewers often are prepared in this manner, the location plan appearing at the top of the sheet and the profile below it.

Any information that may make the profile more valuable should be added. Thus, the names of the streets or streams and the stations at which they are crossed should appear. The locations and elevations of bench marks may appear as notes on the map. There should be a title giving the following information: what the profile represents, its location, its scales, the date of the survey, and the names of the surveyor and the draftsman.

3-49. **Grade Lines.** The irregular line in Fig. 3-43 represents the original ground surface along which the profile has been taken. The line to which this surface is brought by grading operations is called the grade line. When planning a railroad, the grade line represents the proposed position of the base of the rail. For a street or highway, the grade line is the finished surface at the center line. For construction purposes, it is usually more convenient to let the grade line represent the subgrade, that is, the base of the ballast on a railroad or the bottom of the pavement slab on a paved highway.

The principal purpose for which a profile is constructed is to enable the engineer to establish the grade line. The aim of the engineer is to keep the volume of earthwork at a minimum, to have the grade line straight for considerable distances and its inclination within the allowable limit, and to have the excavation and the embankment balance over reasonably short stretches. To determine the best grade line may require considerable study, but the saving of even a few hundred cubic yards of grading will pay for many hours of such study.

Where changes in the inclination of the grade line occur, the straight grades are connected by vertical curves. (See Sec. 9-15.)

3-50. Rate of Grade. The inclination of the grade line to the horizontal can be expressed by the ratio of the rise or fall of the line to the corresponding horizontal distance. The amount by which the grade line rises or falls in a unit of horizontal distance is called the rate of grade or the gradient. The rate of grade is usually expressed as a percentage; that is, as the rise or fall in a horizontal distance of 100 ft. If the grade line rises 2 ft in 100 ft, it has an ascending grade of 2 per cent, which is written + 2 per cent. If the grade line falls 1.83 ft in 100 ft, it has a descending grade of 1.83 per cent, which is written − 1.83 per cent. The sign + indicates a rising grade line and the sign − indicates a falling grade line.

The rate of grade is written along the grade line on the profile. The elevation of grade is written at the extremities of the line, and also at each point where the rate of grade changes. It is common practice to enclose in small circles the points on the profile where the rate of grade changes.

The rate of grade, in per cent, is equal to the total rise or fall in any horizontal distance divided by the horizontal distance expressed in stations of 100 ft. The total rise or fall of a grade line in any given horizontal distance is equal to the rate of grade, in per cent, multiplied by the horizontal distance in stations. The horizontal distance, in stations of 100 ft, in which a given grade line will rise or fall a certain number of feet is equal to the amount of the required rise or fall divided by the rate of grade, in per cent.

PROBLEMS

3-1. Compute the departure of a level surface from a horizontal plane at a distance of 35 miles from the point of tangency.

3-2. A backsight of 8.250 ft is taken on a point 200 ft from the level. A foresight of 3.134 ft is then taken on a point 825 ft from the level. Compute the correct difference in elevation between the two points.

3-3. A vertical angle of −2° 06′ 20″ is read to a signal which is 18.0 ft above ground station B. The telescope of the instrument is 5.0 ft above ground station A. The distance AB is 34,200 ft. The elevation of station B is 465 ft. Compute the elevation of Station A.

3-4. Three altimeters, A, B, and C, read the same when held on a bench mark whose elevation is 416 ft. Altimeter A is kept at this bench mark; altimeter B is taken to a bench mark at an elevation of 1402 ft; altimeter C is used as a field altimeter. The following readings were taken:

Time	Altimeter A	Altimeter B	Altimeter C
1:10	1391	2358	1402
1:25	1394	2358	1616
1:45	1396	2360	1580
1:50	1398	2366	1890
2:30	1406	2376	2205

Determine the elevations of the five field points.

3-5. The radius of curvature of the bubble tube of an engineer's level is 67 ft. The graduations on the tube are 2 mm apart. What is the sensitiveness of the bubble in seconds?

3-6. A level is set up, and the end of the level bubble is carefully brought to a graduation on the tube. A reading of 3.466 ft is taken on a rod held 340 ft from the level. The level is then tilted so as to cause the end of the bubble to move over six divisions, and the rod is again read. This second reading is 3.341 ft. What is the sensitiveness of the bubble?

3-7. How much error will be introduced in a rod reading of 11.905 ft, if the rod is 13 ft long and the top leans 0.5 ft away from the level? What is the error if the rod reading is 2.000 ft?

3-8. By means of an instrument set 5.0 ft above a point A, a vertical angle of +1° 58′ is read to a signal which is 14.0 ft above a point B. With the instrument set up 5.0 ft above B, a vertical angle of −1° 58′ is read to a target which is 5.0 ft above A. The horizontal distance between A and B is 12,000 ft. What is the difference in elevation between the two points to the nearest tenth of a foot?

3-9. If the horizontal distance in Problem 3-8 is in error by 120 ft, what is the resulting error in the difference in elevation?

3-10. Complete the accompanying set of notes recorded in running differential levels between two bench marks. Prove the notes to detect arithmetical mistakes.

Sta.	B.S.	H.I.	F.S.	Elev.
B.M. 16	4.64			232.20
T.P. 1	5.80		5.06	
T.P. 2	2.25		5.02	
B.M. 17	6.02		5.85	
T.P. 3	8.96		4.34	
T.P. 4	8.06		3.22	
T.P. 5	9.45		3.71	
T.P. 6	12.32		2.02	
B.M. 18			1.98	

3-11. Reduce and prove the accompanying set of profile level notes.

Sta.	B.S.	H.I.	F.S.	I.F.S.	Elev.
B.M. 3	4.45				976.28
T.P. 1	4.18		2.90		
0 + 00				3.2	
1 + 00				1.9	
1 + 20				1.4	
2 + 00				3.3	
2 + 50				3.2	
3 + 00				4.9	
3 + 80				7.2	
T.P. 2	2.02		7.08		
4 + 00				2.9	
5 + 00				3.0	
6 + 00				5.0	
T.P. 3	6.84		4.91		
6 + 42				7.7	
6 + 46				9.9	
6 + 60				9.7	
7 + 00				6.8	
8 + 00				1.3	
B.M. 4			1.44		

3-12. Using a horizontal scale of $1'' = 1$ station and a vertical scale of $1'' = 5$ ft, plot the profile of the line to which the notes of Problem 3-11 apply.

3-13. The grade elevation at station $25 + 42.00$ is to be 2456.70 ft. What will be the grade elevation at station $39 + 14.25$, if the grade line falls at the rate of 3.25 per cent between these two points.

3-14. The grade elevation of station $152 + 50$ is 763.60 ft, and the grade elevation of station $159 + 75$ is 785.44 ft. What is the rate of grade, in per cent, of a slope joining these two stations?

3-15. Compute the slope of the line of sight of a level from the following observations taken in each instance with the level bubble centered. From the first instrument set-up, the reading on a rod at A is 3.729 ft and that on a rod at B is 4.286 ft. The distance from the level to A is 20 ft, and the distance to B is 220 ft. From the second instrument set-up, the reading on the rod at A is 4.368 ft and that at B is 4.908 ft. The distance to A is 200 ft, and that to B is 15 ft.

4

Random Errors

4-1. Nature of Random Errors. In the processes of taping and leveling described in Chapters 2 and 3, several sources of errors and mistakes were discussed. Mistakes are eliminated when the observer takes such precautions as measuring a distance in both directions, proving level notes, and using other procedures which will help to avoid or detect the mistakes. Systematic errors can be practically eliminated by using calibrated tapes, by correcting taped distances for temperature, tension, sag, and slope, by balancing backsight and foresight distances in leveling, by alternating the sequence of taking backsight and foresight readings, and by having the leveling rod plumb when it is read.

Random errors, often called accidental errors, are unpredictable in regard to both size and algebraic sign. They are truly accidental and cannot be avoided. The statements in the articles to follow are based on three important principles of random errors: 1) A plus error will occur as frequently as will a minus error; 2) small errors will occur more frequently than large errors; and 3) very large errors do not occur at all, or the chance for a large error to occur is remote.

4-2. Probability of an Error Occurring. If serious thought is given to some of the examples of sources of random errors discussed in Chapters 2 and 3, it will be seen that any one single error can be considered to be in itself the result of an indefinite number of very small elementary errors introduced together at any one time. The size and algebraic sign of the resultant random error are determined by the manner in which these elementary errors build up when combined in a measurement. Each element of error is thought of as having an equal chance of being plus or minus, and each element is further considered as having the same size as each other element. For a given number of these elements, or units, of error acting together, we can determine the possible number of combinations of the units, the size of the resultant error from each combination and the probability of each such size occurring.

Assume that the size of each unit of error is unity. If one unit acts alone, the size of the resultant error is 1 and the possible number of combinations is two, since the error may be either $+ 1$ or $- 1$. The probability of either combination occurring is ½, or 1 out of 2. Probability is defined as the number of times a given value should occur divided by the total number of times all values can occur. If two units act together, there are four possible combinations. These are $+ 1$ and $+ 1$, $+ 1$ and $- 1$, $- 1$ and $- 1$, and $- 1$ and $+ 1$. The sizes of the resultant errors are, respectively, $+ 2, 0, - 2$, and 0. The probability of $+ 2$ occurring is ¼, that of 0 occurring is ¾, and that of $- 2$ occurring is ¼.

Each time the number of units acting at any one time is increased by one, the number of possible combinations will double. Three units

TABLE 4-1

CHARACTERISTICS OF RANDOM ERRORS

Number of Units Combining at One Time	Units in Combination	Number of Combinations	Total Number of Combinations	Size of Resultant Error	Probability of Occurrence of Resultant Error
1	$+ 1$	1		$+ 1$	1/2
	$- 1$	1	2	$- 1$	1/2
2	$+ 1, + 1$	1		$+ 2$	1/4
	$+ 1, - 1$	2		0	2/4
	$- 1, - 1$	1	4	$- 2$	1/4
3	$+ 1, + 1, + 1$	1		$+ 3$	1/8
	$+ 1, + 1, - 1$	3		$+ 1$	3/8
	$+ 1, - 1, - 1$	3		$- 1$	3/8
	$- 1, - 1, - 1$	1	8	$- 3$	1/8
4	$+ 1, + 1, + 1, + 1$	1		$+ 4$	1/16
	$+ 1, + 1, + 1, - 1$	4		$+ 2$	4/16
	$+ 1, + 1, - 1, - 1$	6		0	6/16
	$+ 1, - 1, - 1, - 1$	4		$- 2$	4/16
	$- 1, - 1, - 1, - 1$	1	16	$- 4$	1/16
5	$+ 1, + 1, + 1, + 1, + 1$	1		$+ 5$	1/32
	$+ 1, + 1, + 1, + 1, - 1$	5		$+ 3$	5/32
	$+ 1, + 1, + 1, - 1, - 1$	10		$+ 1$	10/32
	$+ 1, + 1, - 1, - 1, - 1$	10		$- 1$	10/32
	$+ 1, - 1, - 1, - 1, - 1$	5		$- 3$	5/32
	$- 1, - 1, - 1, - 1, - 1$	1	32	$- 5$	1/32
6	$+ 1, + 1, + 1, + 1, + 1, + 1$	1		$+ 6$	1/64
	$+ 1, + 1, + 1, + 1, + 1, - 1$	6		$+ 4$	6/64
	$+ 1, + 1, + 1, + 1, - 1, - 1$	15		$+ 2$	15/64
	$+ 1, + 1, + 1, - 1, - 1, - 1$	20		0	20/64
	$+ 1, + 1, - 1, - 1, - 1, - 1$	15		$- 2$	15/64
	$+ 1, - 1, - 1, - 1, - 1, - 1$	6		$- 4$	6/64
	$- 1, - 1, - 1, - 1, - 1, - 1$	1	64	$- 6$	1/64

of error acting together give eight possible combinations; four units give sixteen combinations, and so on. Table 4-1 shows the relationship between the number of combinations and the probability that an error of a given size will occur.

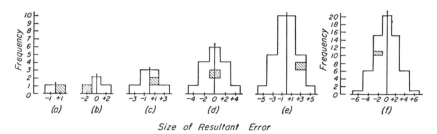

FIG. 4–1. Plot of size of resultant error vs. frequency based on plus and minus unit errors.

The results of Table 4-1 are plotted in Fig. 4-1, views (a) through (f). The shaded rectangle represents the following probability. In (a), ½; in (b), ¼; in (c), ⅛; in (d), ⅟₁₆; in (e), ⅟₃₂; and in (f), ⅟₆₄. It is to be noted that the total area in each case is one. In Fig. 4-1 (f), the vertical scale has been reduced to one-half of that in the other five views.

If the number of units of error were increased indefinitely, the graphical representation of the size of the resultant errors and the frequency of their occurrence would approach a bell-shaped curve called the *probability curve,* or the *normal error distribution curve.*

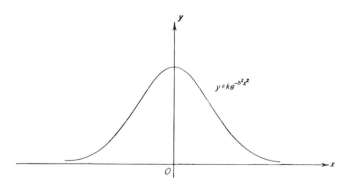

FIG. 4–2. Probability curve.

Such a curve is shown in Fig. 4-2. This curve portrays the three principles of random errors stated in Sec. 4-1. The equation of this curve is

$$y = ke^{-h^2 x^2} \qquad (4\text{-}1)$$

in which y = relative probability of occurrence of an error of a given
size;

x = size of the error;

k and h = constants which determine the shape of the curve;

e = base of natural logarithms.

The values of k and h under a given set of circumstances will be discussed in Sec. 4-4.

4-3. Condition of Least Squares. In Sec. 1-9, an error is defined as the difference between the true value of a quantity and the measured value of the same quantity. Since the true value of a quantity can never be determined, the errors in the measurements can be determined only to the extent that systematic errors can theoretically be computed and eliminated. Let it be presumed that a quantity has been measured several times, and that a slightly different value has been obtained from each measurement. Then by an extended investigation of Eq. 4-1, the value of the quantity which has the most frequent chance of occurrence, or which has the *maximum probability* of occurrence, is the one which will render the sum of the squares of the errors a minimum.

Suppose, for example, that in a given set of measurements, M_1, $M_2, \ldots, M_n$, some value is adopted to represent the best possible value of the measured quantity obtainable from the set. Let this be denoted as M. The following subtractions are then made:

$$M_1 - M = v_1$$
$$M_2 - M = v_2$$
$$\vdots$$
$$M_n - M = v_n$$

The v's on the right-hand side are termed *residuals*. They are similar to errors (x's), but errors are obtained by subtracting the true value, rather than the best possible value, from the measurements. The equation of the probability curve, or Eq. 4-1, can then be written in terms of the residuals as follows:

$$y = ke^{-h^2 v^2} \qquad (4\text{-}2)$$

in which v is the size of the residual, and the other terms are defined as for Eq. 4-1.

The probability of the occurrence of, for example, v_1 is then the area of the probability curve at this value. This area is obtained by

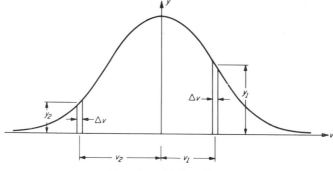

FIG. 4-3. Probability.

multiplying the ordinate by an arbitrary increment Δv, as shown in Fig. 4-3. If a probability is denoted by P, the probability that v_1, v_2, ..., v_n will occur in the set of measurements is as follows:

$$P_{v_1} = y_1 \, \Delta v = ke^{-h^2 v_1^2} \, \Delta v$$

$$P_{v_2} = y_2 \, \Delta v = ke^{-h^2 v_2^2} \, \Delta v$$

$$\cdot$$
$$\cdot$$
$$\cdot$$

$$P_{v_n} = y_n \, \Delta v = ke^{-h^2 v_n^2} \, \Delta v$$

Also, the probability that the various v's will occur simultaneously in a set is equal to the product of the separate probabilities. Thus,

$$P_{(v_1,\, v_2,\, \ldots,\, v_n)} = (ke^{-h^2 v_1^2} \, \Delta v)\,(ke^{-h^2 v_2^2} \, \Delta v) \ldots (ke^{-h^2 v_n^2} \, \Delta v)$$

or

$$P_{(v_1,\, v_2,\, \ldots,\, v_n)} = k^n \, (\Delta v)^n \, e^{-h^2 (v_1^2 + v_2^2 + \ldots + v_n^2)} \qquad (4\text{-}2a)$$

The quantity M must be selected so as to give the maximum probability of the simultaneous occurrence of the v's. According to Eq. 4-2a, that unique set of v's which has the highest probability of occurring is the one which will make $P_{(v_1,\, v_2,\, \ldots,\, v_n)}$ a maximum. This condition exists when the negative exponent of e in Eq. 4-2a has a minimum value. That is, for maximum probability,

$$v_1^2 + v_2^2 + \ldots + v_n^2 = \text{minimum}$$

or

$$\Sigma v^2 = \text{minimum} \qquad (4\text{-}3)$$

Equation 4-3 expresses the *condition of least squares* that is imposed upon a set of measurements when each is made with the same reliability (see Sec. 4-10) and the resulting set of residuals conforms to the principles relating to random errors stated in Sec. 4-1.

When a quantity is measured directly several times, the best value or most probable value, of the quantity is the arithmetic mean of the measured values. This can be shown as follows:

$$v_1 = M_1 - M \; ; \; v_1^2 = (M_1 - M)^2$$

$$v_2 = M_2 - M \; ; \; v_2^2 = (M_2 - M)^2$$

$$\vdots$$

$$v_n = M_n - M \; ; \; v_n^2 = (M_n - M)^2$$

$$\Sigma v^2 = (M_1 - M)^2 + (M_2 - M)^2 + \ldots + (M_n - M)^2$$

In order to make Σv^2 a minimum, in accordance with Eq. 4-3, the procedure is to differentiate with respect to M and to set the derivative equal to zero. Thus,

$$\frac{d}{dM}(\Sigma v^2) = -2(M_1 - M) - 2(M_2 - M) - \ldots$$
$$-2(M_n - M) = 0 \qquad (4\text{-}4)$$

Then

$$\frac{d^2}{dM^2}(\Sigma v^2) = 2 + 2 + 2 + \ldots + 2 = \text{a positive number}$$

indicating a minimum. Also, from Eq. 4-4,

$$M_1 - M + M_2 - M + \ldots + M_n - M = 0$$

or

$$nM = M_1 + M_2 + \ldots + M_n$$

Hence,

$$M = \frac{M_1 + M_2 + \ldots + M_n}{n} = \text{arithmetic mean}$$

4-4. Standard Error. A residual v is treated as a random error in every respect. Suppose that one hundred measurements of the length of a line were made and that all systematic errors have been eliminated. The mean of all the measurements is the most probable value. If the mean is now subtracted from each measured value, one hundred residuals of varying size would result. If each size of residual is plotted against the frequency of occurrence of that size, the resulting curve will be similar to that of Fig. 4-3. This curve is called the *normal distribution curve*. Its equation is

$$y = \frac{1}{\sigma\sqrt{2\pi}} e^{(-1/2\sigma^2)v^2} \qquad (4\text{-}5)$$

in which y = relative frequency of the occurrence of a residual of a
    given size;

σ = a constant to be determined from the measurements;

v = size of the residual.

The value of σ is obtained from the measurements by the formula

$$\sigma = \sqrt{\frac{\Sigma v^2}{n-1}} \qquad (4\text{-}6)$$

in which Σv^2 is the sum of the squares of the residuals and n is the
number of measurements. The quantity σ is referred to as the
standard error of the group of measurements. It indicates the precision of the measurements relative to any other group of measurements. The smaller σ becomes, the greater is the precision.

The quantity $(n-1)$ in the denominator under the radical in
Eq. 4-6 represents the number of extra measurements taken to determine a value. For example, if a line was measured five times, or
$n = 5$, there are four extra measurements, since one would have been
sufficient although it would not be very reliable. As the number of
extra measurements increases, the standard error becomes smaller.
In statistics, the quantity $(n-1)$ is sometimes referred to as the
number of degrees of freedom. Since a residual is obtained by subtracting the mean value of n measurements from any one of these
measurements, the following statement must be true. If the mean of
n measurements and any $n-1$ of the measurements are given, the
one measurement which was left out can be determined. In other
words, it is a dependent measurement.

EXAMPLE 4-1. The length of a line is measured five times. Four of the
measured lengths are 154.26, 154.29, 154.26, and 154.21 ft. Also the mean of
all the measured lengths is 154.25 ft. What is the value of the dependent
measurement?

Solution: The sum of the five measurements is obviously 5 times the
mean, or $5 \times 154.25 = 771.25$ ft. The sum of the four given measurements is
617.02 ft. The dependent measurement is $771.25 - 617.02 = 154.23$ ft.

A comparison of the probability curve given by Eq. 4-1 and the
curve representing the distribution of errors derived from an actual
set of measurements given by Eq. 4-2 and Eq. 4-5 shows that a
residual v is treated as an error x. Also, the two constants k and h
are obtained in terms of values derived from actual measurements by
the relations

$$k = \frac{1}{\sigma\sqrt{2\pi}}$$

and

$$h^2 = \frac{1}{2\,\sigma^2}$$

It is seen that as k and h increase, so does the precision of the measurements increase. The quantity h is known as the *precision modulus* of the measurements.

4-5. Histograms. A *histogram* is a visual representation of the distribution of a set of measurements or a set of residuals. The representations showing the distribution of unit errors in Fig. 4-1 are histograms. A histogram shows by examination whether the measurements or residuals are symmetrical about some central value, such as the mean value or the zero residual; they show the total spread of values of the measurements or residuals; they show frequencies of the different values; and they show how peaked or how flat the distribution of the values is.

When an area was measured 100 times by means of a polar planimeter, the results expressed in square inches and arranged in ascending order were as shown in the accompanying tabulation. The arithmetic mean of these values, rounded off to the nearest 0.001 square inch, is 1.667. Subtracting the mean from each measured value gives the set of 100 residuals associated with these measurements. The residuals are also arranged in ascending order in the tabulation, and the unit is the square inch.

MEASUREMENTS OF AREA, IN SQUARE INCHES

1.651	1.662	1.665	1.669	1.674
51	63	65	69	74
53	63	66	69	74
53	63	66	69	74
56	63	66	69	74
56	63	66	1.670	75
57	63	66	70	75
57	63	66	70	76
58	63	67	70	76
58	64	67	71	77
58	64	67	71	77
59	64	67	71	78
59	64	67	71	1.680
1.660	64	67	71	80
61	64	67	71	80
61	65	68	71	81
61	65	68	72	83
61	65	68	72	84
61	65	68	73	84
61	65	68	73	85

RESIDUALS, IN SQUARE INCHES

− 0.016	− 0.005	− 0.002	+ 0.002	+ 0.007
16	04	02	02	07
14	04	01	02	07
14	04	01	02	07
11	04	01	02	07
11	04	01	03	08
10	04	01	03	08
10	04	01	03	09
09	04	0	03	09
09	03	0	04	+ 0.010
09	03	0	04	10
08	03	0	04	11
08	03	0	04	13
07	03	0	04	13
06	03	0	04	13
06	02	+ 0.001	04	14
06	02	01	05	16
06	02	01	05	17
06	02	01	06	17
06	02	01	06	18

A histogram can be drawn for each set of tabulated values. In Fig. 4-4, which is the histogram for the first set, the abscissas are the measurements in the range from 1.649 sq in. to 1.685 sq in. plotted at intervals of 0.001 sq in. Thus, each interval is given a discrete

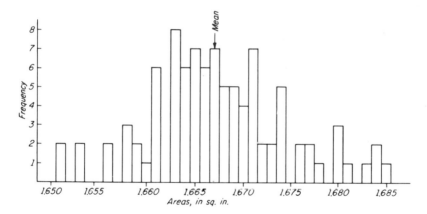

FIG. 4-4. Histogram of polar planimeter measurements.

value. The ordinates show the frequency of occurrence of each given abscissa. In Fig. 4-5, which is the histogram for the set of 100 residuals, the abscissas are the sizes of the residuals in the range from −0.018 sq in. to +0.018 sq in.

The value of σ for this set of residuals can be computed by Eq. 4-6, and the normal distribution curve can be plotted to some arbitrary scale by applying Eq. 4-5. However, it is usually desirable

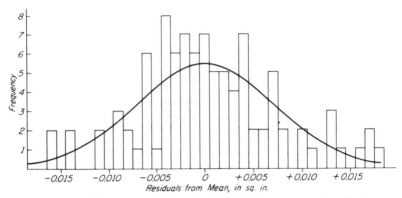

FIG. 4-5. Histogram and normal distribution curve of residuals.

to plot the normal distribution curve to the same scale as the residual histogram in Fig. 4-5. In order that this may be done, Eq. 4-5 must be modified as follows: Let the abscissa interval, which is designated the class interval, be denoted by I, and let n denote the number of measurements or residuals. Then Eq. 4-5 takes the form

$$y = \frac{nI}{\sigma\sqrt{2\pi}} e^{(-1/2\sigma^2) v^2} \qquad (4\text{-}5a)$$

After the value of σ has been determined from the residuals, it is possible to compute the following constant quantities for the set:

$$\frac{nI}{\sigma\sqrt{2\pi}} = K_1 \quad \text{and} \quad \frac{1}{2\sigma^2} = K_2$$

When these constants are substituted in Eq. 4-5a, that equation becomes

$$y = \frac{K_1}{e^{K_2 v^2}} \qquad (4\text{-}7)$$

This form is convenient for slide-rule computation.

EXAMPLE 4-2. For the normal distribution curve for the set of residuals shown in histogram form in Fig. 4-5, compute the ordinates corresponding to abscissas that are multiples of 0.002. Plot the curve onto the histogram.

Solution: The sum of the squares of the residuals, or Σv^2, is found by computation to be 0.005235. These computations are not shown, but the procedure is similar to that indicated in Example 4-3. The standard error is then

$$\sigma = \sqrt{\frac{0.005235}{100 - 1}} = \pm\, 0.0073 \text{ sq in.}$$

Since $n = 100$ and $I = 0.001$ sq in., the value of K_1 in Eq. 4-7 is

$$K_1 = \frac{100 \times 0.001}{0.0073\sqrt{2\pi}} = 5.46$$

Also,

$$K_2 = 9460$$

v	v^2	$K_2 v^2$	$e^{K_2 v^2}$	$y = \dfrac{K_1}{e^{K_2 v^2}}$
0	0	0	1.000	5.46
± 0.002	0.000004	0.0378	1.039	5.26
± 0.004	0.000016	0.1514	1.162	4.70
± 0.006	0.000036	0.340	1.405	3.88
± 0.008	0.000064	0.605	1.83	2.98
± 0.010	0.000100	0.946	2.58	2.12
± 0.012	0.000144	1.362	3.90	1.40
± 0.014	0.000196	1.855	6.40	0.85
± 0.016	0.000256	2.42	11.2	0.49
± 0.018	0.000324	3.10	22.2	0.25

The remainder of the computations are arranged in tabular form, as shown. The computed values of y have been plotted on the histogram in Fig. 4-5, and the normal distribution curve has been drawn as a continuous line through the plotted points. Note that the area under the curve is essentially the same as the area bounded by the histogram, as it should be. Note also that if the histogram of residuals had not been prepared, the normal distribution curve could have been plotted on the histogram of the measurements shown in Fig. 4-4 by renumbering the abscissa scale so that $v = 0$ occurs at the mean measured value of 1.667 sq in.

4-6. Measures of Precision. Both the standard error σ and the precision modulus h are measures of precision of a set of measurements. If the curve for Eq. 4-5 were to be integrated between the limits $-\sigma$ and $+\sigma$, the area between these limits would be 0.6826 times the total area under the curve, the total area being unity. In other words, approximately 68 per cent of all the residuals for the set of measurements should be equal to or less than the standard error. In Example 4-2, 72 per cent of the residuals fall between -0.0073 and $+0.0073$ sq in. For further analysis, the curve plotted in Fig. 4-5 is redrawn in Fig. 4-6.

The area under the curve between the limits $-\sigma$ and $+\sigma$ is indicated. Also, as can be seen on this curve, the standard error occurs at the point of inflection on each side of the center.

Let it be desired to find the size of a residual, plus or minus, within which one half, or 50 per cent, of the residuals should fall. This size would be the fractional part of σ for which the area under the curve will be 0.50. The limits of this area are the dashed lines in Fig. 4-6. The error of a size embracing 50 per cent of all residuals is called the *probable error*. It is obtained by the formula

$$E = 0.6745\,\sigma = 0.6745\sqrt{\frac{\Sigma v^2}{n-1}} \tag{4-8}$$

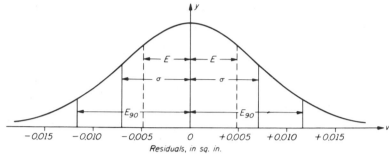

FIG. 4-6. Measures of precision.

in which E is the probable error of any one of the measurements, and the other symbols have the meanings previously given. Another way of indicating the meaning of probable error is to say that the residual of any one measurement has an equal chance of being either less than E or greater than E. In Example 4-2, the probable error is ± 0.0048 sq in. It is seen that 55 per cent of the residuals fall in the range between -0.0048 and $+0.0048$ sq in.

EXAMPLE 4-1. The measurements of the difference in elevation between two points by three-wire leveling are listed in the accompanying tabulation. What are the standard error and the probable error of any one of these measurements?

Measurement Number	Measured Differences in Elevation (ft)	Residual v (ft)	v^2
1	21.232	-0.001	0.000001
2	21.235	$+0.002$	0.000004
3	21.233	0	0
4	21.225	-0.008	0.000064
5	21.233	0	0
6	21.221	-0.012	0.000144
7	21.239	$+0.006$	0.000036
8	21.244	$+0.011$	0.000121
9	21.232	-0.001	0.000001
10	21.234	$+0.001$	0.000001
11	21.229	-0.004	0.000016
12	21.235	$+0.002$	0.000004
13	21.237	$+0.004$	0.000016
14	21.230	-0.003	0.000009
15	21.235	$+0.002$	0.000004

Sum = 318.494
Mean = 21.233

$\Sigma v^2 = 0.000421$

Solution: First find the mean of the measured differences in elevation. Then compute each residual and its square, and get Σv^2. The standard error of any one of these measurements is, by Eq. 4-3,

$$\sigma = \sqrt{\frac{0.000421}{15 - 1}} = \pm 0.0055 \text{ ft}$$

The probable error of any one of these measurements is, by Eq. 4-4,

$$E = 0.6745 \, (\pm 0.0055) = \pm 0.0037 \, \text{ft}$$

Theoretically, one half of the residuals should lie between $+ 0.0037$ ft and $- 0.0037$ ft.

The probable error E, as well as the quantities h and σ, is a measure of the precision of a given set of measurements and can be computed after the measurements have been made. The quantity E is sometimes referred to as the *50 per cent error*, because 50 per cent of all the residuals are theoretically expected to fall between $+ E$ and $- E$.

Another very useful measure of precision is the *90 per cent error*, or the value below which 90 per cent of all residuals of a set of measurements are expected to fall. The 90 per cent error is determined from the standard error by the relation

$$E_{90} = 1.6449 \, \sigma$$

Thus, the 90 per cent error is about 2½ times the size of the probable error. This measure of precision is valuable in deciding the worth of a given set of measurements, since it indicates the size of the residual that is exceeded by only 10 per cent of the residuals. In Example 4-2, E_{90} is ± 0.0118 sq in. Actually, a total of 88 per cent of the residuals fall in the range between -0.0118 and $+0.0118$ sq in.

4-7. Propagation of Random Errors. One fundamental principle derived from the laws of probability is that the standard error of the sum of several measured quantities is equal to the square root of the sum of the squares of the standard errors of the individual quantities. In algebraic form this relationship is

$$\sigma_s = \sqrt{\sigma_1{}^2 + \sigma_2{}^2 + \cdots + \sigma_n{}^2} \qquad (4\text{-}9)$$

where σ_s is the standard error of the sum of the measurements each of which has a standard error designated by σ with a numerical subscript. In Example 4-3, the sum of all the measurements has a standard error σ_s equal to the square root of the sum of the squares of the standard errors for all the listed measurements. Therefore, for the measurements in Example 4-3,

$$\sigma_s = \sqrt{0.0055^2 + 0.0055^2 + \cdots + 0.0055^2} = \sqrt{15} \, \sqrt{0.0055^2}$$

Since the mean value of the measurements is the sum divided by the number of measurements, or n, the standard error of the mean is equal to the standard error of the sum divided by n. For the values in Example 4-3,

$$\sigma_m = \frac{\sqrt{15}\sqrt{0.0055^2}}{15} = \frac{\pm 0.0055}{\sqrt{15}}$$

where σ_m is the standard error of the mean. The standard error of the mean of several measured quantities, all made with the same degree of precision, is therefore given by the relation

$$\sigma_m = \frac{\sigma}{\sqrt{n}} \qquad (4\text{-}10)$$

in which σ is the standard error of any one of the measurements computed from Eq. 4-6 and n is the number of measurements.

Similarly, the probable error of the mean of a group of measurements of a quantity is given by

$$E_m = \frac{E}{\sqrt{n}} \qquad (4\text{-}11)$$

Also the probable error of the sum of several measurements is

$$E_s = \sqrt{E_1^2 + E_1^2 + \cdots + E_n^2} \qquad (4\text{-}12)$$

where the probable error of each individual measurement is designated by E with a numerical subscript.

EXAMPLE 4-4. A line is measured in six sections, and the lengths of the sections together with the probable error in the length of each section are given in the accompanying tabulation. What is the probable error in the length of the line?

Section	Length (ft)	E (ft)
1	961.22	± 0.044
2	433.12	± 0.031
3	1545.90	± 0.060
4	355.40	± 0.021
5	1252.54	± 0.100
6	320.40	± 0.075

Solution: The sum of the lengths is 4868.58 ft, and the probable error in the total length of the line is, by Eq. 4-12.

$$E_s = \sqrt{0.044^2 + 0.031^2 + 0.060^2 + 0.021^2 + 0.100^2 + 0.075^2}$$
$$= \pm 0.150 \text{ ft}$$

EXAMPLE 4-5. A line is laid out by using a 200-ft tape. Each tape length laid out is assumed to be subject to a probable error of ± 0.03 ft. If 12 tape lengths are laid out, giving a total length of 2400 ft, what is the probable error in the length of the line?

Solution: Since each tape length is subject to the same probable error E, Eq. 4-12, may be reduced to

$$E_s = E\sqrt{n} \qquad (4\text{-}12a)$$

Hence, the probable error in the 2400-ft distance is $0.03\sqrt{12} = \pm 0.104$ ft.

Example 4-5 illustrates the following very important concept of random errors: If a series of measurements are made with the same degree of refinement, then the probable error may be considered proportional to the square root of the number of opportunities for introducing an error. For example, each time a set-up is made in leveling, an opportunity for introducing an error presents itself. Therefore, the errors tend to accumulate in proportion to the square root of the number of instrument set-ups. If all set-ups have about the same lengths of backsight and foresight distances, then the errors tend to accumulate in proportion to the square root of the distance. This concept was presented in Sec. 2-25 and Sec. 3-39.

The basic equation expressing the manner in which random errors are propagated is given here. Let U be some function of measured quantities denoted by $X, Y, Z, \cdots N$. Then the standard error of U is related to the standard errors in the measured values of $X, Y, Z, \cdots N$ by the equation

$$\sigma_U{}^2 = \left(\frac{\partial U}{\partial X}\right)^2 \sigma_X{}^2 + \left(\frac{\partial U}{\partial Y}\right)^2 \sigma_Y{}^2 + \left(\frac{\partial U}{\partial Z}\right)^2 \sigma_Z{}^2 + \cdots + \left(\frac{\partial U}{\partial N}\right)^2 \sigma_N{}^2 \tag{4-13}$$

Let $U = X + Y + Z$, where X, Y, and Z are three measured quantities. Then, from Eq. 4-13,

$$\sigma_U = \sqrt{\sigma_X{}^2 + \sigma_Y{}^2 + \sigma_Z{}^2}$$

which is identical with Eq. 4-9.

Let $U = X - Y$, where X and Y are two measured quantities. Then, from Eq. 4-13,

$$\sigma_U = \sqrt{\sigma_X{}^2 + \sigma_Y{}^2} \tag{4-14}$$

Let $U = XY$, where X and Y are two measured quantities. Then, from Eq. 4-13,

$$\sigma_U = \sqrt{Y^2 \sigma_X{}^2 + X^2 \sigma_Y{}^2} \tag{4-15}$$

Let $U = AX$, where A is a constant and X is a measured quantity. Then, from Eq. 4-13,

$$\sigma_U = A\, \sigma_X \tag{4-16}$$

In Eqs. 4-13 through 4-16, the probable error E can be substituted for the standard error σ, since the relationship between E and σ is constant as given by Eq. 4-8.

EXAMPLE 4-6. If the probable error in a backsight reading from a set-up of a level is ± 0.02 ft, and the probable error in the foresight reading from the same set-up is also ± 0.02 ft, what is the probable error in the difference in elevation between the two turning points on which the readings are taken?

Solution: The difference in elevation between the two turning points is equal to the backsight minus the foresight. Then by Eq. 4-14, the probable error in the difference in elevation is

$$E = \sqrt{0.022^2 + 0.022^2} = \pm\, 0.028 \text{ ft}$$

EXAMPLE 4-7. The dimensions of a rectangular field are measured with a steel tape and found to be 550.00 ft with a probable error of $\pm$ 0.07 ft and 800.00 ft with a probable error of $\pm$ 0.12 ft. What are the area of the field and the probable error in the area?

Solution: The area of the field is $550.00 \times 800.00 = 440{,}000$ sq ft. The probable error in the area is, by Eq. 4-11,

$$E = \sqrt{550^2 \times 0.12^2 + 800^2 \times 0.07^2} = \pm\, 86.6 \text{ sq ft}$$

EXAMPLE 4-8. What is the probable error in the determination of the area in Example 4-7, in acres?

Solution: Since one acre equals 43,560 sq ft, the probable error of the area in acres is, by Eq. 4-16,

$$E = (1/43{,}560)\,(\pm\, 86.6) = \pm\, 0.00199 \text{ acre}$$

EXAMPLE 4-9. The diameter D of the base of a cone is measured as 3.002 in., with a standard error of $\pm$ 0.0005 in. The height h of the cone is measured as 5.45 in., with a standard error of $\pm$ 0.01 in. What are the volume of the cone and the standard error of the volume?

Solution: The volume of a cone is

$$V = \frac{\pi D^2 h}{12} = \frac{\pi \times 3.002^2 \times 5.45}{12} = 12.86 \text{ cu in.}$$

The standard error of the volume can be expressed, according to Eq. 4-13, as follows:

$$\sigma_V = \sqrt{\left(\frac{\partial V}{\partial D}\,\sigma_D\right)^2 + \left(\frac{\partial V}{\partial h}\,\sigma_h\right)^2}$$

Then

$$\frac{\partial V}{\partial D} = \frac{\pi D h}{6} = \frac{\pi \times 3.002 \times 5.45}{6} = 8.567 \text{ cu in./in.}$$

and

$$\frac{\partial V}{\partial h} = \frac{\pi D^2}{12} = \frac{\pi \times 3.002^2}{12} = 2.359 \text{ cu in./in.}$$

Hence, the standard error of the volume is

$$\sigma_V = \sqrt{(8.567 \times 0.0005)^2 + (2.359 \times 0.01)^2} = \pm\, 0.024 \text{ cu in.}$$

EXAMPLE 4-10. Two sides and the included angle of a triangle were measured with the following results: $a = 472.58$ ft and $\sigma_a = \pm$ 0.09 ft; $b = 214.55$ ft and $\sigma_b = \pm$ 0.06 ft; $C = 37° \ 15'$ and $\sigma_c = \pm$ 30″. Compute the area of the triangle, in square feet, and compute the standard error of the area.

Solution: The area A of the triangle is given by the relationship

$$A = \frac{1}{2}\, ab \sin C = \frac{1}{2} \times 472.58 \times 214.55 \sin 37°15' = 30{,}686 \text{ sq ft}$$

The standard error of the area is, by Eq. 4-13,

$$\sigma_A = \sqrt{\left(\frac{\partial A}{\partial a}\sigma_a\right)^2 + \left(\frac{\partial A}{\partial b}\sigma_b\right)^2 + \left(\frac{\partial A}{\partial C}\sigma_c\right)^2}$$

Then

$$\frac{\partial A}{\partial a} = \frac{1}{2}b\sin C = \frac{1}{2} \times 214.55 \sin 37°15' = 64.93 \text{ sq ft/ft}$$

$$\frac{\partial A}{\partial b} = \frac{1}{2}a\sin C = \frac{1}{2} \times 472.58 \sin 37°15' = 143.03 \text{ sq ft/ft}$$

and

$$\frac{\partial A}{\partial C} = \frac{1}{2}ab\cos C = \frac{1}{2} \times 472.58 \times 214.55 \cos 37°15' = 40,354 \text{ sq ft/radian}$$

Since σ_C expressed in radians is $30 \times 0.00000485 = 0.0001455$ radian, the standard error of the computed area is

$$\sigma_V = \sqrt{(64.93 \times 0.09)^2 + (143.03 \times 0.06)^2 + (40,354 \times 0.0001455)^2} =$$
$$\pm 12 \text{ sq ft}$$

The standard errors in Examples 4-9 and 4-10 can obviously be computed by slide rule with more than sufficient accuracy.

4-8. Weighted Measurements. The *weight* of a measurement can be thought of as the value or the worth of that measurement relative to any other measurement. In order to investigate the relationship between the weight of a given observation and the measures of precision E, σ, and h, consider the length of a line to have been measured fifteen times by using the same measuring technique, the same degree of refinement, the same experienced personnel, and so on. Suppose that the fifteen values are as shown in the accompanying tabulation.

Measurement Number	Value (ft)	Measurement Number	Value (ft)	Measurement Number	Value (ft)
1	432.33	6	432.33	11	432.36
2	432.33	7	432.36	12	432.33
3	432.36	8	432.31	13	432.33
4	432.33	9	432.33	14	432.36
5	432.31	10	432.36	15	432.33

Each of the listed values has equal weight, because all conditions of measurement were identical. The most probable value of the length of the line may therefore be obtained by adding all the values and dividing by 15, that is, by finding the mean value. Since the value 432.33 appears 8 times, the value 432.36 appears 5 times, and the value 432.31 appears 2 times, the mean can be computed as follows:

$$8 \times 432.33 = 3458.64$$
$$5 \times 432.36 = 2161.80$$
$$\underline{2 \times 432.31 = 864.62}$$
$$\overline{15} \qquad\qquad 6485.06/15 = 432.337 \text{ ft}$$

The fifteen measurements can be considered equivalent to three measurements with the relative worths, or weights, of 8, 5, and 2. By analysis of the arithmetic in the assumed example, an expression for a *weighted mean* can be formed as follows:

$$\overline{M} = \frac{p_1 M_1 + p_2 M_2 + \cdots + p_n M_n}{p_1 + p_2 + \cdots + p_n} = \frac{\Sigma\,(pM)}{\Sigma\,p} \qquad (4\text{-}17)$$

where $\overline{M}$ is the weighted mean of several measurements of a quantity, M_1, M_2, and so on are the measurements, and p_1, p_2, and so on are the relative weights of the measurements.

Now suppose that each of the fifteen measurements of the line in the assumed example contains a standard error of ±0.04 ft. The mean of the eight values of 432.33 ft has a standard error of $\pm0.04/\sqrt{8}$ ft by Eq. 4-10; the mean of the five values of 432.36 ft has a standard error of $\pm0.04/\sqrt{5}$ ft, and the mean of the two values of 432.31 ft has a standard error of $\pm0.04/\sqrt{2}$ ft. For convenient reference, the values of the three means, their weights, and their standard errors are given in the following tabulation.

Value (ft)	Weight p	Standard Error (ft)
432.33	8	$\pm\,0.04/\sqrt{8}$
432.36	5	$\pm\,0.04/\sqrt{5}$
432.31	2	$\pm\,0.04/\sqrt{2}$

The assumed example demonstrates the following very important relationship between relative weights and measures of precision: The weight of a measured value is inversely proportional to the square of the probable error of the measurement, inversely proportional to the square of the standard error of the measurement, and directly proportional to the square of the precision modulus. That is,

$$p \propto \frac{1}{E^2} \propto \frac{1}{\sigma^2} \propto h^2 \qquad (4\text{-}18)$$

In the preceding discussion, the value ±0.04 is assumed to be the standard error of each individual measurement of the set, and each measurement has the same weight. This quantity is sometimes referred to as the standard error of unit weight, and is designated σ_0. The standard error of the weighted values can then be expressed in terms of their weights and the standard error of unit weight, as follows:

$$\sigma_p = \sigma_0 \sqrt{\frac{1}{p}} \qquad (4\text{-}19)$$

in which σ_p is the standard error of a weighted value, and p is the weight. Of course, if the weight of a measurement is unity, then $\sigma = \sigma_0$. The quantity $\frac{1}{p}$, which is the reciprocal of the weight, is referred to as a weight number.

EXAMPLE 4-11. Three lines of levels were run between B. M. 20 and B. M. 21 by different routes, but each set-up and each rod reading were made with the same degree of care. On the first line, 17 set-ups were required and the measured difference in elevation was 29.492 ft; on the second line, 9 set-ups were required and the measured difference in elevation was 29.440 ft; on the third line, 10 set-ups were required and the measured difference in elevation was 29.480 ft. What is the weighted mean of the measured differences in elevation between B. M. 20 and B. M. 21?

Solution: According to Eq. 4-12a in Example 4-5, the probable error in the determination of the difference in elevation between two points is proportional to the square root of the number of set-ups required. Therefore, the probable errors of lines 1, 2, and 3 are in proportion to the quantities $\sqrt{17}$, $\sqrt{9}$, and $\sqrt{10}$. The relative weights of the values of the difference in elevation obtained from lines 1, 2, and 3, are, by Eq. 4-18, 1/17, 1/9, and 1/10, respectively. Then, by Eq. 4-17, the weighted mean of the measured differences in elevation is

$$\overline{M} = \frac{(1/17)\,(29.492) + (1/9)\,(29.440) + (1/10)\,(29.480)}{1/17 + 1/9 + 1/10} = 29.466 \text{ ft}$$

If the weighted mean is computed by Eq. 4-17, the standard error of the weighted mean is given by the expression

$$\overline{\sigma} = \sqrt{\frac{\Sigma\,(pv^2)}{\Sigma\,p\,(n-1)}} \qquad (4\text{-}20)$$

Also the probable error of the weighted mean is given by the relation

$$\overline{E} = 0.6745\,\overline{\sigma} = 0.6745 \sqrt{\frac{\Sigma\,(pv^2)}{\Sigma\,p\,(n-1)}} \qquad (4\text{-}21)$$

EXAMPLE 4-12. Determine the standard error and the probable error of the weighted mean difference in elevation in Example 4-11.

Solution: The calculations may be arranged as follows:

$$v_1 = 29.492 - 29.466 = +0.026 \qquad v_1{}^2 = 0.000676$$

$$v_2 = 29.440 - 29.466 = -0.026 \qquad v_2{}^2 = 0.000676$$

$$v_3 = 29.480 - 29.466 = + 0.014 \qquad v_3{}^2 = 0.000196$$

$$p_1 v_1{}^2 = \frac{1}{17} \times 0.000676 = 0.0000398 \qquad \Sigma \, p = 0.2693$$

$$p_2 v_2{}^2 = \frac{1}{9} \times 0.000676 = 0.0000744 \qquad \overline{\sigma} = \sqrt{\frac{0.0001338}{0.2693 \,(3 - 1)}} = \pm \, 0.0157 \text{ ft}$$

$$p_3 v_3{}^2 = \frac{1}{10} \times 0.000196 = \overline{0.0000196} \qquad \overline{E} = 0.6745 \times 0.0157 = \pm \, 0.0106 \text{ ft}$$

$$\Sigma \,(pv^2) = \overline{0.0001338}$$

4-9. Simple Adjustment of Measurements. If the three angles in a triangle were to be measured by methods described in Chapter 6 and each angle were measured with the same degree of precision, then

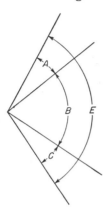

each of the three measured angles would carry the same weight. If the sum of the three measured angles is not 180°, then it is expected that each measured angle would be corrected by the same amount. The reasonableness of this adjustment is proved by an extended investigation of the principle of least squares developed in Sec. 4-3.

If three angles are measured about a point, as the angles A, B, and C in Fig. 4-7, and the total angle, as E, is also measured, and if all measurements are made with the same precision, $A + B + C$ should equal E. If the sum of the measured values of A, B, and C does not equal the measured value of E, then each of the measured angles must receive the same amount of correction, because their weights are identical.

Fig. 4–7. Angles measured about a point.

EXAMPLE 4-13. In Fig. 4-7, the measured angles are: $A = 22° \, 10' \, 10''$; $B = 71° \, 05' \, 50''$; $C = 24° \, 16' \, 00''$; and $E = 117° \, 31' \, 00''$. What are the corrected angles?

Solution: The computations may be arranged as in the accompanying tabulation.

Angle	Measured Value	Correction	Adjusted Value
A	22° 10′ 10″	− 15″	22° 09′ 55″
B	71° 05′ 50″	− 15″	71° 05′ 35″
C	24° 16′ 00″	− 15″	24° 15′ 45″
Sum =	117° 32′ 00″		117° 31′ 15″
E	117° 31′ 00″	+ 15″	117° 31′ 15″
Error =	1′ 00″		

If a series of angles closing the horizon about a point are measured, their total should be 360°. If the total is not 360° and all angles were measured with the same degree of refinement, each should be corrected by an equal amount. Obviously this amount is found by taking the difference between $360°$ and the measured total and dividing that difference by the number of angles.

4-10. Adjustment of Weighted Measurements. The corrections to be applied to weighted measurements are inversely proportional to their weights. Equation 4-3 is the statement of the condition of least squares which applies to measurements of equal or unit weight. Assume now a set of measurements M_1, M_2, . . . , M_n with varying weights p_1, p_2, . . . , p_n and the corresponding residuals v_1, v_2, . . . , v_n. By Eq. 4-18, p is directly proportional to h^2. The probability P that v_1, v_2, . . . , v_n will occur in the set is as follows:

$$P_{v_1} = y_1 \, \Delta v = k_1 e^{-h_1^2 v_1^2} \, \Delta v$$

$$P_{v_2} = y_2 \, \Delta v = k_2 e^{-h_2^2 v_2^2} \, \Delta v$$

$$\vdots$$

$$P_{v_n} = y_n \, \Delta v = k_n e^{-h_n^2 v_n^2} \, \Delta v$$

Also, since the probability that residuals will occur simultaneously in the set is equal to the product of their separate probabilities,

$$P_{(v_1, \, v_2, \, \ldots, \, v_n)} = (k_1 e^{-h_1^2 v_1^2} \, \Delta v)(k_2 e^{-h_2^2 v_2^2} \, \Delta v) \ldots (k_n e^{-h_n^2 v_n^2} \, \Delta v)$$

or

$$P_{(v_1, \, v_2, \, \ldots, \, v_n)} = (k_1 k_2 \ldots k_n) \, \Delta v^n e^{-(h_1^2 v_1^2 + h_2^2 v_2^2 + \ldots + h_n^2 v_n^2)}$$

Obviously, if P is to be a maximum in order to give the most probable value from the measurements, the negative exponent of e must be made a minimum. That is,

$$h_1^2 v_1^2 + h_2^2 v_2^2 + \ldots + h_n^2 v_n^2 - \text{a minimum}$$

Since p is proportional to h^2, then

$$p_1 v_1^2 + p_2 v_2^2 + \ldots + p_n v_n^2 = \text{a minimum}$$

or

$$\Sigma \, (pv^2) = \text{minimum} \tag{4-22}$$

The residual v for any value is defined as the measured value minus the most probable value, or $v_i = M_i - M$, where M_i is the ith measured value and M is the most probable value. Thus, the most probable value, or the adjusted value, is $M = M_i - v_i$. It can be seen that if the quantity $-v$ is added to the measured value, the adjusted value is obtained. But, $-v$ must be the correction to the measured value. Thus,

$$c = -v \qquad (4\text{-}23)$$

in which c is the correction.

Note that c^2 has both the same magnitude and the same algebraic sign as v^2. Then, if Eq. 4-22 is to be satisfied, the corrections must be inversely proportional to the weights. For example, if one measurement is, say, five times as good as another like measurement, then the correction to the first measurement should be only one-fifth of the correction to the second measurement. As an illustration of the adjustment of weighted measurements, consider the three angles of the triangle in Fig. 4-8. Assume that the mean value of six mea-

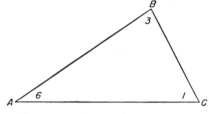

FIG. 4–8. Angles in a triangle.

surements of angle A is $32°\ 40'\ 15''$, the mean value of three measurements of angle B is $84°\ 33'\ 15''$, and a single measurement of angle C is $62°\ 46'\ 00''$. Also assume that each measurement of an angle is made with the same degree of refinement, and that the probable error of each single measurement is ± 1 minute. Then, by Eq. 4-11, the probable error in the mean of the six measurements of A is $\pm 1'/\sqrt{6}$; the probable error in the mean of the three measurements of B is $\pm 1'/\sqrt{3}$; and the probable error in the measurement of C is $\pm 1'/\sqrt{1}$. So, by Eq. 4-18, the relative weights are $p_A = 6$, $p_B = 3$, and $p_C = 1$. In general the number of repetitions of an angle indicates its relative weight.

The computations for determining the adjusted angles may be arranged as shown in the accompanying tabulation. Since the sum of

Angle	Number of Measurements	Mean Value of Angle	Relative Corrections	Corrections	Adjusted Value
A	6	$32°\ 40'\ 15''$	1/6 or 1/9	$1/9 \times 30'' = 3.3''$	$32°\ 40'\ 18.3''$
B	3	$84°\ 33'\ 15''$	2/6 or 2/9	$2/9 \times 30'' = 6.7''$	$84°\ 33'\ 21.7''$
C	1	$62°\ 46'\ 00''$	6/6 or 6/9	$6/9 \times 30'' = 20.0''$	$62°\ 46'\ 20.0''$
		$179°\ 59'\ 30''$	9/6 9/9		$180°\ 00'\ 00.0''$

the observed angles is 179° 59′ 30″, the total of the three corrections must be 30″. Also, the correction to the mean value of angle A is only one-half that of the correction to the mean value of angle B and is only one-sixth that of the correction to the mean value of angle C. The relative corrections to the three angles A, B, and C are therefore ⅙, ⅓, and ¼ or ⅙, ⅔, and ⁶⁄₆. Now the sum of these relative corrections should be found, and the numerator of this sum, or 9, should be used as the denominator of each of a second set of relative corrections. The sum of this second set should be unity. The corrections to the measured angles are then obtained by multiplying the second set of relative corrections by the total error, and the adjusted angles are determined.

4-11. Adjustment of a Level Circuit. The adjustment of a level circuit is a special case of adjusting weighted observations. When several lines of levels between two points are compared, the weight of each line is inversely proportional to the number of set-ups, as shown in Example 4-11. It was also pointed out that the probable error of a line is proportional to the square root of the length of the line. Then, by Eq. 4-18, the weight of a line of levels is inversely proportional to the distance along the line. This fact is the basis of the following principle for adjusting a line or circuit of levels: Corrections to measured elevations of points are proportional to the distances from the beginning of the line or circuit to the points, or are proportional to the numbers of set-ups between the beginning of the line or circuit and the points.

EXAMPLE 4-14. A line of levels is run from B. M. 30 to B. M. 33, the elevations of which have been previously established. As shown in Fig. 4-9, two inter-

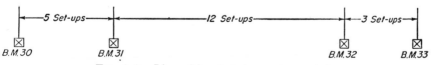

FIG. 4–9.   Line of levels between two points.

mediate bench marks, B. M. 31 and B. M. 32 are established. The fixed elevation of B. M. 30 is 453.52 ft, and the fixed elevation of B. M. 33 is 482.10 ft. As a result of the fieldwork, the elevation of B. M. 31 is 440.98 ft; that of B. M. 32 is 464.25 ft; and that of B. M. 33 is 482.23 ft. The error of closure is therefore + 0.13 ft. There are a total of 20 set-ups distributed as shown in Fig. 4-9. The relative corrections for bench marks 31, 32, and 33 are therefore 5/20, 17/20, and 20/20, respectively.

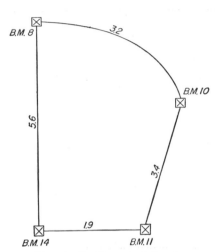

FIG. 4–10. Circuit of levels.

The correction to the elevation of B. M. 31 is $5/20 \times 0.13 = 0.03$ ft; that to the elevation of B. M. 32 is $17/20 \times 0.13 = 0.11$ ft; and that to the elevation of B. M. 33 is $20/20 \times 0.13 = 0.13$ ft. The adjusted elevations of bench marks 31, 32, and 33 are, respectively, 440.95, 464.14, and 482.10 ft.

EXAMPLE 4-15. A circuit of levels is shown in Fig.4-10.It starts and ends at B. M. 8 and passes through B. M. 10, B. M. 11, and B. M. 14. The distances between the several bench marks, in thousands of feet, are given on the diagram. Also the known elevation of B. M. 8 is 445.108 ft, and the measured elevations of the bench marks are as shown in the accompanying tabulation. What are the adjusted elevations of bench marks 10, 11, and 14?

Bench Mark	Measured Elevation (ft)	Distance from B.M. 8 (1000) (ft)	Correction (ft)	Adjusted Elevation (ft)
8	445.108	0	0	445.108 (fixed)
10	430.166	3.2	$3.2/14.1 \times 0.074 = 0.017$	430.183
11	433.421	6.6	$6.6/14.1 \times 0.074 = 0.035$	433.456
14	440.380	8.5	$8.5/14.1 \times 0.074 = 0.045$	440.425
8	445.034	14.1	$14.1/14.1 \times 0.074 = 0.074$	445.108

Solution: The closing error on B. M. 8 is $445.108 - 445.034 = 0.074$ ft. The corrections to the measured elevations of the bench marks are computed as shown in the table. Since the measured elevation of B. M. 8 is too small, the corrections are added to the measured elevations of the other bench marks.

4-12. Other Adjustments. The necessity for applying corrections to observations which are subject to random errors enters into all types of surveying measurements. The adjustment of the various types of measurements will be discussed in the separate chapters where the need arises. The Appendix shows the adjustment of elementary surveying measurements by the principle of least squares.

PROBLEMS

4-1. If six coins are tossed in the air at random, what is the probability that exactly three coins will turn up heads?

4-2. Three dice are rolled at random. Determine the probability *a*) that the sum of the marks on the upper faces of the dice will be 3; *b*) that it will be 4; and *c*) that it will be 5.

4-3. The accuracy with which a rod reading can be obtained by means of a tilting level equipped with an optical micrometer is to be evaluated. A leveling rod is set up at a distance of 150 ft from the level. The level itself is mounted firmly on a concrete pedestal. After each reading has been taken, the tilting knob is disturbed in order to throw the bubble off, and the focus knob is disturbed to introduce parallax. Thus, each reading is made independently. The following fifty readings in feet, were observed.

3.2593	3.2490	3.2572	3.2593	3.2586
3.2590	3.2575	3.2579	3.2569	3.2562
3.2644	3.2484	3.2590	3.2581	3.2492
3.2581	3.2557	3.2518	3.2514	3.2592
3.2571	3.2648	3.2556	3.2542	3.2559
3.2564	3.2555	3.2491	3.2588	3.2568
3.2510	3.2562	3.2550	3.2485	3.2570
3.2543	3.2504	3.2542	3.2591	3.2498
3.2550	3.2584	3.2592	3.2543	3.2550
3.2544	3.2496	3.2514	3.2536	3.2545

a) Plot these observations in the form of a histogram with a class interval of 0.0020 ft, beginning with 3.2480 ft.

b) Compute the mean of the observed values, the standard error of the observations, the standard error of the mean, and the probable error of the mean.

c) Using the standard error of the observations, compute ordinates to the normal distribution curve representing this set of observations. Plot the curve on the histogram in *(a)*.

d) Locate the positions of $+ \sigma$ and $- \sigma$ and of $+ E$ and $- E$ on the curve in *(c)*.

4-4. A line 1600 ft long is measured with a 100-ft tape. The following standard errors are assumed for each tape length: calibrated length, $\pm$ 0.004 ft; temperature, $\pm$ 10 deg F; misalignment, $\pm$ 0.6 ft; setting forward mark, $\pm$ 0.004 ft; and indexing rear mark, $\pm$ 0.004 ft. What is the standard error of the measured length?

4-5. The probable error of a rod reading due to multiple causes is assumed to be $\pm$ 0.008 ft. A line of levels 1 mile long is run between bench marks. The average length of sights is 175 ft. What is the probable error of the measured elevation of the last bench mark?

4-6. A line is broken into sections for measurement with a tape. The results are: $AB = 452.26$ ft $\pm$ 0.030 ft; $BC = 816.80$ ft $\pm$ 0.055 ft; $CD = 212.16$ ft $\pm$ 0.027 ft; $DE = 516.78$ ft $\pm$ 0.044 ft. Determine the length of the line and the probable error of the length.

4-7. When the line AE in Problem 4-6 is measured with an electronic instrument, the length is given as 1998.25 ft $\pm$ 0.070 ft. What is the most probable length of the line?

4-8. Four different instruments are used to measure an angle. The results are: instrument A, 32° 15′ 20″ $\pm$ 10″; instrument B, 32° 15′ 24″ $\pm$ 04″; instrument C, 32° 15′ 15″ $\pm$ 20″; instrument D, 32° 15′ 15″ $\pm$ 20″. What is the best value of the angle, and what is the probable error of this value?

4-9. The height of a radio tower is determined by measuring the horizontal distance from the center of its base to an instrument located 510.20 ft away and by measuring a vertical angle of $+ 40°$ 25′ to its top. The elevation of the instrument telescope is assumed to be the same as the elevation of the base of the tower. If the standard error of the measured distance σ_D is $\pm\ 0.10$ ft and the standard error of the vertical angle σ_a is $\pm\ 30$ sec., what is the height of the tower and what is the standard error of this value?

4-10. The distance s through which a freely falling object under the influence of gravity falls in time t beginning with an initial velocity v_0 is given by the expression $s = v_0 t + \frac{1}{2}\, gt^2$, where g is the acceleration of gravity. The initial velocity is estimated as 30 ft per sec; the time for which the body fell is measured as 18.20 sec; the value of g is 32.2 ft per sec per sec. Assume that $\sigma_{v_0} = \pm\ 2$ ft per sec; $\sigma_t = \pm\ 0.05$ sec; $\sigma_g = \pm\ 0.04$ ft per sec per sec. Compute the distance the body fell and the standard error of this value.

4-11. One side and two adjacent angles of a triangle are measured in order to determine the lengths of the other two sides, because the vertex opposite the measured side is inaccessible. The side c measures 412.50 ft $\pm\ 0.08$ ft; angle A measures $65°\ 20'\ \pm\ 30''$; angle B measures $72°\ 14'\ \pm\ 15''$. Compute angle C, side a, and side b. Compute the standard error of each quantity.

4-12. The weight of an angle is assumed to be proportional to the number of times it has been repeated (see Sec. 6-14). Five angles in a five-sided figure are measured with the following results:

Angle	Observed Value	Number of Repetitions
1	92° 15′ 35″	2
2	163° 42′ 25″	2
3	77° 58′ 50″	4
4	140° 50′ 20″	4
5	65° 12′ 30″	6

Compute the adjusted values of the angles.

4-13. A line of levels was run between B. M. 40 at an elevation of 618.66 ft and B. M. 46, the fixed elevation of which is 419.80 ft. Five intermediate bench marks 41, 42, 43, 44, and 45 were set as the levels were taken. The results are as shown in the tabulation. What are the adjusted elevations of the bench marks to the nearest 0.01 ft?

B.M.	Observed Elevation (ft)	Number of Set-ups Between Bench Marks
40	618.66 (fixed)	
		7
41	602.20	
		9
42	573.58	
		13
43	510.95	
		5
44	473.16	
		18
45	418.02	
		8
46	419.68	

4-14. Three contiguous angles were measured separately at point A, and then the total angle was measured. The results are as follows:

From	To	Measured Value	Number of Repetitions
B	C	14° 15′ 52″	6
C	D	26° 25′ 40″	4
D	E	60° 54′ 26″	6
B	E	101° 35′ 46″	12

Compute the adjusted angles to the nearest tenth of a second.

5

The Direction of a Line

5-1. Astronomical Meridian. A plane passing through a point on the surface of the earth and containing the earth's axis of rotation defines the *astronomical meridian* at the point. The direction of this plane may be established by observing the position of the sun or a star, as described in Chapter 12, or by observing a planet. By popular usage, the intersection of this meridian plane with the surface of the earth is known as the *true meridian*.

5-2. Magnetic Meridian. The earth acts very much like a bar magnet with a north magnetic pole located considerably south of the north pole defined by the earth's rotational axis. The magnetic pole is not fixed in position, but rather it changes its position continually. A magnetized needle, freely suspended on a pivot, will come to rest in a position parallel to the magnetic lines of force acting in the vicinity of the needle. Generally, the greatest component of the magnetic force at a point is that created by the earth's magnetic field, but other components may be created by other magnetic fields such as those around electric-power lines, reinforcing bars in roads and structures, and iron deposits. The direction of the magnetized needle defines the *magnetic meridian* at the point at a specific time. Unlike the true meridian, whose direction is fixed, the magnetic meridian varies in direction.

A gradual shift in the earth's magnetic poles back and forth over a great many years causes a secular change, or variation, which amounts to several degrees in a cycle. An annual variation of negligible magnitude is experienced by the earth's magnetic field. A daily variation causes the needle to swing back and forth through an angle of not much more than one-tenth of a degree each day.

Local attraction, the term applied to the magnetic attractions other than that of the earth's magnetic field, may change at a given location. This change may be caused by a variation in the voltage carried by a power line or by a gradual increase or decrease of a magnetic field in reinforcing bars, wire fences, underground utility pipes, or other metal parts.

5-3. Assumed Meridian. For convenience in a survey of limited extent, any line of the survey may be assumed to be a meridian or a line of reference. An assumed meridian is usually taken to be in the general direction of the true meridian.

5-4. Convergence of Meridians. True meridians on the surface of the earth are lines of geographic longitude, and they converge toward each other as the distance from the equator toward either of the poles increases. The amount of convergence between two meridians in a given vicinity depends on 1) its distance north or south of the equator and 2) the difference between the longitudes of the two meridians. Magnetic meridians tend to converge at the magnetic poles, but the convergence is not regular and it is not readily obtainable.

5-5. Grid Meridian. Another assumption is convenient in a survey of limited extent. When a line through one point of the survey has been adopted as a reference meridian, whether true or assumed north, all the other meridians in the area are considered to be parallel to the reference meridian. This assumption eliminates the necessity for determining convergence. The methods of plane surveying assume that all measurements are projected to a horizontal plane and that all meridians are parallel straight lines. These are known as *grid meridians*.

Two basic systems of grids are used in the United States to allow plane surveying to be carried statewide without any appreciable loss of accuracy. In each separate grid one true meridian is selected. This is called the *central meridian*. All other north-south lines in that grid are parallel to this line. The two systems, which are known as the Lambert Conformal Projection and the Transverse Mercator Projection, are the subject of Chapter 11.

5-6. Azimuth of a Line. The azimuth of a line on the ground is the horizontal angle measured from the plane of the meridian to the vertical plane containing the line. Azimuth gives the direction of the line with respect to the meridian. It is usually measured in a clockwise direction with respect to either the north meridian or the south meridian. In astronomical and geodetic work, azimuths are measured from the south meridian. In plane surveying, azimuths are generally measured from north.

Since the advent of the state grid systems mentioned in Sec. 5-5, engineers and surveyors are using more and more the control monuments established by the large federal agencies engaged in control surveys. These agencies publish the azimuths of lines in their control networks as measured from the south. Because of this practice, an increasing number of engineers engaged in state-wide, county-wide, and city-wide control surveying are using azimuths measured from the south.

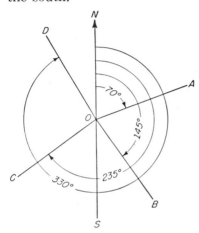

FIG. 5–1.   Azimuths.

A line may have an azimuth between 0° and 360°. In Fig. 5-1, the line NS represents the meridian passing through point O, with N toward the north. The azimuth of the line OA measured from the north is 70°; that of OB is 145°; that of OC is 235°; and that of OD is 330°. Azimuths are called true azimuths when measured from the true meridian, magnetic azimuths when measured from the magnetic meridian, assumed azimuths when referred to an arbitrary north-south line, and grid azimuths when referred to the central meridian in a grid system.

5-7. Back Azimuth. When the azimuth of a line is stated, it is understood to be that of the line directed from an original point to a terminal point. Thus, a line LP has its origin at L and its terminus at P. If the azimuth of LP is stated as 85°, then the azimuth of the

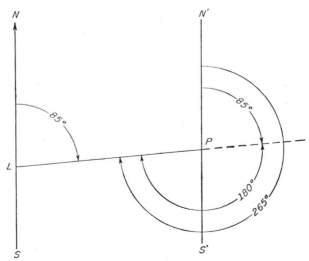

FIG. 5–2.   The relationship between azimuth and back azimuth.

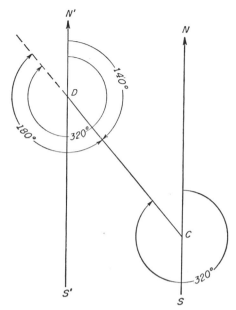

FIG. 5-3. Azimuth and back azimuth.

line *PL* must have some other value since *LP* and *PL* do not have the same direction. One direction is the reverse of the other. For the purpose of discussing back azimuth, consider the line *LP* in Fig. 5-2. In the diagram, *NS* is the meridian through *L*, and *N'S'* is the meridian through *P*. According to the assumption in plane surveying, the two meridians are parallel to each other. If the azimuth of *LP* is 85°, then the azimuth of *PL* is 85° + 180°, or 265°. Thus, the back azimuth of *LP* is the same as the azimuth of *PL*. In Fig. 5-3, the azimuth of *CD* is 320° and the back azimuth of *CD*, which is the azimuth of *DC*, is 320° − 180°, or 140°.

From the preceding explanation, it is seen that the back azimuth of a line can be found from its forward azimuth as follows: If the azimuth of the line is less than 180°, add 180° to find the back azimuth. When the azimuth of the line is greater than 180°, subtract 180° to obtain the back azimuth.

5-8. **Bearing of a Line.** The bearing of a line also gives the direction of the line with respect to the reference meridian. Unlike an azimuth, which is always an angle measured in a definite direction from a definite half of the meridian, a bearing angle is never greater than 90°. The bearing states whether the angle is measured from the north or the south and also whether the angle is measured toward the east or toward the west. For example, if a line has a bearing of

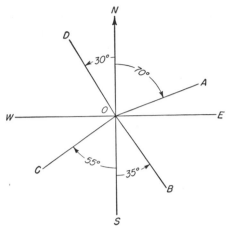

Fig. 5–4. Bearings.

S 35° E, called south 35° east, the bearing angle 35° is measured from the south meridian eastward. In Fig. 5-4 are shown four lines, the origin in each case being point *O*. Each line lies in a different quadrant. The bearing of *OA* is N 70° E; that of *OB* is S 35° E; that of *OC* is S 55° W; and that of *OD* is N 30° W.

It is apparent from Fig. 5-4 that the bearing angle of a line must be between 0° and 90°. A stated bearing is a *true bearing*, a *magnetic bearing*, an *assumed bearing*, or a *grid bearing*, according to whether the reference meridian is true, magnetic, assumed, or grid. In land surveying, and in the conveyance of title to property, references are made to maps, notes, and plats of previous surveys which are recorded with the various counties throughout the United States. When reference is made to a bearing in such a previous survey, the term *record bearing* is used. If reference is made to a property deed, the term *deed bearing* is used. The terms deed bearing and record bearing are commonly used interchangeably.

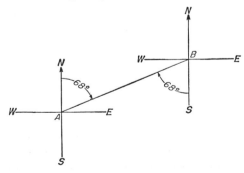

Fig. 5–5. Bearing and back bearing.

5-9. **Back Bearing.** The back bearing of a line is the bearing of a line running in the reverse direction. In Fig. 5-5, the bearing of the line *AB* is N 68° E, and the bearing of *BA*, which is in the reverse direction, is S 68° W.

The bearing of a line in the direction in which a survey containing several lines is progressing is called the forward bearing, while the bearing of the line in the direction opposite to that of progress is the back bearing. The back bearing can be obtained from the forward bearing by simply changing the letter *N* to *S* or *S* to *N* and also changing *E* to *W* or *W* to *E*.

5-10. **Relation Between Azimuths and Bearings.** To simplify computations based on survey data, bearings may be converted to azimuths and azimuths may be converted to bearings. The instances when such conversion is convenient will become apparent in later chapters. The conversion itself is quite simple.

An inspection of Fig. 5-1 will show that the line *OA* whose azimuth from north is 70° lies in the northeast quadrant, since the angle eastward from the meridian is less than 90°. Furthermore it is apparent that the bearing angle and the azimuth are identical. Therefore, the bearing of *OA* is N 70° E. The line *OB* is 145° from the north meridian. It lies south of a due-east line and is therefore in the southeast quadrant. The problem in this case is to determine the angle from the south meridian. Since the north meridian and the south meridian are 180° apart, the problem is solved by subtracting the azimuth, or 145°, from 180° to arrive at the bearing angle, which is 35°. Therefore the bearing of the line *OB* is S 35° E. The line *OC* is 235° from the north meridian in a clockwise direction and is beyond the south meridian in a westerly direction by an angle of 235° − 180° or 55°. Therefore if the azimuth is 235°, the bearing is S 55° W. For the line *OD* the angle from the north meridian is 330° in a clockwise direction. The angle from the north meridian in a counterclockwise or westerly direction is 360° − 330° or 30°. The line *OD* lies in the northwest quadrant, and its bearing is N 30° W.

The rules to observe in converting from azimuths to bearings are very quickly established in a person's mind after the rules have been put to practice a few times. They are as follows: 1) If an azimuth from north is between 0° and 90°, the line is in the northeast quadrant, and the bearing angle is equal to the azimuth. 2) If an azimuth from north is between 90° and 180°, the line is in the southeast quadrant, and the bearing angle is 180° minus the azimuth. 3) If the azimuth from north is between 180° and 270°, the line is in the southwest quadrant, and the bearing angle is the azimuth minus 180°.

4) If the azimuth from north is between 270° and 360°, the line is in the northwest quadrant, and the bearing angle is 360° minus the azimuth. These conversions should be performed mentally. For example, to determine the bearing of a line whose azimuth is 142° 29′ 54″, mentally subtract 142 from 179° and write 37°; mentally subtract 29′ from 59′ and write 30′; subtract 54″ from 60″ and write 06″. The bearing is S 37° 30′ 06″ E. Such mental subtraction is highly efficient in all phases of surveying computations, and you should practice it at the outset.

To convert from bearings to azimuths it is only necessary to reverse the foregoing rules, and the computations should be made with the same mental ease. The azimuth of a line in the northeast quadrant is equal to the bearing angle; that of a line in the southeast quadrant is 180° minus the bearing angle; that of a line in the southwest quadrant is 180° plus the bearing angle; that of a line in the northwest quadrant is 360° minus the bearing angle. As an example, the azimuth of a line whose bearing is N 77° 43′ 16″ W is 282° 16′ 44″.

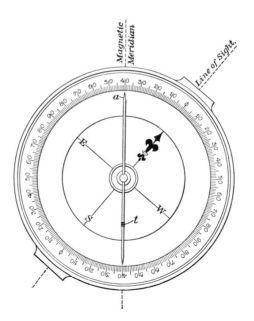

Fɪɢ. 5–6.   Compass box.

5-11. The Magnetic Compass. Since a freely suspended magnetized needle will lie in the magnetic meridian, the direction of a line can be determined with respect to the needle, and thus to the magnetic meridian, by measuring the angle between the line and the needle. The magnetic compass is constructed so as to allow a needle to swing freely on a pivot when in use, and to allow a line of sight to be directed from the occupied point to a terminal point. As shown in Fig. 5-6, a graduated circle is rotated as the line of sight is rotated. The north-seeking end of the compass needle is read against the circle to obtain the angle between the magnetic meridian and the line of sight.

The circle and the needle are encased in a metal compass box and are covered with a glass plate. The line of sight normally is fixed in line with the zero mark or the north graduation on the circle. Thus if a line of sight is directed along the north magnetic meridian, the needle will point to the zero mark or to the north graduation. As the line of sight is turned clockwise from magnetic north, the needle remains in the magnetic meridian, but the graduated circle is turned clockwise through the corresponding angle. When the line of sight is turned exactly 90° east of north, then the letter E is brought opposite the north end of the compass needle. The circle thus indicates that the magnetic bearing is due east, as it should. If the line of sight is turned exactly 180° from north, the letter S is brought opposite the north end of the needle and the magnetic bearing of the line of sight is shown to be due south.

Three general types of compasses are used in surveying. The pocket compass of various designs is used where only rough estimates of directions are needed. It is easily carried, and is held in the hand when used. The line of sight is established by a combination of a peep-sight and a slotted vane, whereby the observer sights from the origin towards the terminus of the line whose bearing he wishes to determine. In order that the compass needle may swing freely on its pivot, the

FIG. 5–7. Brunton compass. (Courtesy of Keuffel & Esser Co.)

pivot must be kept very sharp. If the compass needle is allowed to jostle around inside the compass box, the constant jarring against the pivot will in time dull the pivot point and render the compass useless. The pocket compass is constructed so that when the sights are folded down the needle is lifted off its pivot and held against the glass cover. Some types of pocket compasses, as the Brunton compass shown in Fig. 5-7, contain a pin which when depressed will clamp the compass needle. Thus, when the observer has made a sight, he depresses the pin and can then conveniently read the bearing.

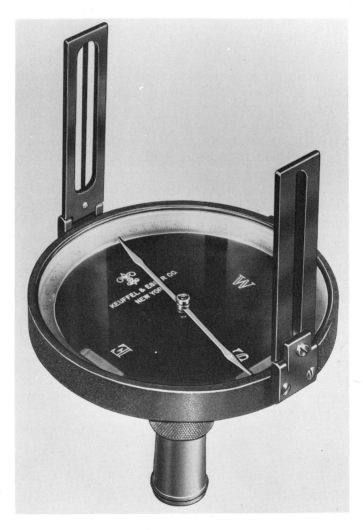

FIG. 5–8.   Surveyor's compass. (Courtesy of Keuffel & Esser Co.)

The surveyor's compass, Fig. 5-8, is the instrument that was used in the past to run surveys of reasonable accuracy. Its main part is the compass box containing the graduated circle between 4 and 6 in. in diameter, the magnetic needle, one or two level bubbles to allow the circle to be brought horizontal, long sight vanes to allow fairly accurate pointings along rather steeply inclined lines, and a screw for lifting the needle off the pivot and against the glass cover plate. The compass box is fitted with a spindle which rotates in a socket. The socket fits in a leveling head consisting of a ball-and-socket joint, and the whole compass assembly is leveled about the ball-and-socket against friction applied by a clamping nut. The leveling head is fastened to a tripod or to a staff and is used in the field in this fashion. The circle is usually graduated in half-degrees. Just as on the pocket compass, the sight vanes are aligned so that the line of sight passes through the north graduation on the circle.

The transit compass is similar to the surveyor's compass in all respects save for the method of leveling and for the line of sight. The compass box sets in the center of the horizontal limb of the transit, astride of which are the standards which hold the telescope. See Fig. 6-8 in Chapter 6. The method of leveling the transit, and thus the compass box, will be described in Sec. 6-11 in Chapter 6. The line of sight for the transit compass is the collimation line of the telescope defined by the center of the objective lens and the intersection of the cross hairs. The telescope of the transit is capable of being raised or depressed for sighting along inclined lines. The letter N on the compass circle is normally under the objective end of the telescope when the telescope is in the direct position. See Sec. 6-13 in Chapter 6. The letter S is under the eyepiece. Therefore, this arrangement keeps the north graduation directed along the line of sight just as in the case of the pocket compass and the surveyor's compass.

5-12. **Dip of the Compass Needle.** The lines of force created by the earth's magnetic field are directed toward the north and south magnetic poles and are horizontal only at points about halfway between the poles. From the halfway point toward the poles these lines of force become increasingly steep, and at the poles they are practically vertical.

A magnetic needle pivoted at its center of gravity would dip down on one end in order to remain oriented parallel to the lines of force in the vicinity. In the northern hemisphere, the north end of the needle would dip down. To overcome the dip of the needle and to cause it to come to rest about its pivot in a horizontal position, a coil of wire or a small clip of nonmagnetic metal is fastened to the end of the needle opposite that of the direction of dip to act as a counterweight. The metal is adjusted along the needle until, when the compass is level, the top surface of the needle coincides, or nearly coincides, with the top surface of the graduated circle. The counterbalance tells at a glance which is the north end of the compass needle. In the northern hemisphere the weight is usually on the south end, although with some needles this is not true. The observer must determine the north end for himself.

If a given compass is used in the same general vicinity, the position of the weight rarely needs to be changed. If, however, the compass is used in areas widely separated in a north-south direction, then the weight must be shifted accordingly. Although shifting the weight is a simple operation in itself, it must be done with great delicacy and with a fine touch so as not to dull the pivot in taking up or replacing the needle and so as to keep from bending the needle.

5-13. Determining Directions with the Magnetic Compass. When using a pocket compass, the observer occupies one end of the line whose magnetic bearing he wishes to obtain. He holds the compass level, releases the needle by lifting the sights to their sighting position, sights the other end of the line, and allows the needle to come to rest. He then depresses the needle clamp and reads the circle at the north end of the compass needle. This reading gives him the magnetic bearing of the line directed from his position to the point sighted.

When using a surveyor's compass or a transit, the observer occupies one end of the line, centers the instrument over the point, and levels the instrument. He releases the clamp holding the needle, allowing it to rest on the pivot. He then directs the line of sight toward a point at the other end of the line and brings it on that point. When the needle comes to rest, he reads the circle at the north end of the needle to obtain the bearing of the line from the occupied point to the point sighted on. He then clamps the needle before disturbing the instrument.

To obtain the back magnetic bearing as a check, he occupies the second point and sights back to the first point, reading the north end of the needle as before. The bearing angles should show reasonable agreement, and the letters N and S as well as E and W should be reversed on the back bearing. This check should be made before leaving the point. The use of the compass will be discussed further in Chapters 6 and 8.

5-14. **Magnetic Declination.** The magnetic poles do not coincide with the poles defined by the earth's rotational axis, and certain irregularities in the earth's magnetic field cause local and regional variations in the position of the needle. Therefore, except in a very narrow band around the earth, the magnetic needle does not point in the direction of true north. In some areas the needle points east of true north; in other areas the needle points west of true north. The amount and direction by which the magnetic needle is off the true meridian is called the magnetic declination (formerly called variation). Declination is positive or plus when the needle points east of true north, and it is negative or minus when the needle points west of true north. The declination varies from $+ 24°$ in the state of Washington to $- 22°$ in the state of Maine, the total range over the United States being $46°$.

The declination can be determined for a given locality at a certain date by referring to the Isogonic Chart for Magnetic Declination prepared by the United States Coast and Geodetic Survey about every five years. The Isogonic Chart for 1960 is shown in Fig. 5-9. As seen on the chart, a narrow band, or line, running through portions of the states of Michigan, Indiana, Ohio, Kentucky, Tennessee, North Carolina, South Carolina, and Georgia shows zero declination. This is called the *agonic line.* All portions to the east of this line have a west or minus declination. Those portions to the west of this line have an east or plus declination.

As noted in Sec. 5-2, the direction of the magnetic meridian at a given point is changing continually. The change to be considered when the compass is used for surveying is the secular variation, which causes the declination to change slowly in one direction in a given locality over a great many years and then change in the other direction. The cycles through which the change in declination occurs vary in length. Furthermore, this variation cannot be predicted, because not enough is known about secular variation.

If the declination in a given vicinity for a previous year is desired, the declination for a year for which an isogonic chart has been published should be determined. Then by referring to the dashed lines on the chart, the annual change is determined. This annual change is multiplied by the difference between the desired year and the charted year to give the total change in declination from the charted year to the desired year. The proper correction is applied to the declination at the time of charting. As an example, suppose that the declination at Denver in 1948 is desired. Consult the isogonic chart for either 1945 or 1950. The procedure with the 1945 chart follows:

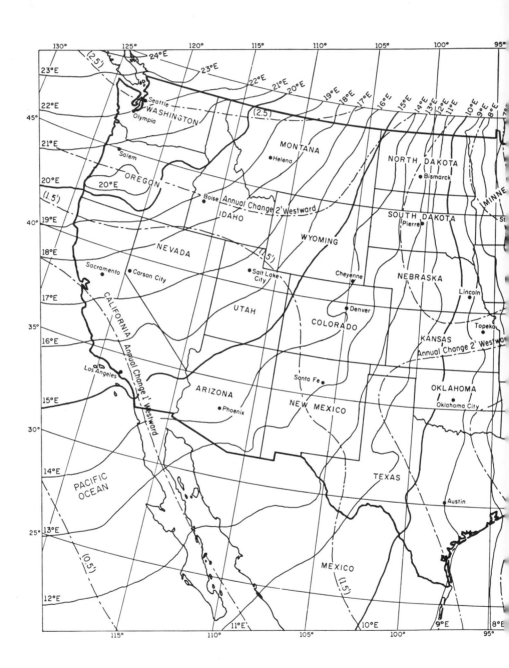

FIG. 5-9. Lines of equal magnetic declination and of equal annual change in

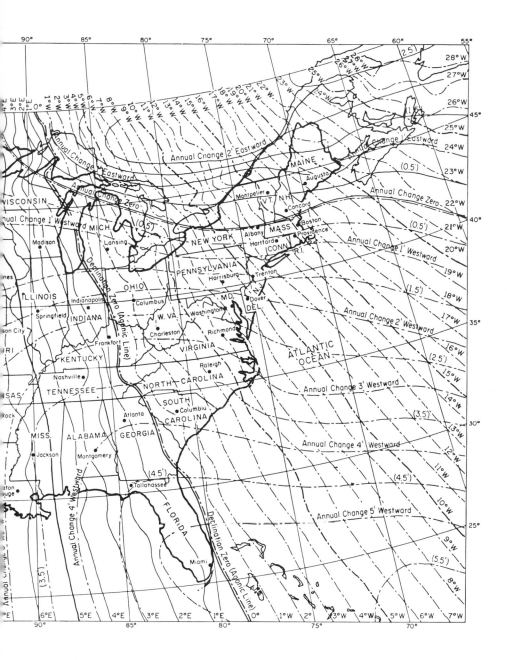

the United States for 1960. (By permission of U.S. Coast & Geodetic Survey.)

Annual change at Denver in 1945 $= -2'$
Lapse of time covered $= +3$ years
Total change in declination $= (+3) \times (-2') = -6'$
Declination at Denver in 1945 $= +14° \ 16'$
                                                 $-06'$
                                       _____
Declination at Denver in 1948 $= +14° \ 10'$

If the 1950 chart is used, this is the work:

Annual change at Denver in 1950 $= -1.8'$
Lapse of time covered $= -2$ years
Total change in declination $= (-2) \times (-1.8') = +3.6'$
Declination at Denver in 1950 $= +14° \ 00.0'$
                                                 $+3.6'$
                                       _____
Declination at Denver in 1948 $= +14° \ 03.6'$

The difference between the two results is due in part to interpolation and in part to inaccuracy in the charts. If the declination at Denver for 1860 is required, the approximate declination could be obtained by working backward from a recent chart, but the better way would be to obtain the values from a chart prepared as near to 1860 as possible. This refinement is not always justified, since magnetic bearings shown on charts in many instances are only approximate at best, and local irregularities can be several times as great as any error caused by using a chart for a different year.

5-15. Relation Between True and Magnetic Bearings and Azimuths. True azimuths differ from magnetic azimuths by the magnitude of the magnetic declination at the time. If the declination is east of north, then all magnetic azimuths will be less than corresponding true azimuths by the amount of declination; if the declination is west of north, then magnetic azimuths will be larger than corresponding true azimuths by the amount of declination. Conversion between true and magnetic directions is best made by means of azimuths.

EXAMPLE 5-1. The magnetic declination on a certain date at a given place is 15° 15′ W. The magnetic azimuth of a line is 124° 20′. What is the true azimuth of the line?

Solution: The solution to this problem is shown in Fig. 5-10. The magnetic azimuth is seen to be larger than the true azimuth by 15° 15′, and the true azimuth is therefore 124° 20′ − 15° 15′ or 109° 05′.

FIG. 5-10. Relationship between true and magnetic azimuth.

EXAMPLE 5-2. The magnetic bearing of a line was observed as S 12° 30′ E when the magnetic declination was 22° E. What is the true bearing of the line?

Solution: This problem is solved best by making the conversion by azimuths. The work follows:

$$
\begin{aligned}
\text{Magnetic bearing} &= \text{S} \quad 12°\ 30′\ \text{E} \\
\text{Magnetic azimuth} &= \quad\quad 167°\ 30′ \\
\text{Declination} &= +\ 22°
\end{aligned}
$$

$$
\begin{aligned}
\text{True azimuth} &\quad - \quad 189°\ 30′ \\
\text{True bearing} &= \text{S} \quad 9°\ 30′\ \text{W}
\end{aligned}
$$

EXAMPLE 5-3. The magnetic bearing of a line was recorded as S 80° 15′ W in 1880 at a place which had a declination of 16° E in that year. What is the magnetic bearing if the declination is now 4° 30′ E?

Solution: The reduction to true azimuth in this problem is made in the following manner:

$$
\begin{aligned}
\text{Magnetic bearing in 1880} &= \text{S } 80°\ 15′\ \text{W} \\
\text{Magnetic azimuth in 1880} &= \quad 260°\ 15′ \\
\text{Declination in 1880} &= +\ 16°
\end{aligned}
$$

$$
\begin{aligned}
\text{True azimuth in 1880} &= \quad 276°\ 15′ \\
\text{Declination at present} &= -\ 4°\ 30′
\end{aligned}
$$

$$
\begin{aligned}
\text{Magnetic azimuth at present} &= \quad 271°\ 45′ \\
\text{Magnetic bearing at present} &= \text{N } 88°\ 15′\ \text{W}
\end{aligned}
$$

EXAMPLE 5-4. The true azimuth, from north, of a line is given as 144° 15′. This line is to be traced by using a compass when the declination is 3° 30′ W. What should be the reading on the compass to observe this line?

Solution: The computations follow:

$$
\begin{aligned}
\text{True azimuth} &= \quad 144°\ 15′ \\
\text{Declination} &= +\ 3°\ 30′
\end{aligned}
$$

$$
\begin{aligned}
\text{Magnetic azimuth} &= \quad 147°\ 45′ \\
\text{Magnetic bearing} &= \text{S } 32°\ 15′\ \text{E}
\end{aligned}
$$

From the foregoing examples, you may consider the process to be unnecessarily long. This may be true if the conversion of only one or two lines is involved. When the survey involves several lines, however, the method of converting directions from one meridian to another through azimuths is consistent throughout, and its use tends to reduce mistakes involving algebraic signs. Also, in making conversions, you are strongly urged to draw a diagram like that in Fig. 5-10, showing the angles to relatively correct size before deciding in each case whether a declination is to be added to or subtracted from an azimuth or a bearing angle.

Computations involving azimuths and bearings will be treated in more comprehensive examples in Chapters 6 and 8.

PROBLEMS

5-1. Express the following azimuths as bearings: *a*) 32° 14′ 20″; *b*) 127° 58′ 15″; *c*) 188° 44′ 30″; *d*) 264° 02′ 10″; *e*) 272° 10′ 10″; *f*) 302° 25′ 45″; *g*) 90° 02′ 20″.

5-2. Convert the following bearings to azimuths: *a*) N 71° 02′ 45″ W; *b*) S 1° 10′ 15″ W; *c*) S 1° 10′ 15″ E; *d*) S 48° 14′ 50″ E; *e*) N 3° 22′ 10″ E.

5-3. The true azimuth of a line is known to be 324° 27′. The observed magnetic bearing of this line is N 1° 15′ E. What is the magnetic declination at the point of observation?

5-4. Given the following magnetic bearings: *a*) N 1° 50′ E; *b*) N 1° 50′ W; *c*) S 20° 12′ E; *d*) S 2° 40′ E; *e*) S 45° 00′ W; *f*) N 38° 10′ W. The magnetic declination is 15° 30′ E. Compute the true bearings.

5-5. Using the Isogonic Chart for 1960, determine the magnetic declination at Olympia, Wash., in 1930; at Denver, Colo., in 1945; at Little Rock, Ark., in 1910; at Boston, Mass., in 1920.

5-6. At the time a survey was run, the magnetic declination was 5° 20′ W. The magnetic bearings of several lines observed at the time were: *AB* = N 42° 20′ W; *BC* = S 14° 40′ E; *CD* = S 60° 00′ E; *DE* = S 65° 14′ E; *EF* = N 13° 20′ E. These lines are to be retraced by using a compass when the declination is 2° 40′ E. What bearings should be set off on the compass?

6

The Measurement of Angles

6-1. Horizontal Angle. A horizontal angle is the angle formed by two intersecting vertical planes. The vertical planes intersect along a vertical line which contains the vertex of the angle. In surveying, an instrument for measuring angles occupies this vertex, and the vertical line formed by the two vertical planes coincides with the vertical axis of the instrument. In Fig. 6-1, two vertical planes, OAZ and OBZ, intersect along the vertical line OZ and form the horizontal angle AOB. Point C lies in the vertical plane containing line OA. Therefore, the direction of OC is the same as that of OA. Point D lies in the vertical plane containing line OB, and so the direction of OD is the same as that of OB. Point O, being the vertex of the angle, is the *at* station. The angle at O from A to B is the angle AOB, point A being the *from* or backsight station and point B being the *to* or foresight station. In Fig. 6-1, the horizontal angle at O from C to D is exactly the same as angle AOB. The horizontal projection of OC is

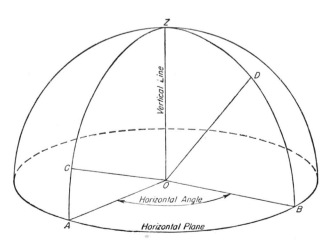

FIG. 6–1. Horizontal angle.

131

OA, and the horizontal projection of *OD* is *OB*. The horizontal angle between two lines, therefore, is the angle between the projections of the lines onto a horizontal plane.

A horizontal angle in surveying has a direction or sense; that is, it is measured or designated to the right or to the left, or it is considered clockwise or counterclockwise. In Fig. 6-1, the angle at *O* from *A* to *B* is counterclockwise and the angle at *O* from *D* to *A* is clockwise.

The common methods of measuring horizontal angles are: by tape, by transit, by compass, by plane table, and by sextant.

6-2. Measuring Angles by Tape. It is possible to make simple surveys by using just a tape, the angles being computed from the linear measurements. One method of doing this is to divide the survey area into a series of connected triangles, the sides of which are measured. From the lengths of the resulting triangle sides, the angles at all the vertices are computed by using the formulae of plane trigonometry, and the various separate angles are added to obtain the whole angle at each vertex. If all the

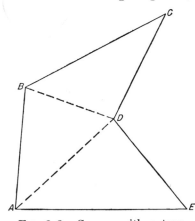

FIG. 6–2.   Survey with a tape.

sides in Fig. 6-2 are measured by using the tape, all the angles in the tract can be computed by solving triangles *ABD*, *CDB*, and *EAD*. To obtain the angle at *D* from *E* to *C*, for example, the three angles at *D* from the individual triangles are added.

To avoid measuring the interior lines in a tract, as in Fig. 6-2, the angle at each vertex may be determined directly by the chord method or by the tangent method. In the chord method, Fig. 6-3, equal distances are laid off from *B* on the two lines *BA* and *BC*, and

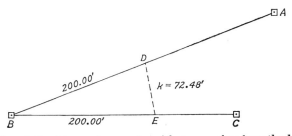

FIG. 6–3.   Measuring angle with tape—chord method.

points D and E are set. These points should be lined in carefully. The chord distance DE, or k, is then measured. The angle is computed from the relation sin ½ $ABC = k/2BD$. Thus, if BD and BE are each 200 ft and k is 72.48 ft, then sin ½ $ABC = 72.48/(2 \times 200) = 0.1812$; ½ $ABC = 10° 26½'$; and $ABC = 20° 53'$.

In the tangent method, Fig. 6-4, a perpendicular to BC is established at P. (See Sec. 6-3 for a method of laying out a right angle.) Point Q is set on the line BA. The distances BP and PQ are measured with the tape, and the relation tan $ABC = PQ/BP$ gives the angle at B. This method becomes weaker as the angle increases, and it is

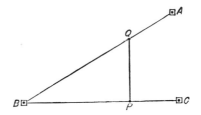

FIG. 6–4. Measuring angle with tape—tangent method.

not satisfactory for angles much over 45° since the line representing the perpendicular may not be a true perpendicular and its intersection with the line, as at Q in Fig. 6-4, will be doubtful. An extremely small angle can be measured quite accurately with the tape by using the tangent method, since the perpendicular will be relatively short.

The accuracy of the values obtained by these methods is dependent on the size of the angle, on the care with which the points are set on line, on the accuracy of the measured lengths, and when the tangent method is used, on the care taken in erecting the perpendicular. With reasonable care, the value of an angle determined by one of these methods would agree with the value obtained with the transit within 1 or 2 minutes.

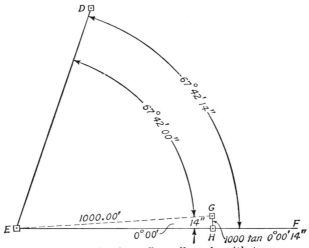

FIG. 6–5. Laying off small angle with tape.

6-3. Laying off Angles with the Tape. It is sometimes necessary to stake out an angle more accurately than it can be done with the ordinary transit. Since it is impossible to lay off directly with the transit the angle of 67° 42′ 14″ shown in Fig. 6-5, the angle is laid off as exactly as possible with the instrument and a point G, 1000 ft from E, is established. The angle DEG is measured by the repetition method described in Sec. 6-14. A point H is next located from G at a distance $GH = 1000 \tan (67°\ 42′\ 14″ - DEG)$. The line through E and H will make the required angle with the line ED. This method is used in land surveying, where a line is frequently extended several miles and where a small error in an angle may cause a considerable discrepancy in the location of a point at the end of the line.

A perpendicular to a line can be constructed with a tape by the 3-4-5 method. Since a triangle is right-angled if its sides are proportional to the numbers 3, 4, and 5, a right angle can be laid out by constructing a triangle whose sides are in these proportions. Thus, in Fig. 6-6, let it be required to erect a perpendicular to the line AD at A. First, a temporary point B is established on the line AD and 30 ft from A. Then, by using A and B as centers and swinging arcs with radii of 40 ft and 50 ft, respectively, the point C is located at the intersection of these two arcs. This can be most easily done if two tapes are available. If but a single 100-ft tape is at

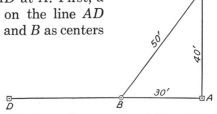

FIG. 6–6.   Constructing right angle with tape.

hand, the zero mark can be held at B and the 100-ft mark held at A, while the point C is located by holding the 50-ft and 60-ft marks to-

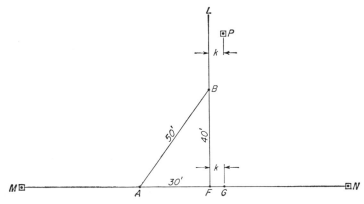

FIG. 6–7.   Perpendicular to a line through a point off the line.

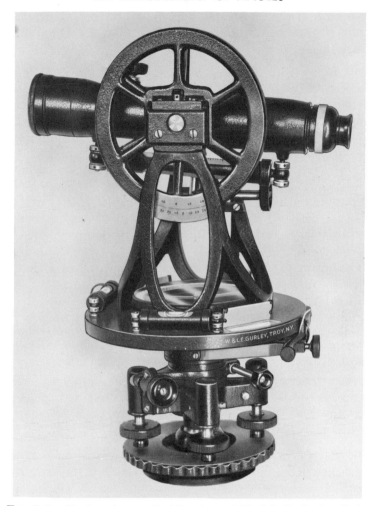

FIG. 6–8.   Engineer's transit. (Courtesy of W. & L. E. Gurley Co.)

gether and stretching the tape tight. After a stake has been driven at C, the exact point on the stake can be found by striking two arcs on the top of the stake. One arc is struck at a time; and the intersection of the two arcs is the required point. Instead of the 30-ft, 40-ft, and 50-ft lengths, any other convenient lengths that are in the same proportions can be used.

A perpendicular to a given line through a point off the line can be constructed by first estimating where the perpendicular will intersect the line. To drop a perpendicular from point P to line MN in Fig. 6-7, first select point F on MN. The line FL is established by the 3-4-5 method, points being set at A and at B. The offset distance k

from *FL* to *P* is then measured, and this distance is laid off on line *MN* from *F* to establish point *G*. Thus the line *GP* is perpendicular to the line *MN*.

6-4. Angles with Transit. The engineer's or surveyor's transit, Fig. 6-8, is an instrument of great versatility. By means of a telescope, the line of sight is well defined. As a result, long sights and accurate sighting are possible. The transit contains a horizontal circle which is graduated every 30 minutes, 20 minutes, 15 minutes, or 10 minutes, the value of a division depending on the transit. With the aid of a vernier, the transit is capable of measuring or laying off directly horizontal angles of from 1 minute to 10 seconds, the precision depending on the type of transit. A transit also contains a vertical circle and a vernier for measuring or laying off vertical angles. The complete transit contains a compass box by which magnetic bearings may be observed.

The reticule containing the cross hairs is equipped with auxiliary stadia hairs which may be used to determine distances by using the optical constants of the telescope. The telescope is provided with a level bubble which is sensitive enough to allow the transit to be used for spirit leveling and to eliminate uncertainties in measuring vertical angles. The telescope can be rotated about its horizontal axis through a complete circle. This last feature gives the transit its name. The word transit means to pass over or cross over, and the line of sight of the transit can be made to cross over from one side to the other by rotating the telescope about its horizontal axis. A transit is often referred to as a theodolite.

6-5. Parts of the Transit. A modern transit is made up of three subassemblies. These are shown in Fig. 6-9. The upper part is the *alidade*. This contains a circular cover plate which is equipped with two level vials at right angles to one another and is rigidly connected to a solid conical shaft called the inner spindle. The vernier for the horizontal circle is contained in the cover plate. The alidade also contains the frames supporting the telescope which are called the *standards*, the vertical circle and its vernier, the compass box, and finally the telescope and its level vial.

The middle part of a transit contains the *horizontal limb*, which is rigidly connected to a hollow conical shaft called the outer spindle. The inside of the outer spindle is bored with a taper to receive the inner spindle of the alidade. The limb assembly also contains a clamp, called the upper clamp, which allows or prevents rotation of the inner spindle within the outer spindle. The graduated horizontal circle is attached to the upper face of the limb.

FIG. 6–9. Transit showing three subassemblies. (Courtesy of W. & L. E.
Gurley Co.)

The lower part of the transit is the *leveling-head assembly*. It
contains the four leveling screws; a bottom plate which screws onto
the tripod; a shifting device which permits the transit to be moved
about ¼ to ⅜ in. in any direction while the tripod remains stationary;
a half-ball which allows the transit to tilt while being leveled; and
the four-arm piece, or the spider, into the center of which fits the

outer spindle. The assembly also contains a clamp, called the lower clamp, which allows or prevents rotation of the outer spindle, and a hook for attaching a plumb-bob string to the center of the transit. Some of the parts can be seen in Fig. 6-8.

6-6. Transit Telescope. The telescope on the transit shown in Fig. 6-8 is similar to that on an engineer's level, but it is shorter in length. Its main parts are the objective, the focusing wheel, the cross hairs, and the eyepiece. The telescope is attached to the transverse axis, or horizontal axis, which rests on the standards and revolves in bearings at the tops of the standards. The telescope is held at any desired inclination by means of a clamp, called the vertical clamp, and can be rotated slowly in a vertical plane by means of a tangent screw, or slow-motion screw, called the vertical tangent screw, attached to one standard. The telescope in Fig. 6-8 is shown with a dust cap which protects the objective when the instrument is not in use, but this cap is replaced by a sunshade when the transit is being used.

6-7. Rotation of Spindles. The inner and outer spindles, together with the tapered bore in the four-arm piece, provide for rotation of the alidade and the limb about the vertical axis of the instrument. With the instrument set up on a tripod, and with both the lower clamp and the upper clamp in a clamped position, neither the alidade which contains the vernier nor the limb which contains the graduated horizontal circle can move. If the upper clamp remains clamped and the lower clamp is loosened, then the outer spindle is free to rotate in the four-arm piece, but both the alidade and the limb must rotate together about the vertical axis. As a result, the vernier will appear opposite the same horizontal circle graduation during rotation since they move together.

If the lower clamp is clamped and the upper clamp is loosened, the horizontal circle is fixed in position, but the alidade is allowed to rotate about the vertical axis and the vernier moves with it. As the vernier moves around the edge of the fixed graduated circle, the reading on the circle changes correspondingly.

To permit a small rotation of the alidade or the inner spindle in the outer spindle, a tangent screw, or slow-motion screw, is provided. Every tangent screw operates against a spring, which reduces play or backlash in the motion. A small rotation of the outer spindle in the four-arm piece is permitted by a tangent screw similar to that controlling the slow motion of the alidade. Neither of these tangent screws will work unless the corresponding clamp is clamped.

Rotation of the inner spindle in the outer spindle is known as the *upper motion* of the transit. Such rotation is controlled by the upper clamp and the upper tangent screw. Rotation of the outer spindle in the four-arm piece is known as the *lower motion* of the transit. This rotation is controlled by the lower clamp and the lower tangent screw. An upper motion of the transit changes the reading on the horizontal circle. A lower motion of the transit does not change the reading on the horizontal circle because, when the lower motion is used, the vernier on the alidade moves with the horizontal circle on the limb. In other words, either of the motions will rotate the alidade, and thus the line of sight, about the vertical axis of the instrument, but only the upper motion will change the circle reading.

In practice the terms *upper motion* and *lower motion* are also used to refer to the clamps and tangent screws controlling the motions. For instance, when the lower clamp is tightened, it is said, "the lower motion is clamped;" and when the upper clamp is loosened, it is said, "the upper motion is unclamped." Or when a sight is taken with the upper clamp tightened and the lower clamp loosened, it is said, "a sight is taken by means of the lower motion."

6-8. Horizontal Circle and Verniers. The horizontal circle of a transit is located on the periphery of the upper surface of the horizontal limb. It is graduated in various ways, three of which are shown in Fig. 6-10. Each small division on the circle shown in views (*a*) and (*c*) is one-half degree or 30 minutes. A division in view (*b*) is one-third degree or 20 minutes. One in view (*d*) is one-sixth degree or 10 minutes. On the circles in views (*a*), (*b*), and (*c*) the graduations for every 10 degrees are numbered both clockwise and counterclockwise from 0° through 360°. This method of numbering is convenient when measuring angles clockwise or counterclockwise. The circle in view (*d*) is numbered clockwise only. However, it can also be used for measuring counterclockwise angles.

There are two verniers for the horizontal circle of a modern transit. They are intended to be exactly 180° apart. These are called the "A" vernier and the "B" vernier. Each vernier is located in a window in the cover plate and is covered with glass. When the inner spindle is in its proper position in the outer spindle, the outer edge of each vernier comes almost in contact with the inner edge of the graduated circle. Although the scale on the horizontal limb is circular and is graduated in angular units, the principle of a vernier used with this scale is the same as that of a vernier used on a leveling rod and described in Sec. 3-22.

The vernier shown in Fig. 6-10 (*a*) is one of the two verniers of a 1-minute transit. It is actually a double direct vernier, the part to the left of 0 being graduated clockwise and the part to the right of 0 being graduated counterclockwise. The main scale, or the circle, is

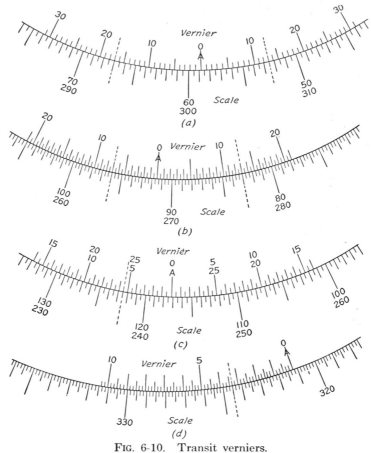

FIG. 6-10.   Transit verniers.

graduated to 30 minutes and there are thirty spaces in each part of the vernier. The least count of the combination is therefore 30′/30 or 1 minute. The clockwise part of the vernier is used with the numbers on the circle increasing clockwise. The counterclockwise part of the vernier is used with the numbers on the circle increasing counterclockwise. The letter A at the zero graduation of the vernier signifies which vernier is being used. The letter B would appear on the vernier on the opposite side of the circle.

In Fig. 6-10 (b) the circle is divided to 20 minutes and there are forty spaces in either the clockwise part of the vernier or the counterclockwise part. Hence the least count of the combination is 20′/40 or ½ minute or 30″. A transit containing such a circle and vernier is known as a 30-second transit. Except for the least count, the verniers in views (a) and (b) are of the same type.

In Fig. 6-10 (*c*) is represented a folded vernier. This type of vernier is used where space for a double vernier is not available. It is to be noted that there are two sets of numbers on the vernier, those of one set increasing clockwise and those of the other increasing counterclockwise. The numbers closest to the circle increase toward the left from 0 at the center up to 15; and from the extreme right, where 15 is repeated, they continue to increase going toward the left to the center mark, which corresponds to 30. The least count of this combination is 30 seconds, since a division on the circle is 30 minutes and the complete vernier contains 60 spaces. In Fig. 6-10 (*d*) is shown a single vernier with sixty spaces. Since a division on the circle is 10 minutes, the least count is $10'/60 = \frac{1}{6}$ minute or $10''$.

Any vernier is read by first noting the graduation on the circle beyond which the vernier index lies, and then adding to the value of that graduation the value of the vernier graduation which coincides with a circle graduation. When the circle in Fig. 6-10 (*a*) is read clockwise, the vernier index lies beyond the 58° 30′ graduation, and the vernier shows coincidence at the 17′ mark. Hence the reading is 58° 30′ + 17′ or 58° 47′. The corresponding counterclockwise reading is 301° 13′. For the clockwise reading in Fig. 6-10 (*b*), the vernier index lies beyond the 91° 20′ graduation, and the vernier shows coincidence at the 7′ mark. Hence the reading is 91° 20′ + 7′ or 91° 27′ 00″. The corresponding counterclockwise reading is 268° 33′ 00″. The readings of the other verniers are: in view (*c*), 117° 05′ 30″ or 242° 54′ 30″; and in view (*d*), 321° 13′ 20″.

The length of a division on the vernier is slightly smaller than that of a division on the circle. So, when an exact coincidence occurs, the two vernier marks on either side of the graduation which coincides with a circle graduation should fall just inside the corresponding circle graduations. If the transit does not have provision for magnification of the graduations by means of an attached microscope, a hand magnifying glass or reading glass should be used. When reading the circle, the observer should look radially along the graduations to eliminate the effect of parallax between the circle and vernier graduations.

6-9. Vertical Circle and Vernier. The vertical circle is rigidly connected to the transverse axis of the telescope and moves as the telescope is raised or depressed. It is clamped in a fixed position by the clamp which controls the vertical motion of the telescope, and after being clamped it can be moved through a small angle by means of the tangent screw. The vertical circle can be either a full circle or a half circle. The former is graduated from 0° to 90° in both directions and then back to zero; the latter is graduated from 0° to 90° in both directions. Each division on either is ½ degree or 30 minutes. On most transits the vernier for reading the vertical circle is mounted on the standard directly beneath the circle and almost comes in contact with the circle. It is a double direct vernier with the graduations numbered from 0 to 30 in both directions. The least count of the vertical circle and its vernier on almost every modern transit is 1 minute.

When the line of sight, and thus the telescope, of a well-adjusted transit is horizontal, the vernier will read 0° on the vertical circle. If some part of the transit is out of adjustment, or if the transit is not carefully leveled, an initial reading other than 0° may be obtained. This is called the index error. On a transit with the vernier rigidly attached to the standard, this initial reading must be determined before a vertical angle can be measured correctly. (See Sec. 6-15.) On some transits, the vernier can be moved slightly on the standard by means of a tangent screw, and its correct position is determined by a level bubble called a control bubble or index bubble. With this arrangement, the circle will read 0° when the index bubble is centered and the line of sight is horizontal, so that the correct vertical angle can be measured directly.

6-10. Transit Stations. The point over which a transit is set up is called a transit station. Such a point should be marked as accurately as possible on some firm object. On many surveys each transit station is marked by a wooden stake or hub driven flush with the ground, and a tack or small nail marks the exact point on the stake. When the survey is intended to be relatively permanent, each point can be marked by a monument of stone or concrete or of iron pipe set in concrete.

Triangulation stations and *traverse stations* of many of the federal, state, county, and city agencies engaged in survey work are marked by bronze disks set in the tops of firmly planted concrete monuments. A point on rock can be marked by a chiseled cross. For identifying such points, the necessary facts can be written on the stone with keel or lumber crayon. To identify a hub and to indicate its location, a projecting stake, which is called a *guard stake* or *witness stake*, is placed near the hub. On this stake are marked in keel the station number of the hub and any other necessary information, such as the name or purpose of the survey.

6-11. **Setting up Transit.** In setting up a transit, it is necessary to have the center of the instrument, which is the point of intersection of the transverse axis and the vertical axis of the instrument, directly over a given point on the ground. Also, the circle and the transverse axis must be horizontal. The position of an ordinary transit over a point on the ground may be indicated by a plumb bob suspended from a hook or ring attached to the lower end of the centers. The plumb-bob string should be held by a sliding knot in order that the height of the bob can be adjusted. The point of the bob should almost touch the mark over which it is desired to set the transit.

In setting up a transit, the tripod legs are spread and their points are so placed that the leveling head is approximately horizontal and the telescope is at a convenient height for sighting. The instrument should be within a foot of the desired point, but no extra care is taken to set it closely at once. When setting up on rough ground, two legs of the tripod should be set at about the same elevation and the leveling head should be made approximately horizontal by shifting the third leg. If the instrument is more than a few inches from the given point, the tripod is lifted bodily without changing the inclinations of the legs, and the instrument is set as near as possible to the point. By pressing the legs firmly into the ground, the plumb bob can usually be brought to within ¼ in. of the point. This brings the point within the range of the shifting head of the instrument.

When the leveling head is approximately horizontal and the plumb bob is very near the point, the bubbles of the plate levels are brought almost to the centers of the tubes by means of the leveling screws. If there are four screws, the plates are rotated until one level is parallel to a line through each pair of opposite screws. Then each bubble is brought to the center separately by turning the screws of the corresponding pair. When the plates are finally leveled up, all four screws should be bearing firmly but should not be so tight as to put a strain in the leveling head. If the leveling screws turn very hard, the cause may be the binding of the ball-and-socket joint at the bottom of the spindle. The tension may be relieved by loosening both screws of the other pair. If there are three leveling screws, the plates are rotated so that one level is parallel to a line through any pair of screws. Both bubbles are then brought to the center in succession by first turning the screws of that pair in opposite directions, and then turning the third screw.

After the bubbles are approximately centered, the instrument is loosened on the tripod plate by loosening two adjacent leveling screws, and the plumb bob is brought exactly over the point on the ground by means of the shifting head. This arrangement allows the head of the transit to be moved laterally without disturbing the tripod. Then the instrument is held securely in position on the tripod plate by tightening the leveling screws that were previously loosened. The bubbles of the plate levels are brought exactly to the centers of the tubes, and the position of the plumb bob over the point is observed. If the bob has moved off the point in leveling up, it is brought back to the proper position by means of the shifting head, and the instrument is leveled again.

When angles are to be measured between points which are at considerable distances from the instrument, it is unnecessary to split hairs in bringing the plumb bob directly over the transit station.

6-12. **Measuring a Horizontal Angle.** With the transit set up, centered, and leveled over the *at* station, the A vernier is usually set to read 0° for convenience. This is done by loosening both the upper and lower clamps and rotating the horizontal limb by slight pressure applied with the finger of one hand to its under side while holding the standards in place with the other hand, until the 0° graduation of the circle is brought almost opposite the index of the vernier. The upper motion is then clamped, and coincidence is obtained between the 0° graduation and the vernier index by using the upper tangent screw. The setting should be made with the aid of the magnifying glass, as this operation constitutes a reading of the circle.

The lower motion being free, the line of sight is directed toward the *from* or backsight station. The lower motion is now clamped, and the line of sight is brought exactly on the backsight station by turning the lower tangent screw. For this sight, the circle reading is observed as 0° 00′ and it is recorded as the initial circle reading.

The final reading is obtained by loosening the upper clamp, rotating the alidade about the vertical axis, and directing the line of sight toward the *to* or foresight station. If the alidade has been turned in a clockwise direction, the reading on the clockwise graduations will increase by the angle of rotation. The upper clamp is tightened, and the line of sight is brought exactly on the foresight station by turning the upper tangent screw. This motion of the upper tangent screw will change the circle reading correspondingly. The reading of the circle for this sight is recorded as the final circle reading.

The difference between the initial reading and the final reading is the angle through which the line of sight was turned in going from the backsight station to the foresight station. As stated before, the A vernier is usually set to read 0° before the backsight is made. However, the vernier need not be set at any particular reading before the backsight is taken, since it is immaterial what the initial reading is. As an example, suppose it is desired to measure the angle at L from M to P in Fig. 6-11, and when a backsight is taken to station M the circle reading is 122° 43′. The upper clamp is loosened, the line of sight is rotated so that it is directed to P, and the upper clamp is

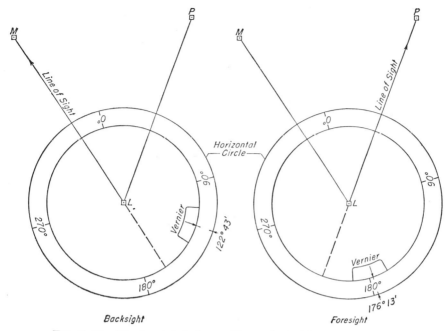

FIG. 6–11. Horizontal-circle readings—backsight and foresight.

then tightened. The line of sight is brought exactly on station P by using the upper tangent screw. The circle reading is now 176° 13'. The angle at L from M to P is therefore the difference between the initial reading and the final reading, which is 176° 13' − 122° 43' − 53° 30'.

The foregoing is the basic procedure in measuring a horizontal angle with the transit. The principles involved are: 1) The backsight is taken by a lower motion, and the backsight reading is the initial circle reading; 2) the foresight is taken by an upper motion, and the foresight reading is the final circle reading; 3) the horizontal angle is obtained by taking the difference between the initial and final circle readings. The procedure as presented is not sufficient in itself to obtain a reliable measurement of a horizontal angle, for the reasons discussed in the following section.

6-13. Double Centering. If the various components of a transit are considered as lines and planes, one finds that the graduated horizontal and vertical circles together with their verniers constitute planes. The line of sight, the transverse or horizontal axis of the telescope, the vertical axis, and the axis of any bubble tube are all lines in space. These lines and planes bear definite relations to one another in a well-adjusted transit. The line of sight is normal to the horizontal axis; the horizontal axis is normal to the vertical axis; the vertical axis is normal to the plane containing the horizontal circle; the line of sight is parallel to the axis of the telescope bubble tube; the axes of the plate levels lie in a plane parallel to the horizontal circle; and the movement of the objective lens in and out when it is focused is parallel to the line of sight. The inner spindle and the outer spindle must be concentric; and the horizontal circle and the verniers must be concentric. The line joining the indices of the A and B verniers must pass through the center of the horizontal circle. A maladjustment of the transit in one or more of these respects is to be expected. In fact, a transit is never in perfect adjustment.

Two procedures for eliminating almost all of the errors due to maladjustment of the transit are: 1) double centering and 2) reading both the A vernier and the B vernier. Of the two, double centering is the more important. Double centering or double sighting consists of making a measurement of a horizontal or a vertical angle once with the telescope in the direct or erect position and once with the telescope in the *reversed, inverted,* or *plunged* position. The act of turning the telescope upside down, that is, rotating it about the transverse axis, is called plunging or transiting the telescope. When the telescope is in its plunged position, the telescope bubble is on top of the telescope.

The most serious mistake an instrumentman can make when measuring an angle with the transit is to fail to double-center, that is, not to measure an angle once with the telescope direct and then once with the telescope reversed. Double centering eliminates blunders and instrumental errors, and increases the accuracy of the angle. The procedure is very simple.

In Sec. 6-12, the transit was set up at station L. A backsight was taken on station M with the telescope direct, and the A-vernier reading was 122° 43′. A foresight was then taken on station P with the telescope still direct, and the A-vernier reading was 176° 13′. The value of the angle by the direct measurement is 53° 30′.

To measure the angle with the telescope reversed or plunged, the vertical clamp is loosened and the telescope is plunged about its transverse axis. The A-vernier reading is still 176° 13′. The lower clamp is loosened to allow the circle to move with the vernier and thus preserve the reading on the circle. The line of sight is now directed toward station M, the lower clamp is tightened, and the line of sight is brought exactly on the station by using the lower tangent screw. The initial reading for this second measurement is thus 176° 13′, which was the final reading for the first measurement. The upper clamp is loosened, the vernier being allowed to move along the circle so as to increase the circle reading, and the line of sight is directed to station P. The upper clamp is tightened and the line of sight is brought exactly on the foresight station with the upper tangent screw. The final circle reading is now observed and recorded. Say this reading is 229° 44′. The second value of the angle at L from M to P is thus 229° 44′ − 176° 13′ or 53° 31′. The mean of the values with the telescope direct and reversed is 53° 30′ 30″, and this mean value is free from errors due to practically all the maladjustments of the instrument.

When an angle is measured with the telescope direct and reversed and the resulting two values disagree by more than the least count of the circle, the whole measurement should be repeated. If double centering is repeated and the discrepancy is always of the same amount and in the same direction, the discrepancy indicates bad adjustment of the transit, but the values can be used. A mean of the two readings should be taken as the best value of the angle.

Suppose that the initial backsight reading is 0°, the initial foresight is 42° 12′, and on repeating with the telescope reversed, the second foresight reading is 84° 28′. Then the first value of the angle is 42° 12′ − 0° = 42° 12′, and the second value is 84° 28′ − 42° 12′ = 42° 16′. There is a discrepancy of 4′ between the two readings. This difference would *not* be detected if the second foresight reading was divided by 2 to obtain the angle. The reading itself is meaningless because the discrepancy is too large. Always obtain the difference between the initial and final readings for each turning, and compare these two differences. If they are acceptable, adopt the mean value. If they are not acceptable, repeat the entire measurement.

6-14. **Angles by Repetition.** Study of Sec. 6-13 indicates that an angle can be measured to the nearest 30 seconds with a 1-minute transit by double centering, that an angle can be measured to the nearest 15 seconds with a 30-second transit by double centering, and so on. This is true. Moreover, an experienced instrumentman with a good 1-minute transit is capable of measuring an angle to the nearest 10 seconds by repeating the angle several times, accumulating the successive readings on the circle, and then dividing by the number of repetitions.

To illustrate the principle of repetition, the accompanying tabulation gives in the left-hand column the successive values of the angle 25° 10′ 23″ multiplied by 1, 2, 3, 4, 5, and 6. In the middle column the tabulation gives the corresponding values of the angle that would be read on a 1-minute transit after 1, 2, 3, 4, 5, and 6 repetitions if the initial backsight reading were 0° and if there were no errors in pointing or mistakes in using the wrong motion. The right-hand column gives the values of the angles in the middle column divided by 1, 2, 3, 4, 5, and 6, respectively.

Number	Multiple Values of True Angle	Successive Transit Readings	Values Obtained From Transit Readings
1	25° 10′ 23″	25° 10′	25° 10′ 00″
2	50° 20′ 46″	50° 21′	25° 10′ 30″
3	75° 31′ 09″	75° 31′	25° 10′ 20″
4	100° 41′ 32″	100° 42′	25° 10′ 30″
5	125° 51′ 55″	125° 52′	25° 10′ 24″
6	151° 02′ 18″	151° 02′	25° 10′ 20″

If the repetitions could go on indefinitely, the transit reading on the 12th repetition divided by 12 would be 25° 10′ 25″, division after the 24th repetition would give 25° 10′ 22.5″, and so on. The practical limit is reached, however, somewhere between the sixth and twelfth repetition because of errors of graduations, eccentricities of centers, play in the instrument, and inability of the observer to point with sufficient speed and accuracy to preserve precision.

The procedure for repeating an angle six times with a transit is to measure it three times with the telescope direct and three times with the telescope reversed, in that order. It is understood that the observer is experienced, that his personal errors will be small, and that he will make no mistakes. Otherwise, there is no justification for repeating angles.

The instrument is set up, centered, and leveled. The initial backsight reading is taken on both the A and B verniers because it is assumed that a great degree of refinement is necessary. The backsight is taken with a lower motion and with the telescope direct. Then with the telescope still in the direct position, the upper clamp is loosened and the pointing on the foresight station is made by using the upper clamp and tangent screw. The first foresight reading is made on the A vernier only to determine the approximate value of the angle. Next, with the telescope direct, the lower clamp is loosened and the line of sight is brought back on the backsight station by using the lower clamp and tangent screw. The upper clamp is loosened and the line of sight is swung around to the foresight station. The circle reading is thus increased. A third backsight is taken on the *from* station and the third foresight is taken on the *to* station. Each repetition increases the circle reading. After the third repetition, the telescope is transited to the reversed position, and the angle is turned off three more times with the telescope reversed. The final readings on both the A vernier and the B vernier are taken. The accompanying four sets of notes will illustrate how the final angle is obtained.

READINGS FOR SET No. 1

At Station *B* (30″ transit)

From	To	Rep.	Tel.	Circle	Vernier A	Vernier B
A	*C*	0	D	0° 00′	00″	00″
		1	D	28° 10′	00	
		6	R	169° 00′	00	30

In the first set the approximate angle is the difference between the initial backsight and foresight readings and is 28° 10′. When this angle is multiplied by 6 and the product is added to the initial reading of 0°, the sum is less than 360°. So the vernier has not gone completely around the circle. The mean of the initial readings on the A and B verniers is 0° 00′ 00″. The mean of the final readings on the A and B verniers is 169° 00′ 15″. The difference is 169° 00′ 15″. This divided by 6 is 28° 10′ 02.5″, which is the accepted value.

READINGS FOR SET No. 2

At Station *B* (30″ transit)

From	To	Rep.	Tel.	Circle	Vernier A	Vernier B
A	*C*	0	D	232° 41′	00″	00″
		1	D	260° 51′		
		6	R	41° 41′	00	30

In the second set of notes, the difference between the initial backsight and foresight readings is 28° 10′. If this angle is multiplied by 6 and the product is added to the initial reading of 232° 41′, the sum is greater than 360°. Consequently, the final reading must be increased by 360°. (The number of complete revolutions is determined by inspection.) The mean of the initial readings on the A and B verniers is 232° 41′ 00″, and that of the final readings on the A and B verniers *increased by 360°* is 401° 41′ 15″. The difference is 169° 00′ 15″. This divided by 6 is 28° 10′ 02.5″, which is the accepted value.

READINGS FOR SET No. 3

At Station 40 + 12.50 (1′ transit)

From	To	Rep.	Tel.	Circle	Vernier A	Vernier B
16 + 22.60	51 + 02.81	0	D	114°	20′	19′
		1	D	274°	52′	
		6	R	357°	33′	33′

In the third set of notes the approximate angle being measured is 274° 52′ − 114° 20′ = 160° 32′. When this angle is multiplied by 6 and the product is added to the initial reading, the sum is 1077° 32′. Obviously, the vernier has passed the 360° mark twice. Consequently, the final reading must be increased by 720°. The mean of the initial readings of the A and B verniers is 114° 19′ 30″; that of the final readings of the A and B verniers *increased by 720°* is 1077° 33′. The difference is 963° 13′ 30″, which is divided by 6. The result, 160° 32′ 15″, is the adopted value.

READINGS FOR SET No. 4

				At Station Dark (30″ transit)		
From	To	Rep.	Tel.	Circle	Vernier A	Vernier B
Bass	Sand	0	D	0° 00′	00″	30̄″
		1	D	26° 22′	30	
		12	R	316° 22′	30	30

In the fourth set of notes the approximate angle is 26° 22′ 30″. When this value is multiplied by 12, which is the number of repetitions, and the product is added to the initial reading, the sum is less than 360°. The recorded reading on the B vernier has a bar drawn above it. Such a bar signifies that the 30″ applies to the next lower minute of the circle reading. The mean of the initial readings on the A and B verniers is therefore 359° 59′ 45″. The mean of the final readings on the A and B verniers is 316° 22′ 30″. To obtain the difference, 360° must be added to the final reading before the initial reading can be subtracted from it. The difference is 316° 22′ 30″ + 360° − 359° 59′ 45″ = 316° 22′ 45″. Dividing by 12 and rounding off the quotient to a whole second gives 26° 21′ 54″ as the adopted value. If an A-vernier reading contains 30″ and the B-vernier reading is on the next higher minute, the reading would be recorded as 60″.

6-15. Vertical Angle. A vertical angle is an angle measured in a vertical plane. In surveying and mapping, a vertical angle is understood to be the angle measured in a vertical plane between a line and a horizontal plane. It is positive if the line is directed upward, and is negative if the line is directed downward. The former is sometimes called an *elevation angle*; the latter is sometimes called a *depression angle*. Both positive and negative vertical angles are measured from zero.

Centering the plate levels on the transit brings the vertical axis of the transit truly vertical, provided that the plate levels are in adjustment. Centering the telescope level brings the telescope, and hence the line of sight, into a truly horizontal position, provided that the telescope level and the line of sight are both in adjustment. When the plate-level bubbles are centered and the telescope is brought to a horizontal position by centering the telescope-level bubble, the vernier should read 0° on the vertical circle. If the plate levels are out of adjustment or are not centered at the time a vertical angle is to be measured, then the vertical circle will not read 0° when the telescope is brought horizontal. It will have an initial reading, which may be positive or negative. Furthermore, as the alidade is rotated in azimuth, that is, rotated about its vertical axis, this initial reading will vary. The initial reading is termed the *index error* of the vertical circle. It is determined for a given vertical angle by pointing the telescope in the direction of the desired line, centering the telescope-level bubble, and reading the vertical circle. This method assumes that the line of sight is parallel to the axis of the telescope bubble, and that the vernier is adjusted.

To measure the vertical angle of the line of sight from one point to another, the transit is set up over the first point, centered, and leveled. The line of sight is brought in the direction of the other point, and the telescope bubble is centered. The reading of the vertical circle is recorded as the initial reading or as the index error. The line of sight is then raised or lowered, and is directed accurately to the second point by means of the vertical clamp and tangent screw. The reading of the vertical circle is recorded as the final reading. The correct vertical angle is the difference between the initial and final readings. In recording both the initial and final readings, it is necessary to give each value its correct algebraic sign; the + for an elevation angle and the − for a depression angle. As an example, suppose that when the telescope bubble is centered the vertical circle reads + 0° 02′. When the line of sight is now raised and directed to the desired point, the vertical circle reads + 14° 37′. The correct vertical angle is the difference between the two readings, or + 14° 37′ − (+ 0° 02′) = + 14° 35′. As a further example, suppose the initial reading is + 0° 02′ and the final reading is − 21° 14′. The difference is − 21° 14′ − (+ 0° 02′) = − 21° 16′, which is the correct vertical angle.

When the initial reading of the vertical circle is recorded as an index error and the final reading is recorded directly as the vertical angle, this angle is corrected by applying the index correction, which is equal to the index error but of opposite sign. Thus, if the index error is + 0° 03′ and the recorded vertical angle is − 16° 48′, the index correction − 0° 03′ is applied to − 16° 48′ to obtain − 16° 51′, which is the correct vertical angle.

If the plate bubbles are out of adjustment, the transit can be leveled very accurately for measuring vertical angles by using the more sensitive telescope bubble. The procedure is as follows. Bring the telescope over a pair of leveling screws, and center the telescope bubble by using the vertical clamp and tangent screw. Rotate the telescope 180° in azimuth. If the telescope bubble does not come to the center, bring it halfway to the center by turning the vertical tangent screw, and then center the bubble by using the two leveling screws. Rotate the telescope again 180° in azimuth. The bubble should remain centered. If it does not, repeat the process of bringing it halfway to center with the tangent screw and the rest of the way with the leveling screws. When the bubble remains centered after the telescope is rotated through 180° in azimuth, bring the telescope over the other pair of leveling screws and bring the bubble to center by using the leveling screws only. This operation makes the vertical axis of the transit truly vertical.

If the axis of the transit is truly vertical, but the line of sight is not parallel to the axis of the telescope level, or the vertical-circle vernier is displaced, or there is a combination of these maladjustments, an index error will result. This error can be detected in a transit having a full vertical circle by reading the vertical angle with the telescope in the direct position and in the reversed position and comparing the two values. If the two disagree, the index error is one-half the difference between the direct and reversed readings. The mean of the direct and reversed readings is free from index error. Measuring a vertical angle with the telescope direct and reversed will not, however, eliminate the error introduced by not having the vertical axis truly vertical. It is therefore necessary to have the transit leveled carefully when vertical angles are to be measured.

The procedure for measuring a vertical angle with a transit equipped with a movable vertical-circle vernier is to sight directly at the point, center the control-level bubble on the vernier by using the control-level tangent screw, and then read the vertical angle. This is free of index error.

One important difference between the horizontal circle and the vertical circle of the transit is in the placement of the vernier with respect to the graduated circle. On the horizontal circle, the vernier is located inside the circle. On the vertical circle, the vernier is located outside the circle. When horizontal and vertical angles are measured concurrently, the observer is alternately reading the horizontal-circle and vertical-circle verniers, and he must be on guard against mistakes in reading the circle for the vernier because of the difference in placement of the verniers.

6-16. Sighting with the Transit. When an observer sights with the telescope of a transit, he must first focus the cross hairs so that they appear sharp to his eye. Then, provided that the cross hairs are in proper focus, he brings the image of the object sighted on into focus by manipulating the focusing knob which moves the objective lens. The focus should be tested for movement between cross hairs and image by moving the eye back and forth slightly. If parallax exists, it is removed by refocusing the objective. If the cross hairs go out of focus, then both the eyepiece and the objective must be refocused.

When making a pointing with the telescope, it is best to sight directly over the top of the telescope and then clamp the upper or lower motion, whichever is being used. The telescope is then raised or lowered and held in position by means of the vertical clamp. When the object to be sighted appears in the field of view, the vertical cross hair is centered on the object with the upper or lower tangent screw, the final motion of the tangent screw being made *against* the spring of the tangent screw. The vertical tangent screw is then used to bring the object sighted in the center of the field of view, that is, near the center horizontal cross hair. This final movement of the telescope may cause the vertical cross hair to go off the point, in which case it is brought on by the upper or lower tangent screw, whichever is being used.

The sight should be made on as small an object as is feasible or is consistent with the length of the sight. If the station is marked on the ground, the ideal sight is, of course, directly on the marked point. If the station is obscured, a pencil or a taping pin held vertically on the station makes a good target. If these are still obscured, a plumb bob centered over the station, either hand held or suspended from a tripod, is satisfactory. It is often difficult to see a plumb-bob string on a sight more than about 500 ft. To make the string visible, a string target can be used. It may be either a commercial type or one fashioned on the spot. A sheet of white paper folded twice makes a good string target. The plumb-bob string is held inside and along the second fold, and the paper is held diagonally so that one corner points downward along the freely suspended plumb-bob string. A line rod, which is from ⅜ to ½ in. in diameter, is a good target for sights between 500 and 1000 ft in length. It must be straight and it must be carefully plumbed. The observer should sight as far down the rod as possible. A range pole from ¾ to 1¼ in. in diameter is satisfactory for sights beyond 500 ft. It, too, must be straight and plumbed over the station.

6-17. **Sources of Error in Transit Angles.** The sources of error in transit angles are instrumental, personal, and natural. Most of the instrumental errors have been discussed in preceding articles.

1) If the line of sight of a telescope is not parallel with the telescope level, an error is introduced in the measurement of vertical angles. This error is eliminated by reading the vertical angle with the telescope both direct and reversed. *Eliminates all following errors*

2) If the vertical-circle vernier is displaced on the standard from its correct position, a corresponding error will result in the measured value of a vertical angle. This error is eliminated by measuring the vertical angle with the telescope both direct and reversed.

3) If the optical axis of the telescope is not parallel with the movement of the objective lens when it is being focused, an error will be introduced into the value of a horizontal angle when the backsight and foresight stations are at considerably different distances from the transit. This error is eliminated by measuring with the telescope direct and reversed. There is no error from this source if the two other stations are at about the same distance from the transit.

4) If the line of sight is not perpendicular to the horizontal axis of the transit and the telescope is rotated on that axis, the line of sight generates a cone whose axis is the horizontal axis. The amount of error c in any pointing is equal to

$$c = e \sec h \qquad (6\text{-}1)$$

where e is the amount by which the line of sight is out of normal, and h is the vertical angle of the line of sight. Consequently, if a horizontal angle is measured between two stations to which the vertical angles are about the same, there will be no error from this source. If, however, the vertical angle to the backsight station is different from that to the foresight station, the total error c_t in the horizontal angle is

$$c_t = e \,(\sec h_F - \sec h_B) \qquad (6\text{-}2)$$

This error is eliminated by measuring the angle with the telescope direct and reversed.

5) If the horizontal axis is not perpendicular to the vertical axis and the telescope is rotated on the horizontal axis, the line of sight will generate a plane which is not vertical, as it would be if the transit were in perfect adjustment. The amount of error c in any pointing is equal to

$$c = e \tan h \qquad (6\text{-}3)$$

where e is the amount by which the horizontal axis is out of normal with the vertical axis, and h is the vertical angle of the line of sight. The resultant error c_t in the measurement of a horizontal angle between two stations is

$$c_t = e \left(\tan h_F - \tan h_B \right) \qquad (6\text{-}4)$$

There is no error from this source if the vertical angles to both the backsight and foresight stations are about the same. The errors from this source are eliminated by measuring the angle with the telescope direct and reversed.

6) If the plate bubbles are out of adjustment, the vertical axis is not truly vertical when the bubbles are centered. This defect causes an error in each pointing which varies both with the direction of pointing and with the vertical angle. When the direction of pointing is in the same direction as the inclination of the vertical axis, no error will result, no matter what the vertical angle may be. If the direction of pointing is at right angles to the direction of inclination of the vertical axis, the error will be greatest. Furthermore the greater the vertical angle becomes, the greater will be the error of pointing. This error is not of great consequence in ordinary transit work. It *cannot* be eliminated by measuring an angle with the telescope direct and reversed. It *can* be eliminated by proper use of the plate bubbles.

When one bubble is brought over a pair of leveling screws, the other bubble is over the opposite pair. Both bubbles are brought to center by turning the leveling screws. The transit is then rotated 180° in azimuth. If both bubbles return to the center of the tube, the vertical axis is truly vertical within the sensitivity of the plate levels. If they do not return to the center, each one is brought *halfway* back by turning the corresponding pairs of leveling screws. This adjustment makes the vertical axis truly vertical. The leveling screws should not be moved after this step while angles are being measured. The vertical axis can be made truly vertical by using the telescope level, as described in Sec. 6-15.

7) If the A and B verniers are not set 180° apart, the two readings will be in disagreement. If the inner and outer spindles do not cause the verniers and the horizontal circle to move concentrically with one another, an error will be introduced which varies from zero at one pointing to a maximum at right angle to the original pointing. These two errors are eliminated by reading both verniers and adopting a mean of the two readings. Since errors due to this source are very small, the A vernier alone is read in most ordinary transit work.

8) Except in work of high precision, the use of an instrument with very small inequalities in the spacing of the graduations around the horizontal circle or around the verniers will not affect the ac-

curacy of ordinary transit work. If the precision of the work warrants it, the error in an angle at a station can be reduced by measuring the angle several times and distributing the initial backsight reading uniformly around the circle.

It is evident from the foregoing discussion that the error caused by defects in adjustment of the transit will be greatest when the survey is being made on hilly terrain with varying vertical angles, and when some points are very close to the transit and others are far away. Practically all instrumental errors can be eliminated by taking the mean of two angles, one of which is observed with the telescope direct and the other with the telescope inverted.

Personal errors are introduced into transit work by the instrumentman and his rodmen. Some of these errors are serious if short sights are encountered, but they are usually negligible on long sights.

Failure to have the instrument centered over the occupied station, bad pointing of the telescope on the target, or failure to have the target directly over the station sighted are all personal errors which affect accuracy in a similar manner.

If the transit is not set up exactly over the station, all angles measured at that point will be in error. The error decreases as the length of the sight increases. The diagram in Fig. 6-12 shows the effect of measuring an angle from B' instead of B, the actual station. The correct angle ABC equals the measured angle $AB'C + e_1 + e_2$.

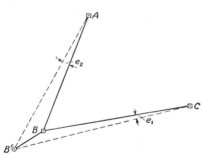

FIG. 6–12.　Transit not properly centered.

The maximum value of e_1 will be obtained when BB' is perpendicular to BC, in which case tan e_1 = BB'/BC. Likewise, the value of e_2 will be greatest when BB' is at right angles to BA, or when tan $e_2 = BB'/BA$. A convenient relation to remember is that the error in a sight will be about 1 minute when the length of the sight is 300 ft and the actual point of set-up is about 1 in. off the theoretical line of sight. Thus, if the distances BA and BC are each about 300 ft and the distance BB' is 1 in., both e_1 and e_2 will be less than 1 minute and the measured angle will be in error by less than 2 minutes. Consequently, when precision is required and when the lengths of the sights are short, the transit must be set up more carefully than when the sights are long or when small errors are of no importance.

The error in an angle due to errors of pointing can also be determined from the relationship just given. Thus, when the pointing is made to a point 1 in. to the right or left of a station 300 ft from the transit, the resulting error in the measured angle will be 1 minute. For a point 100 ft away, this error would be increased to about 3 minutes.

Parallax caused by not having the image of the object sighted focused in the plane of the cross hairs introduces a personal error of varying amounts in the measurement of both horizontal and vertical angles. Its elimination has been discussed in Sec. 6-16.

Faulty centering of level bubbles is a personal error different from maladjustment of the bubbles. Proper manipulation of the level bubbles has been discussed in previous sections.

Errors are introduced when the observer reads the verniers. If the observer does not use a reading glass, or if he does not look radially along the graduations when reading the verniers, he may be one or two graduations in either direction from the correct coincidence. Errors in reading the verniers are not to be confused with mistakes in reading the verniers to be discussed in Sec. 6-18.

The transitman should be very careful in walking about the transit. The tripod is easily disturbed, particularly when it is set up on soft ground. If a tripod leg is accidentally brushed against, the backsight should be checked at once. Of course the plates should be releveled first, if necessary.

Some causes of natural errors are gusts of wind, heat from the sun shining on the instrument, settling of the tripod legs, and horizontal and vertical refraction of the line of sight due to atmospheric conditions. The errors are of little consequence in all but extremely precise work. The transit can be sheltered from the wind and from the rays of the sun if work under unfavorable weather conditions is necessary and accuracy demands such protection. Stakes may be driven to receive the tripod legs in unstable ground. Horizontal refraction is avoided by not allowing transit lines to pass close to such structures as buildings, smokestacks, and stand pipes, which will radiate a great deal of heat. The effect of vertical refraction can be reduced to a minimum when vertical angles are being measured if the vertical angle can be measured at both ends of the line. Otherwise, its effect can be determined by reference to prepared tables discussed in Chapter 12.

6-18. Mistakes in Transit Angles. All mistakes are of a personal nature, but they are not to be confused with personal errors. They are blunders on the part of the surveyor, and are known in the field as "busts." A mistake can have any magnitude and will usually render any observation useless. Some of the more frequent mistakes are forgetting to level the instrument; turning the wrong tangent screw; transposing digits in recording a reading, as writing 291° instead of 219°; dropping a full 20, 30, or 40 minutes from a vernier reading; reading the wrong vernier; reading the wrong circle (clockwise or counterclockwise); reading the wrong side of the vernier; recording a small vertical angle with the wrong algebraic sign; failing to center the control bubble on a vertical circle containing one before reading the circle; sighting on the wrong target; recording the wrong reading on a leveling rod when measuring a vertical angle.

6-19. Repeating and Direction Instruments. There are two types of angle-measuring instruments, the *repeating* instrument and the *direction* instrument. The engineer's transit described in Secs. 6-4 through 6-9 is a repeating instrument. It permits an upper motion and a lower motion. It is capable of repeating horizontal angles, and it allows the addition to accumulate on the horizontal circle.

The direction instrument does not provide for a lower motion. When it is set up over a point, the horizontal circle is essentially fixed in position. Both the backsight reading and the foresight reading are taken by means of one motion, which is the movement of the reading device with respect to the graduated circle. The difference between the backsight reading and the foresight reading is the value of the angle. No predetermined backsight reading is set on the circle, nor can a foresight reading be preserved to make a subsequent backsight, as can be done with the transit. Consequently, the direction instrument cannot accumulate an addition of angles on the circle. The ability to read fractions of a circle graduation is obtained by means of a microscope having a traveling slide moved by a graduated drum. A fixed number of turns of the drum causes the slide to move through one circle graduation. This is known as a micrometer microscope.

As an example of recording and reducing the field notes when using the direction instrument, refer to Fig. 6-13. A direction theodolite, reading to 1 sec, is set up at A for the purpose of measuring the angles between B and C, C and D, and D and E. The telescope in its direct position is pointed at B, the motion is clamped, and the pointing is perfected by means of the tangent screw. The circle is read as 132° 20′ 36″ and recorded as shown in Fig. 6-14 opposite "D" for "direct." The telescope is then turned to C, and the reading of 175° 46′ 21″ is recorded as shown. The telescope is next turned to D, and a reading of 192° 06′ 04″ is recorded. Finally, a reading of 232° 15′ 32″ is obtained by a sight to E.

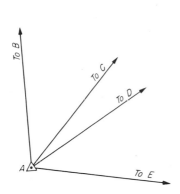

STATION	D or R	CIRCLE READING	MEAN D & R
	⅄	@ STATION A	
B	D	132° 20' 36"	132° 20' 39"
	R	312° 20' 42"	
C	D	175° 46' 21"	175° 46' 23"
	R	355° 46' 25"	
D	D	192° 06' 04"	192° 06' 05"
	R	12° 06' 06"	
E	D	232° 15' 32"	232° 15' 35"
	R	52° 15' 38"	

FIG. 6-13. Angles measured   FIG. 6-14. Direction instru-
by direction instrument.   ment notes.

In order to eliminate instrumental systematic errors, the telescope is now reversed, and the line of sight is directed to B. With the
telescope in this reverse position, the circle reading is displaced 180°
from the direct reading. It is 312° 20' 42", which is recorded opposite
"R" for "reverse." The discrepancy between the 36" in "D" and the
42" in "R" reflects sighting errors and instrumental errors. The mean
of the two values, or 39", is suffixed to the direct reading of 132° 20'
to give the mean of the "D" and "R" values as shown. This mean is
free from instrumental errors, but not from random errors. Sights are
then taken to points C, D, and E to obtain the reversed readings,
which are recorded as shown in the notes.

The directions to the four points are now used to obtain the
angles. The angle at A from B to C is equal to the direction to C
minus the direction to B, and so on. Thus,

$$\angle \text{BAC} = 175° \ 46' \ 23'' - 132° \ 20' \ 39'' = 43° \ 25' \ 44''$$
$$\angle \text{CAD} = 192° \ 06' \ 05'' - 175° \ 46' \ 23'' = 16° \ 19' \ 42''$$
$$\angle \text{DAE} = 232° \ 15' \ 35'' - 192° \ 06' \ 05'' = 40° \ 09' \ 30''$$
$$\angle \text{BAD} = 192° \ 06' \ 05'' - 132° \ 20' \ 39'' = 59° \ 45' \ 26''$$

The direction instrument has provision for advancing the circle
for a new set of readings as just discussed. For the next set, the initial
reading would then be 132° 02' 36" plus a value determined from the
number of sets, or positions, to be read. This added value is 180°/n,
in which n is the number of positions to be observed. Thus, if three
positions are to be observed, the initial reading for the second set
would be 132° 20' 36" + 60° = 192° 20' 36", and the initial reading
for the third set would be 252° 20' 36". For each position, a set of

angles can be computed as just shown for the first position. The final angles are then the means obtained from all the sets.

6-20. Optical Reading Theodolites. An optical reading theodo-

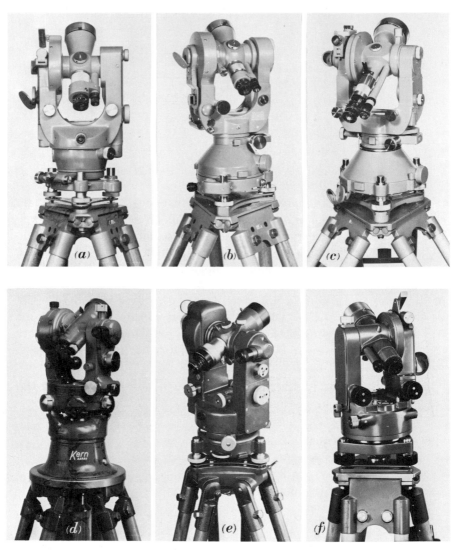

FIG. 6-15. Optical reading instruments. *Top* (left to right): Wild T1, 1 min repeating instrument; Wild T2, 1 sec. direction instrument; Wild T3, 0.2 sec. direction instrument. (Courtesy of Wild Heerbrugg Instruments, Inc.) *Bottom* (left to right): Kern DKM1, 10 sec. direction instrument. (Courtesy of Kern Instruments, Inc.) Watts Microptic No. 2, 1 sec. direction instrument; Filotechnica 4150 NE, 6 sec. direction instrument. (Courtesy of A. Lietz Co. of San Francisco.)

lite, several of which are illustrated in Fig. 6-15, is provided with a
horizontal circle and a vertical circle graduated on glass rather than
on metal. On some instruments, the images of diametrically opposite
sides of the graduated circle are brought together by means of prisms
and then carried through an optical train to a reading microscope

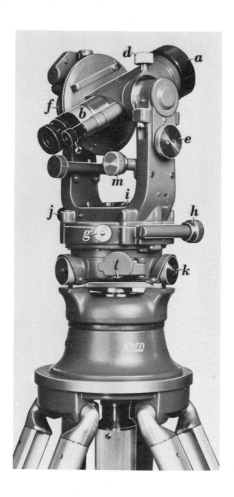

(a) Main telescope	(g) Clamp of horizontal circle
(b) Focusing ring	(h) Azimuth tangent screw
(c) Reading microscope	(i) Horizontal level
(d) Clamp of vertical circle	(j) Optical plummet
(e) Micrometer operating screw	(k) Levelling screw
(f) Lighting mirror	(l) Circle orientating gear

(m) Altitude tangent screw

FIG. 6-16. Optical reading theodolite. (Courtesy of Kern Instruments, Inc.)

located adjacent to the telescope eyepiece. On others, just the image of one side of each circle is carried to the reading microscope. A mirror located on the side of one of the standards directs light into the optical system, thereby illuminating the circles. The reading microscope thus presents a brilliant magnified image of both the horizontal circle and the vertical circle. Some of the features of an optical reading theodolite are shown in Fig. 6-16.

Four general methods are employed to enable the observer to make the circle readings. The first method is by obtaining one part of the value from the reading of a fixed index mark and the other part from the position of one of the diametrically opposite graduations. This method is illustrated in Fig. 6-17. The upper window is for the vertical circle, while the lower window is for the horizontal circle. In each window the notch represents the index mark. The index for the vertical circle reads 69° 20′. The index for the horizontal circle reads 215° 30′, since the index is more than halfway between the 20′ mark and the 40′ mark.

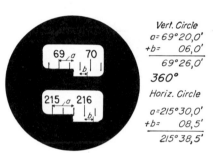

The distance b on the vertical circle is the fraction of 10 minutes that must be added to the index reading to get the gross value. This is estimated as 6.0′. (Since the images of the diametrically opposite graduations move in opposite directions, a movement of the lower line in the vertical-circle window with respect to the upper lines actually represents twice the absolute movement.) The complete vertical circle reading is 69° 20′ + 6.0′ = 69° 26.0′. The distance b on the horizontal circle is estimated as 8.5′, and so the complete horizontal-circle reading is 215° 30′ + 8.5′ = 215° 38.5′.

Fig. 6–17. Circle reading with fixed index mark.

The second method, illustrated in Fig. 6-18, does not employ an index mark. On viewing each circle, the observer sees two sets of figures, one set normal and the other set inverted. The inverted set is different from the normal set by 180° on the horizontal circle, and the two sets are identical on the vertical circle. One part of the reading is obtained by noting which normal figure has a corresponding inverted figure *lying to the right*. In Fig. 6-18, such a figure on the horizontal circle is 156°, since 336° lies to the right. The amount to be added to 156° is obtained by counting the number of spaces between the 156° mark and the 336° mark. Each space is worth 10′

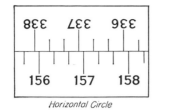

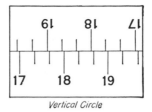

FIG. 6–18.   Circle reading with no index mark.

because the two sets of graduations appear to move in opposite directions. The amount to be added is seen to be 5.6 spaces, or 56'. The reading on the horizontal circle is therefore 156° 56'. The reading on the vertical circle is 18° 18'.

The third method is a refinement of the second method in that the fraction of the space between the last 10' mark and the corresponding inverted graduation is measured directly by means of an optical micrometer. The micrometer is turned by means of an operating knob until a normal graduation and the corresponding inverted graduation coincide with one another, and the amount of travel of the micrometer is shown in the window on the glass micrometer drum. The value of a division on the micrometer drum depends on the type and precision of the instrument. It may be 0.1', 1", 0.2", or 0.1". In Fig. 6-19 are shown the horizontal circle and the micrometer as seen through the reading microscope both before and after the micrometer knob is turned to make coincidence. The micrometer reading before making coincidence is meaningless. After coincidence, it is seen that 265° has its corresponding reading of 85° to the right of it. Furthermore there are four spaces between the two figures, each having an absolute value of 10'. On the micrometer drum, the number

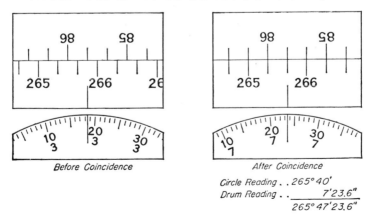

FIG. 6–19.   Circle reading with optical micrometer.

that is repeated is the number of minutes to be added to the multiple of 10'. In Fig. 6-19, this is 7'. The graduations give the number of seconds as 23.6". The reading is therefore 265° 40' + 7' + 23.6" or 265° 47' 23.6".

In the fourth method, an optical micrometer moves a single- or double-line index to a circle graduation, measuring this amount of movement and indicating it as a micrometer reading on the micrometer scale. In Fig. 6-20(*a*), the two sides of the circle are shown opposite one another, with the graduations offset from each other by a small amount. This is accomplished by the prism arrangement inside the instrument. The single-line index is made to bisect the space between two graduations by turning the micrometer knob, thus auto-

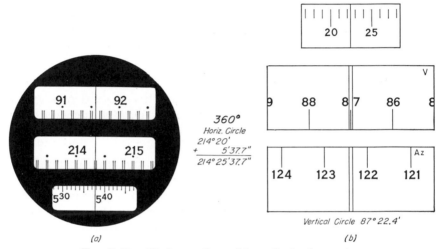

FIG. 6-20. Circle reading with optical micrometer.

matically obtaining a mean of diametrically opposite readings of the circle. The micrometer is read below. The reading for the setting on the horizontal circle (center window) is 214° 25' 37.7". If the vertical-circle reading were to be desired, the micrometer drum would be rotated until the index line bisects the small space at either 91° 30' or 91° 40', and the micrometer would be read as before. The index line can be moved to only one of the spaces. In Fig. 6-20(*b*) is shown the reading for an instrument in which only one side of the circle is brought to the reading microscope. The double-line index is made to straddle the 87° graduation on the vertical circle. The micrometer drum gives the rest of the reading. The vertical circle for this setting reads 87° 22.4'.

The four methods here described are basic. Slight variations from one instrument to another will be found. In some optical reading theodolites, a knob must be turned to shift from a view of the horizontal circle to that of the vertical circle. The reading time with an optical reading theodolite is much less than the time required to read the vernier of an engineer's transit. Furthermore, on instruments which show the opposite sides of the circle coinciding with one another, the reading is the mean of two readings, whereas such a mean is obtainable on the engineer's transit only by reading both the A vernier and the B vernier.

Some of the optical reading theodolites are equipped with a vertical line of collimation called the optical plummet. It is used to center the instrument over the ground station, and takes the place of a plumb bob. The eyepiece for the optical plummet is located on the side of the instrument, usually just above the head of the tripod. The instrument must be leveled before the optical plummet is used. Furthermore, the instrument must be moved parallel to itself when being centered, since a rotation will cause it to go off level.

Optical reading theodolites are constructed either as repeating instruments or as direction instruments. The direction instrument is graduated with more precision, and the micrometer is graduated to smaller intervals than is that of the repeating instrument.

6-21. Angles by Compass. The pocket compass, the surveyor's compass, and the transit compass are used not only for determining the direction of a line with respect to the magnetic meridian but also for determining horizontal angles. The angles obtained by using the compass are accurate to within the limits of reading the compass circle or about 10 minutes of arc.

When the sole function of the compass is to determine a horizontal angle by sighting to two points from the vertex of the angle, neither the declination of the compass needle nor local attraction need be taken into account, since at each pointing from the vertex the corrections to the bearings for both these factors are of the same magnitude and direction and will cancel out when the two observed directions are used to determine the angle.

In Fig. 6-21 are shown a series of magnetic bearings read at station O to stations H, J, K, M, and P. The bearings of the lines are as follows:

Line	Magnetic Bearing
OH	N 41° 00′ E
OJ	S 72° 30′ E
OK	S 8° 00′ W
OM	S 67° 15′ W
OP	N 36° 30′ W

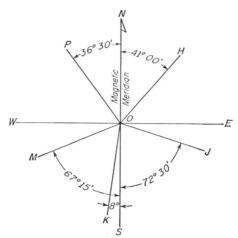

FIG. 6–21. Magnetic bearings.

The values of the various angles about station O reckoned in a clockwise direction are as follows:

From	To		Angle
H	J	$180° - (41° 00' + 72° 30')$	$= 66° 30'$
H	K	$180° - 41° 00' + 8° 00'$	$= 147° 00'$
H	P	$360° - (36° 30' + 41° 00')$	$= 282° 30'$
J	K	$72° 30' + 8° 00'$	$= 80° 30'$
J	H	$180° + 41° 00' + 72° 30'$	$= 293° 30'$
K	M	$67° 15' - 8° 00'$	$= 59° 15'$
K	P	$180° - (8° 00' + 36° 30')$	$= 135° 30'$
P	H	$36° 30' + 41° 00'$	$= 77° 30'$
P	J	$180° - 72° 30' + 36° 30'$	$= 144° 00'$

When determining angles from bearings, it is advisable to draw a sketch showing the lines in their proper quadrants and indicating on the sketch the angles off the meridian, as in Fig. 6-21.

When using the transit, the compass is used only for providing a rough check on the value of an angle determined more precisely by the horizontal circle and verniers. The compass on the transit is used also to read bearings to reference marks which in the future will help to rediscover the transit station.

There are only two instrumental errors of any consequence when using a compass to measure horizontal angles. The sight vanes on the pocket compass or the surveyor's compass may become bent normal to the line of sight. Such bending will introduce an error in an angle if the sights to the two stations are at different vertical angles. The vanes may be checked by sighting on a plumb-bob string to determine whether or not they are vertical when the compass is leveled. The second error is introduced if the pivot is bent, causing the center of the compass needle to be displaced from the center of the compass circle. The error varies as the compass is rotated in azimuth. It can never become appreciably large, because if the pivot is sufficiently bent, the needle will not swing freely. A bent compass needle, although introducing an error in each pointing, will not affect the value of an angle, since the errors in the two pointings are canceled.

Personal errors are introduced in centering the compass over the station, in faulty pointing, by the rodman giving a bad sight, and in reading the compass circle. Their effects are small, considering the low degree of accuracy of angles measured with the compass.

Natural errors mentioned in Sec. 6-17 are of no consequence in compass work.

6-22. Angles with the Plane Table. The plane table affords a means of measuring a horizontal angle graphically. If, on a sheet of paper, lines are drawn along the lines of sight to two objects, the result is a graphical representation of the angle between the two lines of sight. This method is largely used in topographic surveying and is described in Chapter 13.

6-23. Description of Sextant. The sextant is a hand instrument for measuring either horizontal or vertical angles. By means of it the angle between two lines of sight can be measured by a single operation. When the observations are taken, the instrument is held in the hand, and successive angular measurements can be made with great rapidity. The sextant is especially well suited for use in a boat, where the motion of the boat renders the use of fixed instruments impracticable.

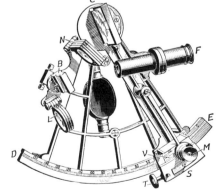

FIG. 6-22.　Sextant.

A sextant, as represented in Fig. 6-22, consists of a metal frame CDE, and an arm CS, called an index arm, which is fitted with a vernier and rotates about the center of the sextant. To this index arm is also attached the index mirror C. To the arm CD is fixed the horizon glass B. Half of this glass is silvered on the back to serve as a mirror, while the other half is transparent. A telescope F directed toward the horizon glass B can be attached to the frame of the sextant. Thus, in Fig. 6-23, while the telescope is directed to an object H, the rays of light from another

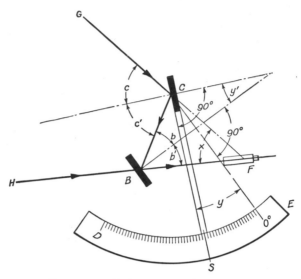

FIG. 6–23. Principles of the sextant.

body G are reflected first from the mirror C to the silvered half of the mirror B, and then from this mirror to the telescope in the direction HBF. The observer will thus see both bodies H and G in the field of the telescope together.

In order that the ray of light GC, Fig. 6-23, may enter the telescope after reflection, the index arm CS must be turned about the pivot at C until the mirror C is brought into the proper position with respect to the ray GC and the mirror B. When the index S is at $0°$ on the scale DE (assuming there is no index error in the sextant), the two mirrors are parallel. When S has been moved forward until the ray of light GC enters the telescope after two reflections, the arc y, over which the arm CS has been moved, will be equal to exactly one-half the angle x between GC and HF.

This relationship can be proved from the angles shown in Fig. 6-23. By the law of reflection, $c = c'$ and $b = b'$. Since the two sides of y are mutually perpendicular to the two sides of y', $y = y'$. In the triangles formed by the rays of light and lines perpendicular to the mirrors, $c + c' = b + b' + x$, or $2c' = 2b + x$; and $c' = b + y'$, or $2c' = 2b + 2y'$. Hence, $x = 2y'$ and $y = \frac{1}{2} x$.

Since the angle y is one-half the true angle between GC and HB, the arc ED has each half-degree marked as a whole degree, so that ED, which is an arc of $60°$, is divided into 120 equal parts and each part is assumed to represent $1°$. This is done merely to spare the observer the trouble of multiplying the reading by 2.

6-24. Measuring Angles with the Sextant. Before an angle is measured with the sextant, the index error must be determined. This is done by setting the index at zero and then looking through the telescope at a very distant object and noting whether the direct and reflected images of the object coincide. If they coincide, the index error is zero. If they do not, the index arm is moved until they coincide and is clamped in this position. The reading of the index in this position is called the index error. If the error is off the arc, that is, if the index is to the right of the zero mark, it is added to all readings. If the error is on the arc, that is, if the index is to the left of the zero mark, the error is subtracted from all readings.

To measure an angle between two objects with a sextant, hold the plane of the limb in the plane of the two objects, look through the telescope toward the less distinct object, and move the index arm until the reflected image of the brighter object comes in contact with the direct image of the less distinct object. Clamp the index arm and turn the tangent screw T, Fig. 6-22, to bring the two images exactly together. Note the reading of the vernier V with the aid of the magnifying glass M, and apply the correction for the index error. In order to have the plane of the limb in the plane of the two objects when the telescope is directed toward the less distinct object, it may sometimes be necessary to hold the sextant upside down.

The sextant is used in determining a ship's position at sea by measuring horizontal angles between points on the shore, or by measuring the vertical angle between the horizon and some heavenly body, as the sun or a star. When the sun is being observed, the colored glasses shown at L and N in Fig. 6-22 are placed in front of the mirrors to protect the eye of the observer.

When the altitude of a heavenly body is measured on land, an artificial horizon must be used. A shallow basin of mercury or a pan

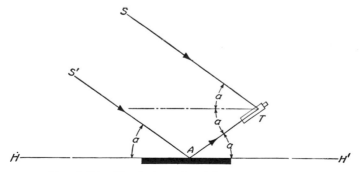

Fig. 6–24. Vertical angle with artificial horizon.

nearly filled with a mixture of oil and lampblack can be used for this purpose. The observer measures the angle between the image of the heavenly body reflected in the mercury or oil and the body itself. Thus, in Fig. 6-24, the angle ATS is measured with the sextant. This angle corrected for index error is double the required angle $S'AH$.

6-25. Precision of Sextant Angles. In the measurement of vertical angles to heavenly bodies for astronomical determinations, the results obtained with the sextant are likely to be more precise than those obtained with the ordinary transit. The principal reason for this is that the least count of the vertical-circle vernier on most transits is 1 minute, while the least count of the sextant vernier may be 10 seconds. Thus, the error of observation may be cut from 30″ to 5″.

In the measurement of horizontal angles, the use of the sextant is limited to work where the lengths of the lines are considerable. It is apparent from Fig. 6-23 that the position of the vertex of the angle x is dependent on the size of the angle. If the angle is very small, this vertex may be several feet back of the index mirror. The effect on the measured angle is the same as that caused by not setting the transit directly over a station. This condition is discussed in Sec. 6-17. On lines 1000 ft long, the error from this source will be less than 1 minute.

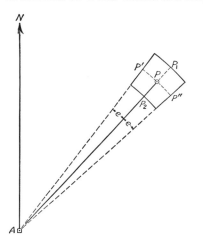

FIG. 6–25. Relation between angular and linear errors.

6-26. Accuracy Required in Measuring Angles. The accuracy required in the measurement of horizontal angles is largely determined by the purpose of the survey, and by the accuracy with which the linear measurements are made. A balance should be maintained between the precision of the angular measurements and the precision of the linear measurements.

The location of a point is frequently determined by a horizontal angle from some line of reference and a distance from the vertex of the angle. Thus, in Fig. 6-25, a point P can be located by the angle NAP and the distance AP, neither of which can be measured exactly. If the angular error is $\pm e$, and it is assumed that there is no linear error, the position of P would be between P' and P''. On the other hand, if it is assumed that there is no angular error, the effect of linear error would be to locate P somewhere between P_1 and P_2. If the precision of the angular measurements is consistent with the precision of the linear measurements, the values of $P'P$, P_2P, $P''P$, and P_1P should all be equal, and the located position of P will fall somewhere within an approximate square.

When the allowable linear error in a distance l is assumed to be d, the corresponding allowable angular error e can be computed from the relation, $\tan e = d/l$. If the linear error is expressed as a ratio, this ratio will also be $\tan e$. Where the angular error e is assumed, the allowable error in distance will be the length of the line times the tangent of the angle e.

In Table 6-1 the allowable errors in angles and the allowable errors in linear measurements are given for various assumed pre-

TABLE 6-1

RELATIONS BETWEEN LINEAR AND ANGULAR ERRORS

ALLOWABLE ANGULAR ERROR FOR GIVEN LINEAR PRECISION		ALLOWABLE LINEAR ERROR FOR GIVEN ANGULAR PRECISION					
Precision of Linear Measurements	Allowable Angular Error	Least Reading in Angular Measurements	Allowable Linear Error in				Ratio
			100'	500'	1000'	5000'	
$\dfrac{1}{500}$	6'53"	5'	.145	.727	1.454	7.272	$\dfrac{1}{688}$
$\dfrac{1}{1000}$	3 26	1'	.029	.145	.291	1.454	$\dfrac{1}{3440}$
$\dfrac{1}{5000}$	0 41	30"	.015	.073	.145	.727	$\dfrac{1}{6880}$
$\dfrac{1}{10,000}$	0 21	20"	.010	.049	.097	.485	$\dfrac{1}{10,300}$
$\dfrac{1}{50,000}$	0 04	10"	.005	.024	.049	.242	$\dfrac{1}{20,600}$
$\dfrac{1}{100,000}$	0 02	5"	.002	.012	.024	.121	$\dfrac{1}{41,200}$
$\dfrac{1}{1,000,000}$	0 00.2	2"	.001	.005	.010	.048	$\dfrac{1}{103,100}$
		1"		.002	.005	.024	$\dfrac{1}{206,300}$

cisions of linear and angular measurements. From this tabulation it is evident that, if the distances are being obtained by the stadia method with a precision of 1/500, the angles need be measured only to the nearest 5 minutes; whereas, if a precision of 1/10,000 is required, the angles should be known to 20″.

6-27. Precision of Angles Used in Trigonometric Computations. If the measured angles are to be used in trigonometric computations, the values in Table 6-1 may be somewhat misleading. It appears from the table that, with an angular error of 1 minute, the corresponding linear precision should be 1/3440. If the measured angle is used in computing the length of an unknown side, the precision of the computed length may be considerably less than this, the exact error depending on the size of the angle and the particular function used.

As an example, let it be assumed that in Fig. 6-26 the distance AC has been measured with no error and the angle at A is accurate within 1 minute. The distance BC is $AC \sin A$. With $A = 30° \pm 01'$

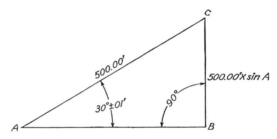

Fɪɢ. 6–26.   Precision of angles in trigonometric computations.

and $AC = 500.00$ ft, BC will be 250.00 ± 0.126 ft. The precision of this computed value is, therefore, 0.126/250 or 1/1980. If the base AB of the triangle had been measured, and BC had been computed from the relation $BC = AB \tan A$, the precision of the computed result would be still less than when the sine is used. With $AB = 500.00$ and $A = 30° \pm 01'$, $BC = 288.68 \pm 0.194$ ft, and the precision of the result is 0.194/288.68 or 1/1490.

In Table 6-2 is shown the precision of computed results involving the sines and cosines and the tangents and cotangents of various angles for angular errors of 1′, 30″, 20″, 10″, and 5″. From this table it is evident that when the sine of an angle of approximately 45° is to be used in a computation and the precision of the computed result is to be 1/10,000, the angle must be measured to the nearest 20″. When the tangent of 45° is used, the angle must be measured to 10″ to maintain the same precision. The precision of computations involving the sines, tangents, or cotangents of small angles or the cosines, tangents, or cotangents of angles near 90° will be very low, unless these angles are measured much more exactly than is usually the case.

TABLE 6-2

PRECISION OF VALUES CALCULATED BY TRIGONOMETRY

SIZE OF ANGLE AND FUNCTION		ANGULAR ERROR				
		1′	30″	20″	10″	5″
		Precision of computed value using sine or cosine				
sin 5° or cos 85°		$\frac{1}{300}$	$\frac{1}{600}$	$\frac{1}{900}$	$\frac{1}{1800}$	$\frac{1}{3600}$
10	80	$\frac{1}{610}$	$\frac{1}{1210}$	$\frac{1}{1820}$	$\frac{1}{3640}$	$\frac{1}{7280}$
20	70	$\frac{1}{1250}$	$\frac{1}{2500}$	$\frac{1}{3750}$	$\frac{1}{7500}$	$\frac{1}{15,000}$
30	60	$\frac{1}{1990}$	$\frac{1}{3970}$	$\frac{1}{5960}$	$\frac{1}{11,970}$	$\frac{1}{23,940}$
40	50	$\frac{1}{2890}$	$\frac{1}{5770}$	$\frac{1}{8660}$	$\frac{1}{17,310}$	$\frac{1}{34,620}$
50	40	$\frac{1}{4100}$	$\frac{1}{8190}$	$\frac{1}{12,290}$	$\frac{1}{24,580}$	$\frac{1}{49,160}$
60	30	$\frac{1}{5950}$	$\frac{1}{11,900}$	$\frac{1}{17,860}$	$\frac{1}{35,720}$	$\frac{1}{71,440}$
70	20	$\frac{1}{9450}$	$\frac{1}{18,900}$	$\frac{1}{28,330}$	$\frac{1}{56,670}$	$\frac{1}{113,340}$
80	10	$\frac{1}{19,500}$	$\frac{1}{39,000}$	$\frac{1}{58,500}$	$\frac{1}{117.000}$	$\frac{1}{234,000}$
		Precision of computed value using tan or cot				
tan or cot 5°		$\frac{1}{300}$	$\frac{1}{600}$	$\frac{1}{900}$	$\frac{1}{1790}$	$\frac{1}{3580}$
10		$\frac{1}{590}$	$\frac{1}{1180}$	$\frac{1}{1760}$	$\frac{1}{3530}$	$\frac{1}{7050}$
20		$\frac{1}{1100}$	$\frac{1}{2210}$	$\frac{1}{3310}$	$\frac{1}{6620}$	$\frac{1}{13,250}$
30		$\frac{1}{1490}$	$\frac{1}{2980}$	$\frac{1}{4470}$	$\frac{1}{8930}$	$\frac{1}{17,870}$
40		$\frac{1}{1690}$	$\frac{1}{3390}$	$\frac{1}{5080}$	$\frac{1}{10,160}$	$\frac{1}{20,320}$
45		$\frac{1}{1720}$	$\frac{1}{3440}$	$\frac{1}{5160}$	$\frac{1}{10,310}$	$\frac{1}{20,630}$
50		$\frac{1}{1690}$	$\frac{1}{3390}$	$\frac{1}{5080}$	$\frac{1}{10,160}$	$\frac{1}{20,320}$
60		$\frac{1}{1490}$	$\frac{1}{2980}$	$\frac{1}{4470}$	$\frac{1}{8930}$	$\frac{1}{17,870}$
70		$\frac{1}{1100}$	$\frac{1}{2210}$	$\frac{1}{3310}$	$\frac{1}{6620}$	$\frac{1}{13,250}$
80		$\frac{1}{590}$	$\frac{1}{1180}$	$\frac{1}{1760}$	$\frac{1}{3530}$	$\frac{1}{7050}$
85		$\frac{1}{300}$	$\frac{1}{600}$	$\frac{1}{900}$	$\frac{1}{1790}$	$\frac{1}{3580}$

174   THE MEASUREMENT OF ANGLES

PROBLEMS

6-1. The sides of a triangle measure 142.56, 435.82, and 390.05 ft. Compute the three angles.

6-2. If the distances BD and BE in Fig. 6-3 are laid out 100.00 ft long, and the distance k measures 66.62 ft, what is the value of the angle?

6-3. A pointing error of 0.40 ft is made in a distance of 872.66 ft. What angular error does this represent? Express the result to the nearest second.

6-4. An angle is measured by repetition with a 1-minute transit. The mean of the readings of the A and B verniers for the initial backsight is 125° 52′ 00″. After the first repetition, the A vernier reads 202° 15′. After the sixth repetition the mean reading of the A and B verniers is 224° 12′ 30″. Compute the value of the angle.

6-5. If angles are measured to the nearest 10 sec, and the precisions of the angular and linear measurements are to be consistent, what should be the allowable linear error in a 1000-ft distance?

6-6. A vertical angle is measured to a signal on top of a building. With the telescope in the direct position, the vertical circle reads + 6° 18′. With the telescope in the reversed position, the vertical circle reads + 6° 21′. What is the correct vertical angle? What is the index error with the telescope in the direct position?

6-7. The line of sight of a transit makes an angle of 89° 54′ with the transverse axis. A backsight is taken to a point at an elevation angle of + 42° 00′. A foresight is then taken on a point at a depression angle of − 20° 00′. What error is introduced in the measured horizontal angle?

6-8. The transverse axis of a transit is inclined 04′ with the horizontal, the right-hand end being high when the observer looks in the direction of the line of sight. A backsight is taken at an elevation angle of + 45° 00′. A foresight is then taken with the line of sight level. What error is introduced in the measured angle? Is the measured angle too large or too small?

6-9. An engineer wishes to establish a construction line perpendicular to a base line. Using a 1-minute transit, he backsights along the base line with the circle reading 0° 00′. He then sets the upper motion to a circle reading of 90° 00′ and sets a point on the line of sight 750 ft away from the transit. Next, he measures the angle by repetition and finds the angle to be 90° 00′ 25″. What offset should be measured perpendicular to the construction line at the far point (see Fig. 6-5)?

6-10. A direction theodolite is used to measure angles about a point. Four positions of the circle are used. The resulting directions are listed below.

Station Sighted	Mean D & R Position 1	Mean D & R Position 2	Mean D & R Position 3	Mean D & R Position 4
B	123° 14′ 22.6″	168° 14′ 18.0″	213° 14′ 25.9″	258° 14′ 23.5″
C	160° 52′ 03.0″	205° 52′ 03.6″	250° 52′ 09.9″	295° 52′ 06.6″
D	191° 03′ 56.2″	236° 03′ 55.4″	281° 04′ 02.1″	326° 04′ 03.1″
E	233° 27′ 44.4″	278° 27′ 41.4″	323° 27′ 52.3″	8° 27′ 54.7″

Compute the three angles for each position. Compute the mean of each of the three angles from the four positions.

6-11. A compass is used to observe the bearing of lines AB and AC. The magnetic bearing to B is S 42° 15' W; the magnetic bearing to C is N 4° 00' W. What is the angle at A from B to C?

6-12. Assume that, in Fig. 6-26, $AC = 358.58$ ft and $A = 18°$ 22' with a precision of 30". What will be the precision of the computed side BC?

7

Field Operations with the Transit

7-1. Introduction. Chapter 6 dealt with the construction of the transit and the methods by which horizontal and vertical angles are measured with it. Also the various errors introduced into the measurement of angles when using the transit were discussed. Chapter 7 will describe tne various operations for which the transit is used in the field, without going into the fundamentals of angle measurement or into instrumental errors except to point out instances where they are eliminated by certain field techniques.

7-2. Measuring Interior Angles. The angles formed within a closed figure between the adjacent sides are known as interior angles. In Fig. 7-1, there are five interior angles to be measured. They are the angles at L, M, N, O, and P. If the transit is set up at each station in turn in the order just given, all the interior angles would be measured in a counterclockwise direction. Thus, the interior angle at L is measured from P to M, that at M from L to N, that at N from M

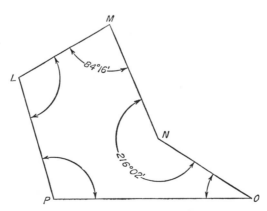

Fig. 7-1. Interior angles.

Station	From To Station	Circle	Interior Angle
	L	0° 00′	
M		84° 16′	84° 16′
	N	168° 32′	84° 16′
		Mean	84° 16′ 00″
	M	0° 04′	
N		216° 06′	216° 02′
	O	72° 09′	216° 03′
		Mean	216° 02′ 30″

Fig. 7-2. Notes for recording interior angles.

to O, that at O from N to P, and that at P from O to L. On the other hand, if the transit is set up in turn at L, P, O, N, and M, then all the interior angles would be measured clockwise. In the first instance, the graduation numbers of the horizontal circle and vernier that increase in a counterclockwise direction would be used; in the second instance, those that increase in a clockwise direction would be used.

The form of notes used to record the interior angles is a matter of importance, since the notes are the record of the measurements. The form of notes shown in Fig. 7-2 is a record of interior angles measured at stations M and N of Fig. 7-1, each angle being measured once with the telescope direct and once with it reversed.

The occupied station appears under the column headed *Station*. The backsight station and the foresight station appear respectively above and below under the column headed $\frac{From}{To}$ *Station*. The three readings under the column headed *Circle* are the initial backsight reading, the initial foresight reading, and the second foresight reading. The first value of the interior angle at station N from M to O, measured with the telescope direct, is obtained by subtracting 0° 04′ from 216° 06′ and is recorded under the column headed *Interior Angle* as 216° 02′. The second value, measured with the telescope reversed, is obtained by subtracting 216° 06′ from (72° 09′ + 360°) and is recorded as 216° 03′. The mean of the two angles is recorded as 216° 02′ 30″. At both M and N, the counterclockwise circle was read, since the angles are counterclockwise interior angles.

If interior angles are measured in a counterclockwise direction with a transit on which the circle is graduated in a clockwise direction only, then the circle readings would decrease when the angles

Station	From To Station	Circle	Interior Angle
	L	0° 00′	
M		275° 44′	84° 16′
	N	191° 28′	84° 16′
	Mean		84° 16′ 00″

FIG. 7-3.   Notes for recording interior angles with transit
having only clockwise numbering.

are turned. The angle would be obtained by subtracting the lower
reading from the upper reading. As an example, if the angle at M in
Fig. 7-1 was measured from L to N with such a transit, the notes
would be as shown in Fig. 7-3.

The first value of the interior angle is obtained by subtracting
275° 44′ from (0° 00′ + 360° 00′). The second value is obtained by
subtracting 191° 28′ from 275° 44′. In order to avoid confusion, interior angles should be measured clockwise if the circle does not contain a counterclockwise system of graduation numbers.

The sum of the interior angles in a closed plane figure must equal
$(n - 2) \times 180°$, where n is the number of sides in the figure. This relation furnishes a check on the accuracy of the field measurements of
the angles and a basis for distributing the errors in measurement.

7-3. Measuring Angles to the Right. Most surveys performed
to establish horizontal control by traversing between fixed control
points are made by measuring all the angles from the backsight to
the foresight station in a clockwise direction. Angles to the right are
shown in Fig. 7-4, where a traverse is run from station Park to station
Church through stations *1, 2, 3,* and *4.* The form for recording the
notes is the same as those for recording readings for interior angles.

The check on the angles measured to the right is made by comparing the final azimuth, as computed from the angles, with a fixed
azimuth. This check is fully discussed in Sec. 8-6 in Chapter 8.

FIG. 7-4.   Angles to the right.

7-4. Measuring Deflection Angles. A deflection angle, as shown in Fig. 7-5, is the angle made by the foresight with the prolongation of the backsight. Thus, at station 17 + 42.86, a deflection to the *left* of 18° 26' is shown; at station 38 + 14.53, the deflection is 40° 12' 30" to the *right*.

To measure the deflection angle with the transit occupying station 17 + 42.86, a backsight is taken on station 0 with the telescope direct. The circle is read and the value is recorded as the initial circle reading. Say the reading is 0° 00'. The telescope is plunged to the reversed position so that the line of sight is now directed along the prolongation of the line from station 0 to station 17 + 42.86. The circle still reads 0° 00' since no angle has been turned.

The upper clamp is loosened and the line of sight is turned to the left and directed to station 38 + 14.53. When the line of sight is brought exactly on the point with the upper tangent screw, the circle is read. If the clockwise circle is read, the reading will have decreased from 0° (or 360°) to 341° 34', the difference being 18° 26'. If the counterclockwise circle is read, the reading will have increased from 0° to 18° 26', the difference being 18° 26'.

The angle is now measured a second time. With the telescope still in the *reversed* position, the lower clamp is loosened and the line of sight is directed toward the backsight station. The line of sight is brought exactly on station 0 by means of the lower tangent screw. The clockwise circle still reads 341° 34', and the counterclockwise circle still reads 18° 26'. The telescope is plunged again (it is thus brought back to its direct position) so that the line of sight is now directed along the prolongation of the backsight. The clockwise circle still reads 341° 34', and the counterclockwise circle still reads 18° 26'.

The upper clamp is loosened and the line of sight is turned to the left and brought on station 38 + 14.53. The circle is read to obtain the final reading. If the clockwise circle is read, the reading will have decreased from 341° 34' to 323° 08', the difference being 18° 26'. If the counterclockwise circle is read, the reading will have increased from 18° 26' to 36° 52', the difference being 18° 26'. The direction of the deflection angle, in this case *left*, is as important as the magnitude of the angle.

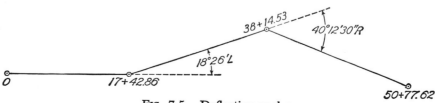

Fig. 7-5. Deflection angles.

The two angles shown in Fig. 7-5 would be recorded from the clockwise-circle readings as shown in the form in Fig. 7-6.

Station	From Station To	Circle	Deflection Angle
	0 + 00	0° 00′	
17 + 42.86		341° 34′	18° 26′
	38 + 14.53	323° 08′	18° 26′
		Mean	18° 26′ 00″ Left
	17 + 42.86	0° 00′	
38 + 14.53		40° 13′	40° 13′
	50 + 77.62	80° 25′	40° 12′
		Mean	40° 12′ 30″ Right

FIG. 7-6.   Deflection-angle notes with clockwise circle.

If the counterclockwise circle is read, the readings would be recorded as shown in the form in Fig. 7-7.

Station	From Station To	Circle	Deflection Angle
	0 + 00	0° 00′	
17 + 42.86		18° 26′	18° 26′
	38 + 14.53	36° 52′	18° 26′
		Mean	18° 26′ 00″ Left
	17 + 42.86	0° 00′	
38 + 14.53		319° 47′	40° 13′
	50 + 77.62	279° 35′	40° 12′
		Mean	40° 12′ 30″ Right

FIG. 7-7.   Deflection-angle notes with counterclockwise circle.

When a deflection angle is measured only once, the more serious instrumental errors are introduced into the measurement. If a deflection angle is measured by double centering, most of the instrumental errors are eliminated, and the second value of the angle affords a check on the first value.

Deflection angles are used frequently in surveys for highways, railroads, transmission lines, and similar routes, which extend in the same general direction, although they are employed by many surveyors and engineers in running traverse lines. The principal advantages of using deflection angles are: 1) Azimuths are easily computed from deflection angles (see Sec. 8-5 in Chapter 8); 2) the deflection angles are used in the computation of circular curves for highway and railroad work; 3) deflection angles are easily plotted. One distinct disadvantage is the likelihood of the notekeeper making a mistake in recording the direction of the deflection angle.

A procedure which helps to guard against a mistake in recording is to read the clockwise circle at all times, as shown in Fig. 7-6. Then a glance at the notes will indicate whether the angle was turned to the right or to the left. If the circle readings increase, the angle is to the right; if the circle readings decrease, the angle is to the left.

You should bear in mind the fact that a deflection angle can never be greater than 180°. Suppose that the observer backsights with a reading of 0° 00′ on the circle, plunges the telescope, turns off the deflection angle, and reads 180° 10′ on the *clockwise* circle. The deflection angle is the difference between the initial and final circle readings. In this instance, the reading either increased from 0° to 180° 10′ or decreased from 360° to 180° 10′. The former assumption would indicate a right deflection angle of 180° 10′, which is impossible. The latter assumption would indicate a left deflection angle of 179° 50′, which is correct.

In a closed figure in which the sides do not cross one another, the difference between the sum of the right deflection angles and the sum of the left deflection angles should equal 360°. In a closed survey where the lines cross once, as in a figure eight, the sum of the right deflection angles should equal the sum of the left deflection angles. If the lines do not cross or cross any *even* number of times, the difference between the sums should equal 360°. If the lines cross any *odd* number of times, the sums should equal one another.

7-5. Laying off Angles. In all types of construction work, for laying out highways, bridges, buildings, and other structures, it becomes necessary to establish lines in given directions, and thus to lay off both horizontal and vertical angles. A line called a *base line* is established in the vicinity of the work. The base line may or may not be a portion of a control traverse, its position depending on circumstances. Nevertheless, it acts as the control for the construction. Stations along the base line are occupied by the transit, and backsights are made to other base line stations. The angles called for on construction plans and drawings are laid off with respect to the base line.

The principle of double centering is employed in turning angles from the base line. If construction lines are quite long, the principle of repetition may be employed. For example, to lay off an angle of 55° 12′ 30″ by double centering with a 1-minute transit, a backsight is taken on a base-line station with the circle reading 0° 00′. The upper clamp is loosened, and the telescope is turned until the circle reading is approximately 55° 12′. The upper clamp is tightened, and the vernier is made to read 55° 12′ as closely as possible by turning the upper tangent screw. A point is set on the line of sight, preferably being marked by a tack in a stake or a hub. The telescope is inverted and a second backsight is taken on the base-line station by a lower motion. When the backsight has been made, the upper clamp is loosened and the telescope is turned until approximately 2 × 55° 12′ 30″, or 110° 25′, is read. The upper clamp is tightened and the exact reading of 110° 25′ is made by turning the upper tangent screw. A second point is set on the line of sight alongside the first point. The second angle is 55° 13′. A third point halfway between the other two points is the correct point, and the line joining this point and the transit station makes the desired angle with the base line.

To lay off an angle by repetition, see Secs. 6-3 and 6-14 in Chapter 6.

To lay off a vertical angle with a transit having a full vertical circle, carefully level the transit by using either the plate levels as described in Sec. 6-17 or the telescope level as described in Sec. 6-15. Rotate the telescope in the direction of the point to be set, and incline the telescope until the vertical circle reads approximately the angle to be laid off. Clamp the vertical clamp, and set off the exact reading by using the vertical tangent screw. The point is marked by reference to the center horizontal cross hair. Invert the telescope and rotate the transit on its vertical axis until the line of sight is in the desired direction. Sight the first point and clamp the vertical clamp. If the vertical circle reads the desired angle when the horizontal cross hair is brought on the point previously set, it may be concluded that the index error was zero and the point has been correctly set. If the vertical circle does not read the desired angle, the vertical tangent screw is turned until it does. A second point is set above or below the first point. A third point halfway between the two will be in very nearly the correct position.

To lay off a vertical angle with a transit having a half vertical circle, level the instrument as before and rotate the telescope until the line of sight is in the direction of the desired point. Bring the telescope horizontal, and center the telescope bubble by using the vertical tangent screw. Read the vertical circle to obtain the index error. Add the index error algebraically to the desired vertical angle to obtain the correct circle reading. Set off the correct circle reading by using the vertical clamp and tangent screw. The line of sight is now directed along the desired vertical angle and the point is set on line.

7-6. Straight Line by Double Centering. Whenever a straight line is to be accurately extended for any considerable distance, the method of double centering should be used. If, in Fig. 7-8, the line AB is to be extended to the right, the transit is set up at B, and a backsight is taken on A with the telescope in the normal or direct position. The telescope is then plunged. If the transit is in adjustment, the line of sight will then be the line BC. If the transit is not in adjustment, it may be either the line BC' or the line BC''. A stake is driven on the line of sight, and the exact line is marked by a point on the stake. The backsight having first been checked to see that the telescope has not moved off line, either the upper clamp or the lower clamp is loosened and a second backsight is taken on A, this time with the telescope in the inverted position. The telescope is again plunged, and the line of sight is again directed toward C. If the instrument is in adjustment, the line of sight will strike the point previously set. If it is out of adjustment, the line of sight will now miss that point and a second point should be set on this line. A third point, midway between the two points already set, will be on the line AB extended. Thus, if C' is the first point set, C'' will be the second one, and the correct line will be marked by C, which is midway between C' and C''.

The line can be extended further by moving the transit to C and repeating the procedure, a fourth point D being located midway between D' and D''. The first backsight might, of course, be made with the telescope in the inverted position. If this is done, the second backsight is taken with it normal. In Fig. 7-8 the scale is very much distorted. With an instrument in reasonably good adjustment, the three points, C', C'', and C, should all fall on the same 2-in. stake at a distance of 1200 to 1500 ft from the transit. If they do not, the instrument should be adjusted. Otherwise, unnecessary time will be spent in driving stakes when this kind of work is being done.

Establishing a straight line by the method of double centering is nothing more than laying off a zero deflection angle twice, the first backsight being taken with the telescope direct and the second one with it reversed.

FIG. 7-8.   Extending straight line by double centering.

7-7. Establishing Points on a Straight Line. The simplest case of establishing points on a straight line is when the two ends of the line are marked and the entire line is visible from one end or the other. Thus, if it is necessary to establish additional points between *A* or *B* in Fig. 7-8, the transit can be set up at either *A* or *B* and a sight taken to the other end of the line. The rodman is then directed by motions to the right or the left to the point that is on the line. The rodman may use a line rod if the lengths are considerable. When they are short and the ground is clear, he may have the transitman line in the stake or other object on which the point is to be marked. A point on the top of the stake may be obtained by lining in the line rod again or a pencil or a plumb-bob string.

If the ground surface is so shaped that the telescope does not have to be raised or lowered appreciably after taking the sight on the opposite end of the line, and if the focus of the telescope is likewise unchanged, this work can be done with a transit that is not in perfect adjustment. If the inclination of the telescope must be changed considerably and the focus altered, important points should be checked by taking two sights, one with the telescope normal and another with it inverted.

If points are to be established between *B* and *C*, the distant point *C* should first be established by the method of double-centering and a foresight should be taken on *C*, before line is given for the intermediate points. Where points are being set at regular intervals, as in a route survey, the transit is moved only when the foresight distance becomes so great that it is impossible to give line accurately, or when the ground conditions prevent further accurate sighting. The forward transit station should be set by the method of double-centering. The careful transitman will use this procedure as a check, even when he is reasonably certain that his instrument is in good adjustment.

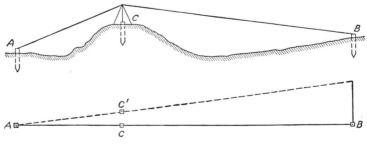

FIG. 7-9. Balancing-in.

7-8. Balancing-In. It often happens that the two ends of a line are not intervisible but some intermediate point can be found from which the ends can be seen. Thus, in Fig. 7-9, both A and B can be seen from the top of an embankment. The method of finding, by trial, the location of a point C that will be on the line AB is called *balancing-in*. The transit is first set up at C', which is as nearly on the line as can be estimated. A backsight is taken on A, and the telescope is plunged. From the sketch it is evident that the line of sight strikes considerably to the left of B. The amount by which it fails to strike B is measured or estimated, and the transit is moved a proportionate amount (in the sketch about one-third) of this distance and the procedure is repeated. After a few trials the line of sight should strike B. The final movement of the instrument can often be made with the shifting head of the transit. Until the transit is near the correct point, it is unnecessary to level the instrument carefully.

To check the position of the transit, backsight on A with the telescope in the inverted position, plunge the telescope, and check to see whether or not the line of sight is directed on B. If it is, then the transit is on line. If it is to one side of B, measure the distance by which it misses B and move the transit in the opposite direction a proportionate amount of this distance.

After the correct position of the transit at C has been established, any additional points between C and A or between C and B can be set by the method described in the preceding section.

7-9. Random Lines. In Fig. 7-10 the distance from A to B may be very great and the ground may be so thickly wooded or so hilly that it is impossible to see directly from A to B or to find an intermediate point from which both A and B can be seen. Under any of these conditions, a trial straight line, or *random line*, is run as near as can be estimated to the true line. This line, as $ACDEF$, is run by the method of double centering to a point from which B can be seen. The length AF of the random line, the distance FB, and the angle at F from A to B are then measured. In the triangle ABF, two sides and the included angle are known, and the angle at A can be computed. The transit is set up again at A, the computed angle is turned off from the line AF by using the method described in Sec. 6-3 or Sec. 7-5, and

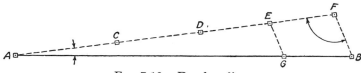

Fig. 7-10.   Random line.

the line AB is run. If this new line fails to strike B exactly, points along the line can be shifted slightly to bring them on line, the amounts they are to be moved being obtained by proportion.

A second method of locating points on the required line is to set up the transit at points on the random line, turn off angles equal to the measured angle AFB, and measure distances obtained by proportion. Thus, in Fig. 7-10, if the angle at E is made equal to the angle at F, then $EG = FB \times (AE/AF)$. Points adjacent to C and D may be set in a similar manner.

Another method of locating points along the line AB is discussed in Chapter 8. In this method a closed random traverse is run, instead of a straight line, and points on the traverse are located with respect to the line AB by computation. From these traverse points, computed angles and distances are laid off to determine additional points on AB. Furthermore, these additional points may be set on AB at any desired distances from A or B.

7-10. Intersection of Two Straight Lines. Two examples of the intersection of straight lines are shown in Fig. 7-11. To find the intersection of lines AB and CD in view (a), the transit is set up at either A or B and a sight is taken along the line AB. Stakes, known as

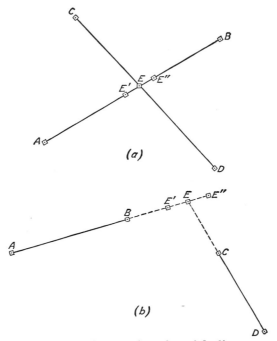

FIG. 7-11.   Intersection of straight lines.

straddle stakes, are then set at E' and E'', being so located that the point of intersection will fall somewhere between them. These stakes should be set so close together that a string can be stretched between them. If it is difficult to estimate where the intersection is to be, more than two such stakes can be set.

The transit is next moved to C or D and a sight is taken along the line CD. The point E is then found at the intersection of the line of sight and the string stretched between E' and E''. If two transits are available, one can be set up on each line and E can be found at the intersection of the two lines of sight.

In Fig. 7-11 (b) the intersection of the lines AB and CD is on the prolongations of both lines. If the lines are short, the stakes at E' and E'' can be set by placing the transit at A, sighting on B, and extending this line to E' and E''. When the lines are long, the transit is set up at B and points on the straddle stakes are set by double centering. The intersection is determined by moving the transit to either C or D and finding where the new line of sight strikes the string stretched between E' and E''. If the transit is at C, the method of double centering should be used.

7-11. Obstacles on a Line. When a boundary line is being extended by the method developed in Sec. 7-6, or when the center line for a highway or railroad is being staked out in preparation for construction, the problem of extending the line through heavily wooded or congested areas is invariably faced. Where timber cannot be cut, as in a boundary survey, or where buildings are not removed until immediately before construction begins, and an obstacle is on the line, it becomes necessary to leave the line in order to pass the obstacle. Two methods for passing an obstacle are given here.

The first method, illustrated in Fig. 7-12, consists of establishing two equal perpendicular offsets from the desired line AF, as BB' and CC'. To provide a check, an equal offset from A to A' is also laid off. The line $A'B'C'$ is parallel to the line ABC and is extended beyond the obstacle to points D', E', and F' by the methods described in Secs. 7-6 and 7-7, the point F' being set as a check. Perpendicular offsets equal in length to BB' and CC' are established at these points to locate points D, E, and F. If measurements are to be carried along

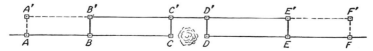

FIG. 7-12. Prolonging line past obstacle.

the line being run, then the offsets at C and D' should be made parallel by using the transit, so that the unmeasurable distance CD will be equal to $C'D'$, which can be measured.

The second method, illustrated in Fig. 7-13, is used where there are many obstacles on the desired line and where running an offset

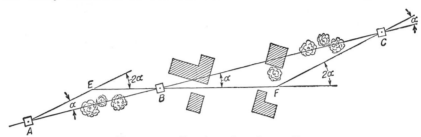

FIG. 7-13.   Passing obstacles on line.

parallel line as just described is not feasible. This method consists of laying off a small deflection angle α from the desired line at a convenient point as A, setting point E at a measured distance from A, then laying off a deflection angle 2α from line AE in the opposite direction, and setting point B on the new line of sight so that $EB = AE$. If the deflection angle α is now turned from line EB at B, the line of sight will be directed along the desired line. If there is an obstacle between B and C, the line EB may be extended to a point at F. The angle 2α is then laid off at F and the distance FC is laid off equal to BF. The procedure is repeated until the obstructed area has been traversed. Finally the direction of the desired line beyond C can be established by laying off the angle α at C.

This method is convenient in that isosceles triangles are laid off, and the angles α and 2α can have the same values throughout. A random traverse discussed in Chapter 8 will accomplish the same results with perhaps more speed in the field, but more computations will be needed. Using a random traverse also requires computed distances and angles to be laid out, necessitating additional field work.

7-12.   Parallel Lines.   The principles of plane geometry are used in the establishment of parallel lines. In Fig. 7-12 the lines AF and $A'F'$ are made parallel by making the distance between them the

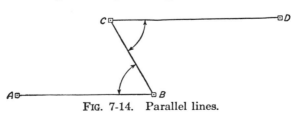

FIG. 7-14.   Parallel lines.

same at B, C, D and E. Equal offsets at two points are sufficient to establish the position of the parallel line, but the field work can be checked if offsets are made at three or more points.

In Fig. 7-14 the line CD is made parallel to the line AB by making the alternate interior angles at B and C equal. In the field, the angle ABC would be measured and the direction of CD determined by laying off the angle BCD equal to the measured angle ABC. If the length of CD is more than a very few feet, these angles should be measured by repetition.

7-13. Location of a Point. The field location of a point involves the measurement of enough angles and distances to enable a person in the office to plot the point in its correct position, either with respect to two fixed points, or with respect to a fixed point and a fixed line through that point. As the two fixed points and the required point are the vertexes of some triangle, the position of the required point will also be fixed when the triangle is determined.

A triangle is determined by: *a*) two sides and the included angle; *b*) a side and the two adjacent angles; *c*) three sides; *d*) two sides and the angle opposite one of these sides. The field applications of these methods of locating a point are shown in Fig. 7-15. In view (*a*) the point P is located from A by the measurement of an angle from the known line AB and a distance. In view (*b*) two angles are measured at the known points A and B, while in view (*c*) two dis-

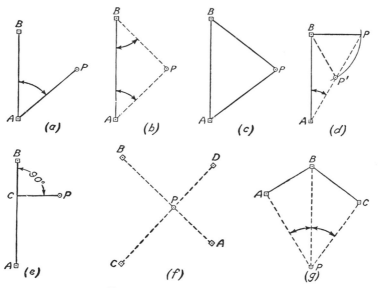

Fig. 7-15. Locating a point.

tances from A and B are required. In view (d) an angle at the known point A and the side opposite from the known point B are measured. In view (e) the measurements are the perpendicular distance CP from P to the line AB and the distance BC or AC. In view (f) the point P is at the intersection of the known lines AB and CD. The location of P in view (g) is determined by measuring the angles at P between the lines to three fixed points A, B, and C.

Although each of these methods has its particular uses, the first one shown—the measurement of an angle and a distance—is used much more frequently than the others. The shape of the figure may sometimes preclude the use of some particular method. Thus, in view (b), where two angles are measured, the location will be very uncertain if the angles at A and B are so small as to give an indefinite intersection when the lines AP and BP are, for example, drawn on a map. This method is used when the measurement of distances is difficult or impossible. It is also the basis of triangulation, where, with one side and all the angles of a triangle known, the unknown sides are computed.

The method in view (c) can be used when the survey is being made with only a tape. The location of P will be best when the angle at P is near 90° and will be uncertain when this angle approaches 0° or 180°. In such cases the method shown in view (d) will give a better location. This method can also be used when the measurement of the side AP is impossible. When this method is adopted, the approximate shape of the triangle must be known as, in general, there will be two solutions of a triangle in which two sides and the angle opposite one of them are known. In every case it must be known whether the located point is to the right or left of the line of reference.

The method represented in view (e) is frequently used in route surveying to locate objects with respect to the center line. It is most advantageously used when extreme precision is unnecessary, as considerable field work is involved in locating the point C exactly. On construction work, important points that are liable to be disturbed during the progress of the work can be replaced if their location is determined by the intersection of lines, as shown in view (f). The location will be more certain if the distances from P to A, B, C, and D are also measured.

In view (g) is shown a *three-point resection* to determine the position of the point P occupied by an instrument when this position is not known before the instrument is set up. The positions of points A, B, and C are known, and the angles at P from A to B and from B to C are measured. The computations necessary to determine the position of P are described in Chapter 8 in Sec. 8-34. In hydrographic work, the two angles at *P* are measured between shore stations at the boat position by means of two sextants. In plane-table operations, the three-point resection is solved graphically to determine the map position of the plane table.

PROBLEMS

7-1. The interior angles in a six-sided figure are measured as follows: *a*, 142° 16′ 00″; *b*, 78° 19′ 30″; *c*, 148° 43′ 30″; *d*, 133° 56′ 00″; *e*, 92° 14′ 30″; *f*, 124° 28′ 00″. All angles have equal weights. Compute the adjusted interior angles.

7-2. The following equal-weight deflection angles were measured in a six-sided traverse that closes on itself: *A*, 78° 32′ R; *B*, 93° 10′ R; *C*, 88° 19′ R; *D*, 104° 04′ L; *E*, 117° 47′ R; *F*, 86° 19′ R. Compute the adjusted deflection angles.

7-3. The line of sight of a transit makes an angle of 89° 56′ 20″ with the transverse axis. What will be the angular error in the line *CD* in Fig. 7-8 if each extension of the line *AB* was made with only one plunging and each backsight was made with the telescope in the direct position?

7-4. If each of the distances *AB*, *BC*, and *CD* in Problem 7-3 is 350 ft, how far off the true prolongation of *AB* will point *D* lie?

7-5. In Fig. 7-10, *AC* = 389.90 ft; *CD* = 360.25 ft; *DE* = 295.56 ft; *EF* = 288.63 ft; and *FB* = 22.11 ft. The angle at *F* from *B* to *E* is measured as 102° 16′. What is the angle at *A* from *F* to *B*? What is the distance *EG*, if *EG* is parallel to *FB*?

7-6. In Fig. 7-13, *AE* = *EB* = 150.00 ft, *BF* = *FC* = 275.00 ft, and angle α = 2° 30′. What is the length of the line *AC*?

8

Traverse Surveys and Computations

8-1. **Traverse.** A traverse is a series of connected lines of known length related to one another by known angles. The lengths of the lines are determined by direct measurement of horizontal distances, by slope measurement, or by indirect measurement based on the methods of stadia or the subtense bar. These methods are discussed in Chapters 2 and 13. The angles at the traverse stations between the lines of the traverse are measured with the instruments discussed in Chapter 6. They can be interior angles, deflection angles, or angles to the right.

The results of field measurements related to a traverse will be a series of connected lines whose lengths and azimuths, or whose lengths and bearings, are known. The lengths are horizontal distances; the azimuths or bearings are true, magnetic, assumed, or grid.

In general, traverses are of two classes. One of the first class is an open traverse. It originates either at a point of known horizontal position with respect to a horizontal datum or at an assumed horizontal position, and terminates at an unknown horizontal position. A traverse of the second class is a closed traverse, which can be described in any one of the following three ways: 1) It originates at an assumed horizontal position and terminates at that same point; 2) it originates at a known horizontal position with respect to a horizontal datum and terminates at that same point; 3) it originates at a known horizontal position and terminates at another known horizontal position. A known horizontal position is defined by its geographic latitude and longitude, by its Y- and X-coordinates on a grid system, or by its location on or in relation to a fixed boundary.

Traverse surveys are made for many purposes and types of projects, some of which follow:

a) To determine the positions of existing boundary markers.

b) To establish the positions of boundary lines.

c) To determine the area encompassed within the confines of a boundary.

d) To determine the positions of arbitrary points from which data may be obtained for preparing various types of maps, that is, to establish *control* for mapping.

e) To establish ground control for photogrammetric mapping.

f) To establish control for gathering data regarding earthwork quantities in railroad, highway, utility, and other construction work.

g) To establish control for locating railroads, highways, and other construction work.

8-2. Open Traverse. An open traverse is usually run for exploratory purposes. There are no arithmetical checks on the field measurements. Since the figure formed by the surveyed lines does not close, the angles cannot be summed up to a known mathematical condition. None of the positions of the traverse stations can be verified, since no known or assumed position is included except that of the starting station. To strengthen an open traverse, that is, to render it more reliable, several techniques may be employed. Each distance can be measured in both directions and can be roughly checked by using the stadia hairs of the transit (see Chapter 13). The measurements of the angles at the stations can be repeated by using the methods of Chapters 6 and 7 and checked approximately by observing magnetic bearings. The directions of the lines can be checked by observing the sun or the stars to determine true azimuths or bearings of selected lines in the traverse. An open traverse should not be run for any permanent project or for any of the projects indicated in Sec. 8-1, because it does not reveal mistakes or errors and the results are always open to doubt.

8-3. Closed Traverse. A traverse that closes on itself immediately affords a check on the accuracy of the measured angles, provided that the angle at each station has been measured. As will be discussed later, a traverse that closes on itself gives an indication of the consistency of measuring distances as well as angles by affording a check on the position closure of the traverse. Unless astronomical observations for azimuths have been made at selected stations of a traverse which closes on itself, the only provision for verifying the directions of the lines is that afforded by the angular closure. In this type of traverse, there is no check on the systematic errors introduced into the measurement of lengths. Therefore, when this type of traverse is executed for a major project, the taping apparatus must be carefully calibrated to determine the systematic errors and to eliminate them.

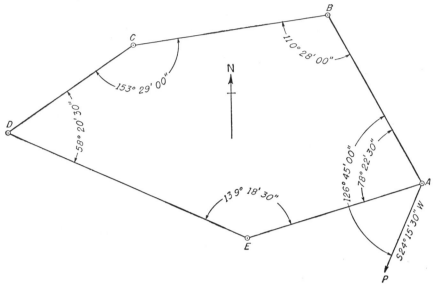

FIG. 8–1. Interior-angle traverse.

A traverse that originates at a known position and closes on another known position is by far the most reliable, because a check on the position of the final point checks both the linear and angular measurements of the traverse. When a point of known position is referred to, it is understood that such a point has been located by procedures as precise as, or more precise than, those used in the traverse being executed. These procedures are the methods of either traversing or triangulation. Triangulation is the subject of Chapter 10.

8-4. Interior-Angle Traverse. An interior-angle traverse is shown in Fig. 8-1. The azimuth or bearing of the line AP is known. The lengths of the traverse lines are measured to determine the horizontal distances. With the transit at A, the angle at A from P to B is measured to determine the azimuth of line AB. The angle at A from E to B is also measured, as this is one of the interior angles in the figure. Magnetic bearings to P, E, and B are observed to provide a rough check on the values of the measured angles. The instrument is then set up at B, C, D, and E in succession, and the indicated angles are measured and magnetic bearings are observed. The notes for the angles are recorded as indicated in Chapter 6, but an additional column is used in the angle notes for recording the observed magnetic bearings. Had the azimuth of one of the traverse sides been known, then there would have been no necessity for measuring the angle at A from P to B.

To test the angular closure, the interior angles are added and their sum is compared to $(n-2)\ 180°$, which in this example is $(5-2)$ $180° = 540°$. The total angular error, or the closure, is $1'\ 30''$. In the accompanying tabulation, the measured angles are adjusted by assuming that the angular error is of the same amount at each station.

Station	Measured Angle	Correction	Adjusted Angle
A	78° 22' 30"	+ 18"	78° 22' 48"
B	110 28 00	+ 18"	110 28 18
C	153 29 00	+ 18"	153 29 18
D	58 20 30	+ 18"	58 20 48
E	1°9 18 30	+ 18"	139 18 48
	539° 58' 30" − 540° 00' 00" Closure = − 1' 30"		540° 00' 00"

This assumption may not be valid, because an error in angular measurement, all other things being equal, will increase as the lengths of the adjacent sides decrease. For example, since the angles in this illustration were measured to the nearest 30", the discrepancy could be distributed by correcting the angles at A, B, and C by 30" each, or by correcting the angles at A, C, and D by 30" each.

After the adjusted angles are computed, they should always be added to see whether their sum is, in fact, the proper amount. A mistake in arithmetic either in adding the measured angles or in applying the corrections will become apparent.

The azimuth of the line AP in Fig. 8-1 is known, and the azimuths of all the traverse sides can be determined by using the measured angle at A from P to B and the adjusted interior angles in the closed figure. Since the bearing of AP is S 24° 15' 30" W, the azimuth of AP reckoned from north is 204° 15' 30". As indicated in Fig. 8-2, the azimuth of AB is equal to the azimuth of AP plus the angle at A from P to B, or 204° 15' 30" + 126° 45' 00" = 331° 00' 30". The azimuths of the other lines are computed systematically by applying the adjusted angle at each station to the azimuth of each backsight line in turn. To determine the azimuth of BC, compute the azimuth of BA by subtracting 180° from the azimuth of AB, and then add the adjusted angle at B from A to C. A similar procedure is adopted at each station (see the accompanying tabulation).

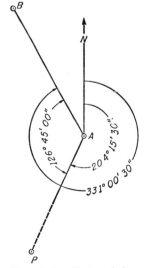

FIG. 8–2.   Determining azimuth of line AB.

Line	Azimuth	Bearing
AP	204° 15′ 30″	S 24° 15′ 30″ W
	(+ ∠ A) + 126 45 00	
AB	331 00 30	N 28 59 30 W
BA	151 00 30	
	(+ ∠ B) + 110 28 18	
BC	261 28 48	S 81 28 48 W
CB	81 28 48	
	(+ ∠ C) + 153 29 18	
CD	234 58 06	S 54 58 06 W
DC	54 58 06	
	(+ ∠ D) + 58 20 48	
DE	113 18 54	S 66 41 06 E
ED	293 18 54	
	(+ ∠ E) + 139 18 48	
EA	432 37 42	
EA	72 37 42	N 72 37 42 E
AE	252 37 42	
	(+ ∠ A) + 78 22 48	
AB	331 00 30 Check	N 28 59 30 W

The azimuths of the lines can also be computed by applying the angles at *A, E, D, C,* and *B* in that order. Then each interior angle would be subtracted from the azimuth of the proper back line. This is apparent from a study of Fig. 8-1.

The bearing of each line, if desired, is determined from its azimuth. Since the conversion from azimuths to bearings is easily made, it is unwise to attempt to compute the bearing of each line directly by applying the proper angle in the traverse to the bearing of the adjacent line.

In a traverse of *n* sides or stations, the closure of the measured angles should not exceed the least count of the vernier of the instrument times the square root of *n*. With care in sighting, in centering the instrument, and in reading the verniers, the angular closure can be expected to be half this allowable amount. Of course, with few traverse stations, this precision may not be obtainable since the opportunities for random errors to compensate are few.

One very important point to observe in the preceding example of an interior-angle traverse is that there is no check on the angle at *A* from *P* to *B*. If this angle is in error, then the error affects the azimuth of each line in the traverse. To avoid the possibility of making a mistake in measuring this angle, the clockwise angle at *A* from *B* to *P* should also be measured. This measurement immediately

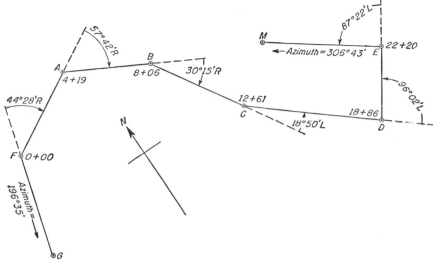

FIG. 8–3.   Deflection-angle traverse between fixed azimuths.

affords a check at station A, since the angle at A from P to B and the angle at A from B to P should total 360°. If the azimuth of one of the sides of the traverse were known, then this uncertainty would have been avoided, because the test of the accuracy in this case is simply that the sum of the interior angles should equal $(n - 2)$ 180°.

8-5. Deflection-Angle Traverse. A deflection-angle traverse that originates at station 0 + 00 and closes on station 22 + 20 is shown in Fig. 8-3. The azimuth of the line FG is fixed as 196° 35′ and the azimuth of EM is fixed as 306° 43′, these directions having been established by previous surveys. The traverse is made to fit between these two fixed azimuths. After the deflection angles and the lengths of the several courses have been measured, the check on angular closure is made by carrying azimuths through the traverse by applying the deflection angles. In Fig. 8-4 the azimuth of GF is 16° 35′, obtained by subtracting 180° from the azimuth of FG. So the azimuth of the line FA is 16° 35′ plus 44° 28′, which is the right deflection angle at F from G to A. The addition gives 61° 03′ as the azimuth of FA. Now to determine

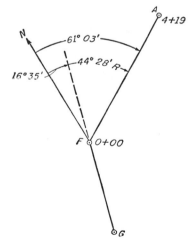

FIG. 8–4.   Determining azimuth of line FA.

the azimuth of the next line *AB*, the right deflection angle at *A* from *F* to *B* is added to the azimuth of *FA*. This sum is 61° 03′ + 57° 42′ = 118° 45′. Observe that no back azimuths need be computed, as was the case for the interior-angle traverse. To compute an azimuth by using a deflection angle, simply add a right deflection angle to the *forward* azimuth of the backsight to obtain the *forward* azimuth of the foresight; or subtract a left deflection angle from the *forward* azimuth of the backsight to obtain the *forward* azimuth of the foresight. A computation of azimuths in deflection-angle traverse follows.

Line	Azimuth		Correction	Adjusted Azimuth	Adjusted Bearing
GF		16° 35′	Fixed		N 16° 35′ 00″ E
	(+ ∠ F) +	44 28			
FA		61 03	− 0′ 30″	61° 02′ 30″	N 61 02 30 E
	(+ ∠ A) +	57 42			
AB		118 45	− 1′ 00″	118 44 00	S 61 16 00 E
	(+ ∠ B) +	30 15			
BC		149 00	− 1′ 30″	148 58 30	S 31 01 30 E
	(− ∠ C) −	18 50			
CD		130 10	− 2′ 00″	130 08 00	S 49 52 00 E
	(− ∠ D) −	96 02			
DE		34 08	− 2′ 30″	34 05 30	N 34 05 30 E
DE		394 08			
	(− ∠ E) −	87 22			
EM		306 46	− 3′ 00″	306 43 00	N 53 17 00 W
		306 43	Fixed		
	Closure =	+ 03′			

In the example in Fig. 8-3, the computed azimuth of *EM* failed to check by 3′. Since six deflection angles were measured, the correction to each angle is 30″. Instead of applying this correction to each angle and recomputing the azimuths, the azimuths themselves are adjusted. The azimuth of *FA* receives a 30″ correction, since this azimuth was obtained by considering only one measured angle; the azimuth of *AB* receives a 1′ 00″ correction, since this azimuth was obtained by using two angles, and so on. The correction to the last azimuth is 6 × 30″ = 3′ 00″, since this azimuth was obtained by using all six deflection angles.

In Fig. 8-5 is illustrated a deflection-angle traverse that closes on the point of origin at *L*. The bearing of the line *OP* is known to be N 66° 02′ W. Before the bearings of the remaining sides are computed, the angles must be adjusted so that the difference between the sum of the right deflection angles and the sum of the left deflection angles is 360°. It is found that the sum of the right deflection angles must be reduced and the sum of the left deflection angles must be increased. The correction in this case is distributed equally among

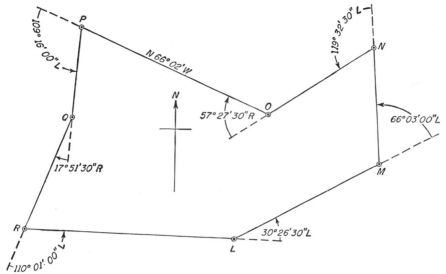

Fig. 8–5.   Deflection-angle traverse that closes on point of origin.
(Adjusted angles are shown.)

all of the angles. Had the angular closure been only 01′, then 30″ could have logically been added to the angle at N and subtracted from the angle at Q, since these two angles are formed by the shortest lines of sight. The following tabulation shows this adjustment of deflection angles.

Station	Deflection Angle	Correction	Adjusted Deflection Angle
L	30° 26′ 00″ L	+ 30″	30° 26′ 30″ L
M	66 02 30 L	+ 30″	66 03 00 L
N	119 32 00 L	+ 30″	119 32 30 L
O	57 28 00 R	− 30″	57 27 30 R
P	109 15 30 L	+ 30″	109 16 00 L
Q	17 52 00 R	− 30″	17 51 30 R
R	110 00 30 L	+ 30″	110 01 00 L
	Σ Right 75 20 00		Σ Right 75 19 00
	Σ Left 435 16 30		Σ Left 435 19 00
	Diff. 359 56 30		360 00 00 Check
	Closure 3 30		

Bearings of the sides of the traverse are computed by first converting the bearing of OP to an azimuth, then applying the adjusted deflection angles to obtain azimuths, and finally converting the azimuths to bearings as shown in the accompanying tabulation.

The angular closure of a deflection-angle traverse should be no more than the least count of the vernier of the instrument times the square root of the number of angles in the traverse. A deflection

Line	Azimuth	Bearing
OP	293° 58′ 00″	N 66° 02′ 00″ W
	(− ∠ P) − 109 16 00	
PQ	184 42 00	S 4 42 00 W
	(+ ∠ Q) + 17 51 30	
QR	202 33 30	S 22 33 30 W
	(− ∠ R) − 110 01 00	
RL	92 32 30	S 87 27 30 E
	(− ∠ L) − 30 26 30	
LM	62 06 00	N 62 06 00 E
LM	422 06 00	
	(− ∠ M) − 66 03 00	
MN	356 03 00	N 3 57 00 W
	(− ∠ N) − 119 32 30	
NO	236 30 30	S 56 30 30 W
	(+ ∠ O) + 57 27 30	
OP	293 58 00 Check	N 66 02 00 W

angle should never be measured without double centering the instrument, because the error caused by the line of sight not being normal to the horizontal axis of the instrument may be too large to be tolerated.

8-6. Angle-to-the-Right Traverse. Either an open traverse or a closed traverse can be executed by measuring angles to the right. The method of measuring the angles is described in Sec. 7-3. The method of computing azimuths from a given fixed azimuth is similar to that employed in an interior-angle traverse. A forward azimuth is always obtained by *adding* the angle to the right to the azimuth of the back-

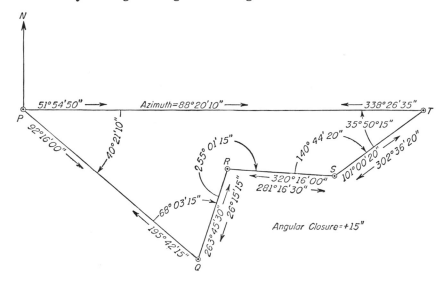

Fɪɢ. 8–6.   Angles to the right from direction-instrument readings.

sight. Angles to the right are always employed when a traverse is executed with a direction instrument.

As an illustration of an angle-to-the-right traverse executed by use of a direction instrument, refer to Fig. 8-6. Station P is occupied, a backsight is taken on station T, and the circle is read. A foresight is taken on station Q, and the circle is read. This procedure is repeated at each station along the traverse, each backsight and foresight being observed with the telescope both direct and reversed. Notes for a 10-second direction instrument are given in the accompanying tabulation.

Station		D or R	Reading	Mean
At P	T	D	51° 54′ 50″	51° 54′ 50″
		R	231 54 50	
	Q	D	92 15 50	92 16 00
		R	272 16 10	
At Q	P	D	195 42 10	195 42 15
		R	15 42 20	
	R	D	263 45 20	263 45 30
		R	83 45 40	
At R	Q	D	26 15 10	26 15 15
		R	206 15 20	
	S	D	281 16 30	281 16 30
		R	101 16 30	
At S	R	D	320 16 00	320 16 00
		R	140 16 00	
	T	D	101 00 10	101 00 20
		R	281 00 30	
At T	S	D	302 36 10	302 36 20
		R	122 36 30	
	P	D	338 26 30	338 26 35
		R	158 26 40	

Assume that the azimuth of PT is known to be 88° 20′ 10″. The azimuth of the line PQ is the azimuth of PT plus the angle to the right at P. The angle to the right at P from T to Q can be obtained by subtracting the circle reading to T from the circle reading to Q. This angle, as computed from the notes, is 92° 16′ 00″ − 51° 54′ 50″ = 40° 21′ 10″. Then the azimuth of PQ is 88° 20′ 10″ + 40° 21′ 10″ = 128° 41′ 20″. This computation can be simplified if the circle reading to Q is added to the azimuth of PT, and then the circle reading to T is subtracted from the sum. In this manner, the circle reading for the foresight is always added and the circle reading for the backsight is always subtracted.

The computation is shown in the accompanying tabulation as it would be made without the aid of a calculating machine designed for adding and subtracting angles on the sexagesimal system. If such a calculating machine is used, only the forward azimuth of each line

Line	Azimuth	Correction	Adjusted Azimuth
PT	88° 20′ 10″ Fixed		
	+ 92 16 00		
	180 36 10		
	− 51 54 50		
PQ	128 41 20	− 3″	128° 41′ 17″
QP	308 41 20		
	+ 263 45 30		
	572 26 50		
	− 195 42 15		
QR	376 44 35		
QR	16 44 35	− 6″	16 44 29
RQ	196 44 35		
	+ 281 16 30		
	478 01 05		
	− 26 15 15		
RS	451 45 50		
RS	91 45 50	− 9″	91 45 41
SR	271 45 50		
	+ 101 00 20		
	372 46 10		
	− 320 16 00		
ST	52 30 10	− 12″	52 29 58
TS	232 30 10		
	+ 338 26 35		
	570 56 45		
	− 302 36 20		
TP	268 20 25	− 15″	268 20 10
PT	88 20 25		
	88 20 10 Fixed		
	Closure + 15″		

of the traverse need be recorded on the computation sheet. The resulting azimuths are then adjusted to the fixed azimuth, and bearings may be obtained from the adjusted azimuths.

8-7. Traverse-by-Azimuth Method. In running a traverse for the purpose of establishing a lower order of control for mapping and for locating the positions of ground objects with respect to such a supplementary traverse, the transit can be handled so that the clockwise circle reading at all times indicates the azimuth of the line of sight. This procedure eliminates the need for computing azimuths from interior angles, deflection angles, or angles to the right.

In Fig. 8-7 is shown a portion of a supplementary traverse in which the line *DE* has an azimuth of 96° 22′. This may be a true,

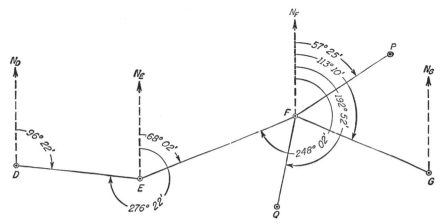

FIG. 8–7.   Traverse by azimuth method.

magnetic, assumed, or grid azimuth. The transit is set up at station *E* and the clockwise circle is set to read the azimuth of the line *ED*, which is 276° 22'. A lower motion is used to take a backsight along the line *ED*. The transit and the horizontal circle are now oriented. In other words, when any sight is taken by an upper motion, the clockwise circle reading will always indicate the azimuth of the line of sight. If a pointing is made on station *F* and the clockwise circle reads 68° 02', this is the azimuth of the line *EF* and is recorded as such.

When the transit is set up at *F*, the circle is oriented by setting the azimuth of *FE*, which is 248° 02', on the clockwise circle and backsighting along the line *FE* by a lower motion. A sight taken on point *P* by an upper motion will give the azimuth of the line *FP* directly on the clockwise circle. The readings to *P*, *Q*, and *G* are shown to be, respectively, 57° 25', 192° 52', and 113° 10'.

The advantages of executing a traverse by observing azimuths are that the transit is allowed to do the work of adding and subtracting angles, and that the field notes are easily reduced to map form by having all lines related to the same meridian directly in the notes.

The disadvantage of such a procedure is in not realizing the benefit of double centering, which eliminates instrumental errors and which makes mistakes in reading the circle quite obvious. The purpose of the traverse, however, is usually such that small errors are of little consequence. See Sec. 13-8.

If a traverse is to be run on magnetic azimuths, and the directions of the lines are to be consistent with one another, the initial set-up determines the specific magnetic meridian to which all other lines are referred. To orient on the magnetic meridian, set the clock-

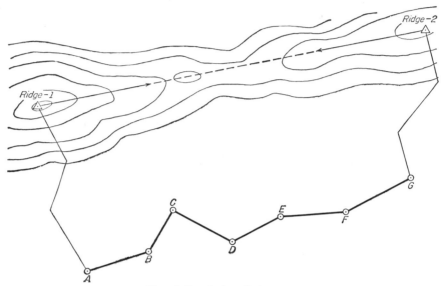

FIG. 8–8.   Azimuth traverse.

wise circle to read zero, unclamp the compass needle, loosen the lower clamp, and rotate the transit until the compass needle points to the north point of the compass circle. Tighten the lower clamp, and make an exact setting by using the tangent screw. The transit is then oriented for measuring magnetic azimuths. The procedure for carrying azimuths through the remaining lines in the traverse is the same as that previously described.

8-8. Azimuth Traverse.   An azimuth traverse is a continuous series of lines of sight related to one another by measured angles only. The distances between the transit stations are not measured. An azimuth traverse serves one of two purposes. The first purpose is to permit the determination of directions far removed from a beginning azimuth without the necessity of measuring distances. As an example, consider a pair of intervisible stations, such as Ridge-1 and Ridge-2 in Fig. 8-8, situated high on a ridge, and assume that the azimuth of the line joining these stations is known. A traverse is to be run in an adjacent valley, and the basis of azimuths of this traverse is to be the same as that for the line along the ridge.

To carry the azimuth down into the valley, one end of the known line, as Ridge-1, is occupied and the other end of the line, Ridge-2, is used as a backsight for measuring an angle to the right, a deflection angle, or, if the traverse is to close by occupying station Ridge-2, an interior angle. All the other points are occupied by the instrument,

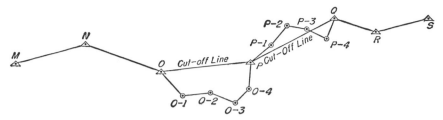

FIG. 8–9.   Azimuth traverse by cut-off lines.

and angles are measured. That portion of the survey from Ridge-1 to A and the portion from G to Ridge-2 are azimuth traverses. The lengths of the lines from AB through FG are measured along with the angles. The angular closure can be computed, and the traverse from A to G will be on the same basis of azimuths as is the straight line from Ridge-1 to Ridge-2.

The second purpose of an azimuth traverse is to avoid carrying azimuths through extremely short traverse sides. Since the angular error will increase as the lines of sight become shorter, the desirable traverse is one with long sights. Such sights may not be practical, however, for several reasons. The ground over which the traverse must follow may be rough and the sides may have to be short to alleviate difficult taping; the traverse may run through a city where every street corner or every point at a break in the street center line is a transit station; the traverse may be run along a curving right of way where intervening brush would interfere with the measurement of the lengths of long traverse sides. In these situations, the angular errors accumulating from short lines of sight can be isolated by employing an azimuth traverse of one or more stations through which the azimuth is computed. This use of an azimuth traverse is illustrated in Fig. 8-9. The azimuth is carried through lines MN, NO, OP, PQ, QR, and RS, although the azimuths of the lines forming the loops that have been cut off must also be determined. The lengths of the cut-off lines OP and PQ would not be measured. All the remaining distances would be measured.

8-9. Compass Traverse.   In Sec. 6-21 it was shown how angles may be measured by using a compass. The surveyor's compass can give reasonably accurate values of interior angles, the limit of error in each measurement being about 10 minutes. When a traverse is executed with the compass, the lengths of the traverse sides are measured with a tape, and at each station both the bearing of the backsight and the bearing of the foresight must be observed. If the bearing of one line of a compass traverse is known, then the bearings

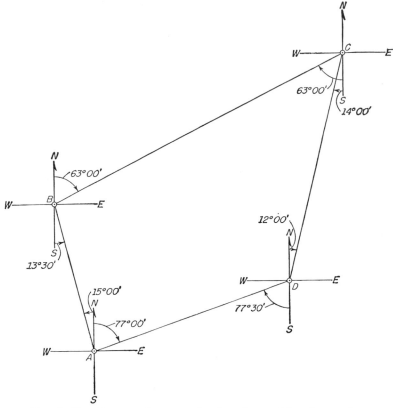

Fig. 8–10. Compass traverse showing observed bearing angles.

of all the remaining lines are adjusted to this one bearing. If no bearing is known, then the bearing of some one line must be assumed, and all the remaining lines are adjusted to the assumed bearing.

In Fig. 8-10 the lengths of the sides of the four-sided traverse are measured. Also the interior angles are measured with the compass. The compass is set up at A, and the bearing of line AD is observed and is recorded as the back bearing of the line DA. The bearing of the line AB is observed and is recorded as such. Stations B, C, and D are occupied in turn, and the bearings of both the backsight and the foresight are observed at each point. The notes for the observed bearings are shown in the accompanying tabulation.

Line	Observed Bearing	Observed Back Bearing
AB	N 15° 00′ W	S 13° 30′ E
BC	N 63° 00′ E	S 63° 00′ W
CD	S 14° 00′ W	N 12° 00′ E
DA	S 77° 30′ W	N 77° 00′ E

The two bearings observed at A are used to determine the interior angle at A. These bearings are N 77° E to D and N 15° W to B. As seen in Fig. 8-10, the angle at A is 77° + 15° = 92°. Calculations for each angle are also tabulated.

Station	Angle	Correction	Adjusted Angle
A	77° + 15° = 92° 00′	+ 15′	92° 15′
B	180° − (63° + 13° 30′) = 103° 30′	+ 15′	103 45
C	63° − 14° = 49° 00′	+ 15′	49 15
D	180° − 77° 30′ + 12° = 114° 30′	+ 15′	114 45
	Sum 359° 00′		360° 00′
	Closure − 1° 00′		

The closure is caused by setting the compass off center, making an improper pointing, holding the signal for the backsight or foresight off the point, and reading the compass needle inaccurately. It is *not* caused by the declination of the compass needle nor by local attraction, since these effects combine to establish the magnetic meridian at a given station and the meridian normally will not change during the time the readings are taken at the station.

To determine the adjusted bearings of the sides if no bearing is known, one must be assumed. Let the bearing of the line AB be assumed as N 15° 00′ W. Then the adjusted bearing of the line BA is S 15° 00′ E. Applying the adjusted angle at B gives the adjusted bearing of BC. The bearing angle of BC is 180° − (15° + 103° 45′) = 61° 15′. The adjusted bearing of BC is therefore N 61° 15′ E and the adjusted bearing of CB is S 61° 15′ W. The adjusted bearing angle of line CD is 61° 15′ − 49° 15′ = 12° 00′. So the adjusted bearing of CD is S 12° 00′ W, and the adjusted bearing of DC is N 12° 00′ E. Applying the adjusted interior angle at D gives the adjusted bearing of the line DA. The bearing angle is 180° + 12° − 114° 45′ = 77° 15′. The adjusted bearing of DA is therefore S 77° 15′ W and that of AD is N 77° 15′ E. All the adjusted bearings have been determined, but to provide a check on the computations the adjusted angle at A is applied to the bearing of AD to see whether the resulting bearing of AB is the same as that which was assumed. The computed bearing angle of AB is 92° 15′ − 77° 15′ = 15°, which checks with the value initially assumed.

For an open compass traverse, angles at each station are computed as shown in Sec. 6-21, but no check on the angles is provided. To make the bearings of the traverse lines consistent, it is necessary to start with either a known bearing or an assumed bearing and then to base each of the other bearings on this starting direction and the angle computed at each station.

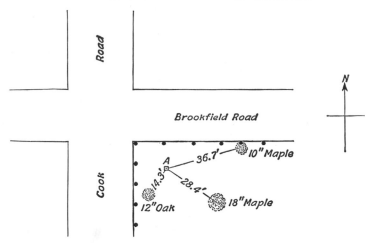

FIG. 8–11.   Referencing a point.

8-10.   Referencing a Traverse Station. As an aid in relocating a point which may become hidden by vegetation or buried beneath the surface of the ground, or as a means of replacing a point which may have been destroyed, measurements are made to nearby permanent or semipermanent objects. This process is known as *referencing* or *witnessing* the point. Property corners and, on important surveys, all transit stations are usually referenced.

In Fig. 8-11 are shown the locations of the witness points with respect to station *A*. If the stake at *A* cannot be found at a later time, its position can be determined by locating the intersection of the arcs struck with the trees as centers. The point would, of course, be determined by two arcs, but a third measurement is taken to serve as a check. If it is likely that any of the witness points will be destroyed, additional witnesses are located.

The method of recording the witnesses is the same as that used in notes for all United States land surveys. (See Chapter 17.) First, the object is described. If it is a tree, its diameter is given. Next, the bearing from the station to the witness point is given. Lastly the distance is recorded. If the measurement is made to any definite point, such as a nail driven in the root or side of a tree, that fact should be stated. To be of the most value in replacing a missing station, the witnesses should be less than 100 ft from the station and, if possible, the arcs should intersect approximately at right angles.

On many surveys no permanent objects may be available as witnesses. In such cases additional stakes can be driven. The method illustrated in Fig. 7-11(*f*) is the most satisfactory way of referencing a point so that it can be replaced in its original position. In this figure the point P is at the intersection of the lines AB and CD. If the distances from P to the four stakes are measured carefully, the point can be replaced if any two of the stakes remain, and the relocation can be checked if three of them can be found. This method is commonly used in referencing transit stations on route surveys, where it is known that all center-line stakes will be destroyed as soon as grading operations are begun.

In addition to the specific witnesses, a general description of the location of the transit station should be given, so that a person searching for it will have a fairly good idea of where to begin his search.

8-11. Traverse Computation. The result of the field work in executing a traverse of any kind is a series of connected lines whose directions and lengths are known. The angular closure is distributed to give a series of preliminary adjusted azimuths or bearings. Errors in the measured lengths of the traverse sides, however, will tend to alter the shape of the traverse. The steps involved in adjusting a traverse whose preliminary adjusted azimuths have been determined are as follows:

a) Determine the distance that each line of the traverse extends in a north or south direction, and the distance that each line extends in an east or west direction. These distances are called, respectively, *latitudes* and *departures*.

b) Determine the algebraic sum of the latitudes and the algebraic sum of the departures, and compare them with the fixed latitude and departure of a straight line from the origin to the closing point. This presumes a closed traverse.

c) Adjust the discrepancy found in step (*b*) by apportioning the closure in latitudes and the closure in departures on a reasonable and logical basis.

d) Determine the adjusted position of each traverse station with respect to some origin. This position is defined by its Y-coordinate and its X-coordinate with respect to a plane rectangular-coordinate system, the origin being the intersection of the Y-axis and the X-axis, and the Y-axis being in the direction of the meridian.

When these computations have been performed, the position of each traverse station is known with respect to any other traverse station. Furthermore, each station is related in position to any other point which is defined on the same coordinate system, even though the point is not included in the traverse.

If the purpose of the survey is merely to control a map of a limited area and the positions of the traverse stations are to be located on the map sheet by distances and deflection angles, or by distances and bearings, then there is no need for computing the latitudes and departures or the coordinates, since the ultimate position will be determined graphically.

Surveying computations are performed by longhand methods, slide rule, manually operated desk calculators, electrically operated desk calculators, logarithms, graphical methods, or electronic computing machines. The selection of the method depends on several factors, which include the accuracy of the field work, the number of significant figures necessary, the availability of electrical power, the size of the project and the extent of the computations, the complexity of the computations, the cost, the time restriction, the availability of trained personnel, and the availability of computing equipment.

Very few traverses are computed by longhand means. Electrically operated desk calculators are used most for performing traverse computations. Where electrical power is not available, logarithms are efficiently employed, or hand computers are used. Many large mapping agencies which do extensive traverse work employ calculating machines designed specifically for traverse computations. They also employ electronic computing machines of small or medium capacity.

8-12. Latitudes and Departures. The latitude of a line is the distance which the line extends in a north or south direction. A line running in a northerly direction has a plus latitude; one running in a southerly direction has a minus latitude.

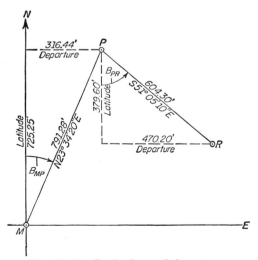

FIG. 8–12. Latitudes and departures.

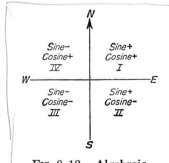

FIG. 8–13. Algebraic signs of azimuth-angle functions.

The departure of a line is the distance which the line extends in an east or west direction. A departure to the east is considered plus; a departure to the west is minus.

In Fig. 8-12, the bearing of the line MP is N 23° 34′ 20″ E and its length is 791.28 ft. The bearing of PR is S 51° 05′ 10″ E and its length is 604.30 ft. The line MP has a latitude of + 725.25 ft and a departure of + 316.44 ft. The line PR has a latitude of − 379.60 ft and a departure of + 470.20 ft. From Fig. 8-12, it is seen that the latitude of each line is the length of the line times the cosine of the bearing angle, and that the departure of each line is the length of the line times the sine of the bearing angle. If D represents the length of the line and B is the bearing angle, then

$$\text{Latitude} = D \cos B \qquad\qquad (8\text{-}1)$$

$$\text{Departure} = D \sin B \qquad\qquad (8\text{-}2)$$

If the direction of the line is given in terms of its azimuth from north and A represents that azimuth, then

$$\text{Latitude} = D \cos A \qquad\qquad (8\text{-}3)$$

$$\text{Departure} = D \sin A \qquad\qquad (8\text{-}4)$$

When bearings are used, the sine and cosine of the bearing angle are always considered positive, and the algebraic signs of the latitude and departure are obtained from the quadrant. When azimuths are used, a table giving the functions of angles from 0° to 360° together with the proper algebraic signs is most convenient. The signs of the sine and cosine of an azimuth in each of the four quadrants (northeast, southeast, southwest, and northwest) are shown in Fig. 8-13, where Roman numerals are used for the quadrants. These signs agree, respectively, with the algebraic signs of the functions of angles lying in the four quadrants defined in trigonometry. If a table of functions of angles to 360° is not available, then converting the azimuths to bearings is most convenient, since the quadrant obtained from the bearing gives the algebraic signs of the latitude and departure.

The calculation of latitudes and departures for the traverse of Fig. 8-14 is shown in the accompanying tabulation as it would be set up for using a desk calculating machine. The bearings given in the tabulation are those computed after an adjustment was made for the angular closure of the traverse. Several variations of the form of computation will be found in practice. The form can be extended to include the calculation of coordinates. It should be noted that the length is placed in the keyboard of the calculating machine once, and then is

CALCULATION OF LATITUDES AND DEPARTURES BY DESK CALCULATING MACHINE

Station	Bearing	Length	Cosine	Sine	Latitude +	Latitude −	Departure +	Departure −
A	N 47° 28' 00" E	483.52	0.676019	0.736884	326.87		356.30	
B	S 8° 27' 30" W	392.28	0.989123	0.147090		388.01		57.70
C	S 56° 27' 00" W	886.04	0.552665	0.833404		489.68		738.43
D	N 26° 16' 30" E	452.66	0.896680	0.442680	405.89		200.39	
E	N 39° 18' 00" W	279.33	0.773840	0.633381	216.16			176.92
F	S 80° 20' 30" E	421.97	0.167773	0.985826		70.79	415.99	
A		2915.80			948.92	948.48	972.68	973.05
					− 948.48		− 973.05	
					+ 0.44		− 0.37	

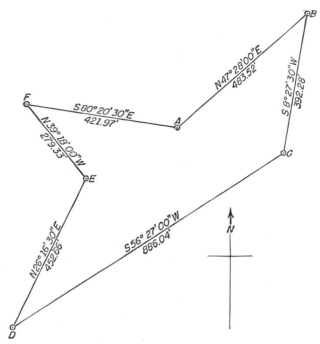

FIG. 8–14.   Traverse showing lengths and bearings.

multiplied in turn by the cosine and the sine of the azimuth or bearing angle. The results of these two multiplications are entered as the latitude and departure under the proper algebraic sign in the heading.

8-13. **Closure in Latitudes and Departures.** In a traverse which closes on the point of origin, the algebraic sum of the latitudes should be zero, and the algebraic sum of the departures should be zero. In the traverse of Fig. 8-14, the sum of the plus latitudes is 948.92 ft, and the sum of the minus latitudes is 948.48 ft. The closure in latitude is therefore + 0.44 ft. The sum of the plus departures is 972.68 ft, and the sum of the minus departures is 973.05 ft. Thus, the closure in departure is − 0.37 ft. These closures result from errors in measuring angles and distances when executing the traverse. Even though an adjustment has been made to eliminate the angular closure, each angle has not necessarily received the correct amount of adjustment.

In a traverse which originates at one known position and closes on another known position, the algebraic sum of the latitudes and the algebraic sum of the departures must equal, respectively, the latitude and departure of the line joining the origin and the closing point. The latitude and departure of this line are usually given as a difference in Y-coordinates and a difference in X-coordinates, respectively, be-

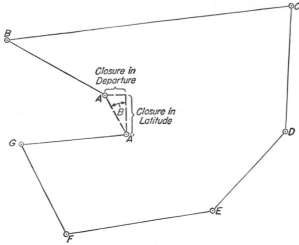

FIG. 8–15.   Traverse closure.

tween the point of beginning and the closing point. An example of a traverse computation between two known positions will be given following a discussion of coordinates.

If the error in latitudes or the error in departures is large, a mistake is indicated. The first place to search for the mistake is in the computations. Sources of mistakes are, of course, very numerous. One common mistake is to interchange the sine and the cosine. Before latitudes and departures are computed, a check should be made to avoid this mistake. The cosines of angles between 0° and 45° are greater than the sines; the sines of angles between 45° and 90° are the greater. Another common mistake is to misplace the decimal point. This frequently happens when logarithms are used. The characteristic of the logarithm of the departure or latitude may be wrong, especially when sines of angles near 0° and cosines of angles near 90° are involved in the computations. If no mistakes can be found in the computations, then a large discrepancy in latitudes or departures or both indicates a mistake in the field work of measuring either an angle or a distance. If the length of one line contains a mistake, the line itself may be selected from the remainder of the traverse by analyzing the traverse closure.

8-14. Traverse Closure. The closure of a traverse is the line which will exactly close the traverse. In Fig. 8-15, the line $A'A$ is the closure of a traverse which theoretically closes on itself. The angle B that this line makes with the meridian is determined by the relation

$$\tan B = \frac{\text{closure in departure}}{\text{closure in latitude}} \tag{8-5}$$

The length D of the line is given by the equation

$$D = \sqrt{(\text{closure in latitude})^2 + (\text{closure in departure})^2} \quad (8\text{-}6)$$

In the traverse computed in Sec. 8-12 and shown in Fig. 8-14, the bearing angle of the traverse closure is $\tan^{-1} (0.37/0.44) = 40°$.

Since the algebraic sum of the latitudes is positive, the latitude of the closure must be negative; and since the algebraic sum of the departures is negative, the departure of the closure must be positive. So the bearing of the closure must be S 40° E. The length of the closure is $\sqrt{0.37^2 + 0.44^2} = 0.57$ ft.

A *closure precision* for a given traverse may be obtained by dividing the length of the traverse closure by the total length of the traverse. It is to be expected that the length of the traverse closure will be greater in long surveys than in short ones if the same precautions are taken in both cases. Therefore, the lengths of the traverse closures of two surveys of different lengths do not indicate the relative degrees of accuracy of the surveys. The closure precisions, however, do indicate the relative degrees of accuracy of the two surveys. The length of the closure of the traverse computed in Sec. 8-12 is 0.57 ft and the total length of the traverse is 2915.80 ft. The closure precision is therefore 0.57/2915.80 or about 1/5120. If a traverse which was twice as long had the same length of closure, its closure precision would be about 1/10,240. Traverse work is often rated as to order of accuracy on the basis of the closure precision.

It should be noted that the traverse closure is the result of random errors, rather than of systematic errors, if the traverse begins and ends at the same point. Thus if a traverse of this kind is run with a tape of incorrect length, the actual error in the length of each line in the traverse can be considerable, even though the traverse closure and the closure precision are very small. Also, if the beginning azimuth or bearing is wrong, and if the azimuths or bearings of the remaining sides have been determined by using the adjusted angles in the figure, then the azimuths or bearings of all the sides are wrong by approximately the same amount. If a traverse begins on one known position and closes on another known position, then the amount by which it fails to close on the basis of the computations reflects both systematic and random errors in the field work. The amount by which it reflects the systematic errors depends on the shape of the traverse. If the traverse is run in a direct line between the two known points, then all the systematic errors are represented. If the two points lie on an east-west line, for example, and if the traverse is run north for a considerable distance, then east, and then south for a considerable distance to the point of closure, the systematic errors accumulated in traveling north will be canceled by those accumulated in traveling south, insofar as they affect the traverse closure.

3-15. Balancing a Traverse. Before the results of a traverse are usable for determining areas or coordinates, for publishing the data, or for computing lines to be located from the traverse stations, the traverse must be mathematically consistent, that is, the closures in latitudes and departures must be adjusted out. Applying corrections to the individual latitudes and departures so that they will sum up to a given condition is called balancing a traverse.

At this point, it will be well to examine Table 6-1 to appreciate the relationship between the precision in angular measurements and the precision in linear measurements. For example, according to Table 6-1, a precision of 1 part in 5000 in linear measurements requires that the error in angular measurements must not be greater than about 0' 41". This accuracy is obtained by using a 1-minute transit if the angles are turned once direct and once reversed. On the other hand, if angles are measured within 1' 00", the distances should be measured to a precision of 1 part in 3440 which is about 1½ ft per mile. In each of these examples, the two types of measurements will be consistent with one another.

Only three basic conditions can exist. 1) The angular precision is higher than the linear precision; 2) the angular precision is the same as the linear precision; 3) the angular precision is lower than the linear precision. An extreme example of the first condition is a traverse, executed in rugged terrain, in which angles are measured directly to one second and distances are determined by holding the tape horizontally throughout the measurements. The angular precision is expected to be high, while the linear precision is expected to be low because it is necessary to break tape. The second condition is exemplified by a traverse, executed in fairly level terrain, in which angles are measured with a 30-second or 1-minute transit and the tape is handled by experienced personnel; or a similar traverse in which angles are measured with a 1-second instrument and the tape is supported on posts or taping bucks and is handled by experienced personnel. The third condition is represented by a traverse, run over level terrain, in which directions are obtained by compass bearings and the tape is handled by experienced personnel. There are, of course, various degrees of the three basic conditions.

In order to balance a traverse properly, the conditions should be known because the conditions themselves govern the selection of the method employed. In general, traverses are executed so as to satisfy the second condition as a matter of policy, economy, and common sense. The method of balancing based on this condition is known as the compass rule.

8-16. Balancing by the Compass Rule. According to the compass rule, the correction to the latitude of a side is to the length of that side as the closure in latitude of the traverse is to the total length of the traverse; and the correction to the departure of a side is to the length of that side as the closure in departure of the traverse is to the total length of the traverse. For example, in the traverse computed in Sec. 8-12, the compass rule states that the correction c_L to the latitude of the line CD may be found from the proportion $c_L/886.04 = 0.44/2915.80$; and the proportion for finding the correction c_D to the departure of the line CD is $c_D/886.04 = 0.37/2915.80$. Both c_L and c_D have algebraic signs opposite to those of the closure in latitude of the traverse and the closure in departure of the traverse. Thus, for the line CD, $c_L = -0.13$ ft and $c_D = +0.11$ ft.

If a traverse of many sides is to be balanced by the compass rule, the corrections are most conveniently computed by first determining the number of feet of length that receives a correction of 0.01 ft of latitude, and the number of feet of length that receives a correction of 0.01 ft of departure. Let L_L denote the number of feet receiving a correction of 0.01 ft of latitude, and let L_D denote the number of feet receiving a correction of 0.01 ft of departure. Then, in the traverse of Sec. 8-12, $0.01/L_L = 0.44/2915.80$ and $0.01/L_D = 0.37/2915.80$. Thus $L_L = 66.3$ ft and $L_D = 78.7$ ft. This calculation may be made with sufficient accuracy on the slide rule or mentally. For the line AB, c_L in hundredths of a foot is $483.52/66.3$ and c_D in hundredths of a foot is $483.52/78.7$; or $c_L = -0.07$ ft and $c_D = +0.06$ ft. The corrections to the latitudes and departures for each line in the traverse are shown in the accompanying tabulation.

After the corrections have been computed, they should be added to check whether, in fact, their sums equal the closures in latitude and departure. In the example, the sum of the latitude corrections as first computed was less than the closure in latitude by 0.01 ft. This is a rounding-off error and is corrected by adding the 0.01 ft to that correction which lies nearest to the next higher 0.01 ft. Thus, the correction to the latitude of the line FA has been changed from -0.06 to -0.07.

After the balanced latitudes and departures have been computed, they should be added in order to provide a check on the computations.

8-17. Balancing by Transit Rule. A rule which has been adopted by many surveyors and engineers, presumably on the assumption that

CORRECTIONS TO LATITUDES AND DEPARTURES

Station	Length	Latitudes +	Latitudes −	Departures +	Departures −	c_L	c_D	Balanced Latitudes +	Balanced Latitudes −	Balanced Departures +	Balanced Departures −
A	483.52	326.87		356.30		− 0.07	+ 0.06	326.80		356.36	
B	392.28		388.01		57.70	− 0.06	+ 0.05		388.07		57.65
C	886.04		489.68		738.43	− 0.13	+ 0.11		489.81		738.32
D	452.66	405.89		200.39		− 0.07	+ 0.06	405.82		200.45	
E	279.33	216.16			176.92	− 0.04	+ 0.04	216.12			176.88
F	421.97		70.79	415.99		− 0.06	+ 0.05		70.86	416.04	
A	2915.80	948.92	948.48	972.68	973.05	− 0.44	+ 0.37	948.74	948.74	972.85	972.85
		− 948.48		− 973.05							
		+ 0.44		− 0.37							

$L_L = 66.3$ ft $L_D = 78.7$ ft

the angles in the traverse are measured with a higher degree of precision than are the lengths of the sides, is the so-called *transit rule*. According to the transit rule, the correction to the latitude of a line is to the latitude of that line as the closure in latitude is to the sum of all the latitudes, regardless of sign; and the correction to the departure of a line is to the departure of that line as the closure in departure is to the sum of all the departures, regardless of sign. Although the transit rule is valid for selected lines in a given traverse, it is usually contrary to the assumptions made. Since the compass rule is easier to apply and is valid in most traverse adjustment, there is little justification for use of the transit rule.

8-18. **Least-Squares Adjustment.** The least-squares method of adjustment of a simple closed traverse gives the minimum value for the sum of the squares of the corrections to either the angles or the lengths. This method is based on the mathematical law of probabilities and random errors. There are but two conditions which can justify the application of the method of least squares. The first is that the directions of all the lines are absolutely correct and only the lengths of the lines are adjusted to give a consistent geometrical figure. The second is that all the lengths are absolutely correct and only the directions of the lines are adjusted to give a consistent geometrical figure. These conditions are the extremes of conditions (1) and (3) of Sec. 8-15. For discussions of the application of least squares, you are referred to textbooks on least squares, to special publications of the U. S. Coast and Geodetic Survey on the subject, and to a paper by Mr. H. S. Rappleye in *Proceedings of the American Society of Civil Engineers* for November, 1929.

8-19. **Remarks on Adjustments.** A traverse is balanced to make the figure formed by the traverse geometrically consistent. If the traverse is run to establish control points for other traverses of equal or lower order, the adjusted positions of the points furnish checks on the work to follow. If the traverse is run to determine areas, the consistency in the figure affords a check on the calculations. In many surveys, however, no balancing will be required, particularly when the latitudes and departures are to be used only in plotting the positions of the stations on a map and when the closure is too small to be scaled on the map.

8-20. **Traverse Computation by Logarithms.** The traverse shown in Fig. 8-14 was computed in Sec. 8-12 by a desk calculating machine and was adjusted by the compass rule in Sec. 8-16. When a desk computer is used, the length of a line is multiplied successively by the natural cosine and the natural sine of the azimuth or the bearing angle of the line to give, respectively, the latitude and the departure of the line. When logarithms are used, the logarithm of the length of the line is added successively to the logarithmic cosine and the logarithmic sine of the azimuth or the bearing angle to give, respectively, the logarithm of the latitude and the logarithm of the departure. From these logarithms the latitude and the departure are determined. Since the logarithm of the length is used in two additions, the form shown in the accompanying tabulation is convenient. The logarithm of the length of each line need then be entered only once. Adding upward gives the logarithm of the latitude; adding downward gives the logarithm of the departure.

TRAVERSE COMPUTATION BY LOGARITHMS

Line Length Bearing	AB 483.52 N 47° 28′ 00″ E	BC 392.28 S 8° 27′ 30″ W	CD 886.04 S 56° 27′ 00″ W
Lat. log lat.	+ 326.87 2.51 4373	− 388.01 2.58 8846	− 489.68 2.68 9916
log cos B log length log sin B	9.82 9959 2.68 4414 9.86 7399	9.99 5250 2.59 3596 9.16 7583	9.74 2462 2.94 7454 9.92 0856
log dep. Dep.	2.55 1813 + 356.30	1.76 1179 − 57.70	2.86 8310 − 738.43
Line Length Bearing	DE 452.66 N 26° 16′ 30″ E	EF 279.33 N 39° 18′ 00″ W	FA 421.97 S 80° 20′ 30″ E
Lat. log lat.	+ 405.89 2.60 8411	+ 216.16 2.33 4769	− 70.79 1.85 0001
log cos B log length log sin B	9.95 2638 2.65 5773 9.64 6090	9.88 8651 2.44 6118 9.80 1665	9.22 4720 2.62 5281 9.99 3800
log dep. Dep.	2.30 1863 + 200.39	2.24 7783 − 176.92	2.61 9081 + 415.99

Line	Latitude		Departure	
	+	−	+	−
AB	326.87		356.30	
BC		388.01		57.70
CD		489.68		738.43
DE	405.89		200.39	
EF	216.16			176.92
FA		70.79	415.99	
	948.92 − 948.48	948.48	972.68 − 973.05	973.05
	+ 0.44		− 0.37	

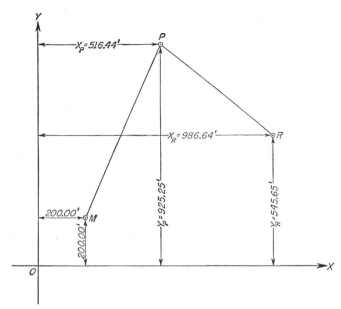

FIG. 8–16. Rectangular coordinates.

When 6-place logarithms are used, it is advisable to allow a space between the second and third digits after the decimal point, as shown in the computation. This space helps to prevent mistakes in addition. When 7-place logarithms are used, the space should come between the third and fourth digits after the decimal point.

One of the most common mistakes in computing a traverse by logarithms is to put down the wrong characteristic of a logarithm. Attention is called to the logarithm of the latitude of *FA* and the logarithm of the departure of *BC*. Each of these logarithms has 1 as its characteristic, whereas the logarithms of all remaining latitudes and departures have 2 as the characteristic. A second common mistake is the transposition of the logarithmic cosine and the logarithmic sine. The entries should be checked in the following way before the additions are made. If the bearing angle is less than 45°, the logarithmic cosine should be larger than the sine; and if the bearing angle is greater than 45°, the logarithmic sine should be larger.

In the tabulation shown, the algebraic signs of the latitude and departure of each line are obtained by an inspection of the bearing, which shows in what quadrant the line is situated.

8-21. Rectangular Coordinates. The rectangular coordinates of a point are the distances measured to the point from a pair of mutually perpendicular axes. As in analytic geometry, the distance from the X-axis is the Y-coordinate of the point, and the distance from the Y-axis is the X-coordinate of the point. In plane surveying conducted in the United States, the north part of the meridian on which the survey is based is the positive Y-axis, and a line perpendicular to this meridian through an assumed origin is the X-axis. The X-axis is positive in an easterly direction. Also, the Y- and X-coordinates are expressed in feet. In Fig. 8-16, the Y- and X-coordinates of M are, respectively, $+ 200.00$ ft and $+ 200.00$ ft; those of P are $+ 925.25$ ft and $+ 516.44$ ft; and those of R are $+ 545.65$ ft and $+ 986.64$ ft.

In general, the origin of coordinates is situated far enough south and west of the area to make the coordinates of all points in the survey positive quantities. This practice reduces the chances of making mistakes in computations involving the coordinates. Furthermore, there is no need to assign an algebraic sign to the coordinates of a point, since it is understood that all coordinates are positive. In subsequent examples in this chapter, the origin is selected so as to render all the coordinates positive.

Before the coordinates of the stations of a traverse can be computed, the coordinates of at least one station must be known or else they must be assumed. In Fig. 8-16, the coordinates of station M were assumed to be 200.00 and 200.00. The Y-coordinate of station P is determined by adding the latitude of the line MP to the Y-coordinate of station M; the X-coordinate of P is determined by adding the departure of MP to the X-coordinate of M. If the subscript 1 is used for the first station and the subscript 2 is used for the second station of the line 1-2, then

$$Y_2 = Y_1 + \text{latitude of } 1\text{-}2 \qquad (8\text{-}7)$$

$$X_2 = X_1 + \text{departure of } 1\text{-}2 \qquad (8\text{-}8)$$

These equations can be applied to obtain Y- and X-coordinates all the way around a traverse. If a traverse originates and closes on the same point, then the final Y- and X-coordinates of the point of beginning computed by using the latitudes and departures of the traverse sides should be the same as the beginning Y- and X-coordinates. This will be true provided the traverse has been balanced. An addition to the tabulation of the computations for the traverse of Sec. 8-12 is given here to show the calculation of coordinates of the points in the traverse. The columns headed Balanced Latitudes and Balanced Departures are repeated for continuity. The coordinates of station A are known to be $Y = 4166.20$ and $X = 6154.22$.

A check on the arithmetic is provided by computing the coordinates of station A from those of station F to see whether or not they are the same as the given coordinates of A.

COMPUTATION OF COORDINATES WITH DESK CALCULATING MACHINE

Station	Balanced Latitudes		Balanced Departures		Y-Coordinate	X-Coordinate
	+	−	+	−		
A					4166.20	6154.22
	326.80		356.36			
B					4493.00	6510.58
		388.07		57.65		
C					4104.93	6452.93
		489.81		738.32		
D					3615.12	5714.61
	405.82		200.45			
E					4020.94	5915.06
	216.12			176.88		
F					4237.06	5738.18
		70.86	416.04			
A					4166.20	6154.22

8-22. Adjustment of Traverse by Coordinate Adjustment. The coordinates of traverse stations may be computed directly from the measured lengths of the sides of the traverse, the preliminary azimuths or bearings of the sides, and the coordinates of the point of beginning. This work is done conveniently with a desk calculator by first putting the Y-coordinate of the point of beginning into the calculator, adding the product of the distance and the cosine of the bearing angle of the first side, and using the result as the Y-coordinate of the second point. This result is simply the sum of the latitude of the first line and the Y-coordinate of the point of beginning, as called for by Eq. 8-7. The sum is combined with the product $D \cos B$ of the second line, and the procedure is repeated for successive lines. Due regard must be paid to algebraic signs. Each intermediate result is the Y-coordinate of a point in the traverse. In a closed traverse, the computed Y-coordinate of the point on which the traverse closes will differ from its known Y-coordinate by the closure in latitude.

Next, the X-coordinate of the point of beginning is put into the calculator, and to this is added the product $D \sin B$ for the first line. The result is the X-coordinate of the second point, as the operation is simply the application of Eq. 8-8, or the addition of the departure of the first line to the X-coordinate of the point of beginning. Similarly, the product $D \sin B$ for each successive line is used, due regard being paid to algebraic signs, and each intermediate result is taken as the X-coordinate of a point in the traverse. The computed X-coordinate of the point on which the traverse closes will differ from the known X-coordinate by the closure in departure. If you are familiar with the modern desk computer, you will realize that the Y-coordinate and the X-coordinate can be computed for each point at the same time by a simple shift of the carriage on the computer. The distance

COMPUTATION OF COORDINATES WITH DESK CALCULATOR

Station	Distance	Total Dist.	Azimuth	Cosine	Sine	Y	X
Richmond						28,221.34	20,370.66
A	2872.45	2,872	110° 10′ 20″	− 0.3448432	+ 0.9386603	27,230.80	23,066.91
B	1977.14	4,850	184° 22′ 15″	− 0.9970916	− 0.0762115	25,259.41	22,916.23
C	1440.40	6,290	177° 49′ 54″	− 0.9992841	+ 0.0378355	23,820.04	22,970.73
D	1635.97	7,926	167° 02′ 11″	− 0.9745127	+ 0.2243322	22,225.77	23,337.73
E	3230.84	11,157	212° 18′ 28″	− 0.8451893	− 0.5344671	19,495.10	21,610.95
F	1491.48	12,648	284° 50′ 23″	+ 0.2561160	− 0.9666461	19,877.09	20,169.22
G	2231.98	14,880	270° 42′ 25″	+ 0.0123382	− 0.9999239	19,904.63	17,937.41
Kenney	1220.96	16,101	220° 20′ 12″	− 0.7622542	− 0.6472777	18,973.95	17,147.11
					Fixed	18,972.77	17,146.82
					Closure	+ 1.18	+ 0.29

$$\text{Closure precision} = \frac{\sqrt{1.18^2 + 0.29^2}}{16,101} = \frac{1}{13,200}$$

is used as the multiplicand, and the cosine and the sine are used as successive multipliers.

After the preliminary coordinates have been computed, the correction to be applied to each Y-coordinate is found by multiplying the closure in latitude by the ratio of the distance of the point from the point of beginning to the total length of the traverse. An adjustment is then made to each X-coordinate in the same manner. That is, the correction to a Y-coordinate is to the discrepancy in Y-coordinates (closure in latitude) as the distance from the point of beginning is to the total length of the traverse. Similarly, the correction to an X-coordinate is to the discrepancy in X-coordinates (closure in departure) as the distance from the point of beginning is to the total length of the traverse. If a discrepancy is plus, the corrections to all coordinates are minus; if a discrepancy is minus, the corrections to all coordinates are plus.

The accompanying tabulations show the computation and adjustment of coordinates of traverse stations. The traverse originates on station Richmond, whose coordinates are $Y = 28,221.34$ and $X = 20,370.66$, and closes on station Kenney, whose coordinates are $Y = 18,972.77$ and $X = 17,146.82$. The azimuths are preliminary azimuths obtained after an adjustment of the measured angles in the traverse. The column headed Total Dist. is the distance from the point of beginning to the station in question. It is needed only to the nearest foot, because it is used to compute the corrections which are, or should be, relatively small.

The computed Y-coordinate of station Kenney is too large by 1.18 ft. This is comparable to a closure in latitude of $+ 1.18$ ft. The computed X-coordinate of station Kenney is too large by 0.29 ft. Thus, it is apparent that the Y-coordinate of each point must be reduced by an amount proportionate to the distance from the beginning point to the point under consideration, and that the X-coordinate of each point must be reduced in the same proportion. The amount of each correction can be computed by using the slide rule, since no more than three significant figures are involved.

The Y-coordinate of station A is reduced by an amount equal to $(1.18)(2872)/16,101 = 0.21$ ft; the Y-coordinate of B is reduced by $(1.18)(4850)/16,101 = 0.35$ ft; and so on. The X-coordinate of A is reduced by $(0.29)(2872)/16,101 = 0.05$ ft; the X-coordinate of B is reduced by $(0.29)(4850)/16,101 = 0.09$ ft; and so on.

The corrections to all the coordinates, together with the adjusted coordinates, are shown in the accompanying tabulation. Actually, these results can be combined with the previous computations in one

ADJUSTMENT OF COORDINATES

Station	Total Dist.	Y-Correction	X-Correction	Adjusted Y	Adjusted X
Richmond				28,221.34	20,370.66
A	2,872	− 0.21	− 0.05	27,230.59	23,066.86
B	4,850	− 0.35	− 0.09	25,259.06	22,916.14
C	6,290	− 0.46	− 0.11	23,819.58	22,970.62
D	7,926	− 0.58	− 0.14	22,225.19	23,337.59
E	11,157	− 0.82	− 0.20	19,494.28	21,610.75
F	12,648	− 0.93	− 0.23	19,876.16	20,168.99
G	14,880	− 1.09	− 0.27	19,903.54	17,937.14
Kenney	16,101	− 1.18	− 0.29	18,972.77	17,146.82

tabulation, which shows the unadjusted and adjusted coordinates. Each adjusted coordinate may be entered directly below the corresponding unadjusted coordinate or alongside it in a separate column; or the last few digits of the unadjusted coordinate may be struck out, and the adjusted figures entered above them. The two separate tabulations are shown here for the sake of clarity.

You should observe that the adjustment of the coordinates is really an application of the compass rule, which states that corrections are proportional to lengths or distances. The adjustment of latitudes and departures differs from the adjustment of coordinates in this way, however. As a rule some latitudes and some departures receive plus corrections, while others receive minus corrections; whereas all Y-coordinates must receive a correction of the same algebraic sign, and so must all the X-coordinates. There are, of course, exceptions to the former condition, as in the case of a traverse with all plus latitudes or all minus departures. This situation occurs frequently when a traverse originates on one point and closes on another point.

8-23. The Use of Rectangular Coordinates. The rectangular coordinates of a point uniquely define its position with respect to a known horizontal datum. Therefore, the use of coordinates is the most convenient method of publishing the horizontal positions of points which have been located in the field. The coordinates of a point give its position with respect to any other point located on the same coordinate system or horizontal datum.

If the coordinates of two stations 1 and 2 are known, the latitude and departure of the line from station 1 to station 2 are obtained by transposing terms of Eqs. 8-7 and 8-8 to give the following relations:

$$\text{Latitude of } 1\text{-}2 = Y_2 - Y_1 \qquad (8\text{-}9)$$

$$\text{Departure of } 1\text{-}2 = X_2 - X_1 \qquad (8\text{-}10)$$

The tangent of the bearing angle B of the line joining the two stations is given by the equation

$$\tan B = \frac{X_2 - X_1}{Y_2 - Y_1} \qquad (8\text{-}11)$$

The distance D between the two points is given by any one of the following equations:

$$D = \sqrt{(Y_2 - Y_1)^2 + (X_2 - X_1)^2} \qquad (8\text{-}12)$$

$$D = \frac{Y_2 - Y_1}{\cos B} \qquad (8\text{-}13)$$

$$D = \frac{X_2 - X_1}{\sin B} \qquad (8\text{-}14)$$

Equation 8-12 is convenient only when using the desk calculating machine. Equations 8-13 and 8-14 are convenient when using logarithms or a desk calculating machine. If the quantity $Y_2 - Y_1$ is greater than $X_2 - X_1$, Eq. 8-13 is used. If the quantity $X_2 - X_1$ is greater, Eq. 8-14 is used.

The azimuth A_N of a line *1-2* measured from the north meridian is given by the equation

$$\tan A_N = \frac{X_2 - X_1}{Y_2 - Y_1} \qquad (8\text{-}15)$$

The azimuth A_S of the same line measured from the south meridian is given by the equation

$$\tan A_S = \frac{X_1 - X_2}{Y_1 - Y_2} \qquad (8\text{-}16)$$

In Eqs. 8-9, 8-10, 8-11, 8-15, and 8-16, due consideration must be given to the algebraic signs of the coordinates and the differences in coordinates.

The equations of straight lines and second-degree curves given by the methods of analytic geometry are equally applicable to problems in surveying when coordinates are used. The slope of a straight line in analytic geometry is given as $m = \tan \alpha$, where α is the angle measured from the positive X-axis. As seen in Fig. 8-17, the slope of the line OP

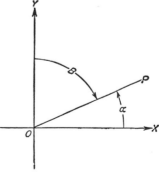

FIG. 8–17. Slope of a line.

is $m = \tan \alpha$. The angle α is the complement of the bearing angle B of the line or of its azimuth from north. Therefore, in surveying, the slope of the line is given as $\cot B$ or $\cot A_N$, the choice depending on whether bearings or azimuths from north are used. If azimuths from south are used, then the slope of the line is given as $-\cot A_S$. The following equations from analytic geometry, applicable to surveying, are given here for convenience.

  a) Equation of a straight line: When the coordinates (X_1, Y_1) and (X_2, Y_2) of two points are given,

$$\frac{Y - Y_1}{Y_2 - Y_1} = \frac{X - X_1}{X_2 - X_1} \tag{8-17}$$

When the coordinates (X_1, Y_1) of one point and the bearing angle B of the line are given,

$$Y - Y_1 = \cot B \ (X - X_1) \tag{8-18}$$

When the line passes through the origin and its bearing angle is given,

$$Y = X \cot B \tag{8-19}$$

  b) Equation of a circle of radius R: When its center is at the origin,

$$X^2 + Y^2 = R^2 \tag{8-20}$$

When the coordinates of its center are $X_c = H$ and $Y_c = K$,

$$(X - H)^2 + (Y - K)^2 = R^2 \tag{8-21}$$

  c) Area of polygon:

$$2A = X_1(Y_2 - Y_n) + X_2(Y_3 - Y_1) + \cdots$$
$$+ X_{n-1}(Y_n - Y_{n-2}) + X_n(Y_1 - Y_{n-1}) \tag{8-22}$$

or

$$2A = Y_1(X_2 - X_n) + Y_2(X_3 - X_1) + \cdots$$
$$+ Y_{n-1}(X_n - X_{n-2}) + Y_n(X_1 - X_{n-1}) \tag{8-23}$$

  d) Dividing a line into two parts in the proportion R_1/R_2:

$$X_0 = \frac{X_1 R_2 + X_2 R_1}{R_1 + R_2} \qquad Y_0 = \frac{Y_1 R_2 + Y_2 R_1}{R_1 + R_2} \tag{8-24}$$

where the coordinates of the points at the ends of the line are (X_1, Y_1) and (X_2, Y_2) and the coordinates of the division point are (X_0, Y_0).

  The foregoing equations are but a few of many which can be taken from analytic geometry and applied to surveying computations.

Engineers and surveyors in the past have been prone to apply the more cumbersome methods of trigonometry to the solution of surveying problems, but when a desk calculator is available, the methods of analytic geometry are much more efficient than are trigonometric methods. The following examples are given to show how easily some of the methods of analytic geometry are applied.

EXAMPLE 8-1. For the traverse computed in Sec. 8-12, determine the Y- and X coordinates of the intersection of the line joining points E and C with the line joining points D and A.

Solution: The equation of each of these lines may be written from the coordinates computed in Sec. 8-20 by using Eq. 8-17. The equation of the line EC is

(1a)
$$\frac{Y - 4020.94}{4104.93 - 4020.94} = \frac{X - 5915.06}{6452.93 - 5915.06}$$

and the equation of the line DA is

(2a)
$$\frac{Y - 3615.12}{4166.20 - 3615.12} = \frac{X - 5714.61}{6154.22 - 5714.61}$$

Because the actual coordinates are relatively large numbers which give terms with many significant figures in the calculations, the values of the coordinates should be reduced by subtracting a constant from each Y- and X-coordinate. In this problem, each Y-coordinate is reduced by 3000 ft, and each X-coordinate is reduced by 5000 ft. The two line equations then become

(1b)
$$\frac{Y' - 1020.94}{1104.93 - 1020.94} = \frac{X' - 915.06}{1452.93 - 915.06}$$

(2b)
$$\frac{Y' - 615.12}{1166.20 - 615.12} = \frac{X' - 714.61}{1154.22 - 714.61}$$

Rearranging and collecting terms, we get

(1c) $83.99\, X' - 537.87\, Y' = -\,472{,}277.11$

(2c) $551.08\, X' - 439.61\, Y' = +\,123{,}394.38$

These two equations are solved simultaneously to find the coordinates of the intersection. If Eq. 2c is multiplied by 537.87/439.61, and Eq. 1c is subtracted from the new equation, the work is as follows:

$$674.26\, X' - 537.87\, Y' = +\,150{,}975.04$$
$$83.99\, X' - 537.87\, Y' = -\,472{,}277.11$$

$$590.27\, X' \qquad\qquad = +\,623{,}252.15$$
$$X' \qquad\qquad = +\,1055.876$$

Substituting the value of X' in Eqs. 1c and 2c to provide a check gives Y' as 1042.93. The coordinates of the point of intersection are, therefore,

$$Y = 1042.93 + 3000 = 4042.93$$
$$X = 1055.88 + 5000 = 6055.88$$

EXAMPLE 8-2. For the traverse computed in Sec. 8-12, determine the coordinates of the intersection of a line passing through point B and parallel to line CD with the line AF.

Solution: The equations of these two lines are written and then solved simultaneously to obtain the coordinates of the point of intersection. The bearing of the line passing through B is the same as that of CD. Therefore, $\tan B_{CD} = 5714.61 - 6452.95)/(3615.12 - 4104.93)$ or $\cot B = (3615.12 - 4104.93)/(5714.61 - 6452.95) = +0.663393$, and the equation of the line through B is, by Eq. 8-18,

(1a) $$Y - 4493.00 = +0.663393\,(X - 6510.58)$$

The equation of the line AF is, by Eq. 8-17,

(2a) $$\frac{Y - 4166.20}{4237.06 - 4166.20} = \frac{X - 6154.22}{5738.18 - 6154.22}$$

In order to keep the number of significant figures in the calculations as small as possible, each Y-coordinate is reduced by 4000 ft and each X-coordinate by 5000 ft. The two line equations then become

(1b) $$Y' - 493.00 = +0.663393\,(X' - 1510.58)$$

(2b) $$\frac{Y' - 166.20}{237.06 - 166.20} = \frac{X' - 1154.22}{738.18 - 1154.22}$$

Rearranging and collecting terms gives

(1c) $$0.663393\,X' - Y' = +509.11$$

(2c) $$70.86\,X' + 416.04\,Y' = +150{,}933.88$$

These equations are solved simultaneously to give the coordinates of the intersection. When Eq. 1c is multiplied by $70.86/0.663393$, and the new equation is subtracted from Eq. 2c, the work is as follows:

$$
\begin{array}{r}
70.86\,X' - 106.81\,Y' = +\;54{,}380.34 \\
70.86\,X' + 416.04\,Y' = +\,150{,}933.88 \\
\hline
+522.85\,Y' = +\;96{,}553.54 \\
Y' = +184.668
\end{array}
$$

From Eqs. 1c and 2c, it is found that $X' = 1045.81$ and $X' = 1045.79$. The adopted value is 1045.80. The final coordinates are, therefore,

$$Y = \;\;184.67 + 4000 = 4184.67$$
$$X = 1045.80 + 5000 = 6045.80$$

EXAMPLE 8-3. The coordinates of the center of a circular curve defining the center line of a highway are $Y = 2655.10$ and $X = 17{,}255.35$. The radius of the curve is 750.00 ft. Determine the coordinates of the intersection of this center line with a line passing through a point whose coordinates are $Y = 3844.20$ and $X = 17{,}000.00$ and having a bearing S 30° E. See Fig. 8-18.

Solution: The equation of the circular curve is, by Eq. 8-21,

(1a) $$(X - 17{,}255.35)^2 + (Y - 2655.10)^2 = 750.00^2$$

The equation of the straight line is, by Eq. 8-18,

(2a) $$Y - 3844.20 = -\cot 30°\,(X - 17{,}000.00)$$

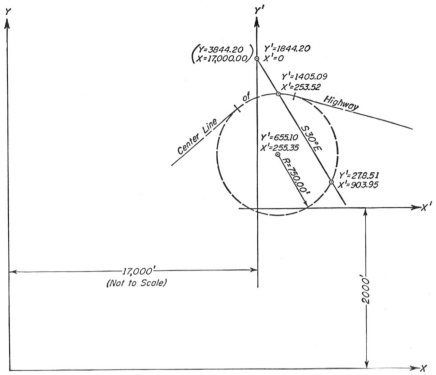

FIG. 8–18.   Intersection of circular curve and straight line.

The cotangent is minus because the bearing is in the southeast quadrant. The calculations may be simplified by subtracting 2000 ft from each Y-coordinate and 17,000 ft from each X-coordinate before the equations are solved, and then adding these amounts to the computed coordinates. Therefore,

(1b) $(X' - 255.35)^2 + (Y' - 655.10)^2 = 750.00^2$

(2b) $Y' - 1844.20 = -1.732051 (X' - 0)$

To solve these simultaneous equations, first the value of Y' obtained from Eq. 2b is substituted in Eq. 1b. Thus,

(2c) $Y' = -1.732051 X' + 1844.20$

(1c) $(X' - 255.35)^2 + (-1.732051 X' + 1844.20 - 655.10)^2 = 750.00^2$

Expanding, rearranging, and collecting terms gives

$$4 X'^2 - 4629.86 X' + 916,662.43 = 0$$

This is a quadratic equation of the form $ax^2 + bx + c = 0$ whose solution is $x = (-b \pm \sqrt{b^2 - 4ac})/2a$, and its solution will give two values of X', as follows:

$$X' = \frac{4629.86 \pm \sqrt{21,435,603.6196 - 14,666,598.8800}}{8}$$

$$X' = 903.95 \quad \text{or} \quad X' = 253.52$$

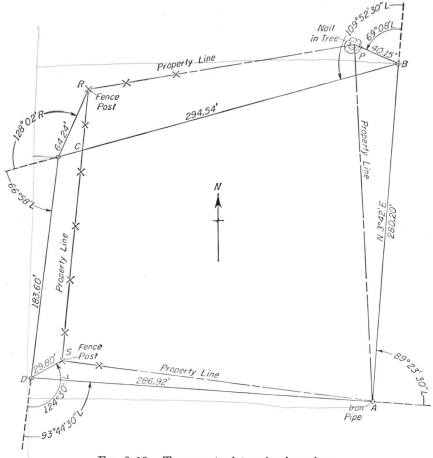

Fig. 8–19.　Traverse to determine boundary.

Substituting the values of X' in Eq. 2c gives

$$Y' = 278.51 \qquad \text{or} \qquad Y' = 1405.09$$

As a check on the computation, both values of X' and Y' may be substituted in Eq. 1b to see whether both values satisfy the equation. An inspection of Fig. 8-18 shows that the values obtained by using the smaller value of X' are the coordinates of the desired point. The final coordinates of the point are obtained by adding 2000 ft to Y' and 17,000 ft to X'. The results are $Y = 3405.09$ ft and $X = 17,253.52$ ft.

8-24. Coordinates of Unoccupied Points. In order to determine the coordinates of points which cannot be included in the traverse because it is not possible to set the transit up over such points, spur lines or tie lines must be run from the traverse to these points. For example, in Fig. 8-19 the boundaries of a parcel of land are defined by an iron pipe, a nail in a tree, and two fence posts. The only corner that can be occupied is the one marked by the iron pipe. The problem is to determine the lengths and bearings of the property lines.

It will be assumed that the coordinates of the iron pipe at point A and the bearing of the line AB are known. The procedure is then as follows:

a) Measure the lengths of the traverse sides AB, BC, CD, and DA, and also the lengths of the three tie lines BP, CR, and DS.

b) Measure the angles in the traverse $ABCD$, and also the angles between traverse lines and the tie lines to P, R, and S, as shown in Fig. 8-19.

c) Adjust the angles in the traverse $ABCD$, and compute the bearings of lines BC, CD, and DA based on the known bearing of the line AB.

d) Balance the traverse $ABCD$.

e) Compute the coordinates of points B, C, and D.

f) Determine the bearings of the lines BC, CD, and DA based on the coordinates computed in (*e*).

g) Compute the bearings of the tie lines from the bearings computed in (*f*) and the measured angles.

h) Compute the latitudes and departures of the tie lines.

i) Compute the coordinates of the unoccupied stations from the coordinates of traverse stations B, C, and D and the latitudes and departures of the lines BP, CR, and DS, respectively.

When the coordinates of P, R, and S have been computed, the bearings and lengths of the boundary lines may be computed by Eq. 8-11 and Eq. 8-12, 8-13, or 8-14.

EXAMPLE 8-4. The following deflection angles were measured at stations A, B, C, and D of the traverse in Fig. 8-19.

Station	From	To	Deflection Angle	Adjusted Deflection Angle
A	D	B	89° 23′ 30″ L*	89° 24′ 00″ L
B	A	C	109° 52′ 00″ L*	109° 52′ 30″ L
B	A	P	69° 08′ 00″ L	
C	B	D	66° 58′ 00″ L*	66° 58′ 30″ L
C	B	R	128° 02′ 00″ R	
D	C	A	93° 44′ 30″ L*	93° 45′ 00″ L
D	C	S	124° 30′ 00″ L	
			Check	360° 00′ 00″

The lengths as determined in the field are as follows:

Line	Length
AB	280.20 ft
BC	294.54
BP	40.15
CD	183.60
CR	64.24
DA	286.92
DS	29.80

Determine the lengths and bearings of the boundary lines *AP, PR, RS,* and *SA*.

Solution: The sum of the four angles in the closed traverse shown by an asterisk (*) is 359° 58'. These angles are adjusted to total 360°, as shown in the last column. The bearing of the line *AB* is known to be N 3° 42' E. The bearings of the other traverse sides (not including the tie lines) are computed by subtracting each left deflection angle from the forward azimuth of each backsight as outlined in Sec. 8-5. When these azimuths are converted to bearings, the results are as follows:

Line	Adjusted Bearing
AB	N 3° 42' 00" E
BC	S 73° 49' 30" W
CD	S 6° 51' 00" W
DA	S 86° 54' 00" E

From the adjusted bearings and the measured lengths of the traverse sides, the latitudes and departures are computed and balanced. From the balanced latitudes and departures, the coordinates of *B, C,* and *D* are determined, a check being made by computing the coordinates of *A* from point *D*. For the sake of brevity, the tabulation on page 235 shows only unbalanced and balanced latitudes and departures of the traverse sides, together with the computed coordinates of the traverse stations.

From the coordinates of the traverse stations, the azimuths of the lines *AB, BC,* and *CD* are computed, since these azimuths are needed to determine the azimuths of the tie lines. Then for line *AB,*

$$\tan A_N = \frac{+\,18.13}{+\,279.68} \qquad A = \quad 3° 42' 30''$$

For line *BC,*

$$\tan A_N = \frac{-\,282.82}{-\,81.98} \qquad A = 253° 50' 00''$$

For line *CD,*

$$\tan A_N = \frac{-\,21.86}{-\,182.25} \qquad A = 186° 50' 30''$$

The azimuths and bearings of the tie lines are determined as shown in the tabulation on page 235.

COMPUTATION OF COORDINATES OF TRAVERSE STATIONS

Station	Latitude +	Latitude −	Departure +	Departure −	Balanced Latitude +	Balanced Latitude −	Balanced Departure +	Balanced Departure −	Y-Coordinate	X-Coordinate
A									1000.00	1000.00
B	279.62		18.08		279.68		18.13		1279.68	1018.13
C		82.05		282.88		81.98		282.82	1197.70	735.31
D		182.29		21.90		182.25		21.86	1015.45	713.45
A		15.52	286.50			15.45	286.55		1000.00	1000.00
	279.62	279.86	304.58	304.78	279.68	279.68	304.68	304.68		

COMPUTATION OF AZIMUTHS OF TIE LINES

Line	Azimuth	Line	Azimuth	Line	Azimuth
AB	3° 42' 30"	BC	253° 50' 00"	CD	186° 50' 30"
AB	363° 42' 30"	$(+ \angle C)$	+ 128° 02' 00"	$(- \angle D)$	− 124° 30' 00"
$(- \angle B)$	− 69° 08' 00"	CR	381° 52' 00"	DS	62° 20' 30"
BP	294° 34' 30"	CR	21° 52' 00"	DS	N 62° 20' 30" E
BP	N 65° 25' 30" W	CR	N 21° 52' 00" E		

From the bearings and lengths of the tie lines, the latitudes and departures and then the coordinates are computed, as shown in the accompanying tabulation.

COMPUTATION OF COORDINATES OF BOUNDARY CORNERS

Sta-tion	Length	Bearing	Latitude		Departure		Y-Co-ordinate	X-Co-ordinate
			+	−	+	−		
B							1279.68	1018.13
	40.15	N 65° 25′ 30″ W	16.70			36.51		
P							1296.38	981.62
C							1197.70	735.31
	64.24	N 21° 52′ 00″ E	59.62		23.93			
R							1257.32	759.24
D							1015.45	713.45
	29.80	N 62° 20′ 30″ E	13.83		26.39			
S							1029.28	739.84

Since the coordinates of each boundary corner are known, the bearings and lengths of the boundary lines may now be computed by Eq. 8-11 and Eq. 8-12, 8-13, or 8-14. Equation 8-12 is employed only when a desk calculator is used. Equation 8-13 or 8-14 is employed when the computations are made by using logarithms or a desk calculator. The work with logarithms may be arranged as follows:

For line AP:

$X_P − X_A = − 18.38$
$Y_P − Y_A = + 296.38$

$\log − 18.38 = 1.26\ 4346\ (n)$
$\log + 296.38 = 2.47\ 1849$

$\log \tan B = 8.79\ 2497\ (n)$
$B = N\ 3°\ 33′\ 00″\ W$

$\log 296.38 = 2.47\ 1849$
$\log \cos B = 9.99\ 9166$

$\log D = 2.47\ 2683$
$D = 296.95\ ft$

For line PR:

$X_R − X_P = − 222.38$
$Y_R − Y_P = − 39.06$

$\log − 222.38 = 2.34\ 7096\ (n)$
$\log − 39.06 = 1.59\ 1732\ (n)$

$\log \tan B = 0.75\ 5364$
$B = S\ 80°\ 02′\ 20″\ W$

$\log 222.38 = 2.34\ 7096$
$\log \sin B = 9.99\ 3403$

$\log D = 2.35\ 3693$
$D = 225.78\ ft$

For line RS:

$X_S − X_R = − 19.40$
$Y_S − Y_R = − 228.04$

$\log − 19.40 = 1.28\ 7802\ (n)$
$\log − 228.04 = 2.35\ 8011\ (n)$

$\log \tan B = 8.92\ 9791$
$B = S\ 4°\ 51′\ 50″\ W$

$\log 228.04 = 2.35\ 8011$
$\log \cos B = 9.99\ 8433$

$\log D = 2.35\ 9578$
$D = 228.86\ ft$

For line SA:

$X_A − X_S = + 260.16$
$Y_A − Y_S = − 29.28$

$\log + 260.16 = 2.41\ 5241$
$\log − 29.28 = 1.46\ 6571\ (n)$

$\log \tan B = 0.94\ 8670\ (n)$
$B = S\ 83°\ 34′\ 40″\ E$

$\log 260.16 = 2.41\ 5241$
$\log \sin B = 9.99\ 7266$

$\log D = 2.41\ 7975$
$D = 261.80\ ft$

In reviewing the computations shown in this example, it should be realized that computations for the azimuths of AB, BC, and CD

from coordinates may be an unnecessary refinement, since the distances are relatively short. The azimuths of the tie lines could have been determined by applying the deflection angles from the traverse lines to the tie lines directly to the preliminary adjusted azimuths of the traverse lines. Then the latitudes and departures of the tie lines could be determined from their lengths and these azimuths. The results would not be appreciably different from those just obtained. On more extensive and complex traverses, however, it is advisable to compute new azimuths of the traverse lines from balanced latitudes and departures and adjusted coordinates.

8-25. Location of a Line Based on Computations. The problem of locating a desired line in the field by measurement from stations in a control traverse is constantly faced in location surveys, construction surveys, and boundary surveys. In Secs. 7-9 and 7-11 two methods were discussed for laying out a straight line in the field by means of a straight random traverse and by a traverse such as that illustrated in Fig. 7-9. Either of these problems can be solved by running a control random traverse between the two ends of the line. Latitudes and departures can be computed for the lines in the random traverse, and coordinates can be computed for the traverse stations. From the coordinates of the two ends of the desired line, its length and bearing can be computed. Furthermore, the coordinates of any point on the desired line can be computed.

By use of the computed coordinates at selected points on the desired line, the bearings and lengths of tie lines from the control-traverse stations can be computed. The angle to be laid off from a control-traverse line to run a tie line is computed from the known bearing of the tie line and that of the traverse line. In this manner, all the necessary angles are computed, and the points are set on the desired line by reoccupying the traverse stations and running the tie lines on the computed bearings and for the computed distances.

8-26. Area from Rectangular Coordinates. The area of a figure for which coordinates have been computed is determined by either Eq. 8-22 or 8-23 of Sec. 8-23. In evaluating each term of this equation, some of the terms will be positive and some negative giving the possibility of a net positive area or a net negative area. This is of no consequence unless the result is subject to further analytical treatment. See Sec. 8-33. The application of Eq. 8-22 to the area enclosed within the *boundary* of Fig. 8-19, the coordinates of which were computed in Sec. 8-24, is shown in the accompanying tabulation.

COMPUTATION OF AREA WITHIN A BOUNDARY BY COORDINATES

	+	−
$X_1 (Y_2 - Y_4) = 1000.00 \ (1296.38 - 1029.28) =$	267,100	
$X_2 (Y_3 - Y_1) = \ \ 981.62 \ (1257.32 - 1000.00) =$	252,590	
$X_3 (Y_4 - Y_2) = \ \ 759.24 \ (1029.28 - 1296.38) =$		202,793
$X_4 (Y_1 - Y_3) = \ \ 739.84 \ (1000.00 - 1257.32) =$		190,376
	519,690	393,169
	− 393,169	
	2)126,521	

Area =   63,260 sq ft

8.27. **Area from Latitudes and Double Meridian Distances.**
Where the primary purpose of a traverse survey is the determination
of the area of a tract, and where the transit lines coincide with the
boundaries of the required area, the method of using latitudes and
double meridian distances is commonly preferred. The double
meridian distance, or D.M.D., of a traverse line is twice the distance
from a meridian through the most westerly station of the traverse to
the middle point of the line.

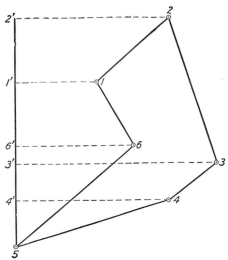

FIG. 8–20. Area from latitudes
and double meridian distances.

The double meridian dis-
tance of a traverse line can also
be defined as the sum of the
lengths of the two parallel
bases of the trapezoid formed
by drawing perpendiculars from
the ends of the line to the
meridian through the most
westerly traverse station. In
Fig. 8-20 the double meridian
distance of the side *1-2* is the
sum of the two parallel distances *2'2* and *1'1*. A triangle
may be considered as a trapezoid with one base equal to
zero. The area of a trapezoid is
one-half the sum of the two
parallel bases multiplied by the
altitude. So the area of the trapezoid *1'1 2 2'* is one-half the D.M.D.
of side *1-2* multiplied by the latitude of the side.

If the double meridian distances of traverse sides are computed
by beginning with the most westerly station of the traverse, all of

COMPUTATION FOR AREA OF TRAVERSE BY DOUBLE MERIDIAN DISTANCES

Line	D.M.D.		Latitude	Double Area	
				+	
DA	D.M.D. = + 286.55 Dep. DA + 286.55 Dep. AB + 18.13		− 15.45		4,427
AB	D.M.D. = + 591.23 Dep. AB + 18.13		+ 279.68	165,355	
		+ 609.36 Dep. BC − 282.82			
BC	D.M.D. = + 326.54 Dep. BC − 282.82		− 81.98		26,770
		+ 43.72 Dep. CD − 21.86			
CD	D.M.D. = + 21.86		− 182.25		3,984
				+ 165,355 − 35,181	− 35,181
				2) + 130,174	
				65,087	

$$\text{Area} = \quad 65{,}090 \text{ sq ft}$$

them are positive and can be computed readily from the departures of the sides by the following rules: The D.M.D. of the first side is the departure of that side. The D.M.D. of each succeeding side is the D.M.D. of the preceding side, plus the departure of the preceding side, plus the departure of the side itself. When adjusted departures have been used, all double meridian distances can be easily checked, since the D.M.D. of the last side should be equal numerically to the departure of the last side, but should have the opposite sign.

The double areas for the traverse sides are obtained by multiplying each D.M.D. by the adjusted latitude of that side. Those areas which are obtained from plus latitudes should be considered positive, and those areas which are found from minus latitudes are negative. The algebraic sum of these double areas will be twice the area of the traverse. The sign of the area may be either positive or negative. The negative sign has no particular significance. Had the survey progressed around the same figure in the opposite direction, the sign of the area would have been reversed.

The advantage of this D.M.D. method is that it can be used where no coordinates have been calculated. It can be used also as a means of checking an area which has been obtained from coordinates.

The D.M.D. area can be checked by using double latitude distances, computed by beginning with the most southerly station. The trapezoids and triangles are then formed by dropping vertical lines from the stations to an east-and-west line through the most southerly station.

The most westerly station or the most southerly station can be determined from the coordinates, when they have been calculated; or from a rough sketch of the figure; or from an inspection of the departures and latitudes, by noting at which station the departures change from west to east or where the latitudes change from south to north.

The computation of the area enclosed within the traverse $ABCD$ of Sec. 8-24 is shown in the tabulation on page 239. This traverse is not to be confused with the boundary of the tract $APRS$. Since station D is the most westerly station, the line DA is the first line to consider.

8-28. Areas from Maps. When a map of a required area is available, the area can be obtained by dividing the figure into geometrical shapes (triangles, trapezoids, and rectangles), and computing the areas of these figures from the dimensions scaled from the map. This method is limited to figures which are bounded by approximately straight lines. When the three sides a, b, and c of a triangle have been scaled from the map, the area may be found by the formula

$$\text{Area} = \sqrt{s(s-a)\ (s-b)\ (s-c)} \qquad (8\text{-}25)$$

where $s = \frac{1}{2}\,(a + b + c)$. These lengths are sometimes the result of direct field measurements.

When two sides a and b and the included angle C of a triangle are known, the formula for the area is

$$\text{Area} = \frac{1}{2}\,ab \sin C \qquad (8\text{-}26)$$

If the figure is very irregular in shape, as is generally the case when the boundaries are bodies of water, its area can be obtained most accurately by the use of the planimeter. The planimeter can be used also to check an area which has been computed from the field measurements.

The larger planimeters having adjustable arms are generally more carefully constructed and, hence, are more accurate than the smaller ones. The precision of the resulting area is dependent on the scale to which the map is drawn, and on the skill of the operator of the planimeter. With care, areas which are accurate within 1 per cent can be obtained by means of the planimeter.

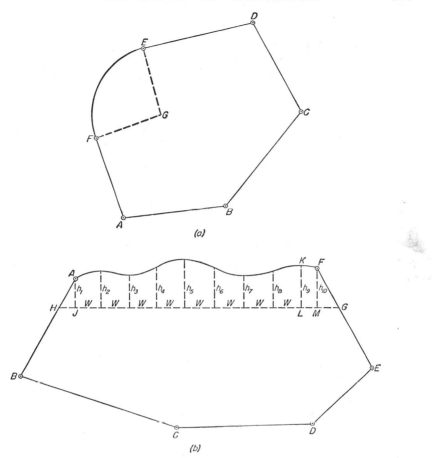

Fɪɢ. 8–21.   Areas with one curved boundary.

8-29. Area with One Curved Boundary. Two examples of areas with one curved boundary are shown in Fig. 8-21. In view (*a*) one side of the figure is a circular arc with radius R and central angle FGE. This area can be calculated in two parts, namely, the sector EFG and the part $ABCDEGFA$ bounded by straight lines. The area of the sector is $\pi R^2 \times$ angle $FGE/360°$.

In Fig. 8-21(*b*), the boundary AF is an irregular curve. The area of this figure can be divided into two parts by the straight line GH, and computations for the portion bounded by straight lines can be made by any of the ordinary methods. If perpendicular offsets from the straight line GH to the curved boundary are measured, either on the ground or on a map, the irregular portion can be considered as a series of triangles and trapezoids. These offsets should be measured at all breaks in the curved boundary. The area of each triangle and each trapezoid can be computed separately. When the boundary is sufficiently regular, the offsets can be taken at equal intervals along the line GH, and the computations can thus be simplified considerably. The area of the regular portion $AJLK$ in Fig. 8-21(b) can be obtained by a single multiplication by applying the trapezoidal rule, which is

$$\text{Area} = W \left(\frac{h_1 + h_n}{2} + h_2 + h_3 + \cdots + h_{n-1} \right) \qquad (8\text{-}27)$$

where W is the common spacing of the offsets and n is the number of offsets.

EXAMPLE 8-5. Determine the area $AFGH$ in Fig. 8-21(b) by using the trapezoidal rule for the regular portion. The distances are as follows:

$h_1 = 22.6$ ft	$h_6 = 36.9$ ft	$HJ = 14$ ft
$h_2 = 28.0$	$h_7 = 30.0$	$LM = 13.5$ ft
$h_3 = 27.1$	$h_8 = 31.5$	$MG = 21$ ft
$h_4 = 30.6$	$h_9 = 34.8$	$W = 25$ ft = common spacing
$h_5 = 38.5$	$h_{10} = 35.0$	

Solution: The computations follow:

$$\text{Area } AJH = \frac{(14.0)\ (22.6)}{2} = 158 \text{ sq ft}$$

$$\text{Area } KFML = \frac{(34.8 + 35.0)\ (13.5)}{2} = 471 \text{ sq ft}$$

$$\text{Area } FGM = \frac{(21.0)\ (35.0)}{2} = 368 \text{ sq ft}$$

$$\text{Area } AJLK = 25 \left(\frac{22.6 + 34.8}{2} + 28.0 + 27.1 + 30.6 + 38.5 \right.$$
$$\left. + 36.9 + 30.0 + 31.5 \right) = 6283 \text{ sq ft}$$

The total area $AFGH$ is therefore 7280 sq ft.

The assumption made in using the trapezoidal rule is that the curved boundary is composed of chords connecting the ends of the offsets. When the offsets are taken closely enough together, and when the curves are flat, no considerable error is introduced by this assumption.

A more accurate value for the area between a straight line and an irregular boundary may be obtained by taking offsets at regular intervals and applying Simpson's one-third rule to that portion lying between an *odd* number of offsets. Simpson's one-third rule assumes that the curve through each successive three points

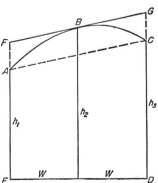

FIG. 8–22. Area by Simpson's one-third rule.

is a portion of a parabola. In Fig. 8-22 the curve through points A, B, and C is assumed to be a segment of a parabola cut off by the chord AC. The area between the chord and the parabola, found by the calculus, is equal to two-thirds the area of the parallelogram $AFGC$. The area of $ABCDE$ is, therefore,

$$\text{Area} = 2W \left(\frac{h_1 + h_3}{2}\right) + \frac{2}{3} \times 2W \left(h_2 - \frac{h_1 + h_3}{2}\right)$$

Expanding and collecting terms gives

$$\text{Area} = \frac{W}{3} (h_1 + 4h_2 + h_3)$$

For the next three offsets, the area would be, by the same reasoning,

$$\text{Area} = \frac{W}{3} (h_3 + 4h_4 + h_5)$$

By extending this reasoning to any *odd* number of offsets, and summing up the results, we obtain the following relation:

$$\text{Area} = \frac{W}{3} [h_1 + 2(h_3 + h_5 + \cdots + h_{n-2})$$
$$+ 4(h_2 + h_4 + \cdots + h_{n-1}) + h_n]$$

where h_1 = first offset;
$\quad h_n$ = last odd-numbered offset;
$\quad W$ = common interval at which the offsets are taken.

In its condensed form, Simpson's one-third rule may be expressed as follows:

$$\text{Area} = \frac{W}{3} (h_1 + h_n + 2 \, \Sigma \, h_{odd} + 4 \, \Sigma \, h_{even}) \qquad (8\text{-}28)$$

EXAMPLE 8-6. Determine the area $AFGH$ in Fig. 8-21 (*b*) by using Simpson's one-third rule where it applies.

Solution: Obviously Simpson's one-third rule applies only between the first and the ninth offsets. The area of the remaining portion will be computed by the trapezoidal rule. Thus,

$$\text{Area } AJLK = \tfrac{25}{3} [22.6 + 34.8 + 2 \, (27.1 + 38.5 + 30.0)$$
$$+ 4 \, (28.0 + 30.6 + 36.9 + 31.5)] = 6305 \text{ sq ft}$$

The remaining area, as computed in the preceding example, is 997 sq ft. Therefore the total area $AFGH$ is 7302 sq ft, which is 22 sq ft more than that obtained by the trapezoidal rule. This difference is due to the fact that the

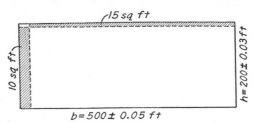

irregular boundary is generally concave toward the line *HG*. If the irregular boundary is concave away from the straight line from which offsets have been measured, Simpson's one-third rule will give a smaller area than will the trapezoidal rule.

8-30.   Errors in Areas. The accuracy of a computed area is dependent on the accuracy of the field measurements, on the geometric shape of the area, and on the elements of the area (sides or angles) which have been measured. For example, let us consider the case of a rectangular field with a length a and width b, and let the standard errors of these measurements be σ_a and σ_b, respectively. Then, by Eq. 4-15, the standard error of the area A is

$$\sigma_A = \sqrt{(b\sigma_a)^2 + (a\sigma_b)^2}$$

The maximum error in the area is obtained by assuming that both errors in the dimensions are positive or that both are negative. According to the theory of random errors, the maximum error to be expected in a measured quantity is approximately 3σ. Thus, the maximum error in the area of a rectangle is approximately

$$e_{max} = \pm\,(3b\sigma_a + 3a\sigma_b)$$

If the dimensions of the rectangle shown in Fig. 8-23 are 500 ft and 200 ft, with standard errors of $\pm$ 0.05 ft and $\pm$ 0.03 ft, respectively, the standard error of the area is $\pm \sqrt{10^2 + 15^2}\ = \pm 18$ sq ft. The maximum error could then be approximately 75 sq ft.

The computed area of a triangle in which two sides and the included angle have been measured is $\tfrac{1}{2}ab \sin C$. In Example 4-10, the standard error of the computed area is

$$\sigma_A = \sqrt{[(\tfrac{1}{2}b \sin C)\sigma_a]^2 + [(\tfrac{1}{2}a \sin C)\sigma_b]^2 + [(\tfrac{1}{2}ab \cos C)\sigma_c]^2}$$

and the maximum error of the area is approximately

$$e_{max} = \pm\,[(\tfrac{3}{2}b \sin C)\sigma_a + (\tfrac{3}{2}a \sin C)\sigma_b + (\tfrac{3}{2}ab \cos C)\sigma_c]$$

8-31.   Significant Figures in Areas. The precision of an area is dependent on the number of significant figures in the dimensions from which the area is calculated. The number of significant figures in an observed length is the number of digits which are known. Thus, a length of 428.52 ft, if accurate to hundredths of a foot, contains five significant figures, 428.5 ft contains four, and 428 ft contains three significant figures. If a distance of 4800 ft is known to the nearest hundred feet only, it contains but two significant figures, the zeros merely showing the position of the decimal point. Similarly, 0.0004 contains but one significant figure, the zeros again indicating the position of the decimal point.

The number of correct significant figures in a product or a quotient can be no greater than the number in the least accurate term. This limitation will be apparent from an investigation of the product and the quotient of 21.4215 ft and 12.5 ft. The distance 12.5 ft, which is measured to the nearest tenth of a foot, may have any value between 12.46 and 12.54 ft. If the more exact value is 12.51 ft, the approximate product and quotient are $21.4215 \times 12.5 = 267.76875$ and $21.4215 \div 12.5 = 1.714$, while the more accurate values are $21.4215 \times 12.51 = 267.982965$ and $21.4215 \div 12.51 = 1.712$. Thus a change of 0.01 ft in the less accurate term produces a change in the fourth significant figure of the product or the quotient. In other words, there can be but three certain figures, and the product should be given as 268 and the quotient as 1.71, results which could have been obtained by using 21.4 and 12.5. It is a waste of effort to retain six figures in the more accurate term, when the same result can be obtained after dropping at least two of them. In order to insure the desired precision in the final figure of a result, it will usually be necessary to carry one uncertain figure in the intermediate work.

8-32. Problems in Omitted Measurements. The common examples of omitted measurements are shown in Fig. 8-24. In view (a), the length or the azimuth, or both the length and the azimuth, of the side EA may be unknown. The latitudes and departures of the known sides are computed. The latitude $E'A$ of the line EA equals the algebraic sum of the latitudes of the known sides *with opposite sign*. The departure EE' of the line EA equals the algebraic sum of the departures of the known sides *with opposite sign*. The bearing angle B or the azimuth A_N from north of the line EA is obtained by the equation

$$\tan B = \tan A_N = \frac{\text{departure}}{\text{latitude}} \tag{8-29}$$

The length D of the line EA is obtained by any of the following three equations:

$$D = \sqrt{\text{latitude}^2 + \text{departure}^2} \tag{8-30}$$

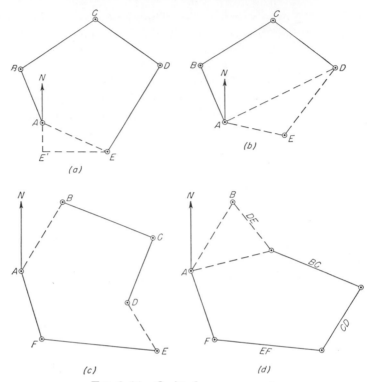

FIG. 8–24. Omitted measurements.

$$D = \frac{\text{latitude}}{\cos B} \tag{8-31}$$

$$D = \frac{\text{departure}}{\sin B} \tag{8-32}$$

These four equations are the same as Eqs. 8-11, 8-12, 8-13, and 8-14, because the latitude corresponds to $(Y_2 - Y_1)$ and the departure corresponds to $(X_2 - X_1)$.

In Fig. 8-24(b), two adjacent sides are involved in the missing measurements. Both lengths, both azimuths, or the azimuth of one line and the length of the other may be unknown. From the latitudes and departures of the known sides, the azimuth and length of the closing line DA are computed. The triangle ADE can now be solved. When the lengths of DE and EA are missing, the triangle is solved from the computed length DA and the three angles, which can be calculated from the known azimuths. When the azimuths of DE and EA are unknown, the three sides of the triangle are known and the angles are computed. When the azimuth of one of the sides and the length of the other are unknown, the triangle is solved from the two known sides and the angle opposite one of the known sides. Frequently, there will be two solutions in this last case, and the approximate shape of the figure must then be known. The trigonometric formulas for the solution of oblique triangles are given in Table I at the end of this text.

In Fig. 8-24(c), the omitted measurements occur on sides that are not adjacent. Since the latitudes and departures of equal parallel lines are equal, this problem can be solved by shifting the line DE until it is adjacent to AB, so as to form the closed figure shown in view (d). The solution of this problem is the same as that outlined for view (b).

8-33. Parting off Land. One of the common problems of land surveying is the division of an irregular polygon into two or more parts with known areas. The division may be made by a line of known direction, or it may be made by a line from a given starting point on the perimeter of the polygon.

In Fig. 8-25, let the problem be the division of the polygon ABCDEF into two equal parts by a line parallel to AF. The azimuths and lengths of the sides being known, the first step is the calculation of the entire area. This can be done by either the D.M.D. method or the coordinate method. If a rough sketch is made from the field measurements, the appropriate position of the line HI, which is to divide the area into two equal parts, can be determined. From the figure it is evident that H will be somewhere on the line BC. The exact location of HI is determined most easily by first including an imaginary line BG parallel to AF and calculating the area of the part ABGF. This area will probably be less than the required area, and the trapezoid BHIG must be added. The area of this trapezoid should equal the required area minus the area of ABGF.

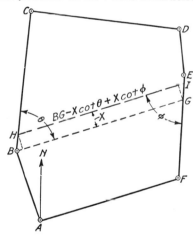

FIG. 8–25. Parting off land.

Before the area of ABGF can be computed, the lengths of BG and GF must be calculated by the methods of the preceding section. In the trapezoid BHIG, the area, the base BG, and the angles will be known; the base HI and the altitude X are unknown. The length of HI can be expressed in terms of BG, the cotangents of the angles

θ and ϕ, and the altitude X. Thus, in Fig. 8-25, $HI = BG - X \cot \theta + X \cot \phi$. Also,

$$\text{Area of } BHIG = \tfrac{1}{2} X [BG + BG - X (\cot \theta - \cot \phi)]$$

$$= X \times BG - \frac{(\cot \theta - \cot \phi)}{2} X^2$$

When the known quantities are substituted, the resulting equation is a quadratic of the form $aX^2 + bX + c = 0$, the solution of which is expressed as

$$X = \frac{-b \pm \sqrt{b^2 - 4ac}}{2a}$$

After the altitude X of the trapezoid $BHIG$ has been found, the distances BH and GI can be computed from the relations $BH = X/\sin \theta$ and $GI = X/\sin \phi$. The computations can be checked by calculating the latitudes and departures of CH, HI, and IE and getting the area of $HCDEI$, which should equal one-half the area of the entire field $ABCDEF$.

In the tabulation on page 249 are shown numerical values for the azimuths and lengths of the sides of the field $ABCDEF$ of Fig. 8-25, and the computations for dividing this field into two equal parts by a line HI. The only work not shown is that for finding the lengths of BG and FG.

Differentials frequently can be used to advantage in solving the quadratic $aX^2 + bX + c = 0$. Differentiation of $Y = aX^2 + bX + c$ gives $\delta Y = (2aX + b)\, \delta X$. If for δY is substituted the value of Y found when an approximate value of X is used, the resulting value of δX is the correction to be applied to the approximate value of X. Although the value of X can be obtained with any desired degree of accuracy by successive trials, usually but one or two trials are necessary. Thus, in the numerical example given here, the figure $BGIH$ is roughly a parallelogram, and X is equal approximately to the area divided by the length of BG, or $46{,}215 \div 763.2 = 60$. Also, $Y = 46{,}215 - 763.2\, X + 0.0324\, X^2$, and $\delta Y = (-763.2 + 0.0648\, X)\, \delta X$. When $X = 60$, then $Y = 46{,}215 - 45{,}792 + 117 = 540$ and $\delta Y = (-763.2 + 3.9)\, \delta X = -759.3\, \delta X$. Since Y should equal zero, -540 is equated to $-759.3\, \delta X$, whence $\delta X = 0.71$ and the more exact value of X is 60.71.

A more direct solution of the problem is obtained by the methods of analytic geometry. The rectangular coordinates of the corners are determined from the latitudes and departures of the sides. For con-

COMPUTATIONS FOR PARTING OFF LAND

Total Area

Side	Azimuth	Length	Departures +	Departures −	Latitudes +	Latitudes −	D.M.D.	Double Area
AB	340° 12′	320.4		108.5	301.5		108.5	+ 32,713
BC	5° 38′	618.6	60.7		615.6		60.7	+ 37,367
CD	96° 26′	654.3	650.2			73.3	771.6	− 56,558
DE	174° 34′	200.6	19.0			199.7	1440.8	− 287,728
EF	182° 27′	447.5		19.1		447.1	1440.7	− 644,137
FA	251° 53′	633.7		602.3		197.0	819.3	− 161,402
			729.9	729.9	917.1	917.1		2)1,079,745

Area = 539,870

Area of $ABGF$

Side	Azimuth	Length	Departures +	Departures −	Latitudes +	Latitudes −	D.M.D.	Double Area
AB				108.5	301.5		108.5	+ 32,713
BG	71° 53′	763.2	725.4		237.3		725.4	+ 172,137
GF	182° 27′	342.2		14.6		341.8	1436.2	− 490,893
FA				602.3		197.0	819.3	− 161,402
			725.4	725.4	538.8	538.8		2) 447,445

Area = 223,720

Lengths

Total area = 539,870 sq ft

One-half total area = 269,935

Area $ABGF$ = 223,720

Area $BGIH$ = 46,215

$\cot 66° 15' = 0.4400105$

$\cot 69° 26' = 0.3752115$

0.0647990

$$46,215 = 763.2X - \tfrac{1}{2} (\cot 66° 15' - \cot 69° 26') X^2$$

$$46,215 = 763.2X - 0.0324X^2$$

$$X = \frac{763.2 - \sqrt{582,474.24 - 5989.46}}{0.0648} = \frac{763.2 - 759.26}{0.0648} = \frac{3.94}{0.0648} = 60.8$$

$$BH = \frac{60.8}{\sin 66° 15'} = \frac{60.8}{0.9153} = 66.5$$

$$CH = BC - BH = 618.6 - 66.5 = 552.1$$

$$HI = 763.2 - 60.8 \times 0.0648 = 759.2$$

$$GI = \frac{60.8}{\sin 69° 26'} = \frac{60.8}{0.9363} = 64.9$$

$$FI = FG + GI = 342.2 + 64.9 = 407.1$$

$$EI = EF - FI = 447.5 - 407.1 = 40.4$$

venience, the Y-axis should be chosen through B and the X-axis through A. The coordinates are as shown in the accompanying tabulation along with the determination of the area of the entire field found by Eq. 8-22.

COMPUTATION OF AREA BY COORDINATES

Station	Y	X		+	−
$A\ (=1)$	0	108.5	108.5 (301.5 − 197.0) =	11,338	
$B\ (=2)$	301.5	0	0 (917.1 − 0) =		
$C\ (=3)$	917.1	60.7	60.7 (843.8 − 301.5) =	32,918	
$D\ (=4)$	843.8	710.9	710.9 (644.1 − 917.1) =		194,076
$E\ (=5)$	644.1	729.9	729.9 (197.0 − 843.8) =		472,099
$F\ (=6)$	197.0	710.8	710.8 (0 − 644.1) =		457,826
				+ 44,256	1,124,001
					+ 44,256
					2) −1,079,745
					Area = − 539,873

This area is − 539,870 sq ft. The algebraic sign is significant in this solution, since one-half this area, or − 269,935 sq ft, is a term in one of the equations to be used in solving the problem analytically.

From Fig. 8-25 and from the conditions in the problem, the following four statements are apparent: 1) Point H lies on the line BC; 2) point I lies on the line EF; 3) the area of $ABHIF$ is one-half the total area, or − 269,935 sq ft; 4) the line HI has the same bearing as does the line AF. If the coordinates of the unknown point H are denoted by Y_H and X_H and the coordinates of the unknown point I by Y_I and X_I, the following four equations may be written:

By Eq. 8-17,

$$\frac{Y_H - Y_B}{Y_C - Y_B} = \frac{X_H - X_B}{X_C - X_B}$$

By Eq. 8-17,

$$\frac{Y_I - Y_E}{Y_F - Y_E} = \frac{X_I - X_E}{X_F - X_E}$$

By Eq. 8-22,

$$X_A (Y_B - Y_F) + X_B (Y_H - Y_A) + X_H (Y_I - Y_B)$$

$$+ X_I (Y_F - Y_H) + X_F (Y_A - Y_I) = 2 (- 269,935)$$

By Eq. 8-11,

$$\frac{X_F - X_A}{Y_F - Y_A} = \tan B_{AF} = \tan B_{HI} = \frac{X_I - X_H}{Y_I - Y_H}$$

Substituting the known values of the coordinates in these equations gives four equations which may be solved simultaneously to obtain the values of the four unknowns X_H, Y_H, X_I, and Y_I. These equations are:

(1a)
$$\frac{Y_H - 301.5}{615.6} = \frac{X_H - 0}{60.7}$$

(2a)
$$\frac{Y_I - 644.1}{-447.1} = \frac{X_I - 729.9}{-19.1}$$

(3a) $(108.5)\,(104.5) + 0\,(Y_H - 0) + X_H\,(Y_I - 301.5)$
$$+ X_I\,(197.0 - Y_H) + 710.8\,(0 - Y_I) = -539{,}870$$

(4a)
$$\frac{X_I - X_H}{Y_I - Y_H} = \frac{602.3}{197.0}$$

The results obtained by cross multiplying and rearranging and collecting terms follow:

(1b) $\qquad$ $615.6\,X_H - 60.7\,Y_H + 18{,}301.05 = 0$

(2b) $\qquad$ $447.1\,X_I - 19.1\,Y_I - 314{,}035.98 = 0$

(3b) $\quad$ $301.5\,X_H - 197.0\,X_I - X_H Y_I + X_I Y_H + 710.8\,Y_I - 551{,}208 = 0$

(4b) $\qquad$ $X_H - X_I - 3.05736\,Y_H + 3.05736\,Y_I = 0$

Expressing Y_H in terms of X_H from Eq. 1b gives

(1c) $\qquad$ $Y_H = 10.14168\,X_H + 301.5$

Expressing Y_I in terms of X_I from Eq. 2b gives

(2c) $\qquad$ $Y_I = 23.40838\,X_I - 16{,}441.7$

When these values of Y_H and Y_I are substituted in Eqs. 3b and 4b, the results are:

(3c) $16{,}743.2\,X_H + 16{,}743.2\,X_I - 13.26670\,X_H X_I - 12{,}237{,}968 = 0$

(4c) $\qquad$ $30.00677\,X_H - 70.56784\,X_I + 51{,}190 = 0$

or $\qquad\qquad$ $X_I = 0.42522\,X_H + 725.40$

Substituting the value of X_I from Eq. 4c in Eq. 3c gives

(3d) $\qquad$ $5.64127\,X_H{}^2 - 14{,}239\,X_H + 92{,}451 = 0$

From this quadratic equation, $X_H = 6.5588$. By Eq. 4c, $X_I = 728.19$. By Eq. 1c, $Y_H = 368.0$. By Eq. 2c, $Y_I = 604.0$. By Eq. 8-12, $BH = 66.8$ ft; $EI = 40.1$ ft; $HI = 759.2$ ft.

The small discrepancies in the lengths of BH and EI are round-ing-off errors in the solution of the equation. The constant term in Eq. 3a is rounded off from a more exact value of $-539,873$ computed in the tabulation for area.

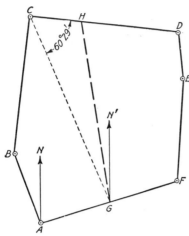

FIG. 8–26.   Parting off land.

In Fig. 8-26 let the problem be the division of the polygon $ABCDEF$ of Fig. 8-25 into two equal parts by a line GH from the middle point of the side AF. The required area can be considered as made up of two parts, namely, the quadrilateral $ABCG$ and the tri-angle GCH. From the latitudes and departures of the sides, the area of the quadrilateral and the azimuth and length of CG can be computed. The area of the triangle CGH will be the difference between the re-quired area and the area of the quadrilateral. In the triangle, the area, the length CG, and the angle HCG are known, and the length CH is computed from the following relationship:

$$\text{Area} = \tfrac{1}{2}\, CG \times CH \times \sin HCG$$

The computations can be checked by computing the area of $HDEFG$, which should equal the required area. For the field for which the azimuths and lengths of the sides were given on page 249, the com-putations, except those for the area of the original polygon, are shown in the accompanying tabulation.

This same problem is solved by analytic geometry by first com-puting coordinates of the traverse stations and then computing the area from the coordinates. The coordinates of point G are $Y = 98.5$ and $X = 409.6$, which are equal to the means of the coordinates of A and F since G is the middle point of the line AF. From Fig. 8-26, and from the conditions in the problem, two statements are apparent: 1) Point H lies on line CD; 2) the area of $ABCHG$ is one-half the total area. Two equations suffice to compute the coordinates X_H and Y_H of the unknown point H. The equations are as follows: By Eq. 8-17,

$$\frac{Y_H - Y_C}{Y_D - Y_C} = \frac{X_H - X_C}{X_D - X_C}$$

By Eq. 8-22,

COMPUTATIONS FOR PARTING OFF LAND

Area of $ABCG$

Side	Azimuth	Length	Departures +	Departures −	Latitudes +	Latitudes −	D.M.D.	Double Areas
GA	251° 53′	316.85		301.2		98.5	518.2	− 51,043
AB	340° 12′	320.4		108.5	301.5		108.5	+ 32,713
BC	5° 38′	618.6	60.7		615.6		60.7	+ 37,367
CG	(156° 55′)	(889.8)	(349.0)			(818.6)	470.4	− 385,069
			409.7	409.7	917.1	917.1	2)	366,032

Area = 183,016

Azimuth and Length of CG

log 349.0 = 2.54 2825   log 818.6 = 2.91 3072
log 818.6 = 2.91 3072   log cos 23° 05′ = 9.96 3757

log tan CGN' = 9.62 9753   log CG = 2.94 9315
CGN' = 23° 05′ CG = 889.8
Azimuth CG = 180° − 23° 05′ = 156° 55′
Azimuth CD = 96° 26′

Angle HCG = 60° 29′

Length of CH

Required area = 269,935 sq ft
Area $ABCG$ = 183,016

Area CGH = 86,919 = ½ × 889.8 × CH × sin 60° 29′

log 2 = 0.30 1030
log 86,919 = 4.93 9115
colog 889.8 = 7.05 0685
colog sin 60° 29′ = 0.06 0375

$$CH = \frac{2 \times 86,919}{889.8 \times \sin 60° 29'}$$

log CH = 2.35 1205
CH = 224.5 ft

Length and Azimuth of GH

The triangle CHG can now be solved for the length of GH and the angle at G, from which the azimuth of GH can be calculated.

$$X_A(Y_B - Y_G) + X_B(Y_C - Y_A) + X_C(Y_H - Y_B)$$
$$+ X_H(Y_G - Y_C) + X_G(Y_A - Y_H) = -2(269,935)$$

It is only necessary to substitute the values of the known coordinates in these equations and solve the simultaneous equations thus obtained. The work follows:

(1a)   73.3 X_H + 650.2 Y_H −   600,747.7 = 0
(2a)   818.6 X_H + 348.9 Y_H −   543,594.4 = 0

(1b)   73.3 X_H + 650.2 Y_H −   600,747.7 = 0
(2b)   1525.5 X_H + 650.2 Y_H − 1,013,026.9 = 0

$$1452.2\,X_H \qquad\qquad -\quad 412{,}279.2 = 0$$

$$X_H = 283.9 \qquad Y_H = 891.9$$

By Eq. 8-12, $CH = 224.5$ ft and $GH = 803.3$ ft. By Eq. 8-11, the bearing of GH is N 9° 00′ W.

8-34. Three-Point Resection. In field work it often becomes desirable to locate a point without running a traverse from known points or without resorting to triangulation (see Chapter 10). This situation arises when traversing is uneconomical and when it is difficult or impossible to occupy known points in a triangulation net. One method of locating the desired point is by a three-point resection. The prerequisites for a three-point resection are three well-defined control points visible from the station whose position is as yet unknown.

In Fig. 8-27, A, B, and C are points whose positions (coordinates) are known and which are visible from the unknown station P. If sta-

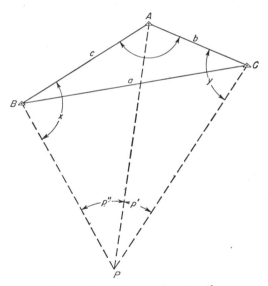

FIG. 8–27.   Three-point resection.

tion P is occupied and the angles p'' and p' are measured, then these angles and the coordinates of the control points are sufficient to determine the position of P. The lengths and azimuths of the lines AB, BC, and CA are computed from the coordinates of these three points. The angle at A from C to B may be computed from the azimuths of the lines AC and AB. Let the angle at B from A to P be denoted by x and the angle at C from P to A be denoted by y, as shown in Fig.

8-27. Then, since the sum of the interior angles in a four-sided figure is 360°,

$$x + y + A + p'' + p' = 360°$$

Therefore, $x + y = 360° - (A + p'' + p')$, and

$$\tfrac{1}{2}(x + y) = 180° - \tfrac{1}{2}(A + p'' + p') \tag{8-33}$$

Furthermore, $\sin x/AP = \sin p''/c$ and $\sin y/AP = \sin p'/b$. So

$$AP = \frac{c \sin x}{\sin p''} = \frac{b \sin y}{\sin p'}$$

Let $\sin y/\sin x = \tan Z$. Then

$$\tan Z = \frac{c \sin p'}{b \sin p''} \tag{8-34}$$

When 1 is added to each side of the equation $\sin y/\sin x = \tan Z$, the result is

$$\frac{\sin y}{\sin x} + 1 = \tan Z + 1$$

or

$$\frac{\sin x + \sin y}{\sin x} = \tan Z + \tan 45° \tag{a}$$

When each side of the same equation is subtracted from 1, the result is

$$1 - \frac{\sin y}{\sin x} = 1 - \tan Z$$

or

$$\frac{\sin x - \sin y}{\sin x} = 1 - \tan Z \tan 45° \tag{b}$$

Dividing Eq. b by Eq. a gives

$$\frac{\sin x - \sin y}{\sin x + \sin y} = \frac{1 - \tan Z \tan 45°}{\tan Z + \tan 45°}$$

$$= \frac{1}{\tan (Z + 45°)} = \cot (Z + 45°)$$

The left-hand side of this last equation may be expressed in terms of the product of two functions, rather than in terms of the sum of two functions. Thus,

$$\frac{2 \cos \tfrac{1}{2}(x + y) \sin \tfrac{1}{2}(x - y)}{2 \sin \tfrac{1}{2}(x + y) \cos \tfrac{1}{2}(x - y)} = \cot (Z + 45°)$$

or

$$\cot \tfrac{1}{2} (x + y) \tan \tfrac{1}{2} (x - y) = \cot (Z + 45°)$$

Hence,

$$\tan \tfrac{1}{2} (x - y) = \cot (Z + 45°) \tan \tfrac{1}{2} (x + y) \qquad (8\text{-}35)$$

When the triangle ABC has been solved for the angle at A and the lengths b and c, the angle $\tfrac{1}{2} (x + y)$ is computed by Eq. 8-33. Then $\tan Z$ is computed by Eq. 8-34, and the angle $\tfrac{1}{2} (x - y)$ is computed by Eq. 8-35. Adding $\tfrac{1}{2} (x + y)$ and $\tfrac{1}{2} (x - y)$ gives x; subtracting $\tfrac{1}{2} (x - y)$ from $\tfrac{1}{2} (x + y)$ gives y. These two angles complete the data necessary to solve the triangles PBA and PAC, the length of the common side PA affording a check on the computations. The azimuths of the three lines BP, AP, and CP are determined from the known angles and azimuths. Their lengths are determined from the triangle solutions. The latitude and departure of any one of the lines are computed to determine the coordinates of P. The latitude and departure of another of the lines will afford a check on the coordinates of P.

A numerical example, indicating the manner in which the computations for solving a three-point resection by logarithms may be tabulated, is shown on page 257. Due regard must be given to the algebraic sign of $\tan \tfrac{1}{2} (x + y)$ and also of $\cot (Z + 45°)$ in the solution of Eq. 8-35. This determines whether $\tfrac{1}{2} (x - y)$ is positive or negative. If $\tfrac{1}{2} (x + y)$ is 90°, then the position of the unknown point is indeterminate, since it lies on the circle passing through the three control stations.

In Fig. 8-28 (a), $\tfrac{1}{2} (x + y) = 180° - \tfrac{1}{2} (A + p'' + p')$, as in Fig. 8-27. However, in Fig. 8-28 (b), $\tfrac{1}{2} (x + y) = \tfrac{1}{2} (A - p'' - p')$. Otherwise, the solution for x and y is the same for the conditions in Fig. 8-28(b) as for those in Figs. 8-27 and 8-28(a).

A three-point resection can always be made to check mathematically, but *the mathematical checks do not provide a check on the field work or on the control points used.* The field angles may be checked by measuring the angles p'', p', and the exterior angle at P, since the sum of these three angles should be 360°.

The value of a three-point resection may be increased considerably by sighting on a *fourth* control point. The result is a conditioned three-point resection, since there are two independent solutions which should give the same position for the unknown point. If the discrepancy between the two computed positions of the point based on a conditioned resection is unreasonably large, then the cause may be that the observer has sighted on an erroneously identified control

Logarithmic Computation of Three-Point Resection

Determination of Angles

$$c = 1642.83 \text{ ft} \quad p' = 38°\ 12'\ 20''$$
$$b = 1076.44 \text{ ft} \quad p'' = 49°\ 36'\ 10''$$
$$A = 141°\ 28'\ 30''$$
$$\text{sum} = \overline{229°\ 17'\ 00''}$$
$$\tfrac{1}{2}\text{ sum} = 114°\ 38'\ 30''$$
$$\tfrac{1}{2}(x+y) = 180° - \tfrac{1}{2}\text{ sum} = 65°\ 21'\ 30''$$

$$\log c = 3.21\ 5593$$
$$\log \sin p' = 9.79\ 1329$$
$$\text{colog } b = 6.96\ 8010$$
$$\text{colog } \sin p'' = 0.11\ 8290$$
$$\log \tan Z = \overline{0.09\ 3222}$$
$$Z = 51°\ 06'\ 09''$$
$$Z + 45° = 96°\ 06'\ 09''$$

$$\log \cot (Z + 45°) = 9.02\ 9031\ (n)$$
$$\log \tan \tfrac{1}{2}(x+y) = 0.33\ 8456$$
$$\log \tan \tfrac{1}{2}(x-y) = \overline{9.36\ 7487\ (n)}$$

$$\tfrac{1}{2}(x-y) = -\ 13°\ 07'\ 11''$$
$$\tfrac{1}{2}(x+y) = 65°\ 21'\ 30''$$
$$x = \overline{52°\ 14'\ 19''}$$
$$y = 78°\ 28'\ 41''$$

Solution of Triangles

$p'' = 49°\ 36'\ 10''$	$p' = 38°\ 12'\ 20''$
$x = 52°\ 14'\ 19''$	$y = 78°\ 28'\ 41''$
$\text{sum} = 101°\ 50'\ 29''$	$\text{sum} = 116°\ 41'\ 01''$
$180° - \text{sum} = 78°\ 09'\ 31'' = PAB$	$180° - \text{sum} = 63°\ 18'\ 59'' = PAC$
$BP = \dfrac{c \sin PAB}{\sin p''}$	$CP = \dfrac{b \sin PAC}{\sin p'}$
$\log c = 3.21\ 5593$	$\log b = 3.03\ 1990$
$\log \sin PAB = 9.99\ 0658$	$\log \sin PAC = 9.95\ 1095$
$\text{colog } \sin p'' = 0.11\ 8290$	$\text{colog } \sin p' = 0.20\ 8671$
$\log BP = 3.32\ 4541$	$\log CP = 3.19\ 1756$
$BP = 2111.26$	$CP = 1555.09$
$AP = \dfrac{c \sin x}{\sin p''}$	$AP = \dfrac{b \sin y}{\sin p'}$
$\log c = 3.21\ 5593$	$\log b = 3.03\ 1990$
$\log \sin x = 9.89\ 7939$	$\log \sin y = 9.99\ 1159$
$\text{colog } \sin p'' = 0.11\ 8290$	$\text{colog } \sin p' = 0.20\ 8671$
$\log AP = 3.23\ 1822$	$\log AP = 3.23\ 1820 \text{ check}$
$AP = 1705.38$	$AP = 1705.38$

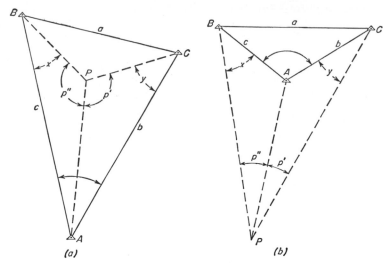

FIG. 8–28.   Three-point resection.

point, the published position of a control point was wrong, a mistake was made in measuring the angles, or a mistake was made in the computations. If the control points are correct and the discrepancy is within reason, then its amount will give an indication of the precision of the field work.

8-35. Methods of Plotting Traverses. A traverse can be plotted by using the computed coordinates of the stations, or by laying off directly on the map the angles and distances which were measured in the field. These angles may be interior, deflection, azimuth, or bearing angles. They can be plotted by means of a protractor or by means of their trigonometric functions. The scale and the size of the map, and the required precision, will determine the method to be used.

8-36. Plotting by Protractor. Circular and semicircular protractors made of paper, celluloid, or metal are available in diameters up to 14 in. The smaller varieties are graduated in degrees or half-degrees, while some of the larger metal ones have movable arms with an attached vernier that can be read to minutes. The small protractors are used mostly for checking angles which have been plotted by some more accurate means.

The first step in plotting a traverse to a specified scale is to make a rough sketch, so that the approximate shape and size will be known. From this sketch the size of paper necessary can be ascertained, and a suitable position and direction of the first line of the survey can be determined. If azimuths or bearings have been measured in the field, this first line will be the meridian through the first station; otherwise, it will be the first transit line of the survey. This line is drawn on the map in its proper place, and the first transit station is indicated by a point marked with a needle or a very sharp hard pencil and surrounded with a light penciled circle. The line is extended a sufficient distance beyond the station to permit the protractor to be centered accurately and oriented over the station, and the angle at that station is plotted. The protractor is then removed, the line is drawn, and the distance to the next station is laid off with the scale. If the angles are azimuths or bearings, a line parallel to the meridian is drawn through this new point, the protractor is again oriented, and the next course is plotted. If interior or deflection angles have been measured, the angle is laid off from the preceding course. By this means the remaining stations are plotted.

In any closed traverse, the plotting should close, of course, on paper. If the traverse fails to close, the error may be due to the inaccurate plotting of either an angle or a distance, or there may be an error in the field measurements. The position of an error in the field work can be detected by computing the latitudes and departures of the sides. If the error is in a plotted distance, the angles being correct, the error will be found in the length of a side parallel to the line which represents the closure. An error in a plotted angle may be located by plotting the lines backward to the point where the two positions of a plotted station agree. There will be less chance for the small errors of plotting to accumulate if half the traverse is plotted in each direction from the starting point and the closure is made midway around the figure.

Another method of checking angles, which should be used to check open traverses, is to plot two different angles. Thus, if the traverse has been plotted by interior of deflection angles, the bearings or azimuths of the sides should be calculated and these used to check the original plotting. When there is an angular error in a traverse of many sides, the location of the error can be narrowed down to a few stations by checking the bearing of every fourth or fifth side. Another method of checking is to plot by some other method.

The length of the sides of an open traverse can be checked by graphically adding the plotted lengths along the edge of a long straight piece of paper, and then comparing the scaled length of this total with the mathematical total.

8-37. Plotting by Natural Tangents. Although the tangent method can be used for plotting any angle, it is particularly well

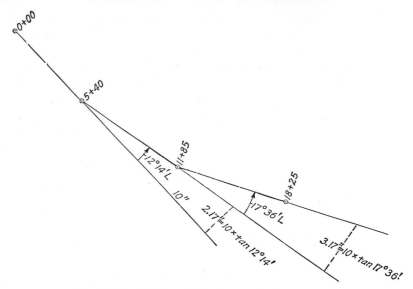

FIG. 8–29.   Plotting deflection angles by tangents.

adapted to the plotting of route surveys, where deflection angles have
been measured. This method of plotting is shown in Fig. 8-29. At station 5 + 40, it is required to lay off a deflection angle of 12° 14′ to
the left. The line from station 0 to station 5 + 40 is prolonged 10 in.
beyond station 5 + 40, and a perpendicular is erected at the 10-in.
point. On this perpendicular is laid off the distance 10 × tan 12°
14′ = 2.17 in. By connecting this point with station 5 + 40, the direction of the new line is given. Station 11 + 85 is located on this line,
and the line is extended 10 in. beyond the new station. A perpendicular is erected at this point, and 10 × tan 17° 36′ = 3.17 in. is laid
off on the perpendicular. This point connected with station 11 + 85
gives the direction of the new line on which station 18 + 25 is located.

The method just described is applicable to deflection angles less
than 45° or greater than 135°. If a deflection angle lies between 45°
and 135°, first a perpendicular is carefully erected at the vertex of the
deflection angle, and a 10-in. distance is laid off along this perpendicular. Then a second perpendicular is erected at the 10-in. mark,
and 10 times the cotangent of the deflection angle is scaled off along
this line.

When the map is too small to permit the use of the 10-in. lengths,
10 units on any edge of the triangular engineer's scale can be used,
but the same edge must be used for laying off the perpendicular
distance.

On a small map, a traverse which has been run by the azimuth

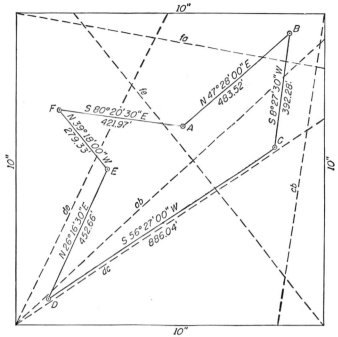

FIG. 8–30.   Plotting traverse by tangents of bearing angles.

or bearing method can be plotted by first constructing a 10-in. square near the center of the sheet and laying off all the bearings or azimuths within this square by the tangent method. The directions are then transferred to their proper positions by parallel lines. When the bearing angle exceeds 45°, the angle is plotted by using the tangent of 90° minus the angle. In Fig. 8-30 the traverse from Sec. 8-12 has been plotted by this method.

When angles are plotted by the tangent method, the precision will be considerably greater than that obtained when the protractor is used, especially if the protractor is a small one. The precision is dependent on the care with which the tangent is laid off, and on the size of the triangle formed. Small discrepancies in the measurements will have less effect if the 10-in. lengths can be used than when a smaller unit must be used.

The tangent method is widely used in plotting open traverses, and also in plotting closed traverses when the latitudes and departures have not been computed.

8-38. **Plotting by Rectangular Coordinates.**   The method by rectangular coordinates is the most accurate method of plotting a traverse and has advantages not possessed by any of the preceding

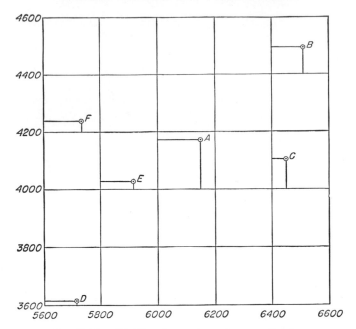

FIG. 8–31.   Plotting by rectangular coordinates.

methods. It is known in advance that the traverse closes. The erroneous plotting of any point does not affect the location of any of the succeeding points, as the plotting of each point is independent of the rest. Each point can be checked as soon as plotted by comparing the scaled distance to the preceding station with the length measured in the field. The proper size of sheet for the map may be determined by an inspection of the coordinates.

A series of *grid* lines is carefully constructed. The lines of the two sets are perpendicular to one another, and those of each set are spaced at intervals of 50, 100, 500, or 1000 ft, or at some other regular interval, the distance depending on the scale to which the traverse or map is to be plotted. All these grid lines should be plotted in as brief a period of time as possible, so that the measurements are consistent with one another under the given ambient conditions of temperature and humidity. Each grid line is labeled with its proper Y-coordinate or X-coordinate, and finally the several points are plotted, according to their coordinates, from the nearest grid lines. Plotting by coordinates is shown in Fig. 8-31, where the stations of the traverse of Sec. 8-12 are plotted by using a 200-ft grid spacing. When all the points have been plotted, their positions are checked by scaling the distances between successive points and comparing them with the known distances.

Grid lines and coordinates can be plotted mechanically by means

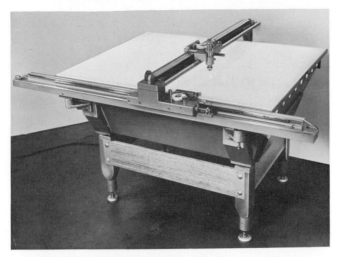

FIG. 8-32. Coordinatograph. (Courtesy of Unitech Corp.)

of an instrument called a coordinatograph. One is shown in Fig. 8-32. A girder travels in the X-direction, and its motion is capable of being read or set by means of a scale and rotating dial to an accuracy of approximately $\pm$ 0.003 in. or less than 0.1 mm. A pencil, pen, or needle holder travels along the girder in the Y-direction, and its motion also can be read or set to the same accuracy. Grid lines are ruled in both directions by appropriate settings of the scales and dials, which are determined by the choice of the plotting scale. Each point is then plotted, according to its coordinates, by making appropriate settings of the scales and dials.

The value of a map may be increased considerably by retaining the grid lines on the finished map, either as complete lines or as tick marks at the edges of the sheet and cross marks at the grid intersections in the interior portion. The map user can then detect any change in scale in any or all portions of the map by measuring between grid lines or between grid ticks. Where accurate lengths are to be determined between well-defined points, the coordinates of the points defining the ends of the lines are scaled from the nearest grid lines, and the scaled distances are either increased or decreased to allow for the scale change. The lengths may then be computed by Eq. 8-12. In Fig. 8-32, the grid was originally plotted with 5-in. spacings representing 1000 ft. The scaled distances to point P from the grid lines representing $Y = 6000$ ft and $X = 10,000$ ft are 420 ft and 775 ft, respectively. The actual distance between the grid lines in the Y-direction is 5.012 in., and the distance in the X-direction is 4.980 in. The Y-coordinate of the point P is therefore 6000 + (420) (5)/5.012

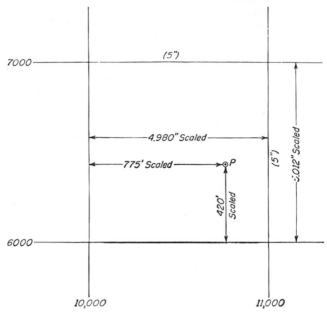

FIG. 8–33. Scaling coordinates.

= 6419 ft, and the X-coordinate is 10,000 + (775) (5)/4.980 = 10,777 ft.

8-39. **Scales.** The scales commonly used on maps intended for engineering purposes are those found on the edges of an engineer's scale. Thus, 1 in. on the paper represents some multiple of 10, 20, 30, 40, 50, or 60 ft on the ground. Maps are generally classed as large-scale when the scale is greater than 1 in. = 100 ft; as intermediate-scale when the scale is between 1 in. = 100 ft and 1 in. = 1000 ft; and as small-scale when the scale is less than 1 in. = 1000 ft. The large scales are used when a large amount of detail is to be shown, or where the area covered by the map is small. In general, the scale should be as small as possible, and still represent the detail with sufficient precision. Maps intended for the design of engineering projects are commonly plotted to scales between 1 in. = 20 ft and 1 in. = 800 ft, the exact scale depending on the detail to be shown and the area covered.

Surveys made for architects are often plotted to the scales used by architects, namely 1 in. = 4 ft, 1 in. = 8 ft, and 1 in. = 16 ft.

The topographic maps prepared by the U. S. Geological Survey and the U. S. Coast and Geodetic Survey are plotted to so-called natural scales. These scales are expressed as ratios. On a map drawn to a scale of 1/20,000, one unit on the map represents 20,000 units on the ground. Thus, 1 in. on the paper represents 20,000 in. on the ground, 1 ft represents 20,000 ft, and 1 meter represents 20,000 meters on the ground.

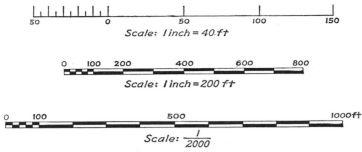

Scale: 1 inch = 40 ft

Scale: 1 inch = 200 ft

Scale: $\frac{1}{2000}$

FIG. 8–34. Graphical scales.

As previously stated, the scale of a map may change slightly because of the shrinkage or stretching of the drawing paper. The scale is changed also when the map is reproduced. The change may be slight in blueprinted reproductions, or it may be considerable when photographic reductions or enlargements are made. Since the original scale no longer applies to the duplicates, a graphical scale, similar to one of those shown in Fig. 8-34, should appear on the map.

8-40. Meridian Arrow. A meridian arrow should appear on the map. It should be simple in design and, while it should be of sufficient length to permit the reasonably accurate scaling of directions on any part of the map, it should not be so conspicuous as to convey the impression that the map is a drawing of an arrow. The proportions of an arrow which can be constructed easily with drawing instruments are shown in Fig. 8-35. The dotted circle does not appear on the finished drawing. When both true and magnetic directions are known, two arrows are combined as in Fig. 8-35, a full-headed arrow usually indicating true north, and a half-headed arrow indicating magnetic north. The magnetic declination is shown in figures.

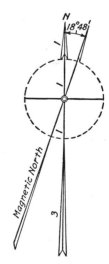

FIG. 8–35.
Meridian arrows.

8-41. Titles. On an engineering drawing the title appears in the lower right-hand corner of the sheet. This same convention is followed as far as possible on maps, although on many maps the shape of the area covered may be such that the title is placed elsewhere on the sheet to give the drawing a more balanced appearance.

As maps may pass through many hands and may be intended as permanent records, more time is spent on the lettering than would be justified on the shop drawings for an engineering project. The very ornate lettering found on older maps is no longer used, carefully constructed Roman or Gothic capitals being used instead. Legends and notes, separated from the main title, may be shown in single-stroke Reinhardt letters.

The title should be sufficiently complete to permit the identification of the map. It should include the purpose of the survey, the name of the owner or the organization for whom the survey is made, the location (city or township, county, and state), the date of the survey, the name of the engineer or surveyor responsible for the work, and the scale. The name of the draftsman may also appear.

PROBLEMS

8-1. The adjusted interior angles in a traverse which originates and closes on point A are as follows:

Sta.	From	To	Adjusted Interior Angle
A	G	B	132° 16′ 40″
B	A	C	114° 37′ 10″
C	B	D	83° 30′ 00″
D	C	E	226° 07′ 30″
E	D	F	40° 10′ 10″
F	E	G	272° 42′ 00″
G	F	A	30° 36′ 30″

All angles are considered clockwise. The line AB bears S 42° 10′ 20″ W. Compute the azimuths and bearings of the remaining sides of the traverse.

8-2. The following deflection angles were measured in a traverse which originates at point A with a backsight on P and closes at point G with a foresight on Q.

Sta.	From	To	Deflection Angle
A	P	B	33° 14′ 00″ R
B	A	C	79° 18′ 00″ R
C	B	D	48° 00′ 30″ R
D	C	E	50° 22′ 00″ L
E	D	F	56° 10′ 00″ L
F	E	G	42° 26′ 30″ L
G	F	Q	38° 55′ 30″ R

The fixed azimuth of PA is 336° 20′ 30″, and the fixed azimuth of GQ is 26° 49′ 25″. What are the adjusted azimuths and bearings of the intermediate traverse sides?

8-3. The lengths in feet and the adjusted bearings of the sides of a closed traverse follow:

Side	Length	Bearing	Side	Length	Bearing
AB	250.32	N 36° 22′ 20″ W	DE	506.12	S 19° 38′ 50″ E
BC	322.94	N 57° 40′ 00″ E	EF	110.84	S 44° 27′ 10″ W
CD	408.60	N 83° 28′ 40″ E	FA	637.68	N 77° 44′ 20″ W

Compute the latitudes and departures of the sides.

8-4. Balance the traverse in Problem 8-3 by the compass rule. Then compute the coordinates of the stations, taking X_A as 30,000.00 ft and Y_A as 24,500.00 ft.

8-5. Balance the traverse in Problem 8-3 by the transit rule.

8-6. Using the results in Problem 8-4, compute the area bounded by the traverse in Problem 8-3 by the coordinate method.

8-7. Compute the area bounded by the traverse in Problem 8-3 by the D.M.D. method, using the adjusted latitudes and departures computed in Problem 8-4.

8-8. Compute the length of the line BD in Fig. 8-14 by using the adjusted coordinates of the traverse given in Sec. 8-12.

8-9. A line passing through point E in Fig. 8-14 bears N 12° 20′ E. At what distance from point A does this line intersect the line FA?

8-10. The following perpendicular offsets in feet are measured from a straight line to an irregular boundary at regular intervals of 50 ft:

$h_1 = 78.2$	$h_6 = 140.4$	$h_{11} = 172.0$
$h_2 = 76.0$	$h_7 = 172.9$	$h_{12} = 118.6$
$h_3 = 61.6$	$h_8 = 176.8$	$h_{13} = 80.3$
$h_4 = 68.2$	$h_9 = 172.2$	$h_{14} = 52.8$
$h_5 = 98.7$	$h_{10} = 172.8$	$h_{15} = 30.0$

Compute the area lying between the straight line and the irregular boundary by the trapezoid rule.

8-11. Compute the area in Problem 8-10 by Simpson's one-third rule.

8-12. In the traverse in Fig. 8-24(b) the following lengths and bearings were measured:

Side	Length (ft)	Bearing
AB	400.15	N 16° 26′ W
BC	550.05	N 67° 38′ E
CD	492.16	S 40° 20′ E
DE	540.36	. . . .
EA	. . . . . .	N 82° 46′ W

Compute the missing length and bearing.

8-13. In the traverse in Fig. 8-24(c) the following lengths and bearings were measured:

Side	Length (ft)	Bearing	Side	Length (ft)	Bearing
AB	. . . . . .	N 31° 22′ E	DE	. . . . . .	S 21° 36′ E
BC	235.52	S 82° 14′ E	EF	263.96	N 88° 18′ W
CD	311.25	S 14° 44′ W	FA	193.81	N 20° 10′ W

Compute the missing sides.

8-14. Part off the southwesterly one-fourth portion of the area enclosed by the traverse in Fig. 8-14 by a line passing through point E. Give the position of the partition point along line CD with respect to point D.

8-15. Part off the northeasterly one-fourth portion of the area of the traverse in Fig. 8-14 by a north-south line. Give the length of the line and its position with respect to points A and C.

8-16. The coordinates in feet of three control points are as follows:

Point	Y	X
A	98,202.66	38,762.50
B	110,002.65	61,252.84
C	89,102.32	78,565.12

a) From an unknown point P_1 lying southerly from A, the clockwise angle from A to B is measured as 22° 36′ 14.6″, and that from B to C as 29° 58′ 50.6″. Compute the coordinates of P_1.

b) From a point P_2 lying easterly from A and inside the triangle formed by the control points, the clockwise angle from A to B is measured as 112° 28′ 29.7″, and that from B to C as 86° 00′ 04.4″. Compute the coordinates of P_2.

c) From a point P_3 lying northerly from B, the clockwise angle from C to B is measured as 12° 32′ 22.6″, and that from B to A as 55° 28′ 33.4″. Compute the coordinates of P_3.

8-17. The observed compass bearings of the five sides of a closed traverse follow:

Side	Observed Bearing	Observed Back Bearing
AB	S 43° 30′ E	N 45° 00′ W
BC	S 20° 00′ W	N 20° 30′ E
CD	S 82° 30′ W	N 83° 30′ E
DE	N 0° 30′ E	S 0° 30′ E
EA	N 52° 00′ E	S 51° 00′ W

Determine the measured interior angles, and adjust them by applying an equal correction to each angle. Assuming that the bearing of AB is fixed, compute the adjusted bearings of the remaining sides. Show a check on the computations.

9

Horizontal and Vertical Curves

9-1. Remarks. The center line of a highway, railroad, or canal consists of a series of straight lines connected by curves. The grade line on a profile of any length is likewise made up of straight lines and curves. These curves may be arcs of circles, parabolas, or curves whose equations are of the third degree. The parabola is generally used as a vertical curve on grade lines, while the circle and the higher-degree curves are used as horizontal curves. On modern highways and railroads the horizontal curves are made up of circles with easement or transition curves at the two ends.

9-2. Notation for Circular Curves. The notation commonly used on circular curves is shown in Fig. 9-1. The point at which the two tangents to the curve intersect is called the *vertex*, which is designated V, or the *point of intersection*, abbreviated *P.I.* The deflection angle between the tangents, which is equal to the angle at the center of the curve, is denoted by I or Δ. If the survey, shown in Fig. 9-1, is progressing to the right, the straight line to the left of the *P.I.* is the *back tangent*, and the one to the right is the *forward tangent*. The beginning point of the curve is called the *point of curvature*, abbreviated *P.C.* This is sometimes referred to as the *tangent-to-curve point*, abbreviated *T.C.* The end of the curve is the *point of tangency*, or the *P.T.* This is also referred to as the *curve-to-tangent point*, abbreviated *C.T.*

The distance from the *P.I.* to the *P.C.* or the *P.T.* is the *tangent distance, T.* The distance from the *P.I.* to the middle point of the curve, measured along the bisector of the central angle, is the *external distance, E.* The distance from the middle point of the curve to the middle point of the chord joining the *P.C.* and the *P.T.* is the *middle ordinate, M.* The angle subtended at the center of the curve by a 100-ft chord is the *degree of curve, D,* by *chord* definition. The angle subtended at the center of the curve by a 100-ft arc is the *degree of*

269

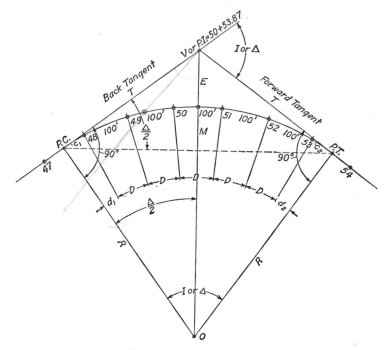

FIG. 9–1.   Circular curve.

curve, D, by *arc* definition. The *radius* of the curve is designated by R.

As the station method is commonly used in recording the horizontal distances, and as the *P.C.* of a curve will rarely be at a full station, the distance c_1 from the *P.C.* to the first full station on the curve will be, in general, less than 100 ft. The central angle subtended by this chord is d_1. The distance from the last full station on the curve to the *P.T.* is c_2, and the corresponding central angle is d_2.

A curve can be designated by either the radius or the degree of curve. The designation by the radius is finding widespread use in highway practice. Usually some integral multiple of 50 ft is used as the radius of the curve.

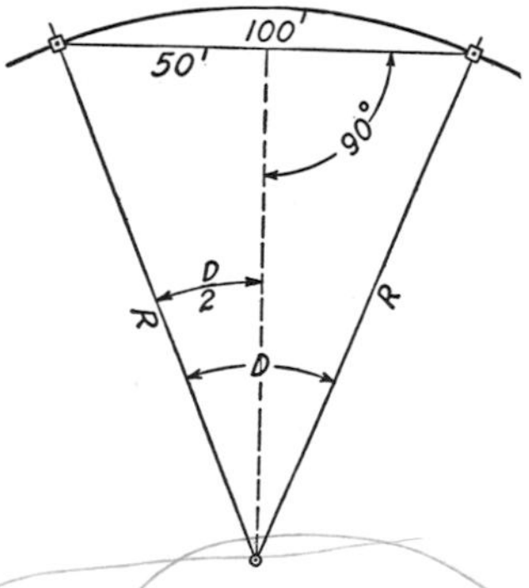

The *length of a curve* is the difference in stationing between the *P.C.* and the *P.T.* of the curve. By arc definition, this corresponds to the length of the curve measured along the actual arc. By chord definition it does not correspond either to the length measured along the arc or to the length measured along a series of chords unless the curve is, by chance.

FIG. 9–2.   Relation between R and D by chord definition.

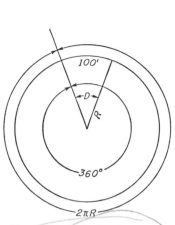

Fig. 9–3. Relation between
R and D by arc definition.

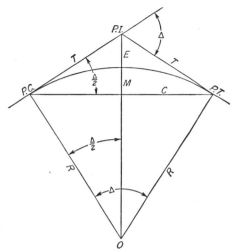

Fig. 9–4. Elements of a circular curve.

composed of full 100-ft chords only. The length L of a curve herein defined is a mathematical value used to compute other elements used in
laying out the curve in the field.

9-3. Radius and Degree of Curve. The relationship between
the radius and the degree of curve by chord definition is shown in
Fig. 9-2. In either of the two right-angled triangles formed by bisecting the central angle D,

$$\sin \tfrac{1}{2} D = \frac{50}{R} \tag{9-1}$$

from which

$$R = \frac{50}{\sin \tfrac{1}{2} D} \qquad CHORD \tag{9-2}$$

The relationship between the radius and the degree of curve by
arc definition is shown in Fig. 9-3. When D is expressed in degrees,

$$\frac{100}{D} = \frac{2 \pi R}{360°}$$

from which

$$R = \frac{5729.58}{D} \tag{9-3}$$

or

$$D = \frac{5729.58}{R} \qquad ARC \tag{9-4}$$

9-4. Equations for Circular Curves. The relationships involving the radius R of a circular curve, the deflection angle Δ between

the tangents, and other elements of the circular curve are shown in
Fig. 9-4. The following equations apply to both the chord definition
and the arc definition.

$$T = R \tan \tfrac{1}{2} \Delta \qquad (9\text{-}5)$$

or

$$E = R \sec \tfrac{1}{2} \Delta - R = R (\sec \tfrac{1}{2} \Delta - 1)$$

$$E = R \operatorname{exsec} \tfrac{1}{2} \Delta \qquad (9\text{-}6)$$

or

$$M = R - R \cos \tfrac{1}{2} \Delta = R (1 - \cos \tfrac{1}{2} \Delta)$$

$$M = R \operatorname{vers} \tfrac{1}{2} \Delta \qquad (9\text{-}7)$$

$$C = 2 R \sin \tfrac{1}{2} \Delta \qquad (9\text{-}8)$$

The full deflection angle for the curve is the angle at the *P.C.*
from the *P.I.* to the *P.T.* and is seen to be ½ Δ.

The length of the curve, or the difference in stationing between
the *P.C.* and the *P.T.*, is computed by the relationship

$$L = 100 \, \frac{\Delta}{D} \qquad CHORD \qquad (9\text{-}9)$$

9-5. Selection of Curve. Any two given tangents can be connected by an infinite number of circular arcs. The curve to be used
in a particular case is determined by assuming $D, R, T, E,$ or L. Since
all these quantities are interdependent, only one can be assumed.
The other values are calculated from the relationships developed in
the preceding section.

Field conditions frequently decide which quantity should be
assumed. Thus, when the survey is following the bank of a stream,
the external distance may be the limiting factor. On a winding road
the tangent lengths may be restricted. On high-speed modern pavements and railroads, an attempt is made to keep the degree of curve
below a given maximum. Wherever possible a radius of more than
1000 ft is adopted. This radius corresponds to a degree of curve of
about 5° 44′.

9-6. Stations of *P.I.*, *P.C.*, and *P.T.* The station of the *P.I.* is
determined when the center-line tangents have been located in the
field. It is equal to the distance, in hundreds of feet and plusses, from
the point selected as station 0 + 00 as described in Sec. 3-45. The
station of the *P.C.* is obtained by subtracting the tangent distance T
from the *P.I.* station. The *P.T.* station is obtained by adding the
length of the curve L to the *P.C.* station. In algebraic form,

$$P.C. = P.I. - T \qquad (9\text{-}10)$$

$$P.T. = P.C. + L \qquad (9\text{-}11)$$

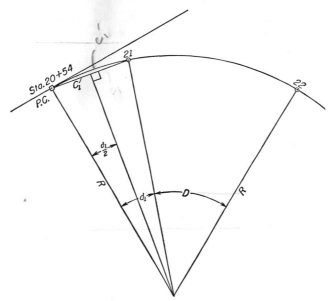

FIG. 9–5.   Relation between central angle
and deflection angle.

9-7. **Central Angle and Chord to First Curve Station.** In Fig. 9-5, the $P.C.$ station is $20 + 54.00$, the first curve station is $21 + 00$, and the second curve station is $22 + 00$. By either the chord or the arc definition, the angle at the center subtending a full station is equal to the degree of curve D. Let c'_1, called the nominal subchord, equal the *difference in stationing* between the $P.C.$ and the first station on the curve. Then, by direct proportion,

$$\frac{d_1}{D} = \frac{c'_1}{100}$$

or

$$\boxed{d_1 = \frac{c'_1 D}{100}} \tag{9-12}$$

In Fig. 9-5, let $D = 15°$. Then, since $c'_1 = 46.00$ ft, $d_1 = 46.0 \times 15/100 = 6.90° = 6° 54'$.

The *actual* chord length between the $P.C.$ and station $21 + 00$, designated c_1, is used to lay out the point on the ground. It is found from the relationship

$$\frac{\frac{1}{2} c_1}{R} = \sin \tfrac{1}{2} d_1$$

from which

$$\boxed{c_1 = 2 R \sin \tfrac{1}{2} d_1} \tag{9-13}$$

The value of c_1 in Fig. 9-5 will depend on whether the degree of curve is determined by the chord or arc definition, since the value of R will be different for the two definitions for a given D.

9-8. Central Angle and Chord from Last Curve Station to P.T. If c'_2 denotes the difference in stationing between the last station on the curve and the P.T., then the central angle d_2 between these two points is

$$d_2 = \frac{c'_2 D}{100} \qquad (9\text{-}14)$$

The actual chord length c_2 between the last curve station and the P.T. is

$$c_2 = 2 R \sin \tfrac{1}{2} d_2 \qquad (9\text{-}15)$$

9-9. Central Angle and Chord Between Any Two Curve Points. From Secs. 9-7 and 9-8, it is obvious that the angle at the center subtended between any two points on the curve is proportional to the difference in stationing between the two points. Let c' = the difference in stationing between any two points on the curve, d = the central angle between the two points, and D = the degree of curve, either by chord or arc definition. Then

$$d = \frac{c' D}{100} \qquad (9\text{-}16)$$

The actual chord distance c between the same two points, either by chord or arc definition, is given by the relationship

$$c = 2 R \sin \tfrac{1}{2} d \qquad (9\text{-}17)$$

9-10. Deflection Angles to Points on Curve. The angle formed between the back tangent and a line from the P.C. to a point on the curve is the *deflection angle* to the point. This deflection angle, measured at the P.C. between the tangent and the line to the point, is one-half the central angle subtended between the P.C. and the point. This relationship comes directly from the geometry of a circle. An angle between a tangent and a chord is measured by one-half the intercepted arc, while the central angle is measured by the whole arc. Thus, in Fig. 9-6, the central angle d_1 between the P.C. at station $12 + 62.50$ and the first full station on the curve is $3°$, and the deflection angle $\tfrac{1}{2} d_1$ between the back tangent and the line directed to station $13 + 00$ is $1° 30'$. Similarly the central angle between the P.C. and the second full station on the curve is $d_1 + D = 3° + 8° = 11°$,

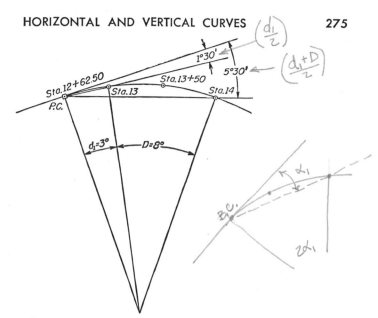

FIG. 9–6.   Deflection angles to points
on curve.

and the deflection angle, which is $\frac{1}{2} d_1 + \frac{1}{2} D$, is 5° 30'. If each half-station were to be located, then the deflection angle to station 13 + 50 in Fig. 9-6 would be $\frac{1}{2} d_1 + \frac{1}{4} D = 3°\ 30'$.

The deflection angle to each succeeding full station is obtained by adding the value $\frac{1}{2} D$ to the preceding deflection angle. To locate half-stations, $\frac{1}{4} D$ is added; to locate quarter-stations, $\frac{1}{8} D$ is added.

9-11. Curve Location. To locate the position of a simple curve in the field, the intersection angle Δ is measured. Based on an assumed value for one of the elements of the curve, the other elements and the stationing of the $P.C.$ and the $P.T.$ are computed. A table of deflection angles is prepared for locating full stations, half-stations, or quarter-stations. For any curve the final deflection angle should be checked against the full deflection angle $\frac{1}{2}$ Δ. With the transit still at the $P.I.$, the $P.C.$ and the $P.T.$ are located by laying off the tangent distance T.

The transit is next set up at the $P.C.$ and a backsight is taken along the back tangent toward the $P.I.$ The first deflection angle $\frac{1}{2} d_1$ is turned off, and the actual chord distance c_1 is laid off on the line of sight to locate the first curve station. When full stations are located, the second deflection angle $\frac{1}{2} d_1 + \frac{1}{2} D$ is turned off by setting the horizontal circle to this reading. The chord distance between the first and second curve stations is laid off by measuring from the first station, and the forward end of the chord is brought on the line

Computations for Circular Curve by Deflection Angles

$\Delta = 23° 18'$ $\tfrac{1}{2}\Delta = 11° 39'$ D (assumed) $= 4° 00'$ chord def.

$P.I.$ = station $50 + 53.87$
$T =$ $2 + 95.39$

(1) $R = \dfrac{50}{\sin \tfrac{1}{2}D}$

$P.C.$ = station $47 + 58.48$ (3)
$L =$ $5 + 82.50$

$\log 50 = 1.69\ 8970$
$\log \sin 2° 00' = 8.54\ 2819$

$P.T.$ = station $53 + 40.98$ (5)

$\log R = 3.15\ 6151$
$\log 2 = 0.30\ 1030$

$c'_1 = 41.52$ (6)
$c'_2 = 40.98$ (7)
$c_1 = 41.52$ (10)
$c_2 = 40.99$ (11)

(2) $\log 2R = 3.45\ 7181$
$T = R \tan \tfrac{1}{2}\Delta$
$\log R = 3.15\ 6151$
$\log \tan 11° 39' = 9.31\ 4247$

$\log T = 2.47\ 0398$
$T = 295.39$

Station	Deflection Angle (12)
$P.C.$ = $47 + 58.48$	$0° 00' 00''$
48	$0° 49' 49''$
49	$2° 49' 49''$
50	$4° 49' 49''$
51	$6° 49' 49''$
52	$8° 49' 49''$
53	$10° 49' 49''$
$P.T.$ = $53 + 40.98$	$11° 39' 00''$
	(checks $\tfrac{1}{2}\Delta$)

(4) $L = 100\dfrac{\Delta}{D} = \dfrac{2330}{4}$
$L = 582.50$

(8) $\tfrac{1}{2}d_1 = \dfrac{c'_1 D}{200}$
$\tfrac{1}{2}d_1 = 0° 49' 49''$

(9) $\tfrac{1}{2}d_2 = \dfrac{c'_2 D}{200}$
$\tfrac{1}{2}d_2 = 0° 49' 11''$

(10) $c_1 = 2R\sin\tfrac{1}{2}d_1$
$\log 2R = 3.45\ 7181$
$\log \sin 0° 49' 49'' = 8.16\ 1086$

$\log c_1 = 1.61\ 8267$

(11) $c_2 = 2R\sin\tfrac{1}{2}d_2$
$\log 2R = 3.45\ 7181$
$\log \sin 0° 49' 11'' = 8.15\ 5529$

$\log c_2 = 1.61\ 2710$

of sight. This procedure establishes the second curve station. Each station is located by a line of sight from the $P.C.$ and a chord distance from the preceding station, until the end of the curve is reached, or until a set-up on the curve becomes necessary. The previously located position of the $P.T.$ provides a check on the accuracy of the field work.

The complete computations for the curve shown in Fig. 9-1 are given in the above table. The order in which these computations are made is indicated by the numbers in parentheses. The deflection angles are computed more exactly than the angles can be turned off in the field. This is done to check the value of the final deflection angle, since it must agree with $\tfrac{1}{2}\Delta$. The curve is based on the chord definition for degree of curve.

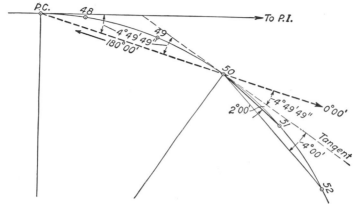

FIG. 9–7. Moving up on curve.

9-12. Moving up on Curve. It will happen frequently that, because of the length of the curve, or because of obstacles on the line, the entire curve cannot be staked out with the transit at the *P.C.* of the curve. If the transit is properly manipulated, it can be moved forward along the curve as many times as may be necessary, and the deflection angles previously computed can be used in staking out the remaining portions of the curve.

A portion of the curve for which the computations are tabulated on page 276 is shown in Fig. 9-7 to a distorted scale. Let it be assumed that the transit is moved to station 50, which has been located by turning off a deflection angle of 4° 49′ 49″ from the tangent at the *P.C.* If a backsight is taken on the *P.C.* with vernier *A* reading 180°, it is apparent that vernier *A* will read 4° 49′ 49″ when the line of sight is directed forward along the tangent at station 50. Since the angle between this tangent and the chord to station 51 is ½ *D*, or 2° 00′, vernier *A* will read 6° 49′ 49″ when the line of sight is directed along the chord to station 51. This reading of 6° 49′ 49″ is the previously computed deflection angle for station 51. The reading of 8° 49′ 49″, previously computed for station 52, will be the reading when the line of sight is directed along the chord from station 50 to station 52.

Thus, if the vernier is set at 180° and a backsight is taken on the *P.C.*, the previously computed deflection angles can be used in locating stations beyond the one occupied by the transit. From Fig. 9-7 it should be evident that, if a backsight is taken to any other station, vernier *A* should be set at 180° plus the deflection angle for that station, since the curve shown is to the right. For a curve to the left, the reading should be 180° minus the deflection angle for the station on which a backsight is taken.

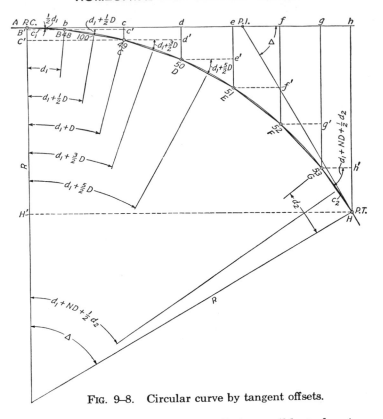

FIG. 9–8.   Circular curve by tangent offsets.

9-13. Curve by Tangent Offsets. It is possible to locate a curve on the ground by using only steel tapes. Although the precision attained will not be so great as when the transit is used, it will be sufficient for many purposes. The tangent-offset method can be used either with or without a transit, and can be used also in plotting a curve of large radius when a beam compass cannot be used conveniently.

The tangent-offset method of staking out a curve is illustrated in Fig. 9-8. The field work consists in locating temporary points, as b, c, d, and e, on the back tangent and determining stations on the curve by intersecting two arcs. The first point B at station 48 is located by using the $P.C.$ as a center and c_1 as the radius for one arc, and using b as a center and $bB = t_1$ as a radius for the second arc. The intersection of these two arcs determines the location of B, the first full station on the curve. This station is then used as a center, with 100 ft as a radius, and the arc thus located is intersected with a second arc struck with c as a center and cC as a radius. Each succeeding station is located by using the preceding station as a center and 100 ft as a radius for one arc and intersecting that arc with one for which a point such as d, e, or f is the center and a distance such as dD, eE, or fF, is the radius. The field work can be checked by comparing the measured distance from the last full station to the $P.T.$ with the computed value of c_2, and by comparing the perpendicular offset hH from the tangent to the $P.T.$ with the computed value of this offset.

When the transit is used, the temporary points such as b, c, and d can be lined in with the instrument; otherwise, they are lined in by eye. The deflection angle at the $P.I.$ can be measured by the method described in Sec. 6-2, in case a transit is not available.

The tangent offsets and the distances along the tangent can be computed in two ways. The offset at the first station on the curve, or station 48, is $bB = AB' = R$ vers d_1, and the distance along the tangent is $Ab = B'B = R \sin d_1$; or, $bB = c_1 \sin \frac{1}{2} d_1 = c_1^2/2R$, and $Ab = c_1 \cos \frac{1}{2} d_1$. At station 49, $cC = AC' = R$ vers $(d_1 + D)$, and $Ac = C'C = R \sin (d_1 + D)$; or, $cC = cc' + c'C = bB + c'C = c_1 \sin \frac{1}{2} d_1 + 100 \sin (d_1 + \frac{1}{2} D)$, and $Ac = Ab + bc = Ab + Bc' = c_1 \cos \frac{1}{2} d_1 + 100 \cos (d_1 + \frac{1}{2} D)$. The second method is preferable, since a check is provided on the computations of the offsets and tangent distances. The last offset, or that to the $P.T.$, is $hH = bB + c'C + d'D + \ldots + h'H = AH' = R$ vers Δ, and the tangent distance $Ah = Ab + Bc' + Cd' + \ldots + Gh' = H'H = R \sin \Delta$.

9-14. Intersection of Curve and Straight Line. One of the common problems in right-of-way surveys is the intersection of a straight line with a curve. Thus, in Fig. 9-9, DG represents a property line intersected by the curve ABC. When the curve is flat, the intersection B can be located on the ground by setting points at E and F on the curve on both sides of the intersection and close enough together so that no appreciable error will be introduced by considering the curve to be a straight line between these two points. The point B is found at the intersection of the chord EF and the property line DG.

The intersection can be obtained mathematically if the distance AV' and the angle $GV'V$ are measured on the ground. The figure $V'BOA$ can be considered as a traverse with two missing quantities, the length $V'B$ and the direction of the line BO. These values can be calculated by the methods of Sec. 8-32. From the computed direction, the central angle AOB and the station of B on the curve can be calculated.

A second mathematical solution will be apparent from the following relationships. In Fig. 9-9, angle $GV'V$ = angle $DV'A$ = angle $IOA = a$. In triangle AOH, $AH = R \sin a$ and $OH = R \cos a$. In tri-

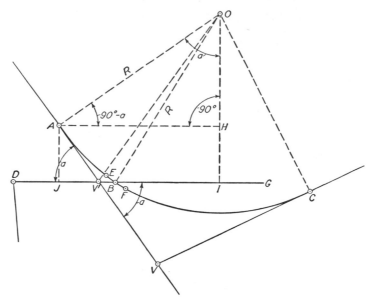

FIG. 9-9.   Intersection of curve and straight line.

angle $AV'J$, $V'J = AV' \cos a$ and $AJ = AV' \sin a$. Also, $V'I = AH - V'J$, $OI = OH + AJ$, $\cos IOB = OI/R$, $\tan IOV' = V'I/OI$, $BI = R \sin IOB$, $V'B = V'I - BI$, and angle $AOB =$ angle $AOI -$ angle IOB. When these computations have been completed, B may be located by measuring the computed distance $V'B$ along $V'G$, or by means of a deflection angle and a chord measured from the $P.C.$ of the curve. The length of the chord AB is $2\,R \sin \frac{1}{2}\,AOB$.

The problem of intersecting a line with a curve can be solved by the methods given in Sec. 8-23 if the line and the curve are both on a coordinate system.

9-15. Vertical Curves. When the grade line of a highway or a railroad changes grade, provision must be made for a vehicle to negotiate this transition smoothly and to provide vision over the crest of a hill far enough ahead to give the operator of the vehicle ample time to react to a dangerous situation. The parabola is most commonly used for connecting two different grades, in order to provide for this transition. It is easy to compute elevations on a parabola, and such a curve also provides a constant rate of change of grade. The results of the vertical-curve computations are the grade elevations at selected points along a route from the beginning of the curve to its end. These elevations are used, in turn, to control grading operations when the roadbed is to be brought to the desired grade by excavation and the construction of embankments.

The length of a vertical curve in 100-ft stations is designated as L and is measured along the horizontal. The two grades in the direction of stationing are g_1 and g_2. The total change in grade is $(g_2 - g_1)$. The rate of change of grade per station, designated as r, is found by dividing the total change in grade by the length of the curve in stations. Thus,

$$r = \frac{g_2 - g_1}{L} \qquad (9\text{-}18)$$

where r = rate of change of grade per station;
   g_1 = initial grade, in per cent;
   g_2 = final grade, in per cent;
   L = length of the curve, in stations.

When r is specified, the required length L is found by the relationship

$$L = \frac{g_2 - g_1}{r} \qquad (9\text{-}19)$$

If two given grades are to be connected by a vertical curve, then either r or L must be assumed and the other value is computed. The sharpness of a vertical curve in railroad location is usually defined by the allowable rate of change of grade.

When a vertical curve is laid out so that the intersection of the grade lines, called the point of grade intersection and designated as V, lies midway between the two ends of the curve measured horizontally, then the vertical curve is called an *equal-tangent* parabolic vertical curve.

Two methods are available for computing the elements of a vertical curve. The first method, presented in Sec. 9-16, treats the curve analytically. By this method, problems involving high and low points on the curve, vertical clearance, and curve intersections can be dealt with most efficiently. Also, the analytic method can be adapted to computer programming very easily. The second method, presented in Sec. 9-17, is somewhat more easily applied for simple vertical-curve problems. It takes advantage of the geometric properties of the parabola. The solution of a complicated curve problem, however, is more difficult by the geometric method.

9-16. Vertical Curves by Equation of Parabola. As shown in Fig. 9-10, the beginning of a vertical curve is designated as *B.V.C.*, the intersection of the tangents as V, and the end of the vertical curve as *E.V.C.* The initial grade is g_1 and the final grade is g_2.

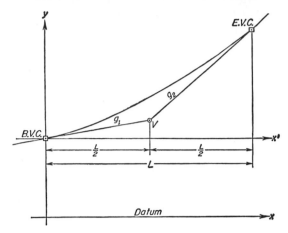

FIG. 9–10. Parabola with rectangular-coordinate axes.

The y-values are elevations in feet, and the x-values are stations beyond the $B.V.C.$ The y-axis is passed through the $B.V.C.$, and the x-axis lies on the datum. The equation of a parabola with the axis in the y-direction is

$$y = ax^2 + bx + c \qquad (9\text{-}20)$$

When $x = 0$, y is the elevation of the $B.V.C.$ Therefore, c is the elevation of the $B.V.C.$, and Eq. 9-20 becomes

$$y = ax^2 + bx + (\text{elev. of } B.V.C.) \qquad (9\text{-}21)$$

The first derivative of y with respect to x from Eq. 9-20 is

$$\frac{dy}{dx} = 2ax + b \qquad (9\text{-}22)$$

When $x = 0$, the slope of the curve is g_1. Since this slope equals the first derivative of the curve at $x = 0$, it follows that $b = g_1$. Equation 9-20 then becomes

$$y = ax^2 + g_1x + (\text{elev. of } B.V.C.) \qquad (9\text{-}23)$$

The second derivative is the rate of change of slope or grade of the curve. So $2a = r$, and Eq. 9-20 becomes

$$y = \frac{r}{2} x^2 + g_1x + (\text{elev. of } B.V.C.) \qquad (9\text{-}24)$$

which is the equation of the equal-tangent parabolic vertical curve used to connect two grades. In Eq. 9-24, y is the elevation of a point on the curve, and x is the distance in stations between the $B.V.C.$ and the point. If the elevations of the points above or below the $B.V.C.$

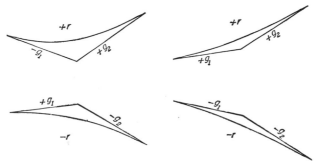

FIG. 9–11. Algebraic signs of r.

are desired, the x-axis becomes the x'-axis, as shown in Fig. 9-10, and c becomes 0. For these conditions,

$$y' = \frac{r}{2} x^2 + g_1 x \qquad (9\text{-}25)$$

The value of r must be assigned its proper algebraic sign. Equation 9-18 gives the algebraic sign directly. In Fig. 9-11, it is seen that if the vertical curve opens upward, r is plus; and if it opens downward, r is minus.

EXAMPLE 9-1. Two grades, for which $g_1 = +1.25$ per cent and $g_2 = -2.75$ per cent, intersect at station $18 + 00$, and the elevation of the intersection is 886.10 ft. If the length of the curve is to be 600 ft, what are the elevations of the B.V.C., the E.V.C., and all full stations on the curve?

Solution: See Fig. 9-12. The B.V.C. is at station 15, and the E.V.C. is at station 21. The elevation of the B.V.C. is obtained by going backward along grade g_1 from the point of intersection for a distance of 300 ft. The elevation of the

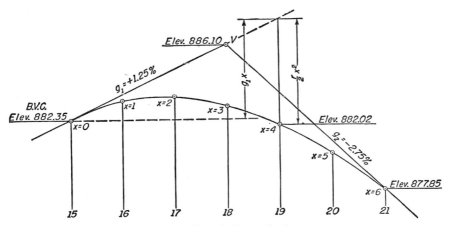

FIG. 9–12. Parabolic vertical curve.

E.V.C. is obtained by going forward from the point of intersection along grade g_2 for 300 ft. The computations follow:

$$\text{Elev. } B.V.C. = 886.10 - 3 \times 1.25 = 882.35 \text{ ft}$$

$$\text{Elev. } E.V.C. = 886.10 - 3 \times 2.75 = 877.85 \text{ ft}$$

By Eq. 9-18, the change of grade per station is

$$r = \frac{-2.75 - 1.25}{6} = -0.667 \text{ per cent}$$

The equation of the curve is $y = -0.333\, x^2 + 1.25\, x + 882.35$.

The elevations of the points on the curve are computed by preparing the accompanying table. Note that the elevation of a point is the sum of the values in the fourth, fifth, and sixth columns of the table.

COMPUTATIONS FOR VERTICAL CURVE BY EQUATION OF PARABOLA

Station	x	x^2	$\dfrac{r}{2} x^2$	$g_1 x$	Elev. B.V.C.	Elev. Curve
B.V.C. = 15	0	0	0	0	882.35	882.35
16	1	1	− 0.33	+ 1.25	882.35	883.27
17	2	4	− 1.33	+ 2.50	882.35	883.52
18	3	9	− 3.00	+ 3.75	882.35	883.10
19	4	16	− 5.33	+ 5.00	882.35	882.02
20	5	25	− 8.33	+ 6.25	882.35	880.27
E.V.C. = 21	6	36	− 12.00	+ 7.50	882.35	877.85

9-17. Vertical Curves by Tangent Offsets from Grade Lines. Three properties of an equal-tangent vertical curve are as follows:

1) The offsets from the tangent to the curve at a point are proportional to the squares of the horizontal distances from the point.

2) Offsets from the two grade lines are symmetrical with respect to the point of intersection of the two grade lines.

3) The curve lies midway between the point of intersection of the grade lines and the middle point of the chord joining the *B.V.C.* and the *E.V.C.*

Proof of these properties is left to the reader.

In Fig. 9-13, by the first property, $bB = 4\ aA$; $cC = 9\ aA$; $OV = 16\ aA$; $eE = 4\ fF$; $dD = 9\ fF$; $OV = 16\ fF$. By the second property, $aA = fF$; $bB = eE$; $cC = dD$. By the third property, $MO = OV$, or $OV = \frac{1}{2} MV$. The distance MV is obtained by subtracting the elevation of V from the elevation of M. The elevation of M is the mean of the elevations of the *B.V.C.* and the *E.V.C.*, since it lies at the middle point of the chord joining the two points. The elevations of points A, B, C, D, E, and F, the *B.V.C.*, and the *E.V.C.* are computed from the assigned grades of the two tangents. By employing the properties of the curve, the elevations of the points on the curve can then be computed.

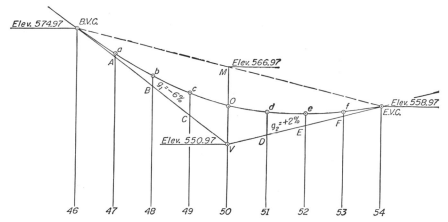

Fig. 9–13. Properties of the vertical curve.

EXAMPLE 9-2. For the two grade lines of Fig. 9-13, $g_1 = -6$ per cent and $g_2 = +2$ per cent. The elevation of the intersection of the grade lines at station 50 is 550.97 ft. The length of the curve is 800 ft. Compute the stations and elevations of the B.V.C. and the E.V.C. and the elevations at all other stations on the curve.

Solution: The computations may be arranged as follows:

Station of $B.V.C. = 50 - 4 =$ station 46
Elev. of $B.V.C. = 550.97 + 4 \times 6 = 574.97$ ft
Station of $E.V.C. = 50 + 4 =$ station 54
Elev. of $E.V.C. = 550.97 + 4 \times 2 = 558.97$ ft

$$\text{Elev. of middle point of chord} = \frac{574.97 + 558.97}{2} = 566.97 \text{ ft}$$

$$\text{Offset to curve at intersection} = \frac{566.97 - 550.97}{2} = 8.00 \text{ ft} = VO$$

Offset at A and $F = (\frac{1}{4})^2 \times 8.00 = 0.50$ ft
Offset at B and $E = (\frac{2}{4})^2 \times 8.00 = 2.00$ ft
Offset at C and $D = (\frac{3}{4})^2 \times 8.00 = 4.50$ ft
Elev. of $A = 574.97 - 6.00 = 568.97$ ft
Elev. of $B = 568.97 - 6.00 = 562.97$ ft
Elev. of $C = 562.97 - 6.00 = 556.97$ ft
Elev. of $V = 556.97 - 6.00 = 550.97$ ft
Elev. of $F = 558.97 - 2.00 = 556.97$ ft
Elev. of $E = 556.97 - 2.00 = 554.97$ ft
Elev. of $D = 554.97 - 2.00 = 552.97$ ft
Elev. of $V = 552.97 - 2.00 = 550.97$ ft (check)
Elev. of $a =$ station $47 = 568.97 + 0.50 = 569.47$ ft
Elev. of $b =$ station $48 = 562.97 + 2.00 = 564.97$ ft
Elev. of $c =$ station $49 = 556.97 + 4.50 = 561.47$ ft
Elev. of $o =$ station $50 = 550.97 + 8.00 = 558.97$ ft
Elev. of $d =$ station $51 = 552.97 + 4.50 = 557.47$ ft
Elev. of $e =$ station $52 = 554.97 + 2.00 = 556.97$ ft
Elev. of $f =$ station $53 = 556.97 + 0.50 = 557.47$ ft

The foregoing computations should be arranged as shown in the accompanying tabulation.

COMPUTATIONS FOR VERTICAL CURVE BY OFFSETS FROM BOTH TANGENTS

Station	Tangent Elev.	Offset from Tangent	Elev. Curve
B.V.C. = 46	574.97	0	574.97
47	568.97	+ 0.50	569.47
48	562.97	+ 2.00	564.97
49	556.97	+ 4.50	561.47
50	550.97	+ 8.00	558.97
51	552.97	+ 4.50	557.47
52	554.97	+ 2.00	556.97
53	556.97	+ 0.50	557.47
E.V.C. = 54	558.97	0	558.97

9-18. Intermediate Points on Vertical Curves. Occasions will frequently arise where the elevations of points on vertical curves must be computed at intervals of 50 ft, 25 ft, or even 10 ft. Also the elevations of random points on the curve are quite frequently necessary. The most direct way of computing the elevations of these intermediate points is by use of Eq. 9-24 where x is the station or plus beyond the B.V.C. and y is the elevation of the point in feet. In Example 9-1, if the elevation of station 17 + 22.33 is desired, then $x = 2.2233$ stations beyond the B.V.C. The elevation of station 17 + 22.33 is, therefore,

$$y = (- 0.333)(2.2233)^2 + (1.25)(2.2233) + 882.35 = 883.48 \text{ ft}$$

The elevation of an intermediate point can be computed by the tangent-offset method, although not quite so readily as by using the equation of the curve. In Example 9-2, the elevation of station 49 + 52 is obtained by first computing the tangent elevation at the station and then by computing the tangent offset at the station. The tangent elevation is $574.97 - (3.52)(6) = 553.85$ ft. The tangent offset is $(3.52/4)^2 \times 8.00 = 6.20$ ft. Therefore the elevation of the curve at station 49 + 52 is $553.85 + 6.20 = 560.05$ ft.

9-19. Location of Highest or Lowest Point. When g_1 and g_2 have opposite algebraic signs, either a high point or a low point will occur between the B.V.C. and the E.V.C. Furthermore, this point may not fall on a full station or on a previously selected point. Sometimes it is necessary to determine the station and elevation of the high point or the low point, in order to locate a clearance point, a drainage structure, or some other feature. The tangent to the curve at this point will be a horizontal line, that is, the slope of the curve will be zero. The position of the point can be determined, then, by equating to zero the first derivative of Eq. 9-24. For the high or low point,

$$\frac{dy}{dx} = rx + g_1 = 0$$

or

$$x = -\frac{g_1}{r} \tag{9-26}$$

The value of x in Eq. 9-26 is the distance in stations from the $B.V.C.$ to the high or low point. The elevation of the point is found by substituting the value of x obtained from Eq. 9-26 in Eq. 9-24, and solving for y.

The high point of the curve of Example 9-1 occurs at $x = 1.25/0.666 = 1.875$ stations beyond the $B.V.C.$ Thus, the summit is at station $16 + 87.5$. The elevation at the point is 883.52 ft.

In Example 9-2, the value of r found by Eq. 9-18 is $[2 - (-6)]/8 = + 1.00$, and the low point occurs at $x = 6/1.00 = 6$ stations beyond the $B.V.C.$ It is at station 52 where the elevation was previously computed.

9-20. Minimum Length of Vertical Curve. The length of a vertical curve on a highway should be ample to provide a clear sight which is sufficiently long to prevent accidents. The American Association of State Highway Officials (AASHO) has developed criteria for the distance required to pass another vehicle traveling in the same direction on a vertical curve and also for the distance required to stop a vehicle in an emergency. The former distance, called the safe passing sight distance and designated as S_{sp}, is based on the assumptions that the eyes of the driver of a vehicle are about 3.75 ft above the payment and the top of an on-coming vehicle is about 4.50 ft above the pavement. The latter required distance, called the safe stopping sight distance and designated as S_{np}, is based on the assumption that an obstruction ahead of the vehicle is 0.50 ft above the pavement. The values of S_{sp} and S_{np} are given in Table 9-1.

TABLE 9-1

AASHO Sight-Distance Recommendations

Design Speed (mph)	S_{sp} (ft)	S_{np} (ft)
30	800	200
40	1300	275
50	1700	350
60	2000	475
70	2300	600

If it is assumed that the safe passing sight distance is less than the length L of the curve, then

$$L = \frac{S^2_{sp} (g_1 - g_2)}{33.0} \tag{9-27}$$

where distances are in feet and g_1 and g_2 are expressed as ratios. If it is assumed that S_{sp} is longer than the curve, then

$$L = 2 S_{sp} - \frac{33.0}{g_1 - g_2} \tag{9-28}$$

If the safe stopping sight distance is less than the length of the curve, then

$$L = \frac{S^2_{np} (g_1 - g_2)}{14.0} \tag{9-29}$$

If S_{np} is longer than the curve, then

$$L = 2 S_{np} - \frac{14.0}{g_1 - g_2} \tag{9-30}$$

On a highway with four or more traffic lanes, the safe stopping sight distance can be used to determine the required length of a vertical curve, because there is little probability of meeting oncoming vehicles in the passing lane. On a two-lane highway, however, the safe passing sight distance must be used if a vehicle is permitted to pass another one traveling in the same direction on the vertical curve. Use of the safe passing sight distance results in excessive lengths of vertical curves, and in most instances causes excessive excavation. (See Chapter 16.) Two methods are employed on two-lane roads to allow the safe stopping sight distance to be used for computing L. One method is to prohibit passing on crests and to indicate the restriction by appropriate center-line marking. The second method is to widen the pavement at the crest to permit two lanes in both directions for a sufficient distance.

EXAMPLE 9-3. The grades at a crest are $g_1 = + 2$ per cent and $g_2 = - 3$ per cent, and the design speed is 60 mph. Compute the lengths of the vertical curves required for the safe passing sight distance and the safe stopping sight distance recommended by the AASHO.

Solution: By Eq. 9-27 and Table 9-1,

$$L = \frac{2000^2 \times 0.05}{33} = 6060 \text{ ft}$$

Also, by Eq. 9-28,

$$L = 2 \times 2000 - \frac{33}{0.05} = 3340 \text{ ft}$$

The length required for safe passing is therefore 6060 ft, since S_{sp} is less than L.

By Eq. 9-29,

$$L = \frac{475^2 \times 0.05}{14} = 806 \text{ ft}$$

Also, by Eq. 9-30,

$$L = 2 \times 475 - \frac{14}{0.05} = 670 \text{ ft}$$

The length required for safe stopping is thus 806 ft, since S_{np} is less than L.

In this example, it would not be necessary to apply Eq. 9-28 or Eq. 9-30 after it is found by Eq. 9-27 or 9-29 that the required sight distance is less than L.

9-21. Compound Curves. A compound curve consists of two or more consecutive circular arcs, the $P.T.$ of one curve being the $P.C.$ of the next and the centers of the curves being on the same side of the curve. Such a curve is shown in Fig. 9-14. While it is beyond the scope of this text to go deeply into the problems of compound curves, it may be pointed out that many of the compound-curve equations can be developed by considering the polygon *1-2-3-4-5* in Fig. 9-14 as a five-sided traverse.

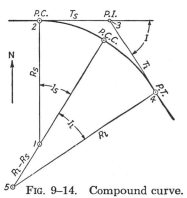

FIG. 9–14. Compound curve.

The values for this traverse are shown in Table 9-2.

TABLE 9-2

BASIS OF EQUATIONS FOR COMPOUND CURVES

Side	Azimuth	Length	Departures		Latitudes	
			E	W	N	S
1-2	$0°$	R_s	0		R_s	
2-3	$90°$	T_s	T_s			0
3-4	$90° + I$	T_l	$T_l \cos I$			$T_l \sin I$
4-5	$180° + I$	R_l		$R_l \sin I$		$R_l \cos I$
5-1	I_s	$R_l - R_s$	$(R_l - R_s) \sin I_s$		$(R_l - R_s) \cos I_s$	

Since the traverse is a closed one, the algebraic sums of the latitudes and departures must equal zero. From the departures,

$$T_s + T_l \cos I - R_l \sin I + (R_l - R_s) \sin I_s = 0 \qquad (9\text{-}31)$$

From the latitudes, north latitudes being considered negative for convenience, $- R_s + T_l \sin I + R_l \cos I - (R_l - R_s) \cos I_s = 0$. If R_l is added and subtracted, this equation can be written

$$(R_l - R_s) - (R_l - R_s) \cos I_s + T_l \sin I - (R_l - R_l \cos I) = 0 \qquad (9\text{-}32)$$

Since $1 - \cos a = \text{vers } a$, this reduces to

$$(R_l - R_s) \text{ vers } I_s + T_l \sin I - R_l \text{ vers } I = 0 \qquad (9\text{-}33)$$

From Eqs. 9-31 and 9-32 or 9-33 and the relation $I = I_s + I_l$, the values of T_s, I_l, and I_s can be found when I, T_l, R_s, and R_l are known. For a complete discussion of compound curves, you should consult a text on route surveying.

9-22. Reversed Curves. A reversed curve is composed of two simple curves turning in opposite directions, as shown in Fig. 9-15. The point of reverse curve, $P.R.C.$, is the $P.T.$ of the first curve and the $P.C.$ of the second one.

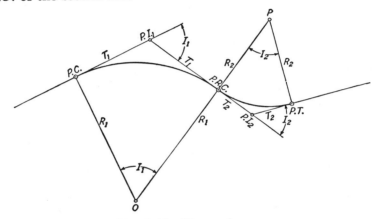

FIG. 9–15. Reversed curve.

If the angles I_1 and I_2 and the distance between intersection points $P.I._1$ and $P.I._2$ have been measured in the field, one radius, or one degree of curve, can be assumed and the other calculated. If R_1 is assumed, the first tangent distance T_1 is computed from the relationship

$$T_1 = R_1 \tan \tfrac{1}{2} I_1$$

This length subtracted from the total distance between the intersection points gives the value of T_2. Then

$$R_2 = T_2 \cot \tfrac{1}{2} I_2$$

The use of reversed curves on railroads is limited to sidings and crossovers. The necessity of elevating the outer rail on a railroad, and the outer edge of a highway, prevents the use of reversed curves except where very low speeds are encountered.

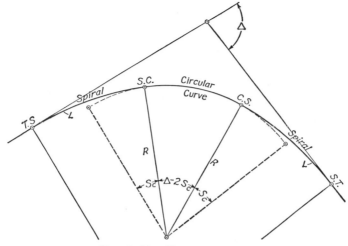

FIG. 9–16. Easement curve.

9-23. Easement Curves. The amount of superelevation, in feet per foot of width, on a curve can be determined from the equation

$$e = \frac{v^2}{32.2R} = 0.067\,\frac{V^2}{R} \qquad (9\text{-}34)$$

where v = velocity, in feet per second;
V = velocity, in miles per hour;
R = radius of the curve, in feet.

On a straight track or pavement, the two edges are at the same elevation. On a circular arc, the outer edge is elevated the proper amount for the radius of the curve and for the speed expected. These two requirements lead to an impossible condition at the *P.C.* of a simple curve, since the *P.C.* is both on the curve and on the tangent, and at the same point there should be superelevation for the curve and none for the tangent.

The introduction of a spiral easement, or transition, curve between the tangent and the circular arc, as indicated in Fig. 9-16, permits the gradual elevation of the outer edge. There are many curves which can be used as easement curves. However, the one recommended by the American Railway Engineering Association (A.R.E.A.) is probably as simple as any. With the aid of tables found in railroad engineering handbooks, the computations can be made almost as quickly as the computations for a simple curve.

The A.R.E.A. spiral is based on the assumption that the superelevation is to change at a uniform rate along the spiral. The equation of this curve is

$$y = \frac{l^3}{6RL}$$

where y = tangent offset at any point whose distance from the beginning point $T.S.$ (tangent to spiral) of the spiral is l;

R = radius of the circular arc;

L = length of the spiral.

The radius of this curve decreased from infinity at the $T.S.$ to R at the $S.C.$ (spiral to curve). Between the circular arc and the forward tangent is a second spiral whose ends are the $C.S.$ (curve to spiral) and the $S.T.$ (spiral to tangent).

The principal differences between the circular curve and the spiral are: The length of the spiral is twice the length of a circular arc with radius R and central angle S_c. In the case of the usual spiral, it is accurate enough for practical purposes to assume that the deflection angle from the tangent at the $T.S.$ to any point on the spiral is one-third (instead of one-half) the central angle subtended by the chord from the $T.S.$ to the point. The deflection angles are proportional to the squares of the distances along the spiral (rather than to the distances themselves, as in the case of the circular curve).

For the development of spirals and their applications, you should refer to Meyer's *Route Surveying*, or Skelton's *Route Surveys*. These texts contain tables which simplify the field computations.

PROBLEMS

9-1. A circular curve is to connect two tangents that intersect at an angle Δ of 29° 14′ at station 56 + 42.32. The tangent distance must be less than 425 ft. Using the chord definition, determine the degree (to the nearest 30′) of the flattest possible curve which will satisfy the conditions. Compute the deflection angle to each full curve station.

9-2. A circular curve is to join two tangents that intersect at an angle Δ of 19° 15′ at station 32 + 20.44. Using the arc definition, compute the radius (to a full 100 ft) of the flattest possible curve for which the external distance does not exceed 50 ft. Compute the deflection angle to each full curve station. Compute the length of the chord joining two successive 100-ft stations.

9-3. The length of a circular curve is not to exceed 350 ft. The two tangents intersect at station 58 + 46.32 and make a deflection angle Δ of 41° 20′ with each other. Using the arc definition, compute the degree (to the nearest 30′) of the flattest possible curve that will join the two tangents. Compute T, E, M, and C for this curve.

9-4. A circular curve is to be located by offsets from the tangent, as discussed in Sec. 9-13. The degree of curve (chord definition) is 2° 30′. The deflection angle to the $P.T.$ at station 24 + 89.60 is 16° 22′. Compute the distance along the tangent and the offset necessary to locate each curve station.

9-5. Compute the chord length to the nearest 0.001 ft joining two adjacent full stations on a circular curve *a*) when the degree (by arc definition) is 15°; *b*) when it is 10°; *c*) when it is 5°.

9-6. Compute the chord length to the nearest 0.001 ft joining station 20 and station 20 + 50 *a*) when the degree of curve by chord definition is 15°; *b*) when it is 10°; *c*) when it is 5°.

9-7. The *P.C.* of a circular curve is located at station 63 + 52.45. The degree of curve *D* is 2° 30′. The curve is to be located by deflection angles. Stations 64 to 68 can be located with the transit set up at the *P.C.* Because of an obstruction beyond station 68, the transit must be moved up to occupy station 68 in order to locate the remainder of the curve. If a backsight of 0° 00′ is taken on the *P.C.* with the telescope inverted and the telescope is then plunged back to normal, what deflection angles should be turned to locate stations 69, 70, 71, and 71 + 56.30, which is the *P.T.?*

9-8. In Fig. 9-9, $\Delta = 38°$ 16′; $D = 4°$ 00′ (by arc definition); the *P.C.* at *A* is at station 12 + 46.66; $AV' = 388.49$ ft; and angle $GV'V = 62°$ 12′. Compute $V'B$ and the stationing of *B* on the curve.

9-9. A vertical curve joining two grade lines is to be 900 ft long. Also, $g_1 = + 2.2$ per cent and $g_2 = - 3.0$ per cent. The intersection of the grade lines at station 60 is at elevation 763.66 ft. Compute the elevation at each half-station on the curve.

9-10. Compute the station and elevation of the summit of the curve in Problem 9-9.

9-11. A 1600-ft vertical curve is to join two grades for which $g_1 = - 2.8$ per cent and $g_2 = + 1.9$ per cent. The intersection is at station 154 + 16.50 and at elevation 1566.40 ft. Compute the stationing and elevation of the low point of the curve. Compute the elevations of stations 150 and 160.

9-12. At what station or stations on the curve in Problem 9-11 is the elevation 1580.00 ft?

9-13. A grade g_1 of $- 3$ per cent passes station 40 at an elevation of 456.20 ft, and a grade g_2 of $+ 2.5$ per cent passes station 70 at an elevation of 502.60 ft. Compute the station and elevation of the point of intersection of these two grades. (The point-slope form of the equation of a line may be used.) Compute the elevations of the *B.V.C.*, the *E.V.C.*, and each full station of an 800-ft curve joining these two grades.

9-14. If g_1 is $+ 3.75$ per cent and g_2 is $- 2.25$ per cent, compute the minimum length of a vertical curve necessary to provide the safe passing sight distance for a design speed of 50 mph. Compute the length necessary to provide the safe stopping sight distance for a design speed of 70 mph.

9-15. In Fig. 9-14, $T_s = 250$ ft; $R_s = 360$ ft; $I_s = 20°$ 30′; $I = 45°$ 00′; and the *P.I.* is at station 42 + 25.50. Using the chord definition for degree of curve, compute T_l, R_l, I_l, and the station numbers of the *P.C.C.* and the *P.T.*

9-16. A pavement 60 ft wide is to be superelevated to allow safe negotiation of a 3° circular curve (arc definition) at the design speed of 60 mph. What will be the theoretical difference in elevation between opposite edges of the pavement?

10

Triangulation

10-1. Basis of Triangulation. The method of surveying called triangulation is based on the trigonometric proposition that, if one side and the three angles of a triangle are known, the remaining sides can be computed. Furthermore, if the direction of one side is known, the directions of the remaining sides can be determined.

The methods of triangulation are quite demanding. They require a considerable amount of precise angle measurement with a minimum amount of distance measurement. The triangles are developed into a net of interconnected figures, and certain lines, called base lines, must be measured in order to compute the lengths of the other lines in the net. The base lines must be measured with extreme precision, since errors propagated through the system originate with these measured lines.

In order to eliminate the effects of random errors as much as possible, triangulation systems always include more than the minimum number of measurements necessary to fix the positions of the points in the triangulation net. These extra, or redundant, measurements provide the data necessary for the adjustment of the net, usually by the method of least squares.

Triangulation nets are of two types. One is the arc or chain type, which is shown in Fig. 10-1. This is the type used for the main horizontal control net of the nation. The other is the area triangulation net, which is shown in Fig. 18-1 on page 587, especially in the southeasterly portion. An area net is usually developed for county and municipal surveys and is invariably tied to arc triangulation to establish the overall position and orientation of the net.

10-2. Purposes of Triangulation. Triangulation as a form of horizontal control is applied when a large area is to be surveyed, and where the methods of traversing would not be expected to maintain a uniformly high accuracy over the entire area. Thus, the United States Coast and Geodetic Survey employs triangulation to establish

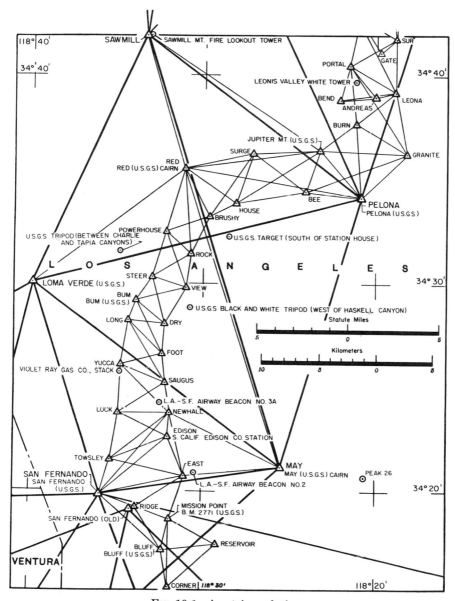

FIG. 10-1. Arc triangulation.

a basic network of high-order control throughout the country. Also, the United States Geological Survey uses triangulation to form the control necessary for its national mapping activities.

Triangulation is employed in every sizable city to form a network of consistently accurate control monuments from which the city and private engineers can work in locating streets and utilities. Triangulation is necessary to control the locations of large bridge structures, state and federal highways, dams, canals, and other engineering works of a massive nature. A large project, such as boundary location, power development, water-resources development, flood control, irrigation, or reclamation, requires triangulation in order to maintain the necessary accuracy throughout the system.

Once a triangulation system, whether large or small, has been developed, measured, and adjusted, the points in the system then furnish control for subsequent traversing and minor triangulation needed for day-to-day engineering operations.

10-3. Classes of Triangulation. Triangulation surveys are executed under varying field standards of accuracy. The standards for a particular survey depend on the purpose of the survey. The United States Bureau of the Budget has developed criteria for different classes of triangulation to correspond to their functions. The classification has been made in consultation with the U.S. Coast and Geodetic Survey, the U.S. Geological Survey, the Bureau of Land Management, the U.S. Forest Service, the U.S. Soil Conservation Service, the U.S. Defense Department, the American Society of Civil Engineers, and the American Congress on Surveying and Mapping, as well as with public and private organizations and individuals engaged in control surveys throughout the country.

There are three orders of accuracy, namely, first, second, and third. First order is the highest accuracy. It is, in turn, broken down into three classes. Class I, which is the most accurate, applies to highly developed urban land, to measurements of small crustal movements of the earth in earthquake areas, and to concentrated nets used for measuring the performance of space vehicles, ballistic systems, electronic measuring systems, precision cameras, and other engineering and scientific developments requiring high precision over moderately large distances.

First-order triangulation of class II is used to develop the basic network of horizontal control throughout the United States. This network consists of triangulation arcs spaced at intervals of approximately 60 miles in each direction. Thus, when this network is completed, no point in the country should be more than 25 or 30 miles from a first order, class II triangulation station.

First-order, class III triangulation is the former primary triangulation classification, which was later called first order with no class designation. A great deal of the triangulation which exists in the national network is of first order, class III accuracy. This class is applicable to large highway and water-development projects, county-wide control nets, and surveys for bridge and dam location, where a high degree of accuracy must be maintained over fairly great distances but the tolerances are more liberal than those of the national net.

Second-order triangulation is subdivided into class I and class II. Class I applies to the national control used to fill in between the large national arcs. It is usually planned as area triangulation in which the triangulation stations are uniformly dispersed over the area. Because of topographic limitations, however, it can also be developed as small arcs or chains of triangles crossing between the main arcs in both directions.

Second-order, class II triangulation is very important to the engineer, as it is the lowest classification permissible for designating points on the state plane coordinate systems. See Chapter 11. It also is the criterion for establishing control for hydrographic surveys along the shore line and inland waterways.

Third-order triangulation has only one class designation. It is adopted for the control of topographic mapping, and is tied directly to the triangulation control of higher order.

The requirements for the different orders of accuracy are given in Table 10-1. The significance of strength of figures indicated in the table is presented in Sec. 10-5. The significance of the side check and that of the closure in length are given in Sec. 10-29 and Sec. 10-30.

10-4. Reconnaissance. The success of any triangulation depends to a great extent on the reconnaissance, which is the most difficult and exacting task of an extensive survey. Although no two regions call for exactly the same treatment, certain general principles apply to all such work. The reconnaissance preliminary to minor triangulation for some isolated project may be very simple. Reconnaissance for triangulation of the largest size is a matter of much complexity and demands skill, experience, and judgment.

During the reconnaissance the sites for the future stations are selected and all information that will be valuable in the operations of the building and observing parties is collected. Heavily wooded country is the most difficult in which to carry on triangulation. A valley of proper width, with peaks on either side, is the most favorable. The stations are located on the higher points, provided their locations will give the best-shaped triangles. The ideal location is one in which low towers can be used and where there is little or no clearing to be done. A most important and difficult part of the reconnaissance is the determination of the heights of the towers necessary to make the line

TABLE 10-1
CLASSIFICATION OF TRIANGULATION SYSTEMS

	First Order		Class III (Standard)	Second Order		Third Order
	Class I (Special)	Class II (Optimum)		Class I	Class II	
Spacing of arcs or principal stations	Stations: 1 to 5 miles or greater as required	Arcs: 60 miles; Stations: 10 to 15 miles	Stations: 10 to 15 miles	Stations: 4 to 10 miles	As required	As required
Strength of figure: ΣR_1 between bases						
Desirable limit	25	60	80	80	100	125
Maximum limit	30	80	110	120	130	175
Single figure Desirable limit						
R_1	5	10	15	15	25	25
R_2	10	30	50	70	80	120
Maximum limit						
R_1	10	25	25	25	40	50
R_2	15	60	80	100	120	170
Base Measurement:						
Actual error not to exceed	1 part in 300,000	1 part in 300,000	1 part in 300,000	1 part in 300,000	1 part in 150,000	1 part in 75,000
Probable error not to exceed	1 part in 1,000,000	1 part in 1,000,000	1 part in 1,000,000	1 part in 1,000,000	1 part in 500,000	1 part in 250,000
Triangle closure:						
Average not to exceed	1"	1"	1"	1.5"	3"	5"
Maximum seldom to exceed	3"	3"	3"	5"	5"	10"
Side check: Ratio of maximum difference of logs of sides to tab. diff. for 1" of log sine of smallest angle	1.5	1.5 to 2	2	2 to 4	4	10 to 12
Astronomic azimuth:						
Spacing (figures)	6 to 8	6 to 10	8 to 10	8 to 10	10 to 12	12 to 15
Probable error	0.3"	0.3"	0.3"	0.3"	0.5"	2.0"
Closure in length: Maximum after side and angle conditions have been satisfied	1 part in 100,000	1 part in 50,000	1 part in 25,000	1 part in 20,000	1 part in 10,000	1 part in 5,000

of sight between any two of them clear of all obstructions. A mistake on the part of the person making the reconnaissance may delay the large observing party an entire day while the line is being cleared, or higher towers are being erected. This will be particularly true on first-order and second-order work, as practically all the observing is done after dark.

10-5. Strength of Figure. Since computed lengths are likely to be uncertain when the sines of small angles are involved, no very small angles should be included in a triangulation scheme, if those angles are to be used in the computations. The U. S. Coast and Geodetic Survey employs a method of testing the precision that may be expected in any given case. This method is based on the probable error of a computed length. The square of the probable error E of the logarithm of a side of a figure is

$$E^2 = \frac{4}{3}\,(d^2)\,\frac{D-C}{D}\,\Sigma\,(\delta_A{}^2 + \delta_A\,\delta_B + \delta_B{}^2) \qquad (10\text{-}1)$$

where d = probable error of an observed direction;
D = number of directions observed in the figure;
C = number of conditions to be satisfied in the figure;
$\delta_A,\ \delta_B$ = respective logarithmic differences of the sines;
Σ = summation.

The respective logarithmic differences of the sines corresponding to a change of 1 second in the angles A and B used in the computation of the triangle are expressed in units of the sixth decimal place. The summation Σ is to be taken for the triangles used in computing the value of the side in question from the side supposed to be absolutely known.

In determining the value of D for any figure, the starting line is supposed to be completely fixed, and hence the directions observed along that line are not included. When all stations are occupied and all lines are observed, there will be two directions for all lines except the starting line. Thus, for a triangle, $D = 4$; and for a quadrilateral, shown in Fig. 10-2, $D = 10$.

The number of conditions C to be satisfied in any figure can be computed from the following relationship:

$$C = (n' - s' + 1) + (n - 2s + 3) \qquad (10\text{-}2)$$

where n = total number of lines;
n' = number of lines observed in both directions;
s = total number of stations;
s' = number of stations occupied.

Thus, for a triangle with all stations occupied, $C = (3 - 3 + 1) + (3 - 6 + 3) = 1$, as is to be expected, since the only condition involved in a triangle is that the sum of the three angles should equal $180°$. For a quadrilateral, with all stations occupied, $C = (6 - 4 + 1) + (6 - 8 + 3) = 4$.

In Eq. 10-1, the values of the two terms $(D - C)/D$ and $\Sigma(\delta_A{}^2 + \delta_A \delta_B + \delta_B{}^2)$ depend entirely on the figure chosen and are independent of the accuracy with which the angles are measured. The product of these two terms is, therefore, a measure of the strength of the figure with respect to length, in so far as the strength depends on the selection of stations and of lines over which observations are made. Hence, the strength of a figure is

$$R = \frac{D - C}{D} \Sigma (\delta_A{}^2 + \delta_A \delta_B + \delta_B{}^2) \qquad (10\text{-}3)$$

When a required distance can be computed through two or more chains of triangles, the strengths of the figures are designated by R_1 and R_2 for the best and second-best chains, respectively.

In Table 10-2 the values $(\delta_A{}^2 + \delta_A \delta_B + \delta_B{}^2)$ are tabulated. The two arguments of the table are the distance angles in degrees, the smaller distance angle being given at the top of the table. The distance angles are the angles in each triangle opposite the known side and the required side.

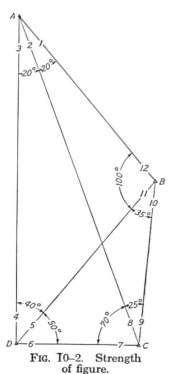

FIG. 10–2. Strength of figure.

If, in the quadrilateral shown in Fig. 10-2, the side AB is the known length, the side CD might be computed in four different ways. One solution would be first to find the side BD in the triangle ABD by using the distance angles $40°$ and $40°$. The required side CD could then be found from the triangle BCD by using the angles $95°$ and $35°$. In the quadrilateral there are a total of 12 directions, indicated by the numbered lines. Since the line AB is assumed fixed in direction and length, $D = 10$, $C = 4$, and $(D - C)/D = 0.60$. For convenience in illustrating the use of Table 10-2, the angles here given are in whole degrees. The strength of this figure is $0.60 \times (19 + 9) = 17$.

TABLE 10-2

Factors for Determining Strength of Figure

°	10°	12°	14°	16°	18°	20°	22°	24°	26°	28°	30°	35°	40°	45°	50°	55°	60°	65°	70°	75°	80°	85°	90°
10	428	359																					
12	359	295	253																				
14	315	253	214	187																			
16	284	225	187	162	143																		
18	262	204	168	143	126	113																	
20	245	189	153	130	113	100	91																
22	232	177	142	119	103	91	81	74															
24	221	167	134	111	95	83	74	67	61														
26	213	160	126	104	89	77	68	61	56	51													
28	206	153	120	99	83	72	63	57	51	47	43												
30	199	148	115	94	79	68	59	53	48	43	40	33											
35	188	137	106	85	71	60	52	46	41	37	33	27	23										
40	179	129	99	79	65	54	47	41	36	32	29	23	19	16									
45	172	124	93	74	60	50	43	37	32	28	25	20	16	13	11								
50	167	119	89	70	57	47	39	34	29	26	23	18	14	11	9	8							
55	162	115	86	67	54	44	37	32	27	24	21	16	12	10	8	7	5						
60	159	112	83	64	51	42	35	30	25	22	19	14	11	9	7	5	4	4					
65	155	109	80	62	49	40	33	28	24	21	18	13	10	7	6	5	4	3	2				
70	152	106	78	60	48	38	32	27	23	19	17	12	9	7	5	4	3	2	2	1			
75	150	104	76	58	46	37	30	25	21	18	16	11	8	6	4	3	2	2	1	1	1		
80	147	102	74	57	45	36	29	24	20	17	15	10	7	5	4	3	2	1	1	1	0	0	
85	145	100	73	55	43	34	28	23	19	16	14	10	7	5	3	2	2	1	1	0	0	0	0
90	143	98	71	54	42	33	27	22	19	16	13	9	6	4	3	2	1	1	1	0	0	0	0
95	140	96	70	53	41	32	26	22	18	15	13	9	6	4	3	2	1	1	0	0	0	0	
100	138	95	68	51	40	31	25	21	17	14	12	8	6	4	3	2	1	1	0	0	0		
105	136	93	67	50	39	30	25	20	17	14	12	8	5	4	2	2	1	1	0	0			
110	134	91	65	49	38	30	24	19	16	13	11	7	5	3	2	2	1	1	1				
115	132	89	64	48	37	29	23	19	15	13	11	7	5	3	2	2	1	1					
120	129	88	62	46	36	28	22	18	15	12	10	7	5	3	2	2	1						
125	127	86	61	45	35	27	22	18	14	12	10	7	5	4	3	2							
130	125	84	59	44	34	26	21	17	14	12	10	7	5	4	3								
135	122	82	58	43	33	26	21	17	14	12	10	7	5	4									
140	119	80	56	42	32	25	20	17	14	12	10	8	6										
145	116	77	55	41	32	25	21	17	15	13	11	9											
150	112	75	54	40	32	26	21	18	16	15	13												
152	111	75	53	40	32	26	22	19	17	16													
154	110	74	53	41	33	27	23	21	19														
156	105	74	54	42	34	28	25	22															
158	107	74	54	43	35	30	27																
160	107	74	56	45	35	33																	
162	107	76	59	48	42																		
164	109	79	63	54																			
166	113	86	71																				
168	122	98																					
170	143																						

The accompanying tabulation shows the strength of figure for all four sets of computations.

The values of R_1 and R_2 are 17 and 26, respectively. The value for R_1 is slightly above the desirable limit for a single figure in first-order, class III triangulation, as shown in Table 10-1, but is well below the maximum limit. This figure could be strengthened by shortening the line AD and thus increasing each angle at station A.

COMPUTATIONS FOR STRENGTH OF FIGURE

Triangle	Known Side	Computed Side	Distance Angles		$\delta_A{}^2 + \delta_A\delta_B + \delta_B{}^2$
ABD	AB	BD	40°	40°	19
BCD	BD	CD	95°	35°	9
					$\overline{28} \times 0.6 = 17 = R_1$
ABC	AB	AC	25°	135°	15
ACD	AC	CD	90°	20°	33
					$\overline{48} \times 0.6 = 29$
ABD	AB	AD	40°	100°	6
ACD	AD	CD	70°	20°	38
					$\overline{44} \times 0.6 = 26 = R_2$
ABC	AB	BC	25°	20°	80
BCD	BC	CD	50°	35°	18
					$\overline{98} \times 0.6 = 59$

10-6. Lengths of Lines. In the earlier days, when it was necessary to extend the first-order triangulation across the country rapidly, very long lines were used whenever possible, these lines in many cases being over 100 miles in length. Since one of the objectives of present-day work is to establish points for the use of the local surveyor and engineer, much shorter lines are used. Most of them range from 8 to 15 miles, with an occasional maximum of about 40 miles.

The average length of sight is usually determined by the nature of the country. With very short lines, extremely accurate centering of signals and instrument is required, many more stations must be occupied to accomplish the same linear advance, the area covered becomes a comparatively narrow strip, and the computations are increased. If the objective of the work is to distribute useful points with specified frequency for the purpose of a local survey, this consideration may govern the lengths of the lines used in the main figures. It should be noted, however, that all the stations required probably do not need to be main stations. Satisfactory intersected points that will meet the specifications usually can be distributed among the main stations. If long sights are desired, the stations selected must be at commanding elevations so as to overlook the intervening country. Visibility is better in some regions than in others. Since it varies with the seasons, the prevalent atmospheric conditions should be introduced as a factor in considering the lengths of lines to be used.

10-7. Station Marks. Except where the triangulation is of a temporary nature, the stations should be permanently marked and referenced. Bronze or copper markers cemented into solid ledge rock make the best station marks. In earth, a concrete monument makes an excellent permanent mark. It should be set deep enough in the ground to prevent movement by frost action.

The name or number of the station and the year in which the mark is set are stamped on the mark. The name is chosen with due regard to geographic significance, meaningless names being used only when names of geographical significance cannot be found.

Each station must have an azimuth mark at a distance of not less than ¼ mile from the station, and must also have at least two reference marks. An azimuth mark or a reference mark consists of a metal tablet similar to one used for a station mark, and bears an arrow pointing to the station. When a mark is set in a concrete post, the post may be smaller in diameter and shorter than one for the station mark.

In order that a station may be of future use to other engineers and surveyors, a very complete description of the station and its location should be prepared. This description should include the type of monument and references used, and its location. The description of the location begins with the state and county, and the distance and direction from the nearest town; and includes also the position in a particular quarter-section, and the position with respect to the reference marks and nearby topographic features.

10-8. Signals. The type of signal used will depend on the length of the line and the precision required. As experience has shown that the air is steadier and that lateral refraction is a minimum between dark and daylight, most precise work is done during those hours. The signal used for such work is practically an automobile headlight, the current for the light being supplied by dry batteries. A simple rheostat, operated by a light tender, is placed in the circuit to control the intensity of the light.

For third-order triangulation work, a small pole signal that is 5 or 6 ft high and is braced or guyed with wire is satisfactory for a sight under 3 or 4 miles. The signal can be found and identified more easily if a flag is attached and if the pole is painted black (or red) and white on alternate sections. For a greater distance, the pole should carry two cross targets made of cloth stretched on wooden frames and set at right angles to each other. Targets 3 ft square can usually be seen without difficulty at a distance up to 8 or 10 miles under average conditions. Tall signals, made of poles guyed with wire, may be necessary to project above obstructions, such as trees or buildings.

A tripod or quadripod surmounted by a pole with a flag or with cross targets is more substantial, and a signal of this kind should be built if the work is of such a nature that the station is to be used frequently for a considerable period, as in the case of a long tunnel or an important bridge. The best design is that in which the center pole does not come all the way to the ground, but is elevated sufficiently to allow space and headroom to set up the instrument over the station mark under the pole. The legs should be well anchored to prevent the structure from overturning in the wind.

Church spires, windmills, water tanks, and other prominent objects can be conveniently located by intersection.

The use of signals subject to phase should be avoided. If a signal is so situated that one side is illuminated by the sun while the other is in shadow, it is likely that a distant observer will see only the illuminated or the shaded side and his readings will be affected accordingly. A solid square or cylindrical object that is light in color is particularly bad in this respect. A signal consisting of cross targets set on a pole is nearly free from phase, if the targets are set about a foot apart so that the upper one will not cast a shadow on the lower one. The color should be such that the target can be seen easily against the background.

10-9. Towers. The most favorable country for triangulation is one with numerous high points on which the stations can be located. Where the ground is flat or the timber is dense, the theodolite and the signals must be elevated sufficiently to provide clear sights. The amount of this elevation may vary from a few feet to more than 100 ft in particularly difficult country or where extremely long sights are taken.

The U. S. Coast and Geodetic Survey has developed a steel tower which can be easily erected and dismantled. It is built of light sections similar to those used on windmills. This tower consists of two independent structures. The instrument rests on the inner one, which is undisturbed by the movements of the observer on the outer one. When the instrument need be raised only a few feet above the ground, a substantial tripod of 2 in. by 4 in. lumber is built, and the observer stands on a platform which is entirely separated from this tripod.

On third-order triangulation the intervisibility of stations should be checked in the field, and for reasons of economy the use of towers and elevated signals should be kept to a minimum. When the lines extend across a flat terrain, or across a large body of water, the curvature of the earth and the effects of refraction are definite factors. In Sec. 3-2 it was seen that the combined effect of these two factors can be approximated from the relationship

$$h = 0.574 \, K^2 \qquad\qquad (10\text{-}4)$$

where $h =$ required height of eye, in feet;
$K =$ length of sight, in miles.

Thus, if it is desired to see a point 10 miles away on the surface of a body of water, it would be necessary to elevate the eye of the observer 57.4 ft. If two towers of equal height are built, the line of sight would be tangent to the earth's surface at a distance of 5 miles, and two towers 14.4 ft high would replace the 57.4-ft tower. On account of refraction, it is desirable that the line of sight clear intervening objects by at least 10 ft. Hence, towers about 24 ft high would be required.

10-10. Base Lines. Since the computed sides of a triangulation system can be no more accurate than the base lines, every precaution to insure accuracy is taken in measuring these lines. The length of any base is determined primarily by the desirability of securing strong figures in the base net. Ordinarily, the longer the base, the easier it will be found to secure strong figures.

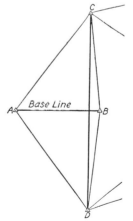

The base is connected to the triangulation system through a base net. This connection may be made through a simple figure, as shown in Fig. 10-3, or through a much more complicated figure. The net shown is a strong one, as it is expanded from the base line AB to the side CD, which is a side of a main triangle of the triangulation system.

Because of errors in the angular measurements, the precision of the computed lengths will decrease as the distance from the base line increases. On extensive triangulation the precision is maintained by measuring additional base lines. The required frequency of the bases is dependent on the strength of the figures, a new base being measured whenever the sum of the values of R_1 in the triangles through which the computations are carried reaches a certain

Fig. 10-3.   Base net.

FIG. 10-4. Geodimeter used for base-line measurement. (Courtesy of Berg, Hedstrom & Co., Inc.)

limit. These limits for first-order, second-order, and third-order work are shown in Table 10-1. They will be found to correspond to a chain of from 5 to 30 triangles, the number depending on the strengths of the figures involved.

Base lines are measured either by using invar tapes and related apparatus or by electronic measuring systems discussed in Secs. 2-5, 2-6, and 2-7. If a first-order base is to be measured electronically, the large precise model of the geodimeter, which is shown in Fig. 10-4, must be used to insure the necessary accuracy. On less precise triangulation work, the measurement of base lines can frequently be eliminated by connecting the work to a triangulation system of a higher order.

10-11. Preparation of Base Line for Taping. When a base line is to be measured by taping, the ground is prepared for the measurement by first clearing away obstructions, in order that the tape may hang freely when under tension. Stakes are then set on, or nearly on, the line at distances apart equal to the length of the tape to be used in measuring the base. Copper strips are fastened to the tops of these stakes for marking the tape lengths. The tape is supported at the middle point, as well as at the ends. For the intermediate support, stakes are set with their edges on line, and nails are driven in the sides to support the middle of the tape on line with the tops of the adjacent stakes. Where the grade of the base is uniform, the stakes need not project more than 1½ to 2 ft above the ground surface, since the lower height makes them more rigid.

For first-order base lines, 4 in. by 4 in. stakes are used at the tape ends, with 2 in. by 4 in. stakes at the middle points, the stakes being lined in with a transit. The accuracy of the alignment should be such that, when a 50-meter tape is to be used, no stake is more than 6 in. off the line between the terminal stations, and no marking strip is more than 1 in. off the line joining the strips on the two adjacent stakes.

For base lines of less precision, 2 in. by 4 in. and 1 in. by 4 in. stakes can be used. For second-order precision and when a 50-meter tape is to be used for measuring, no part of the measured line should be more than 6 in. off the straight line between the terminal stations, nor should any one marking strip on a stake be more than 2 in. off the line between the strips on the two adjacent stakes. For third-order precision, the stakes should be so located that the error in the length of the base caused by poor alignment will not exceed 1 part in 150,000.

10-12. Base-Line Levels. Levels should be run along the base line to determine the differences of elevation between the stakes. These differences of elevation are used in determining the corrections necessary to reduce the slope measurements to the horizontal. The accuracy with which the differences of elevation must be obtained depends on the rate of grade and the distances between the stakes.

The difference between an inclined distance and the corresponding horizontal distance is, by Eq. 2-3, Sec. 2-13, $C_h = (h^2/2s) + (h^4/8s^3)$. When the first term of this correction is differentiated, the result is

$$dC_h = \frac{2h\,dh}{2s} = \frac{h\,dh}{s}$$

where dC_h represents the error in the correction corresponding to an error dh in the difference of elevation, when the difference in elevation is h and the distance between the stakes is s. This error can be expressed as a ratio by dividing each member of the preceding equation by s. Thus,

$$\frac{dC_h}{s} = \frac{h\, dh}{s^2} \qquad\qquad (10\text{-}5)$$

When the stakes are set at 100-ft intervals, and 1/100,000 is to be the maximum error due to incorrect difference in elevation, $1/100{,}000 = h\, dh/100^2$, and $dh = 0.1/h$. When $h = 1.0$ ft, $dh = 0.10$ ft. Hence, when the rate of grade is 1 per cent, an error of 0.10 ft in the difference of elevation will produce an error equivalent to 1/100,000 in that tape length. When $h = 5.0$ ft, $dh = 0.02$ ft; and when $h = 10.0$ ft, $dh = 0.01$ ft. Thus, it is evident that when the slopes are steep the leveling must be more accurate than when the base line is on more level ground. Nomograms prepared for tape lengths of 100, 75, 50, and 25 ft and for a precision of 1/100,000 are shown in Fig. 10-5. From these curves it will be seen that the leveling must also be more precise when short measurements are made.

10-13. Tapes. The base lines of the U. S. Coast and Geodetic Survey are measured with 50-meter invar tapes. These tapes, made of an alloy of about 35 per cent nickel to 65 per cent steel, have coefficients of expansion from about 1/25 to 1/30 times that of steel. They have a very unstable molecular arrangement and are easily kinked unless handled very carefully. They should not be reeled or unreeled rapidly or under a heavy tension, nor wound on a reel having a small diameter, nor dragged over the ground, nor shaken violently, nor subjected to sudden large changes in temperature. When the tape is not on a reel, a slight tension must be maintained constantly to prevent it from kinking.

These tapes are standardized by the Bureau of Standards, a tension of 15 kilograms being used. The following data are supplied by the Bureau: the weight of the tape in grams per meter; the coefficient of expansion per degree centigrade; the length at a specified temperature when supported at the 0-, 25-, and 50-meter points; length at a specified temperature when supported at the 0-, 12.5-, 25-, 37.5-, and 50-meter points; length at a specified temperature when supported throughout.

The standardized length for the tape supported throughout presupposes a frictionless surface as a support for the tape. Second-order bases are sometimes measured along railroad rails. In such cases, the rail should be dry and care should be taken in lowering the tape to the rail. On first-order bases, it is not desirable to have the tape supported throughout, because the error due to friction will vary with the surface conditions of the rail.

When a base line must be measured with steel tapes, the measure-

The curved lines in this nomogram are the loci of the points representing those conditions of difference of elevation between tape ends and error in determining same which will produce an error of 1 part in 100,000 in the reduced length. Each curve is for the length of tape indicated. For example, for a 100-ft tape length and a difference of elevation of 5.0 ft, an error of 0.02 ft in determining the difference of elevation would cause an error of 1 part in 100,000 in the reduced length.

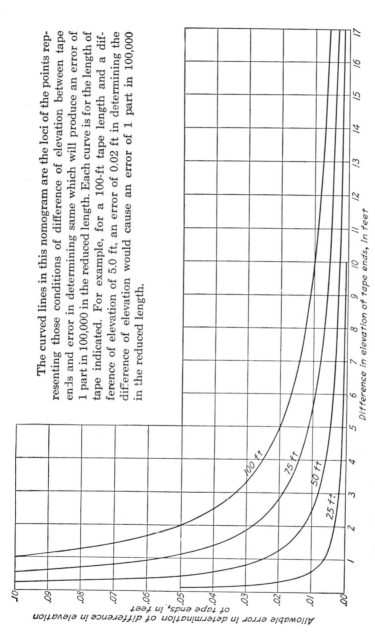

Fig. 10-5.   Allowable error in measured difference of elevation between tape ends.

ments should be made either on a cloudy day or early in the morning or late in the afternoon, when the temperature of the tape will be the same as that of the surrounding air. Since the coefficient of expansion of steel is about 0.0000065 per degree Fahrenheit, the temperature must be known more accurately than when invar tapes are used, if equal precision is to be attained. The steel tapes should be standardized before any important base is measured.

10-14. Thermometers. The field temperature for each tape length is determined by two thermometers. Those used by the U. S. Coast and Geodetic Survey are supported in channel-bar holders, which are fastened to the tape with narrow bands of adhesive tape. The thermometers are attached at the same points at which they are placed during the standardization of the tape, namely, at points 1 meter toward the center from the terminal marks, the distances being measured from the marks to the nearer ends of the thermometer. The thermometers used on first-order and second-order bases are correct to within 0.3 degree C.

10-15. Spring Balances. The tension in the tape should be maintained by a spring balance. This balance should be sufficiently sensitive to permit maintaining a tension within 100 grams, or about ¼ pound, of the standard tension. The balance should be tested before and after each day's work, also at midday if practicable, and oftener if it is suspected that the position of the pointer has changed.

10-16. Tape-Stretching Apparatus. Steel tubes pointed at the ends or ordinary steel line rods can be used in applying tension to the tape. A leather loop attached to the rear end of the tape and one attached to the spring balance at the forward end of the tape slip over the rods. These loops can be slipped up and down on the rods to correspond to the heights of the stakes.

10-17. Base-Line Field Party. The field party for measuring a base line consists of six men, namely, front and rear tension men, front and rear contact men, a middle man, and a recorder. Usually, the chief of the party makes the forward contact, as in that position he can best supervise the manipulation of the tape and can set the pace of measurement. If any of the men are inexperienced, it is better to measure a practice section of several hundred feet before the recorded measurements are begun, each man being drilled in his position by an experienced man.

10-18. Measuring Base Line. In the actual measurement of the base line, the line is broken up into sections about 1 kilometer in length, and at least two measurements of a section are made with different tapes before proceeding to the next section. When three tapes are available, the total length is divided into three divisions of approximately equal length, and a different pairing of the tapes is used for the measurement of each division. For first-order and for second-order, class I accuracy, the discrepancy, in millimeters, between the duplicate measurements of a section should not exceed $10\sqrt{k}$, where k is the length of the section in kilometers. This is equivalent to a discrepancy, in feet, of about $0.04\sqrt{M}$, where M is the length in miles. For second-order, class II accuracy, the corresponding values are $20\sqrt{k}$ and $0.08\sqrt{M}$; for third-order work, the figures are $25\sqrt{k}$ and $0.10\sqrt{M}$. When the discrepancy exceeds these values, additional measurements of the section must be made, preferably with the same tapes, until two measurements are secured which agree within these limits.

10-19. Corrections to Base-Line Measurements. The principal corrections applied to the field measurements of a base line are for incorrect length of tape, for temperature, for slope, and for reduction of the length to sea-level length. The corrections for sag and tension are usually avoided by having the tape standardized under the conditions to which it will be subjected in the field.

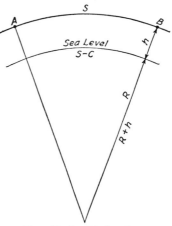

FIG. 10–6. Reduction to sea level.

When the triangulation system is extensive, all linear distances are reduced to their equivalent sea-level lengths. In Fig. 10-6, A and B are two points on the earth's surface at an average elevation h above sea level. Since the lengths of arcs are proportional to their radii, $(S - C)/R = S/(R + h)$. This equation may be expanded into the form

$$\frac{S}{R} - \frac{C}{R} = \frac{S}{R} - S\frac{h}{R^2} + S\frac{h^2}{R^3} - S\frac{h^3}{R^4} + \cdots$$

Whence,

$$C = S\frac{h}{R} - S\frac{h^2}{R^2} + S\frac{h^3}{R^3} - \cdots \qquad (10\text{-}6)$$

where C = correction to be subtracted from the measured length S, at an average elevation h;
R = radius of curvature of the earth.

For most work, the first term is sufficient and an average value of R can be used. When h is in feet, $\log R = 7.32027$; for h in meters, $\log R = 6.80429$. The more exact values of R are dependent on the mean latitude and the azimuth of the base.

For a base line at an average elevation of 6100 ft and a measured length of 4324.186 ft, the correction is obtained as follows:

$$
\begin{aligned}
\log S \ (4324) &= 3.63589 \\
\log h \ (6100) &= 3.78533 \\
\text{colog } R \ (\text{ft}) &= 2.67973 \\
\hline
\log C &= 0.10095 \\
C &= 1.262 \text{ ft}
\end{aligned}
$$

The corrections for incorrect length of tape, temperature, slope, sag, and other conditions have been discussed in Chapter 2.

10-20. Probable Error of Base Line. The probable error of the mean of two or more measurements of a base line, or of a section if the base was measured in sections, is found by the equation

$$ E_m = 0.6745 \sqrt{\frac{\Sigma v^2}{n(n-1)}} $$

When only two measurements are made, E_m is equal to 0.6745 times one-half the difference between the two measurements. When the base line has been measured in sections, the probable error of the entire line is the square root of the sum of the squares of the probable errors of the sections. (See Sec. 4-7.)

10-21. Base-Line Measurement by Use of Electronic Systems. The use of electronic distance-measuring devices eliminates the need for elaborate base-line preparation. The general requirement for a base line which is to be measured by means of one of these instruments is a clear line of sight between the two ends of the base. A base line may be chosen between two prominent triangulation stations, since the measurement with an electronic device is completely independent of the character of the intervening terrain.

If a base line is to be measured across a body of water, use of the geodimeter presents no particular problems as long as the transmitter and the reflector are sufficiently elevated, say by towers, to give a clear line of sight. However, when a microwave system is used, reflections off the water surface may be severe enough in some cases to preclude the possibility of obtaining reliable readings free from the effect of swing. Attempts at shielding the transmitter and receiver from incoming reflected waves by physical masking of the instruments have met with a moderate degree of success.

The time required to make the necessary instrument readings during the actual measuring operation is independent of the length of the base line. When an electronic device is used under normal conditions, the instruments can be set up and aligned, and all the readings can be made in about an hour. There is a tremendous saving in time, especially when base lines 20 to 30 miles in length are considered.

Because of the ease with which bases can be measured by using the electronic equipment, check bases can be selected at more frequent intervals than when base lines must be measured with tapes. Check bases tend to strengthen the entire triangulation network.

10-22. Measuring Angles in Triangulation. The instruments to be used in measuring the angles in the triangulation network depend on the desired accuracy of the positions of the triangulation stations. For first-order work, direction theodolites which can be read directly to 0.2 second should be used. An example of such an instrument is shown in Fig. 10-7. For second-order work, the instrument should be capable of reading directly to 1 second. An example of a second-order direction theodolite is shown in Fig. 6-16. For third-order triangu-

FIG. 10–7. First-order direction theodolite.
(Courtesy of Kern Instruments, Inc.)

lation, an engineer's transit reading to 30 or 20 seconds can be employed if advantage is taken of the added precision gained by repeating angles.

Before the angles at a triangulation station which are to be used in the computations are measured accurately, a preliminary list of directions should be prepared by occupying the station and measuring either the angles or the directions to other stations in the network. This list eliminates much unnecessary delay in reading the final angles because it allows the instrument to be pointed almost directly to the sighted stations by means of precomputed circle settings. Thus, a distant station which may not be readily seen with the naked eye can be picked up in the field of the telescope after the circle setting is made.

10-23. Triangulation Angles by Repetition. The repetition method of measuring triangulation angles is the same as that described in Sec. 6-14. In Fig. 10-8, each one of the angles a through e is measured by repetition, either three times with the telescope direct and three times with it reversed, or six times direct and six times reversed. The number of turnings depends on the required accuracy and on the number of sets of repetitions to be taken. When all the angles about the station have been measured by using the required number of repetitions, the complete procedure constitutes one *set* of observations. For third-order triangulation, six sets of six repetitions or three sets of twelve repetitions will suffice when a 30-second transit is used. The mean value of each measured angle is used to find the sum of the angles about the station, and then each angle receives an equal correction. A list of directions based on the adjusted angles is then prepared for subsequent use in computations, the initial direction being taken as 0° 00′ 00.0″.

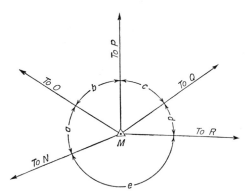

Fɪɢ. 10–8.   Angles about a station.

EXAMPLE 10-1. As shown in Fig. 10-8, five angles were measured about station *M*. Each set of measurements consisted of six repetitions with the telescope direct and six with the telescope reversed, and three sets of measurements were taken. The mean values of the angles are shown in the second column of the accompanying tabulation. Adjust the mean angles and prepare an abstract of directions to the observed stations. Take the direction to station *N* as 0° 00′ 00.0″.

STATION ADJUSTMENT AND ABSTRACT OF DIRECTIONS

Angle	Mean Value	Corr.	Adjusted Value (sec)	To Station	Abstracted Direction
a	54° 02′ 15.0″	+ 0.8″	15.8″	N	0° 00′ 00.0″
b	57° 33′ 12.7″	+ 0.8″	13.5″	O	54° 02′ 15.8″
c	55° 42′ 42.5″	+ 0.8″	43.3″	P	111° 35′ 29.3″
d	36° 57′ 22.5″	+ 0.8″	23.3″	Q	167° 18′ 12.6″
e	155° 44′ 23.3″	+ 0.8″	24.1″	R	204° 15′ 35.9″
	359° 59′ 56.0″		00.0″	N	360° 00′ 00.0″
	Closure = − 4.0″				

Solution: Since the sum of the measured angles is 359° 59′ 56.0″, the angles are adjusted by adding 0.8″ to each measured value. The seconds in the adjusted angles are entered in the fourth column of the tabulation.

The directions in the last column are obtained by adding each adjusted angle in succession to the preceding direction. As a check the angle *e* is added to the direction of *R* to see if the sum is exactly 360°.

10-24. Triangulation Angles by Direction Method. As indicated in Sec. 6-19, the direction instrument does not have a lower clamp. So it cannot be used to repeat angles. However, provision is made to advance the position of the horizontal circle relative to the reading microscope without rotating the telescope in azimuth. Angles in almost all first-order and second-order triangulations are measured by using an optical reading direction instrument as described in Sec. 6-20.

With the direction instrument set up over a selected triangulation station and the telescope direct, the line of sight is directed at each adjacent station in turn, the telescope being rotated in a clockwise direction, and the circle is read at each pointing by means of the optical micrometer. The telescope is then reversed, and another round of directions is observed. This entire set of readings constitutes one *position.* For first-order work, a total of between 8 and 16 positions are observed, the number depending on the precision of the instrument. For second-order work, a total of between 4 and 8 positions are observed. The circle reading should be advanced by 180°/*n* for each new position, where *n* is the number of positions to be observed. This interval tends to distribute the readings over the entire circle and eliminates the errors of graduation of the circle.

Each position gives a set of angles, as shown by way of illustration in Sec. 6-19. If four positions have been observed, then each angle will have four values. The mean value of each angle must be obtained, and an abstract is then prepared.

EXAMPLE 10-2. The angles *a* through *e* in Fig. 10-8 have been measured by observing the directions from *M* to *N, O, P, Q,* and *R* with four positions of a direction theodolite, and the results are as shown in the accompany tabulation. Taking the direction to station *N* as 0° 00′ 00.00″, prepare an abstract of directions to the observed stations.

Angle	Position 1	Position 2	Position 3	Position 4	Mean Angle
a	54° 02′ 13.5″	54° 02′ 15.0″	54° 02′ 18.4″	54° 02′ 12.0″	54° 02′ 14.72″
b	57° 33′ 14.0″	57° 33′ 14.0″	57° 33′ 10.2″	57° 33′ 15.6″	57° 33′ 13.45″
c	55° 42′ 46.1″	55° 42′ 44.3″	55° 42′ 42.4″	55° 42′ 46.3″	55° 42′ 44.77″
d	36° 57′ 21.0″	36° 57′ 18.8″	36° 57′ 24.1″	36° 57′ 21.8″	36° 57′ 21.43″
e	155° 44′ 25.4″	155° 44′ 27.9″	155° 44′ 24.9″	155° 44′ 24.3″	155° 44′ 25.63″
	360° 00′ 00.0″	360° 00′ 00.0″	360° 00′ 00.0″	360° 00′ 00.0″	360° 00′ 00.00″

Solution: The angles resulting from each position are added to verify that their sum is 360°. If it is not, a mistake has been made in obtaining the angles. The average of the four values of each angle is then computed. Finally, the direction abstract is obtained as in Example 10-1.

To Station	Abstracted Direction
N	00° 00′ 00.00″
O	54° 02′ 14.72″
P	111° 35′ 28.17″
Q	167° 18′ 12.94″
R	204° 15′ 34.37″
N	360° 00′ 00.00″

As a check, the angle *e* is added to the direction of *R*, as was done in Example 10-1.

10-25. Nature of Triangulation Computations. The purpose of triangulation is to compute some inaccessible distance or to obtain the coordinates of triangulation stations, as a basis for further surveys. Before such computations are made, the errors in the field measurements must be eliminated or distributed. This distribution can be made by approximate methods or by the more exact method of least squares.

In a triangulation net which contains fixed control points, lines of fixed azimuth, and more than one measured base, five kinds of discrepancies are encountered. 1) The sum of the three angles in each triangle will seldom equal exactly 180° plus spherical excess (see Sec. 10-28). 2) In a quadrilateral, the length of any unknown side will have two different values when computed through two different sets of triangles. 3) The measured lengths of the additional base lines will not agree with their computed lengths as obtained from the preceding base and the measured angles. 4) The azimuths of fixed lines will not agree with the azimuths computed from the measured angles. 5) The fixed position (coordinates) of a point will disagree with its position as computed through the triangle nets. Consequently, before triangulation computations can be made, the measured values must be adjusted in order to distribute the random errors in such fashion that the sum of the squares of the corrections to the measured angles will be a minimum.

In the adjustment procedure, the five kinds of inconsistencies cited above give rise to five conditions which must be satisfied. These are referred to, respectively, as follows: a) angle condition; b) side condition; c) length condition; d) azimuth condition; and e) position condition. The least squares adjustment is made to satisfy all these conditions.

The triangulation can be adjusted as a whole by the so-called simultaneous method, or it can be adjusted in sections by the sectional method. From the standpoint of accuracy in the final results, the simultaneous method is the better. Where large numbers of stations are involved, however, the computations become so unwieldy that it is often necessary to divide the triangulation into sections and to adjust each section separately.

The order of the calculations is as follows: 1) reduction to center, when the transit has not been placed exactly over a given station; 2) correction for eccentricity of signal, where the signal has not corresponded exactly with the station; 3) spherical excess; 4) approximate adjustment, or least-squares adjustment; 5) computation of the lengths of the sides; 6) computation of coordinates.

10-26. Reduction to Center. In the measurement of triangulation angles, it often is not possible to occupy a station directly below an excellent target, such as a church spire or a lighthouse. Also, targets are frequently blown out of position and the angles read on them have to be corrected to the true position of the triangulation station. There are thus two types of problems: 1) when the instrument point is not the true station and the measured angles must be corrected to what they would be at the station; 2) when the target is out of position. In the example shown in Fig. 10-9 the angles were measured at an eccentric station A' instead of the true station A.

In computing the corrections to be applied to the measured angles or directions, the simplest method is to calculate first the directions of the lines with respect to the line between the eccentric station and the true station as a meridian. The corrections to refer these directions to the true station are obtained by solving the triangles

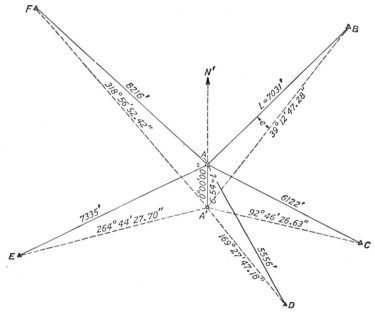

FIG. 10–9. Reduction to center.

such as ABA', ACA', and ADA' for the angles at the stations B, C, D, E, and F. In the triangle ABA',

$$\sin e = \frac{l}{L} \sin a$$

where e = angle $A'BA$;

$l = AA'$ or the distance between the true station and the eccentric station;

$L = AB$ or the distance from the true station to B;

a = direction of $A'B$ measured at the eccentric station with respect to the meridian through A' and A.

Since the angles at B, C, D, E, and F will be very small, their values in seconds can be obtained by dividing both sides of the preceding equation by sin 1″. Thus, if e'' denotes the angle in seconds,

$$e'' = \frac{l}{\sin 1''} \times \frac{\sin a}{L} \tag{10-7}$$

For any given case, $l/\sin 1''$ will be a constant for solving all the triangles that are involved. In the accompanying tabulation are shown the computations for reducing to the true station A, Fig. 10-9, the

Stations	B	C	D	E	F
Dist.	7,031′	6,122′	5,556′	7,335′	8,216′
a	39°12′47.28″	92°46′26.63″	169°27′47.18″	264°44′27.70″	318°56′52.42″
log sin a	9.80086	9.99949	9.26213	9.99817 (n)	9.81740 (n)
colog dist.	6.15298	6.21311	6.25524	6.13460	6.08534
log (l/sin 1″)	6.13001	6.13001	6.13001	6.13001	6.13001
log e″	2.08385	2.34261	1.64738	2.26278 (n)	2.03275 (n)
e″	+ 121.30″	+ 220.10″	+ 44.40″	− 183.14″	− 107.83″
Corr. Direct.	39°14′48.58″	92°50′06.73″	169°28′31.58″	264°41′24.56″	318°55′04.59″

directions measured from the eccentric station A'. The distance l from A to A' is 6.54 ft and log $(l / \sin 1'') = 6.13001$. The signs of the corrections are the same as the signs of sin a, negative values being indicated by (n).

The angles at station A can be obtained from the corrected directions. If the values of L used in the computations for e'' differ considerably from the more exact values, it may be necessary to make other computations in which the corrected lengths are used. Since the eccentric distance l will, in general, be small compared with the lengths of the sides, this recalculation will seldom be required.

10-27. Correction for Eccentric Signal. If, in Fig. 10-9, A' represents the station and A the eccentric signal. the corrections to be applied to the directions measured to the eccentric signal from stations B, C, D, E, and F will be the same as those computed in the preceding section.

10-28. Spherical Excess. The amount by which the sum of the three angles of a spherical triangle exceeds 180° is called the spherical excess. Before the closing error in the angles of a large triangle can be ascertained, the spherical excess must be known. The amount of this excess is dependent on the area of the triangle and on the latitudes of the vertexes. It is approximately equal to 1 second for every 75.5 square miles of area. A more exact value for the excess in seconds is

$$E'' = \frac{bc \sin A}{2R^2 \sin 1''} = mbc \sin A \qquad (10\text{-}8)$$

where b, c, and A = two sides and the included angle of the triangle;
$\qquad R$ = radius of curvature of the earth.

Most tables intended for geodetic computations contain values of log m for various latitudes. When the triangles are small, as will be those encountered in third-order triangulation work, and even those in much first-order and second-order triangulation, the mean radius of the earth can be used. For a triangle in latitude 45°, log m = 0.3720 when the dimensions are in feet and log m = 1.4040 when the dimensions are in meters. The excess is divided equally between the three angles of the triangle, the corrections being subtracted from the observed values.

10-29. Triangulation Adjustment. When two or more points are to be connected by a triangulation system, the connection can be made either by a chain of trian-

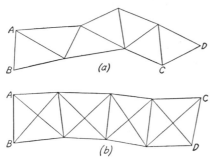

gles, as shown in Fig. 10-10 (*a*), or by means of connected quadrilaterals, as shown in view (*b*). When triangles are used, the only adjustment to be made is to satisfy the condition that the sums of the angles of the individual triangles shall equal 180°. This adjustment is made ordinarily by

FIG. 10–10. Triangulation nets.

correcting each angle by one-third of the closure in that triangle. Although this method involves the reading of fewer angles, and simplifies the computations, the only check on the computed lengths of the sides is afforded by the measurement of a second base line, such as *CD* in Fig. 10-10 (*a*).

When the connection is made by means of quadrilaterals, additional checks on the angular measurements are provided by the added geometrical conditions. Checks on the computed lengths are afforded, since any length can be obtained through the use of two different sets of triangles. Unless the measured angles have been adjusted, it is unlikely that the two computed values will agree exactly. The purpose of the adjustment is to correct the observed angles so that the various conditions relative to the sums of the angles will be satisfied, and in addition so that the computed length of a side will have the same numerical value, regardless of the triangles used in the computation.

In the quadrilateral shown in Fig. 10-11, the sum of the eight angles should equal 360° and the sums of the angles of any triangle should equal 180°. In addition, $b + c = f + g$, and $h + a = d + e$. The side condition is developed as follows: In the triangle *ABC*,

$$BC = \frac{AB \sin b}{\sin e}$$

In the triangle *BCD*,

$$CD = \frac{BC \sin d}{\sin g} = \frac{AB \sin b \sin d}{\sin e \sin g}$$

In the triangle *CDA*,

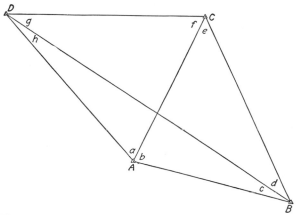

FIG. 10–11. Triangulation adjustment in quadrilateral.

$$DA = \frac{CD \sin f}{\sin a} = \frac{AB \sin b \sin d \sin f}{\sin a \sin e \sin g}$$

In the triangle DAB,

$$AB = \frac{DA \sin h}{\sin c} = \frac{AB \sin b \sin d \sin f \sin h}{\sin a \sin c \sin e \sin g}$$

Hence,

$$1 = \frac{\sin b \sin d \sin f \sin h}{\sin a \sin c \sin e \sin g}$$

If the logarithms of both members of the equation are considered,

$$(\log \sin b + \log \sin d + \log \sin f + \log \sin h)$$

$$- (\log \sin a + \log \sin c + \log \sin e + \log \sin g) = 0$$

Unless this condition is satisfied, the value of a computed length will depend on the triangles used in the computation.

The most accurate method of making the adjustments is according to the theory of least squares, as the most probable values for the measured angles and the computed lengths are then obtained. For the application of the least-squares method, refer to the adjustment of a quadrilateral given in the Appendix.

If the sides are less than a mile in length, the computations can be made without an adjustment when the angles have been quite accurately measured, and when extreme precision in the computed lengths is unnecessary. When greater precision is required, approximate methods of adjusting will give computed lengths which will agree very closely with the least-squares values.

10-30. Approximate Adjustment of a Quadrilateral. The first step in the adjustment of a quadrilateral like that in Fig. 10-11 by the approximate method is to correct each of the eight angles so that their sum will be exactly 360°. In the numerical example for which the computations are shown on page 323, a total correction of + 1.71″ is necessary. Hence, five of the angles are increased by 0.21″, and three of them are increased by 0.22″. The sums of the opposite angles are next made to agree by correcting each angle by one-fourth of the error in the sums. Thus, a and h are increased by ¼ × 2.32″ = 0.58″, and d and e are decreased by equal amounts. In a like manner, b and c are diminished, and f and g are increased, by 1.39″.

The logarithmic sines and the differences in the logarithms for 1 second of angle are tabulated next, the corrected values just obtained being used for the angles. Note that 7-place logarithms are used in the adjustment. The sums of the alternate logarithmic sines fail to agree by 290, and hence the angles must be corrected by amounts which will eliminate this difference. The change must be effected by correcting each angle by an equal amount. The value of the correction in seconds is found by dividing the total change in logarithmic sines, or 290, by the total difference in logarithmic sines for 1 second of angle, or 252.7. The quotient 1.15″ is the correction applied to each angle, being added to the four angles whose logarithmic sines are to be increased and subtracted from the other four. If the corrections are accurate and are properly applied, the sums of the logarithmic sines of the corrected angles will agree within 1 or 2 in the last decimal place.

10-31. Computation of Lengths. Two sides of each triangle are computed by using the law of sines, since one side of the triangle is always known and the three angles have been measured and adjusted. In computing the sides of the triangles in a quadrilateral, such as that shown in Fig. 10-11, the solution of two triangles is sufficient to compute the positions of the forward triangulation stations. The two triangles chosen must be the strongest route through the quadrilateral. In Fig. 10-11 the side AB is the known or measured line of the quadrilateral, and the strongest route is obtained by considering triangle CBA and triangle DCA in that order. To check the accuracy of the field work or the consistency of the figure after adjustment, the two triangles DBA and CBD can be computed in that order. This computation gives a check on the length of the side CD, which is the forward side of the quadrilateral. However, only the result for the strongest route can be used to solve the following quadrilateral.

In the tabulation on page 324 are shown the computations of

COMPUTATIONS FOR ADJUSTMENT OF QUADRILATERAL BY APPROXIMATE METHOD

Observed Angles	For 360°	For Opposite Angles	Log Sines of Adjusted Angles		Diff. for 1″	Corrected Angles	Corrected Log Sines	
a = 63° 17′ 26.18″	26.39″	26.97″	9.950 9970		10.6	63° 17′ 28.12″	9.950 9982	
b = 84° 18′ 22.69″	22.91″	21.52″		9.997 8518	2.1	84° 18′ 20.37″		9.997 8516
c = 17° 52′ 26.72″	26.93″	25.54″	9.487 0263		65.3	17° 52′ 26.69″	9.487 0338	
d = 30° 41′ 18.49″	18.71″	18.13″		9.707 8838	35.5	30° 41′ 16.98″		9.707 8797
e = 47° 07′ 55.18″	55.39″	54.81″	9.865 0576		19.5	47° 07′ 55.96″	9.865 0598	
f = 66° 35′ 54.84″	55.06″	56.45″		9.962 7234	9.1	66° 35′ 55.30″		9.962 7224
g = 35° 34′ 49.01″	49.22″	50.61″	9.764 8106		29.4	35° 34′ 51.76″	9.764 8140	
h = 14° 31′ 45.18″	45.39″	45.97″		9.399 4615	81.2	14° 31′ 44.82″		9.399 4522
359° 59′ 58.29″	00.00″	00.00″	39.067 8915	39.067 9205	252.7	360° 00′ 00.00″	39.067 9058	39.067 9059
8)1.71				8915				
+ 0.21″				290				

$a + h$ = 77° 49′ 11.78″ $b + c$ = 102° 10′ 49.84″

$d + e$ = 77° 49′ 14.10″ $f + g$ = 102° 10′ 44.28″

4)2.32″   4)5.56″

0.58″   1.39″

$$\frac{290}{252.7} = 1.15″$$

COMPUTATION OF LENGTHS BY USE OF 7-PLACE LOGARITHMS

Sides	Stations	Angles	Corrected Angles	Distances	Logarithms
BA				2899.06	3.462 2572
	C	e	47° 07′ 55.96″		0.134 9402
	B	c + d	48° 33′ 43.67″		9.874 8723
	A	b	84° 18′ 20.37″		9.997 8516
AC			180° 00′ 00.00″	2965.31	3.472 0697
CB				3935.94	3.595 0490
CA				2965.31	3.472 0697
	D	g + h	50° 06′ 36.58″		0.115 0467
	C	f	66° 35′ 55.30″		9.962 7224
	A	a	63° 17′ 28.12″		9.950 9982
AD			180° 00′ 00.00″	3546.82	3.549 8388
DC				3452.35	3.538 1146
BA				2899.06	3.462 2572
	D	h	14° 31′ 44.82″		0.600 5478
	B	c	17° 52′ 26.69″		9.487 0338
	A	a + b	147° 35′ 48.49″		9.729 0626
AD			180° 00′ 00.00″	3546.82	3.549 8388
DB				6192.52	3.791 8676
BD				6192.52	3.791 8676
	C	e + f	113° 43′ 51.26″		0.038 3675
	B	d	30° 41′ 16.98″		9.707 8797
	D	g	35° 34′ 51.76″		9.764 8140
DC			180° 00′ 00.00″	3452.35	3.538 1148
CB				3935.95	3.595 0491

determining the lengths of the sides of the quadrilateral in Fig. 10-11 by using the corrected angles found on page 323. The stations in the triangle CBA are listed in the order determined by beginning with the unknown point C and going around the triangle in a clockwise direction. The adjusted angles are filled in as shown. With the side BA known, the sides AC and CB are computed by using the law of sines. Thus, $AC = BA \sin (c + d)/\sin e$, and $CB = BA \sin b/\sin e$. In the tabulation, log BA, colog sin e, log sin $(c + d)$, and log sin b are listed in that order. It is convenient to use colog sin e because sin e is the common divisor in the application of the law of sines. The sum of the first three logarithms is log AC, and the sum of the first, second, and fourth logarithms is log CB.

The triangle DCA is next considered, and the adjusted angles are filled in. The value of log CA found by solving the first triangle is carried down as the logarithm of the now known side of the second triangle. Then colog sin $(g + h)$, log sin f, and log sin a are listed in that order. The sum of the first three logarithms for the second triangle is log AD, and the sum of the first, second, and fourth logarithms is log DC.

The two triangles DBA and CBD in the second route are solved by starting from side BA and following a similar procedure. This route provides a check on the side DC and also shows the consistency of the sides AD and CB.

If a desk computer is used, the values of the natural sines would be entered directly in the column headed "Distances." This arrangement is shown in the accompanying tabulation for the first triangle. The distance AC is obtained by first multiplying the side BA by sin $(c + d)$ and then dividing the product by sin e; the distance CB is obtained by multiplying the side BA by sin b and dividing the product by sin e.

Sides	Stations	Angles	Corrected Angles	Distances
BA				2899.06
	C	e	47° 07′ 55.96″	0.732 92548
	B	$c + d$	48° 33′ 43.67″	0.749 67381
	A	b	84° 18′ 20.37″	0.995 06538
AC				2965.31
CB				3935.94

10-32. Computation of Plane Coordinates. The objective of triangulation is to establish the horizontal positions of the triangulation stations in the network relative to one another and with respect to a horizontal datum. In Chapter 11 are described the state plane coordinate systems which should be the basis of any triangulation to be established on a plane coordinate system. The triangulation network must include at least one point, and preferably should include two or more points, the horizontal position of which is known with respect to the state plane coordinate system. In the network of Fig. 10-10(b), if A and B are points with known coordinates, the length and azimuth of the line AB can be computed by using suitable equations in the group 8-12 through 8-16. If point C is also a point with known coordinates, then a check on the entire network is provided, because the discrepancy between the fixed position of C and its position as computed through the quadrilaterals can be determined.

If the coordinates of stations A and B in Fig. 10-11 are known, the length of line BA computed by Eq. 8-12 is used as the starting line in the computations for the lengths of the sides of the quadrilateral shown on page 324. The azimuth from north of the line AB is determined by Eq. 8-15. The azimuth of the line AC is equal to the azimuth of AB minus angle b. The azimuth of BC is equal to the azimuth of BA plus angle $(c + d)$. Furthermore, when the azimuths of AC and BC have been computed, the difference between the two must be equal to angle e. The discrepancy represents the triangle closure.

DOUBLE-POSITION COMPUTATION FOR POSITIONS OF TRIANGULATION STATIONS

Azimuth AB = 104° 42' 56.60"	Azimuth BA = 284° 42' 56.60"
− Angle b = − 84° 18' 20.37"	+ Angle $(c + d)$ = + 48° 33' 43.67"
Azimuth AC = 20° 24' 36.23"	Azimuth BC = 333° 16' 40.27"
+ 360°	
380° 24' 36.23"	
− 333° 16' 40.27"	
Angle e = 47° 07' 55.96" (check)	

log AC = 3.472 0697	log BC = 3.595 0490	log BC = 3.595 0490
l. sin NAC = 9.542 4977	l. cos NBC = 9.950 9476	l. sin NBC = 9.652 8884
l. dep. AC = 3.014 5674	l. lat. BC = 3.545 9966	l. dep. BC = 3.247 9374
X_A = 1,442,416.25	Y_B = 621,779.78	X_B = 1,445,220.22
dep. AC = +1,034.11	lat. BC = +3,515.58	dep. BC = −1,769.85
X_C = 1,443,450.36	Y_C = 625,295.36	X_C = 1,443,450.37

Azimuth AC = 20° 24' 36.23"	Azimuth CA = 200° 24' 36.23"
− Angle a = − 63° 17' 28.12"	+ Angle f = + 66° 35' 55.30"
Azimuth AD = 317° 07' 08.11"	Azimuth CD = 267° 00' 31.53"
− 267° 00' 31.53"	
Angle $(g + h)$ = 50° 06' 36.58" (check)	

log AC = 3.472 0697	log CD = 3.538 1146	log CD = 3.538 1146
l. cos NAC = 9.971 8419	l. cos NCD = 8.717 5315	l. sin NCD = 9.999 4079
l. lat. AC = 3.443 9116	l. lat. CD = 2.255 6461	l. dep. CD = 3.537 5225
Y_A = 622,516.21	Y_C = 625,295.36	X_C = 1,443,450.36
lat. AC = +2,779.15	lat. CD = − 180.15	dep. CD = − 3,447.64
Y_C = 625,295.36	Y_D = 625,115.21	X_D = 1,440,002.72

log AD = 3.549 8388	log AD = 3.549 8388
l. cos NAD = 9.864 9663	l. sin NAD = 9.832 8147
l. lat. AD = 3.414 8051	l. dep. AD = 3.382 6535
Y_A = 622,516.21	X_A = 1,442,416.25
lat. AD = +2,598.99	dep. AD = − 2,413.53
Y_D = 625,115.20	X_D = 1,440,002.72

After the lengths of the lines AC and BC have been computed by solving the triangles and the azimuths of the lines AC and BC have been determined, the latitudes and departures of these two lines are computed by Eqs. 8-3 and 8-4. Applying the latitudes and departures of AC and BC to the coordinates of A and B, respectively, in accordance with Eqs. 8-7 and 8-8, gives two sets of values of the coordinates of C. These two sets of values should not differ by more than 0.01 or 0.02 ft. The slight discrepancy is due either to rounding-off errors or to slight inconsistencies in the triangles.

The computation just discussed is known as a *double-position computation*. In the tabulation on page 326 is shown the double-position computation for the quadrilateral in Fig. 10-11 when the angles determined on page 323 and the lengths determined on page 324 are used. To save space in the logarithmic work, l. is used instead of log and the azimuth of a side is indicated by putting N before the letters at the ends of the side. When the position of C has been determined, a double-position computation for D is performed by using triangle DCA. Note that the actual lengths of the sides shown on page 324 are not necessary because the logarithms of the sides are used in the double-position computation.

These same computations can be set up for machine computation by using the natural sines and cosines of the azimuths. The azimuths are computed by following the procedure shown on page 326. Then each triangle is solved as if it were a traverse beginning on a known point and closing on a known point. The slight discrepancies are caused by rounding-off errors. In the accompanying tabulation is shown how the double-position computation on page 326 would be arranged when the work is performed by a desk computer.

Station	Length	Cos Azimuth	Sin Azimuth	Y	X
A				622,516.21	1,442,416.25
	2965.31	+0.937 22075	+0.348 73667	+2,779.15	+ 1,034.11
C				625,295.36	1,443,450.36
	3935.94	−0.893 19764	+0.449 66429	−3,515.57	+ 1,769.85
B				621,779.79	1,445,220.21
			Fixed	621,779.78	1,445,220.22
A				622,516.21	1,442,416.25
	3546.82	+0.732 76763	−0.680 47894	+2,598.99	− 2,413.54
D				625,115.20	1,440,002.71
	3452.35	+0.052 18331	+0.998 63752	+ 180.16	+ 3,447.65
C				625,295.36	1,443,450.36
			Fixed	625,295.36	1,443,450.36

The coordinates of all the stations throughout the triangulation system are computed by using the strongest route of triangles in the network. When a station is reached whose coordinates are fixed, the positions of the intermediate stations can then be adjusted. If the triangulation system is of great extent and high precision, this adjustment should be made by an application of the least-squares principle. If the system is moderate in extent, an application of the compass rule described in Sec. 8-16 will give highly satisfactory results. In this case, a traverse extending from one fixed point to another fixed point and including all the intermediate triangulation stations is selected in as direct a line as possible. This traverse is then adjusted by the compass rule.

10-33. Spherical Coordinates. When the triangulation system extends over a large area, as does the work of the U. S. Coast and Geodetic Survey, the coordinates of the stations are given as the latitudes and longitudes. In computing these geographic positions, the latitude ϕ and the longitude λ of one station either must be known or must be determined by astronomical observations. The coordinates ϕ' and λ' of any adjacent station can be computed when the azimuth a (reckoned from the south point) and the length s of the line connecting the two stations are known. The difference in latitude $\Delta\phi$ and the difference in longitude $\Delta\lambda$, in seconds of arc, which correspond with the latitude and departure of a side of a plane traverse, are calculated from the equations that follow:

$$- \Delta\phi = s \cos a \cdot B + s^2 \sin^2 a \cdot C + (\delta\phi)^2 D - hs^2 \sin^2 a \cdot E \quad (10\text{-}9)$$

$$\Delta\lambda = s \sin a \sec \phi' \cdot A \quad (10\text{-}10)$$

$$\phi' = \phi + \Delta\phi \quad (10\text{-}11)$$

$$\lambda' = \lambda + \Delta\lambda \quad (10\text{-}12)$$

$$- \delta\phi = s \cos a \cdot B + s^2 \sin^2 a \cdot C - hs^2 \sin^2 a \cdot E \quad (10\text{-}13)$$

$$h = s \cos a \cdot B \quad (10\text{-}14)$$

Because of the convergence of meridians, the difference between the forward azimuth and the back azimuth of a line will not be exactly 180°. The amount of this convergence, Δa, can be found from the relationship

$$- \Delta a = \Delta\lambda \sin \tfrac{1}{2} (\phi + \phi') \sec \tfrac{1}{2} (\Delta\phi) + (\Delta\lambda)^3 F \quad (10\text{-}15)$$

and the back azimuth is

$$a' = a + \Delta a + 180° \quad (10\text{-}16)$$

Logarithms of A, B, C, D, E, and F, for distances in meters, and forms for making the computations are given in *Special Publication No. 8* of the U. S. Coast and Geodetic Survey, entitled "Formulas and Tables for the Computation of Geodetic Positions," and in *Bulletin* 650 of the U. S. Geological Survey, entitled "Geographic Tables and Formulas." These tables in abbreviated form and the derivations of the formulas used in the calculations appear in most texts on geodesy. The derivations are given also in *Special Publication No. 8*.

When the length of a side is less than 15 miles, the computations can be shortened by omitting the term involving E in $\Delta\phi$, as well as the factor sec ½ ($\Delta\phi$) and the term involving F in Δa.

By means of the preceding equations, the reverse problem can also be solved; that is, when the geographic positions of two points are known, the azimuth and length of the line connecting them can be computed.

10-34. Precise Traverse. Under certain conditions, a traverse of high precision may be substituted for a triangulation network. In flat, heavily-wooded country the construction of towers and signals is a large item of expense in establishing a triangulation system. When such an area is crossed by railroads and paved highways, traverses may replace the triangulation. In establishing control for a city survey, where many control points are needed, the traverse can frequently be used to advantage.

In deciding between triangulation and traverse, the following considerations should be kept in mind. Traverse stations will usually be more available for the control of local surveys than will triangulation stations, since the latter are generally located in places more difficult of access. Because of this inaccessibility, the transportation of materials for the erection of towers and signals may be impossible and thus preclude the use of triangulation. On the other hand, triangulation stations are usually on high ground, and therefore are visible from much larger areas than are traverse stations. Besides, an arc of triangulation covers a belt of country at least 10 or 15 miles wide while the traverse is just a single line.

The electronic distance-measuring systems are successfully employed in measuring the lengths of lines in precise traverses. Their use, however, is restricted to traverses composed of lines at least ½ mile in length. The amount of time needed to measure a line ½ mile long with the electronic device is about the same as that required to measure the same line by using a tape. On shorter lines, taping the lines will prove more economical. Also, the inherent instrument errors, representing only a very small fraction of the length of a long line, are too large for lines under ½ mile in length.

As in the case of triangulation, traverses are classified as first-order, second-order, or third-order, according to the degree of precision attained. The requirements for the various orders are shown in Table 10-3.

TABLE 10-3
CLASSIFICATION OF TRAVERSES

	First-Order	Second-Order	Third-Order
Number of azimuth courses between azimuth checks not to exceed	15	25	50
Astronomical azimuth: Probable error of result	0.5″	2.0″	5.0″
Azimuth closure, in seconds, at azimuth check points not to exceed*	$2 \sqrt{N}$ or 1.0 per station	$10 \sqrt{N}$ or 3.0 per station	$30 \sqrt{N}$ or 8.0 per station
Distance measurements accurate within	1 in 35,000	1 in 15,000	1 in 7,500
After azimuth adjustment, closing error in position, in feet, not to exceed*	$0.66 \sqrt{M}$ or 1 in 25,000	$1.67 \sqrt{M}$ or 1 in 10,000	$3.34 \sqrt{M}$ or 1 in 5,000

*N is the number of stations for carrying azimuth
M is the distance in miles
The expressions for closing errors in traverse surveys are given in two forms.
The expression containing the square root is designed for longer lines where higher proportional accuracy is required. The requirement which gives the smaller permissible closure should be used.

No check on the precision of the traverse is available until the traverse has been closed and the latitudes and departures and the closures have been computed. The discrepancy is sometimes of such size that it is difficult to tell whether it is caused by a blunder or by an accumulation of small errors in the traverse. When a blunder has been made, it is often difficult to locate the incorrect value and it may be necessary to rerun a large part or all of the traverse line. In triangulation, as each quadrilateral is completed in the field, there are checks on both the angles and the lengths. Furthermore, the office computations for the adjustment of triangulation have automatic mathematical checks which are lacking in the computations for a traverse.

The lengths of lines used on traverses will, as a rule, be shorter than those for triangulation of the same order of precision, 5 miles being about the maximum length. The angles in a traverse are measured in the same manner as triangulation angles, that is, either by the direction method or by repetition. The measurement of the sides is conducted in the same manner as for base lines, except that the measurements are made wherever possible along a rail or along a paved highway. When the measurements must leave such lines, the tape is supported by driving stakes, as is done on base-line measurements. Some organizations that specialize in establishing control for city surveys use heavy cast-iron cradles, or taping bucks, for supporting the tape when measuring along city streets or sidewalks.

10-35. Trilateration. Because of the development of highly accurate electronic distance-measuring devices, a triangulation system can be completely observed, computed, and adjusted by measuring the lengths of the sides in the network. This procedure is known as *trilateration.* No horizontal angles need be measured because the lengths of the sides are sufficient to permit both the horizontal angles and the positions of the stations to be computed. However, in order to maintain accuracy in the azimuths of the lines in the trilateration net, astronomical observations are made at selected stations. These azimuths impose conditions on the network in the adjustment process.

Before the lengths of the lines can be used in any subsequent computations, their slope lengths determined by the instrument and corrected for atmospheric conditions must be reduced to the corresponding sea-level distances. Just as slope measurements discussed in Sec. 2-13 require auxiliary measurements to determine slope corrections, so do the lines in the trilateration net. The auxiliary data are either reciprocal vertical angles measured at the two ends of each line or the elevations of the two ends of each line.

10-36. Reduction of Slope Distance by Vertical Angles. In Fig. 10-12, the positive vertical angle α and the negative vertical angle β are measured from stations A and B, respectively. Vertical distances and angles have been greatly exaggerated in the diagram. The angle e is the refraction angle of the line of sight, assumed to be the same at both stations. It is further assumed that the height of the instrument above the ground and the height of the signal above the ground in each instance are the same, or that the two angles have been reduced to an equivalent situation.

The angle subtended at the center of the earth between the vertical lines through A and B is θ. In triangle OVB, the angle at V is $90° - \theta$, as shown, because the angle at B is $90°$.

The distance G is measured along the refracted line from A to B by the electronic instrument. This distance, within the range of the instrument, can be taken as the straight-line slope distance AB. The difference between the two distances in 100 miles is less than a foot, decreasing to a negligible amount in the range of the instruments.

In the triangle AVB,

$$(\beta + e) + (90° - \theta) + [(90° - \alpha) + e] = 180°$$

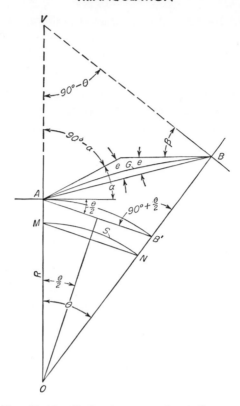

FIG. 10–12.   Reduction to sea-level distance.

or
$$2e = \alpha + \theta - \beta$$

and
$$e = \frac{\alpha}{2} - \frac{\beta}{2} + \frac{\theta}{2}$$

In the triangle ABB',

$$\angle\, BAB' = \alpha - e + \frac{\theta}{2} = \alpha - \left(\frac{\alpha}{2} - \frac{\beta}{2} + \frac{\theta}{2}\right) + \frac{\theta}{2}$$

or

$$\angle\, BAB' = \frac{\alpha + \beta}{2} \qquad\qquad\qquad (10\text{-}17)$$

Also the distance AB' is very nearly

$$AB' = AB \cos BAB' \qquad (\text{approx.}) \qquad\qquad (10\text{-}18)$$

With the approximate value of AB', the value of θ can be obtained with sufficient accuracy by the relationship

$$\sin \frac{\theta}{2} = \frac{AB'}{2R} \qquad (10\text{-}19)$$

where R is the radius of the earth in the area.

In the triangle ABB',

$$\angle ABB' = 90° - \frac{\theta}{2} - \angle BAB' \qquad (10\text{-}20)$$

The triangle ABB' can now be solved by the law of sines to give a more exact value of the distance AB'. Thus,

$$AB' = \frac{AB \sin ABB'}{\sin [90° + (\theta/2)]} \qquad (10\text{-}21)$$

The distance MN is the length of a chord connecting the sea-level positions of stations A and B, and is less than the length of the chord AB'. The amount to be subtracted from AB' is determined by an analysis of the sea-level correction given in Sec. 10-19. If C_1 denotes the amount by which the chord AB' must be reduced to obtain the chord MN,

$$C_1 = AB' \frac{h_A}{R} - AB' \frac{h_A^2}{R^2} \qquad (10\text{-}22)$$

where h_A = elevation of station A;

R = radius of the earth for the latitude of the area.

The sea-level length s is greater than the corresponding chord length MN. The amount to be added to MN to obtain s is found as follows:

$$MN = 2R \sin \frac{\theta}{2} = 2R \left(\frac{\theta}{2} - \frac{\theta^3}{48} + \frac{\theta^5}{3840} - \cdots \right)$$

$$s = R\theta = 2R \frac{\theta}{2}$$

$$s - MN = 2R \frac{\theta}{2} - 2R \frac{\theta}{2} + 2R \frac{\theta^3}{48} - 2R \frac{\theta^5}{3840}$$

If the last term is neglected, the result is

$$C_2 = R \frac{\theta^3}{24} = \frac{\overline{MN}^3}{24 R^2} \qquad (10\text{-}23)$$

where C_2 = amount to be added to the chord length to obtain the sea-level length of the line;

R = radius of the earth expressed in the same units as the measured distance;

θ = angle subtended by the line at the center of the earth, expressed in radians.

The value of C_2 is about 14 ft in a distance of 100 miles.

10-37. Reduction of Slope Distance by Station Elevations. In Fig. 10-13, the elevations of A and B are shown. The distance AB is

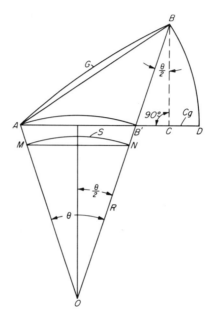

Fig. 10-13. Reduction to sea-level distance by station elevations.

again assumed to be the straight-line distance measured with the electronic instrument. This distance must be reduced to the chord distance AB'. The vertical distance BB' is the difference in elevation between A and B. Since the slopes are not great when trilateration is suitable, only the first term of the correction for grade in Eq. 2-3 is used to compute the difference between AB and AC. Since $AB = AD$, then $AB - AC = CD$. By Eq. 2-3, the correction for grade, in feet, is

$$CD = \frac{\overline{BB'}^2}{2\,AB} = \frac{(\Delta h)^2}{2G} \tag{10-24}$$

in which Δh is the difference in elevation, in feet, between the two ends of the line, and G is the measured slope distance, also in feet. If a line is 5 miles long and the difference in elevation between the two ends is 1000 ft, the second term in Eq. 2-3 amounts to about 0.07 ft. So, for shorter lines and large differences of elevation, the second term should be evaluated.

The angle $\theta/2$ in Fig. 10-13 may be obtained by Eq. 10-19. But the value of AB' is not known. Its approximate value, however, is AC, which can be found by subtracting the distance CD computed by Eq. 10-24 from the measured distance G; and the distance AC can be used in Eq. 10-19 instead of AB'. Also,

and

$$\sin \frac{\theta}{2} = \frac{B'C}{BB'} = \frac{B'C}{\Delta h}$$

$$B'C = \Delta h \sin \frac{\theta}{2} \tag{10-25}$$

Then, the distance $AB' = AB - (B'C + CD)$. Finally, the distance AB' is reduced to the sea level distance by applying Eqs. 10-22 and 10-23.

10-38. Adjustment of Trilateration. Although there are several ways in which a quadrilateral or a network of figures in a trilateration system can be adjusted, one which can be used when extreme accuracy is not required is as follows: The angles in each of the triangles are computed from the lengths of the sides, and then these angles are adjusted by methods given in Sec. 10-30. Formulas for the solution of oblique triangles where all the sides are known are given at the end of this book. As a check on the computed angles, the three angles in any triangle must add up to 180° exactly, whether or not spherical excess exists. If the spherical angles in a large triangle are needed for computation of spherical coordinates, one-third of the spherical excess is added to each computed angle.

Any approximate adjustment of trilateration will produce inconsistencies in subsequent computations. Therefore, if the work is on a large project where high accuracy is to be obtained, then a least-squares method of adjustment must be investigated.

One difficult problem in adjusting a trilateration net is that of assigning weights to the measured lengths. The probable errors for relatively short lines may be just as great as those for long lines, because of the inherent errors in the measuring system. The order of precision of a long line is higher than that of a short line because these inherent errors are rather constant. For example, suppose that an inherent error of 2 in. exists in the instrument. Then the precision for a line 1 mile long, is 1 part in 31,680, while the precision for a line 20 miles long, is 1 part in 633,600. If the probable error of each line can be determined by repeated measurements of each line, then the weights can be assumed to be inversely proportional to the squares of the probable errors, in accordance with Eq. 4-18. For a limited net with relatively few lines, all of which have lengths of the same order of magnitude, then a unit weight can be given to each line.

10-39. Computation of Lengths of Sides. If an approximate method of adjustment of the computed angles is used first, the lengths of the sides must be recomputed to be consistent with the adjusted angles. Before this recalculation can be performed, the strongest triangle in each of the quadrilaterals must be selected, and one side of this triangle must be held fixed and equal to the reduced sea-level distance. If, however, the trilateration begins from a line joining two points with fixed positions, then the fixed length of that line will be used to compute the sides.

10-40. Computation of Plane Coordinates. The positions of the stations in the trilateration system may be computed by applying the procedures described in Sec. 10-32.

BIBLIOGRAPHY

BOMFORD, BRIGADIER G. *Geodesy,* 2nd ed. London: Oxford University Press, 1962.

FORMULAS AND TABLES FOR THE COMPUTATION OF GEODETIC POSITIONS. *Special Publication No. 8,* U.S. Coast and Geodetic Survey, Government Printing Office.

HODGSON, C. V. "Manual of First-Order Triangulation," *Special Publication No. 120,* U.S. Coast and Geodetic Survey, Government Printing Office.

―――. "Manual of Second- and Third-Order Triangulation and Traverse," *Special Publication No. 145,* U.S. Coast and Geodetic Survey, Government Printing Office.

HOSMER, G. L. *Geodesy,* 2d ed. New York: John Wiley & Sons, Inc., 1930.

LAURILA, S. *Electronic Surveying and Mapping.* The Ohio State University, 1960.

REYNOLDS, W. F. "Manual of Triangulation Computations and Adjustment," *Special Publication No. 138,* U.S. Coast and Geodetic Survey, Government Printing Office.

PROBLEMS

10-1. Determine R_1 and R_2 for each of the quadrilaterals shown in the accompanying illustration. The starting side is AB.

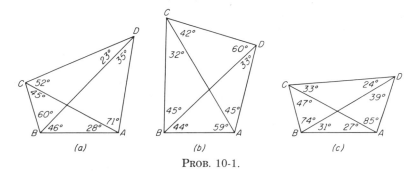

PROB. 10-1.

10-2. Determine the value of D and C for each of the figures shown in the illustration. In (a) the center point is occupied. A dashed line going into a station means that a sight was made on that station, but that the line was not sighted from that station. If all lines going into a station are dashed, the station is presumed not to have been occupied.

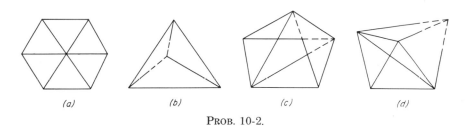

PROB. 10-2.

10-3. Towers of equal heights are to be erected on opposite shores of a body of water 18 miles wide. The line of sight is to clear the water by 20 ft. The theodolite is presumed to sit atop each tower, and so no allowance need be made for the height of a tripod. Scaffolding is constructed around each tower but independent of the tower, so that the observer may move without disturbing the instrument. How high must the towers be?

10-4. A signal is to be erected on the opposite side of a bay from a triangulation station. The bay is 16 miles wide along this line. If the theodolite stands on its tripod 5 ft above the triangulation station, how high must the signal be raised in order that the line of sight from the theodolite to the signal will just clear the water?

10-5. The coefficient of thermal expansion of a 50-meter invar base-line tape is 2.0×10^{-7} per deg F. What is the effect on a 10-mile base line measured with the tape, if the temperature differs 15 deg F from standard?

10-6. The difference in elevation between the tops of two base-line posts set 50 meters apart is 16.35 ft. If this difference is in error by 0.10 ft, what is the effect on the correction for grade? Round off the result to the nearest 0.0001 meter.

10-7. The average elevation of a base line is 3760 ft, and the length of the base is 27,326.22 ft. What is the length reduced to sea level?

10-8. A direction theodolite is set up at E in the accompanying illustration. The following directions were observed.

To Station	Mean Direction
A	266° 14′ 26.8″
B	341° 28′ 19.1″
C	50° 52′ 03.2″
D	96° 31′ 32.0″
G	158° 57′ 43.8″

Compute the directions from A to B, C, D, and G. Prepare an abstract of these directions, taking the direction from A to B as 0° 00′ 00.0″.

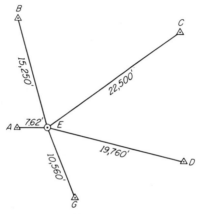

PROB. 10-8.

10-9. The hypotenuse of a triangle with angles of 45°, 45°, and 90° is 38 miles long. The triangle lies in latitude 45°. Compute the spherical excess.

10-10. In the quadrilateral represented in the accompanying illustration,

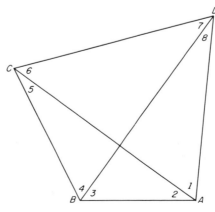

PROB. 10-10.

all angles were measured with the same degree of precision, and the results were as follows:

Angle	Value	Angle	Value
1	56° 24′ 10.0″	5	25° 18′ 16.8″
2	33° 53′ 35.0″	6	58° 54′ 57.5″
3	62° 03′ 27.6″	7	37° 02′ 04.4″
4	58° 44′ 39.0″	8	27° 38′ 46.5″

Adjust the quadrilateral by the approximate method of Sec. 10-30.

10-11. In the quadrilateral in Problem 10-10, the coordinates of A are $X_A = 1,524,472.25$ ft and $Y_A = 624,502.34$ ft; and the coordinates of B are $X_B = 1,510,235.70$ ft and $Y_B = 627,355.52$ ft. Compute the length and azimuth of AB. Then solve the triangle DAB. Finally, compute the coordinates of D by a double-position computation.

10-12. Using the length of DB computed in Problem 10-11, solve the triangle CDB, and compute the coordinates of C by a double-position computation.

10-13. Trilateration station A is at an elevation of 1360 ft above sea level; and station B is at an elevation of 4980 ft. The distance from station A to station B, as measured by using a geodimeter, is 28,545.60 meters. The line lies in latitude 45° approximately, and log R in meters for that latitude is 6.80 4701. Reduce this distance to sea level.

11

State Plane Coordinate Systems

11-1. Purpose. In Chapter 8 was discussed the use of plane rectangular coordinates as applied to plane surveying, not only for defining the positions of survey stations, but also for solving such diverse problems as determining areas, locating the intersections of lines and curves, parting off land, and computing lengths and azimuths. No mention was made, however, of the extent of any given plane coordinate system. The methods of plane surveying are based on the assumption that all distances and directions are projected onto a horizontal plane surface which is tangent to the surface of the earth at one point within the area of the survey.

If two surveys are made independently of each other, then the measurements in each survey are referred to two different horizontal planes which, of course, do not coincide. Furthermore, if the Y-axis of a plane coordinate system for each of the two surveys is assumed to be parallel to the true meridian at one station of the survey, then even the Y-axes of the two systems are not parallel with one another because of the convergence of the meridians. In a given system, the farther the survey departs from the point of tangency, the more will the distances and angles as measured on the ground differ from the corresponding distances and angles as projected onto the horizontal plane. When this discrepancy becomes intolerable, then the limits of plane surveying and its inherent simplicity have been reached.

In Chapter 10 are discussed briefly the methods of geodetic surveying wherein all distances are reduced to a common reference surface conforming closely to the sea-level surface. Angles in triangles are considered as spherical (sometimes spheroidal) angles. Coordinates of points are computed with reference to parallels of latitude and meridians of longitude by using angles computed near the center of the earth rather than distances. Geodetic surveying is employed so that precise surveys may be extended over great distances in any direction without suffering the limitations of plane-surveying methods. Geodetic-surveying methods are more complex and more expensive, they involve more difficult computations, and they require specialized personnel in their execution.

For more than a century, large surveying and mapping organizations of the Federal government, notably the U. S. Coast and Geodetic Survey, have established horizontal control monuments in the form of triangulation, traverse, and intersection stations. These stations have been located by the methods of geodetic surveying. The network formed by these control points is being constantly filled in and added to by the same organizations. All the control points throughout the country bear a definite relationship, one to another, being referred to one common spheroidal surface.

The state plane coordinate systems have been devised to allow methods of plane surveying to be used over great distances in any direction. At the same time, a precision approaching that of geodetic surveying is maintained. As a result surveyors and engineers can incorporate the network of control established by geodetic surveying into their own surveys for purposes of coordination, checking, and reestablishing lost points.

If a land surveyor runs a traverse from one of these stations to the nearest corner of the land which he is to survey, he can calculate readily the state-coordinate position for each corner of the land and has in effect keyed his survey to all the stations of the national geodetic survey. As a result, all stations of the national geodetic survey become witnesses to the positions of the land corners whose coordinates on a state system are known. The material marks of the land corners, such as trees, stones, fence posts, or other monuments, may be destroyed, and yet the positions they occupied on the ground can be closely reproduced from any recoverable stations of the national survey which are within practical distances of these corners. In this manner, a survey station or land corner which is described in terms of a state coordinate system is practically indestructible.

The system is of great value to highway engineers and others whose work covers very large areas. Many surveys, which in the past would have been open traverses with few checks on their accuracy, can now start from one known point and end on another, these points providing a closure for the traverse.

The state coordinate systems are shown on many federal maps, particularly on topographic maps. These maps thus become useful to engineers who desire data for reducing their surveys to a state grid.

At the same time their own surveys become available for transfer to the map.

11-2. Limits of State Plane Coordinate Systems. Just as a map of a considerable portion of the earth's surface is a compromise when compiled on a plane surface, namely, the map sheet, so must a state plane coordinate system be a compromise since it represents a spheroidal surface projected onto a curved surface which may be developed into a plane surface. However, this compromise does not prove to be at all serious for two reasons: 1) Any distortion suffered through the transformation of the spheroidal surface to the plane surface may be allowed for by simple arithmetic. 2) If the extent of the earth's surface to be represented by a plane surface is limited, then the distortion may be neglected entirely except for a special survey requiring great accuracy; in such a case, the distortion is eliminated by simple computation.

If a state is not too large, the entire state can be embraced in one projection. If the state is of such size that the distortions in one projection would be too great to be ignored, then the state is divided into *zones* of appropriate size. These zones are broken along county lines to permit an entire county to be included in the same zone.

Two types of projections are employed in developing the state plane coordinate systems, namely, the *transverse Mercator projection* and the *Lambert conformal projection*. The transverse Mercator projection employs a cylindrical surface, the axis of which is normal to the earth's axis of rotation and which intersects the surface of the earth along two ellipses equidistant from a meridian plane through the center of the area to be projected. The distortions occur in the east-west direction, and therefore the projection is used for states or zones which have relatively short east-west dimensions. An example is Vermont.

The Lambert conformal projection employs a conical surface, the axis of which coincides with the earth's axis of rotation and which intersects the surface of the earth along two parallels of latitude that are approximately equidistant from a parallel lying in the center of the area to be projected. The distortions occur in a north-south direction, and therefore the projection is used for states or zones with relatively short north-south dimensions. An example is Tennessee.

If the distance in an east-west direction in a transverse Mercator projection is limited to about 158 miles, or if the distance in a north-south direction in a Lambert projection is limited to about 158 miles, then the distortions will be such that a distance at sea level will not differ from the corresponding projected distance by any more than 1

TABLE 11-1

State Plane Coordinate Systems

State and Zone	Grid	State and Zone	Grid
Alabama		Illinois	
East	Tr. Merc.	East	Tr. Merc.
West	Tr. Merc.	West	Tr. Merc.
Alaska*		Indiana	
		East	Tr. Merc.
Arizona		West	Tr. Merc.
East	Tr. Merc.		
Central	Tr. Merc.	Iowa	
West	Tr. Merc.	North	Lambert
		South	Lambert
Arkansas			
North	Lambert	Kansas	
South	Lambert	North	Lambert
		South	Lambert
California			
Zone 1	Lambert	Kentucky	
Zone 2	Lambert	North	Lambert
Zone 3	Lambert	South	Lambert
Zone 4	Lambert		
Zone 5	Lambert	Louisiana	
Zone 6	Lambert	North	Lambert
Zone 7	Lambert	South	Lambert
Colorado			
North	Lambert	Maine	
Central	Lambert	East	Tr. Merc.
South	Lambert	West	Tr. Merc.
Connecticut	Lambert	Maryland	Lambert
Delaware	Tr. Merc.	Massachusetts	
		Mainland	Lambert
Florida		Island	Lambert
East	Tr. Merc.		
West	Tr. Merc.	Michigan	
North	Lambert	East	Tr. Merc.
		Central	Tr. Merc.
Georgia		West	Tr. Merc.
East	Tr. Merc.		
West	Tr. Merc.	Minnesota	
		North	Lambert
Hawaii		Central	Lambert
Zone 1	Tr. Merc.	South	Lambert
Zone 2	Tr. Merc.		
Zone 3	Tr. Merc.	Mississippi	
Zone 4	Tr. Merc.	East	Tr. Merc.
Zone 5	Tr. Merc.	West	Tr. Merc.
Idaho		Missouri	
East	Tr. Merc.	East	Tr. Merc.
Central	Tr. Merc.	Central	Tr. Merc.
West	Tr. Merc.	West	Tr. Merc.

*Alaska is divided into 10 zones although projection tables are not available. Zone 1 is an oblique transverse Mercator projection; Zones 2 through 9 are Mercator transverse projections; and Zone 10 is a Lambert projection.

Table 11-1 (Continued)

State and Zone	Grid	State and Zone	Grid
Montana		Rhode Island	Tr. Merc.
North	Lambert		
Central	Lambert	South Carolina	
South	Lambert	North	Lambert
		South	Lambert
Nebraska			
North	Lambert	South Dakota	
South	Lambert	North	Lambert
		South	Lambert
Nevada			
East	Tr. Merc.	Tennessee	Lambert
Central	Tr. Merc.		
West	Tr. Merc.	Texas	
		North	Lambert
New Hampshire	Tr. Merc.	North Cent.	Lambert
		Central	Lambert
New Jersey	Tr. Merc.	South Cent.	Lambert
		South	Lambert
New Mexico			
East	Tr. Merc.	Utah	
Central	Tr. Merc.	North	Lambert
West	Tr. Merc.	Central	Lambert
		South	Lambert
New York			
Long Island	Lambert	Vermont	Tr. Merc.
East	Tr. Merc.		
Central	Tr. Merc.	Virginia	
West	Tr. Merc.	North	Lambert
		South	Lambert
North Carolina	Lambert		
		Washington	
North Dakota		North	Lambert
North	Lambert	South	Lambert
South	Lambert		
		West Virginia	
Ohio		North	Lambert
North	Lambert	South	Lambert
South	Lambert		
		Wisconsin	
Oklahoma		North	Lambert
North	Lambert	Central	Lambert
South	Lambert	South	Lambert
Oregon		Wyoming	
North	Lambert	Zone I	Tr. Merc.
South	Lambert	Zone II	Tr. Merc.
		Zone III	Tr. Merc.
Pennsylvania		Zone IV	Tr. Merc.
North	Lambert		
South	Lambert		

part in 10,000. Thus it becomes necessary to assign more than one projection to some individual states. California, for example, has seven Lambert zones; Michigan has three transverse Mercator zones; New York has three transverse Mercator zones to cover all but Long Island, which is covered by one Lambert zone. Florida has two transverse Mercator zones covering the peninsula proper and one Lambert zone which covers the western portion of the state. In Table 11-1 are shown the number and type of projections covering the various states.

11-3. Geodetic and Grid Azimuths. In placing a survey on a system of plane rectangular coordinates, all bearings or azimuths are referred to the same meridian. Since the system is rectangular, all grid north-and-south lines are parallel to a *central meridian*. In general there is a difference between the grid azimuth or bearing of a line and its geodetic azimuth or bearing. This difference is caused by the convergence of meridians, the amount increasing with the latitude and the distance from the central meridian. When the grid coordinates of the two ends of a starting line are known, its azimuth may be computed by either Eq. 8-15 or Eq. 8-16, and its length by Eq. 8-12.

The geodetic azimuth of a line is a computed azimuth based on triangulation and traverse observations, computations, and adjustments resulting from geodetic surveying. It is always reckoned from the south part of the meridian. The difference between true or astronomical azimuth as defined in Sec. 5-6 and geodetic azimuth is relatively small and is caused by the fact that the plumb line at a station is deflected from a true normal to the spheroid of computation for geodetic positions. The geodetic azimuth of a line is that published by the U. S. Coast and Geodetic Survey along with the geodetic positions in triangulation and traverse networks.

It is frequently important for the surveyor to know the difference between the geodetic and grid azimuths of a survey line, for purposes of obtaining a check on a computed value, or to provide a starting azimuth for a survey. On the Lambert grid, the angle between the geodetic and grid azimuths is designated by θ and is listed in the state projection tables. On the transverse Mercator grid the angle is $\Delta\alpha$, employed in geodetic computations to represent the convergence of the meridians. In current publications of state-coordinate position data, the appropriate value of θ or $\Delta\alpha$ is listed for each station.

A line on the surface of the spheroid representing a line of sight between two points or, more exactly, representing the most direct path between the two points, can be thought of as a "great circle," as would be the case if the sea-level surface were a true sphere. This line is referred to as a geodetic line. The geodetic line projected onto the Lambert grid or the transverse Mercator grid would in general show a slight curvature. Thus, if long lines are involved and utmost accuracy is to be obtained, the difference between geodetic and grid azimuths is slightly different from the values of θ and $\Delta\alpha$ (see Secs. 11-5 and 11-9).

11-4. Transverse Mercator Projection. The transverse Mercator projection is represented diagrammatically in Fig. 11-1. In view (*a*) is shown the sea-level surface of the earth intersected by a cylindrical surface along the two ellipses $AE'A'$ and $BE''B'$, which are equidistant from a *central meridian PES*. In view (*b*) is shown a portion of the cylindrical surface developed into a plane surface on which have been projected mathematically the meridians and parallels of the earth's surface. On the development each ellipse appears as a straight line parallel to and equidistant from the central meridian.

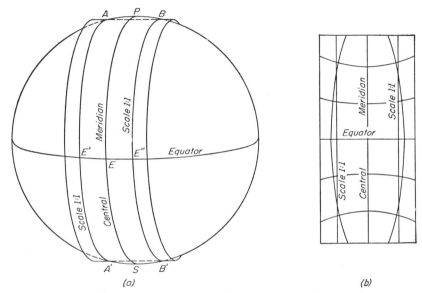

Fig. 11-1. Transverse Mercator projection.

Along either of these two lines, a distance on the projection is the same as the corresponding distance on the sea-level surface. Between the two lines, a distance on the projection is smaller than the corresponding distance on the sea-level surface. Outside the two lines, a distance on the projection is larger than the corresponding distance on the sea-level surface. The discrepancy between these corresponding distances depends on the position of the line being considered with respect to the central meridian. It is seen that the scale of a line running in an east-west direction varies from point to point. It is also seen, however, that a line on the projection parallel to the central meridian has a constant scale throughout its length, whether this scale be larger than, equal to, or less than that on the corresponding sea-level line.

To apply the transverse Mercator projection to a state or a zone, the width of the projection is limited to 158 miles, and the lines along which the scale of the projection is exact are separated by about two-thirds this distance. At no point within these limits will the discrepancy between a sea-level distance and the projected distance, called the *grid distance*, be greater than 1 part in 10,000.

11-5. Grid Azimuth on Transverse Mercator Projection. With but two exceptions, a line run on the surface of the earth as a straight line does not have a constant azimuth with respect to the true meridians, because of the convergence of these meridians. The exceptions are a straight line run along the true meridian from which the azimuth angle is measured and a line run along the equator. For example, a secant line run to establish a parallel of latitude, as described in Sec. 17-8, extends due east or due west at one point only. Immediately on leaving this point, the secant runs in a southeasterly or southwesterly direction.

In the transverse Mercator system of plane coordinates, the azimuth of any line is referred to the central meridian. This azimuth is also referred to any line parallel to the central meridian. The direction of each of this series of parallel lines is *grid north*. Thus, a straight line on the transverse Mercator projection has a constant azimuth throughout its length. The angle between the grid north and the true north at a point on this projection depends on two things: 1) the distance from the central meridian to the point ; 2) the latitude of the point.

In Fig. 11-2, P is a station whose latitude and longitude are, respectively, ϕ and λ. The line parallel to the central meridian passing through P is grid north. The curved line making the angle $\Delta\alpha$ with grid north at P is the true meridian through P. The straight line PP', making an angle of 90° with the central meridian, is the projection of the arc of a great circle (nearly) passing through P. It intersects the central meridian at P', whose coordinates are ϕ' and λ_m. The parallel of latitude through P is a curved line intersecting the central meridian at R. The latitude of R is ϕ. The value of $\Delta\alpha$ is the

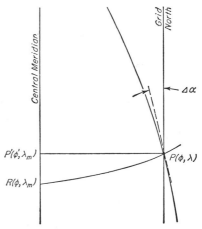

FIG. 11-2. Relationship between geodetic and grid azimuths on transverse Mercator projection.

same as that given in Chapter 10 for computing geodetic positions. Thus,

$$- \Delta\alpha = \Delta\lambda \sin \tfrac{1}{2} (\phi + \phi') \sec \tfrac{1}{2} (\phi - \phi') + (\Delta\lambda)^3 F \qquad (11\text{-}1)$$

Since the value of $\sec \tfrac{1}{2} (\phi - \phi')$ is practically unity, and since the term containing F is small except for very exact determinations, the equation for $\Delta\alpha$ may be reduced to

$$- \Delta\alpha = \Delta\lambda \sin \tfrac{1}{2} (\phi + \phi') \qquad (11\text{-}1a)$$

where $\Delta\lambda$ is the difference between the longitude of the station and the longitude of the central meridian for the given projection. It is found from the relationship

$$\Delta\lambda = \lambda_m - \lambda \qquad (11\text{-}2)$$

where λ_m = longitude of the central meridian;
λ = longitude of the station.

If the station lies east of the central meridian, then $\Delta\lambda$ is positive (+). If the station lies west of the central meridian, $\Delta\lambda$ is negative (−). Because the direction in which $\Delta\lambda$ is computed by Eq. 11-2 is opposite to that in which it is reckoned in Chapter 10, the algebraic sign of $\Delta\alpha$ as computed by Eq. 11-1a is the same as the algebraic sign of $\Delta\lambda$. Thus, if the station lies east of the central meridian, $\Delta\alpha$ is positive; and if to the west, $\Delta\alpha$ is negative.

The relationship between the true azimuth and the grid azimuth of a line originating in P is given by the expression

$$\text{Geodetic azimuth} - \text{grid azimuth} = \Delta\alpha \qquad (11\text{-}3)$$

The difference between the true and geodetic azimuths is explained in Sec. 11-3.

In Fig. 11-3, lines AB and CD lie to the west of the central meridian, and EF and GH lie to the east of the central meridian. The grid lines joining the end points are straight lines in every case. The ground line, or geodetic line, joining any pair of end points, however, is curved when projected onto the grid. Furthermore, this curvature, which is greatly exaggerated in Fig. 11-3, increases outward from the central meridian. To allow for this curvature in going from the geodetic azimuth to the grid azimuth, or vice versa, when a line longer than 5 miles is involved, Eq. 11-3 must be modified by a small correction term. Thus,

Geodetic azimuth − grid azimuth

$$= \Delta\alpha + \frac{(Y_2 - Y_1)(2X'_1 + X'_2)}{(6\rho_0{}^2 \sin 1'')_g} \qquad (11\text{-}3a)$$

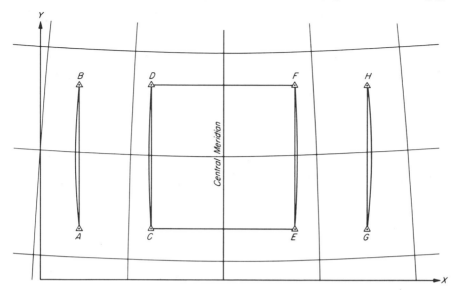

FIG. 11–3. Curvature of geodetic lines on transverse Mercator projection.

in which X'_1 and X'_2 are the X-coordinates of the origin and terminal of the line, respectively, *referred to the central meridian* (see Eq. 11-9); Y_1 and Y_2 are the Y-coordinates; and ρ_0 is the mean radius of the earth in the vicinity of the projection. The subscript g indicates that the value of ρ_0 has been reduced by a scale factor. Due regard must be given to the sign of the X'-coordinates and of the value $Y_2 - Y_1$. Notice that if the line is grid east-west, as is the line DF or CE in Fig. 11-3, no correction need be applied to $\Delta\alpha$ since $Y_2 - Y_1 = 0$.

11-6. Geographic to Plane Coordinates on Transverse Mercator Projection. The origin of coordinates on the transverse Mercator projection is taken far enough south and west of the zone covered to render all values of coordinates positive. To make all the X-coordinates positive, the central meridian, which is the Y-axis, is assigned a large X-value denoted by X_0; usually, $X_0 = 500,000$ ft.* The X-axis is a line perpendicular to the central meridian where $Y = 0$.

The Y-coordinate of a point on the central meridian is equal to the sea-level distance along the central meridian measured from the intersection of the X-axis and the central meridian to the point and adjusted for the scale along the central meridian. The X-coordinate of a point on the central meridian is, of course, the same as the X-value of the central meridian.

* Exceptions are: Rhode Island, 600,000 ft; Georgia East, 2,000,000 ft; and Georgia West, 2,000,000 ft.

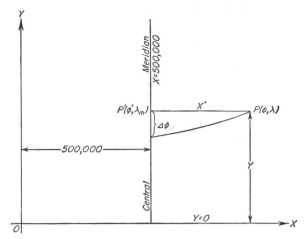

FIG. 11–4.   Rectangular coordinates on transverse
Mercator projection.

Before the Y- and X-coordinates of any point whose latitude and longitude are known can be determined, the sea-level length of a line passing through the point and perpendicular to the central meridian must first be computed. The latitude of the foot of this perpendicular on the central meridian must then be determined. In Fig. 11-4, P is a point whose latitude and longitude are ϕ and λ. The line $P'P$ is the sea-level line passing through P and perpendicular to the central meridian at P'. The azimuth (from south) of the line from P' to P is therefore 270°. The sea-level length of this line may be determined by the equation for $\Delta\lambda$ in the computation for geodetic positions. (See Chapter 10 and *Special Publication 8*, U. S. Coast and Geodetic Survey.) This length is given by the equation

$$\log \Delta\lambda = \log s + c_{\log \Delta\lambda} - c_{\log s} + \log \sin \alpha + \log A + \log \sec \phi$$

where $\Delta\lambda$ = difference in longitude between the point and the central meridian;

  s = sea-level length of the line $P'P$, in meters;

  α = azimuth of $P'P$;

  A = factor A for the known point P;

  ϕ = latitude of point P.

The terms denoted by c are the correction sine to arc of the angle $\Delta\lambda$ and the correction arc to sine of the distance s, obtained from *Special Publication 8*. Since the azimuth of $P'P$ is 270°, $\log \sin \alpha = 0$. Transposing terms then gives the following equation for the distance s, in meters:

$$\log s = \log \Delta\lambda - c_{\log \Delta\lambda} + \log \cos \phi + \text{colog } A + c_{\log s} \quad (11\text{-}4)$$

In Eq. 11-4, $\Delta\lambda$ is positive if the point is east of the central meridian and is negative if the point is west of the central meridian.

The latitude of P' is determined from the equation for $-\Delta\phi$ in the computation for geodetic position, which is

$$-\Delta\phi = B\,s\cos\alpha + C\,s^2\sin^2\alpha + (\delta\,\phi)^2\,D - E\,h\,s^2\sin^2\alpha$$

where $-\Delta\phi =$ minus the difference in latitude going from P' to P;

$\qquad\quad C =$ factor C for the unknown point P';

$\qquad\quad \alpha =$ azimuth of the line $P'P$, which is $270°$.

Since $\cos\alpha = 0$, the first term drops out. Also, because the difference in latitude between P' and P can never be very large, the terms containing D and E are both neglected. So

$$-\Delta\phi = C\,s^2 \qquad\qquad (11\text{-}5)$$

The distance s in meters is obtained from Eq. 11-4. The value of C should be obtained for the latitude of P'. However, since this is as yet unknown, the preliminary value of C for the known latitude of the point P is used. Then, when the preliminary value of ϕ' is determined, a better value of C is obtained to give a corrected value of $-\Delta\phi$. It should be noted that the numerical value of $\Delta\phi$ is always added to the latitude ϕ of point P to obtain ϕ'. Therefore,

$$\phi' = \phi + \Delta\phi \qquad\qquad (11\text{-}6)$$

Once the value of ϕ' has been determined, the Y-coordinate of P', and hence of P, is obtained by interpolation in Table I of the tables prepared for the particular projection by the U. S. Coast and Geodetic Survey. This coordinate is a true length along the central meridian reduced for the scale along the central meridian. Therefore it may be tabulated for each latitude.

The length of the line $P'P$ on the plane projection is obtained by the equation

$$X' = s_g + \frac{s_g{}^3}{(6\,\rho_0{}^2)_g} \qquad\qquad (11\text{-}7)$$

where $X' =$ grid length of $P'P$ corresponding to s (the sea-level length of $P'P$);

$\qquad\quad s_g =$ distance s converted to feet and reduced by the over-all scale reduction of the projection;

$\qquad\quad \rho_0 =$ the mean radius of curvature of the spheroid, in feet, in the vicinity of the projection.

This radius is assumed to be constant for any given projection, and has also been reduced by the over-all scale reduction.

The X-coordinate of the point P may now be determined by adding the value of X' to the X-coordinate of the central meridian. Thus,

$$X = X_0 + X' \tag{11-8}$$

If $\Delta\lambda$ is negative, then s and consequently X' will also be minus, and the value of X will be less than X_0.

To summarize, the equations are here repeated in their order of solution as follows:

$$\Delta\lambda = \lambda_m - \lambda \tag{[11-2]}$$

$$\log s = \log \Delta\lambda - c_{\log \Delta\lambda} + \log \cos \phi + \mathrm{colog}\, A + c_{\log s} \tag{[11-4]}$$

$$-\Delta\phi = C\, s^2 \tag{[11-5]}$$

$$\phi' = \phi + \Delta\phi \tag{[11-6]}$$

The value Y is found by interpolating in table with ϕ' as argument.

$$X' = s_g + \frac{s_g{}^3}{(6\, \rho_0{}^2)_g} \tag{[11-7]}$$

$$X = X_0 + X' \tag{[11-8]}$$

The values of $c_{\log \Delta\lambda}$ and $c_{\log s}$ are given in *Special Publication 8*, U. S. Coast and Geodetic Survey. The values of the other quantities are found from suitable tables described in the following section.

11-7. Tables for Transverse Mercator Projections. The U. S. Coast and Geodetic Survey has prepared tables for each projection in each state and makes them available through the Government Printing Office. In addition to these prepared tables, *Special Publication 8* is needed, as explained in the preceding section. The accompanying tabulation shows a portion of Tables I, II, and III for Rhode Island, which is covered by a single zone.

Table I is provided to find the value of Y by using ϕ' computed from Eq. 11-6 as the argument. Table II gives the value of colog A used in Eq. 11-4 and also the value of log C used in Eq. 11-5. To find colog A, the latitude of the point is used as the argument. To find log C, the latitude ϕ of the point is first used as the argument, and the more accurate value is found when ϕ' has been determined approximately.

Table III gives the amount by which a sea-level length must be increased or decreased to give the corresponding grid length. If logarithms are used, one column gives the amount by which the logarithm of a sea-level length must be increased or decreased to get the logarithm of a grid length. The other column gives the scale factor which

TRANSVERSE MERCATOR PROJECTION FOR RHODE ISLAND

Table I

Latitude	Y (feet)	Tabular Difference (for 1 second of latitude)
41° 11′	36,434.99	101.20933
12′	42,507.55	101.20967
13′	48,580.13	101.20983
14′	54,652.72	101.21033
15′	60,725.34	101.21050

Table II

Latitude	Colog A	Log C
41° 11′	1.490 91165	1.34 6361
12′	208	6614
13′	250	6867
14′	293	7120
15′	335	7374

Table III

X′ (feet)	Scale (in units of 7th place of logs)	Scale (expressed as ratio)
65,000	− 6.1	0.999 9986
70,000	− 2.8	0.999 9994
75,000	+ 0.8	1.000 0002
80,000	+ 4.7	1.000 0011
85,000	+ 8.8	1.000 0020

Constants

λ_m (central meridian) $= 71° 30′ 00.000″$
$R = -27.1$
$\log 1/(6\rho_0^2)_g = 4.580\ 8361$
$\log 1/(6\rho_0^2 \sin 1″)_g = 9.895\ 2612 - 20$
$X = 600,000 + X′$

is multiplied by the sea-level length to get the corresponding grid length. The argument to be used in determining these values is the distance $X′$ to the point or area from the central meridian. If the X-coordinate of a point is known, the proper scale factor is determined from the table by first computing $X′$ by applying the equation

$$X′ = X - X_0 \qquad (11\text{-}9)$$

The value without the algebraic sign is used as the argument.

The constants given are the longitude λ_m of the central meridian; the value of R, which is the over-all scale-reduction factor needed to solve Eq. 11-7; $\log 1/(6\rho_0^2)_g$, which is also used in Eq. 11-7; $\log 1/(6\rho_0^2 \sin 1″)_g$, which is used in the second term of Eq. 11-3a; and the value of X_0. The value of R is the number of units applied to the seventh decimal place in log s, expressed in feet.

EXAMPLE 11-1. The latitude and longitude of a control point in Rhoae Island are $\phi = 41° 12' 24.220''$ and $\lambda = 71° 02' 15.463''$. Compute the coordinates of the control point on the transverse Mercator grid for Rhode Island.

Solution: The difference in longitude is first computed by Eq. 11-2. Thus,
$$\Delta\lambda = 71° 30' 00.000'' - 71° 02' 15.463'' = + 0° 27' 44.537'' = + 1664.537''$$
Next the value of s is computed. This is the sea-level length of the line perpendicular to the central meridian from the point to the central meridian. Since s is not known as yet, the value $c_{\log s}$ must initially be left out of Eq. 11-4. The work then proceeds as follows:

$\log \Delta\lambda =$	3.221 2935	
$c_{\log} \Delta\lambda =$	-48	(Spec. Pub. 8, reverse sign)
$\log \Delta\lambda_1 =$	3.221 2887	
$\log \cos \phi =$	9.876 4127	(Latitude of given point)
$\mathrm{colog}\ A =$	1.490 9123	(Table II of Projection Tables)
$\log s_1 =$	4.588 6137	
$c_{\log s} =$	$+27$	(Spec. Pub. 8, reverse sign)
$\log s_m =$	4.588 6164	(Used in Eq. 11-5)
$\log 3937/1200 =$	0.515 9842	(Convert from meters to feet)
$\log R =$	-27	(From constants in Projection Tables)
$\log s_g =$	5.104 5979	(Distance s reduced to scale of projection)
$\log s_g{}^3 =$	15.313 7937	(Used in Eq. 11-7)
$\log 1/(6\rho_0{}^2)_g =$	4.580 8361-20	(From constants in Projection Tables)
$\log s_g{}^3/(6\rho_0{}^2)_g =$	9.894 6298-10	(Used in Eq. 11-7)
$s_g =$	$+127{,}232.46$	
$s_g{}^3/(6\rho_0{}^2)_g =$	$+0.78$	
$X' =$	$+127{,}233.24$	(By Eq. 11-7)
$X_0 =$	$600{,}000.00$	
$X =$	$727{,}233.24$	(By Eq. 11-8)
$\log s_m{}^2 =$	9.17 7233	(Used in Eq. 11-5)
$\log C =$	1.34 6716	(for lat. ϕ, Table II of Projection Tables)
$\log \Delta\phi =$	0.52 3949	(By Eq. 11-5, tentative)
$\phi =$	$41° 12' 24.220''$	
$\Delta\phi =$	$+3.342''$	
$\phi' =$	$41° 12' 27.562''$	(By Eq. 11-6, tentative)
$\log s_m{}^2 =$	9.17 7233	
$\log C =$	1.34 6730	(for lat. ϕ' tentative, Table II)
$\log \Delta\phi =$	0.52 3963	(By Eq. 11-5)
$\phi =$	$41° 12' 24.220''$	
$\Delta\phi =$	$+3.342''$	
$\phi' =$	$41° 12' 27.562''$	(By Eq. 11-6)

Y (for minutes of ϕ') =	42,507.55	(Table I)
Y (for seconds of ϕ') =	2,789.54	(101.20967 × 27.562, Table I)
$Y =$	45,297.09	

EXAMPLE 11-2. A line joins the control point in Example 11-1 with a point whose coordinates are $X = 710,206.91$ ft and $Y = 131,643.20$ ft. Compute the geodetic azimuth of this line in the direction of the second point. Evaluate the term in Eq. 11-1 containing F in determining $\Delta\alpha$.

Solution: Apply Eq. 8-16 as follows:

$$X_1 = 727,233.24 \qquad Y_1 = 45,297.09 \qquad \log(X_1 - X_2) = 4.231\ 1210$$
$$X_2 = 710,206.91 \qquad Y_2 = 131,643.20 \qquad \log(Y_1 - Y_2) = 4.936\ 2428\ (n)$$
$$\Delta X = +17,026.33 \qquad \Delta Y = -86,346.11 \qquad \log \tan \alpha_s = 9.294\ 8782\ (n)$$
$$\text{Grid azimuth from south} = 168°\ 50'\ 42.46''$$

The grid azimuth is taken from the south in this example because a geodetic azimuth is always reckoned from the south meridian.

The value of $(\Delta\lambda)^3 F$ in Eq. 11-1 is found to be negligible. Thus,

$$\log(\Delta\lambda)^3 = 9.663$$
$$\log F = 7.863\text{-}20$$
$$\log(\Delta\lambda)^3 F = 7.526\text{-}10$$
$$(\Delta\lambda)^3 F = 0.003'' \text{ (not significant)}$$

Then compute $\Delta\alpha$ by Eq. 11-1a.

$$\tfrac{1}{2}(\phi + \phi') = 41°\ 12'\ 25.84$$
$$\log \sin \tfrac{1}{2}(\phi + \phi') = 9.818\ 7429$$
$$\log \Delta\lambda = 3.221\ 2935$$
$$\log \Delta\alpha = 3.040\ 0364$$
$$\Delta\alpha = 1096.57'' = 0°\ 18'\ 16.57''$$

Now determine the correction term in Eq. 11-3a.

$$Y_2 = 131,643.20 \qquad X_1 = 727,233.24 \qquad X_2 = 710,206.91$$
$$Y_1 = 45,297.09 \qquad X_0 = 600,000.00 \qquad X_0 = 600,000.00$$
$$(Y_2 - Y_1) = +86,346.11 \qquad X'_1 = 127,233.24 \qquad X'_2 = 110,206.91$$
$$2X'_1 = 254,466.48$$
$$(2X'_1 + X'_2) = 364,473.39$$

$$\log(Y_2 - Y_1) = 4.936\ 2428$$
$$\log(2X'_1 + X'_2) = 5.561\ 6658$$
$$\log 1/(6\rho_0^2 \sin 1'')_g = 9.895\ 2612\text{-}20$$
$$\log \text{corr. term} = 0.393\ 1698$$
$$\text{corr. term} = 2.47''$$

Finally, apply Eq. 11-3a.

$$\text{Grid azimuth} = 168°\ 50'\ 42.46''$$
$$\Delta\alpha = +\ 18'\ 16.57''$$
$$\text{corr. term} = +\ 2.47''$$
$$\text{Geodetic azimuth} = 169°\ 09'\ 01.50''$$

You should examine the magnitudes of the different quantities in Examples 11-1 and 11-2 to appreciate which steps are sensitive and which involve only a few significant figures. The calculation of X' taxes 7-place logarithms because when this value is expressed to hundreds of a foot, it contains 8 significant figures. But the value of

$(\Delta\lambda)^3F$ in Eq. 11-1 is usually insignificant. Also, the value of the correction term in Eq. 11-3a is fairly small, and does not require 7-place logarithms. Note also that in Example 11-1 the value of C determined from the given latitude of the point would have been sufficiently accurate for computing ϕ', and it was not necessary to determine a second value. These examples are adaptable to machine computations if the numerical values of the quantities needed in the solution are given together with or instead of their logarithms.

EXAMPLE 11-3. The state plane coordinates of a point on the Rhode Island system are $X = 795{,}452.20$ ft and $Y = 56{,}483.95$ ft. Determine the latitude and longitude of the point.

Solution: An example of this type is the inverse of Example 11-1, and it is solved by performing the calculations in reverse order, as shown on page 354. Although s_g is not known, the value of the last term in Eq. 11-7 can be computed by using X' instead of s_g. The exact value of s_g is then determined by Eq. 11-7. The work then proceeds as shown in the left-hand column of the calculations to the point at which log A is needed. Since A depends on ϕ, the latitude must be computed as shown in the right-hand column of the calculations. The value of log cos ϕ is listed in this column for convenience. The computations then continue in the left-hand column to determine the value of λ.

$$X = \quad 795{,}452.20$$
$$X_0 = \quad 600{,}000.00$$
$$X' = \quad 195{,}452.20 \qquad \text{[Use as } s_g \text{ to obtain } s_g{}^3/(6\rho_0{}^2)_g\text{]}$$
$$\log X' = 5.291\ 0406$$
$$\log X'^3 = 15.873\ 1218 \qquad\qquad\qquad Y = 56{,}483.95$$
$$\log (6\rho_0{}^2)_g = \quad 4.580\ 8361\text{-}20 \qquad (Y \text{ for minutes of } \phi') = 54{,}652.72 = 41°\ 14'$$
$$\log s_g{}^3/(6\rho_0{}^2)_g = \quad 0.453\ 9579 \qquad (Y \text{ for seconds of } \phi') = \quad 1{,}831.23$$
$$X' = \quad 195{,}452.20 \qquad\qquad \text{seconds of } \phi' = \dfrac{1{,}831.23}{101.21033} = 18.093''$$
$$s_g{}^3/(6\rho_0{}^2)_g = \qquad\quad 2.84 \qquad\qquad\qquad\qquad\qquad \phi' = 41°\ 14'\ 18.093''$$
$$s_g = \quad 195{,}449.36 \qquad\qquad\qquad \log s_m{}^2 = 9.55\ 0106$$
$$\log s_g = 5.291\ 0343 \qquad\qquad\qquad\quad \log C = 1.34\ 7196$$
$$\log R = \qquad\quad +27 \qquad\qquad\qquad\quad \log \Delta\phi = 0.89\ 7302$$
$$\text{sum} = 5.291\ 0370 \qquad\qquad\qquad\qquad \Delta\phi = \quad 7.894''$$
$$\log 3937/1200 = 0.515\ 9842 \qquad\qquad\qquad \phi = 41°\ 14'\ 10.199''$$
$$\log s_m = 4.775\ 0528 \qquad\qquad\qquad \log \cos \phi = 9.876\ 2172$$
$$c_{\log s} = \qquad\quad -63$$
$$\log s_1 = 4.775\ 0465$$
$$\log A = 8.509\ 0870$$
$$\log \sec \phi = 0.123\ 7828$$
$$\log \Delta\lambda_1 = 3.407\ 9163$$
$$c_{\log\Delta\lambda} = \qquad\quad +111$$
$$\log \Delta\lambda = 3.407\ 9274$$
$$\Delta\lambda = 2558.158''$$

$$\lambda_m = 71°\ 30'\ 00.000''$$
$$\Delta\lambda = \quad 0°\ 42'\ 38.158''$$
$$\lambda = 70°\ 47'\ 21.842''$$

11-8. Lambert Conformal Projection. The Lambert projection is represented diagrammatically in Fig. 11-5. In view (*a*) is shown the sea-level surface of the earth intersected by a cone along two parallels of latitude AL_1B and CL_2D. These are known as the *standard parallels* of the projection. In view (*b*) is shown a portion of the conical surface developed into a plane surface on which the meridians and parallels of the earth's surface have been projected mathematically. The developments of the two parallels appear as arcs of concentric circles with the center at the apex of the developed cone (not shown on the illustration). Along these two parallels, the distances on the projection are the same as corresponding distances on the sea-level surface. Between the two parallels, a distance on the projection is smaller than the corresponding distance on the sea-level surface. Outside the two parallels, a projected distance is larger. The discrepancy between these corresponding distances depends on the position of the line being considered with respect to the two standard parallels. It is seen that the scale of a line running in a north-south

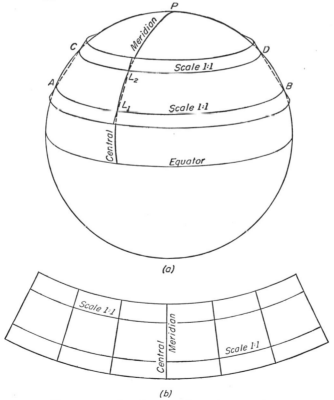

Fig. 11-5. Lambert conformal projection.

direction varies from point to point. It is also seen, however, that a due east-west line has a constant scale throughout its length, whether this scale be larger than, equal to, or less than that on the corresponding sea-level line.

To apply the Lambert conformal projection to a state or a zone, the width of the projection in a north-south direction is limited to 158 miles, and the standard parallels are separated by about two-thirds this distance. At no point within these limits will the discrepancy between a sea-level distance and the grid distance be greater than 1 part in 10,000.

11-9. Grid Azimuth on Lambert Conformal Projection. The central meridian and all lines parallel thereto on the Lambert projection are grid-north lines. Therefore, the azimuth of any line on the plane projection is referred to any of these grid-north lines. The relationship between geodetic azimuth and grid azimuth is indicated in Fig. 11-6. The point P has geographic coordinates ϕ and λ. Two true meridians are shown. Line AB is the central meridian of the projection, and PB is the meridian through P. The line through P, parallel to the central meridian, is the grid meridian or grid-north line at P. The point B is the apex of the developed cone. The angle at B between the meridian through P and the central meridian, which is designated θ, is known as the *mapping angle* for the point.

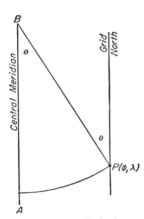

FIG. 11-6. Relationship between geodetic and grid azimuths on Lambert projection.

To compute the mapping angle for a point, first determine the difference in longitude $\Delta\lambda$ between the central meridian and the point by the equation

$$\Delta\lambda = \lambda_m - \lambda \qquad (11\text{-}10)$$

Then multiply $\Delta\lambda$ by a constant of the given projection which gives the relationship between $\Delta\lambda$ and θ. That is,

$$\theta = l\,\Delta\lambda \qquad (11\text{-}11)$$

where l is the constant. If the point is east of the central meridian, then $\Delta\lambda$ and θ are positive. If the point is west of the central meridian, $\Delta\lambda$ and θ are negative.

As seen from Fig. 11-6, the relationship between the geodetic azimuth and the grid azimuth at a point is

$$\text{Geodetic azimuth} - \text{grid azimuth} = +\theta \qquad (11\text{-}12)$$

Due regard must be paid to the algebraic sign of θ. Tables giving the value of θ for every minute of longitude are available for the various Lambert projections. These tables are discussed in Sec. 11-11.

In Fig. 11-7, the arc designated by ϕ_0 is a certain parallel of latitude lying slightly north of an arc midway between the standard parallels. The Y-coordinate of the intersection of this parallel with the central meridian is designated by Y_0, as shown. The line AB lies

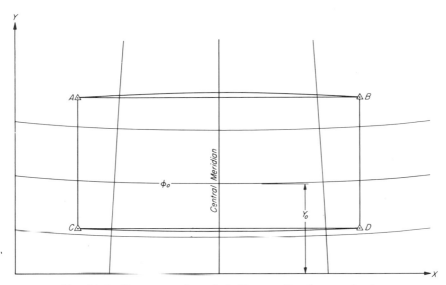

FIG. 11–7. Curvature of geodetic lines on Lambert projection.

north of this parallel. The grid line joining the two points A and B is a straight line. The geodetic line joining the two points, when projected onto the grid, is seen to curve outward away from the parallel designated by ϕ_0. The geodetic line CD is also seen to curve outward away from this parallel, whereas the grid line between C and D is straight. To allow for this curvature in going from the geodetic azimuth to the grid azimuth, or vice versa, when a long line is involved, Eq. 11-12 must be modified by a small correction term. Thus,

Geodetic azimuth $-$ grid azimuth

$$= + \theta - \frac{X_2 - X_1}{2\rho_0{}^2 \sin 1''} \left(Y_1 - Y_0 + \frac{Y_2 - Y_1}{3} \right) \qquad (11\text{-}12a)$$

in which X_1 and Y_1 and X_2 and Y_2 are the coordinates of the ends of the line, Y_0 is as defined above, and ρ_0 is the mean radius of curvature of the earth at latitude ϕ_0. The value of $1/(2\rho_0^2 \sin 1'')$ and the value of Y_0 are given in the projection tables for each zone.

Notice that if a line runs grid north or grid south, as does the line AC or BD in Fig. 11-7, there is no correction term to θ because $X_2 - X_1 = 0$. Also, if a line other than a grid north-south line crosses the parallel designated by ϕ_0, its projection onto the grid will have a reverse curvature.

11-10. Geographic to Plane Coordinates on Lambert Conformal Projection. On a Lambert projection, the central meridian is the Y-axis, and the X-axis is perpendicular to the central meridian. The origin of coordinates is far enough south and west to render all the coordinate values positive. The Y-axis is assigned a large X-value. It is usually, but not always, 2,000,000 ft. This large value is designated by X_0; that is, $X_0 = 2,000,000$ ft. Except for three projections, the Y-value of the X-axis is 0 ft.

In Fig. 11-8, P is a point whose geographic coordinates are ϕ and λ. The parallel of latitude through P is a circle whose radius is R. As the latitude increases, the corresponding value of R decreases. The value of R for any latitude may be obtained from the tables to be discussed in the next section. The mapping angle θ for point P may be determined by Eq. 11-11, or it may be obtained by interpolation in the proper table for the given projection. The distance along the central meridian from the X-axis to point B is designated by R_b. It is

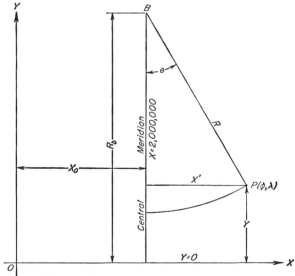

FIG. 11–8.   Rectangular coordinates on Lambert projection.

constant for a given projection. Thus, the X-axis is at a distance R_b south of B.

If the latitude of point P in Fig. 11-8 is known, R can be obtained. Also, if the longitude of the point P is known, θ can be obtained. Then the Y- and X-coordinates of P can be computed by means of the following equations:

$$Y = R_b - R \cos \theta \qquad (11\text{-}13)$$

$$X = X_0 + R \sin \theta \qquad (11\text{-}14)$$

These coordinates are most easily computed by using tables of sines and cosines of small angles to 10 places, since the values of R_b and R are given to 10 significant figures. Furthermore, the computations should be performed on a 10-bank desk calculator.

If logarithms are to be used in computing the Y- and X-coordinates from geographic coordinates, then the equation for Y must be revised to avoid having numbers with many significant figures. In Fig. 11-9, the distance Y' is the Y-coordinate of the intersection of the parallel of latitude through point P in latitude ϕ with the central meridian. As the latitude increases, Y' increases by the same amount by which R decreases. It should be noted that $Y' + R = R_b$. The value of Y' for every minute of latitude is available in prepared tables. The distance Y'' may be computed by the relationship

$$Y'' = R - R \cos \theta = R (1 - \cos \theta)$$

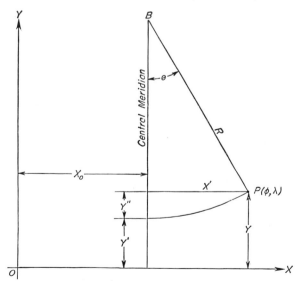

FIG. 11–9. Rectangular coordinates on Lambert projection.

or

$$Y'' = 2\,R \sin^2 \frac{\theta}{2} \tag{11-15}$$

From Fig. 11-7, it is apparent that $Y = Y' + Y''$. Therefore,

$$Y = Y' + 2\,R \sin^2 \frac{\theta}{2} \tag{11-16}$$

The value of Y'' is relatively small, and 7-place logarithms are more than sufficient when Eq. 11-15 is applied.

Equation 11-14 is easily solved by using 7-place logarithms. There will, however, be uncertainty in the hundredths of a foot when the value of $R \sin \theta$ becomes large enough to contain seven significant figures.

11-11. Tables for Lambert Projections. The U. S. Coast and Geodetic Survey has prepared tables for each projection in each state and makes them available through the Government Printing Office. In addition to these prepared tables, *Special Publication 246* gives to 10 places the sines, cosines, and tangents of angles from 0° to 6° for use with Lambert projections. This range includes all values of θ to be encountered. The accompanying tabulation shows a portion of Tables I and II for the north zone of the State of Ohio.

Table I gives for every minute of latitude the value of R, the Y-coordinate of the intersection of the parallel of latitude with the central meridian, and the tabular difference for 1 second of latitude for both R and Y'. The values of R decrease, while the values of Y' increase. Table I also shows the amount by which a sea-level length must be increased or decreased to obtain the corresponding grid length. If logarithms are used, one column gives the amount by which the logarithm of a sea-level length must be increased or decreased to obtain the logarithm of the corresponding grid length. The values in the last column of Table I are the scale factors by which the sea-level lengths are multiplied to give the corresponding grid lengths. Note that the scale varies with the latitude.

In Table II the value of θ is given for each full minute of longitude. To interpolate, the number of seconds of longitude is multiplied by the constant appearing in the heading, and the product is added to or subtracted from the tabular value. Table II is not really necessary, since $\Delta\lambda$ is readily obtained by Eq. 11-10. The value of θ can then be found by Eq. 11-11, where l is the value given at the head of Table II or is included among the constants of the projection.

The constants following Table II are those discussed in Secs. 11-8, 11-9, and 11-10.

LAMBERT PROJECTION FOR OHIO—NORTH

Table I

Latitude	R (feet)	Y' Y-value on Cent. Merid. (feet)	Tab. Diff. for 1 Sec of Latitude (feet)	Scale in Units of 7th Place of Logs	Scale Expressed as a Ratio
40° 51′	24,128,050.71	431,107.76	101.19850	− 233.2	0.9999463
40° 52′	24,121,978.80	437,179.67	101.19883	− 237.8	0.9999452
40° 53′	24,115,906.87	443,251.60	101.19883	− 242.0	0.9999443
40° 54′	24,109,834.94	449,323.53	101.19917	− 245.8	0.9999434
40° 55′	24,103,762.99	455,395.48	101.19950	− 249.3	0.9999426

Table II

1″ of long. = 0.65695032″ of θ

Longitude	θ
84° 46′	− 1° 29′ 20.71461″
84° 47′	− 1° 30′ 00.13163″
84° 48′	− 1° 30′ 39.54865″
84° 49′	− 1° 31′ 18.96567″
84° 50′	− 1° 31′ 58.38269″

Constants

$$R_b = 24,559,158.47 \text{ ft}$$
$$X_0 = C = 2,000,000 \text{ ft}$$
$$Y_0 = 510,419.96 \text{ ft}$$
$$l = 0.65695032$$
$$\lambda_m \text{ (central meridian)} = 82° 30' 00.000''$$
$$1/(2\, \rho_0{}^2 \sin 1'') = 2.3574 \times 10^{-10}$$
$$\log 1/(2\, \rho_0{}^2 \sin 1'') = 0.372\ 4381-10$$

EXAMPLE 11-4. The latitude and longitude of a control point in Ohio are $\phi = 40° 52' 44.602''$ and $\lambda = 84° 48' 16.225''$. Compute the plane coordinates of the control point on the projection for the Ohio-North zone.

Solution: The value of R for the point is obtained from Table I by interpolation, as follows:

$$R \text{ for } 40° 52' = 24,121,978.80 \text{ ft}$$
$$101.19883 \times 44.602'' = \underline{\qquad -4,513.67}$$
$$R \text{ for } 40° 52' 44.602'' = 24,117,465.13 \text{ ft}$$

The value of θ is obtained from Table II by interpolation.
$$\theta \text{ for } 84° 48' = -1° 30' 39.54865''$$
$$0.656\ 95032 \times 16.225'' = \underline{\qquad -10.65902''}$$
$$\theta \text{ for } 84° 48' 16.225'' = -1° 30' 50.20767''$$

From Special Publication 246, $\sin \theta = -0.02642\ 02778$ and $\cos \theta = +0.99965\ 09235$.

Then the plane coordinates may be computed by Eqs. 11-13 and 11-14.

$$R_b = 24,559,158.47 \qquad\qquad X_0 = 2,000,000.00$$
$$R \cos \theta = 24,109,046.29 \qquad\qquad R \sin \theta = -637,190.01$$
$$\overline{Y = \qquad 450,112.18 \text{ ft}} \qquad\qquad \overline{X = 1,362,809.99 \text{ ft}}$$

EXAMPLE 11-5. A line joins the control point in Example 11-4 with a point whose coordinates are $X = 1,414,516.20$ ft and $Y = 602,168.24$ ft. Compute the geodetic azimuth of this line in the direction of the second point.

Solution: The grid azimuth is found by Eq. 8-16.

$$X_1 = 1,362,809.99 \qquad Y_1 = 450,112.18$$
$$X_2 = 1,414,516.20 \qquad Y_2 = 459,168.24$$
$$\overline{\Delta X = -51,706.21} \qquad \overline{\Delta Y = -9,056.06}$$

$$\tan \alpha_s = \frac{-51,706.21}{-9,056.06} = +5.709\ 57016$$

Grid $\alpha_s = 260°\ 03'\ 56.59''$

The grid azimuth is taken from the south in this example because a geodetic azimuth is always reckoned from the south meridian.

The value of θ for the first point was determined in Example 11-4 by using the longitude of the point. However, in this example, we will assume that only the plane coordinates of the ends of the line are known. It can be seen from Fig. 11-8 that

$$\tan \theta = \frac{X'}{R_b - Y} = \frac{X - X_0}{R_b - Y} \tag{11-17}$$

The computations for determining θ follow:

$$X = 1,362,809.99 \qquad R_b = 24,559,158.47 \qquad \tan \theta = \frac{-637,190.01}{24,109,046.29}$$
$$X_0 = 2,000,000.00 \qquad Y = 450,112.18 \qquad \tan \theta = -0.02642\ 94988$$
$$\overline{X' = -637,190.01} \qquad \overline{R_b - Y = 24,109,046.29} \qquad \theta = -1°\ 30'\ 50.21''$$

The correction term in Eq. 11-12a is now computed.

$$X_2 - X_1 = +51,706.21 \qquad\qquad Y_1 = 450,112.18$$
$$Y_2 - Y_1 = +\ 9,056.06 \qquad\qquad Y_0 = 510,419.96$$
$$\qquad\qquad\qquad\qquad\qquad\qquad Y_1 - Y_0 = \overline{-60,307.78}$$
$$1/(2\rho_0{}^2 \sin 1'') = 2.357 \times 10^{-10} \qquad (Y_2 - Y_1)/3 = +3,018.69$$
$$\qquad\qquad\qquad\qquad\qquad\qquad\qquad\qquad\qquad \overline{-57,289.09}$$

Correction term $= 5.171 \times 10^4 \times 2.357 \times 10^{-10} \times -0.573 \times 10^5 = -0.70''$
Note that this correction term can be evaluated by slide rule.

Finally, the geodetic azimuth is determined by applying Eq. 11-12a.

$$\text{Grid azimuth} = 260°\ 03'\ 56.59''$$
$$+ \theta = -1°\ 30'\ 50.21''$$
$$\overline{258°\ 33'\ 06.38''}$$
$$- \text{correction term} = +0.70''$$
$$\text{Geodetic azimuth} = 258°\ 33'\ 07.08''$$

EXAMPLE 11-6. The state plane coordinates of a point in the Ohio-North zone are $X = 2,097,462.33$ ft and $Y = 440,028.92$ ft. Determine the latitude and longitude of the point.

Solution: The value of θ is obtained by Eq. 11-17 given in Example 11-5, as follows:

$$X = 2,097,462.33 \qquad R_b = 24,559.158.47 \qquad \tan \theta = \frac{+\ 97,462.33}{24,119,129.55}$$
$$X_0 = 2,000,000.00 \qquad Y = 440,028.92 \qquad \tan \theta = +0.00404\ 08726$$
$$\overline{X' = +97,462.33} \qquad \overline{R_b - Y = 24,119,129.55} \qquad \theta = +0°\ 13'\ 53.4853''$$
$$\qquad\qquad\qquad\qquad\qquad\qquad\qquad\qquad\qquad\qquad \theta = +833.4853''$$

By Eq. 11-11,

$$\Delta\lambda = \frac{+\,833.4853}{0.656\ 95032} = +\,1268.719'' = +\,0°\ 21'\ 08.719''$$

By Eq. 11-10, the longitude is

$$\lambda = 82°\ 30'\ 00.000'' - 0°\ 21'\ 08.719''$$
$$\lambda = 82°\ 08'\ 51.281''$$

The value of R can be obtained by a rearrangement of Eq. 11-13. Thus,

$$R = \frac{R_b - Y}{\cos\theta} = \frac{24,119,129.55}{0.99999\ 18355} = 24,119,326.47$$

Finally, the latitude is obtained from the value of R by interpolating in Table I of the projection tables.

$$R \text{ for } 40°\ 52' = 24,121,978.80$$
$$R \text{ for point} = 24,119,326.47$$
$$\text{Diff. for seconds} = 2,652.33$$
$$\text{Number of seconds} = \frac{2,652.33}{101.19833} = 26.209''$$
$$\theta = 40°\ 52'\ 26.209''$$

11-12. Application of the State Coordinate Systems. As mentioned in Sec. 11-1, the national network of horizontal control monuments is available to any engineer or surveyor who desires to connect his work with the federal system by methods of plane surveying. It is made usable through the state coordinate systems computed for each state, because the positions of these monuments are published both in geographic and state plane coordinates. If a point to be used is one whose Y- and X-coordinates are not known, they may be computed from the latitude and longitude of the point by the equations discussed in Secs. 11-6 and 11-10.

When a federal monument has been established, it is the practice to set also a second monument, called an azimuth mark, which is far enough away to give an accurate point for backsighting. In addition to the azimuth marks so set, other control monuments in the vicinity can be used as backsights. The grid azimuths, as well as the geodetic azimuths, of these lines to azimuth marks are usually published along with the position data. If, however, no grid azimuth is available for a particular line whose geodetic azimuth is known, then the angle $\Delta\alpha$ or the angle θ is computed as explained in Sec. 11-5 or Sec. 11-9 and the grid azimuth may be obtained by Eq. 11-3 or 11-3a or by Eq. 11-12 or 11-12a. If the plane coordinates of the two ends of the line are known, then the grid azimuth may be determined by Eq. 8-15 or 8-16 of Sec. 8-23.

When a traverse survey is to be related to the state plane coordinate system, the first consideration is the necessary accuracy of the results. If the relative precision that is expected is no better than,

say, 1 part in 5000, then the traverse may be related to the state coordinate system simply by beginning at a point whose state coordinates are known, carrying the traverse on grid azimuths, closing on
another point whose state coordinates are known, and then adjusting
the traverse to fit between these two points. This type of traverse is
described in Sec. 8-22.

If the expected relative precision is 1 part in 10,000 or better,
then a slight amount of additional computation is necessary. As
stated previously, geographic positions are referred to one common
surface which practically coincides with the sea-level surface. Furthermore, the transverse Mercator projections and the Lambert conformal
projections are computed for this sea-level surface. Therefore, distances measured on the ground at elevations other than sea level
must be reduced to their corresponding sea-level lengths by the
method described in Chapter 10. Since the grid length coincides with
the sea-level length in only limited areas on either of the two types
of projections, the sea-level length of a line outside these areas must
be either increased or decreased by multiplying it by the scale factor
that applies to the area under consideration. The scale factor was
discussed in Secs. 11-7 and 11-11.

As suggested in Sec. 11-3, when high precision is to be maintained over long lines, the conversion between grid and geodetic
azimuths requires that a small correction be applied to $\Delta\alpha$ or θ. The
application of these small corrections is illustrated in Examples 11-2
and 11-5. The value of $\Delta\alpha$ or θ is usually given for control points of
the national network discussed in Chapter 10. However, the occasion
arises when an astronomical determination of the azimuth of a line in
the survey is necessary to prevent angular errors from accumulating.
Since the survey is computed by grid coordinates, the conversion
from the astronomically determined azimuth to the grid azimuth is
necessary for the comparison with the computed grid azimuth.

When the grid lengths of all the traverse lines have been determined, their latitudes and departures are computed by the ordinary
method of plane surveying, either grid azimuths or grid bearings being
used. The coordinates of the traverse stations may then be computed
and adjusted.

It is often desirable and expedient to assign a combination factor
for sea-level and grid lengths to an area whose elevation does not
fluctuate too much. For example, if the average elevation in a given
area is 2600 ft above sea level, the sea-level reduction factor is
0.9998750. If the area is in such a latitude on a Lambert projection
that the grid scale factor is 0.9999000, the combination factor in this
area would be $(0.9998750)(0.9999000) = 0.9997750$. A ground length

of 1000 ft in this area would therefore correspond to a grid length of 999.775 ft.

A problem frequently arises in which a large survey extends from one coordinate-projection zone into an adjacent zone. The solution requires a conversion from plane coordinates of one zone to geodetic coordinates, as illustrated in Examples 11-3 and 11-6, and then a conversion from geodetic coordinates to plane coordinates of the next zone, as illustrated in Examples 11-1 and 11-4. The transition usually requires that at least two points in each zone near the common boundary of the two zones be converted, in order that a line of known grid azimuth may be established for each zone.

Triangulation of moderate extent may be executed and computed by using Y- and X-coordinates on the state coordinate systems. A line makes an ideal base line when the coordinates of both ends are known beforehand, since both the grid azimuth and the grid distance may be computed from the coordinates. Plane angles are used to solve the triangles and to carry grid azimuths through the triangulation system. A triangulation network based on a state coordinate system should always begin on a pair of control monuments and end on another pair of control monuments. This tie-in gives the greatest possible reliability to the intermediate triangulation stations.

11-13. Land Areas from State Coordinates. If the state coordinates of the corners of a parcel of land are known, the grid area encompassed within the boundary may be computed by Eq. 8-22 or 8-23 of Sec. 8-23. Since this grid area does not as a rule correspond to the actual ground area, it should be *divided* by the *square* of the combination factor used to determine grid lengths from ground lengths. For example, if the grid area of a parcel of land lying in an area whose combination factor is 0.9997750 was computed by Eq. 8-22 of Sec. 8-23 to be 45,675 sq ft, then the actual ground area is $(45,675)/(0.9997750)^2 = 45,696$ sq ft.

11-14. Lost and Obliterated Corners. When the coordinates of a land corner on a state system are known and the corner cannot be found by the usual methods, its ground position can be determined by locating the point corresponding to those coordinates. This is accomplished by running a traverse from other stations, for which the state-coordinate data are available, to a new point in the immediate vicinity of the point sought for. The coordinates of the new point and the sought-for point are compared, and the azimuth and distance from the new point to the old one are laid out on the ground. The point thus established is the ground position corresponding to the coordinates of the required corner. If any remnants of the original corner remain in position, they may be found by a careful and detailed examination of the ground within a short distance of the restored position.

Marks which are otherwise difficult to find, and which if found are apt to be considered as of doubtful origin, may be recovered and proved authentic by the use of the state coordinate system. A fragment of stone or a piece of decayed wood may constitute a satisfactory recovery if found in the ground position corresponding to the coordinates of the landmark. If no marks are found in the position indicated by the coordinates, it may safely be concluded that the monument has been destroyed, and the coordinate position may be accepted as primary evidence of the ground location.

As the accuracy of the restored position reflects the errors of both the original survey and the restoration survey, care must be taken to maintain a high order of accuracy in the restoration survey, especially when the restoration survey is longer than the original one. Although it is not necessary to employ the same stations in the resurvey that were used in the original survey, it is desirable to use stations which were in the same traverse or survey net. A station on some other traverse may not be so well related in position to the lost mark, because of the methods which were used in the previous adjustment.

11-15. Descriptions by Coordinates. A legal description of a parcel of land identifies the land for title purposes and provides information necessary for locating the land on the ground. A description which is satisfactory for title purposes may be wholly inadequate for a field location of the property. One of the simplest forms of land description for title purposes is afforded by the public-land method of surveying, where a description by reference to township, range, and section can apply to one and only one parcel of land. Thus, "the northwest quarter of the southeast quarter (NW¼SE¼) of Section Ten (10), Township Two South (T2S), Range Six East (R6E) of the Meridian of Michigan" is satisfactory for title purposes. It is also satisfactory for survey purposes as long as the controlling monuments are in existence. For the sake of perpetuating the corners, it would be helpful to add the coordinates of the center of the section, its south and east quarter-corners, and its southeast corner. If a corner monument is later obliterated, these coordinates will provide an effective means of recovering and identifying any part of the monument that may remain in position. If the original monument is entirely destroyed, the coordinates become primary evidence of where it stood and make possible an accurate replacement.

When the description is by metes and bounds, it may be simplified by reference to a plat which is made a part of the conveyance. The azimuths and lengths of the sides of the parcel, as well as the coordinates of the place of beginning, can be shown on this plat.

Where no plat is available, the following form taken from the Second Progress Report of the Joint Committee of the Real Property Division, American Bar Association, and the Surveying and Mapping Division, American Society of Civil Engineers, Proceedings, A.S.C.E., June, 1941, may be used:

"_____situated in the Town of_____, County of _____, State of_____, and bounded as follows:

"Beginning at a drill hole in a stone bound which is set in the corner of a stone wall on the north line of Farm Road at the southwest corner of land of Peter L. Prince and at the southeast corner of land hereby conveyed, the coordinates of which monument referred to the Massachusetts Coordinate System, Mainland Zone, are: $x =$ 417,603.29, $y =$ 316,042.17. Thence, on an azimuth of 81° 39' 30", 123.39 feet along the northerly line of Farm Road to an iron pin at the southwest corner of the tract hereby conveyed; thence, on an azimuth of 181° 47' 30", 145.82 feet along the easterly line of land of Arthur C. Hicks to an iron pin in a stone wall at the northwest corner of the tract hereby conveyed; thence, on an azimuth of 276° 32' 00", 62.04 feet along a stone wall on the southerly line of land of Peter L. Prince to a drill hole in a stone bound in the wall at the northeast corner of land hereby conveyed; thence, on an azimuth of 335° 10' 20", 133.09 feet along a stone wall on the westerly line of land of said Prince, to the place of beginning.

"Zero azimuth is grid south in the Massachusetts Coordinate System, Mainland Zone.

"This description was written June 1, 1939, from data secured by survey made by Fred L. Connor, Civil Engineer, in March and April, 1939."

11-16. Establishment of State Systems. The text of the bill for establishing the legal status of the Michigan Coordinate System is typical. The title is "An Act to describe, define, and officially adopt a system of coordinates for designating and stating the positions of points on the surface of the earth within the State of Michigan." The text follows:

The People of the State of Michigan enact:

Section 1. The system of plane coordinates which has been established by the United States Coast and Geodetic Survey for defining and stating the positions or locations of points on the surface of the earth within the State of Michigan is hereafter to be known and designated as the "Michigan Coordinate System."

For the purpose of the use of this system the State is divided into an "East Zone," a "Central Zone," and a "West Zone."

The area now included in the following counties shall constitute the East Zone: (There follows a list of the counties included in the East Zone.)

The area now included in the following counties shall constitute the Central Zone: (The counties are then listed.)

The area now included in the following counties shall constitute the West Zone: Baraga, Dickinson, Gogebic, Houghton, Iron, Keweenaw, Marquette, Menominee, and Ontonagon.

Section 2. As established for use in the East Zone, the Michigan Coordinate System shall be named, and in any land description in which it is used it shall be designated, the "Michigan Coordinate System, East Zone."

As established for use in the Central Zone, the Michigan Coordinate System shall be named, and in any land description in which it is used it shall be designated, the "Michigan Coordinate System, Central Zone."

As established for use in the West Zone, the Michigan Coordinate System shall be named, and in any land description in which it is used it shall be designated, the "Michigan Coordinate System, West Zone."

Section 3. The plane coordinates of a point on the earth's surface, to be used in expressing the position or location of such point in the appropriate zone of this system, shall consist of two distances, expressed in feet and decimals of a foot. One of these distances, to be known as the "x-coordinate," shall give the position in an east-and-west direction; the other, to be known as the "y-coordinate," shall give the position in a north-and-south direction. These coordinates shall be made to depend upon and conform to the coordinates, on the Michigan Coordinate System, of the triangulation and traverse stations of the United States Coast and Geodetic Survey within the State of Michigan, as those coordinates have been determined by said survey.

Section 4. When any tract of land to be defined by a single description extends from one into another of the above coordinate zones, the positions of all points on its boundaries may be referred to either of such zones, the zone which is used being specifically named in the description.

Section 5. (a) For purposes of more precisely defining the Michigan Coordinate System, the following definition by the United States Coast and Geodetic Survey is adopted:

The Michigan Coordinate System, East Zone, is a transverse Mercator projection of the Clarke spheroid of 1866, having a central meridian 83° 40' west of Greenwich, on which meridian the scale is set at one part in 17,500 too small. The origin of coordinates is at the intersection of the meridian 83° 40' west of Greenwich and the parallel 41° 30' north latitude. This origin is given the coordinates: $x = 500,000$ feet and $y = 0$ feet.

The Michigan Coordinate System, Central Zone, is a transverse Mercator projection of the Clarke spheroid of 1866, having a central meridian 85° 45' west of Greenwich, on which meridian the scale is set at one part in 11,000 too small. The origin of coordinates is at the intersection of the meridian 85° 45' west of Greenwich and the parallel 41° 30' north latitude. This origin is given the coordinates: $x = 500,000$ feet and $y = 0$ feet.

The Michigan Coordinate System, West Zone, is a transverse Mercator projection of the Clarke spheroid of 1866, having a central meridian 88° 45' west of Greenwich, on which meridian the scale is set at one part in 11,000 too small. The origin of coordinates is at the intersection of the meridian 88° 45' west of Greenwich and the parallel 41° 30' north latitude. This origin is given the coordinates: $x = 500,000$ feet and $y = 0$ feet.

(b) The position of the Michigan Coordinate System shall be as marked on the ground by triangulation or traverse stations established in conformity with standards adopted by the United States Coast and Geodetic Survey for first-order and second-order work, whose geodetic positions have been rigidly adjusted on the North American datum of 1927, and whose coordinates have been computed on the system herein defined. Any such station may be used for establishing a survey connection with the Michigan Coordinate System.

Section 6. No coordinates based on the Michigan Coordinate System, purporting to define the position of a point on a land boundary, shall be presented to be recorded in any public land records or deed records unless such point is within one-half mile of a triangulation or traverse station established in conformity with the standards prescribed in Section 5 of this Act; provided that such one-half mile limitation may be modified by a duly authorized State agency to meet local conditions.

Section 7. The use of the term "Michigan Coordinate System" on any map, report of survey, or other document shall be limited to coordinates based on the Michigan Coordinate System as defined in this Act.

Section 8. Whenever coordinates based on the Michigan Coordinate System are used to describe any tract of land which in the said document is also described by reference to any subdivision, line, or corner of the United States public land surveys, the description by coordinates shall be construed as supplemental to the basic description of such subdivision, line, or corner contained in the official plats and field notes filed of record, and in the event of any conflict the description by reference to the subdivision, line, or corner of the United States public land surveys shall prevail over the description by coordinates.

Section 9. Nothing contained in this Act shall require any purchaser or mortgagee to rely on a description, any part of which depends exclusively upon the Michigan Coordinate System.

Section 10. If any provision of this Act shall be declared invalid, such invalidity shall not affect any other portion of this Act which can be given effect without the invalid portion, and to this end the provisions of this Act are declared to be severable.

Section 11. This Act is to take effect⸻⸻⸻⸻⸻⸻.

11-17. Remarks on the State Coordinate Systems. The various state coordinate systems are made possible by virtue of the highly precise geodetic-surveying methods used in establishing the initial framework of horizontal control which defines these systems. Each traverse or local triangulation network which has been executed by methods to give position closures of 1 in 10,000 or better is an addition to the state system and helps to define it more completely. At present, many areas of the country are rather sparsely covered by the federal network. This condition will not last indefinitely, since the U. S. Coast and Geodetic Survey is continuously breaking the larger triangulation networks down to more usable control for local surveyors and engineers. In turn, the highway departments. utilities, railroads, and county and city engineers are filling in between the federally established control. The fact that these surveys are all related to the state coordinate systems means that they are all related to one another. This is the most singular advantage of the state coordinate systems.

Other advantages of using the state coordinate system are: 1) A traverse of relatively low accuracy run between a pair of control points is actually raised in accuracy after an adjustment between the control points is made. 2) The use of well-established control points in a traverse eliminates serious mistakes in measuring both distances and angles. 3) A point whose Y- and X-coordinates have been determined can, if lost, always be replaced with the degree of precision with which it was originally established. 4) Maps which have been controlled by coordinated points will always conform when joined, no matter how unrelated were the projects which necessitated the maps. 5) The use of a common reference system for surveys reduces or eliminates costly duplication in the way of numerous control surveys over the same area by various engineers and surveyors. 6) The use of the state coordinate system permits surveys to be carried over state-wide distances by using plane-surveying methods with results which approach those obtained by geodetic methods. 7) Photogrammetric mapping can be conducted at much less expense when all control points in the area to be mapped are on the same system.

Many additional advantages and applications of the state coordinate systems could be listed. You are urged to take this subject under serious consideration when practicing the civil-engineering profession. The use of the state systems continues to increase, and many economies are being realized by their application.

BIBLIOGRAPHY

ADAMS, O. S., and C. N. CLAIRE. "Manual of Plane Coordinate Computation," *Special Publication No. 193,* U. S. Coast and Geodetic Survey, Government Printing Office.

———. "Manual of Traverse Computation on the Lambert Grid," *Special Publication No. 194,* U. S. Coast and Geodetic Survey, Government Printing Office.

———. "Manual of Traverse Computation on the Transverse Mercator Grid," *Special Publication No. 195,* U. S. Coast and Geodetic Survey, Government Printing Office.

"Formulas and Tables for the Computation of Geodetic Positions," *Special Publication No. 8,* U. S. Coast and Geodetic Survey, Government Printing Office.

MITCHELL, H. C., and L. G. SIMMONS. "The State Coordinate Systems (A Manual for Surveyors)," *Special Publication No. 235,* U. S. Coast and Geodetic Survey, Government Printing Office.

"Ten-Place Tables of Sines, Cosines, and Tangents from 0° to 6°," *Special Publication No. 246,* U. S. Coast and Geodetic Survey, Government Printing Office.

WHITMORE, G. D. *Advanced Surveying and Mapping.* Scranton, Pa.: International Textbook Company, 1949.

PROBLEMS

11-1. The latitude and longitude of a point on the Rhode Island projection are, respectively, 41° 13′ 16.622″ N and 71° 01′ 50.202″ W. Compute the state plane coordinates of the point. Neglect the corrections $c_{\log \Delta \gamma}$ and $c_{\log s}$.

11-2. The plane coordinates of a point on the Rhode Island projection are $X = 528,462.60$ ft and $Y = 44,165.62$ ft. Compute the latitude and longitude of the point.

11-3. The grid azimuth of a line AB on the Rhode Island projection is $202°\ 16'\ 22.3''$ measured clockwise from the north. The coordinates of A are $X_A = 636,565.21$ ft and $Y_A = 50,025.50$ ft. The grid length of AB is $42,415.26$ ft. Compute the geodetic azimuth of AB measured from the south. Neglect the term containing F. Note: In a situation such as that in this problem, the latitude of point A could be scaled with sufficient accuracy from a good map to give the value of $\frac{1}{2}\ (\phi + \phi')$ used in Eq. 11-1a. The longitude can be scaled with an accuracy sufficient to determine $\Delta\alpha$ to about one-half second.

11-4. The latitude and longitude of a point on the Ohio-North projection are, respectively, $40°\ 54'\ 10.035''$ N and $84°\ 46'\ 52.242''$ W. Compute the state plane coordinates of the point.

11-5. The plane coordinates of a point on the Ohio-North projection are $X = 1,885,242.20$ ft and $Y = 439,176.22$ ft. Compute the latitude and longitude of the point.

11-6. The coordinates of two points A and B on the Ohio-North projection are $X_A = 1,989,476.22$ ft and $Y_A = 444,526.24$ ft and $X_B = 2,008,196.21$ ft and $Y_B = 439,986.22$ ft. Compute the geodetic azimuths of AB and BA, both measured from the south.

11-7. The line in Problem 11-6 lies at an average elevation of 2400 ft. What is the ground length of the line?

11-8. The area of a parcel of land, as determined by Eq. 8-22 from the state plane coordinates of the corners, is 15.252 acres. The parcel is located in the Ohio-North grid projection at an average latitude of $40°\ 55'$. Its average elevation is 750 ft. Determine the ground area of the parcel, in acres.

12

KNOW

Practical Astronomy

12-1. **Use of Astronomy.** The engineer or surveyor needs a knowledge of practical astronomy in order to make intelligently the observations and computations necessary for the determination of latitude, time, longitude, and azimuth. The purpose of the present chapter is not to supplant a text on astronomy, but rather to present, in condensed form, methods of observation and computation which can be used when the survey is being conducted with an ordinary engineer's transit. For the development of the formulas used, and for more exact methods, you are referred to the bibliography at the end of the chapter.

The various heavenly bodies are considered to be located on the surface of a sphere of infinite radius. The center of this sphere is the center of the earth. The field observations usually consist of the measurement of horizontal and vertical angles to some heavenly body. The computations involve the solution of the spherical triangle formed by the zenith, the celestial north pole, and the heavenly body.

Where only moderate precision is required, the field observations can be made either with a sextant or with a transit that is equipped preferably with a full vertical circle and a prismatic eyepiece. A good watch is needed for determining the instant at which the observation is made. For the computations, trigonometric tables and an ephemeris are required. The American Nautical Almanac, which is printed each year by the Government Printing Office, contains tables that furnish the positions of the principal heavenly bodies. The various instrument positions of the principal heavenly bodies. The various instrument makers publish small pocket editions containing essential data for solar and Polaris calculations.

While the engineer is ordinarily interested primarily in the azimuth of a certain line, most azimuth methods in use require that the instant at which the observation is made be known within a very few minutes, and that the latitude also be known. It is thus frequently

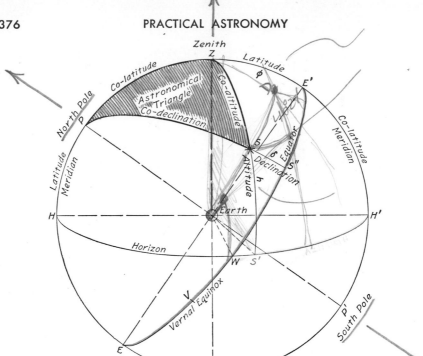

Fig. 12–1.   Celestial sphere.

necessary to determine the time and the latitude, by observation, before the azimuth can be ascertained.

12-2. **Definitions.** In Fig. 12-1 are shown the *astronomical triangle PZS* and the principal points and planes on the celestial sphere.
The *celestial poles* P and P' are the points of intersection, with the
celestial sphere, of the axis of rotation of the earth, if that axis be
extended indefinitely. The *celestial equator* $E'S''WVE$ is the intersection of the celestial sphere with the plane passing through the
center of the earth and perpendicular to the axis of rotation.

  If a vertical line at any point on the earth's surface is extended,
it intersects the upper portion of the celestial sphere at the *zenith* Z,
and the lower portion of the sphere at the *nadir*. A *vertical circle* is a
great circle passing through the zenith and the nadir; ZSS' is an arc
of a vertical circle. The *meridian plane HPZE'H'P'E* is a vertical
circle passing through the celestial poles, the *meridian* being the intersection of this plane with the celestial sphere. An *hour circle* is a
great circle passing through the north and south celestial poles; PSS''
is an arc of an hour circle.

  The *horizon* is the intersection of the celestial sphere with the plane that passes through the center of the earth and is perpendicular to a vertical line; $HWS'H'$ is half of the horizon.

The *azimuth* of a heavenly body S is the angular distance $H'S'$, measured along the horizon from the south point of the meridian to the vertical circle through the heavenly body. Azimuth is considered positive when measured clockwise. In the figure the azimuth $H'S'$, measured from the south, equals 180° minus the angle Z in the astronomical triangle. Many engineers prefer to measure azimuth from the north, particularly when observations are made on stars near the north pole.

The *altitude h* of a heavenly body S is the angular distance $S'S$, measured upward from the horizon along a vertical circle. The *co-altitude*, or *zenith distance*, ZS equals 90° minus the altitude.

The *latitude ϕ* of a point on the earth's surface is the angular distance $E'Z$ measured along the meridian from the equator to the zenith of that point. It is numerically equal to the altitude HP of the pole measured at the point. Latitudes north of the equator are considered positive; those south of the equator, negative. The *co-latitude* PZ equals 90° minus the latitude.

The *vernal equinox V* is that intersection of the plane of the earth's orbit with the equator at which the sun appears to cross the equator from south to north. This occurs about March 21. The *right ascension* of a heavenly body S is the angular distance VS'' measured eastward along the equator from the vernal equinox to the hour circle through the body. The *declination δ* of a heavenly body S is the angular distance $S''S$ measured from the equator to the body along the hour circle through the body. If the body is north of the equator, the declination is considered positive; if south, negative. The *co-declination*, or *polar distance*, PS equals 90° minus the declination.

The *hour angle t* of a heavenly body S is the angular distance $E'S''$ measured westward along the equator from the meridian to the hour circle through the heavenly body. Hour angles measured to the west are positive; to the east, negative. Three hour angles are of particular importance. The *local hour angle* (L.H.A.) is the hour angle of a heavenly body with respect to a local meridian. The *Greenwich hour angle* (G.H.A.) is the hour angle with respect to the meridian of Greenwich. Values of the G.H.A. for the vernal equinox, the sun, and the planets used by surveyors and navigators are given in the Nautical Almanac for each hour of the day. The *sidereal hour angle* (S.H.A.) of a heavenly body is its angular distance, measured westward along the equator, from the vernal equinox to the hour circle through the heavenly body. The S.H.A. of a body is equal to 360° minus the right ascension of the body. Values for the more important heavenly bodies are given in the Nautical Almanac. Both the G.H.A. and the S.H.A. are expressed in angular units, while the right ascensions are given in units of time.

The *transit* of a heavenly body is its passage over the observer's meridian. The *upper branch* of the meridian is the half of the meridian, from the north celestial pole to the south celestial pole, that contains the observer's zenith, as arc *PZE'H'P'* in Fig. 12-1. The *lower branch* of the meridian is the half containing the nadir. An *upper transit* of a body occurs at the instant at which the body is on the upper branch of the meridian. A *lower transit* occurs at the instant at which the body is on the lower branch of the meridian.

The *north meridian* is the arc of the meridian from the observer's zenith to the nadir and containing the north celestial pole. This is the arc *ZPHE-nadir* in Fig. 12-1. The *south meridian* contains the south celestial pole.

The *refraction* of a body is the angular increase in its apparent altitude due to the refraction of light. In Fig. 12-2, the angle *S'O'H'* is the measured altitude, and angle *S'O'S* is the refraction. The *correction* for refraction is always negative, as seen from the figure. It is a maximum when the altitude is small and decreases to zero when the altitude is 90°. Values of the correction for refraction are given in Table 12-1. Owing to the uncertainty in the correction when the altitude is small, observations on heavenly bodies within 20° or 30° of the horizon should be avoided if possible.

The values of refraction given in Table 12-1 are based on a barometric pressure of 29.6 in. of mercury and a temperature of 50 deg F. Barometric pressure changes with the weather conditions and

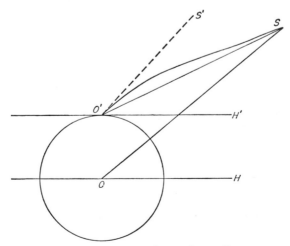

Fig. 12–2.   Refraction and parallax.

also with the elevation. Since atmospheric refraction is a function of temperature and pressure, the mean values given in Table 12-1 should be modified according to the multipliers given in Table 12-2.

EXAMPLE 12-1. The observed altitude to a star is 33° 15′ when the temperature is 72 deg F and the barometer reads 28.0 in. What is the refraction correction?

Solution: The mean refraction for an altitude of 33° 15′, from Table 12-1, is − 1′ 28″ = − 88″. From Table 12-2, the pressure multiplier is 0.95 and the temperature multiplier is 0.96. The refraction correction is, therefore, − 88″ × 0.95 × 0.96 = − 80″ = − 1′ 20″.

TABLE 12-1

MEAN REFRACTION
(To be subtracted from observed altitudes)

App. Alt.	Refrac.	App. Alt.	Refrac.	App. Alt.	Refrac.	App. Alt.	Refrac.
0° 00′	34′ 54″	16° 00′	3′ 19″	32°	1′ 32″	64°	0′ 28″
30′	29′ 04″	30′	3′ 13″	33°	1′ 29″	65°	27″
1° 00′	24′ 25″	17° 00′	3′ 07″	34°	1′ 25″	66°	26″
30′	20′ 51″	30′	3′ 02″	35°	1′ 22″	67°	25″
2° 00′	18′ 09″	18° 00′	2′ 56″	36°	1′ 19″	68°	0′ 23″
30′	16′ 01″	30′	2′ 51″	37°	1′ 17″	69°	22″
3° 00′	14′ 15″	19° 00′	2′ 46″	38°	1′ 14″	70°	21″
30′	12′ 48″	30′	2′ 42″	39°	1′ 11″	71°	20″
4° 00′	11′ 39″	20° 00′	2′ 37″	40°	1′ 09″	72°	0′ 19″
30′	10′ 40″	30′	2′ 33″	41°	1′ 06″	73°	18″
5° 00′	9′ 47″	21° 00′	2′ 29″	42°	1′ 04″	74°	17″
30′	9′ 02″	30′	2′ 26″	43°	1′ 02″	75°	16″
6° 00′	8′ 23″	22° 00′	2′ 22″	44°	1′ 00″	76°	0′ 14″
30′	7′ 50″	30′	2′ 18″	45°	0′ 58″	77°	13″
7° 00′	7′ 20″	23° 00′	2′ 15″	46°	0′ 56″	78°	12″
30′	6′ 53″	30′	2′ 12″	47°	0′ 54″	79°	11″
8° 00′	6′ 30″	24° 00′	2′ 09″	48°	0′ 52″	80°	0′ 10″
30′	6′ 08″	30′	2′ 06″	49°	50″	81°	09″
9° 00′	5′ 49″	25° 00′	2′ 03″	50°	48″	82°	08″
30′	5′ 32″	30′	2′ 00″	51°	47″	83°	07″
10° 00′	5′ 16″	26° 00′	1′ 58″	52°	0′ 45″	84°	0′ 06″
30′	5′ 02″	30′	1′ 55″	53°	44″	85°	05″
11° 00′	4′ 49″	27° 00′	1′ 53″	54°	42″	86°	04″
30′	4′ 36″	30′	1′ 50″	55°	40″	87°	03″
12° 00′	4′ 25″	28° 00′	1′ 48″	56°	0′ 39″	88°	0′ 02″
30′	4′ 15″	30′	1′ 46″	57°	38″	89°	01″
13° 00′	4′ 05″	29° 00′	1′ 44″	58°	36″	90°	00″
30′	3′ 56″	30′	1′ 42″	59°	35″		
14° 00′	3′ 47″	30° 00′	1′ 40″	60°	0′ 33″		
30′	3′ 39″	30′	1′ 38″	61°	32″		
15° 00′	3′ 32″	31° 00′	1′ 36″	62°	31″		
30′	3′ 25″	30′	1′ 34″	63°	29″		
16° 00′	3′ 19″	32° 00′	1′ 32″	64°	28″		

TABLE 12-2
CORRECTIONS TO MEAN REFRACTION
(Multiply Mean Refraction by Tabular Values)

Barometric Pressure or Elevation

Bar. (in.)	Elev. (ft)	Multiplier	Bar. (in.)	Elev. (ft)	Multiplier	Bar. (in.)	Elev. (ft)	Multiplier
30.5	− 451	1.03	27.2	2670	0.92	23.6	6538	0.80
30.2	− 181	1.02	26.9	2972	0.91	23.3	6887	0.79
30.0	00	1.01	26.6	3277	0.90	23.0	7239	0.78
29.9	+ 91	1.01	26.3	3586	0.89	22.7	7597	0.77
29.6	366	1.00	26.0	3899	0.88	22.4	7960	0.76
29.3	643	0.99	25.7	4215	0.87	22.1	8327	0.75
29.0	924	0.98	25.4	4535	0.86	21.8	8700	0.74
28.7	1207	0.97	25.1	4859	0.85	21.5	9077	0.73
28.4	1493	0.96	24.8	5186	0.84	21.2	9460	0.72
28.1	1783	0.95	24.5	5518	0.83	20.9	9848	0.71
27.8	2075	0.94	24.2	5854	0.82	20.6	10242	0.70
27.5	2371	0.93	23.9	6194	0.81	20.3	10642	0.69

Temperature

Temp. (Deg F)	Multiplier	Temp. (Deg F)	Multiplier	Temp. (Deg F)	Multiplier
− 20	1.16	+ 30	1.04	+ 80	0.94
− 10	1.13	+ 40	1.02	+ 90	0.93
0	1.11	+ 50	1.00	+ 100	0.91
+ 10	1.08	+ 60	0.98	+ 110	0.90
+ 20	1.06	+ 70	0.96	+ 120	0.88

EXAMPLE 12-2. The observed altitude to the sun's limb is 27° 30′ when the temperature is 48 deg F, the elevation of the point of observation is 4,850 ft, and the barometer reading is unknown. What is the refraction correction?

Solution: Since the barometric pressure is not known, the standard sea-level pressure of 30.0 in. is assumed. From Table 12-1, the mean refraction for an altitude of 27° 30′ is − 1′ 50″ = − 110″. From Table 12-2, the elevation multiplier is 0.85, and the temperature multiplier is 1.00. The refraction correction is, therefore, − 110″ × 0.85 × 1.00 = − 94″ = − 1′ 34″.

The *correction for parallax* (in altitude) is the small angular increase in the apparent altitude of a heavenly body to allow for the fact that the observations are made at the surface of the earth instead of at its center. In Fig. 12-2, the angle SO′H′ is the angle at the surface corrected for refraction. The angle SOH is the true altitude, or the altitude that would be measured at the center of the earth. Observations on the sun, the moon, and the planets must be corrected for parallax. Observations on the stars need no parallax correction because any star is virtually at an infinite distance from the earth. Parallax correction is always added.

12-3. Time. There are three kinds of time which may be involved in astronomical observations, namely, *sidereal time, apparent time,* or *true solar time,* and *mean solar time.* A *sidereal day* is the interval of time between two successive upper transits of the vernal equinox over the same meridian. The sidereal day therefore begins at the instant at which the vernal equinox is on the upper branch of the meridian. The sidereal time at any instant, referred to a particular meridian, is the hour angle of the vernal equinox referred to the same meridian.

An *apparent solar day* is the interval of time between two successive lower transits of the sun's center over the same meridian. Because of the obliquity of the plane of the earth's orbit (which is about 23° 26.5') and because of the variation in the earth's angular velocity about the sun in its elliptical orbit, the interval between two successive lower transits of the sun's center over the same meridian varies from day to day. Since it would not be feasible to keep time on clocks and watches if the apparent solar day were used, the mean solar day is used.

A *mean solar day* is the interval of time between two successive lower transits of the mean sun over the same meridian. The mean sun is a fictitious body which travels at a uniform rate along the equator. The mean sun is sometimes ahead of and sometimes behind the apparent, or true, sun. There are 24 hours in a day. The mean solar time at any instant for a given meridian is the hour angle of the mean sun referred to the same meridian plus 12 hours. At midnight, the hour angle of the mean sun is 12 hours. At mean solar noon, the hour angle of the mean sun is 0 hours.

The difference between apparent solar time and mean solar time is called the *equation of time,* or apparent − mean = equation of time. Its value for each day of the year is given in the ephemeris.

A *solar year* contains 365.2422 solar days. Because the earth rotates on its axis each day and orbits around the sun once a year, any point on the earth faces the sun one time less than it faces any of the stars and the vernal equinox in a period of one year. Therefore the solar year contains 366.2422 sidereal days. The mean solar day is longer than the sidereal day by 3^m 55.909^s of mean solar time or 3^m 56.555^s of sidereal time.

12-4. **Standard Time.** *Standard time* is the mean solar time referred to meridians 15° apart, measured from Greenwich which lies at 0° longitude. Since there are 24 hours in the mean solar day, then $24^h = 360°$ and $1^h = 15°$. Therefore the standard meridians are 1 hour apart. Eastern standard time (E.S.T.) is the time of the 75th meridian west of Greenwich; Central standard time (C.S.T.), of the 90th meridian; Mountain standard time (M.S.T.), of the 105th meridian; and Pacific standard time (P.S.T.), of the 120th meridian.

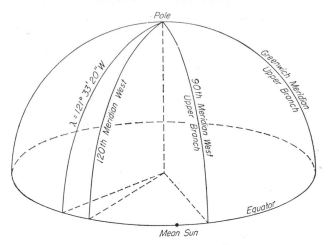

FIG. 12–3. Time (mean).

In Fig. 12-3 the mean sun, which travels westward along the equator, is shown to be about 10° 30′ or 42^m beyond the 90th meridian. Central standard time is therefore 12:42 P.M. At the Greenwich meridian at the same instant, the time is 6^h later. So the Greenwich standard time is 6:42 P.M. The standard time referred to the Greenwich meridian is called Greenwich civil time (G.C.T.), Greenwich mean time (G.M.T.), or universal time. The mean sun has not yet reached the 120th meridian, and the Pacific standard time is therefore before noon. Since the difference between C.S.T. and P.S.T. is 2^h, the Pacific standard time, or time based on the 120th meridian, is 10^h 42^m A.M.

12-5. Local Time. Local time is the time based on the observer's meridian. *Local civil time* (L.C.T.), which is based on mean solar time, is the hour angle of the mean sun measured from the local meridian plus 12 hours. *Local apparent time* (L.A.T.), which is based on the true sun, is the hour angle of the sun's center plus 12 hours. For example, when the actual sun's center is on the observer's meridian, the time is local apparent noon. *Local sidereal time* is the hour angle of the vernal equinox measured from the observer's meridian.

At the meridian in longitude 121° 33′ 20″, standard time is based on the 120th meridian. For the instant shown in Fig. 12-3, the time is 10:42 A.M., P.S.T. Local civil time is earlier by an amount corresponding to 1° 33′ 20″, or 6^m 13.3^s. The local civil time at longitude 121° 33′ 20″ is therefore 10:35:46.7 A.M. The local civil time at longitude 72° 03′ 14″ for the instant shown in Fig. 12-3 is found by adding to the Central standard time the amount corresponding to

$90° - 72° 03' 14''$. The time interval for $90° - 72° 03' 14''$, or $17° 56' 46''$, is $1^h 11^m 47.1^s$, and the L.C.T. is $1^h 53^m 47.1^s$ P.M. Conversion from degrees, minutes, and seconds to hours, minutes, and seconds, or the reverse, is based on the following relationships:

$$360° = 24^h \qquad 24^h = 360°$$
$$1° = 4^m \qquad 1^h = 15°$$
$$1' = 4^s \qquad 1^m = 15'$$
$$1'' = 0.067^s \qquad 1^s - 15''$$

12-6. **Time by Radio.** Where a short-wave radio receiver is available, time may be determined several times daily by picking up the signals sent out by the U. S. Naval Observatory. These signals are also sent out by some broadcasting stations at noon and at 10 P.M., E.S.T. The signals are supposed to be accurate within 0.1 second. Each week the Naval Observatory distributes, on request, a list of corrections.

Time signals are also sent out by radio station WWV of the Bureau of Standards at Washington, D. C., on frequencies of 2.5, 5, 10, and 15 megacycles. These signals are sent out continuously as the ticks of a grandfather clock, superimposed on a 440-cycle hum. There is no tick at the 59th second of each minute. Also the musical tone is cut off at the beginning of each minute that is a multiple of 5 minutes, and is resumed 1 minute later. There is a voice announcement on the hour and the half-hour.

12-7. **Observing the Sun with the Transit.** Observations on the sun are made to determine the altitude or the azimuth of the sun's center or both. Altitude is read on the vertical circle of a transit, while azimuth is related to horizontal-circle readings. Because it is quite difficult to set the intersection of the cross hairs directly on the center of the sun, the cross hairs are usually made to become tangent to the edges of the sun, and then the necessary amounts are added to or subtracted from the circle readings to reduce the observation to the sun's center.

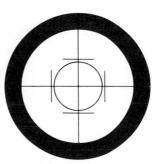

FIG. 12–4. Reticule for sighting sun's center.

In Fig. 12-4 is shown the design of a glass reticule which can be used to great advantage when a survey requires many solar observations. The usual horizontal and vertical cross hairs and the stadia hairs are augmented by a pair of vertical tick marks having the same spacing as the stadia hairs. Inside the stadia hairs and these two tick marks is inscribed a solar circle with an angular radius of 15′ 45″. This is slightly smaller than the *semidiameter* of the sun, which is approximately 0° 16′. The sun's image can thus be centered on this circle with a very high degree of accuracy.

Although the sun can be observed directly through the telescope if the appropriate kind of dark filter is attached to the eyepiece, the usual practice is to view the image of the sun projected onto a white card held behind the eyepiece of the transit, as shown in Fig. 12-5. Two methods will be discussed in this section, each using the white-card technique. The first method is referred to as the center-tangent or disappearing-segment method. The second is known as the quadrant-tangent method.

When the center-tangent method is used, the observation is

Fig. 12–5. Viewing sun's image.

always made on the trailing edge, or *limb*, of the sun. During the morning hours, the sun's altitude is increasing, and the lower limb is observed for altitude (vertical-circle reading). During the afternoon hours, the sun's altitude is decreasing, and the upper limb is observed for altitude. Throughout all hours of the day, the sun moves from east to west, and the east limb is observed for azimuth (horizontal-circle reading).

When the transit is to be leveled over a point for an astronomical observation to measure the altitude of a heavenly body, the bubble of the telescope level must be used as described in Sec. 6-15. This procedure brings the vertical axis of the instrument more perfectly vertical than would be possible by using the plate levels.

With the transit set up and leveled, the telescope is pointed in the direction of the sun, and the telescope bubble is centered. The vertical circle is read to determine the index error (see Sec. 6-15). The telescope is raised and pointed as nearly as possible toward the sun without actually looking through the telescope. A white card is held from 3 to 4 in. behind the eyepiece, and the telescope is rotated both in altitude and azimuth until it casts a circular shadow on the card. See Fig. 12-5. The cross hairs are then focused on the card. The telescope is now focused to make the image of the sun clear and sharp on the card. The image of the sun produced by an erecting telescope will be upside down when the observer looks directly at the card. Therefore, the lower edge of the sun's image is actually the upper limb of the real sun, and the upper edge of the image is the lower limb of the real sun. The right edge of the sun's image, as seen on the card, is the western limb of the real sun; the left edge of the image is the eastern limb of the real sun.

In the morning, when it is desired to make the horizontal cross hair tangent to the lower limb of the sun, the vertical-motion tangent screw is turned so that the horizontal cross hair cuts the sun's image in the position indicated by the dashed lines in Fig. 12-6 (*a*). The altitude of this cross hair now remains stationary. As the sun's image moves downward and to the right, as indicated by the arrow, the small segment becomes smaller. The observer moves the vertical cross hair by means of the upper horizontal-motion tangent screw so that this cross hair continuously bisects the disappearing segment. He stops at the instant the edge of the sun's image becomes tangent to the horizontal cross hair. At this point, the vertical cross hair passes through the center of the sun and the horizontal-circle reading needs no correction. However, the horizontal cross hair is tangent to the lower limb, and the vertical angle must be increased by one-half the angle

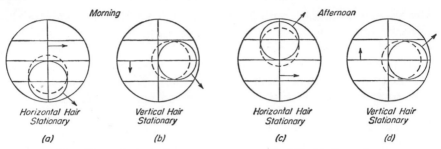

Morning   *Afternoon*

Horizontal Hair Stationary	*Vertical Hair Stationary*	*Horizontal Hair Stationary*	*Vertical Hair Stationary*
(a)	*(b)*	*(c)*	*(d)*

FIG. 12–6. Image of sun as seen on card held behind eyepiece of an erecting telescope.

subtended by the sun. This is the sun's semidiameter, and is about 0° 16′. Its value is given for different times of the year in the ephemeris. The vertical angle is corrected for index error, parallax, and refraction before the semidiameter is added. The observation is repeated with the telescope reversed as explained in Sec. 12-20.

In the afternoon, when it is desired to make the horizontal cross hair tangent to the sun's upper limb, the horizontal cross hair is first set as shown in Fig. 12-6 (c). Also, the semidiameter must be subtracted from the vertical-circle reading, after corrections for index error, parallax, and refraction have been applied.

If it is desired to make the vertical cross hair tangent to the eastern limb of the sun, either in the morning or in the afternoon, the vertical cross hair should be set to cut the sun's image in the position indicated by the dashed lines in Fig. 12-6 (b) or (d). The horizontal cross hair is then moved so as to bisect the disappearing segment continuously until tangency is reached. At this point, the horizontal cross hair passes through the center of the sun, and the vertical-circle reading need be corrected only for index error, parallax, and refraction. The horizontal-circle reading, however, is too small by an amount found by multiplying the semidiameter by sec h, where h is the altitude or vertical angle. This amount is added to the horizontal-circle reading.

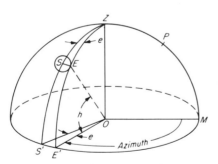

FIG. 12–7. Correction to horizontal circle reading for sun's semidiameter.

In Fig. 12-7, Z is the observer's zenith, P is the pole, arc ZPM is part of the observer's meridian, S is the sun's center, and angle MOS' is the azimuth of the sun's center. The arc ZEE' is part of the vertical circle tangent to the sun's eastern limb. This arc lies in the vertical plane containing the line of sight of the transit when it is brought tangent to the eastern limb. Thus, the azimuth of the sun's eastern limb is the angle MOE', which is smaller than the angle MOS' by the small angle e. In the triangle ZSE, the angle at Z is e, the angle at E is 90°, side ZS is the co-altitude of the sun, or 90° $- h$, and side SE is the sun's semidiameter d. By the law of sines of spherical trigonometry for the triangle ZSE,

$$\frac{\sin Z}{\sin SE} = \frac{\sin E}{\sin ZS} \quad \text{or} \quad \frac{\sin e}{\sin d} = \frac{\sin 90°}{\sin (90°\text{-}h)} = \frac{1}{\cos h} = \sec h$$

Since the semidiameter d is small, it may assumed that

$$\boxed{e = d \sec h} \tag{12-1}$$

in which e is the amount by which the horizontal-circle reading to the sun's eastern limb must be increased. Both d and e are expressed in minutes of arc.

EXAMPLE 12-3. On the morning of October 16, 1958, the horizontal cross hair of a transit was brought tangent to the lower limb of the sun, as indicated in Fig. 12-6 (a), and the vertical circle read $+ 40°$ 22'. The vertical circle read $+ 0°$ 02' when the telescope bubble was centered. If the mean refraction can be assumed, what was the true altitude of the sun's center?

Solution: The computations may be arranged as follows:

Vertical-circle reading	$= + 40°$ 22'
Index correction	$= - 0°$ 02'
	$+ 40°$ 20'
Mean refraction	$= -$ 1' 09" (Table 12-1)
	40° 18' 51"
Sun's parallax	$= +$ 7" (from ephemeris)
	40° 18' 58"
Semidiameter for October 16	$= +$ 16' 05" (from ephemeris)
True altitude of sun's center	$=$ 40° 35' 03"

EXAMPLE 12-4. On the afternoon of May 23, 1958, the vertical cross hair of a transit was brought tangent to the eastern limb of the sun, as indicated in Fig. 12-6 (d). The horizontal-circle reading was 322° 44' 30" and the vertical circle read $+ 27°$ 52'. The index error of the vertical circle was determined to be zero. What was the corrected horizontal-circle reading, and what was the altitude of the sun's center with mean refraction?

Solution: The calculations follow:

Hor.-circle reading	$=$ 322° 44' 30"	Vert.-circle reading	$= + 27°$ 52'
Semidiameter $\times \sec h$	$= +$ 17' 55"	Refraction	$= -$ 1' 48"
Corr. hor.-circle reading	$=$ 323° 02' 25"		$+ 27°$ 50' 12"
		Parallax	$= +$ 8"
		True alt. of sun	$= + 27°$ 50' 20"

When the position of the sun is observed in the manner just described, several observations should be taken in rapid succession, and the mean values of the corrected horizontal-circle readings and the vertical angles should be used. Each of the observed values should be corrected for index error, refraction and parallax, semidiameter, and d sec h. The watch time of each observation should be noted to the nearest second, whether or not the times are exactly correct. Then, after the several horizontal-circle readings and vertical angles have been corrected, both the values of the corrected horizontal-circle readings and the values of the corrected vertical angles should be plotted versus the time. Each plot should be very nearly a straight line. Values that are not close to the adopted straight line should be rejected before the mean values for the group of observations are computed. (See Sec. 12-20.)

When the sun is observed by the quadrant-tangent method, the white card is used in the manner previously described. In Fig. 12-8 is shown the motion of the sun's image as it would be projected through

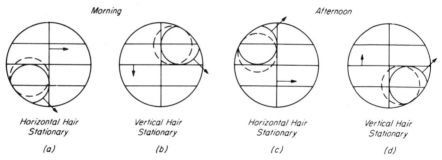

FIG. 12–8. Image of sun as seen on card held behind eyepiece of an erecting telescope (quadrant-tangent method)

an erecting telescope onto the card. In the morning the first part of the observation is made as indicated in Fig. 12-8 (a). The vertical cross hair is always kept tangent to the sun's western, or leading, limb by means of the upper horizontal tangent screw. The vertical motion of the transit is not disturbed, and thus the horizontal cross hair remains at the same altitude. At the instant at which the sun's lower limb (the upper edge of the sun's image) becomes tangent to the horizontal cross hair, as shown by the solid circle, horizontal motion of the transit is stopped. At the same instant, the watch time is noted. Next, the vertical cross hair is held at the same azimuth, as shown in Fig. 12-8 (b), while the horizontal cross hair is kept tangent to the sun's upper limb (the lower edge of the sun's image) by means of the vertical slow-motion screw. At the instant at which the eastern limb becomes tangent to the vertical cross hair, as shown by the solid circle, the transit motion is stopped and the watch time is noted.

In the afternoon, the sun's upper limb is first made tangent, as indicated in Fig. 12-8 (c), and then the eastern limb is made tangent as shown in Fig. 12-8 (d).

When the quadrant-tangent method is used, the observer must watch for tangency at two points of the sun's disc, instead of at only one point in the center-tangent method. It is, therefore, more difficult to make the observation. Presumably, a pair of observations, one carried out as in Fig. 12-8 (a) and the other as in (b), could be made in quick succession, and the readings could be averaged to eliminate the semidiameter corrections to both the horizontal-circle and vertical-circle readings. Moreover, if another pair of observations is made with the telescope reversed, the index error of the vertical circle could also be eliminated. However, a set of solar observations should never be used for computation until all the corrections have been made to the circle readings and the resulting angles have been plotted as a function of time. This plot uncovers any possible mistakes which would otherwise escape notice if all observations are presumed valid and the results are averaged. In each instance shown in Fig. 12-8, the corrections would consist of index correction, refraction and pallalax, semidiameter, and $d \sec h$. In Sec 12-20 is included a discussion of mistakes in observations and the ways in which defective observed values may be rejected on a valid basis.

An ingenious device, which is known as Roelof's solar prism and which can be fitted to the objective of the telescope, produces four overlapping images of the sun to give the solar-disc pattern shown in Fig. 12-9. By direct viewing through the transit, the small diamond-shaped area in the center of the pattern can be bisected simultaneously by the horizontal and vertical cross hairs with a high degree of accuracy. Because of the pattern symmetry, such a pointing is made directly on the sun's center, and the semidiameter corrections are thus eliminated. Because of the direct-viewing feature, the observations can be made quite rapidly. Of course, corrections for index error, refraction, and parallax must be applied to the vertical-circle reading. There is, however, no correction to the horizontal-circle reading.

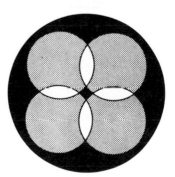

FIG. 12–9. Pattern of sun's image produced by Roelof's solar prism.

12-8. Observing a Star with the Transit. Unlike the sun, a star appears as a point of light in the heavens when view through a transit telescope. It is therefore quite easy to observe the instant at which the star's image crosses either the horizontal cross hair when the star's altitude is being measured or the vertical cross hair when a horizontal angle to the star is being measured. Because observations are taken on stars under such conditions that the amount of natural light coming through the telescope usually is not sufficient to allow the observer to see the cross hairs, artificial light must be provided. A good method is to shine a flashlight obliquely across the objective lens at such an angle that there is sufficient light to make the cross hairs visible, but not enough to blot out the image of the star. Some instruments have internal illumination the brightness of which can be controlled by a rheostat.

If a star is to be observed for determining the azimuth of a line or a backsight has to be made on a ground station during the observation for any other reason, then the ground station itself must be illuminated. Suitable light can usually be provided by holding a flashlight behind the mark when the station is being observed.

Preparations for star observations should be made in daylight or during twilight hours, if possible, simply for convenience. Some stars may actually be observed in the twilight hours. This condition is, of course, most desirable, because the observer and the notekeeper then have at least some natural light in which to work.

12-9. Time by Transit of the Sun. As previously stated, the primary purpose of most astronomical observations on many surveys is the determination of the azimuth of a line, but most methods of observation require that the time be known within a few seconds or a few minutes. Where standard time cannot be obtained, field observations for time may be necessary. Time at an established meridian may be determined by noting the instant of the passage of the sun's center or of a star across that meridian. Where a good map is available, the longitude of the place of observation can be scaled with sufficient accuracy from the map.

When the sun is used, the watch correction is computed by noting the instant at which the sun's center crosses the meridian. This instant is observed by first setting the telescope in the meridian and cutting a small segment from either the upper or lower limb of the sun with the horizontal cross hair by using the vertical-motion tangent screw. The sun's image is then tracked by the vertical-motion tangent screw until the small segment is bisected by the vertical cross hair. The instant of watch time of crossing is noted. This instant is local apparent noon.

The Greenwich apparent time of observation is obtained by adding the longitude (presumed west) in time units to the local apparent time of 12^h. The equation of time, obtained from the ephemeris, is subtracted algebraically to obtain the Greenwich civil time of observation. Finally the longitude of the standard meridian in time units is subtracted from the G.C.T. to give the standard time on which the watch is based. From the correct standard time, the watch error may be computed. Typical computations illustrating the procedure for determining the standard time of the sun's transit are shown in the accompanying tabulation.

COMPUTATIONS FOR TIME FROM SUN'S TRANSIT

Date: October 14, 1964. Longitude: 113° 42' 45" or $7^h 34^m 51^s$. Watch time of transit of sun: $12^h 20^m 04^s$ P.M., M.S.T.

Local apparent time =	$12^h 00^m 00^s$
Longitude west of Greenwich = +	$7^h 34^m 51^s$
Greenwich apparent time =	$19^h 34^m 51^s$
Equation of time at 0^h G.C.T. = +	$00^h 13^m 53^s$ } (from ephemeris
Change for $19^h 34^m 51^s$ = +	$00^h 00^m 11^s$ } of sun)
Equation of time at instant of observation = +	$00^h 14^m 04^s$
Greenwich civil time (G.A.T. − equation of time) =	$19^h 20^m 47^s$
Longitude to M.S.T. = −	$7^h 00^m 00^s$
Mountain standard time =	$12^h 20^m 47^s$
Watch time = −	$12^h 20^m 04^s$
Watch slow	43^s

12-10. Time by Altitude of the Sun. Time may be determined by measuring the altitude of the sun's center at any instant, and the watch error may be found by noting the watch time at the instant the observation is made. Since it is very difficult to locate the sun's center accurately by eye, the altitude is measured to either the lower limb or the upper limb. This observed angle is corrected for the index error of the vertical circle, refraction, parallax, and semidiameter of the sun. Better results can be obtained if several altitudes are measured in quick succession, the corresponding instants of time being noted. The observed limb depends on whether the observation is made in the morning or in the afternoon. See Fig. 12-6 (a) and (c). Corrections for index error, parallax, refraction, and semidiameter are applied to each vertical angle, and the means of the altitudes and the times are used in computing the hour angle by one of the following formulas:

$$\sin \frac{1}{2} t = \sqrt{\frac{\cos s \sin (s - h)}{\cos \phi \sin p}} \tag{12-2}$$

$$\tan \frac{1}{2} t = \sqrt{\frac{\cos s \sin (s - h)}{\cos (s - p) \sin (s - \phi)}} \qquad (12\text{-}3)$$

$$\cos t = \frac{\sin h - \sin \phi \sin \delta}{\cos \phi \cos \delta} \qquad (12\text{-}4)$$

where t = hour angle;

s = ½ $(\phi + h + p)$;

ϕ = latitude obtained from other observations or scaled from a map;

δ = declination obtained from the ephemeris;

h = corrected altitude;

p = polar distance, or 90° minus the declination.

The hour angle t can be converted into time by applying the following relations: 15° of arc = 1 hour, 15′ = 1 minute, and 15″ = 1 second. If the observation is made in the morning, the result is the time interval before local apparent noon. If it is an afternoon observation, the result is the time since local apparent noon. The approximate time must be known for obtaining the declination from the ephemeris. When the time is first computed, it may be found that the estimated time was too much in error, and a second computation must then be made with a corrected declination. The resulting local apparent time can be converted to any standard time by applying the equation of time and the longitude correction, as was done in the example in the preceding section.

The results obtained by this method will usually be unsatisfactory if the observations are made when the sun is close to the horizon or close to the meridian. When the observed altitude is less than 20° to 30°, the refraction correction is likely to be uncertain. For observations made within an hour of local apparent noon, a small error in the observed vertical angle will seriously affect the hour angle.

12-11. Time by Altitude of a Star. The preceding method may also be used for observations made on a star instead of the sun. For accurate results, two stars should be used, one nearly directly east and the other nearly directly west of the place of observation. Both stars should be at least 30° above the horizon. No correction for parallax need be made in the case of a star. Errors of observation will be minimized if several altitudes are measured in quick succession, half with the telescope normal and half with it inverted. By using one star east and one west of the meridian, instrumental and refraction-correction errors are largely eliminated from the mean of the results.

In Fig. 12-1, the arc $E'S''$ along the equator is the hour angle of

Computations for Time from Altitude of Star

Date: Aug. 28, 1945. Latitude: 43° 17′ 13″. Longitude: 110° 40′ 45″. Star (west): α Bootis (Arcturus). Observed vertical angle: 39° 17′ 30″. Watch time: 7ʰ 43ᵐ 34ˢ P. M., M. S. T.

$$\sin \frac{1}{2} t = \sqrt{\frac{\cos s \, \sin \, (s - h)}{\cos \phi \, \sin p}}$$

Observed vertical angle =	39° 17′ 30″
Refraction =	− 1′ 10″
h =	39° 16′ 20″
φ =	43° 17′ 13″
δ (from ephemeris) = 19° 28′ 11″ 90° − δ = p =	70° 31′ 49″
(h + φ + p) =	152° 64′ 82″
s = ½ (h + φ + p) =	76° 32′ 41″
s − h =	37° 16′ 21″
log cos s = 9.3667708	
log sin (s − h) = 9.7821906	
	9.148 9614
log cos φ = 9.8620890	
log sin p = 9.9744278	
	9.836 5168
	2)9.312 4446
log sin ½ t =	9.656 2223
½ t = 26° 56′ 41″	
t = 53° 53′ 22″ =	3ʰ 35ᵐ 33.5ˢ
Right ascension star (from ephemeris) =	14 13 09.3
Local sidereal time =	17 48 42.8
Longitude (time) =	7 22 43
Greenwich sidereal time =	24 70 85.8
Sidereal time, Greenwich 0ʰ, Aug. 29 (from ephemeris) =	22 27 20.3
Sidereal interval since 0ʰ =	2 44 05.5
Correction to solar interval (from Table II, ephem.) =	− 26.9
Greenwich civil time, Aug. 29 =	2 43 38.6
or Greenwich civil time, Aug. 28 =	26 43 38.6
Longitude to Mountain standard time =	7 00 00
Mountain standard time =	19 43 38.6
or Mountain standard time =	7 43 38.6 P. M.
Watch time =	7 43 34
Watch correction =	+ 4.6ˢ

the star, and the arc VS'' is the right ascension of the star. It is thus seen that the local sidereal time equals the local hour angle of the star plus the right ascension of the star. The local sidereal time is reduced to Greenwich sidereal time by adding the longitude (presumed west) in time units. The ephemeris gives the sidereal time corresponding to 0ʰ G.C.T. Since the difference between the sidereal time at 0ʰ G.C.T. and the Greenwich sidereal time of observation is a sidereal interval of time, the corresponding solar interval of time is obtained by subtracting from the sidereal interval 9.83ˢ for each sidereal hour in the interval. The amount to be subtracted is tabulated in the ephemeris. The solar interval of time since 0^h G.C.T. is the Greenwich civil time of the observation. The standard time of observation is obtained by subtracting the longitude of the standard meridian in time units. So the watch error can be easily determined. The computations for a single observation made on a star are given on page 393.

Some ephemerides give the sidereal hour angle of selected stars in angular units, but not the right ascension. Thus, in the computation shown on page 393, the S.H.A. of Arcturus would be $24^h - 14^h\ 13^m\ 09.3^s = 9^h\ 46^m\ 50.7^s$ or $146°\ 42'\ 40''$.

12-12. Time by the Transit of a Star. The most accurate method of determining time is by noting the instant of the passage of a star across the meridian. The stars chosen for this work are those near the equator, as their apparent motions are more rapid. Usually several stars are observed and the mean of the results is used. The stars can be identified by computing beforehand their approximate times of transit and their altitudes. The altitude will equal the co-latitude of the observer plus the declination of the star. Unless the transit is equipped with a prismatic eyepiece, the altitudes should not exceed $55°$ or $60°$. An inspection of Fig. 12-1 will show that the right ascension of a star will be the local sidereal time for the instant at which the star crosses the meridian. The sidereal time is changed to standard time as shown in the accompanying example. Here, again, the S.H.A. of π Sagittarii would be given in some ephemerides as $73°\ 22'\ 05''$ and the right ascension could be obtained from that S.H.A.

COMPUTATIONS FOR TIME FROM TRANSIT OF STAR

Date: Aug. 27, 1945. Longitude: $110°\ 40'\ 45''$. Star: π Sagittarii. Time of upper transit: $9^h\ 04^m\ 17^s$ P. M., M. S. T.

Local sidereal time =	19^h	06^m	31.7^s	= R.A. (from ephemeris)
Longitude West of Greenwich = +	7	22	43	
Greenwich sidereal time =	26	28	74.7	
Sid. time Greenwich 0^h =	22	23	23.8	(eph. of sun for Aug. 28)
Sid. interval since 0^h =	4	05	50.9	
Correction to solar interval = −	0	40.3		(Table II, ephemeris)
Solar interval since 0^h Aug. 28 =	4	05	10.6	
Solar interval since 0^h Aug. 27 =	28	05	10.6	
Longitude to M. S. T. = −	7	00	00	
Mountain standard time =	21	05	10.6	
Mountain standard time =	9	05	10.6	P. M.
Watch time =	9	04	17	
Watch correction =		+ 53.6^s		

12-13. Latitude. The latitude of a point on the earth's surface can be obtained by scaling it from a map, by measuring the altitude of the sun at local apparent noon, or by measuring the altitude of a circumpolar star. Where the latitude is to be used for the computation of time or of azimuth, it is generally accurate enough to scale the latitude from a good map. The final calculated results will probably be as good as can be obtained with the engineer's transit, for they will not be seriously affected by a slight error in the latitude used in the computations.

12-14. Latitude by Sun's Altitude at Noon. Where a meridian has been determined, the latitude can be obtained by measuring the altitude of the sun's lower or upper limb at the instant the sun crosses the meridian. Where the meridian is unknown, this altitude may be measured when the sun reaches the highest point in its path. The observed angle is corrected for the index error of the vertical circle, for refraction and parallax, and for the semidiameter of the sun. The sun's declination at the instant of apparent noon, and the semidiameter of the sun can be obtained from the ephemeris. From Fig. 12-10, which is a section taken in the plane of the meridian, it is evident that the latitude, which is measured by the arc ZE, will be

$$\phi = 90° - (h - \delta) \qquad (12\text{-}5)$$

North declination is considered positive and south declination is negative. Instrumental errors and the correction for semidiameter can be eliminated if one vertical angle is measured to the sun's lower limb with the telescope normal and another is measured immediately afterward to the upper limb with the telescope inverted. If the second observation is made within 1 or 2 minutes of apparent noon, the sun's altitude will not have changed appreciably during that interval.

12-15. Latitude by Observation on Circumpolar Star. From Fig. 12-10 it will be noted that the altitude of the pole is also a measure of the latitude of the observer. Latitude can be determined by meas-

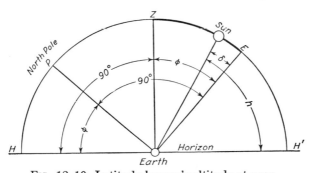

Fig. 12–10. Latitude by sun's altitude at noon.

uring the vertical angle to a circumpolar star when it is on the meridian. The star most frequently used by engineers is Polaris (α Ursae Minoris), because it is quite close to the pole and it can be readily identified. The brighter stars about the north pole are shown in Fig. 12-11. Polaris can usually be identified without difficulty by first locating the *Great Dipper* (Ursa Major). The edge of the dipper that is formed by the stars α and β points toward Polaris.

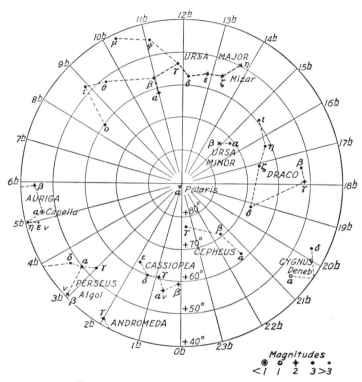

FIG. 12-11. Stars about the north pole.

If the meridian is unknown, the observation can be made when the star reaches either the highest or the lowest point in its path. These positions are known as *upper culmination* and *lower culmination*. Upper culmination occurs when the star is on the upper branch of the meridian, while lower culmination occurs when the star is on the lower branch of the meridian. The time of culmination, which occurs approximately 3^m 56^s earlier each day, may be found with the aid of special tables in the ephemeris or may be computed as follows: At the instant of upper culmination, the local sidereal time equals the right ascension of the star. At lower culmination, it is the right ascension plus 12 hours. The corresponding standard time may be computed from the sidereal time by proceeding as shown in Sec. 12-12.

A special table for determining the time of culmination is provided in the ephemeris. In Table 12-3 is given the local civil time of

TABLE 12-3

LOCAL CIVIL TIME OF UPPER CULMINATION OF POLARIS FOR
THE MERIDIAN OF GREENWICH—1964

Date	Civil Time of Upper Culmination		Variation per Day	Date	Civil Time of Upper Culmination		Variation per Day
1964	h	m	m	1964	h	m	m
Jan. 1	19	17.1	3.95	July 9	6	49.5	3.91
11	18	37.6	3.96	19	6	10.4	3.91
21	17	58.0	3.96	29	5	31.3	3.91
31	17	18.5	3.95	Aug. 8	4	52.3	3.91
Feb. 10	16	38.9	3.96	18	4	13.2	3.91
20	15	59.4	3.95	28	3	34.0	3.92
Mar. 1	15	19.9	3.95	Sept. 7	2	54.9	3.91
11	14	40.4	3.95	17	2	15.8	3.91
21	14	1.0	3.94	27	1	36.6	3.92
31	13	21.6	3.94	Oct. 7	0	57.3	3.93
Apr. 10	12	42.2	3.94	17	0	18.1	3.92
20	12	2.9	3.93	26	23	38.8	3.93
30	11	23.6	3.93	Nov. 5	22	59.5	3.93
May 10	10	44.3	3.93	15	22	20.1	3.94
20	10	5.2	3.91	25	21	40.8	3.93
30	9	26.0	3.92	Dec. 5	21	1.3	3.95
June 9	8	46.8	3.92	15	20	21.9	3.94
19	8	7.7	3.91	25	19	42.4	3.95
29	7	28.6	3.91	1965			
				Jan. 4	19	2.9	3.95

upper culmination of Polaris for the meridian of Greenwich for intervals of 10 days during the year 1964. A similar table for the current year is included in the ephemeris. To find the local time of upper culmination at Greenwich for any date not listed in this table, subtract from the time for the preceding tabular date the product of the variation per day and the number of days elapsed. To find the local time of upper culmination at any other place, subtract 10 seconds for each 15° the place of observation is west of Greenwich or add 10 seconds for each 15° the place is east of Greenwich. If standard time is desired, add or subtract 4 minutes for every degree of longitude by which the place is west or east of the standard time meridian (60°, 75°, 90°, 105°, etc.). To determine the time of lower culmination, add 11^h 58.0^m to the time of upper culmination for the same date if the time of upper culmination is less than 11^h 58.0^m; or subtract 11^h 58.0^m if the time of upper culmination is greater than 11^h 58.0^m.

EXAMPLE 12-5. What is the Pacific standard time of upper culmination of Polaris on Dec. 12, 1964, at a place in longitude 121° 14′ 56″W? What is the P.S.T. of lower culmination on the same date?

Solution: The computations may be arranged as follows:

U.C. for meridian of Greenwich, Dec. 5 (Table 12-3)	$= 21^h 01.3^m$
Correction to Dec. 12, 7×3.95	$= -27.7$
U.C. for meridian of Greenwich, Dec. 12	$= 20^h 33.6^m$
Correction to longitude of place, $(121.25/15) \times 10^s = 81^s$	$= -1.4^m$
U.C. for meridian of place of observation	$= 20^h 32.2^m$
Reduction to P.S.T., 1° 14′ 56″ converted to time	$= +5.0^m$
P.S.T. of U.C. at place of observation	$= 20^h 37.2^m$
	$= 8^h 37.2^m$ P.M.
P.S.T. of U.C., Dec. 12	$= 20^h 37.2^m$
Interval between U.C. and L.C.	$= 11^h 58.0^m$
P.S.T. of L.C., Dec. 12	$= 8^h 39.2^m$ A.M.

Since the altitude of Polaris changes very slowly, a more accurate value of the latitude will be obtained if a number of vertical angles are measured in rapid succession, half of them with the telescope normal and the others with it inverted. The mean of the vertical angle is corrected for refraction. The declination of the star is obtained from the ephemeris. If the observation is made at lower culmination, the latitude is found from the relationship

$$\phi = h + (90° - \delta) \qquad (12\text{-}6)$$

If the observation is made at upper culmination, the relationship is

$$\phi = h - (90° - \delta) \qquad (12\text{-}7)$$

EXAMPLE 12-6. The altitude of Polaris was measured as 38° 14′ 40″ at upper culmination at the place and date given in Example 12-5. The temperature was 42 deg F; the barometric pressure was 29.2 in.; and there was no index error. What is the latitude of the place of observation?

Solution: The declination of Polaris for Dec. 12, 1964, is obtained from the ephemeris as 89° 05′ 41″. Thus, by Eq. 12-7,

Measured $h =$	38° 14′ 40″
Refr. Corr. (Tables 12-1 and 12-2) $=$	−1′ 14″
$h =$	38° 13′ 26″
$- (90° - \delta) =$	−0° 54′ 19″
$\phi =$	37° 19′ 07″

12-16. Latitude from Polaris at Any Hour Angle. During part of the summer, both upper and lower culmination of Polaris may occur during daylight hours. If the time is known within a few minutes, the altitude may be observed whenever the star is visible and the latitude may be computed without serious error by the relationship

$$\phi = h - p \cos t + \tfrac{1}{2} p^2 \sin^2 t \tan h \sin 1'' \qquad (12\text{-}8)$$

where h = true altitude, obtained by correcting the observed altitude for index error and refraction;

t = hour angle, obtained by subtracting the star's right ascension from the sidereal time at the instant of observation;

p = polar distance, expressed in seconds.

The nearer the star is to culmination the smaller will be the error due to errors in time. For hour angles of 3, 9, 15, and 21 hours, an error of 1 minute in time causes an error of about 12″ in the computed latitude. For hour angles of 6 and 18 hours, an error of 1 minute in time causes an error of about 17″ in the computed latitude.

The method of calculating the latitude will be apparent from the example in the accompanying tabulation.

Computations for Latitude from Polaris at Any Hour Angle

Date: Aug. 22, 1945. Longitude: 110° 37′ 01″ W. Time: 7ʰ 22ᵐ 20ˢ P. M., M. S. T. Observed vertical angle on Polaris: 42° 37′ 30″.

Mountain standard time =	19ʰ 22ᵐ 20ˢ
Longitude west from Greenwich = +	7 00 00
Greenwich civil time, Aug. 22 =	26 22 20
Mean solar interval since 0ʰ, Aug. 23 =	2 22 20
Correction to sidereal interval =	+ 23.4 (from Table III, ephem.)
Sidereal interval since 0ʰ, Aug. 23 =	2 22 43.4
Sid. time, Green. 0ʰ, Aug. 23 =	22 03 41.0 (from ephemeris of sun)
Green. sid. time of observation =	24 26 24.4
Long. to place of observation = −	7 22 43
Local sid. time of observation =	17 03 41.4
Right ascension of Polaris = −	1 46 29.0 (from ephemeris)
Hour angle of Polaris =	15 17 12.4
	× 15
Hour angle of Polaris, t =	229° 18′ 06″

$$\phi = h - p \cos t + \tfrac{1}{2} p^2 \sin^2 t \tan h \sin 1''$$

Observed alt. = 42° 37′ 30″	90° 00′ 00.0″
Refraction = − 01′ 02″	δ = 89° 00′ 03.4″ (from ephemeris)
h = 42° 36′ 28″	p = 0° 59′ 56.6″ = 3,596.6″

log p (3,596.6) = 3.555 8921	colog 2 = 9.6990
log cos t (229° 18′ 06″) = 9.814 2985 (negative)	log p^2 = 7.1118
log p cos t = 3.370 1906 (n)	log sin² t = 9.7595
p cos t = − 2,345″ = − 0° 39′ 05″	log tan h = 9.9637
	log sin 1″ = 4.6856
	sum = 1.2196
	$\tfrac{1}{2} p^2 \sin^2 t \tan h \sin 1''$ = 17″

$$\phi = 42° 36′ 28″ - (- 0° 39′ 05″) + 0° 00′ 17″ = 43° 15′ 50″$$

12-17. Longitude. The longitude of a point can be scaled from a map, or it can be calculated by determining the difference in time between the unknown point and some point whose longitude is known. The radio time-signals sent out from the Naval Observatory at Washington provide eastern standard, or 75th-meridian, time. If local mean time is determined by any of the methods of Secs. 12-9 to 12-12, the difference between this local time and 75th-meridian time is the amount the unknown point is east or west of the 75th meridian, expressed in hours, minutes, and seconds. This longitude difference can be changed to degrees, minutes, and seconds of arc by multiplying by 15, and the unknown longitude can be readily determined. Compared with eastern standard time, the local time will be slow if the point is west of the 75th meridian, and it will be fast if the point is east of this meridian.

12-18. Azimuth from Observations on Polaris at Elongation. The two most common methods of determining the azimuth of a line are by observations on circumpolar stars and by solar observations. The simplest method is to observe Polaris either at the apparently most westerly point in its path (western elongation) or at the apparently most easterly point (eastern elongation). The azimuth of Polaris at elongation may be taken from the ephemeris, or it may be computed from the following relationship:

$$\sin Z = \sin p \sec \phi \qquad (12\text{-}9)$$

where Z = azimuth measured from the north;

p = polar distance, or 90° minus the declination;

ϕ = latitude.

The time of elongation can be determined from the time of upper culmination by adding or subtracting the proper interval given in Table 12-4. Also, it can be calculated in the following manner: The hour angle can be computed from the relationship

$$\cos t = \tan \phi \cot \delta \qquad (12\text{-}10)$$

TABLE 12-4

MEAN TIME INTERVAL BETWEEN UPPER CULMINATION
AND ELONGATION*

Latitude	Time Interval	Latitude	Time Interval	Latitude	Time Interval
10°	5ʰ 58.3ᵐ	40°	5ʰ 55.7ᵐ	52°	5ʰ 53.9ᵐ
15°	5ʰ 58.0ᵐ	42°	5ʰ 55.4ᵐ	54°	5ʰ 53.6ᵐ
20°	5ʰ 57.6ᵐ	44°	5ʰ 55.2ᵐ	56°	5ʰ 53.1ᵐ
25°	5ʰ 57.2ᵐ	46°	5ʰ 54.9ᵐ	58°	5ʰ 52.7ᵐ
30°	5ʰ 56.7ᵐ	48°	5ʰ 54.6ᵐ	60°	5ʰ 52.1ᵐ
35°	5ʰ 56.2ᵐ	50°	5ʰ 54.3ᵐ	62°	5ʰ 51.6ᵐ

* Eastern elongation precedes and western elongation follows upper culmination.

The sidereal time at elongation will equal the right ascension of the star plus its hour angle. The sidereal time can be changed to standard time by the method of Sec. 12-12.

If the exact time is unknown, the star can be followed with the vertical cross hair in the transit. When it appears to move vertically on the cross hair, it is at elongation. The horizontal angle is then measured to some fixed point, or the line of sight is brought to the ground, a point on the line is established, and the angle is measured the next morning. If Polaris was at eastern elongation, its azimuth is added to the clockwise-measured angle to obtain the required azimuth of the line. If the star was at western elongation, its azimuth is subtracted from the clockwise-measured angle.

12-19. Azimuth from Observations on Polaris at Any Hour Angle. If the time is accurately known, the observations on Polaris can be made whenever the star is visible and the azimuth can be calculated by either of the two following relationships:

$$\sin Z = - \sin t \cos \delta \sec h \qquad (12\text{-}11)$$

$$\tan Z = \frac{\sin t}{\sin \phi \cos t - \cos \phi \tan \delta} \qquad (12\text{-}12)$$

where Z = azimuth of Polaris, measured from the north;
$\quad t$ = hour angle, obtained from the time as in Sec. 12-16;
$\quad \delta$ = declination, taken from the ephemeris;
$\quad h$ = altitude, obtained by correcting the observed altitude for index error and refraction;
$\quad \phi$ = latitude.

If the latitude is unknown, the altitude is measured and the first equation is used. When the altitude is measured, the same observations can be used for the determination of both azimuth and latitude. The signs of the trigonometric functions must be taken into account in using these equations. When the star is near elongation, the effect of errors in time on the computed azimuth will be negligible. When the star is near culmination, an error of 5 minutes in the time in a latitude of about 40° will cause an error of about 0° 02′ in the computed azimuth.

12-20. **Solar Observation for Azimuth.** If the time is known to within 1 or 2 minutes, the azimuth of a line can be determined by measuring the horizontal angle from the line to the sun's center and measuring the altitude of the sun's center. A total of eight measurements, four with the telescope direct and four with it reversed and

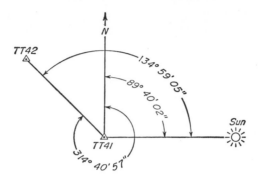

FIG. 12–12. Azimuth of a line by solar observation.

taken in quick succession, will give results reliable to within 15 seconds when a 30″ transit is used.

As shown in Fig. 12-12, the transit is set-up and leveled over a selected point, as station TT41, and the line of sight is directed toward the sun. The telescope bubble is centered and the vertical circle is read to determine the index error, which is recorded. The horizontal circle is set to read 0° 00′ 00″, and a backsight is taken on another selected point, as station TT42. The upper clamp is loosened, the telescope is pointed at the sun, and the image is obtained on a white card as described in Sec. 12-7. Four observations are taken with the image located as indicated in Fig. 12-6 or 12-8. In the morning, these positions would correspond to those in views (a), (b), (a), and (b). In the afternoon the positions would be as in views (c), (d), (c), and (d). For each observation, the time to the nearest second at the instant of tangency, the horizontal-circle reading, and the vertical angle are recorded.

The telescope is then reversed and is again pointed at the sun and adjusted to give an image on the card. This pointing is made with the upper clamp of the transit loosened. Four observations are taken with the telescope reversed, the positions of the image being the same as those with the telescope direct, and the corresponding readings are recorded.

Finally, the upper clamp is loosened, and a sight is taken back to station TT42. The horizontal-circle reading, which should be 180° 00′ 00″, is recorded. Possibly better results could be obtained by reading both verniers each time the horizontal circle is read throughout the series of observations. The index error should be determined after all the observations are made to see whether or not it has changed.

The measured horizontal and vertical angles are corrected to give the true horizontal and vertical angles to the sun's center, as explained in Sec. 12-7 and as demonstrated in Examples 12-3 and 12-4. In order to determine the validity of the observations, a plot is prepared showing corrected horizontal angles and corrected vertical angles as functions of time. If the observations have been made within a period of about 10 minutes or less, the two functions should plot as straight lines.

In Fig. 12-13, eight observations are plotted for an afternoon observation. The horizontal-angle function is shown as a straight line,

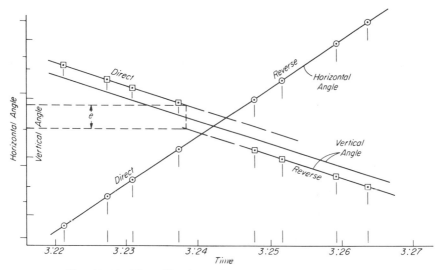

Fig. 12–13. Plot of horizontal and vertical angles vs time.

but the vertical-angle function is shown as two separate straight lines which are parallel. The offset e between these two lines is analyzed as twice the unaccounted-for index error of the instrument. If each vertical angle read with the telescope direct were to be reduced by $e/2$, and each vertical angle read with the telescope reversed were increased by $e/2$, the resulting eight values would plot on one straight line. This, however, is not necessary, since the mean of the eight measured vertical angles is free from the index error.

In Fig. 12-14, eight morning observations have been plotted. The second vertical angle measured with the telescope reversed is seen to be wrong by the amount e. This error is obviously caused by a mistake in reading the vertical circle. Before the means of the observed values are found, both the horizontal angle and the vertical angle for the second reverse readings and the horizontal and vertical angles for the corresponding symmetrical direct readings would be rejected. These latter angles would be those for the third direct readings. This rejection is necessary in order to eliminate systematic transit errors

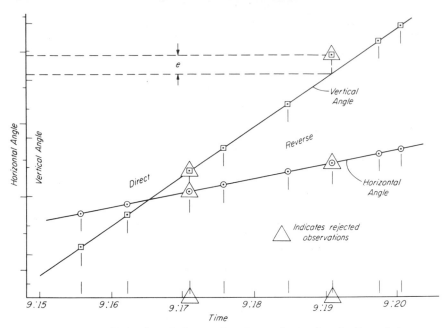

FIG. 12–14. Rejection of observations by analysis of angle-time plot.

to the fullest possible extent. Note that the corresponding two instants of time would also be rejected. The means of the remaining six values of horizontal angles, vertical angles, and times would be used in the computations for azimuth.

Occasionally, the plotted results for a series of solar observations will leave some doubt in regard to the validity of the corrected vertical angles. Since the sun's altitude is a function of time, the change of vertical angle with respect to time can be determined by expressing the altitude h in terms of the sun's hour angle t by solving Eq. 12-4, for sin h. If the resulting equation is differentiated for h with respect to t, the slope of the curve for vertical angle versus time can be expressed as follows:

$$\frac{dh}{dt} = -\frac{\cos \phi \cos \delta \sin t}{\cos h} \tag{12-13}$$

The mean corrected vertical angle for the set of observations gives h. Angle t is obtained by converting the mean watch time of observation first to Greenwich civil time, then to Greenwich apparent time by applying the equation of time, and finally to local apparent time by subtracting the west longitude of the place of observation (or adding if the longitude is east). The result is the hour angle of the sun in hours, minutes, and seconds. This angle is converted to degrees, minutes, and seconds for use in Eq. 12-13. In the morning, the hour angle is considered negative; in the afternoon, positive. If dh/dt is to be expressed as angular minutes of altitude per minute of time, then Eq. 12-13 must be modified to give the following relationship:

$$\frac{dh}{dt} = -\frac{15 \cos \phi \cos \delta \sin t}{\cos h} \tag{12-14}$$

This slope can then be plotted on the diagram for vertical angle versus time, and a line having this slope should be parallel with the line passing through all valid vertical angles. Observations can then be rejected on this basis. If an observation for a vertical angle is rejected, it is necessary to reject also the corresponding horizontal angle. Furthermore, a symmetrical set of observations must also be rejected, as previously mentioned.

The azimuth of the sun is computed from either of the following relationships:

$$\tan \frac{1}{2} Z = \sqrt{\frac{\sin (s - \phi) \sin (s - h)}{\cos s \cos (s - p)}} \tag{12-15}$$

$$\cos Z = \frac{\sin \delta - \sin \phi \sin h}{\cos \phi \cos h} \tag{12-16}$$

where Z = azimuth of the sun, measured from north;
   $s = \frac{1}{2} (\phi + h + p)$;
   ϕ = latitude;
   h = true altitude, obtained from the mean of the corrected vertical angles;
   p = polar distance, or $(90° - \delta)$;
   δ = declination, obtained for the mean instant of time from the ephemeris.

The best results will be obtained if the observations are made when the local mean time is between 8 and 10 A.M. or between 2 and 4 P.M. Except when the observation is made early in the morning or late in the afternoon, Eq. 12-15 should be used to compute the azimuth of the sun.

The horizontal angle between the backsight and the position of the sun represented by the mean of the corrected angles is used with the azimuth of the sun to obtain the azimuth of the line. Computations showing the use of both formulas to determine the azimuth of the line from station TT41 to station TT42 in Fig. 12-12 are given on page 406.

Date: July 24, 1958. Transit at station TT41. Latitude: 43° 00' 37" N.

Mean corrected horizontal angle TT42 to sun = 134° 59' 05"
Mean corrected vertical angle to sun = h = 29° 35' 05"
Mean instant of observation = 8ʰ 38ᵐ 37ˢ A.M., E.S.T.
Longitude of standard meridian = 5 00 00
Greenwich civil time of observation = 13ʰ 38ᵐ 37ˢ
Declination of sun at 0ʰ, G.C.T., July 24, 1958 = +20° 01' 26.8"
Change in declination in 13.65ʰ
= 13.65 × (− 31.287") = 07' 07.1"
Declination at instant of observation = δ = +19° 54' 19.7"

$$\tan \frac{1}{2} Z = \sqrt{\frac{\sin (s - \phi) \sin (s - h)}{\cos s \cos (s - p)}}$$

p = 70° 05' 40"
ϕ = 43° 00' 37"
h = 29° 35' 05"
2) 142° 41' 22"

s =	71° 20' 41"	colog cos s = 0.49 5022
$s - h$ =	41° 45' 36"	log sin $(s - h)$ = 9.82 3482
$s - \phi$ =	28° 20' 04"	log sin $(s - \phi)$ = 9.67 6344
$s - p$ =	1° 15' 01"	colog cos $(s - p)$ = 0.00 0103

2) 9.99 4951
log tan ½ Z = 9.99 7476
½ Z =   44° 50' 01"
Azimuth of sun, Z =   89° 40' 02"
+360°
449° 40' 02"
Horizontal angle = −134° 59' 05"
Azimuth of line from TT41 to TT42 =   314° 40' 57" from north

$$\cos Z = \frac{\sin \delta - \sin \phi \sin h}{\cos \phi \cos h}$$

log sin ϕ (43° 00' 37") = 9.83 3867
log sin h (29° 35' 05") = 9.69 3472   sin δ (+ 19° 54' 19.7") = 0.34 0468
log (sin ϕ sin h) = 9.52 7339   sin ϕ sin h = 0.33 6774
(sin δ − sin ϕ sin h) = 0.00 3694
log (sin δ − sin ϕ sin h) = 7.56 7497

log cos ϕ (43° 00' 37") = 9.86 4055
log cos h (29° 35' 05") = 9.93 9333
log (cos ϕ cos h) = 9.80 3388   log (cos ϕ cos h) = 9.80 3388
log cos Z = 7.76 4109
Azimuth of sun, Z =   89° 40' 02"
+360°
449° 40' 02"
Horizontal angle = −134° 59' 05"
Azimuth of line from TT41 to TT42 =   314° 40' 57"

12-21. Azimuth by Solar Attachment.   The solar attachment is a device fastened to a transit for rapidly determining the direction of a meridian. The three types commonly encountered are the Burt, the Saegmuller, and the Smith attachments. Although these three attachments differ greatly in appearance, the principles involved in their use are the same.

The Saegmuller attachment, shown in Fig. 12-15, consists of an

Fig. 12–15.   Transit equipped with Saegmuller solar attachment.
(Courtesy of Keuffel & Esser Co.)

auxiliary telescope which is equipped with a bubble and has two motions at right angles to each other. If the main telescope is put in the
plane of the meridian and the line of sight is directed to the celestial
equator, as shown in Fig. 12-16, then the vertical axis of the attachment also lies in the meridian and points to the north pole. If the line
of sight of the auxiliary telescope is at right angles to the polar axis, it
will generate an equatorial plane. When the line of sight is inclined
to this plane by an amount equal to, and in the direction of, the sun's
declination, and the telescope is revolved on its polar axis, the line
of sight will follow the sun's path in the heavens for the given day,
the declination being assumed to remain constant.

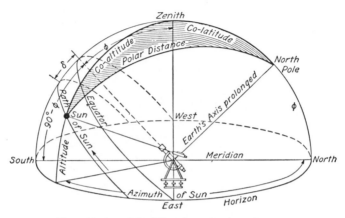

FIG. 12–16.   Meridian by solar attachment.

Thus, when the main telescope is elevated through a vertical
angle equal to the co-latitude and the angle between the planes of
the horizontal cross hairs of the two telescopes is made equal to the
declination of the sun, the main telescope must be in the meridian
when the auxiliary telescope is directed toward the sun. Only one
position for the main telescope can be found which will permit the
smaller telescope to be directed toward the sun. When this position is
found, the main telescope will be in the meridian.

In setting off the declination-angle, the two telescopes are
brought into the same plane by directing the lines of sight to the same
distant object. The main telescope is then depressed or elevated,
according as the declination is north or south, and the declination-
angle is set on the vertical circle. The auxiliary telescope is revolved
about its horizontal axis until its bubble comes to the center of its
tube. The angle between the two telescopic lines of sight will be the
declination-angle. The main telescope is then elevated until its altitude is equal to the co-latitude of the place, and it is clamped in this

position. With the vertical motions of the two telescopes clamped, the horizontal clamps are released and the telescopes are turned until the small telescope is directed toward the sun. The main telescope is then in the meridian.

Because of refraction, the sun will appear higher in the sky than it really is. Hence, the declination-angle used in making the observations is obtained by adding a refraction correction to the declination of the sun as obtained from the ephemeris. The refraction correction is dependent on the declination, hour angle, and latitude. Tables giving the values of this correction are found in the abridged editions of the ephemeris published by the various instrument makers.

Although the solar attachment has been used in the subdivision of much of the public lands, the results obtained may be considerably in error, unless the instrument is in very good adjustment.

12-22. Azimuth by Equal Altitudes. The meridian can be found by means of two equal altitudes of a heavenly body, one east and the other west of the meridian. If the declination of the sun is considered to be constant, its path, as shown in Fig. 12-16, is symmetrical with respect to the meridian. The meridian is, therefore, midway between any two positions of the sun which are at equal distances above the horizon.

To use this method, a horizontal angle is measured between a fixed line of reference and the sun's center when it is at any convenient altitude in the morning and the horizontal cross hair is located as in Fig. 12-6 (a). The horizontal circle and vertical circle are read. The index error is determined and the vertical angle to the sun's lower limb is obtained, uncorrected for parallax and refraction. For the afternoon observation, the vertical angle is increased by the diameter of the sun, and the circle reading is set off on the transit to take into account the index error of this pointing. The sun is tracked until the image reaches the position indicated in Fig. 12-6 (c), at which instant the horizontal cross hair is tangent to the sun's upper limb. Consequently, the altitude of the sun is identical with its altitude in the morning.

Since the sun's declination is not constant, the mean between the two positions of the sun will not be the exact south point. The correction for the change in declination is $C = \frac{1}{2} d / (\cos \phi \sin t)$, where d is the change in declination during the elapsed time, ϕ is the latitude, and t is the hour angle of the sun, or approximately half the time interval between the two observations. If the sun is moving north, the variation per day of the declination is positive, and the mean of the two positions of the sun lies to the west of the south point. When the correction is added to 180°, due heed being paid to the sign of the variation per day, the result is the azimuth, measured from the north, of the sun at the middle position.

When the observations are made at night, a series of observations on different stars can be made. No corrections are needed in this case, since any change in the declination of a star is negligible. An example of the computations for an observation on the sun is shown in the accompanying tabulation.

COMPUTATIONS OF AZIMUTH BY EQUAL ALTITUDES OF SUN

Date: Aug. 17, 1958. Transit at station *1*. Latitude: 43° 17′ N.

M.S.T.	Vernier A	Vernier B	Vert. Angle	To Station
A.M.	0° 00′ 00″	180° 00′ 00″		2
10^h 02^m 43^s	34° 24′ 30″	214° 24′ 30″	+ 46° 38′	☿ Lower Limb
P.M.				
2^h 50^m 52^s	148° 18′ 30″	328° 18′ 30″	+ 47° 10′	☿ Upper Limb
	0° 00′ 00″	180° 00′ 00″		2

Elapsed time $= 4^h\ 48^m\ 09^s$

$t = 2^h\ 24^m\ 05^s = 36°\ 01′$ $\tfrac{1}{2}\,d = (2.4)\,(-47.5″) = -114″$

$\log 114 = 2.05\ 6905\,(n)$ Azimuth of sun at

colog cos 43° 17′ = 0.13 7885   middle position $= 179°\ 55′\ 34″$

colog sin 36° 01′ = 0.23 0607   Mean horizontal angle $=\ \ 91°\ 21′\ 30″$

$\log C = \overline{2.42\ 5397\,(n)}$ Azimuth of line *1-2* $=\ \ 88°\ 34′\ 04″$

$C = -266″ = -0°\ 04′\ 26″$

12-23. Order of Making Observations. In most azimuth observations, the time and the latitude will be known with sufficient accuracy to permit the use of solar observations, or of observations on Polaris at any hour angle. The time is obtained from a good watch, or by comparing a fair one with the time furnished by radio time-signals or any Western Union Telegraph clock. The latitude can usually be scaled with sufficient accuracy from an existing map.

If it is necessary to make observations where no preliminary information is available, an approximate latitude can be obtained by measuring the maximum altitude of the sun. The approximate local apparent time would be obtained at the same observation, since the maximum altitude will occur at the instant of local apparent noon. A more exact latitude could be obtained by measuring the maximum or the minimum altitude of Polaris or any other convenient star.

From the observed latitude, a very close approximation to the true meridian could be established by observations on Polaris at elongation. Local time can be obtained by an observation on the sun at local apparent noon, the previously located meridian being used, or by measuring the altitude of the sun in the manner described in Sec. 12-7.

By repeating the observations and using the data obtained from each preceding observation, the location of the meridian, the local time, and the latitude can eventually be determined with considerable exactness.

The easiest way of determining the longitude is by comparing the local mean time with some standard time, sent out by some radio transmitter. With the small compact short-wave receivers now available, there should be few times when this method cannot be used. Textbooks on astronomy contain methods by which the approximate longitude can be obtained by observations on the moon.

BIBLIOGRAPHY

American Nautical Almanac, Government Printing Office.

BOWIE, "Determination of Time, Longitude, Latitude and Azimuth," *Special Publication No. 14,* U. S. Coast and Geodetic Survey, Government Printing Office.

CHAUVENET, *Spherical and Practical Astronomy.* Philadelphia: J. B. Lippincott Company.

HOSMER, G. L. and ROBBINS, J. M. *Practical Astronomy.* New York: John Wiley & Sons, Inc., 1948.

NASSAU, J. J. *Text Book on Practical Astronomy.* New York: McGraw-Hill Book Company, Inc., 1948.

PROBLEMS*

12-1. Determine the sun's declination and the local apparent time for the instant of 10:42:50 A.M., C.S.T., on Oct. 12 at a place whose longitude is 89° 25' 25" W.

12-2. What is the P.S.T. of local apparent noon on Dec. 12 at a place whose longitude is 121° 35' W? What is the sun's declination at this instant?

12-3. What is the sun's hour angle at a place whose longitude is 76° 22' W at the instant of 5:15:20 A.M., P.S.T.?

12-4. When the altitude of the sun's lower limb is measured at local apparent noon on Sept. 5, the vertical-circle reading is + 44° 25'. The index error is + 0° 03'. What is the latitude of the place of observation if the longitude is 85° 20' W?

12-5. Determine the P.S.T. of eastern and western elongation of Polaris on April 5 at a place whose longitude is 122° 40' W.

12-6. Polaris was observed at upper culmination in longitude 105° 04' 30" W on the night of Dec. 19, and the vertical angle was + 38° 30'. What was the Mountain standard time? What is the latitude of the place of observation?

* The ephemeris for the current year is to be used in the problems for Chapter 12.

12-7. What is the azimuth of Polaris at 8:55:10 P.M., E.S.T., on Feb. 10, at a place whose latitude is 44° 20′ and whose longitude is 74° 21′ 30″ W?

12-8. From the following observations made on Polaris at longitude 7ʰ 22ᵐ 43ˢ west, determine the latitude of the place and the azimuth of the line *AB*.

Date: Sept. 16. Transit at station *A* at elevation of 6110 ft. Temp.: 75 F.

M.S.T. P.M.	Vernier A	Vernier B	Vert. ∠	Tel.	Pointing
7ʰ 12ᵐ 16ˢ 7 14 42	0° 00′ 00″ 54° 24′ 00″ 234° 24′ 30″ 180° 00′ 00″	180° 00′ 00″ 234° 24′ 00″ 54° 25′ 00″ 0° 00′ 30″	+ 42° 58′ 30″ 42° 59′ 00″	Dir. Dir. Rev. Rev.	NWly. to station B Nly. to Polaris Nly. to Polaris NWly. to station B

12-9. The following observations were made on the sun in latitude 42° 16′ 30″ N.

Date: Aug. 12. Transit at station *C* at elevation of 905 ft. Temp.: 82 F.

E.S.T. A.M.	Vernier A	Vernier B	Vert. ∠	Tel.	Pointing

10ʰ 24ᵐ 32ˢ
    25   20
    26   04
    28   12
    28   58
    29   41
	0° 00′ 00″
	268° 48′ 30″
	268° 38′ 00″
	269° 16′ 00″
	88° 58′ 00″
	89° 37′ 00″
	89° 24′ 00″
	180° 00′ 00″
		180° 00′ 00″
		88° 49′ 00″
		88° 38′ 30″
		89° 16′ 00″
		268° 57′ 30″
		269° 37′ 30″
		269° 24′ 30″
		0° 00′ 30″
			+ 49° 57′
			50° 20′
			50° 11′
			51° 18′
			51° 09′
			51° 32′
				Dir.
				Dir.
				Dir.
				Rev.
				Rev.
				Rev.
					SWly. to station D
					Sun's lower limb
					Sun's eastern limb
					Sun's lower limb
					Sun's eastern limb
					Sun's lower limb
					Sun's eastern limb
					SWly. to station D

The longitude of the place of observation is 77° 02′ 20″ W. Correct the horizontal and vertical angles to the sun's center, and plot the corrected values versus the corresponding times of observation. Compute the azimuth of the line *CD* and the watch correction.

13

Methods of Stadia

13-1. Uses of Stadia. The term *stadia* in surveying is used to denote the procedures for obtaining horizontal distances and differences in elevation by indirect methods, which are based on the optical geometry of the instruments employed. The procedure is sometimes referred to as optical distance measurement, telemetry, or tacheometry. The instruments employed are the engineer's transit and the leveling rod or stadia rod, the telescopic alidade and the leveling rod or stadia rod, the theodolite and the subtense bar, the self-reducing theodolite and the leveling rod, the distance wedge and the horizontal distance-rod, and the reduction tacheometer and the horizontal distance-rod. Horizontal distances are obtained with each of these combinations of instruments without resorting to direct taping. Differences in elevation can be determined indirectly with most of the combinations.

Stadia is used to measure the lengths of traverse sides, to check the more accurate taped distances in order to uncover gross errors or mistakes, to determine differences of elevation between points, and to carry lines of levels where a relatively low order of accuracy is permissible. Its most general use is found in the compilation of planimetric and topographic maps by field methods alone, where distances, elevations, and directions to points are to be determined from field control points whose positions have been established by a higher order of accuracy.

The principles of stadia measurement by use of the transit and the leveling rod or stadia rod will be developed thoroughly in this chapter. The other methods will then be discussed. The similarity and the difference in the principles of the various techniques can thus be better understood.

13-2. Principle of Transit Stadia Measurements. For the measurement of stadia distances, the telescope of the transit is equipped with three horizontal cross hairs, the upper and lower hairs being

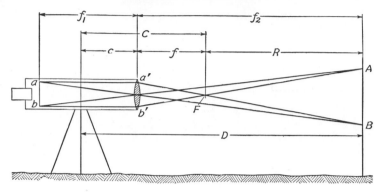

FIG. 13–1.   Principle of transit stadia measurements.

called the stadia hairs. The actual vertical separation of the stadia hairs in the reticule is designated as i. In Fig. 13-1, points a and b represent the positions of the upper and lower stadia hairs with a spacing $ab = i$. By the laws of optics, a ray of light that is parallel with the optical axis of a lens will pass through the *principal focus* of the lens on the opposite side. In Fig. 13-1, point F is the principal focus of the lens, and it is located on the optical axis in front of the lens at a distance f from the center of the lens. The distance f is known as the *focal length* of the lens, and it has a fixed value for a given lens.

Imagine a ray of light to be directed along the line aa', which is parallel with the optical axis of the telescope. This ray of light will be bent by the lens and will continue in the direction $a'FB$. Similarly, a ray along bb' will travel in the direction $b'FA$ on the other side of the lens. The vertical distance AB can be measured on a graduated rod. It is obtained by subtracting the stadia-hair reading at B from the stadia-hair reading at A. The distance AB, designated as s, is called the *stadia interval*.

The distance $a'b'$ is equal to ab and is therefore equal to i. By similar triangles, $a'b'/f = AB/R$, where R is the distance from the principal focus in front of the lens to the graduated rod. So the distance R may be found from the equation

$$R = \frac{f}{i} s \tag{13-1}$$

where f = focal length, which is fixed for a given telescope;
     i = spacing of the stadia hairs, which is also fixed for a given telescope;
    s = vertical distance on the rod between the upper stadia-hair reading and the lower stadia-hair reading.

The ratio f/i is called the *stadia interval factor* and is designated as K. Equation 13-1 thus becomes

$$R = Ks \qquad \text{(13-1a)}$$

The manufacturer can space the stadia hairs with relation to the focal length so as to obtain any convenient value of K desired. The most common value of f/i, or K, is 100.

The horizontal distance, as D in Fig. 13-1, between the center of the instrument and the point at which the rod is held, is $R + f + c$, where c is the distance from the center of the instrument to the lens. This small distance c varies slightly. Its exact value depends on the distance from the instrument to the rod, but the variation is not enough to affect the accuracy of stadia measurements. If C is substituted for $f + c$, then the horizontal distance D from the center of the instrument to the rod is given by the equation

$$D = Ks + C \qquad \text{(13-2)}$$

The distance C is called the stadia constant. Equation 13-2 is the stadia equation for a horizontal line of sight. It is applicable for lines of sight inclined by as much as $3°$ where the distance to be determined is not critical. For this reason, when a stadia interval is measured, it is permissible and desirable to set the lower cross hair on the nearest foot-mark to facilitate reading the interval, even though the line of sight is not quite horizontal.

The value of C will vary from about 0.6 to 1.4 ft, the value depending on the instrument. For most work however, C can be taken as 1 ft. When K is 100, or nearly so, Eq. 13-2 can be written as follows:

$$D = K(s + 0.01) \qquad \text{(13-2a)}$$

where the interval s is simply increased by 0.01 ft.

For long sights, the value of C can be neglected entirely, and Eq. 13-2 can be reduced to the simple form

$$D = Ks \qquad \text{(13-2b)}$$

The stadia interval will become greater than it theoretically should be, because of differential refraction of the upper and lower lines of sight. This effect tends to compensate for neglecting the stadia constant C.

13-3. Determination of Stadia Constant. The stadia constant C is readily determined by setting up the transit, focusing on a distant point at least 1000 ft away, and measuring the distance between the objective lens and the cross-hair ring. This is the focal length f. The telescope is then focused on an object between 200 and 300 ft away. The distance between the objective lens and the center of the instrument is then measured. This is the distance c in Fig. 13-1. The constant C is the sum of f and c.

13-4. Determination of Stadia Interval Factor. If it is desired to determine the stadia interval factor $f/i = K$, a straight line from 400 to 800 ft in length is run on ground that is as nearly level as practicable. The instrument is set on this line, and a point P is located on the line at a distance $f + c = C$ from the center of and in front of the instrument. Points spaced about 50 ft apart are set on line, and the distances R_1, R_2, R_3, and so on are measured from point P to the successive points on line. A leveling rod equipped with two targets is held at each point in succession, and the intervals s_1, s_2, s_3, and so on are determined to the nearest 0.001 ft. Successive values of K are determined by the relationships $K_1 = R_1/s_1$, $K_2 = R_2/s_2$, $K_3 = R_3/s_3$, and so on, and the mean of the values of K thus obtained is taken as the stadia interval factor of the instrument.

13-5. Inclined Stadia Measurements. Inclined stadia measurements are more frequent than are horizontal measurements. Each inclined measurement is reduced to give the horizontal distance from the instrument to the rod and the difference in elevation between the telescope axis at the center of the instrument and the point at which the middle cross hair strikes the rod. This point on the rod is referred to as the middle cross-hair reading. In Fig. 13-2, the instrument is at M, the rod is at O, the horizontal distance be-

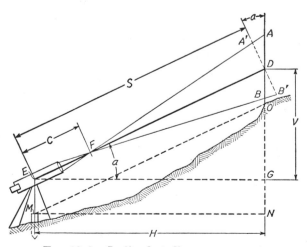

FIG. 13–2.   Inclined stadia measurement.

tween the instrument and the rod is $MN = EG = H$, and the difference in elevation between the telescope axis at E and the middle cross-hair reading D is $DG = V$.

The line of sight is inclined by angle a, and the imaginary line $A'B'$ makes the same angle a with the vertical rod. Since the angle AFB is very small, the angles $DA'F$ and $DB'F$ are considered right angles. Therefore, $A'B' = AB \cos a$. The distance ED is $EF + FD = C + FD = C + Ks \cos a$. But the distance EG is the horizontal distance H, which equals $ED \cos a$. Therefore, the horizontal distance H is given by the equation

$$H = (Ks \cos a + C) \cos a$$

or

$$\boxed{H = Ks \cos^2 a + C \cos a} \qquad (13\text{-}3)$$

where K = stadia interval factor f/i;

s = stadia interval;

C = stadia constant $f + c$;

a = vertical angle of the line of sight, read on the vertical circle of the transit.

The distance DG, which equals $ED \sin a$, is the vertical distance V between the telescope axis and the middle cross-hair reading. Thus, V is given by the equation

$$V = Ks \sin a \cos a + C \sin a \qquad (13\text{-}4)$$

or

$$\boxed{V = \tfrac{1}{2} Ks \sin 2a + C \sin a} \qquad (13\text{-}4a)$$

Table A at the end of this book is used to facilitate the application of Eqs. 13-3 and 13-4a. The column headed "Hor. Dist." gives values of $100 \cos^2 a$ and $C \cos a$ for values of C equal to 0.75, 1.00, and 1.25 ft. The column headed "Vert. Dist." gives values of $\frac{1}{2}$ ($100 \sin 2a$) and $C \sin a$ for values of C equal to 0.75, 1.00, and 1.25 ft. Table A is therefore based on a stadia interval factor K of 100. In using the table, the horizontal distance is obtained by multiplying the value in the "Hor. Dist." column for the given vertical angle by the stadia interval s, and adding the value of $C \cos a$ found at the bottom of the table for the appropriate value of C. The vertical distance between the telescope axis and the middle cross-hair reading is obtained by multiplying the value in the "Vert. Dist." column for the given vertical angle by the stadia interval s, and adding the value of $C \sin a$ found at the bottom of the table for the appropriate value of C.

EXAMPLE 13-1. Stadia readings were made from an instrument set-up to three different points. The stadia interval factor K is 100, and the stadia constant C is 1.00 ft. The recorded values are $s_1 = 3.26$ ft and $a_1 = + 3° 44'$; $s_2 = 5.06$ ft and $a_2 = + 0° 20'$; $s_3 = 4.54$ ft and $a_3 = - 12° 20'$. Find the horizontal distances to the three points and the difference in elevation between the telescope axis and middle cross-hair reading for each sight by using Table A.

Solution: The calculations may be indicated as follows:

$$H_1 = 3.26 \times \quad 99.58 + 1.00 = 325.6 \text{ ft}$$
$$V_1 = 3.26 \times \quad \ 6.50 + 0.06 = + \ 21.25 \text{ ft}$$
$$H_2 = 5.06 \times 100.00 + 1.00 = 507.0 \text{ ft}$$
$$V_2 = 5.06 \times \quad \ 0.58 + 0.01 = + \ 2.94 \text{ ft}$$
$$H_3 = 4.54 \times \quad 95.44 + 0.98 = 434.3 \text{ ft}$$
$$V_3 = 4.54 \times \quad 20.87 + 0.22 = - \ 94.97 \text{ ft}$$

If the value of K for the instrument is not 100, a value determined from the upper part of Table A must be multiplied by the value $K/100$ before the correction for C is added.

EXAMPLE 13-2. Using the instrument readings in Example 13-1 but taking K as 102 and C as 0.75, determine H and V for the three sights.

Solution: In this case, the values are as follows:

$$H_1 = \frac{102}{100} \times 3.26 \times \quad 99.58 + 0.75 = 331.9 \text{ ft}$$

$$V_1 = \frac{102}{100} \times 3.26 \times \quad \ 6.50 + 0.05 = + 21.66 \text{ ft}$$

$$H_2 = \frac{102}{100} \times 5.06 \times 100.00 + 0.75 = 516.9 \text{ ft}$$

$$V_2 = \frac{102}{100} \times 5.06 \times \quad \ 0.58 + 0.01 = + 3.00 \text{ ft}$$

$$H_3 = \frac{102}{100} \times 4.54 \times \quad 95.44 + 0.73 = 442.7 \text{ ft}$$

$$V_3 = \frac{102}{100} \times 4.54 \times \quad 20.87 + 0.16 = - 96.80 \text{ ft}$$

Equations 13-3 and 13-4a can be simplified, if the value of the constant C is assumed to be about 1 ft, by adding 0.01 ft to the stadia interval and neglecting the second term in each formula. Thus, the results are as follows:

$$H = K (s + 0.01) \cos^2 a \qquad (13\text{-}5)$$

$$V = \tfrac{1}{2} K (s + 0.01) \sin 2a \qquad (13\text{-}6)$$

These last two equations are by far the easiest to apply to stadia measurements. An examination of these equations will show they are obtained by making the following assumptions in the last terms of Eqs. 13-3 and 13-4a: K is assumed to be 100; $\cos^2 a$ is assumed to be equal to $\cos a$; and $\tfrac{1}{2} \sin 2a$ is assumed to be equal to $\sin a$. These assumptions are reasonable for any vertical angles encountered in stadia work, when the limited accuracy of the stadia method is considered. When Eqs. 13-5 and 13-6 are used and $K = 100$, the horizontal distance H is obtained by multiplying the value in Table A by the stadia interval increased by 0.01 ft and neglecting the lower part of the table. The vertical distance V is obtained in a similar manner.

EXAMPLE 13-3. Find H and V for each of the three observations in Example 13-1 by using Eqs. 13-5 and 13-6.

Solution: The calculations may be indicated as follows:

$$H_1 = 3.27 \times \quad 99.58 = 325.6 \text{ ft}$$
$$V_1 = 3.27 \times \quad 6.50 = + 21.26 \text{ ft}$$
$$H_2 = 5.07 \times 100.00 = 507.0 \text{ ft}$$
$$V_2 = 5.07 \times \quad 0.58 = + 2.94 \text{ ft}$$
$$H_3 = 4.55 \times \quad 95.44 = 434.3 \text{ ft}$$
$$V_3 = 4.55 \times \quad 20.87 = - 94.96 \text{ ft}$$

These values are practically identical with the values computed in Example 13-1.

13-6. Beaman Stadia Arc. The reduction of stadia readings to corresponding horizontal and vertical distances is greatly simplified if the instrument is equipped with a *Beaman stadia arc*. This arc, which is placed on the vertical circle of the instrument, is composed of two sets of graduations and an index mark for each set. One index mark, designated as H in Fig. 13-3, gives, on the corresponding scale,

FIG. 13–3.   Beaman stadia arc.

the number of feet which must be subtracted for each 100 ft of stadia distance, or for each foot of stadia interval, to obtain the horizontal distance H. The other index mark, designated as V, gives, on the corresponding scale, the number of feet of rise or fall of the line of sight for each 100 ft of stadia distance or for each foot of stadia interval. When the stadia arc is used in place of the vertical circle and the tables, the V-index mark must be set on a whole number before a middle cross-hair reading is taken.

When the telescope is level, the H-scale reads 0, and the V-scale reads 50. A reading on the V-scale greater than 50 indicates a positive vertical angle, while a reading less than 50 indicates a negative vertical angle. If a stadia interval is read as 3.24 ft on a rod with the telescope inclined as shown in Fig. 13-3, and it is assumed that K is 100 and C is 1 ft, the horizontal distance H is 3.25 × 100 − 3.25 × 10 = 292.5 ft. Also, the vertical distance V is 3.25 × (80 − 50) = + 97.50 ft. This is the rise in the line of sight from the instrument to the rod, or the vertical distance between the telescope axis and the middle cross-hair reading.

13-7. **Difference in Elevation Between Two Points.** When stadia methods are used to determine differences in elevation between points, three situations will prevail. In the first situation, which is associated with traversing and mapping details about a point, the difference in elevation between the point on the ground over which the instrument is set up and the point on the ground at which the rod is held is the desired value. In Fig. 13-4, the instrument occupies point M, and the rod is held at point O. A leveling rod or stadia rod is held alongside the instrument, and the height of the telescope axis above point M is measured. This height is recorded in the notes as the H.I., which for this situation is understood to be the height of the instru-

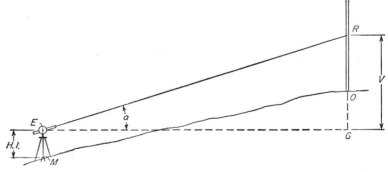

FIG. 13-4.   Difference in elevation between instrument ground station and rod station.

ment *above the ground*. The line of sight is directed at the rod held at O, and the stadia interval is read and recorded. Then the reading of the middle cross hair at R that corresponds to a vertical angle a is read and recorded, along with the vertical angle. The difference in elevation between points M and O is equal to $+ ME + GR - RO$. But the distance ME equals the H.I.; the distance GR is the vertical distance V computed by either Eq. 13-4b or 13-6, by means of Table A, or by the stadia arc; RO is the middle cross-hair reading, which will be referred to simply as the *rod reading*. Therefore, the difference in elevation between M and O is (+ H.I. + V − rod reading) if the vertical angle is positive, or (+ H.I. − V − rod reading) if the vertical angle is negative.

In this situation it is sometimes found convenient to read the vertical angle when the rod reading equals the H.I. The difference in elevation is then + H.I. $\pm V$ − H.I. = $\pm V$ directly. This procedure, however, is convenient only if the middle cross hair can be set at the H.I., and is not a general method.

In the second situation, which is sometimes associated with mapping details about a point, the difference in elevation between the telescope axis and the point on the ground at which the rod is held is the desired value. Again refer to Fig. 13-4, and let it be assumed that the elevation of point M has been established. The distance ME added to the elevation of M gives the elevation of the telescope axis *above the datum*, or the H.I. as understood in differential leveling and defined in Sec. 3-27. Then if the elevation of point O is desired, the difference in elevation between points E and O is added to the H.I. In this instance the difference in elevation between E and O is (+ V − rod reading). If the vertical angle is negative, the desired difference is (− V − rod reading).

In the third situation, which is associated with running a line of levels by stadia, the difference in elevation between two rod stations is desired. The elevation of the ground at the instrument set-up is of no consequence. In Fig. 13-5, the difference in elevation between the backsight station B and the foresight station F is desired. The instrument is set up at A, and a stadia interval, vertical angle a_B, and rod reading R_B are observed on point B and recorded. Then an interval, vertical angle a_F, and rod reading R_F are observed on point F and recorded. The vertical distances $O_B R_B = V_B$ and $O_F R_F = V_F$ are computed by use of the stadia table. The difference in elevation in this instance is (+ backsight rod reading − V_B + V_F − foresight rod reading). You should draw sketches of other situations of this nature, where the backsight and foresight vertical angles are, respectively, + and −, − and −, and − and +. The values to be added and sub-

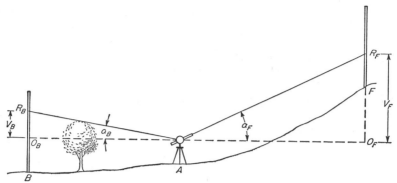

Fig. 13–5.   Difference in elevation between two rod stations.

tracted to arrive at the difference in elevation between the two rod stations will become apparent from the sketches.

13-8.   Stadia Traverse. A stadia traverse is sometimes run to obtain supplementary control based on existing higher-order control. This supplementary control is used to furnish instrument stations for the compilation of field data needed for the production of planimetric and topographic maps, or to provide picture points for controlling photogrammetric mapping. The traverse work may be performed concurrently with the gathering of data, or it may be performed separately from the map-compilation phase.

Three quantities are obtained from the results of the stadia traverse: 1) the length of each traverse side; 2) the azimuth or bearing of each traverse side; 3) the difference in elevation between the ground stations at the ends of each traverse side. The lengths of the sides are obtained by the stadia reduction equations for horizontal distance given in Secs. 13-2, 13-5, and 13-6. The azimuths of the sides are most conveniently determined by carrying a traverse by azimuth as described in Sec. 8-7. Differences in elevation are obtained by the method discussed as the first situation of Sec. 13-7.

The most satisfactory results are obtained if observations for each line of the traverse are taken in both directions. This procedure reveals mistakes, eliminates certain index errors in the vertical circle of the transit, and gives a better value for the horizontal distance and difference in elevation, each of these distances being taken as the mean of two values.

In the stadia traverse of Fig. 13-6, points A and E are established control stations, and the azimuth of the line AE is $200°\ 00'$. Station A, whose elevation is known to be 454.1 ft, is occupied, and the H.I. above the ground is measured by holding the leveling rod

STATION	INTERVAL	HOR. DIST.	AZIMUTH	VERT. ∠	Δ ELEV.	ADJ. ELEV.	
		⊼ @ A	H.I.= 5.0'			454.1	(Fixed)
E			200°00'				
B	2.12	212.7	314°02'	−2°15'	−8.3		
		⊼ @ B	H.I.= 5.1'			446.0	
A	2.12	212.7	134°02'	+2°15'	+8.3		
C	2.13	213.1	223°02'	−3°49'	−14.2		
		⊼ @ C	H.I.= 5.1'			431.9	
B	2.14	213.9	43°02'	+4°02' on 5.8	+14.4		
D	1.88	189.0	167°57'	+0°14'	10.8		
		⊼ @ D	H.I.= 5.0'			432.9	
C	1.88	189.0	347°57'	−0°14'	−0.8		
E	1.83	183.0	95°24'	+4°10'	+13.3		
		⊼ @ E	H.I.= 5.0'			446.4	(Fixed)
D	1.83	183.0	275°24'	−4°10'	−13.3		
A			20°02'				

FIG. 13–6. Stadia traverse notes.

alongside the transit. This H.I., which is 5.0 ft, is recorded in the notes as shown. The value of the azimuth of the line AE is set on the horizontal circle, and a backsight is taken on station E by a lower motion. This method orients the transit circle in azimuth. The transit is now sighted on station B with an upper motion, and the reading of the horizontal circle is observed and recorded as 314° 02'. This is the azimuth of the line AB. A stadia interval of 2.12 is read on the rod held at B and recorded as shown. The middle cross hair is purposely set to read the value of the H.I., or 5.0, and the vertical circle is read and the reading is recorded in the vertical-angle column as − 2° 15'. The value of C of the instrument is 1 ft and K is 100. The horizontal distance and the difference in elevation between the two points are computed and recorded as shown.

The instrument is next set up at station B, the H.I. above the ground is measured, and the back azimuth of the line AB is set on the horizontal circle. This is 134° 02' and is recorded as shown. The transit is oriented by backsighting on station A. The stadia interval is read with the rod held on A and is recorded as 2.12. When the middle cross hair is set at the H.I., the vertical angle is + 2° 15'. The horizontal distance and the difference in elevation are then computed. Station C is next sighted by using an upper motion, and the azimuth of BC, which is read on the horizontal circle, is recorded as 223° 02'. A stadia interval and a vertical angle to the H.I. are read and recorded, and the distance and difference in elevation are computed and recorded.

The procedure just described is repeated at each station, and a final sight is taken on A from E in order to check the azimuth closure. Notice that, when the transit was set up at station C and the rod was held at B, the H.I. could not be sighted with the middle cross hair.

Therefore, the rod reading of 5.8 is recorded, together with the corresponding vertical angle of $+ 4° 02'$.

The data are prepared for traverse computation by first adjusting the azimuth error and then computing the mean value of the length of each traverse side. The traverse is then computed and adjusted by methods described in Chapter 8.

The mean difference in elevation for each line is computed. If the elevation of station E is known, the closure in elevation can be computed. This closure is distributed in proportion to the lengths of the sides. In the traverse of Fig. 13-6, the elevation of station A is 454.1 ft and the elevation of station E is 446.4 ft, giving a difference in elevation of $- 7.7$ ft. The mean values of the differences in elevation of the four lines AB, BC, CD, and DE are, respectively, $- 8.3$, $- 14.3$, $+ 0.8$, and $+ 13.3$ ft. So the measured difference in elevation between A and E is $- 8.5$ ft. The error is $- 0.8$ ft. Since all sides are of about the same length, the error is distributed so that each side receives a correction of $+ 0.2$ ft. The adjusted differences in elevation of the four lines are $- 8.1$, $- 14.1$, $+ 1.0$, and $+ 13.5$ ft, respectively.

13-9. Details About a Point. When the transit stadia method is used to locate details about a point for the purpose of plotting these details, the transit is set up over the point and the H.I. above the ground is determined by the method discussed in the first situation of Sec. 13-7. The horizontal circle is oriented by setting the known azimuth of a line on the circle and backsighting along this line by using the lower motion. The upper motion is then used for all subsequent pointings from the station, so that the azimuth of each line directed to a detail point may be determined. As stadia readings are taken by the instrumentman, the note keeper should keep a detailed sketch up to date in the field notebook, numbering the detail points to correspond with the numbers assigned in the notes. Word descriptions of detail points, such as fence corner, 3' oak, and road int's'n, are used to advantage in documenting the stadia observations.

A form of notes for gathering details about a point is shown in Fig. 13-7. The instrument is set up on station G and oriented by backsighting on station F with the azimuth of the line GF on the horizontal circle. The value of the H.I. is the height of the telescope axis above the ground, and all differences in elevation are applied to the elevation of the ground point. For example, on the sight to point 1, the value of the vertical distance obtained from the stadia table is $3.29 \times 5.75 = - 18.9$ ft. The difference in elevation is then $+ 5.2 - 18.9 - 7.4 = - 21.1$ ft, and the elevation of point 1 is $491.0 - 21.1 = 469.9$ ft. On the sight taken to point 3, the telescope bubble was

POINT	INTERVAL	HOR. DIST.	AZIMUTH	VERT. ∠	ROD READ.	ΔELEV.	ELEV.
	刀 @ STA. G	B.S. 43°22' on STA.F			H.I.= 5.2		491.0
1	3.28	328	37°10'	-3°18'	7.4	-21.1	469.9
2	3.32	333	39°15'	-3°16'	8.1	-21.8	469.2
3	4.06	407	152°50'	—	8.8	-3.6	487.4
4	4.51	452	158°05'	-1°06'	5.2	-8.7	482.3
5	1.29	129	292°22'	+3°45'	5.2	+8.5	499.5
6	1.20	111	316°30'	+16°20'	8.2	+29.7	520.7
7	1.31	124	316°40'	+14°10'	5.2	+31.3	522.3

FIG. 13–7.   Stadia detail notes.

centered when the rod reading was made, and since there was no vertical angle, the difference in elevation is + 5.2 − 8.8 = − 3.6 ft. On the sights taken to points *4*, *5*, and *7*, the middle cross hair was sighted on the H.I. on the rod, and the difference in elevation in each instance is simply the vertical distance determined from the stadia table.

An alternative method of determining elevations is discussed in the second situation of Sec. 13-7. The H.I. above the vertical datum at the instrument set-up is determined, and then the difference in elevation between the telescope axis and the ground point is obtained as described in Sec. 13-7. This method is more effective when using the Beaman arc on the vertical circle. The advantage of sighting on the H.I. measured above the ground to reduce the calculation of differences in elevation is lost when the Beaman arc is used, because the *V*-scale reading must be a whole number, and the rod reading corresponding to this *V*-scale reading must be recorded. It is pure chance if the rod reading happens to be the same as the H.I. above the ground when the *V*-scale is set on a whole number.

The form of notes when the Beaman arc is used is shown in Fig. 13-8. The instrument is set up at station 23, and the H.I. is found to be 237.6 ft. The line of sight is directed toward point *24*, and the stadia interval is read. The *V*-scale is then set on the nearest graduation mark, in this case, 55. The *H*-scale reading is less than 1 and is

POINT	INT.	H% CORR	HOR. DIST.	V	PROD. V×I	ROD READING (−)	ΔELEV.	H.I.	ELEV.
			刀 @ 23					237.6	233.5
24	2.64	—	264	55	+13.2	9.2	+4.0		241.6
25	3.22	—	322	48	-6.4	3.3	-9.7		227.9
26	1.50	5	142	72	+33.0	11.0	+22.0		259.6
27	4.65	—	465	43	-32.6	10.8	-43.4		194.2
28	2.90	3	282	32	-52.2	3.2	-55.4		182.2

FIG. 13–8.   Beaman-arc stadia notes. The value of *C* neglected.

not recorded. The rod reading 9.2 is taken and recorded. The horizontal distance is computed for a value of K equal to 100. The product $V \times I$, where I is the stadia interval, is understood to be the product of $(V - 50)$ and I since 50 represents a horizontal line of sight. Since the rod reading in mapping details about a point will always be a minus quantity, the rod-reading column is headed with a minus sign. The difference in elevation equals the product minus the rod reading. In this case, it is $+ 13.2 - 9.2 = + 4.0$ ft.

The sight to point 28 is downhill. The H-scale reading corresponding to the selected V-scale reading is 3. So, for every 100 ft of stadia distance, 3 ft must be subtracted. The horizontal distance is $100 \times 2.91 - 3 \times 2.91 = 282$ ft. The product $V \times I$ is $(32 - 50) \times 2.91 = - 52.2$ ft, and the difference in elevation is $- 52.2 - 3.2 = - 55.4$ ft.

13-10. Stadia Leveling. The operations in stadia leveling are quite similar to those in differential leveling, but in stadia leveling the line of sight does not have to be horizontal. This feature is advantageous in hilly country where a relatively low order of accuracy is acceptable, because the lines of sight can be quite long.

In Fig. 13-9, a line of stadia levels is run from B.M. 43 to

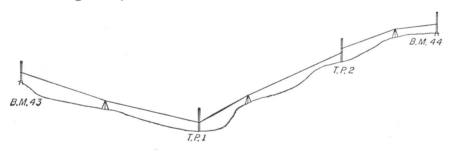

FIG. 13–9.   Stadia leveling.

B.M. 44. The transit is set up, and backsight readings are taken on B.M. 43. These consist of an interval, a rod reading, and a corresponding vertical angle. Foresight readings consisting of an interval, a rod reading, and a corresponding vertical angle are then taken on T.P. 1. This procedure is repeated at the second and third set-ups.

The following procedure is used to detect mistakes in reading the vertical circle and the interval, and in computing the values for the backsights and the foresights. The line of sight is directed at the rod, and the lower stadia hair is set on some foot-mark, as shown in Fig. 13-10 (a). The readings of the lower, middle, and upper cross hairs are observed and recorded. The vertical circle is then read, and the angle is recorded opposite the middle cross-hair reading. Now the

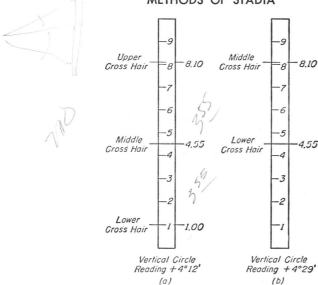

Fig. 13–10. Method of checking
stadia readings.

line of sight is either raised or lowered by means of the vertical tangent screw until the middle cross hair is set on the original reading of the upper or lower cross hair. In Fig. 13-10 (b) the middle cross hair is set on the original reading of the upper cross hair. The vertical circle is again read, and the angle is recorded opposite this cross-hair reading.

If the value of K for the transit is 100 or nearly so, then the angle between the upper and middle cross hairs, or between the middle and lower cross hairs, is $\tan^{-1} (1/200) = 0° 17'$ approximately. Therefore the two values of the vertical angle should differ by about $0° 17'$. If they do not, then a mistake has been made in either a cross-hair or vertical-circle reading, and the readings can be checked before leaving the set-up. The computation of the backsight and foresight values can be checked, because there will be two values for each distance.

A form of notes for stadia leveling is shown in Fig. 13-11. The readings shown are those for the three set-ups of Fig. 13-9. Notice that when the backsight vertical angle is plus, the line of sight actually drops from the rod to the instrument; and when it is minus, the line of sight actually rises from the rod to the instrument.

13-11. Errors in Stadia Measurements. The accuracy of stadia measurements is largely dependent on the instrument and the rod used, and on atmospheric conditions. For sights up to 400 ft, it is usually possible to obtain the intercepted distance on the rod to 0.01 ft.

STATION	ROD	VERT.∠	B.S.	ROD	VERT.∠	F.S.
	9.80	+2°30'				
B.M. 43	6.40	+2°13'	−19.9			
	3.00					
	7.70	−3°08'		8.25	−1°23'	
T.P. 1	5.85	−3°25'	+27.9	4.60	−1°41'	−25.8
	4.00			1.00		
	6.20	−2°21'		8.00	+3°20'	
T.P. 2	4.10	−2°38'	+23.4	4.50	+3°03'	+32.6
	2.00			1.00		
				5.00	+0°27'	
B.M. 44				3.50	+0°10'	−2.6
				2.00		

Fig. 13–11.   Stadia leveling notes.

Consequently, if the stadia interval factor and the rod used are correct, the resulting horizontal distance should be within 1 ft of the correct distance. For longer sights, the error depends on the magnifying power of the telescope, the coarseness of the stadia hairs, the type of rod used, and the weather conditions. Under reasonably favorable conditions, the error should not exceed 10 ft in a 1000-ft sight.

Errors due to imperfections in the graduation of the rod can be kept to a negligible quantity by standardizing the rod. For most stadia work, some type of pattern rod, with coarser graduations than are found on leveling rods, is used. Unless the painting of the rod has been carelessly done, no correction should be necessary for work of moderate precision.

If the rod is not held plumb, the resulting error in horizontal distance will be small when the vertical angle is small, but may be considerable when large vertical angles are encountered. The effect on an observed distance of 1000 ft, determined by reading a 12-ft rod the top of which is 0.5 ft out of plumb, for vertical angles of 0° 30', 10°, and 25°, is as follows:

ERROR IN HORIZONTAL DISTANCE DUE TO ROD BEING OUT OF PLUMB

VERT. ANGLE	OBSERVED DISTANCE	CORRECTED HORIZONTAL DISTANCES		
		Rod Plumb	Rod Leaning Toward	Rod Leaning Away
+ 0° 30'	1000	999.9	999.4	998.7
+ 10° 00'	1000	969.8	976.1	961.9
+ 25° 00'	1000	821.4	836.7	804.7

Errors from this source can be eliminated by using a rod equipped with a plumbing level. In computing the values just given, the constant C has been neglected.

When a cross hair appears to cover an appreciable space on the rod, the observations can be made best by using the tops of the hairs, rather than by attempting to use their centers.

Errors in observing the intercepted distance on the rod will be random in character. On important sights all three hairs can be read. If the hairs are equally spaced, the middle-hair reading should be the mean of the upper and lower readings. When sights are taken between transit stations, observations should be made from both ends of the line.

If systematic errors have been eliminated and the field observations carefully made, the closure of a transit stadia traverse will compare favorably with that for the less precise grades of transit-tape work.

13-12. Errors in Stadia Elevations. The errors in elevations obtained from stadia measurements are caused by errors in measuring the vertical angles and in reading the rod, and by not keeping the rod plumb.

The effect of an error of 1 minute in a vertical angle is practically independent of the size of the angle, but is proportional to the length of the sight. For a distance of 100 ft, the error in elevation is about 0.03 ft.

The effect of an error of 1 ft in an observed inclined distance increases with the size of the vertical angle. An inspection of the stadia reduction table shows the error in elevation to be 0.05 ft for a 3° angle, about 0.1 ft for a 5° angle, about 0.2 ft for a 10° angle, and about 0.4 ft for a 25° angle. It is necessary, therefore, that intervals be observed more carefully when the vertical angles are large.

The error in elevation caused by the rod not being plumb is considerable on a long sight when the vertical angle is large. The effect of the top of a 12-ft rod being 0.5 ft out of plumb when the observed distance is 1000 ft is as shown in the accompanying tabulation.

ERROR IN VERTICAL DISTANCE DUE TO ROD BEING OUT OF PLUMB

VERT. ANGLE	OBSERVED DISTANCE	DIFFERENCES OF ELEVATION		
		Rod Plumb	Rod Leaning Toward	Rod Leaning Away
+ 0° 30′	1000	8.7	8.7	8.7
+ 10° 00′	1000	171.0	172.1	169.6
+ 25° 00′	1000	383.0	390.1	375.2

13-13. Telescopic Alidade. The telescopic alidade, shown in Fig. 13-12, consists of a telescope similar in all details to that of a transit; an upright post, which supports the standards of the horizontal axis of the telescope; and a straightedge, called the blade, whose edges are essentially in the same direction as the line of sight. The blade contains a circular level, a compass trough with provision for raising or

FIG. 13–12.   Telescopic alidade. (Courtesy of
W. & L. E. Gurley Co.)

lowering the compass needle, and a knob at each end to facilitate moving the blade. The eyepiece of the telescope is sometimes fitted with a prism attachment to allow the observer to view downward rather than directly along the line of sight. The telescope can be rotated 180° about its line of sight in a sleeve by loosening the sleeve ring, and can be rotated about its horizontal axis through an elevation angle or depression angle of about 30°. A vertical clamp and tangent screw control the vertical movement of the telescope, just as on a transit.

The vertical circle has three sets of graduations. When the observer faces the circle, the graduations to the left are in degrees and half-degrees and there is a vernier to read directly to the nearest minute. A horizontal line of sight gives a vertical-circle reading of 30°, the circle reading increasing from 30° for an elevation angle and decreasing from 30° for a depression angle. The vertical angle, together with its proper algebraic sign, is therefore equal to the circle reading minus 30°.

The graduations to the right are the *H*-scale and *V*-scale of a Beaman arc, which is identical to that described in Sec. 13-6 and found on some transits. A *V*-scale reading of 50 indicates a horizontal line of sight.

In order to eliminate the index error, the vertical circle is equipped with a level bubble which, when centered, brings the vertical circle vernier and the index marks of the *H*- and *V*-scales in their proper position independent of the rest of the alidade. This level bubble is

FIG. 13–13.   Telescopic microptic alidade. (Courtesy of
A. Lietz Co. of San Francisco.)

called the control bubble, or vernier bubble. Together with the vernier and index marks, it is moved by a tangent screw.

The telescope is made horizontal, when desired, by means of a rather sensitive striding level which sits on a pair of collars on the telescope and is secured by a small knob on the top of the telescope tube. If the striding level is in adjustment and it is centered by means of the vertical clamp and tangent screw, the *V*-scale reading should read 50 when the control bubble is brought to center. The adjustment of the bubbles is described in Chapter 19.

The microptic alidade, shown in Fig. 13-13, contains a vertical circle graduated on glass, and the circle is viewed through the eyepiece directly above the telescope eyepiece. The control bubble is viewed from the eye position by means of a mirror mounted over the bubble. The vertical circle contains the three sets of graduations just mentioned, namely, the V-scale, the H-scale, and the vertical-angle scale. The degrees and minutes are read in an upper window, the V-scale is read in a middle window, and the H-scale is seen in a lower window, as shown in Fig. 13-14. The V-scale on the microptic alidade reads 0 for a horizontal line of sight. For the first eight graduations on either side of 0, a plus sign or a minus sign appears on the scale. Beyond that, the observer must logically deduce the proper alegbraic sign.

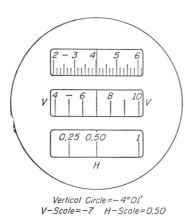

Vertical Circle =− 4°01'
V-Scale=−7   H-Scale=0.50

FIG. 13–14.   Circle readings with microptic alidade.

13-14. Self-Reducing Stadia Instruments. When a major portion of the surveying to be performed consists of stadia measurements, the self-reducing stadia instrument is of particular value. The theodolite shown in Fig. 13-15 is a self-reducing tacheometer in which the stadia hairs are replaced with three curved lines, as shown in Fig. 13-16. The lower curve is referred to as the zero curve. It is placed on a convenient full graduation, which is 1.000 meter in Fig. 13-16. The upper curve then determines the horizontal-distance interval. In (a) this interval is $1.572 - 1.000 = 0.572$ meter. Multiplying by 100 gives the horizontal distance as 57.2 meters. In (b) the interval is 0.485, giving a horizontal distance of $100 \times 0.485 = 48.5$ meters. The middle curve determines the vertical-distance interval, together with the factor for the part of the curve that is being used. In (a), the vertical-distance interval is 0.401 meter, or 40.1 cm. The factor $+ 0.2$ is to be applied to the interval in centimeters, or the factor to be applied to the interval in meters is $+ 20$. The vertical distance is ,therefore, $0.401 \times 20 = 40.1 \times 0.2 = + 8.02$ meters. In (b), the vertical-distance interval is 21.7 cm, and the factor is $- 1$. Hence, the vertical distance is $21.7 \times - 1 = - 21.7$ meters.

As the line of sight is inclined, the curves approach or recede from the zero curve to give a continuous solution of Eqs. 13-3 and 13-4. The vertical-distance curve is interrupted to give a new curve as the line of sight becomes more and more inclined. Each new curve has a different multiplying factor, which is analogous to a different stadia

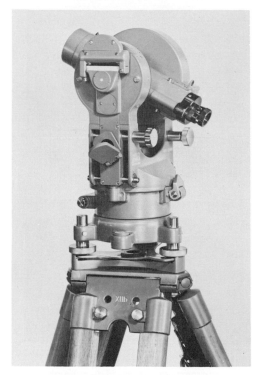

FIG. 13–15. Automatic stadia-reduction instrument. (Courtesy of Wild-Heerbrugg Instruments, Inc.)

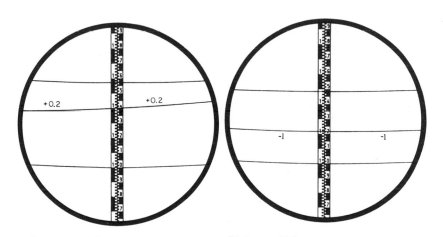

Distance: 57.2 m   Distance: 48.5 m

Diff. of elevation: $+ 0.2 \cdot 40.1 = 8.02$ m   Diff. of elevation: $-1 \cdot 21.7 = -21.7$ m

FIG. 13–16. Stadia intercept curves in field of view of reduction tacheometer.

FIG. 13–17. Self-reducing alidade.
(Courtesy of Kern Instruments,
Inc.)

interval factor in the transit. There is only one horizontal-distance curve, however, and its factor is always 100.

The self-reducing alidade shown in Fig. 13-17 contains a fixed telescope with a tilting objective prism which is used to raise or lower the line of sight. The stadia curves are shown in Fig. 13-18. As the tilting prism is turned, the curves sweep past the field of view, and their spacings are continuously changing so as to automatically solve the stadia equations. The outer curves are for horizontal distance, the factor always being 100. There are three sets of inner curves representing vertical distances. Each of these curves has a different factor. It is 20 for slopes of 0° to 12°, 50 for slopes of 12° to 27°, and 100 for slopes of 27° to 40°. Beyond 40°, the stadia equation is used. In Fig. 13-18 (a) there is a small vertical tick mark on each side. This marking indicates a vertical-distance factor of 100. In Fig. 13-18 (b) there are two such marks on each side to indicate that the factor is 20. The horizontal-distance interval in (b) is $1.717 - 1.500 = 0.217$ meter, and the horizontal distance is $0.217 \times 100 = 21.7$ meters. The vertical-distance interval is $1.662 - 1.551 = 0.111$ meter, and the vertical distance is $0.111 \times 20 = 2.22$ meters. When two sets of five tick marks are visible, the vertical-distance factor is 50.

Field of view of telescope without rod   **Field of view of telescope with rod**

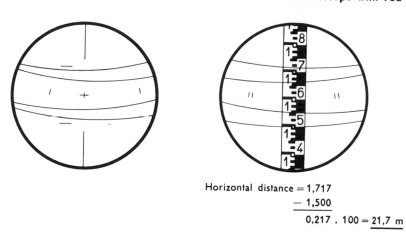

Horizontal distance = 1,717
                    − 1,500
                    0,217 . 100 = 21,7 m

Fig. 13–18. Stadia curves of self-reducing alidade.

13-15. Distance Wedge. In Fig. 13-19 (a) is shown a view obtained by looking down at a telescope, represented by the objective O and the eyepiece e, which is sighted toward a rod oriented in a horizontal position. The line of sight strikes the rod at point a. In Fig. 13-19 (b), a wedge W has been placed in front of the objective so as to cause the line of sight to be deflected by an angle θ and to intersect the rod at b. If the wedge angle and the index of refraction of the glass are such that the angle θ is 0° 34′ 22.6″, then the distance from the wedge to the rod is 100 times the distance ab through which the

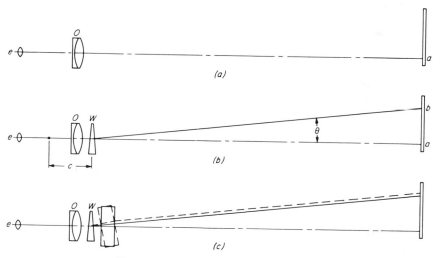

Fig. 13–19. Distance wedge principle.

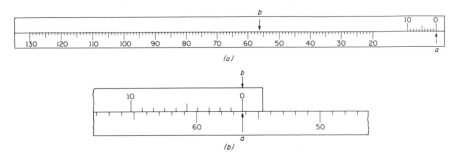

FIG. 13–20. Horizontal distance-rod with vernier.

line of sight has been displaced at the rod. This principle is embodied
in the distance wedge, or stadia prism, which is found in some instruments or in attachments which are adapted to surveying instruments.

In practice, the wedge covers only the central portion of the
objective lens. In effect, the observer is thus permitted to sight a and
b simultaneously. Actually, point a is made to coincide with point b
on the rod. The reading of the rod at b is made more precise by
placing a vernier at a, which superimposes itself on the rod at b.
In Fig. 13-20 (a), the vernier index lies near the right-hand end of
the rod. This position of the index represents point a in Fig. 13-19.
The scale graduations on the rod shown in the lower part of Fig.
13-20 (a) begin at, say, 20 and increase toward the left. In Fig.
13-20 (b) is shown the appearance of the rod as seen through a telescope equipped with a distance wedge. It is seen that the vernier
index lies beyond 56, and the vernier-scale coincidence takes place at
3 on the vernier. Thus, by the principle of the vernier, the reading is
56.3. This position on the rod corresponds to point b in Fig. 13-19.
The distance from the wedge to the rod is, therefore, $56.3 \times 100 =
5630$ units. If each rod graduation is 1 cm, the distance is then
5630 cm or 56.30 meters.

Various types of rods have been designed for use in conjunction
with the distance wedge. Each type is based on the principle just
discussed. Such a rod is shown in Fig. 13-21 as it would be set on its
tripod for use in a field measurement. Because the distance to be
determined is that from the center of the telescope to the face of the
rod, it is necessary to take into account the small distance from the
center of the telescope to the wedge. This distance corresponds to
the stadia constant C and is shown in Fig. 13-19 (b). Allowance for
this distance is made either by the design of the internal optics or by
displacing the vernier in Fig. 13-20 to the left by an amount equal
to $C/100$. The result is to automatically increase the rod reading to
allow for C.

A further refinement in the reading can be made by placing a plano-parallel device in front of the wedge, as shown in Fig. 13-19 (c). This device is an optical micrometer described in Sec. 3-23. A full

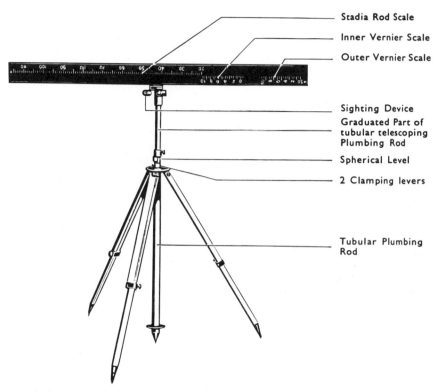

Stadia Rod Scale

Inner Vernier Scale

Outer Vernier Scale

Sighting Device

Graduated Part of tubular telescoping Plumbing Rod

Spherical Level

2 Clamping levers

Tubular Plumbing Rod

FIG. 13–21. Horizontal distance- or stadia-rod mounted on tripod.

rotation of the micrometer drum displaces the vernier through one full vernier division. The use of such a micrometer allows exact coincidence to be made between the vernier and the scale, and a fractional part of the vernier division is then read on the drum.

In Fig. 13-22 are shown the faces of four types of rods used in conjunction with the distance wedge.

The distance determined by means of the combination of a distance wedge and a rod must be reduced to the corresponding horizontal distance. This reduction requires that a vertical angle be read to an index mark on the face of the rod. The horizontal distance is then $s \cos \alpha$, in which s is the distance determined by the wedge and α is the vertical angle. The vertical distance from the center of the instrument to the rod is $s \sin \alpha$. If the rod has been set at the same

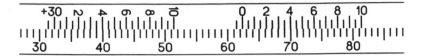

View of the stadia rod as it appears through the telescope with distance
measuring prism device

Stadia reading : **62.35 m** for inner vernier. **32.35 m + 30 m = 62.35 m** for outer vernier.

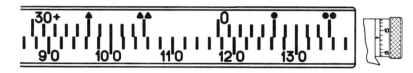

View of the stadia rod as seen through the telescope with stadia prism
with optical micrometer

Stadia reading :   **116**   m reading of rod scale
                + **1.4** m vernier reading
                + **0.115 m** micrometer drum reading
Total stadia dist.:   **117.515 m**

Reading 61.56

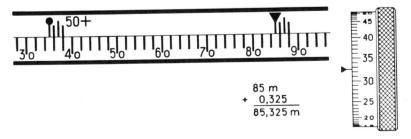

$$85 \text{ m}$$
$$+ \underline{\quad 0,325 \quad}$$
$$85,325 \text{ m}$$

FIG. 13–22. Horizontal distance-rods.

height above the ground as has the center of the instrument, then the vertical distance equals the difference in elevation between the ground points occupied by the instrument and the rod.

13-16. Reduction Tacheometer. The reduction tacheometer is an optical device designed on the principle of the distance wedge. However, there is the following important difference: As the telescope inclination is changed, the deflection of the line of sight is also changed. This feature permits direct determination of horizontal and vertical distances. In Fig. 13-23 the rhombic prism above and in front of the objective lens brings the undeflected part of the field into view.

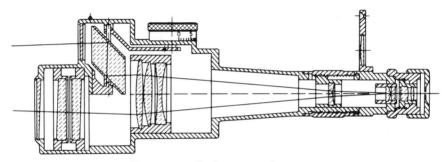

Fig. 13–23. Reduction tacheometer.

This prism is used also as the optical micrometer to shift the image of the rod vernier through one vernier graduation by means of the micrometer drum. Two wedges, which are side by side and are located between the objective and the distance wedge in front, rotate in opposite directions to change the deflection of the line of sight. This rotation is actuated in the process of inclining the telescope.

With the telescope horizontal, the rotating wedges are in a position to cancel their effect, and the deflection is a maximum. This is analogous to the distance-wedge deflection discussed in Sec. 13-15. As the line of sight is inclined up or down, the two wedges change the initial deflection by $\cos \alpha$. Thus, the rod reading gives the horizontal distance directly.

By setting the reduction tacheometer to read vertical distances, the effect of the distance wedge is eliminated when the telescope is horizontal. The deflection then increases from zero by means of the rotating wedges so that it is proportional to $\sin \alpha$. Thus, the reading of the horizontal staff multiplied by 100 gives the vertical distance directly.

The accuracy of distance-wedge measurements is higher than that of transit-stadia measurements by a factor of about 10. This

FIG. 13–24. Subtense bar. (Courtesy of Wild-Heerbrugg Instruments, Inc.)

increase in accuracy is due chiefly to the readings of the vernier and the optical micrometer and to the elimination of parallax error by taking readings on two points on the rod simultaneously. If the work is done with care, short distances can be measured with an accuracy approaching or exceeding that obtainable by direct taping.

13-17. Subtense Bar. The subtense bar, shown in Fig. 13-24, establishes a short but very precise base line at one end of a line to be measured. It contains a target at each end, together with a sighting target at its middle point. The separation of the end targets is controlled by invar wires under a slight but firm spring tension. Although temperature fluctuations cause the bar to expand and contract, the low thermal expansion of the invar holds the targets at practically a fixed distance apart. Slack is increased or taken up by the springs.

The subtense bar is leveled by means of a bulls-eye level and leveling screws, just as is a transit or theodolite. The bar is thus brought into a horizontal plane. Also, the bar is brought perpendicular to the line to be measured by taking a sight to the far end of the line through a small low-power telescope located at the midpoint of the bar.

In Fig. 13-25 is shown a plan view of a subtense measurement. The instrument used to measure the angle γ between the two targets T and T' is located at A. The horizontal distance AB is given by the relationship

$$AB = \frac{TT'}{2} \cot \frac{\gamma}{2}$$

or

$$D = \frac{b}{2} \cot \frac{\gamma}{2} \tag{13-7}$$

in which D is the horizontal distance between the ends of the line; b is the length of the subtense bar, or the distance between the targets; and γ is the subtended angle. Both D and b are, of course, expressed in the same units. The subtense bar is usually 2 meters long. The length of the line in meters is then cot $\gamma/2$. A table is supplied with the subtense bar which gives the distances in meters corresponding to values of γ.

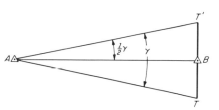

The instrument used to measure the subtended angle must be capable of measuring to 1 second of angle or less. This accuracy can be obtained by measuring the angle with a 1-sec theodolite in several positions of

FIG. 13–25. Subtense-bar principle.

the circle. There is no need to reverse the telescope in these measurements because both targets are at the same vertical angle and at the same distance from the theodolite. Also, the angle is obtained by the difference between the two directions to the targets. Thus, an instrumental error for one pointing equals that for the other pointing. These errors are eliminated by the subtraction of one direction from the other.

The accuracy of subtense measurement is a function of the subtended angle and the length of the bar. Differentiating Eq. 13-7 with respect to γ gives

$$dD - \frac{D^2}{b} d\gamma$$

and differentiation with respect to b gives

$$dD = -\frac{D}{b} db$$

If it is assumed that the uncertainty in $d\gamma$ is $1''$, or 0.00000485, and the uncertainty in db is 0.2 mm, then the uncertainty dD in length for various distances is given in the accompanying tabulation, together with the ratio of dD to the distance D.

D (meters)	dD_γ (meters)	Ratio $dD:D$	dD_b (meters)	Ratio $dD:D$
50	0.006	1:8330	0.0050	1:10,000
75	0.014	1:5350	0.0075	1:10,000
100	0.024	1:4170	0.010	1:10,000
150	0.055	1:2720	0.015	1:10,000
200	0.097	1:2060	0.020	1:10,000
250	0.152	1:1640	0.025	1:10,000
300	0.218	1:1380	0.030	1:10,000
400	0.388	1:1030	0.040	1:10,000
500	0.606	1:820	0.050	1:10,000
600	0.874	1:690	0.060	1:10,000

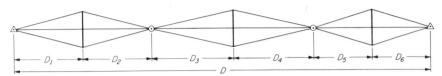

FIG. 13–26. Sectioning line for subtense measurement.

The precision of a distance measured by use of the subtense bar is seen to fall off quite rapidly as the distance increases. This change is caused by the effect of the angular error. As would be expected, an error in the length of the bar produces an error of constant percent in the distance because the ratio of dD to D is constant. If the accuracy of the angular measurement is increased by using multiple pointings, so that the uncertainty is reduced to $\pm 0.5''$, each ratio in the second column is halved. Thus, up to a distance of about 150 meters or about 500 ft, the precision can be held to about 1 part in 5000.

For a line much longer than 500 ft, one or more intermediate points may be set on the line and occupied by the subtense bar or the theodolite, in order to hold each measured length to less than 500 ft. This technique is shown in Fig. 13-26. If the random errors of the measured angle are normally distributed, then according to the principles of random errors discussed in Chapter 4, the standard error of D is proportional to the square root of the sum of the squares of the standard error of each measurement.

If the line to be measured is extremely long, many set-ups may be avoided by employing the technique shown in Fig. 13-27. Line AB is a long line in a survey. At A, a right angle is laid off to establish points S and P, and angles are subtended at A and at P on the subtense bar situated at S. If each of the distances AS and SP is held to less than 200 or 250 ft, the distance AP can be obtained with a precision approaching 1 part in 10,000. Then suitable targets are set at A and P, and the angle β at B from A to P is measured. Thus, the length of AB is $AP \cot \beta$. If AB is approximately 20,000 ft long and the length AP is 400 ft, then an error of $0.5''$ in angle β will produce an error in AB of about 2.42 ft. The precision ratio will be about 1 part in 8330.

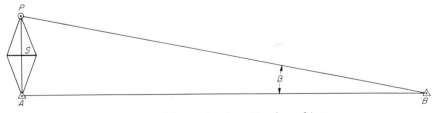

FIG. 13–27. Measuring long line by subtense.

The vertical distance V from a theodolite to a subtense bar can be determined by measuring a vertical angle α to the bar as well as the horizontal distance D. Then,

$$V = D \tan \alpha \qquad (13\text{-}8)$$

The conditions are similar to those in Fig. 3-2 in which D is the horizontal distance DE.

13-18. Plane Table. The plane table, shown in Fig. 13-28, consists of a drawing board which is mounted on a tripod in such a manner that the board can be leveled and rotated in azimuth without

Fig. 13–28.   Plane table and alidade.

disturbing the tripod. This condition is realized by a tripod head, known as the Johnson head, which is shown in Fig. 13-29. One wing nut beneath the head controls the leveling, while the other nut controls the rotation of the board. Standard size boards are 18 in. by 18 in., 18 in. by 24 in., and 24 in. by 31 in.

Fig. 13–29. Johnson head. (Courtesy of
W. & L. E. Gurley Co.)

The plane table itself provides the lower motion for the alidade, and movement of the alidade on the board can be considered as the upper motion, these motions being similar to those of the transit. The rotation of the board is used in backsighting, while the rotation of the alidade over the face of the board is used in foresighting.

The primary use of the combination of the plane table and alidade is in field compilation of maps. For this purpose it is much more versatile than is the transit. The drawing paper used for plane-table work must be of high quality, must be well-seasoned to prevent undue expansion and contraction, must contain a surface with a reasonable amount of tooth or roughness to take pencil lines without undue grooving of the paper, and must be tough enough to stand erasures. For high accuracy, plane-table sheets containing thin aluminum sheets laminated with the paper are used. Celluloid sheets are sometimes used where there is likely to be an accumulation of moisture on the sheets.

In addition to the board and alidade, such accessories as stadia rods, a scale, triangles, plotting needles, pencils, and an eraser are needed. When a map is being compiled, the map is kept clean by first covering it with a piece of low-grade paper, this paper being torn away to expose the map sheet. On threatening days, a cover of plastic or other waterproof material should be provided to protect the map sheet from a sudden shower.

13-19. Plane-Table Traverse. In compiling a map it frequently becomes necessary to establish the control by the plane table itself, rather than by means of a more-precise transit traverse. If high-quality, durable paper is used, and if the plane-table man exercises

care in taking the stadia readings and plotting the points, highly satisfactory traversing can be accomplished by using the plane table.
Two general techniques are in use for running a plane-table traverse.
In the first method, which is applicable to large-scale mapping, each
selected traverse point is occupied by the plane table, and the board
is oriented by backsighting on the previous point. When this method
is used, each line in the traverse can be observed from both directions
so that checks are provided on the values of the distances and differences in elevation between successive traverse stations, as discussed
in Sec. 13-8. In the second method, which is applicable to small-scale
mapping, every other point in the traverse is occupied by the plane
table and the board is oriented with respect to the magnetic meridian
by means of the compass needle on the blade of the alidade. In either
method, the traverse may be run concurrently with the map compilation, or traversing may precede the map compilation. Running the
traverse separately ahead of map compilation affords the advantage
of permitting adjustment of the positions of the traverse stations, and
eliminates much erasing and map revision in the event there is a relatively large closure.

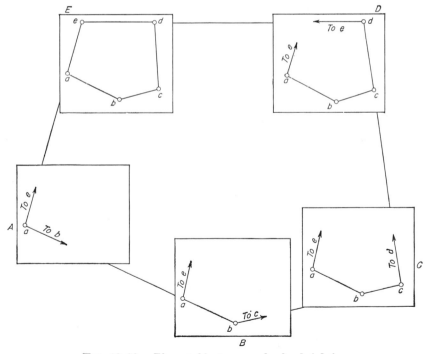

Fig. 13–30.   Plane-table traverse by backsighting.

Method 1: Orienting by Backsighting. In Fig. 13-30, the points
A, *B*, *C*, *D*, and *E* are selected as traverse stations, because these
points are located advantageously with respect to the topography that
is to be mapped. They will be occupied for the purpose of map compilation after the traverse has been plotted on the plane-table sheet.

The plane table is set up over point *A* and leveled by unclamping
both wing nuts of the Johnson head, bringing the circular bubble on
the blade of the alidade to the center by tipping and tilting the board,
and finally clamping the upper wing nut. During this operation, the
alidade must be held on the board, preferably over the center, and
must not be allowed to slip off the board. The board is then so
oriented in azimuth that the entire traverse will fall on the plane-table
sheet. Point *a*, which represents the map position of *A*, is arbitrarily
plotted on the sheet. Point *a* being used as the pivot for the alidade
blade, station *E* is sighted and a line is drawn on the sheet along the
blade in the direction of *E*. The stadia interval is read on a rod held
at *E*; the *V*-scale of the Beaman arc is set at the nearest graduation
mark, and the rod reading of the middle hair is taken and recorded.
The distance *AE* and the difference in elevation between *A* and *E* can
be computed. Next, the blade is pivoted about *a* until the line of sight
is directed toward point *B* and the line *ab* is drawn on the sheet along
the blade. The stadia readings are made, and from them the distance
and difference in elevation between *A* and *B* are computed.

The plane table is next set up over *B*, the blade is aligned along
the line *ba*, and the board is rotated until the line of sight is directed
at *A*. The board is now oriented, and it is clamped in this position.
After the clamp is tightened, the line of sight should be checked to
see whether or not the act of clamping affected the orientation. Stadia
readings are made on station *A*, and the average of the two computed
distances between *A* and *B* is plotted to the selected scale from *a*, to
define the plane-table position *b* of *B*. The blade is next pivoted about
b until the line of sight is directed to station *C*, and the line in the
direction of *bc* is drawn. Stadia readings are made on *C* to determine
the first value of the length of the line *BC* and the difference in
elevation.

The foregoing procedure is repeated at each station. Note that
the position of the forward point is not plotted until two values of the
length of the line are determined. At station *E*, a backsight along the
line through *e* and *d* orients the board, and stadia readings to *D* determine the second value of the length of the line *DE*. The position
of *e* can then be plotted. Stadia readings on *A* from *E* give sufficient
data to plot the final position of *a* along the line *ea*, and the closure
can be adjusted by a graphical application of the compass rule. This

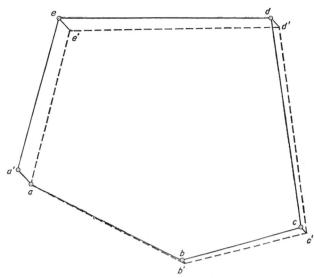

FIG. 13–31. Graphical adjustment of traverse.

adjustment is shown in Fig. 13-31. The point a' is the final position
of a. Lines through points b, c, d, and e are drawn parallel with aa'.
The distances bb', cc', dd', and ee' are in proportion to the distances
from point a to the successive points. The dashed lines are the lines
of the adjusted traverse.

The closure in elevations is found in the manner described in Sec.
13-8. Note that this type of plane-table traverse is similar in all respects to a stadia traverse performed with a transit. Much of plane-
table traversing, however, is graphical work.

Method 2: Orienting by Compass Needle. In Fig. 13-32, the
points A through F are traverse stations whose plane-table positions
are to be obtained. Station A is occupied, and the board is so oriented
that the entire traverse will fall on the map sheet. The compass needle
is unclamped, and the alidade is rotated in azimuth until the compass
needle points to the north graduation on the end of the compass
trough. A line representing the magnetic meridian is drawn the full
length of the blade. The alidade is then pivoted in turn to F and B,
and the rays af and ab are drawn. The necessary stadia readings
are taken to determine the lengths of the lines AF and AB, from
which points f and b are plotted by scaling the distances af and ab.
Differences in elevation are computed for determining the elevations
of F and B.

The plane table is next set up at station C and leveled. The compass needle is released and the blade is aligned with the line repre-

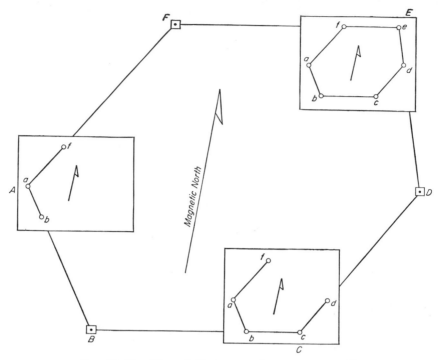

FIG. 13–32.   Plane-table traverse by compass needle.

senting the magnetic meridian. The board is rotated in azimuth until the compass needle points to the north graduation on the end of the compass trough. The board is now oriented. With point b as the pivot, the alidade is rotated until the line of sight is directed to B. The ray bc is drawn back toward c. Stadia readings give the length of the line BC, and the scaled distance bc locates point c. The elevation of station C is also determined from the stadia readings. The alidade is now rotated about point c until station D is sighted, and the ray cd is drawn on the map sheet. Stadia readings give the distance CD, from which point d is plotted. The elevation of station D is also determined from the stadia readings.

At the last set-up on station E, the procedure is the same as that described for the set-up at C. The closure at station F is determined from this set-up, and a graphical adjustment of the traverse is made. The elevations are adjusted by the method described in Sec. 4-11.

13-20. Method of Radiation. When either a point and the magnetic meridian or two intervisible points have been properly located on a plane-table sheet, either by plane-table traverse or by plotting the computed positions from a transit traverse, the details about the

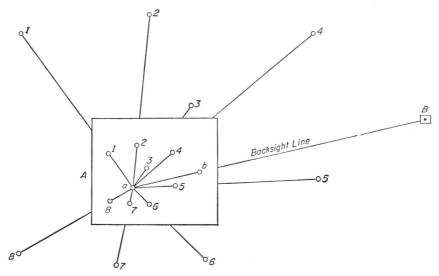

FIG. 13–33. Radiation with plane table.

point can be located on the plane-table sheet by the method of radiation. The plane table is set up and leveled over the point. The board is oriented either by using the compass needle or by backsighting along a plotted line. If the elevation of the ground point is known, the H.I. above the datum is determined by adding the distance from the ground to the telescope axis of the alidade to the elevation of the ground point.

All points whose positions and elevations are to be determined are sighted by using the map position of the occupied point as the pivot for the alidade. Rays are drawn in the directions of the successive points, and the stadia readings on the points give the lengths of the successive lines, from which the points can be plotted by scaling. This procedure is illustrated in Fig. 13-33. The backsight point should be checked frequently to detect any slipping of the board. The elevations of the points are determined as described in Sec. 13-9 and as illustrated in the notes in Fig. 13-8.

13-21. Plane-Table Leveling. The plane-table method of leveling is excellent for getting rapid results of relatively low accuracy. It is in all respects the same as stadia leveling. The plane table is set up at an arbitrary point, as in differential leveling, and a backsight is taken on a point of known elevation. The backsight values consist of the stadia interval, the V-scale reading, and rod reading from which the H.I. above the datum is determined.

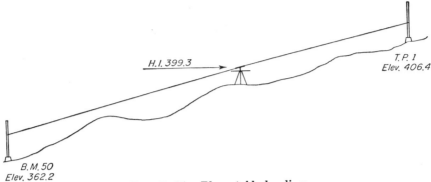

Fig. 13–34.   Plane-table leveling.

In Fig. 13-34, an interval of 9.80 is read on the rod held at B.M. 50 whose elevation is 362.2 ft. The V-scale reading is 47, and the rod reading is 7.7 ft. The product of V and I is $(47 - 50) \times 9.81 = -29.4$. This is the vertical distance by which the line of sight falls from the alidade to the rod reading. The difference in elevation between the foot of the rod and the alidade is $+ 7.7 + 29.4 = + 37.1$ ft, and the H.I. is $362.2 + 37.1 = 399.3$ ft. When a foresight is taken on the rod held at T.P. 1, the interval is 6.64, the V-scale reading is 52, and the rod reading is 6.2 ft. The product is $(52 - 50) \times 6.65 = + 13.3$ ft, and the difference in elevation between the alidade and the foot of the rod at T.P. 1 is $+ 13.3 - 6.2 = + 7.1$ ft. The elevation of T.P. 1 is therefore $399.3 + 7.1 = 406.4$ ft.

A form of notes for plane-table leveling is given in Fig. 13-35. For the backsight taken on T.P. 2 and for the foresight taken on B.M. 51, the telescope is level, giving a V-scale reading of 50 which is not recorded. The interval is recorded on level sights to provide the distances used in adjusting the level line.

13-22. Plane-Table Intersection. One of the decided advantages of the plane table is the ease with which a point can be located by intersection. The procedure is shown in Fig. 13-36 and is described in Sec. 7-13. With the board oriented at station A by backsighting on

STA.	INT.	V	PROD.	ROD	B.S.	INT.	V	PROD.	ROD	F.S.
B.M.50	9.80	47	−29.4	7.7	+37.1					
T.P. 1	3.22	40	−32.2	6.0	+38.2	6.64	52	+13.3	6.2	+7.1
T.P. 2	4.85	—	—	9.7	+9.7	5.08	51	+5.1	4.7	+0.4
T.P. 3	5.50	55	+27.5	3.4	−24.1	7.35	49	−7.4	8.8	−16.2
B.M. 51						4.08	—	—	6.1	−6.1

Fig. 13–35.   Notes for plane-table leveling.

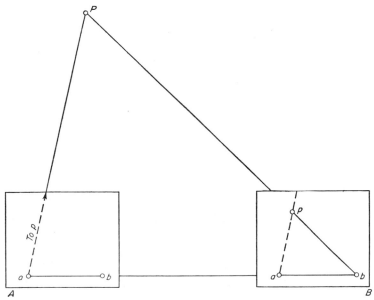

FIG. 13–36.   Intersection with plane table.

station B, the alidade blade is pivoted at a and a ray of indefinite length is drawn toward the point P to be located. The plane table is then set up at station B and the board is oriented by backsighting on A. With the alidade pivoted at b, a ray toward P is drawn on the plane-table sheet. The intersection of these two rays defines the map position p of P. The difference in elevation between A and P and that between B and P can be obtained if the vertical angle to P has been measured from each set-up. The product of the distance AP, scaled from the map, and the tangent of the vertical angle at A is the difference in elevation between the alidade at A and the point P. The difference in elevation between the alidade at B and the point P can be determined in the same manner.

Suppose that the H.I. at A is 714.2 ft, the distance from A to P, scaled on the map, is 1380 ft, and the vertical angle to P is $- 0° 40'$. The elevation of P is $714.2 - 1380 \tan 0° 40' = 698.1$ ft. If the H.I. at B is 708.0 ft, the distance BP scales 1970 ft, and the vertical angle from B to P is $- 0° 18'$, then the elevation of P is $708.0 - 1970 \tan 0° 18' = 697.7$ ft. Thus, a check can be provided against a gross error or a mistake.

13-23. Plane-Table Resection. Resection is of great advantage in an extensive plane-table survey, as it permits the plane table to be set up and oriented at a point which has not been previously located on the map. The method consists in setting the table over a selected point from which two or more control points, which are already plotted, can be seen; determining the position on the map of the point thus occupied; and orienting the table at that point, so that other points may be observed from it and plotted.

If two points that have already been plotted are near at hand and accessible, the station occupied may be located on the plot by determining the distances from it to those two points. If these distances, to the scale of the map, are used as radii, the intersection of the arcs swung from the plotted points will locate the occupied station on the map. Thus, in Fig. 13-37, the point occupied by the plane table is station C, the plotted positions of points A and B are a and b, and it is desired to locate the position of c on the map. The distances CA and

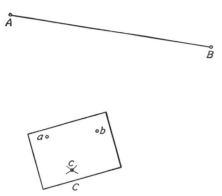

Fig. 13–37.   Resection by distances.

CB are determined either by stadia or by direct measurement. Then, with a and b as centers, arcs are struck with radii that are equal, to the scale of the map, to the distances AC and BC, respectively. The intersection c of these arcs is the plotted position of the point C.

If it is desired to locate additional points from station C, the plane table is oriented by placing the edge of the alidade in contact with ca or cb and turning the board so as to direct the telescope to A or B, as the case may be.

If the station occupied and to be located on the map is on a line

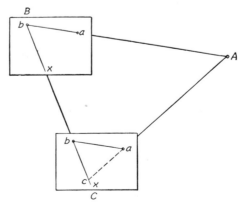

Fig. 13–38.   Resection by intersection.

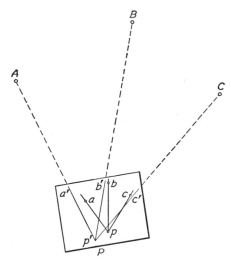

FIG. 13–39. Tracing-paper solution of three-point problem.

that has been plotted from another station, its position on the map is determined as follows: Let C, Fig. 13-38, be a point on the ground to which a line of sight was directed when the table occupied station B, and let bx be the plotted position of that line of sight and a the plotted position of station A. The plane table is oriented at station C by first placing the edge of the alidade on the line xb and directing the telescope to station B. Then, with the board clamped in this position, the edge of the ruler is pivoted at a and the alidade is turned until the line of sight is directed to station A on the ground. The line of sight is plotted, and the intersection c of this line with the line bx is the plotted position of the point C.

13-24. Three-Point Resection. Resection can be performed on three visible points whose positions have been previously plotted. This method is a graphical solution of the three-point problem the analytical solution of which is given in Sec. 8-34. The tracing-paper method of resection is shown in Fig. 13-39. The plane table is to be set over a point P, from which three points A, B, and C, plotted at a, b, and c, respectively, are visible. The problem consists in determining the position of point p on the map corresponding to the point P on the ground; that is, of finding a point on the map whose position with reference to a, b, and c shall be the same as that of P with reference to A, B, and C.

For convenience the board is approximately oriented by eye. A piece of tracing cloth or paper, large enough to cover the three plotted points and the estimated location of the station occupied, is fastened to the board over the plane-table paper. A point p' on the tracing cloth is so chosen that it will have approximately the same position with reference to the points a, b, and c that station P has with reference to the points A, B, and C. With the edge of the alidade pivoted on p', the line of sight is directed successively to A, B, and C, and the lines of sight are plotted, as shown at $p'a'$, $p'b'$, and $p'c'$. The tracing cloth is then unfastened and is shifted on the drawing paper to a position in which the lines $p'a'$, $p'b'$, and $p'c'$ pass through the plotted points a, b, and c. The point p' is then over the required position of p and can be pricked through with a fine needle point. The edge of the alidade is placed in contact with the pricked point p and one of the plotted points, such as a, and the board is turned in azimuth until the line of sight is directed to the corresponding point on the ground. The board is now properly oriented. The position of p can be checked by sighting to the points B and C with the edge of the alidade in contact, respectively, with the points b and c, and plotting the lines of sight. If the work has been done accurately these lines will intersect at p.

If the point P is on the circumference of a circle through A, B, and C, point p will be on the circumference of a circle through a, b, and c, and its position is indeterminate, as an infinite number of positions of the tracing cloth can be found where the lines $p'a'$, $p'b'$, and $p'c'$ will pass through a, b, and c.

The location of the required point can be found quite easily by trial, without the necessity of using tracing paper. When the table has been set up, it is oriented as closely as possible by eye or by the compass. As the table is not properly oriented, resection lines from the three stations will not intersect in a point, but will form a triangle of error, the size of which depends on the error of orientation and the scale of the map.

The position of the point sought can be estimated very closely by applying the following rules. By "point sought" is meant the true position on the plane-table sheet of the station occupied. The topographer is assumed to be facing the signal referred to, when the direction right or left is determined.

The distances to the point sought from the three resection lines drawn through the plotted positions of the fixed points are in proportion to the distances to the actual points from the station occupied. Also, the point sought is on the same side of each of the three resection lines; that is, it is either to the right of all the lines or to the left of all the lines.

When the station to be determined is within the great triangle, or the triangle whose vertexes are the three fixed points, the point sought must be within the triangle of error formed at the intersections of the resection lines.

When the point sought is outside the great circle, or the circle through the three fixed points, it is always on the same side of the resection line from the most distant point as is the intersection of the other two resection lines.

When the point sought is outside the great triangle but inside the great circle, the resection line from the middle point lies between the point sought and the intersection of the other two resection lines.

In practice the topographer first decides if the new station is within the great triangle, outside the great circle, or between the great triangle and the great circle. He then determines whether the point sought lies to the right or to the left of any one of the resection lines. Since it must be on the same side of the other two lines, its general position is established. Finally, he estimates the relative distances of the three actual points from him and marks the position of the point sought at proportionate distances from the three resection lines.

The board is again oriented by placing the edge of the alidade on the line through the plotted positions of the point sought and the most distant station, and sighting to that station. The two nearer stations are then resected. If the table was not oriented accurately at first, a second, but smaller, triangle of error will result, and the operation must be repeated until the correct position of the table is determined.

The method may be understood by reference to Fig. 13-40, in which a, b, and c are the plotted positions of the stations A, B, and C. The triangle of error def, formed at the intersections of the resection lines, is indicated by the heavier lines. In case 1, the plotted position p of the table must lie either in sector 3, to the right of all resection lines, or in sector 6, to the left of all lines. In order that it may be nearer to the line from the nearest station B than to the lines from the other stations, it must lie in sector 6. In case 2, the point p must lie inside the triangle of error. Conditions illustrated in Fig. 13-40 hold good in all cases. If the table is located outside the great triangle for the three control stations, its position on the sheet will lie outside the triangle of error. If it is located inside the great triangle, its plotted position will lie inside the triangle of error.

An additional method of locating the point p from the triangle of error is illustrated in Fig. 13-40, Case 1. Since the angle adb is an accurate delineation of angle APB, the point p will be somewhere on the circumference of the circle passing through a, b, and d. Similarly, p must be on the circle passing through b, c, and f; and also on the circle passing through a, c, and e. Consequently, p must be at the

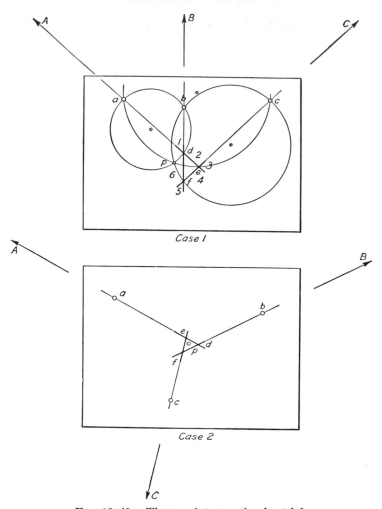

FIG. 13–40. Three-point resection by trial.

intersection of these three circles. In most cases the portions of the arcs used in determining p will be very nearly straight lines that can be sketched without actually locating the centers of the circles. If the new attempt at orientation results in a second triangle of error, which may be called $d'e'f'$, point p will be practically at the intersection of the three lines dd', ee', and ff', since these lines will closely approximate the arcs of the three circles.

13-25. Height of Instrument Following Three-Point Resection. When the plane table is located by the three-point method, the height of the alidade is computed from the elevations of the three known points. Vertical angles are measured to definite points on the signals which are at known distances above the stations. The differences of elevations are computed from these vertical angles and from horizontal distances which are scaled from the plane-table sheet.

As the plane table will seldom be horizontal for all positions of the alidade, the index correction for each vertical angle should be determined by reading the vertical circle with the telescope horizontal. The telescope is brought to a horizontal position by means of the sensitive striding level. To eliminate instrumental errors caused by the horizontal cross hair being out of adjustment, the telescope should be rotated 180° in its sleeve and a second observation should be made with the telescope in this position. Corrections for curvature and refraction should be applied to the computed differences of elevation where the scaled distances are longer than 1500 ft, according to the principles of Sec. 3-2. This correction in feet can be taken as $0.02\ D^2$, where D is the horizontal distance in thousands of feet.

An example of the computations for determining the height of the instrument at station P from observations on stations A, B, and C is shown in the accompanying tabulation. In the tabulation, the

COMPUTATIONS FOR ELEVATION OF ALIDADE

Pointing	Vert. Angle	Index Error	Scaled Dist.	Elev.	Ht. of Pt. Above Sta.	Diff. Elev.	Curv. and Refr.	Elev. Alidade
Sta. A	+ 1° 14′	+ 02′	6230	876.3	+ 16.6	− 130.5	− 0.8	761.6
Sta. B	− 0° 24′	− 03′	10,740	674.8	+ 24.2	+ 65.5	− 2.3	762.2
Sta. C	− 0° 43′	00′	7620	648.9	+ 17.8	+ 95.3	− 1.2	760.8
							Mean	761.5

mean of the two observed values for the vertical angle to station A is + 1° 14′ and the index correction is − 0° 02′. The difference in elevation between the alidade and a point that is 16.6 ft above station A is the scaled horizontal distance 6230 ft times tan 1° 12′ or 130.5 ft. The elevation of the alidade equals the elevation of station A plus the height of the point on which the sight was taken above the station minus the difference in elevation minus the correction for curvature and refraction. The elevation of the alidade is computed in a similar manner from the sights to B and C. The adopted elevation of the alidade, or the H.I., is the mean of the three computed values. A weighted mean could be computed by taking the weight of each value equal to the reciprocal of the distance involved, and then applying Eq. 4-17.

13-26. Errors in Plane-Table Surveys. Errors in plane-table surveys are caused by instrumental errors, by errors in drafting, and by the instability of the board.

The instrumental errors are practically the same as those for transit stadia work. By adjusting and properly manipulating the alidade, error from this source can be kept to a minimum. Except for large-scale maps the error caused by not placing the station on the sheet directly over the station on the ground will cause no perceptible error.

In the case of a small-scale map, the width of a pencil line may represent many feet on the ground, and considerable care must be exercised in drawing the rays on such a map. An extremely hard, well-pointed pencil should be used for this purpose. A needle should be used in plotting station points.

Weather conditions may greatly affect the precision of a plane-table map. Stretching and shrinking of the sheet will be considerable when the weather is changeable. Error from this source can be practically eliminated by using paper sheets that are mounted on thin sheets of aluminum. If mounted sheets are not used, all triangulation control that is to appear on a sheet should be plotted at one time. When the change in the paper is considerable, allowance for it must be made in plotting points. Frequently, the change in the two dimensions will not be the same.

On windy days the measurement of stadia distances may be next to impossible. If a sheltered station can be occupied, sights from the more exposed one should be left for calmer weather. Vertical angles are affected by the board not being perfectly horizontal. As many boards soon become warped, the index correction should be determined for all important pointings by means of the striding level; otherwise, the control bubble must be centered. The topographer must be careful not to lean on the board while sighting or plotting. To guard against possible movement of the board, the orientation should be checked at frequent intervals, particularly when new stations are being located.

PROBLEMS

13-1. Determine the stadia interval factor K of a transit from the accompanying data. The taped distances are from the point of focus of the telescope, which is 1.1 ft in front of the center of the instrument.

Taped Distance (ft)	Stadia Interval (ft)	Taped Distance (ft)	Stadia Interval (ft)
50.0	0.501	300.0	2.997
100.0	1.001	400.0	3.988
150.0	1.502	500.0	4.985
200.0	2.000	600.0	5.982

13-2. The following stadia notes were recorded for a closed traverse:

Sta.	Interval	Hor. Dist.	Azimuth	Vert. $\angle$	Δ Elev.	Elev.	Adj. Elev.
1						250.0	250.0
	3.69		120° 32′	+ 0° 56′			
2							
	5.70		138° 33′	− 0° 16′			
3							
	4.39		180° 19′	− 7° 06′			
4							
	4.87		141° 12′	− 1° 05′			
5							
	4.63		209° 45′	− 7° 29′			
6							
	5.63		231° 03′	− 3° 26′			
7							
	4.92		316° 32′	+ 0° 07′			
8							
	4.39		320° 23′	+ 0° 14′			
9							
	5.02		285° 06′	− 0° 18′			
10							
	5.78		277° 16′	− 0° 32′			
11							
	4.35		62° 38′	+ 1° 06′			
12							
	4.53		83° 38′		0° 50′			
13							
	5.92		46° 46′	+ 2° 33′			
14							
	6.50		7° 05′	+ 10° 50′			
1							

It is to be noted that the observations were made in the forward direction only, and that the middle cross hair was set on the H.I. to obtain the vertical angle. The stadia interval factor K is 100, and the constant C is 1 ft.

a) Compute the horizontal distance and the difference in elevation for each line to the nearest tenth of a foot.

b) Compute the elevations of the traverse stations. Adjust the elevations in accordance with the principles of Sec. 4-11.

c) Plot the stadia traverse to a scale of 1 in. = 200 ft by the method shown in Fig. 8-30. Using a sheet of detail paper 18 in. by 24 in., lay off a 1½-in. border on all sides. With the long dimension in the east-west direction, locate station *1* in the center of that dimension and 1 in. down from the top border. This position will allow the traverse to be conveniently centered on the map sheet.

d) Distribute the error of closure in the position of station *1* by the method shown in Fig. 13-31.

13-3. With a transit set 5.2 ft above station A, a sight is taken on a rod held at station B. The interval is 4.66 ft; the rod reading of the middle hair is 11.6 ft; the vertical angle is $-5° 13'$. With the transit set 5.1 ft above station B, a sight is taken on the rod held at station A. The interval is 4.69 ft; the rod reading of the middle hair is 7.7 ft; the vertical angle is $+6° 00'$. The value of C is 1 ft and $K = 101$. What is the average length of the line AB? What is the average difference in elevation between the two points?

13-4. The following notes were recorded when carrying stadia levels between two temporary bench marks. The value of C is 1 ft and $K = 100$. The elevation of T.B.M. 5 is 1322.2 ft. Compute the elevation of T.B.M. 6.

Station	Backsight			Foresight		
	Int.	Rod	Vert. Angle	Int.	Rod	Vert. Angle
T.B.M. 5	3.14	8.6	$-0° 25'$			
T.P. 1	5.02	4.5	$-3° 15'$	5.02	6.3	$+1° 52'$
T.P. 2	4.88	10.0	$-1° 02'$	2.74	2.2	$+6° 20'$
T.P. 3	6.08	8.0	$+0° 36'$	8.06	5.0	$+0° 13'$
T.P. 4	1.96	5.5	$+5° 52'$	4.81	8.5	$-4° 00'$
T.B.M. 6				5.92	12.2	$-1° 13'$

13-5. A plane table is set up over a control station whose elevation is 772.2 ft. The distance from the ground to the alidade, measured with the stadia rod, is 4.3 ft. Assume that $K = 100$ and $C = 0$. A V-scale reading of 50 on the Beaman arc indicates a level sight. The following notes were recorded from observations made on detail points.

Point	Int. I	H	Hor. Dist.	V	Prod. $(V - 50) \times I$	Rod Reading	Δ Elev.	Elev.
17	0.55	8		78		5.6		
18	1.82	3		67		7.2		
19	1.74	2		38		12.6		
20	3.98	..		55		4.5		
21	6.62	..		49		5.8		
22	4.85	..		50		3.2		

Compute the distance from the plane table to each point and the elevations of the points.

13-6. Compute the error produced in a distance of 204.60 meters determined by means of a distance wedge in which the deflection produced by the wedge is in error by 4 seconds.

13-7. The mean angle measured between the two targets of a 2-meter subtense bar is $0° 30' 14.22''$. The standard error of the angle is $\pm 0.37''$. Assume that the standard error of the distance between the targets is ± 0.25 mm. Compute the distance, in feet, between the theodolite and the subtense bar. Compute the standard error of this distance, in feet.

13-8. After a three-point plane-table resection, a sight is taken to one of the three control points and the vertical circle of the alidade reads $30° 57'$. The telescope is then brought horizontal by means of the striding level and the vertical circle reads $29° 53'$. The distance to the sighted control point scales 6770 ft. The elevation of the control point is 852.4 ft. Compute the elevation of the alidade to the nearest tenth of a foot, making due allowance for curvature and refraction.

14

Topographic Surveys

14-1. General Procedures. Topographic surveying is the process of determining the positions, on the earth's surface, of the natural and artificial features of a given locality, and of determining the configuration of the terrain. The location of the features is referred to as *planimetry*, and the configuration of the ground is referred to as *topography*. The purpose of the survey is to gather data necessary for the construction of a graphical portrayal of planimetric and topographic features. This graphical portrayal is a topographic map. Such a map shows both the horizontal distances between the features and their elevations above a given datum. On some maps the character of the vegetation is shown by means of conventional signs.

Topographic surveying or mapping is accomplished by ground methods requiring the use of the transit, plane table and alidade, level, hand level, tape, and leveling rod in various combinations. Topographic mapping is accomplished also by aerial photogrammetric methods, as described in Chapter 15. In the photogrammetric methods, however, a certain amount of field completion and field editing must be done by ground methods described in this chapter.

The preparation of a topographic map, including the necessary control surveys, is usually the first step in the planning and designing of an engineering project. Such a map is essential in the layout of an industrial plant, the location of a railway or highway, the design of an irrigation or drainage system, the development of hydroelectric power, city planning, and landscape architecture. In time of war, topographic maps are essential to persons directing military operations.

14-2. Scales and Accuracy. Since a topographic map is a representation, on a comparatively small plane area, of a portion of the surface of the earth, the distance between any two points shown on the map must have a known definite ratio to the distance between the corresponding two points on the ground. This ratio is known as the scale of the map. As stated in Sec. 8-39, this scale can be expressed in terms of the distance on the map, in inches, corresponding to a certain distance on the ground, in feet. For example, a scale may be expressed as 1 in. = 200 ft. The scale can be expressed also as a ratio, such as 1:6000, or as a fraction, as 1/6000. In either of these last two cases, 1 in. on the map corresponds to 6000 in. on the ground. A fraction indicating a scale is referred to as the *representative fraction*. It gives the ratio of a unit of measurement on the map to the corresponding number of the same units on the ground.

The scale to which a map is plotted depends primarily on the purpose of the map, that is, the necessary accuracy with which distances must be measured or scaled on the map. The scale of the map must be known before the field work is begun, since the field methods to be employed are determined largely by the scale to which the map is to be drawn. When the scale is to be 1 in. = 50 ft, distances can be plotted to the nearest ½ or 1 ft, while if the scale is 1 in. = 1000 ft, the plotting will be to the nearest 10 or 20 ft and the field measurements can be correspondingly less precise.

14-3. Methods of Representing Topography. Topography may be represented on a map by hachures or hill shading, by contour lines, by form lines, or by tinting. *Hachures* are a series of short lines drawn in the direction of the slope. For a steep slope, the lines are heavy and closely spaced. For a gentle slope, they are fine and widely spaced. Hachures are used to give a general impression of the configuration of the ground, but they do not give the actual elevations of the ground surface.

A *contour line*, or *contour*, is a line that passes through points having the same elevation. It is the line formed by the intersection of a level surface with the surface of the ground. A contour is represented in nature by the shore line of a body of still water. The *contour interval* for a series of contour lines is the constant vertical distance between adjacent contour lines. Since the contour lines on a map are drawn in their true horizontal positions with respect to the ground surface, a topographic map containing contour lines shows not only the elevations of points on the ground, but also the shapes of the various topographic features, such as hills, valleys, escarpments, and ridges.

On maps intended for purposes of navigation, peaks and hilltops along the coast are sometimes shown by means of *form lines*. Such lines resemble contours, but are not drawn with the same degree of accuracy. All points on a form line are supposed to have the same ele-

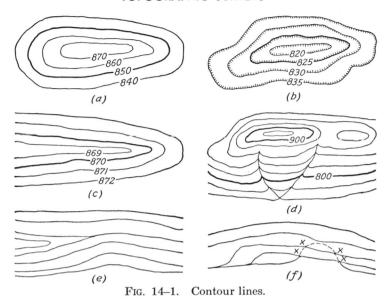

FIG. 14–1. Contour lines.

vation, but not enough points are actually located to conform to the standard of accuracy required for contour lines.

On aeronautical charts and on maps intended for special purposes, such as those which may accompany reports on some engineering projects, elevations may be indicated by tinting. The area lying between two selected contours is colored one tint, the area between two other contours another tint, and so on. The areas to be flooded by the construction of dams of different heights, for example, might be shown in different tints.

14-4. Contour Lines. The configuration of the ground and the elevations of points are most commonly represented by means of contour lines, because contours give a maximum amount of information without obscuring other essential detail portrayed on the map. Some of the principles of contours are represented in Fig. 14-1. Four different contour intervals are shown in views (a), (b), (c), and (d). The steepness of the slopes can be determined from the contour interval and the horizontal spacing of the contours. If all four of these sketches are drawn to the same scale, the ground slopes are the steepest in (d), where the contour interval is 20 ft, and are the flattest in (c), where the interval is 1 ft.

The elevation of any point not falling on a contour line can be determined by interpolating between the two contour lines which bracket the point. Quite often, when the scale of the map is large and the terrain is flat, the successive contours are spaced so far apart hori-

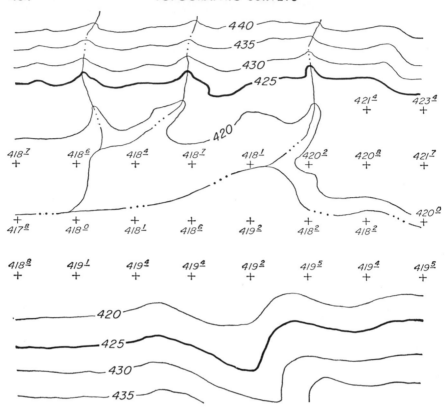

FIG. 14–2.　Spot elevations to supplement contour lines.

zontally that interpolation between adjacent contours does not have much significance. Therefore, in such an instance, the accuracy and utility of the map is greatly increased by showing the elevations of points at regular intervals in some form of a grid pattern. Elevations between these points are then determined by interpolation. Spot elevations are shown on Fig. 14-2.

A contour cannot have an end within the map. It must either close on itself, or commence and end at the edges of the map. A series of closed contours represents either a hill or a depression. From the elevations of the contour lines shown, a hill is represented in Fig. 14-1 (a), and a depression in view (b). As indicated, a depression contour is identified by short hachures on the downhill side of the contour. A ravine is indicated by the contours in Fig. 14-1 (c). If the elevations were reversed, the same contours would represent a ridge. View (e) is incorrect, as two contours are shown meeting and con-tinuing as a single line; this would represent a knife-edged ridge or ravine, something not found in nature. View (f), if not incorrect, is at least unusual. Several contours are shown merging and continuing as a single line. This would be correct only in the case of a vertical slope or a retaining wall. Also, one contour is shown to cross two others. Thus, each point marked x has two elevations, a condition found only at a cave or an overhanging cliff.

A series of equally spaced contour lines represents a constant slope along a line normal to the contours. A series of straight, parallel, equally spaced contours represents man-made excavations or embankments. The steepest direction from any point on a topographic map is that which runs normal to successive contour lines near the point.

As a convenience in scaling elevations from a topographic map, each fifth contour is drawn as a heavier line. When the interval is 1 ft, contours whose elevations are multiples of 5 ft are shown heavy. When the interval is 10 ft, the heavy contours have elevations which are multiples of 50 ft. Enough contours should be numbered to prevent any uncertainty regarding the elevation of a particular contour. Where the contours are fairly regular and closely spaced, only the heavy contours need be numbered.

14-5. Field Methods. Among the factors which influence the field method to be employed in the compilation of a topographic map are the scale of the map, the contour interval, the type of terrain, the nature of the project, the equipment available, the required accuracy, the type of existing control, and the extent of the area to be mapped. The area to be mapped for highway or railroad location and design takes the form of a strip with a width varying from 100 ft to perhaps more than 1000 ft. The control lines are the sides of a traverse which have been established by a preliminary survey and which have been stationed and profiled as outlined in Chapter 2. The method of locating topography most commonly employed for this purpose is the *cross-section* method.

To make an engineering study involving drainage, irrigation, or water impounding, or to prepare an accurate map of an area having little relief, each contour line must be carefully located in its correct horizontal position on the map by following it along the ground. This is the *trace-contour* method.

When an area of limited extent is moderately rolling and has many constant slopes, points forming a grid are located on the ground and the elevations of the grid points are determined. This is the *grid* method of obtaining topography.

If the area to be mapped is rather extensive, the contour lines are located by determining the elevations of well-chosen points from which the positions of points on the contours are determined by interpolation. The topographer determines the shapes of the contours by experience and judgment. This is known as the *controlling-point* method.

14-6. Cross-Section Method. The cross-section method of obtaining topography can be performed by transit and tape, by transit stadia, by level and tape, by hand level and tape, by plane table and tape, or by plane-table stadia. Horizontal control is established by a transit-tape traverse or by a stadia traverse between fixed control points. Stakes are set every 50 or 100 ft or at other pertinent intervals, the spacing depending on the terrain. Vertical control is obtained by profile leveling which may be performed either before the topography is taken or concurrently with the mapping.

When the transit and tape are used, the instrumentman occupies each station or plus station on the line. He determines the H.I. by holding the leveling rod alongside the transit. A right angle is turned off the line, and the rodman, holding one end of the tape, proceeds along this crossline until a break in the slope occurs. If possible, the instrumentman takes a level sight on the rod and records the reading and the distance to the point. If the rod cannot be sighted with the telescope level, a vertical angle is read and the slope distance is recorded. The rise or fall of the line of sight equals the slope distance times the sine of the vertical angle. The horizontal distance to the point is obtained by subtracting the product of the slope distance and the versine of the vertical angle from the slope distance. The rod reading must be taken into account in determining the elevation of the point, as discussed in Sec. 13-7.

The rodman proceeds to the next break in the topography, and the process is repeated. If the width of strip on each side of the line is greater than the length of the tape, a third man is necessary to hold the tape. As the distance out becomes greater, the slope distance cannot be measured directly in case vertical angles must be read, and the true rise or fall of the line of sight will be somewhere between the measured distance times the sine of the vertical angle and the measured distance times the tangent of the angle. Where the accuracy will deteriorate because of this difficulty, another method may be employed.

Instead of the tape, stadia can be used to obtain the horizontal distances to and the elevations of points on the cross section, as outlined in Chapter 13. When stadia is used only to obtain elevations, two men handling the tape can measure the distance to the right or left of the line. Perpendicularity to the line is estimated by the rodman. In this way, the transit need not be set up at each station. The station number, the distance to the right or left of the line, and the elevation of the point are recorded in a systematic manner. It is the best practice to determine the elevation of each point as soon as it is observed, in order to preclude any mistakes or possible misunderstanding at a later date.

When the level and tape are used, the H.I. is determined by backsighting on a point of known elevation. The distances to all points observed are recorded along with their elevations. When the leveling rod is out of sight, a new set-up must be made and the H.I. must be determined either by backsighting on another point of known elevation or by establishing a turning point and backsighting on the turning point.

In any of the foregoing methods, the located points are plotted either in the field or in the office. The positions of the contour lines are obtained by interpolating between the elevations of the plotted points.

The use of the plane table and tape, or plane table and stadia, for cross-section compilation is the same as the use of the transit, except that the topographer does the sketching directly on the plane-table sheet. The sheet is prepared beforehand by plotting the control line to the desired map scale, marking the positions of the stations, and entering the elevations obtained from profile leveling directly on the plane-table sheet. In the field, the board is oriented by backsighting along the line on the ground with the blade of the alidade aligned along the plotted position of the line. As points on the cross lines are observed, their elevations are plotted, the necessary interpolations are made, and the contour lines are sketched in.

In compiling topography by the cross-section method, the positions of all planimetric features, such as buildings, fences, streams, and property lines, must be located with respect to the control line and plotted on the topographic map. The positions of the features can be located by transit-stadia or plane-table methods. The interval and azimuth to various points are read when the transit is used, or the interval is read and the direction is plotted on the plane-table sheet when the plane table and alidade are used. Other methods of locating the positions of points with respect to a traverse line are discussed in Sec. 7-13.

14-7. Methods of Interpolating. In locating contours on a map by interpolation, the positions of points on the contours can be determined either mathematically or mechanically. In Fig. 14-3, it is required to locate the 5-ft contours on the line connecting points a and b, whose elevations are 873.4 and 896.2, respectively. It is evident

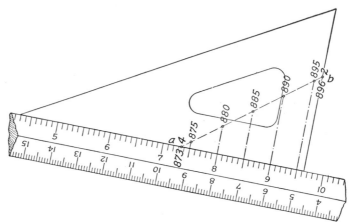

FIG. 14–3. Interpolating with triangle and scale.

that contours at elevations 875, 880, 885, 890, and 895 will cross this line.

The distances on the map from the point a to the contours can be calculated by proportion. The horizontal distance between a and b on the map is scaled and found to be 2.78 in. The corresponding vertical distance on the ground is $896.2 - 873.4 = 22.8$ ft. The vertical distance from a to the 875-ft contour is $875.0 - 873.4 = 1.6$ ft. The horizontal distance from a to the 875-ft contour is $(2.78/22.8)1.6 = 0.17$ in. The distance between two adjacent 5-ft contours is $(2.78/22.8)5 = 0.61$ in. The horizontal distances can also be expressed in terms of the distances on the ground.

In Fig. 14-3 is illustrated a method by which the points on the contours can be located mechanically, a triangular engineer's scale and a small celluloid triangle being used. The method is an application of the geometric method of dividing a line into any number of equal parts. The 7.34-in. mark on the scale is pivoted on a, whose elevation is 873.4 ft; the corner of the triangle is placed at the 9.62-in. mark; and both the scale and the triangle are turned until the edge of the triangle passes through b, whose elevation is 896.2 ft. The scale is then held in place while the corner of the triangle is moved successively to the 9.50-, 9.00-, 8.50-, 8.00-, and 7.50-in. points on the scale. Where the edge of the triangle crosses the line ab in the various positions are the corresponding contour points.

This method is very rapid and accurate and entirely eliminates mathematical computations. Any edge of the triangular scale can be used, provided the length on the scale corresponding to the difference in elevation between the two plotted points is shorter than the length

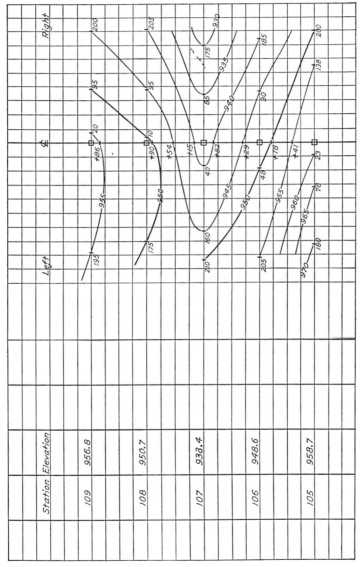

FIG. 14-4. Topography with hand level.

of the straight line between the points on the map. When the difference in elevation is considerable and the map distance is short, it may be necessary to let one division on the scale represent several feet in elevation. Thus, the smallest division on the scale may correspond to a difference in elevation of 10 ft, instead of 1 ft as in Fig. 14-3. By changing the value of a division, some side of the scale can always be used, regardless of the difference in elevation or the length of the line on the map.

Instead of the triangle and scale, a piece of tracing cloth, on which equally-spaced horizontal lines have been ruled, can be used in exactly the same manner. The tracing cloth is turned until lines corresponding to the given elevations pass through the two points on the map. The contour points are then pricked through the tracing cloth to the map beneath.

In most cases, the positions of the contour crossings can be estimated with sufficient precision, and exact interpolation is unnecessary. When the positions of the contour lines have been plotted, the contour lines are sketched in freehand by joining points at the same elevation.

14-8. Contour Location with Hand Level. When the hand level and tape are used, a 5-ft stick is generally used as a support for the hand level. As the rod viewed through the level is not magnified, the length of sight is limited to the visibility of rod readings with the naked eye. A rod with coarse graduations, such as a stadia rod, or a rod equipped with a target is commonly used.

The notes shown in Fig. 14-4 are for the topography between stations 105 and 109. The contours for a 5-ft contour interval are located directly on the ground. On the left-hand page of the notebook are entered the station numbers and the elevations of the ground surface at the stations, as furnished by the profile leveling party. On the right-hand page are sketches showing the locations of the contours to scale. The heavy line at the center of the page is red in the notebook and represents the center line as staked on the ground. The small spaces are ¼ in. square and the scale used for the sketch is 1 in. = 100 ft. The notes begin at the bottom of the page so that, when the topographer faces in the direction in which the station numbers increase, objects on either side of the line can be sketched in their natural positions with reference to the center line.

In Fig. 14-5 is represented the cross section at station 105. To take measurements at this station, the leveler first holds the 5-ft stick, with the hand level resting on it, on the ground at the station, which is marked A in the figure. Since the elevation of the ground at A is 958.7 ft, the hand level is at an elevation of $958.7 + 5 = 963.7$, and to

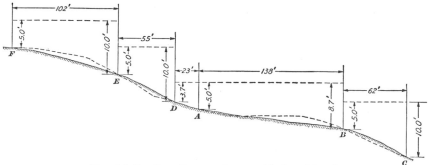

Fɪɢ. 14–5.   Locating contours with hand level.

locate contour 955 the reading on the rod must be 963.7 − 955 = 8.7 ft. The rodman moves the leveling rod along the downhill slope on a line at right angles to the center line until the line of sight of the hand level cuts the 8.7-ft mark on the rod. The rod is then on the 955-ft contour, or at the point marked B in the figure. This point is located by measuring the distance from A, which is found to be 138 ft. The topographer plots the 955-ft contour on the cross-ruled, right-hand page of the notebook, as shown in Fig. 14-4, and marks the distance from the center line to the contour.

The leveler now moves to point B, Fig. 14-5, and holds the hand level on the 5-ft stick at this point. The elevation of the level is 955 + 5 = 960 ft, and to locate the 950-ft contour the rodman moves down the slope until a point is found where the rod reading is 960 − 950 = 10 ft. This point is marked C in Fig. 14-5. The measured distance from B to C is 62 ft, and the total distance from the center line to C is 200 ft. The topographer plots this point, marking its distance from the center line. If the cross sections are to be carried about 200 ft on either side of the line, no further points are necessary on this side.

The contour points on the left-hand side of the station are next determined. The leveler again holds the hand level on the 5-ft stick at the station. Since the elevation of the hand level is 963.7 ft, the rodman moves up the slope at right angles to the center line until the point D is found where the rod reading is 3.7 ft, and thus locates the 960-ft contour. The distance to D from A is found to be 23 ft. This point is plotted on the left-hand side of the center line on the cross-ruled page of the notebook, as shown in Fig. 14-4. Since the ground slopes up from the center line on this side, the leveler goes ahead with the hand level and the rodman holds the leveling rod at point D, Fig. 14-5. The leveler now moves up the slope to a point where, with the hand level held on the 5-ft stick, he makes a reading on the leveling rod of 10 ft. This point, which is marked E, is on the 965-ft contour.

The distance from D to E measures 55 ft, and the topographer plots the point, at a distance of $55 + 23 = 78$ ft from the survey line, on the cross-ruled page of the notebook. In like manner the 970-ft contour is located and its location is plotted. When the ground surface is unobstructed by vegetation, points on the uphill side can be located by the topographer standing at the contour just below the one required. Wherever his line of sight with the hand level on the 5-ft stick strikes the ground, will be the next higher contour.

This procedure is repeated at every station along the line. Points where the contours cross the survey line are also located by plus distances from the preceding stations. In case the ground along a portion of the cross section is so flat that the 5-ft contours are too far apart for a sight, the elevations of points at regular intervals, such as every 50 ft, should be determined, until the next contour or the required width of the section is reached.

The contour lines are drawn through the points of equal elevation, as shown in Fig. 14-4. As soon as a point is plotted in the notebook, the contour line on which it lies is started and the elevation of the contour is marked on the line. When a point at a succeeding station is located in the sketch, the contour having the same elevation is immediately extended to pass through that point, the contour lines being adjusted and smoothed out as the plotting progresses. With the ground before him, an experienced topographer can usually draw the contours quite readily in this manner. When there is any doubt concerning the path of a contour, it may be desirable to plot a few points before the contour lines are drawn. In this case, the elevations of the plotted points, as well as their distances from the traverse line, should be recorded.

14-9. Trace-Contour Method. The trace-contour method of locating contour lines is most effectively performed by using the plane table and alidade, although the transit-stadia method can be employed. Control is provided by a transit-tape, transit-stadia, or plane-table traverse. The traverse is computed, adjusted, and plotted on the plane-table sheet. The elevations of the control points are entered directly on the sheet.

In Fig. 14-6, the plane table is set up at station S, the plotted position of which is s, and is oriented by backsighting on station R. The elevation of station S is 338.1 ft. The rod is held alongside the alidade, and the alidade is found to be 4.1 ft above the station. The H.I. is therefore 342.2 ft. In order to locate the position of the 336-ft contour, the rodman backs off until the topographer reads $342.2 - 336 = 6.2$ ft on the rod with the striding level centered. At this point,

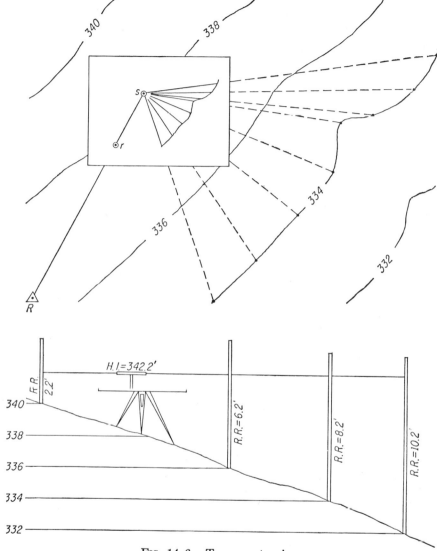

FIG. 14–6. Trace contouring.

the foot of the rod is on the 336-ft contour line. The topographer reads the interval, draws a ray from the plotted position of station *S* in the direction of the rod, and scales the distance along this ray to plot the point. The rodman walks along the contour, and the topographer reads intervals to successive points along the contour line.

When the 336-ft contour line is traced out as far as practicable from this set-up, the topographer locates the 334-ft contour line by obtaining a rod reading of 8.2 ft with the telescope level. All points on the same contour are joined by sketching on the sheet. When the ground is beyond the limit of the rod, the topographer runs a short plane-table traverse to a new set-up, from which additional contours are located. This method of locating contour lines on a topographic map is the most accurate and also the costliest and most time-consuming. However, for certain purposes, it is the only suitable method which gives the required accuracy.

The high-water line of a proposed reservoir may be obtained by a combination of plane-table traversing and trace contouring. The desired contour is at the elevation of the top of the spillway of the reservoir dam. The topographer, in effect, traverses along the water line and determines the position of the high-water line as he proceeds.

When the transit is used for the trace-contour method, the instrumentman sets up on a control point and determines the H.I. by using the leveling rod. He sets the azimuth of the backsight line on the horizontal circle and backsights on another control station by using the lower motion. This orients the horizontal circle. All subsequent pointing is done by using the upper motion. With the telescope bubble centered, he directs the rod man to a contour line by getting the proper reading of the middle cross hair, reads the interval and azimuth to the point, and records these data along with the rod reading.

The sketching may be done in the field or in the office. A 360° protractor is used to plot azimuths. The center of the protractor is set over the point representing the occupied point, and the protractor is rotated so that the reading at the backsight line coincides with its azimuth. This orients the protractor, and any other azimuth may be plotted opposite the corresponding graduation.

Short stadia traverses must be run off the main traverse, as is the case when the plane table is used. These traverses are plotted with respect to the main traverse by using the protractor and scale.

14-10. Grid Method. The grid method of obtaining topography may be used in areas of limited extent where the topography is fairly regular. A level is usually used for determining elevations of the grid points, although a transit can be used by centering the telescope bubble for each sighting.

If the boundary of the area to be mapped has not been previously surveyed, the first step is to run a traverse around the area and establish the corners. Then, in order to determine the topography, the area is usually divided, as far as possible, into squares or rectangles of uniform size. The dimensions of these divisions depend on the required

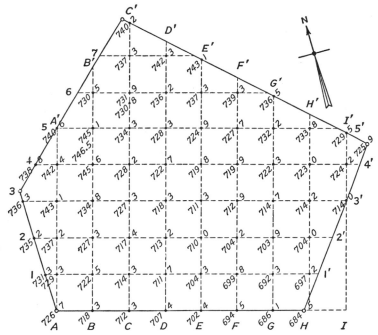

Fig. 14–7. Topography by grid method.

accuracy and the regularity of the topography, but are usually between 25 and 100 ft. The form chosen for the divisions will depend
somewhat on the shape of the area. The size of the divisions should
be such that, for the most part, the ground slopes can be considered
uniform between the grid points at the corners of the divisions. The
grid points either are defined by stakes or are located by ranging out
and measuring from stakes already set.

In Fig. 14-7 is represented a tract of land of which a topographic
map is to be prepared. It is assumed that a traverse survey locating
the boundaries has already been made. The tract is to be divided by
means of lines running in two perpendicular directions and spaced 100
ft apart. When a tract is divided in this manner, it is customary to
designate by letters the lines that extend in one direction, and by
figures the lines at right angles to that direction. The point of intersection of any two lines is then designated by the letter and figure of
the respective intersecting lines. The intersections of the dividing lines
with the exterior boundary lines on the far sides of the tract are designated by the proper letters or numbers affected with an accent or
a subscript, as A', B', $2'$, $3'$.

Different methods may be followed in laying out the tract. Any
method is satisfactory if it accurately defines the positions of the

points of intersection so that they can be readily located when the levels are being taken. For this purpose it is not usually necessary to mark all points of intersection, but enough points should be marked by stakes to permit the remaining points to be located easily and quickly by merely ranging them in from the points that are marked. The rougher and more irregular the surface of the tract, the more stakes must be set. Also, a tract of irregular form usually requires a comparatively greater number of stakes than a tract of rectangular form.

After the required stakes have been set, levels are taken over the tract in order to determine the elevations at all points of intersection and also at any intermediate points where the slope changes abruptly. Such an intermediate point is generally located in a direct line between two intersections by its distance from the intersection having the lower letter or number. This distance is measured with a tape, approximated by pacing, or merely estimated by the eye, according to the conditions and to the degree of accuracy required, and is recorded as a plus. Thus, on line CC' there is a low point 80 ft beyond stake $C5$ and its elevation is 730.8; this point would be designated by $C5 + 80$. The high point whose elevation is 746.5, and which is situated between lines 4 and 5 and between lines A and B, would be designated in the notes as $A + 80, 4 + 45$. The levels should be taken in the order that is most advantageous for the nature of the ground. The object is to take rod readings at each of the intersections and at other points with as few settings of the level as possible. To be sure that rod readings are taken at all the intersections, those taken from each setting are checked off on the sketch, or sketches, in which they are all shown.

After the field work has been completed, the tract boundary and the grid are plotted to the desired map scale. The values of the elevations of the grid intersections are then written at the corresponding map positions of the intersections. Finally, the positions of the contour lines are located and sketched by interpolation between the grid intersections.

14-11. Controlling-Point Method. The compilation of a topographic map by determining the positions and elevations of carefully selected controlling points is applicable to nearly every condition encountered in mapping. It is the method used most extensively in mapping a large area to a relatively small scale because of the economy realized. The method can be applied, instead of the cross-section method, to the mapping of a strip of terrain for route-location studies.

The accuracy of the map, the speed of progress, and the faithful delineation of the true shapes of the contour lines all depend on the experience and judgment of the topographer. The method is the most difficult to master, but it is also the most valuable because of its universal application. Although the accuracy of the map depends on the accuracy of the technical operations of making the observations on the points, the largest contributing factors in the success of mapping by this method are the topographer's knowledge of land shapes, slopes, and stream gradients, his facility for making maximum use of the surveying equipment, and his ability to decide where to select points so that he takes neither too many nor too few observations.

The plane table with telescopic alidade, because of its versatility and because it provides its own drawing board, is the most desirable equipment for this method of compilation. The transit can be used to good advantage, although its use requires that a draftsman having many qualifications of a topographer accompany the field party in order to obtain accuracy, completeness, and true expression of land forms in the map. Only the use of the plane table and alidade will be considered here.

Control. When a given area is to be mapped, the horizontal control may be established by making a simple transit-tape or transit-stadia traverse, which is computed, adjusted, and plotted on the plane-table sheet. The traverse measurements may be performed by using the plane table itself, either prior to or concurrently with the mapping. Unless the traverse is relatively short, it should be executed and adjusted graphically before compilation of the topography begins. The control may consist of a network of interconnected traverses made with transit and tape, transit and stadia, or the plane table. The major lines in the traverse should be adjusted first, and the adjustment of the shorter cross lines should follow. On a very extensive survey, the primary control may be either a simple or a very elaborate triangulation system, and additional control may be provided by traverses connecting the triangulation stations.

Horizontal control may exist in the form of an accurate planimetric map, which contains the horizontal positions of ground features but which does not contain information pertaining to elevations of the ground points. This form of control is most economically produced by photogrammetric methods described in Chapter 15.

Vertical control is established by direct differential leveling, stadia leveling, and plane-table leveling. Bench marks are established by direct leveling, supplemented by less-precise stadia leveling or plane-table leveling.

The accuracy that must be obtained in the basic horizontal and vertical control will depend on the scale to which the map is to be compiled, the contour interval, and the required accuracy of the topography. In general, the horizontal positions of basic control points should be located to within 1/200 in. on the final map. Thus, if the final map scale is 1 in. = 800 ft, the horizontal control should be accurate to within 4 ft. The basic vertical control should be established to within one-tenth of the contour interval.

Locating Contour Lines. With the control plotted on the plane-table sheet, the topographer sets the plane table over a horizontal control point and orients the board by backsighting on another plotted control point; or, if the mapping is to a small scale, he may orient the board by means of the compass needle as described in Sec. 13-19. He determines the H.I. either by backsighting on a vertical control point or, if the elevation of the point over which the plane table is set is known, by measuring the distance from the ground up to the alidade. If the contour interval is 5 ft or greater, the topographer estimates this distance by his experience. It is usually about 4 ft.

Points are selected along ridges, along draws, streams, and drainage channels, at the tops and bottoms of lines with constant grade, and at points between which the topographer can estimate the crossing of the contour lines. As far as the topographer is concerned, drainage has more influence on land form than has any other feature. Consequently, the drainage lines should be located fairly accurately. The positions of the contour lines as they cross the drainage lines are obtained by interpolation, and are sketched in. The elevations of the points at the changes in slope will allow the topographer to interpolate for the contour crossings. The positions and elevations of the points located by the plane table are determined by the method discussed in Sec. 13-20.

In Fig. 14-8 (*a*) the points marked with a cross (x) are controlling points whose plane-table positions have been determined. These points control the positions and gradients of the drainage lines and the tops and bottoms of lines with uniform slopes. From the positions and elevations of these points, the topographer sketches in the drainage lines and the lines along which contour crossings are to be interpolated. He then sketches in the contour crossings, giving them proper forms by analyzing the shapes of the drainage channels and the configuration of the land. Three points on a fence line have been located as shown. The map after the contour sketching has been completed is shown in Fig. 14-8 (*b*).

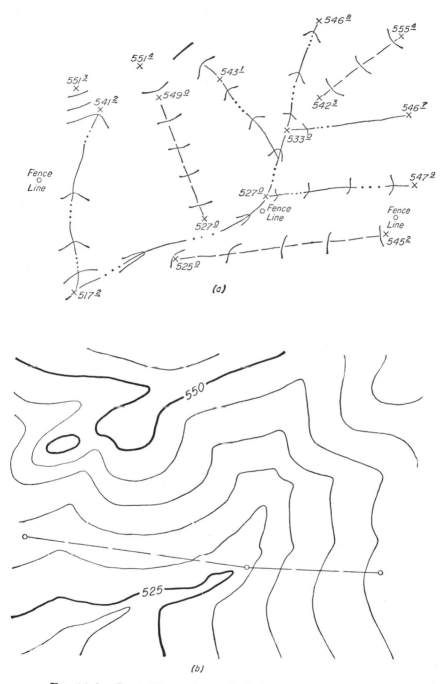

Fig. 14–8. Controlling-point method of locating contour lines.

When the location of points in the area around a plane-table set-up has been completed, the topographer moves to another control point. If the basic control is not sufficiently dense to allow all topography to be completed from the control points themselves, additional points must be located for plane-table set-ups. The supplementary set-ups may be established by traversing between control points, by plane-table intersection, or by resection. These methods were discussed in Chapter 13.

PROBLEMS

14-1. Assuming that the squares shown in Fig. 14-7 are 100 ft on a side, plot the tract to a scale of 1 in. = 100 ft, and draw in the contours for a 2-ft contour interval.

14-2. The cross-section notes on page 481 were taken for the purpose of plotting a strip of topography for road location. The positions of stream crossings are marked (*). Plot the tangent between stations 18 and 27 to a scale of 1 in. = 100 ft, and sketch in each 2-ft contour line.

CROSS-SECTION NOTES

Station	Left			Center Line	Right		
27 + 00	473.1 / 200	461.4 / 107	450.8 / 53	450.4 / 0	439.8 / 200		
26 + 50	458.0 / 200	449.8 / 97	429.3 / 17	427.7 / 0	425.9 / 116	421.3* / 200	
26 + 00		445.2 / 200	428.2 / 65	425.7 / 0	425.3* / 8	423.6 / 94	421.9 / 200
25 + 93				425.5* / 0			
25 + 50		430.8 / 176	429.0 / 140	428.6 / 0	424.3 / 154	422.0 / 200	
25 + 00		436.1 / 200	430.8 / 91	431.0 / 0	430.3 / 65	423.2 / 200	
24 + 90				431.6 / 0	422.5* / 200		
24 + 50			439.3 / 200	432.4 / 0	425.0* / 136	424.8 / 200	
24 + 00		443.2 / 200	435.8 / 93	432.1 / 0	427.7* / 94	428.1 / 115	425.8 / 200
23 + 76		444.9 / 200	433.8 / 73	431.4* / 0	426.9 / 200		
23 + 15		438.4* / 182	438.0 / 150	437.5 / 0	437.5 / 80	431.2 / 200	
23 + 00		440.0 / 200	438.1 / 87	439.2 / 0	438.8 / 113	432.1 / 200	
22 + 00		448.9 / 200	448.2 / 164	450.0 / 0	439.8 / 139	433.7 / 200	
21 + 00	459.9 / 200	460.0 / 153	457.2 / 88	446.8 / 0	433.4 / 102	424.6 / 200	
20 + 00			467.0 / 200	438.6 / 0	420.7 / 143	416.1 / 200	
19 + 00			479.2 / 200	443.5 / 0	422.4 / 111	414.0 / 200	
18 + 00	499.1 / 200	475.4 / 118	461.2 / 63	447.0 / 0	433.2 / 80	419.2 / 200	

15

Photogrammetry

15-1. Scope. Photogrammetry is the science of making measurements on photographs. Terrestrial photogrammetry applies to the measurement of photographs which are taken from a ground station, the position of which usually is known or can be readily determined. Aerial photogrammetry applies to the measurement of photographs taken from the air. As the science of aerial photogrammetry has developed, it has come to include all operations, processes, and products involving the use of aerial photographs. Among these are included the measurement of horizontal distances, the determination of elevations, the compilation of planimetric and topographic maps, the preparation of mosaics, and the interpretation and analysis of aerial photographs for geological and engineering investigation and for evaluating timber stands.

This chapter will discuss the elementary principles of aerial photogrammetry as they apply to the measurement of distances and elevations, the construction of mosaics, and the compilation of planimetric and topographic maps.

15-2. Aerial Camera. The aerial camera is comparable to a surveying instrument in that it gathers data in the form of light rays with certain directions and records the data on a photographic negative. In Fig. 15-1 is shown a schematic diagram of an aerial camera with its component parts. The optical axis usually is supposed to be essentially vertical when a photograph is taken.

The *lens assembly*, which includes the shutter and the diaphragm, forms the photographic image with the proper amount of light admitted. The lens itself is composed of several elements, as shown in Fig. 15-2. It must be highly corrected to satisfy the requirements of a rather wide angular coverage, a high resolution, and a very minor amount of lens distortion. Because of atmospheric haze which contains an overabundance of blue light, the lens is invariable fitted

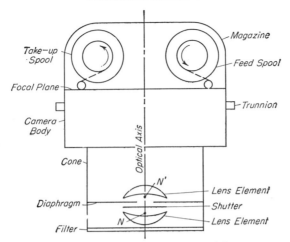

FIG. 15–1. Component parts of aerial camera.

with a yellow, orange, or red filter to absorb some of the blue light. The *cone* and the *camera body* hold the lens assembly in its proper position with respect to the *focal plane*.

The camera body houses the drive mechanism for the shutter assembly and the *magazine*. The upper surface of the camera body, in general, defines the focal plane of the camera. This surface contains four *fiducial* or *collimation marks*, one in the middle of each side of the focal-plane opening. Aerial cameras used for mapping have focal-plane openings with dimension of 9 in. by 9 in., 7 in. by 7 in., or $5\frac{1}{2}$ in. by $5\frac{1}{2}$ in. and produce aerial photographs of corresponding sizes. The purpose of the collimation marks is to define the point at which the optical axis of the lens intersects the focal plane.

The magazine is a light-tight container for the film. It contains a feed spool and a take-up spool, the mechanism for advancing the film after each exposure, and a device for holding the film flat in the focal plane at the instant the exposure is made.

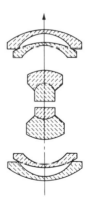

FIG. 15–2. Wild aviogon aerial camera lens.

The two points on the optical axis marked N and N' in Fig. 15-1 are the *front* and *rear nodal points* of the lens system. Any ray of light, on striking the front nodal point, is so refracted by the lens that it appears to emerge from the rear nodal point parallel with its original direction.

The focal length of the lens is the distance between the rear nodal point of the lens and the focal plane. It is designated by the symbol f. The focal length is fixed for a given camera, and its value is precisely determined by calibration. The nominal values of focal lengths used in mapping and in the construction of mosaics are generally 3.5, 4, 6, 6.7, 8.25, and 12 in.

The camera is suspended in a camera mount by means of a pair of trunnions on either side of the camera. It is free to rotate in the mount about all three axes. The mount is secured over an opening in the bottom of the airplane. In Fig. 15-3 is shown an aerial camera installed in the mount. Some of the features just described can be seen in the picture.

FIG. 15-3. Aerial camera installed in mount.

15-3. Types of Aerial Photographs. An aerial photograph taken with the optical axis held essentially vertical is called a *vertical photograph*. Because of movement of the airplane at the instant of exposure, virtually all vertical photographs contain a certain amount of tilt. The optical axis may be inclined as much as 5° from the vertical. Tilt, however, does not present serious difficulties in mapping, and introduces very little difficulty in constructing mosaics. In some of the discussions in this chapter, a vertical photograph is one which is assumed to be truly vertical unless otherwise stated. A vertical photograph is shown in Fig. 15-4.

An aerial photograph taken with the optical axis purposely tilted by a sizable angle from the vertical is called an *oblique photograph*. A high oblique is a photograph on which the apparent horizon appears.

FIG. 15–4. Vertical photograph showing collimation marks at the middles of the four edges. (Courtesy of Clyde Sunderland Aerial Photographs, Oakland, Calif.)

A low oblique is a photograph taken with the optical axis purposely tilted from the vertical, but not enough to include the horizon. Oblique photographs are shown in Fig. 15-5 (a) and (b).

Most planimetric and topographic mapping and most mosaic construction is done by using vertical photographs, although high obliques are used in the preparation of small-scale planimetric maps and charts because of their greater ground coverage. Low obliques taken as convergent photography are used in compiling accurate topographic maps.

15-4. Photographic Scale. Photographic scale is the ratio between a distance measured on a photograph and the corresponding

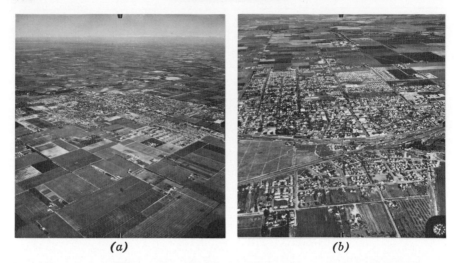

(a) *(b)*

Fɪɢ. 15–5. Oblique photographs. (*a*) High oblique. (*b*) Low oblique.
(Courtesy of Clyde Sunderland Aerial Photographs, Oakland, Calif.)

ground distance. A vertical photograph resembles a planimetric map in that it shows the planimetric and cultural features of a portion of the ground in their relative positions. It is different from a planimetric map, however, in two respects: 1) The vertical photograph does not contain standard map symbols, which are essential to a map. 2) The planimetric map has a uniform scale throughout, whereas the scale of a vertical photograph varies in different portions of the photograph. The photograph is a perspective projection of the ground onto the focal plane of the camera. Consequently, points lying in a plane closer to the camera at the time of exposure will have larger images than those points lying in a plane farther from the camera. The scale will vary across the area of the photograph also because of tilt of the optical axis at the time of exposure.

In Fig. 15-6 (*a*), points A, O, and B all lie at the same elevation. The horizontal distances AO and OB are equal to $A'O'$ and $O'B'$ on a reference datum. A truly vertical photograph taken with the camera at L_1 would show the positions of A, O, and B at a, o, and b. The ratio ao/AO equals the ratio ob/OB, and the scale of the photograph is uniform across the photograph.

In Fig. 15-6 (*b*), points A, O, and B are at different elevations, and the horizontal distances between A and O and between O and B are $A'O'$ and $O'B'$, respectively. If a vertical photograph is taken with the camera at L_2, the points A, O, and B would appear at a, o, and b on the photograph. The ratio $ao/A'O'$ does not equal the ratio $ob/O'B'$, and the scale of the photograph is seen to vary from point

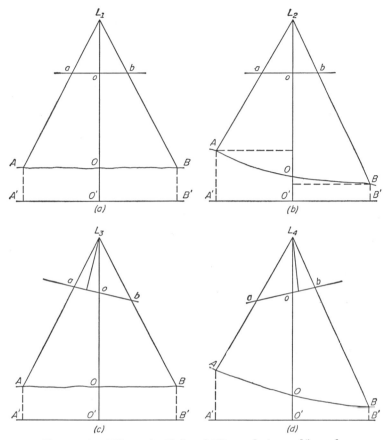

FIG. 15-6. Effect of relief and tilt on photographic scale.

to point because of the variation in the elevations of the ground points.

In Fig. 15-6 (c), points A, O, and B all lie at the same elevation. A tilted photograph taken with the camera at L_3 shows the positions of the ground points at a, o, and b. The ratio ao/AO does not equal the ratio ob/OB, and consequently the scale varies across the photograph. In Fig. 15-6 (d) is shown the combined effect of both relief and tilt on the scale of a photograph.

The scale of a vertical photograph at a point, along a line or in an area, can be determined from the relationship between the focal length of the camera, the flying height of the aircraft at the time of exposure, and the elevation of the point, the line, or the area. In Fig. 15-7, points O and A are at the same elevation, and so $AA' = OO'$ or $h_A = h_O$. Points B and C lie at elevation $h_B = h_C$, and D lies at elevation h_D. By similar triangles, $ao/AO = Lo/LO$, or $ao/AO =$

$f/(H - h_A) = f/(H - h_o)$. Similarly, $bc/BC = f/(H - h_B) = f/(H - h_C)$. But the ratios ao/AO and bc/BC are the scales of the photograph along lines ao and bc, respectively. Therefore, in general,

$$S_E = \frac{f}{H - h} \tag{15-1}$$

where S_E = scale of a vertical photograph for a given elevation;
f = focal length, either in inches or in feet;
H = flying height above the datum, in feet;
h = elevation of the point, line, or area above the datum, in feet.

If f is expressed in inches, the scale is expressed as an engineer's scale, such as 1 in. = 275 ft. If f is expressed in feet, the scale is expressed as a representative fraction, such as 1/5460.

EXAMPLE 15-1. In Fig. 15-7, the elevation of points O and A is 267 ft, that of points B and C is 524 ft, and that of D is 820 ft. The flying height above sea level is 1769 ft, and the focal length of the camera is 8.23 in. Determine the scale of the photograph along the line ao, along the line bc, and at point d, expressing each scale as a number of feet corresponding to 1 in.

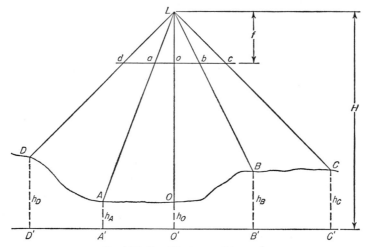

FIG. 15–7.   Photographic scale.

Solution: The value of S_E for line ao is 8.23/(1769 − 267). Reducing the numerator to unity gives a scale of 1 in. = 182.5 ft. The value of S_E for line bc is 8.23/(1769 − 524), and the scale is 1 in. = 151.3 ft.

The value of S_E at point d is 8.23/(1769 − 820), and the scale is 1 in. = 119.3 ft.

Quite often, the average scale of a single photograph or of a set of photographs is desired in order to be able to measure distances in any area of the photograph or photographs. If the average scale is known, it can be applied to a scaled distance to give a reasonable value of the corresponding ground length, provided that the relief is not extremely variable. The average scale is given by the relationship

$$S_A = \frac{f}{H - h_{avg}} \tag{15-2}$$

where S_A = average scale of the photograph, which may be reduced to either an engineer's scale or a representative fraction;

f = focal length, in inches or in feet;

H = flying height above the datum, usually sea level, in feet;

h_{avg} = average elevation of the area covered by the photography, in feet.

The datum scale S_D is the scale of a photograph if all points on the terrain were projected down to the datum and then photographed. The datum scale is given by the equation

$$S_D = \frac{f}{H} \tag{15-3}$$

where the units are as given in Eqs. 15-1 and 15-2. The datum scale of the photograph in Example 15-1 is 1 in. = 215 ft.

The scale of a photograph can be determined by comparing a distance measured on the photograph with the corresponding known ground distance. The ground distance may have been measured directly, or it may be a distance of common knowledge as, for example, the length of a section line (see Chapter 17), a city block, or a stretch of a highway.

If the scale is expressed as an engineer's scale, the ground distance, in feet, is divided by the photograph distance, in inches. If the scale is a representative fraction, the divisor is the photograph distance, in feet.

The scale of a photograph can be determined by comparing a distance measured on the photograph with the corresponding distance measured on a map of known scale.

The photograph scale is then found by the following relationship:

$$D_P = \frac{M}{P} \times D_M \tag{15-4}$$

where D_P = number of feet corresponding to 1 in. in the photograph scale;

M = map distance, in inches;

P = photograph distance, in inches;

D_M = number of feet corresponding to 1 in. in the map scale.

For example, if the distance between two road intersections is 4.34 in. on a photograph and 1.55 in. on a map drawn to a scale of 1 in. = 800 ft,

$$D_P = \frac{1.55}{4.34} \times 800 = 285$$

and the scale of the photograph along the line is 1 in. = 285 ft.

15-5. Relief Displacement. The term *relief displacement* is applied to the displacement of the image of a ground point on a photograph from the position the image would have if the point were on the datum. This displacement is due to the elevation of the ground point above or below the datum. In Fig. 15-8, ground points A and B lie at elevations h_A and h_B above the datum. Their images on a vertical photograph are at points a and b, respectively. The datum positions A' and B' would have images at a' and b' on the photograph. Point o is the center of the photograph, and it is called the *principal point* of

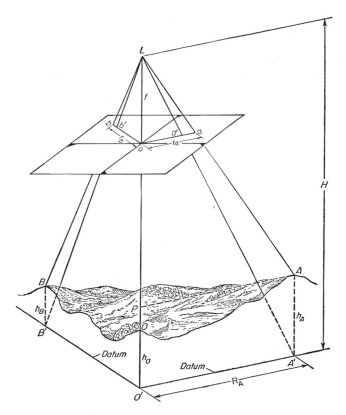

Fig. 15-8. Relief displacement.

the photograph. It is located by joining opposite collimation marks at the edges of the photograph. Because of the elevations of A and B above datum, both a and b have been displaced outward along the radial lines oa and ob, respectively.

In the triangles Loa and LPA, $Lo/LP = r_a/R_A$. Since $Lo = f$ and $LP = H - h_A$,

$$r_a = \frac{R_A f}{H - h_A} \qquad \text{(a)}$$

and

$$R_A = \frac{r_a (H - h_A)}{f} \qquad \text{(b)}$$

Let the relief displacement $a'a$ for point a be denoted by d_a. Then, in the triangles Loa' and $LO'A'$, $Lo/LO' = (r_a - d_a)/R_A$. Since $LO' = H$,

$$r_a - d_a = \frac{R_A f}{H} \qquad \text{(c)}$$

Subtracting Eq. (c) from Eq. (a) gives:

$$r_a - (r_a - d_a) = d_a = \frac{R_A f}{H - h_A} - \frac{R_A f}{H} \qquad \text{(d)}$$

When the value of R_A from Eq. (b) is substituted in Eq. (d) and subscripts are dropped to indicate a general point, the result is

$$d = \frac{rh}{H} \qquad \text{(15-5)}$$

where d = relief displacement of the point, in inches;
     r = radial distance measured from the principal point out to the image of the point, in inches;
     h = elevation of the point, in feet;
     H = flying height above the datum, in feet.

From Eq. 15-5, it is seen that the relief displacement of a point depends on the position of the point on the photograph. At the principal point, the displacement is zero. It increases outward toward the edges of the photograph. Also, the relief displacement increases as the elevation of the ground point increases, and decreases with an increase in flying height.

Assume that a photograph contains all the corners of a tract of land, and that the elevations of these corners are known. Unless all the corners are at the same elevation, the sides of the tract cannot be scaled directly because of variation in scale discussed in Sec. 15-4. The relief displacement of each point can be computed, provided the flying height above sea level has been determined, by measuring the radial distance to each point and applying Eq. 15-5. The positions of the points are then corrected by the amount of relief displacement and the new positions are therefore at a common datum.

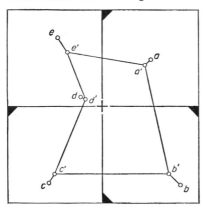

FIG. 15-9.   Points brought
to common datum.

In Fig. 15-9, points a, b, c, d, and e are the photographic images of the corners of a tract of land. The elevations of the points and the flying height above sea level are known. The positions of the five points, corrected to a common datum, are a', b', c', d', and e'. These are the positions of the five points on a map that is at the datum scale of f/H, where H is the flying height used to compute the relief displacements. The corrected lines may be scaled; and the lengths of the lines, the angles between the lines, and the area of the tract can be determined.

If the flying height above the datum for a given photograph is not known, it can be determined with varying accuracy by measuring the length of a ground line, the end points of which lie at about the same elevation, and then scaling the corresponding photograph distance. The scale at the elevation of the line being known, H may be determined by Eq. 15-1. The photographic distance may also be compared with a corresponding map distance to give the scale by Eq. 15-4, and then H may be determined.

In Fig. 15-10 is shown a vertical photograph taken from an altitude of approximately 2000 ft above sea level and covering an area at an average elevation of about 500 ft. The scale is, by Eq. 15-2, about 1/3000 or 1 in. = 250 ft. Lines ab and ac are actually straight fence lines, and the angle at a from b to c is approximately 90° if measured at ground point A from B to C. Because of relief displacement, however, it is obvious that the fence lines are displaced outward from the principal point as the lines go over ridges, and are displaced inward as the lines cross the gulleys. This relief displacement, which is nothing more than a manifestation of perspective in an aerial photograph, is of rather minor consequence in a photograph taken at

FIG. 15–10. Effect of relief displacement on straight lines.

a great altitude over ground with very little relief. However, if a photograph is to be used as a map substitute, then the effect of relief displacement and scale variation must be recognized, especially where the scale of the photograph is large and there is relatively large terrain relief.

15-6. Photograph Overlap. When aerial photography is used for mapping or mosaic construction, flight lines are laid out on a flight map with a spacing that will cause photographs to cover an overlapping strip of ground. This overlap between flight strips amounts to about 25 per cent of the width of the photograph. The actual spacings on the flight map may be determined from the scale at which the photographs are to be made by solving Eq. 15-4. The photographic distance is 75 per cent of the width of the photograph, provided that a

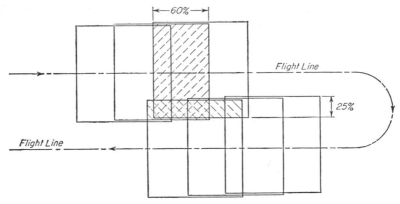

FIG. 15–11. Photographic overlap.

25-per cent overlap between flight strips is to be maintained. This overlap is shown in Fig. 15-11.

Each photograph in the line of flight covers an area which overlaps the area covered by the previous photograph by about 60 per cent. This is illustrated in Figs. 15-11 and 15-12. The large overlap between successive photographs serves three primary purposes. First, it provides coverage of the entire ground area from two viewpoints, such coverage being necessary for stereoscopic viewing and measuring. Second, it allows only the central portion of each photograph to be used in mosaic construction, eliminating to a great extent the effect of relief displacement. Third, the small overlap area between alternate photographs allows horizontal control to be extended along the strip by photogrammetric methods. For example, see Sec. 15-9.

15-7. Ground Control for Photographs. In order that aerial photographs may be used for making simple measurements of distances and elevations, for constructing planimetric and topographic

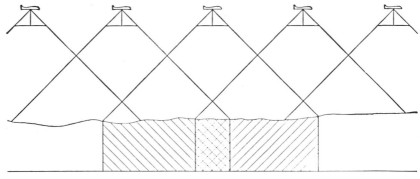

FIG. 15-12.   Overlap along flight line.

maps, and for constructing mosaics, a certain amount of ground control is necessary to fix the scale of the photographs, the map, or the mosaic and to establish a vertical datum with which to establish contour lines on the map. This control may be obtained simply by measuring the ground distance between two identifiable points which appear on a photograph. Or an elaborate system of triangulation and level nets may be required to control the horizontal and vertical positions of identifiable points which appear on the photographs. In general, triangulation and traverse stations and bench marks cannot be identified on the photographs unless they have been marked in the field before the pictures were taken. As a result, shorter traverse lines and level lines, usually of a lower order of accuracy than the main system, are run to points which can be identified. These points are called *picture points*, and the network of picture points in a group of photographs is called *photo control*.

The horizontal photo control may be obtained by running a transit-tape, transit-stadia, or plane-table traverse from a fixed point to the picture points, or it may be obtained by a simple triangulation system of a low order of accuracy. A large amount of photo control work is conducted by a combination of a theodolite and an electronic distance-measuring system. Vertical photo control is obtained by running differential, stadia, or plane-table levels from bench marks to the points, or by using aneroid barometers.

The choice of the field method to be used in establishing photo control depends on the desired accuracy, which in turn depends on the scale of the map or mosaic and the contour interval to be used in compiling the map.

A picture point must be positively identifiable between the photograph and the ground. It must be sharp and well defined as seen on the photograph under magnification. The picture point must fall in the correct position on the photograph. A picture point falling, for example, near the very edge of the photograph may be entirely useless for the purpose for which it is intended. It should be reasonably accessible on the ground so that the expense of the photo-control survey can be kept to a minimum. Finally, the picture point must be well described and documented directly on the photograph used in the field when the photo-control survey is performed.

15-8. Mosaic. A mosaic is an assembly of a series of overlapping aerial photographs to form one continuous picture of the terrain. It may consist of a single strip of photographs, termed a *strip mosaic*, or it may contain many overlapping strips. When photographic film has been processed, each negative of a flight strip is numbered consecutively, and each flight strip bears a number which is also assigned to each photograph of that strip. These identifying numbers appear when the photographs are printed from the negatives. If a set of aerial photographs are laid down and stapled to a board in consecutive order in such a manner that the identifying numbers show on the finished assemblage, the result is a crude mosaic with very little accuracy but with high utility. It is called an *index mosaic* because it is a visual method of indexing each photograph in a set.

A mosaic that is constructed for its pictorial quality alone is usually not controlled to any extent by photo control. To prepare a mosaic for this purpose, all but the central portion of each photograph is trimmed away, leaving a small amount of overlap, and the edges are brought to a feather-edge by sandpapering. The photographs are pasted onto a mounting board, masonite for example, by some type of adhesive. Gum arabic is a common type of mosaic adhesive, because it is easy to work with and can be cleaned off readily with water. Each photograph is laid on the preceding one and is shifted on the board until the images in the overlap areas of the successive photographs match. It is then squeegeed into place.

A mosaic that is constructed to give both high pictorial quality and good accuracy must be controlled by picture points. The accuracy and density of the control is, of course, dependent on the accuracy desired in the finished mosaic. The control provided for mosaics can be obtained by ground surveys supplemented by graphically located points. These supplementary points are located by a method known as *radial-line plotting*, discussed in Sec. 15-9. The control can also be provided in the form of a planimetric map plotted directly on the mounting board to the desired scale of the mosaic. This type of control is used to lay the mosaic shown in Fig. 15-13.

Because of differences of flying heights between successive photographs, and because of displacements of images due to relief and photographic tilt, the photographs of a set must be brought to a common scale, and they must be corrected for tilt displacement and, to a limited extent, for relief displacement. This ratioing to a common scale, while eliminating the effect of tilt at the same time, is performed in an enlarger whose negative holder and easel can be tilted. Such an enlarger is called a *rectifier*. When each negative has been rectified so that it satisfies the positions of the plotted control points, a photograph is made which will be used in the subsequent mosaic construction.

Photographs for a controlled mosaic are trimmed, sanded, and pasted essentially in the manner discussed previously. After the assembly is completed, the mosaic is photographed to the final desired

Fig. 15–13. Laying mosaic to control.
(Courtesy of Hycon Aerial Surveys.)

scale by means of a copy camera, and reproductions of the copy negative are made for use.

Mosaics possess numerous advantages over maps prepared by
conventional ground methods. The mosaic can be produced more
rapidly, and the cost of duplicating by ground surveys the wealth of
detail and completeness found on a mosaic would usually be prohibi-
tive. An objection to the mosaic is that it is not a topographic map,
and elevations cannot be obtained from it. In fact, the mosaic is not
a map at all, because of inherent displacements of images due to relief
and residual tilt effects; but it is an excellent map substitute.

15-9. Radial-Line Plot. On a truly vertical photograph, the angle measured at the principal point between the lines to any pair of points is a horizontal angle. On a photograph with a tilt of as much as 3°, the angles measured about the principal point can be considered horizontal angles for graphical purposes. In Fig. 15-8, the angle at o from b to a is the same as the angle measured with a transit at O from B to A, because the lines ob and OB lie in the same vertical plane and the lines oa and OA also lie in the same vertical plane. The principal point can therefore be considered as an instrument station.

Assume that three picture points appear on a vertical photograph, and that the positions of these three points have been plotted on a map sheet in their correct horizontal positions. The map position of the principal point can be located by the tracing-paper method of three-point resection described in Sec. 13-24. A sheet of tracing paper is placed over the photograph, and rays are drawn from the principal point through the three picture points. The tracing paper is then transferred to the map, and the three rays are caused to pass through the plotted map positions of the picture points. This position of the

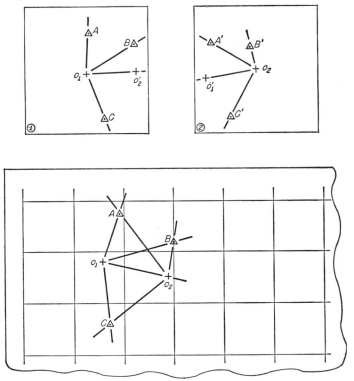

FIG. 15-14. Radial-line plot from first pair of photographs.

paper fixes the correct map position of the principal point.

A pair of overlapping photographs is shown in Fig. 15-14. The point representing the principal point of photograph *1* appears on photograph *2* at position o'_1, and the point representing the principal point of photograph *2* appears on photograph *1* at position o'_2. Picture points *A*, *B*, and *C*, which correspond with *A'*, *B'*, and *C'*, appear on the photographs as shown. Rays drawn through *A*, *B*, *C*, and o'_2 from o_1, and rays drawn through *A'*, *B'*, *C'*, and o'_1 from o_2 are transferred to the map. By resection, the map positions of o_1 and o_2 are located. The line o_1o_2 on the map sheet constitutes a base line from which other points in the overlap area of the pair of photographs can be determined by intersection.

In Fig. 15-15, *e*, *f*, *g*, and *h* are four image points arbitrarily picked in positions opposite the two principal points and out toward the edges of the photographs. These are called *pass points*. The two points *g* and *h* are points which also appear on the photograph *3* because of the small amount of overlap between photographs *1* and *3*. The picture points *A*, *B*, and *C* are omitted from Fig. 15-15 for the

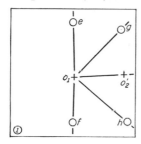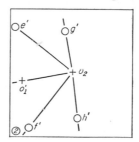

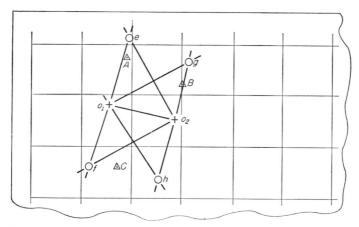

FIG. 15-15. Location of pass points on first pair of photographs.

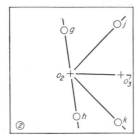
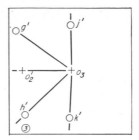

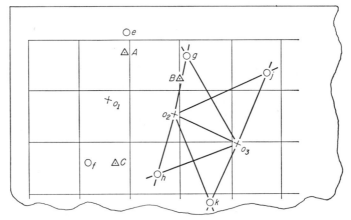

FIG. 15–16.   Location of third photograph and additional
pass points.

sake of clarity. The angles off the base to the four pass points, transferred to the map, fix the map positions of the points by intersection.
The map now contains points g, o_2, and h, which are sufficient to
locate the position of the principal point of photograph 3.

In Fig. 15-16, rays are shown drawn on photograph 2 from o_2
through three additional points j, o'_3, and k, and rays are drawn on
photograph 3 from o_3 through points g', o'_2, h', j', and k'. The map
position of o_3 is located by resecting on the map positions of g, o_2,
and h. As soon as the map position of o_3 has been established, the
map positions of j and k are fixed by intersection of the rays from o_2
and o_3 to the two points.

Use of the process of resection to establish the position of each
principal point, and use of intersection to establish the positions of
the pass points, is continued through the strip of photographs until a
control point is reached. In Fig. 15-17 is shown an assembly of five
sets of rays beginning at points A, B, and C and closing on point D.
This is a small radial-line plot, and its purpose is to obtain graphical
control to supplement the ground control.

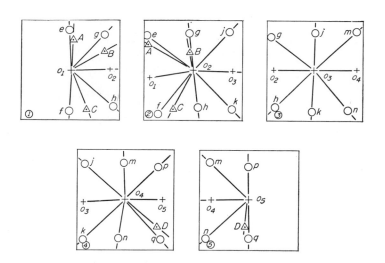

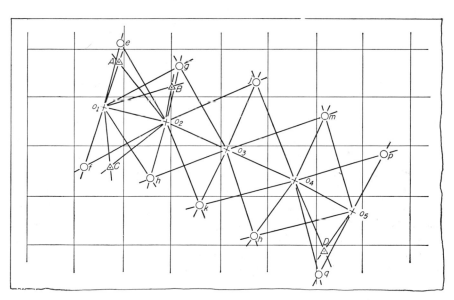

FIG. 15–17. Radial-line plot tied to four control points.

FIG. 15–18.   Radial-line plot with slotted-templets.
(Courtesy of Hycon Aerial Surveys.)

The rays may be transferred from the photograph to the map
sheet by using tracing paper, by using pieces of cardboard with precise slots cut to represent the rays, or by using slotted metal arms held
together at the principal point by means of a nut and bolt. In Fig.
15-18 is shown a radial-line plot being executed by means of slotted
cardboard templates. The positions of the metal studs projecting up
through the slots represent the map positions of the principal points
and the pass points.

It is to be noted that nine control points (six pass points and
three principal points) are established for each photograph. These
control points are in addition to the original photo control obtained
by field methods. This additional control is less accurate than the
ground control, but it fixes the positions of the photographs for compiling planimetric maps and for controlling the assembly of a mosaic.

15-10. Stereoscopy and Parallax. The word *stereoscopy* is defined as the viewing of an object or image in three dimensions and
necessarily implies binocular, or two-eyed, vision. The optical axes of
a person's eyes will converge when looking at an object, and the angle
measured at the object between the two optical axes is called the
parallactic angle. This angle will increase as the object is brought
closer to the eyes, and will decrease as the object recedes from the
eyes. Two objects at different distances will be interpreted by the eyes

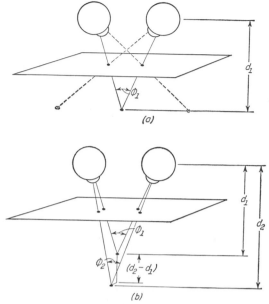

FIG. 15–19.   Stereoscopic vision.

as forming two different parallactic angles, and the difference in the two angles is interpreted as depth.

In Fig. 15-19 (a), two marks of the same size and shape are plotted on a sheet of paper separated by a distance of about 2¼ in. If each eye concentrates on but one mark, the image of the two marks will appear as one mark at a distance d_1, and the parallactic angle formed at this image is ϕ_1. In Fig. 15-19 (b) an additional pair of marks is plotted with a slightly larger separation. The angle ϕ_2 is formed at the single image of this pair, the image appearing to lie at a distance d_2 from the eyes. Thus, the four marks on a plane surface viewed stereoscopically will appear as two marks separated in the third dimension of depth by the amount $d_2 - d_1$.

In Fig. 15-20 (a), a tower is photographed from two consecutive camera stations L and L' and forms images as shown. Notice the relief displacement of the top of the tower with respect to the bottom. The two photographs lined up side by side with the flight line parallel with the eye base will form a three-dimensional image of the tower, as shown in Fig. 15-20 (b). Furthermore, all points in the area of overlap between the two photographs will be seen stereoscopically, that is, in three dimensions. Because of the dimensions of the photograph, and because of the eyes' resistance to focus closely and at the same time diverge abnormally, a stereoscope is used to form the stereoscopic image. The stereoscope can be of a simple lens type shown in Fig.

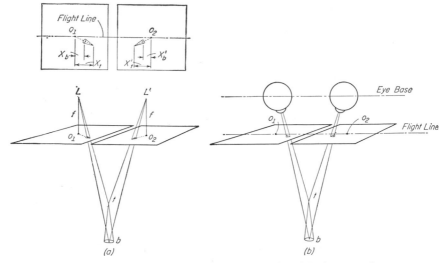

FIG. 15–20. Images of tower on pair of aerial photographs.

15-21 (*a*) or of a mirror type shown in Fig. 15-21 (*b*). When the photographs are laid down, the flight line of one photograph must line up with the same flight line of the other photograph before the stereoscope is placed over the pair. This adjustment is shown in Fig. 15-22.

In Fig. 15-20 (*a*), it is noted that the image of the top of the tower has moved through a total algebraic distance of $x_t - x'_t$ between two successive exposures, and that the image of the bottom of the tower has moved through a total distance of $x_b - x'_b$ between exposures. This movement of an image over the focal plane between exposures is called the *parallax* of the point. Parallax increases as the point lies closer to the camera, that is, as the elevation of the point increases. It is the gradual difference in parallax between successive points as they are photographed from two successive camera stations which gives a gradual difference in the parallactic angles formed between the optical axes of the eyes. Thus a continuous three-dimensional image is formed.

Parallax is a direct indication of elevation and can be measured on a pair of photographs. In Fig. 15-23, point A lies at elevation h_A above the datum; H is the flying height above the datum; B, or distance LL', is the *air base* of the pair of truly vertical photographs; and $a'a$ is the parallax p_a of A. Triangle $La'a$ is similar to triangle $AL'L$, since all sides are mutually parallel. Therefore,

$$\frac{H - h_A}{f} = \frac{B}{p_A}$$

(a)

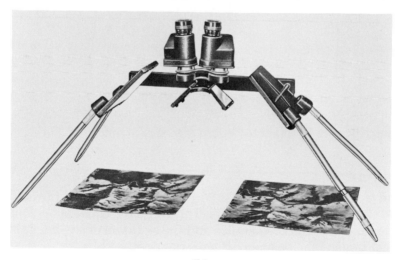

(b)

FIG. 15–21. Stereoscopes. (a) Lens stereoscope. (b) Mirror stereoscope. (Courtesy of Harrison Ryker, Inc., Oakland, Calif.)

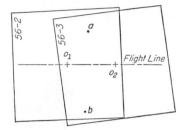

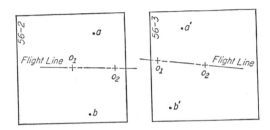

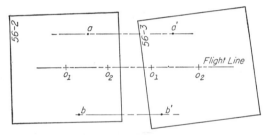

Fig. 15–22.   Adjusting photographs for
stereoscopic viewing.

If subscripts are dropped to denote a general point,

$$H - h = \frac{B}{p} f \qquad (15\text{-}6)$$

where H, B, and h are in feet, and p and f are expressed in the same
units, either inches or millimeters. This is a basic equation, giving the
relationship between the parallax and the elevation of a point. It is the
basis of topographic mapping from aerial photographs.

   The flying height may be determined by methods discussed in
Secs. 15-4 and 15-5. The air base may be determined from a radial-
line plot by scaling the distance between a pair of photograph centers
and converting this distance to feet. If the elevation of one point is
known, its parallax may be determined by Eq. 15-6. By means of a
parallax bar, shown in Fig. 15-24, the difference between the parallax

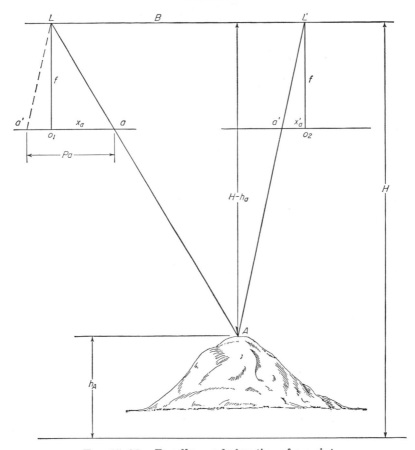

FIG. 15–23. Parallax and elevation of a point.

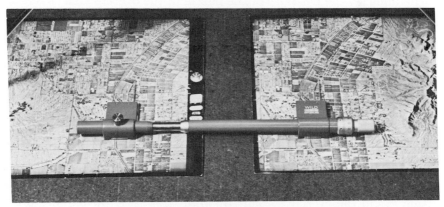

FIG. 15–24. Parallax bar.

of the point of known elevation and that of any other point can be
determined, and the parallax of the other point may be computed.
The elevation of the other point is then computed by Eq. 15-6. For a
discussion of the use of the parallax bar, consult the bibliography at
the end of this chapter.

EXAMPLE 15-2. The scale of a pair of vertical photographs for terrain lying
at an elevation of 670 ft is determined from a map to be 1 in. = 455 ft. The
focal length of the camera used to take the photographs is 153.20 mm. The air
base, scaled from a radial-line plot, is 1680 ft. The difference between the
parallax of a point which lies at an elevation of 653 ft and that of an unknown
point is measured to be + 2.56 mm. Determine the elevation of the unknown
point.

Solution: The focal length f is 153.20 mm = 6.03 in., and the flying height
is computed by Eq. 15-1 as follows:

$$\frac{1}{455} = \frac{6.03}{H - 670} \qquad \text{or} \qquad H = 3414 \text{ ft}$$

The parallax of the point of known elevation is computed by Eq. 15-6
as follows:

$$3414 - 653 = \frac{1680 \times 153.20}{p} \qquad \text{or} \qquad p = 93.22 \text{ mm}$$

The parallax of the unknown point is therefore 93.22 + 2.56 = 95.78 mm,
and the elevation of the unknown point is computed by Eq. 15-6. Thus,

$$3414 - h = \frac{1680 \times 153.20}{95.78} \qquad \text{or} \qquad h = 727 \text{ ft}$$

Because Eq. 15-6 is based on the use of truly vertical photographs
taken from the same flying height above the datum, any tilt in either
or both of the photographs or any inequality in the flying height for
the two photographs will affect the parallax of the points. Tilt and
unequal flying heights, in effect, introduce false parallax, the amount
depending on the positions of the points in the overlap area as well as
on the angle of tilt and the difference in flying heights. The inaccuracies introduced from these sources can be overcome to a limited
extent by having several points of known elevation in the overlap area,
and by then adjusting the measured parallaxes of points lying between
these control points.

Inaccuracies are also introduced in determining elevations from
simple parallax measurements on photographs, because of differential
shrinkage of the photograph during processing and because of distortions of the aerial camera lens.

An approximate parallax equation, which is much simpler to use,
can be derived from Eq. 15-6. Assume that a point of known elevation lies in the overlap area of two photographs. If the parallax difference between this point and a point of unknown elevation is measured

by using the parallax bar, then the difference in elevation between the known point and the unknown point can be obtained by the relationship

$$dh = \frac{dp\,H}{dp + b} \tag{15-7}$$

in which dh is the difference in elevation, in feet; dp is the parallax difference measured with the bar, usually expressed in millimeters; H is the flying height above the known point, in feet; and b is the average length of the line o_1o_2 shown in Fig. 15-22 and measured on both photographs, in the same units as dp. The approximation in Eq. 15-7 is in the assumption that the quantity b is very nearly the parallax of the known point. If the known point lies at an elevation which is equal, or nearly equal, to the average elevation of the two points on the ground imaged at the principal points of the photographs, then the approximation is good. As the point departs from this condition, the approximation becomes weaker.

EXAMPLE 15-3. A pair of overlapping vertical photographs were taken with a lens having a 6-in. focal length. The average scale of the photography is 1:10,000. A vertical control point, whose elevation is 680 ft, appears in the overlap area. The average distance between principal points is 3.660 in., or 92.96 mm. Parallax-bar measurements give the measured differences of parallax between the known control point and five unknown points. These differences are shown in the accompanying tabulation. Compute the elevations of the five points.

Point	dp (mm)	$dp + b$ (mm)	dh (ft)	Elevation (ft)
1	+ 4.62	97.58	+ 206	886
2	− 0.88	92.08	− 48	632
3	+ 1.90	94.86	+ 100	780
4	+ 5.76	98.72	+ 292	972
5	− 3.35	89.61	− 187	493

Solution: We must assume that the elevation of the known point is nearly equal to the average elevation of the area shown on the photographs. Then, by Eq. 15-3, in which the average elevation is assumed to be that of the datum,

$$S_D = \frac{6/12}{H} = \frac{1}{10,000} \quad \text{or} \quad H = 5,000 \text{ ft}$$

With b given as 92.96 mm, the differences of elevation are computed by Eq. 15-7, as shown in the tabulation. Finally, these are used with the elevation of the known point to give the values in the last column.

The method of determining elevations discussed in this section will give values which are accurate to perhaps 1/300 times the flying height, more or less, the error depending on the refinements made in making the measurements and the number of vertical control points in the area of overlap. A rough topographic map can be prepared by obtaining the elevations of controlling points and then, by looking at the stereoscopic image through a stereoscope, sketching in the contour lines according to their proper spacing and shape.

15-11. Stereoscopic Plotting Instruments. A stereoscopic plotting instrument, or plotter, is used to plot planimetric and topographic maps to a predetermined scale by using photographs that have been taken with a precision aerial camera. The elevations of selected ground points measured in a plotter can be determined with varying degrees of accuracy, the error depending on the precision of the plotter. This ranges from 1/1000 times the flying height to as little as 1/5000 times the flying height. The error in contour lines drawn by means of the plotter will vary from 1/500 to 1/2000 times the flying height, the amount again depending on the precision of the plotter and also on the type of ground cover existing at the time the photographs were made.

In order to maintain accuracy, the photographs used in a plotting instrument are printed on glass plates. These glass plates are either the same size as the negatives, or they are reduced in size by a carefully controlled ratio. For use in some plotters, the glass plates are made by projection through a lens which compensates within tolerance the distortions due to the aerial camera lens. In other plotters, the camera-lens distortion is compensated for directly in the projection systems.

Every plotting instrument has four main features: a projection system, a viewing system, a measuring system, and a drawing system. These features will be described with reference to Fig. 15-25, in which is shown a plotting instrument of simple design. This is the Multiplex plotter. Each of the two projectors contains a projector lens with a principal distance of 30 mm, a light source, and a condenser lens which concentrates the light so that it passes through the projector lens. A small reproduction on glass, called a *diapositive* and measuring 2½ in. by 2½ in., is placed in each of the two projectors, corresponding to two overlapping photographs. A blue-green filter is placed below the light source in one projector, and a red filter is put in the other projector. When the lamps of the projectors are turned on, two cones of rays are projected downward toward the map table, each cone of rays having a different color.

Because of tilt in the photographs and because of unequal flying heights, a ray of light through a ground point and coming from one projector may fail to intersect the ray through the same point coming from the other projector; and similarly for other pairs of rays through

FIG. 15–25.   Stereoscopic plotting instrument.
(Courtesy of U. S. Geological Survey.)

other points. Each projector is free to rotate about each of the three axes, and also to move along the three axes. By a systematic manipulation of these motions of each projector, the discrepancies existing between the rays are eliminated, and the two overlapping cones of rays form a stereoscopic image in the area above the map table.

The stereoscopic image is viewed by the operator through a pair of spectacles, the one lens of which is blue-green and the other red. In this way, the cone of rays projected downward from the left projector can be seen with the left eye only, while that coming from the right projector is seen with the right eye only. The operator thus is able to see a three-dimensional image of the overlap area covered by the two successive photographs. This is called the *anaglyphic* method of viewing the stereoscopic image.

The small movable table which sits on the map table is called the tracing table. The tracing table contains a white circular platen which moves up and down by means of a knurled knob, the up and down movement being recorded on a vernier or a counter. In some types of tracing tables, this movement is recorded in millimeters; in other types, it is given directly in feet of elevation. At the center of the platen is a small hole, underneath which is a small light bulb. When the operator views the stereoscopic image formed on the platen, he also sees a small pin-point of light at the center of the platen. This is the measuring mark, and its up-and-down motion is recorded as just mentioned.

Directly beneath the measuring mark is the plotting pencil, which can be raised from or lowered to the map sheet. The position of the plotting pencil can be adjusted in both directions so that the pencil and the measuring mark form a line which is perpendicular to the surface of the map table.

Before the stereoscopic image can be measured and plotted in the form of a planimetric or topographic map, it must be brought to the correct scale and datum. The scale is controlled by the horizontal positions of at least two photo-control points appearing in the area of overlap, their positions having been plotted on the map sheet. By varying the spacing between the two projectors in the direction of the flight line, the scale is varied until the images of the control points received by the measuring mark are directly over the corresponding plotted positions of the control points.

Three, four, or five vertical-control points appearing in the area of overlap are used to bring the image to the correct datum. The operator raises or lowers the measuring mark until it appears to be in contact with a vertical control point as seen in the stereoscopic image. He reads the indicator and determines the discrepancy between the known elevation and the measured elevation. Repeating this at each vertical control point, the operator then analyzes the discrepancy at each point to decide the amount by which the projectors as a unit or the map table must be tipped and tilted to make the measured elevations agree with the known elevations. After the tips and tilts have been introduced, the elevations are again read to determine any minor amount of adjustment which must be made.

The stereoscopic image which has been brought to the correct scale and vertical datum now constitutes a *spatial model* of a portion of the earth's surface. For the equipment in Fig. 15-25, the distance between the two projector lenses is the air base reduced to the scale of the map. The height of the projectors above the map table represents, to the scale of the map, the flying height above a level datum, although not necessarily the sea-level datum. Vertical distances measured above the map sheet to points on the stereoscopic model are elevations, to scale, of the points above the level datum. The stereoscopic model can be measured in all three dimensions by means of the measuring mark.

When plotting planimetric features on the map sheet, the operator follows the features with the measuring mark, raising it when the terrain rises and lowering it when the terrain is falling. The plotting pencil traces these features in their correct orthographic positions on the map sheet.

When plotting a contour line, the operator sets the measuring mark to correspond to the elevation of the contour line to be plotted by reference to the tracing table scale. With the pencil raised from the map sheet, he moves the measuring mark until it appears to come in contact with the spatial model. The measuring mark is thus on the contour line. The operator lowers the pencil to the map sheet and moves the tracing table in such a manner that the measuring mark is at all times in apparent contact with the model. The pencil traces this movement as a contour line orthographically on the map sheet. To verify that he has not missed a contour line at high points, the operator usually measures the elevations of these points and records their values on the map sheet.

The plotting instrument shown in Fig. 15-26 is known as a Balplex plotter. The principles of projection, viewing, and adjusting and measuring the spatial model are identical to those for the Multiplex plotter. The light from the projector lamp is reflected through the lens by means of an ellipsoidal reflector, rather than through condenser lenses. This feature accounts for the dish-shaped light housing. The principal distance of the projector lens is 55 mm. The diapositive is 4¼ in. by 4¼ in. in size. Because of the larger diapositive and the greater projection distance, the Balplex spatial model is about twice as large as the Multiplex model created from the same photography. A higher degree of accuracy is thus obtained from this larger model.

The Kelsh plotter, shown in Fig. 15-27, is used extensively for the compilation of medium-scale and large-scale engineering topographic maps used for design purposes. It is also used for relatively small-scale work. Operating principles are the same as those for the Multiplex and Balplex plotters. The diapositive is the same size as the original negative, or about 9 in. by 9 in. The principal distance of the lens is nominally 6 in., but it can be varied a slight amount to accommodate small variations from the nominal 6-in. focal length of aerial-camera lenses. Illumination of small portions of the diapositives

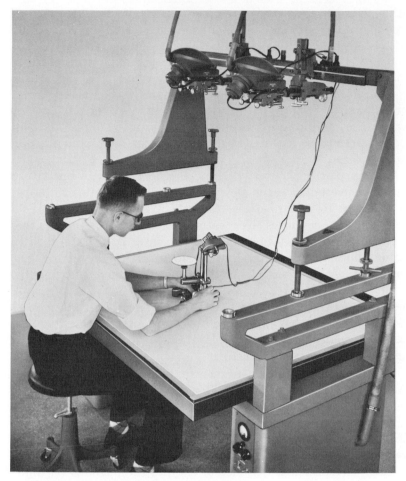

FIG. 15-26.   Balplex plotter.   (Courtesy of Bausch & Lomb, Inc.)

is accomplished by means of two lamps seen in Fig. 15-27. As the tracing table is moved over the map sheet, two guide rods guide the lamps around, illuminating only that part of the model being viewed on the tracing table. The scale of the Kelsh spatial model is about the same as that of the Balplex model from the same aerial photography.

The instrument shown in Fig. 15-28 performs the same function as the plotters previously discussed, but the design and operating principles are quite different. The projection takes place by means of two steel space rods machined to remarkable precision. These rods are analogous to two rays of light coming from two conjugate points on the diapositives and intersecting in space below the projectors. The two space rods, together with their intersection, can be seen in Fig. 15-28. The two diapositive holders can be rotated about three

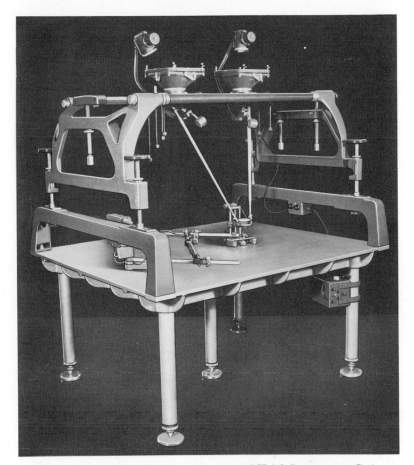

Fig. 15-27.   Kelsh plotter.   (Courtesy of Kelsh Instrument Co.)

axes, and can also be translated in a direction parallel with the flight line. Viewing of the three-dimensional image formed by two diapositives takes place by means of a pair of optical trains commencing on the under sides of the diapositives, continuing through a series of prisms and lenses, and ending at a pair of binocular eyepieces seen in Fig. 15-28.

Two measuring marks, one in each optical train, are superimposed onto the images of the diapositives, and they appear as one floating mark when the viewer observes the stereoscopic image. This feature is similar to the parallax-bar principle mentioned in Sec. 15-10. The image of the mark is caused to move through the model in an X-direction and in a Y-direction by moving the point of intersection of the space rods by using a pair of hand wheels shown in Fig. 15-28. Rotation of a hand wheel causes a corresponding rotation

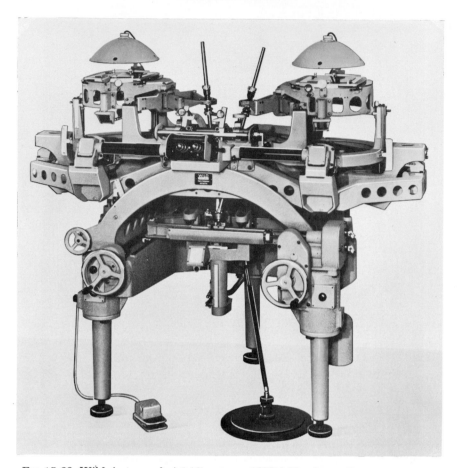

FIG. 15-28. Wild Autograph A8.(Courtesy of Wild-Heerbrugg Instruments, Inc.)

of a spindle of a coordinatograph not shown in Fig. 15-28 (see Fig. 8-32) through a gear box and connecting rods. This movement of the floating mark enables the details seen in the model to be plotted on a map sheet fastened to the coordinatograph. The X-motion and Y-motion can be read to the nearest 0.01 mm by means of appropriate scales on the coordinatograph. The floating mark is made to appear to move up or down by rotating the large foot disk seen in the illustration. The up-and-down motion is registered on a height display and the mark can be set to a selected elevation for following a contour line.

There are no projector lenses in the instrument shown in Fig. 15-28. The perspective centers, replacing the lenses, are located at the pivot points of the space rods and are not seen in the illustration. By physically varying the vertical distance between these pivot points and the plane of the diapositives, focal lengths varying from less than

100 mm to about 210 mm, corresponding to a range from 4 in. to 8¼ in., can be accommodated.

The instruments described above are representative of stereoscopic plotting instruments employed for the compilation of topographic maps. Many variations of the features of these instruments, in addition to completely different principles of design, are incorporated in a multitude of plotters.

15-12. Advantages and Disadvantages of Photogrammetric Mapping. The main advantages of the compilation of topographic maps by using aerial photographs over ground methods are as follows: the speed of compilation, the reduction in the amount of control surveying required to control the mapping, the high accuracy of the locations of planimetric features, the faithful reproduction of the configuration of the ground by continuously-traced contour lines, and the freedom from interference by adverse weather and inaccessible terrain. Also, by the proper selection of flying heights, focal lengths, and plotting instruments, and by proper placement of ground control, photogrammetric mapping can be designed for any map scale ranging from 1 in. = 20 ft down to 1 in. = 20,000 ft and smaller, and for a contour interval as small as ½ ft. Because of the wealth of detail which can be seen in a spatial model, the resultant photogrammetric map will be more complete than will a comparable map produced by ground methods.

Among the disadvantages of mapping by using aerial photographs are the following: the difficulty of plotting in areas containing heavy ground-cover, such as high grass, timber, and underbrush; the high cost per acre of mapping areas 5 acres or less in extent; the difficulty of locating positions of contour lines in flat terrain; and the necessity for field editing and field completion. Field completion is required where the ground cannot be seen in the spatial model because of ground cover, where spot elevations must be measured in flat terrain, and where such planimetric features as overhead and underground utility lines must be located on the map. Editing is necessary to include road classification, boundary lines not showing on the photography, drainage classification, and names of places, roads, and other map features.

BIBLIOGRAPHY

AMERICAN SOCIETY OF PHOTOGRAMMETRY. *Manual of Photogrammetry.* George Banta Publishing Company.
HALLERT, B. *Photogrammetry.* New York: McGraw-Hill Book Co., Inc., 1960.
MOFFITT, F. H. *Photogrammetry.* Scanton, Pa.: International Textbook Company, 1959.

"Topographic Manual, Part II," *Special Publication No. 249,* U.S. Coast and
    Geodetic Survey, Government Printing Office.
Zeller, Dr. M. *Text Book of Photogrammetry.* London: H. K. Lewis Co., Ltd.,
    1952.

PROBLEMS

15-1. A camera with a focal length of 115 mm and a picture size of 5½ in. by 5½ in. is used to photograph gently rolling terrain from an altitude of 8800 ft above sea level. The average ground elevation is 2200 ft above sea level. What is the average scale of the photography?

15-2. In Problem 15-1, what ground area is covered by a single exposure?

15-3. Side lap and overlap of the photography in Problem 15-1 are 25 per cent and 55 per cent, respectively. What is the ground spacing, in feet, between the flight lines? What is the ground spacing between exposures?

15-4. The flight lines in Problem 15-3 are to be plotted on a map which is drawn to a scale of 1:24,000. What is the flight-line spacing on the map, in inches?

15-5. Assuming that the aircraft flies at a true ground speed of 140 mph along a flight line in Problem 15-3, determine the time interval between exposures, in seconds?

15-6. Two points lying at an elevation of 1625 ft appear on a photograph taken as described in Problem 15-1. The distance between the images of these two points scales 38.85 mm. What is the ground distance, in feet, between the points?

15-7. A distance between the images of two points scales 4.63 in. on a photograph taken with a camera for which the focal length is 152.5 mm. The distance between the same two points scales 1.44 in. on a map for which the scale is 1:31,680. Compute the scale of the photograph.

15-8. The image of a radio tower appears on a photograph taken with a lens having a focal length of 6 in. The photo scale is 1 in. = 850 ft. The distance from the principal point to the image of the bottom of the tower is measured as 73.75 mm, and that to the image of the top scales 78.80 mm. Compute the height of the tower, to the nearest foot.

15-9. A 5-mile strip of terrain is to be photographed for highway mapping. The aerial camera contains a lens with a focal length of 8¼ in. and takes 9 in. by 9 in. photographs. The elevation of the terrain varies from 800 ft to 1500 ft, and the average elevation is 1000 ft. The average width of photographic coverage is to be 500 ft.

a) What flying height above sea level should be used on this flight?

b) If the overlap between photos is 60 per cent and the centers of the first and last photographs are to fall outside the limit of the strip, how many photographs will be required?

c) What will be the largest and the smallest photographic scales? Express each as an engineer's scale.

d) Assuming the aircraft ground speed to be 130 mph, compute the time interval between exposures, in seconds.

e) What per cent of the average flying height with respect to the 1000-ft level is represented by the total variation in elevation of the terrain?

15-10. For taking photographs of a certain area, the flying height above sea level is 4800 ft; the camera focal length is 115 mm; and the air base is 2700 ft. The differences in parallax between a control point *A* whose elevation is 385 ft and five other points are measured on an overlapping pair of photographs covering this area. These differences are as follows:

Point	Diff. in Parallax (mm)
B	+ 3.58
C	− 2.34
D	+ 6.22
E	+ 0.31
F	− 1.48

Determine the elevations of the five points, to the nearest foot.

15-11. Aerial photographs are taken for use in the Kelsh plotter. The air base is 1380 ft. After the projectors have been oriented to fit the plotted control, the distance between the projector lenses measures 19.20 in. With the measuring mark of the tracing table set at a point in the spatial model whose ground elevation is 1455 ft, the vertical distance between the tracing-table platen and the projector lenses measures 28.85 in. The platen is elevated 5.02 in. above the map table.

a) What is the flying height above sea level of these photographs?

b) What is the scale of the map?

c) What vertical distance, in feet of ground elevation, is represented by a vertical movement of the measuring mark of 38.7 mm?

d) What datum elevation is represented by the surface of the mapping table?

16

Earthwork

16-1. **Remarks.** Earthwork operations involve the determination of the volumes of materials which must be excavated or embanked on an engineering project to bring the ground surface to a predetermined grade, and the setting of stakes to aid in carrying out the construction work according to the plans. Although the term earthwork is used, the principles involved in determining volumes apply equally well to volumes of concrete structures, to volumes of stock piles of crushed stone, gravel, sand, coal, and ore, and to volumes of reservoirs. The field work includes the measurements of the dimensions of the various geometrical solids which make up the volumes, the setting of grade stakes, and the keeping of the field notes. The office work involves the computations of the measured volumes and the determination of the most economical manner of performing the work.

Because of the inherent accuracy of modern topographic maps of large scale produced by photogrammetric methods, much of the field work to be discussed in this chapter is eliminated, except for earthwork of limited extent. The measurements for the determination of volumes can be made directly on the topographic maps.

16-2. **Cross Sections.** A cross section is a section taken normal to the direction of the proposed center line of an engineering project, such as a highway, railroad, trench, earth dam, or canal. A cross section for a railroad embankment is shown in Fig. 16-1. The cross section for a highway or an earth dam would have similar characteristics. It is bounded by a base b, side slopes, and the natural terrain. The inclination of a side slope is defined by the horizontal distance s on the slope corresponding to a unit vertical distance. The slope may be a rise (in excavation) or a fall (in embankment). A side slope of 3½ to 1, for example, means that for each 3½ ft of horizontal distance the side slope rises or falls 1 ft. This can be designated as 3½ : 1 or 1 on 3½.

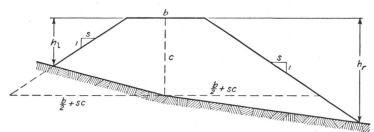

FIG. 16–1.   Cross section for railroad embankment.

16-3. Preliminary Cross Section. In making a preliminary estimate and in determining the location of a facility, such as a highway
or railroad, a preliminary line is located in the field as close to the
final location of the facility as can be determined from a study of the
terrain supplemented by maps or aerial photographs of the area. The
preliminary line is stationed, and profile levels are taken. The configuration of the ground normal to the line is obtained by determining
the elevations of points along sections at right angles to the line. This
is identical to the process of obtaining elevations for topographic mapping described in Sec. 14-6.

The values of the elevations and the corresponding distances out
to the right or left of the line are plotted on specially printed cross-
section paper, at a relatively large scale of from 1 in. = 5 ft to 1 in. =
20 ft. When the location and grade of a trial line representing a
tentative location of the center line of the facility have been established, the offset distance from the preliminary line to the trial line
is plotted, and the grade elevation of this trial line is plotted in relation to the terrain cross section. In Fig. 16-2, the elevations of and
distances to the points plotted on the ground line were determined
with reference to the preliminary center line. These are shown as fractions, with elevations as the numerators and distances from the preliminary line as the denominators. The offset distance of 15 ft from
the preliminary line to the trial line is plotted, and the base of the

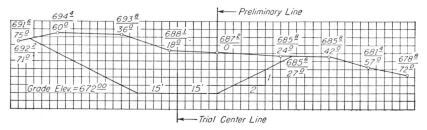

FIG. 16–2.   Preliminary cross section.

roadbed is plotted at grade elevation 672.00 ft. At the edges of the roadbed, the side slopes of 2 to 1 are laid off and drawn to intersect the terrain line at the scaled distances and elevations shown as fractions lying under the terrain line. These points of intersection are called *catch points.*

The cross-sectional area bounded by the base, the side slopes, and the ground line of each trial cross section along the trial line is determined from the plotted cross section by using a planimeter or by computation based on the formulas for areas given in Sec. 8-23. This procedure is discussed in Sec. 16-7. The volumes of excavation and embankment for this trial line are computed from the successive areas and the distances between the areas by the methods described in Secs. 16-8 to 16-11. The volumes for various trial lines are compared. The necessary changes in line and grade are then made to locate the final line and establish the final grade. This location will require a minimum of earthwork and, in the case of a highway project, for example, it will at the same time meet the criteria of curvature, maximum grade, and safe sight distances.

16-4. Final Cross Sections. The line representing the adopted center line of a facility is staked out in the field and stationed. This line is located by computing and running tie lines from the preliminary line as discussed in Sec. 8-25. Deflection angles are measured between successive tangents, and horizontal curves are computed and staked out. Reference stakes are sometimes set opposite each station on both sides of the center line at distances of 25, 50, or 100 ft from the center line. These stakes are used to relocate the center line after grading operations are begun. Stakes at a distance on either side equal to half the base width are sometimes driven to facilitate taking final cross sections and setting construction or slope stakes. The center line and the reference lines are then profiled.

When the final line has been located and profiled, a cross section is taken at each station to determine the area of the cross section and, at the same time, to locate the limits of excavation or embankment. These limits are defined on the ground by stakes. The process of setting these stakes is called *slope-staking.*

In Fig. 16-3, the level is set up and a backsight is taken on the leveling rod held at a station on the center line whose elevation has been determined from the profile levels. The H.I. is established as 880.2 ft. The base width given on the plans is 24 ft, the side slopes are 1½ to 1, and the grade elevation at the station is 878.4 ft. If the leveling rod were held so that the foot of the rod were at grade, the reading of the rod would be 1.8 ft. This is equal to the H.I. minus the

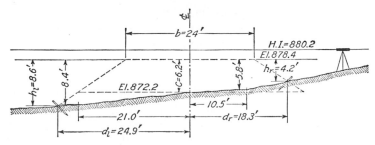

FIG. 16–3.   Slope-staking.

grade elevation, and is called the *grade rod*. The grade rod can be plus
or minus. The vertical distance from a point on the ground line to the
grade line at any section is called the *fill* at the point if the section
is in embankment, or the *cut* if the section is in excavation. It is seen
that the fill at the left edge of the cross section of Fig. 16-3 is 8.6 ft,
at the center line the fill is 6.2 ft, and at the right edge the fill is 4.2 ft.

The grade rod may be determined from the center-line cut or
fill and the rod reading at the center line by the following relationship:

or
$$\left. \begin{array}{l} \text{Grade rod} = \text{ground rod} + \text{center cut} \\ \text{Grade rod} = \text{ground rod} - \text{center fill} \end{array} \right\} \qquad (16\text{-}1)$$

where the ground rod is the rod reading at the center line. The ground
rod in Fig. 16-3 is 8.0 ft. So, the grade rod is $8.0 - 6.2 = 1.8$ ft, as
determined before.

With the grade rod established for the cross section, the amount
of cut or fill at any point in the section can be determined by reading
the rod held at the point and applying the following relationship:

$$\text{Cut or fill} = \text{grade rod} - \text{ground rod} \qquad (16\text{-}2)$$

If the result is plus, the point is above grade, indicating cut (+); if the
result is minus, the point is below grade, indicating fill (−).

The location, on the ground, of the slope stake is determined by
trial. When the ground surface is horizontal, the position of the slope
stake is at a distance from the center line equal to one-half the base
width plus the product of the side-slope ratio and the center cut or
fill. If the ground in Fig. 16-3 were horizontal, each slope stake would
be located at a distance from the center line equal to $12 + 1.5 \times 6.2 =$
21.3 ft. However, since the ground slopes transversely to the center
line, it can be seen that the right slope stake will be less than 21.3 ft
from the center line while the left slope stake will be greater than
21.3 ft from the center line. By trial, a point is found where 12 ft plus
1.5 times the fill equals the actual distance from the center line. With

some experience the point can be found by one or two trials. If it is assumed that the ground appears to rise about 1.5 ft between the center line and the right-hand edge, the fill at the right-hand edge will be $6.2 - 1.5 = 4.7$ ft and the distance out should be $12.0 + 1.5 \times 4.7 = 19.0$ ft. On the basis of this estimate, the rod is held 19 ft from the center line and a rod reading is taken. If the actual reading at this point is found to be 5.8 ft, the depth below the grade is $5.8 - 1.8 = 4.0$ ft. In order that the point will be at the intersection of the side slope with the ground surface, the distance from the center should be $12.0 + 1.5 \times 4.0 = 18.0$ ft. Since the actual distance was 19.0 ft, the trial point is incorrect. The rod is therefore moved nearer the center. Had the ground surface at the right-hand edge been horizontal, the slope stake could have been set at the 18.0-ft point. Since the ground is sloping downward toward the center line, the fill will be somewhat more than 4.0 ft, and the distance out will be greater than 18.0 ft. Consequently, the next trial is taken at 18.2 ft, where a rod reading of 6.0 ft is obtained. The depth below the grade is $6.0 - 1.8 = 4.2$ ft and the distance from the center line should be 18.3 ft. This is within 0.1 ft of where the rod is being held, and so the stake is set at 18.3 ft from the center and the fill is recorded as 4.2 ft.

In the field notes, these two dimensions are recorded in fractional form, the numerator representing the fill and the denominator representing the distance out from the center. To distinguish between cut and fill, either the letters C and F or the signs $+$ and $-$ are used to designate them. As the point is located with respect to the finished grade, a point below grade indicates a fill and is designated by a $-$ sign. The amount of cut or fill is marked on the side of the stake toward the center stake, and the distance out is marked on the opposite side. The stake is usually driven slantingly to distinguish it from a center-line stake and to prevent it from being disturbed during the grading operations.

In Fig. 16-3 there is a decided break in the ground surface between the center line and the right slope stake. This break is located by taking a rod reading there and measuring the distance from the center line. In a similar manner, the break on the left side of the center, and the left slope stake are located. The field notes for this particular station could be recorded as follows:

STATION	ELEV. GRADE	ELEV. GROUND	CROSS SECTION				
			L		C	R	
15 + 00	878.4	872.2	$\dfrac{-8.6}{24.9}$	$\dfrac{-8.4}{21.0}$	$\dfrac{-6.2}{0}$	$\dfrac{-5.8}{10.5}$	$\dfrac{-4.2}{18.3}$

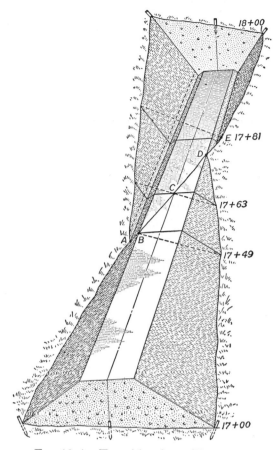

FIG. 16–4.   Transition from fill to cut.

16-5. Cross-Sectioning with Slope Tape and Automatic Leveling Rod. The task of locating the edges of the side slopes can be greatly simplified by the use of a slope tape and an automatic or lightning leveling rod. When this rod is used, the rod reading can be changed to any desired value by shifting the movable band on which the graduations are painted. If, in the example shown in Fig. 16-3, the rod reading with the rod at the center stake is changed to 6.2, then the rod reading at any other point in the cross section will be the distance below the finished grade at that station. A slope tape intended for slopes of 1½:1 has ordinary divisions that are 0.1 ft long on one side and divisions which are 1½ tenths long on the opposite side.

The edge of the side slope can be located by holding the zero of the tape at a distance equal to one-half the width of the roadbed from the center stake, and finding the point where the rod reading and the

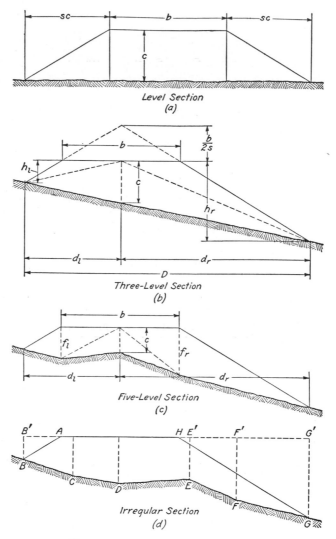

Level Section
(a)

Three-Level Section
(b)

Five-Level Section
(c)

Irregular Section
(d)

Fig. 16–5. Types of cross sections.

tape reading, on that side which has divisions 1½ tenths long, are identical. The horizontal distance from the center line will be half the width of the roadbed plus the distance read on the side of the tape with the regular divisions. The vertical distance below grade will be the reading on the reverse side of the tape, which is the same as the reading on the rod.

16-6. Distance Between Cross Sections. The horizontal distance between cross sections is dependent on the precision required, which in turn is dependent on the price per cubic yard paid for excavation. As the unit cost for highway or railroad grading is usually small, a station distance of 100 ft is generally sufficiently precise. For rock excavation, and for work done under water, the cost per cubic yard mounts very rapidly and the distance between sections is often reduced to 10 ft.

In addition to the cross sections taken at regular intervals, other sections are taken at the P.C. and the P.T. of each curve, at all breaks in the ground surface, and at all grade points. A *grade point* is a point where the ground elevation coincides with the grade elevation. In passing from cut to fill, or from fill to cut, as many as five sections may be needed in computing the volume when the change occurs on a side hill. In Fig. 16-4 these sections are located at A, B, C, D, and E. Unless extreme precision is required, the sections at A and D are usually omitted. Although stakes are set only at the grade points B, C, and E, full cross sections are taken at the stations and the measurements are recorded in the field notes.

It will be noted in Fig. 16-4 that a wider base of cross section is used when excavation is encountered. The additional width is needed to provide ditches for draining the cut.

16-7. Calculation of Areas. Volumes of prismoids are obtained from tables or diagrams, or the areas of the cross sections are determined and the volumes are computed by averaging end areas or by applying the prismoidal formula.

When the cross sections are very irregular, as is frequently the case when an existing highway is to be rebuilt, or when the route traverses land that is badly cut up, the areas can be found by planimetering the plotted cross sections.

When the sections are more regular, the areas can be calculated directly from the field notes. Four classes of sections, shown in Fig. 16-5, are encountered. These sections and their areas are:

a) Level section:

$$\text{Area} = \tfrac{1}{2}(b + sc + b + sc)\,c = \underline{\underline{(b + sc)\,c}} \qquad (16\text{-}3)$$

where $b = $ width of the roadbed;

    $c = $ center fill or cut;

    $s = $ side-slope ratio.

    b) Three-level section:

$$\text{Area} = \tfrac{1}{2} h_l \times \tfrac{1}{2} b + \tfrac{1}{2} c \times d_l + \tfrac{1}{2} c \times d_r + \tfrac{1}{2} h_r \times \tfrac{1}{2} b$$

$$= \tfrac{1}{2} [\tfrac{1}{2} b (h_r + h_l) + c (d_r + d_l)] \tag{16-4}$$

where the notation is as shown in Fig. 16-5 (*b*).

    A second method, which reduces the computation to a single multiplication, is to calculate the area of the figure formed by extending the side slopes to an intersection and subtracting from this area the portion that is above the roadbed. Thus,

$$\text{Area} = \frac{1}{2} \left(c + \frac{b}{2s} \right) \times (d_r + d_l) - \frac{1}{2} \left(b \times \frac{b}{2s} \right)$$

$$= \frac{1}{2} \left(c + \frac{b}{2s} \right) \times D - \frac{b^2}{4s} \tag{16-5}$$

where $D = d_r + d_l$. The area above the roadbed and $b/(2s)$ are constants, as long as the width of the roadbed and the side slopes remain constant.

    c) Five-level section: If the triangles in Fig. 16-5 (*c*) that have common vertical sides are combined,

$$\text{Area} = \tfrac{1}{2} (f_l \times d_l + c \times b + f_r \times d_r) \tag{16-6}$$

    d) Irregular section: The area of the section in Fig. 16-5 (*d*) may be obtained by computing the areas of the trapezoids forming the figure $B'BCDEFGG'$ and subtracting from their sum the areas of the two triangles ABB' and GHG'.

    Another method, which can also be applied to any of the preceding figures, is to consider the cross section as a traverse. The field notes provide the coordinates of the corners with respect to the finished grade and the center line as coordinate axes, the horizontal distances from the center line being the x-coordinates, and the vertical cuts or fills the y-coordinates. For an 8-sided traverse, the area can be expressed by one of the following equations, which are like Eq. 8-22 or Eq. 8-23 in Sec. 8-23.

$$\text{Area} = \tfrac{1}{2} [X_1(Y_2 - Y_8) + X_2(Y_3 - Y_1) + X_3(Y_4 - Y_2) + \cdots]$$

$$\text{Area} = \tfrac{1}{2} [Y_1(X_2 - X_8) + Y_2(X_3 - X_1) + Y_3(X_4 - X_2) + \cdots]$$

Since, for a cross section in earthwork, the y-coordinates of two of the points are zero, the computations will be shortened if the second equation is used. An application of this equation to the area in Fig. 16-5 (*d*) follows:

COMPUTATIONS FOR AREA OF CROSS SECTION

A	B	C	D	E	F	G	H
F 0.0	F 5.2	F 6.8	F 7.2	F 6.1	F 7.4	F 9.6	F 0.0
− 12.0	− 19.8	− 10.0	0	+ 15.0	+ 20.0	+ 26.4	+ 12.0
(1)	(2)	(3)	(4)	(5)	(6)	(7)	(8)

$$Y_n (X_{n+1} - X_{n-1}) \qquad = \text{Double area}$$

$$
\begin{aligned}
0.0 \,(- 19.8 - 12.0) &= 0.0 \\
5.2 \,(- 10.0 + 12.0) &= + 10.4 \\
6.8 \,(0.0 + 19.8) &= + 134.6 \\
7.2 \,(+ 15.0 + 10.0) &= + 180.0 \\
6.1 \,(+ 20.0 - 0.0) &= + 122.0 \\
7.4 \,(+ 26.4 - 15.0) &= + 84.4 \\
9.6 \,(+ 12.0 - 20.0) &= - 76.8 \\
0.0 \,(- 12.0 - 26.4) &= + 0.0
\end{aligned}
$$

$$2\overline{)454.6}$$

$$\text{Area} = \quad 227.3 \text{ sq ft}$$

16-8. Volume by Average End Areas. According to the end-area formula, the volume, in cubic feet, between two cross sections having areas A_0 and A_1 is

$$V_e = \tfrac{1}{2} (A_0 + A_1) L \qquad (16\text{-}7)$$

where L is the distance between the sections. The volume, in cubic yards, is

$$V_e = \frac{1}{2} (A_0 + A_1) \frac{L}{27} = \frac{L}{54} (A_0 + A_1) \qquad (16\text{-}8)$$

Although this relationship is not an exact one when applied to many earthwork sections, it is the one most commonly used, because of the ease of its application and because of the fact that the computed volumes are generally too great and thus the error is in the favor of the contractor.

16-9. Volume by Prismoidal Formula. When the more exact volume must be known, it can be calculated by means of the prismoidal formula

$$V_p = \frac{L}{6} (A_0 + 4M + A_1) \qquad (16\text{-}9)$$

where M is the area of the middle section and V_p is the volume, in cubic feet. In general, M will *not* be the mean of the two end areas. It can be shown that this formula is correct for determining the volumes of prisms, pyramids, wedges, and prismoids that have triangular end sections and sides which are warped surfaces. Since the earthwork solids are included in this group, except for slight irregularities of the ground, the prismoidal formula gives very nearly the correct volume of earthwork. The error in the use of the end-area formula arises chiefly from the fact that in its application the volume of a pyramid is considered to be one-half the product of the base and the altitude, whereas the actual volume is one-third the product of those quantities.

The area of the middle section can be obtained by taking intermediate cross sections on the ground or, when the same number of points have been taken on adjacent sections, by computing the area of a section which has dimensions equal to the means of the corresponding dimensions of the two end sections. An example of this method for three-level sections having bases of 24 ft and side slopes of 1½:1 follows:

COMPUTATION OF VOLUME OF EARTHWORK BY PRISMOIDAL FORMULA

Station	L	C	R	Area
15 + 00	$\dfrac{-8.6}{24.9}$	$\dfrac{-6.4}{0.0}$	$\dfrac{-4.2}{18.3}$	$\dfrac{1}{2} \times 12 \times 12.8 + \dfrac{1}{2} \times 6.4 \times 43.2 = 215.04$ sq ft
16 + 00	$\dfrac{-4.6}{18.9}$	$\dfrac{-2.8}{0.0}$	$\dfrac{-1.4}{14.1}$	$\dfrac{1}{2} \times 12 \times 6.0 + \dfrac{1}{2} \times 2.8 \times 33.0 = 82.20$ sq ft
M	$\dfrac{-6.6}{21.9}$	$\dfrac{-4.6}{0.0}$	$\dfrac{-2.8}{16.2}$	$\dfrac{1}{2} \times 12 \times 9.4 + \dfrac{1}{2} \times 4.6 \times 38.1 = 144.03$ sq ft

$$V_p = \frac{100}{6} \times (215.04 + 4 \times 144.03 + 82.2) = 14{,}556.0 \text{ cu ft} = 539.1 \text{ cu yd}$$

NOTE: above from page 528.

By the end-area formula, $V_e = (100/54)\,(215.04 + 82.20) = 550.4$ cu yd. Thus, the error in applying the end-area formula to this solid is 11.3 cu yd, or about 2 per cent.

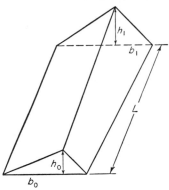

FIG. 16–6. Prism with triangular end sections.

16-10. Prismoidal Correction. Considerably more time is required for computing volumes by the direct application of the prismoidal formula than when the average-end-area method is used. When most of the cross sections are three-level ones, the prismoidal volume can be obtained more easily by applying corrections to the average-end-area volumes. The correction, in cubic feet, for a solid having triangular end sections, as shown in Fig. 16-6, is

$$C = V_e - V_p = \frac{L}{12}\,(b_0 - b_1)\,(h_0 - h_1) \qquad (16\text{-}10)$$

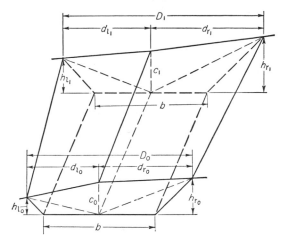

FIG. 16–7.   Prismoid with three-level end sections.

where b_0 and b_1 = bases;

h_0 and h_1 = altitudes of the triangles;

L = distance, in feet, between the cross sections.

In developing this equation for the correction, the average-end-area volume is found from the relationship $V_e = (L/4) \ (b_0 h_0 + b_1 h_1)$. The exact value, $V_p = (L/12) \ (2b_0 h_0 + b_0 h_1 + b_1 h_0 + 2b_1 h_1)$, is obtained either by applying the prismoidal formula or by integral calculus.

Although few earthwork solids have triangular end sections, many of them can be divided into solids which have such end sections. If a solid having three-level end sections is divided into four prisms with triangular end sections, as shown in Fig. 16-7, and Eq. 16-10 is applied to each prism, the corrections are found to be as follows:

Lower left triangle,

$$C = \frac{L}{12} \left(\frac{1}{2} b - \frac{1}{2} b \right) (h_{l_0} - h_{l_1}) = 0$$

Lower right triangle,

$$C = \frac{L}{12} \left(\frac{1}{2} b - \frac{1}{2} b \right) (h_{r_0} - h_{r_1}) = 0$$

Upper left triangle,

$$C = \frac{L}{12} (c_0 - c_1) (d_{l_0} - d_{l_1})$$

Upper right triangle,

$$C = \frac{L}{12} (c_0 - c_1) (d_{r_0} - d_{r_1})$$

The corrections for the lower triangles are zero. Those for the upper triangles can be combined so as to obtain the following relationship:

$$C = \frac{L}{12} (c_0 - c_1)(d_{l_0} + d_{r_0} - d_{l_1} - d_{r_1})$$

or

$$C = \frac{L}{12} (c_0 - c_1)(D_0 - D_1) \qquad (16\text{-}11)$$

where $D_0 = d_{l_0} + d_{r_0}$ and $D_1 = d_{l_1} + d_{r_1}$.

The cross sections of the solid shown in Fig. 16-4, where a change is made from fill to cut, are shown in Fig. 16-8. The prismoidal corrections can be found by dividing the end areas into triangles and applying Eq. 16-10 to the resulting solids. Between stations 17 + 00 and 17 + 49 the correction is

$$C = \tfrac{49}{12}[(c_0 - c_1)(d_{l_0} - \tfrac{1}{2} b) + (c_0 - c_1)(d_{r_0} - d_{r_1})]$$
$$= \tfrac{49}{12}(c_0 - c_1)(D_0 - D_1)$$

Between stations 17 + 49 and 17 + 63 the correction for the volume of fill is

$$C = \tfrac{14}{12}[(c_1 - 0)(\tfrac{1}{2} b - 0) + (c_1 - 0)(d_{r_1} - d_{r_2})]$$
$$= \tfrac{14}{12} c_1 (D_1 - d_{r_2})$$

The correction for the volume of fill between station 17 + 63 and the point D, which may be assumed at station 17 + 81, is

$$C = \tfrac{18}{12}(\tfrac{1}{2} b - 0)(h_{r_2} - 0) = \tfrac{18}{12} \times \tfrac{1}{2} bh_{r_2} = \tfrac{1}{3} V_e$$

The corrections to the volumes of excavation are obtained in a similar manner.

Except in rare cases, the sign of the correction will be positive and the correction is subtracted from the average-end-area volume. When the sign is negative, the correction is added. An inspection of Eq. 16-11 shows that the end-area volume is nearly correct when c_0 and c_1, or D_0 and D_1, are nearly equal, and that the correction will be large when they differ considerably.

The correction to be applied to the end-area volume in the example of the preceding section is

$$C = \tfrac{100}{12}(6.4 - 2.8)(43.2 - 33.0) = 306.0 \text{ cu ft}$$

16-11. Volumes from Tables and Diagrams. Most railroad-engineering and highway-engineering handbooks contain tables and diagrams for the calculation of earthwork volumes. The volumes for level, three-level, and even irregular sections can be obtained more

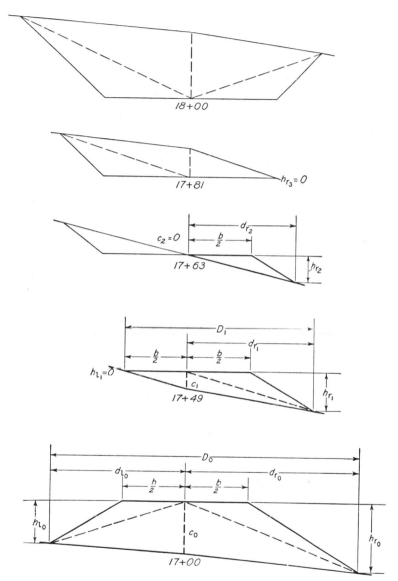

Fig. 16–8. Cross sections in transition from fill to cut.

TABLE FOR COMPUTING EARTHWORK VOLUMES

Base: 16 ft   Side Slopes: 1½:1

c	.0 L	.0 K	.1 L	.1 K	.2 L	.2 K	.3 L	.3 K	.4 L	.4 K	.5 L	.5 K	.6 L	.6 K	.7 L	.7 K	.8 L	.8 K	.9 L	.9 K
0	0.0	7.4	3.0	7.5	6.0	7.7	9.1	7.8	12.3	8.0	15.5	8.1	18.8	8.2	22.1	8.4	25.5	8.5	28.9	8.7
1	32.4	8.8	36.0	8.9	39.6	9.1	43.2	9.2	46.9	9.4	50.7	9.5	54.5	9.6	58.4	9.8	62.3	9.9	66.3	10.0
2	70.4	10.2	74.5	10.3	78.6	10.5	82.8	10.6	87.1	10.7	91.4	10.9	95.8	11.0	100.2	11.2	104.7	11.3	109.3	11.4
3	113.9	11.6	118.5	11.7	123.3	11.9	128.0	12.0	132.9	12.1	137.7	12.3	142.7	12.4	147.7	12.5	152.7	12.7	157.8	12.8
4	163.0	13.0	168.2	13.1	173.4	13.2	178.8	13.4	184.1	13.5	189.6	13.7	195.1	13.8	200.6	13.9	206.2	14.1	211.9	14.2
5	217.6	14.4	223.4	14.5	229.2	14.6	235.1	14.8	241.0	14.9	247.0	15.0	253.0	15.2	259.1	15.3	265.3	15.5	271.5	15.6
6	277.8	15.7	284.1	15.9	290.5	16.0	296.9	16.2	303.4	16.3	310.0	16.4	316.6	16.6	323.2	16.7	329.9	16.9	336.7	17.0
7	343.5	17.1	350.4	17.3	357.3	17.4	364.3	17.5	371.4	17.7	378.5	17.8	385.6	18.0	392.8	18.1	400.1	18.2	407.4	18.4
8	414.8	18.5	422.2	18.7	429.7	18.8	437.3	18.9	444.9	19.1	452.5	19.2	460.3	19.4	468.0	19.5	475.9	19.6	483.7	19.8
9	491.7	19.9	499.7	20.0	507.7	20.2	515.8	20.3	524.0	20.5	532.2	20.6	540.4	20.7	548.8	20.9	557.1	21.0	565.6	21.2

rapidly from these than by computing cross-sectional areas. Tables and diagrams for the prismoidal corrections to be applied to volumes for three-level sections are also included in some of the handbooks.

From Fig. 16-1 it can be seen that the area of a three-level section is equal to that of the level section having the same center fill c, plus the area of the triangle at the lower right, minus the area of the triangle at the lower left. The area of the cross section is

$$A = (b + sc) c + \tfrac{1}{2} (\tfrac{1}{2} b + sc) (h_r - c) - \tfrac{1}{2} (\tfrac{1}{2} b + sc) (c - h_l)$$
$$= (b + sc) c + \tfrac{1}{2} (\tfrac{1}{2} b + sc) (h_r + h_l - 2c)$$

The volume for a length of 50 ft, in cubic yards, is

$$V = \tfrac{50}{27} (b + sc) c + \tfrac{25}{27} (\tfrac{1}{2} b + sc) (h_r + h_l - 2c)$$

The first term of this equation is the volume for a level section for a length of 50 ft, and the second term is a correction by which the volume for a three-level section can be obtained.

The volumes for level sections can be computed for any given width of base and side slopes and for various values of c; the values of $\tfrac{25}{27} (\tfrac{1}{2}b + sc)$ also can be obtained. In the portion of a table for a base of 16 ft and side slopes of $1\tfrac{1}{2}$:1, page 534, the quantities in the columns headed L are the volumes for level sections and those in columns headed K are values of $\tfrac{25}{27} (\tfrac{1}{2}b + sc)$, for values of c differing by 0.1 ft. The volume for a three-level section, for a length of 50 ft, is $L + K$ $(h_r + h_l - 2 c)$.

The average-end-area volume for a length of 100 ft is

$$V_e = 100 \times \frac{(A_0 + A_1)}{2} = 50 A_0 + 50 A_1$$

Since the table gives the values of 50 A, the volume between two end sections can be obtained by addition. An example of the application of the table is shown on the next page.

The volume between stations 17 and 18 is 66.0 + 120.5 = 186.5 cu yd. When $(h_r + h_l - 2c)$ is negative, the correction is subtracted from L to obtain the volume for the three-level sections. If the distance between the sections is other than 100 ft, the volume obtained from the table is multiplied by $D/100$, where D is the distance between the end sections.

16-12. Volume by Truncated Prisms. The volume of a borrow pit or of the excavation for the foundation of a building is frequently found by dividing the surface area into triangles, squares, or rectangles, according to the methods of Sec. 14-10. The original ground-surface elevations at the corners of these figures are determined, usually by direct leveling. The final elevations are obtained either by re-

USE OF TABLE FOR DETERMINING EARTHWORK VOLUMES

Station		Cross Section		
17 + 00		-0.8	-1.6	-3.6
		9.2	0	13.4
18 + 00		-1.2	-2.8	-5.8
		9.8	0	16.7

Sta. 17: $c = 1.6$ $h_r = 3.6$
                      $h_l = 0.8$

$h_r + h_l = 4.4$ $L = \quad 54.5$
$2c = 3.2$ $K\,(h_r + h_l - 2c) = \quad 9.6 \times 1.2 = \quad 11.5$

$h_r + h_l - 2c = 1.2$ Volume for 50 ft $= \quad 66.0$

Sta. 18: $c = 2.8$ $h_r = 5.8$
                      $h_l = 1.2$

$h_r + h_l = 7.0$ $L = 104.7$
$2c = 5.6$ $K\,(h_r + h_l - 2c) = 11.3 \times 1.4 = \quad 15.8$

$h_r + h_l - 2c = 1.4$ Volume for 50 ft $= 120.5$

peating the leveling after the excavation has been completed or, in the case of building foundations, from the plans of the structure. The vertical depth at each corner is calculated by subtracting the final elevation from the original ground-surface elevation.

The volume of any prism is taken as the horizontal area of the prism multiplied by the mean of the corner depths. Thus, if a, b, and c represent the depths at the corners of a truncated triangular prism, the volume is

$$V = A \times \frac{a + b + c}{3} \tag{16-12}$$

where A is the horizontal area of the prism.

When the excavated area has been divided into equal rectangles or equal triangles, the computations can be shortened by noting that some corner heights are common to more than one prism. The volume of the assembled prisms is

$$V = A \times \frac{\Sigma h_1 + 2\Sigma h_2 + 3\Sigma h_3 + 4\Sigma h_4}{4} \tag{16-13}$$

where A = area of one of the equal rectangles or triangles;
   Σh_1 = sum of the vertical heights common to one prism;
   Σh_2 = sum of those heights common to two prisms;
   Σh_3 = sum of those common to three prisms;
   Σh_4 = sum of those common to four prisms.

16-13. Volumes from Topographic Maps. In modern highway-location practice, accurate topographic maps with a large scale and a small contour interval are prepared by photogrammetric methods supplemented by field completion surveys. These maps are known as design maps. The positions of all horizontal-control monuments are accurately plotted by means of their rectangular coordinates with respect to a grid which shows on the map.

The design map is used to study various possible positions for the location of the highway, to aid in establishing the various geometrical properties of the roadbed, to establish limits of the right of way, and to determine the quantities of earthwork for the various possible locations. These quantities are used for comparison of the different lines, for estimates in bidding, and in some instances for determining the actual pay quantities which the contractor is held to.

The design map covers a strip of terrain which usually varies from about 600 ft to 2000 ft in width. When it has been compiled and verified in the field, the design engineer can then project trial lines onto the map with different grade lines. A study of the earthwork involved, together with other controlling factors, will establish a final line on the design map. The coordinates of the points of intersection are scaled from the grid lines, as described in Sec. 8-38, and tie lines from the control monuments are computed. Thus, the final line may be located and staked out in the field by running these tie lines as outlined in Sec. 8-25.

The earthwork quantities for a given trial line are determined from the design map by the method which will now be described. The trial line is laid out on the map, and the curves joining the tangents at their intersections are drawn in. The line is marked from beginning to end at every 50 or 100 ft, the interval depending on the regularity of the terrain and the accuracy desired. These marks are stations and plusses.

A crossline is plotted normal to the trial line at each station and plus, and the elevations of, and distances right or left from the center line to, points representing breaks in the terrain are determined by interpolation between the contour lines and by scaling on the map. These elevations and distances are recorded opposite each station number on a set of notes, with the elevations as the numerators and the distances out from the center line as the denominators. The notes representing these cross sections are called terrain notes. The cross sections are taken far enough out to allow for deep cuts and fills and to allow for line changes on successive trial lines. A cross section, with the terrain notes shown, is represented in Fig. 16-9. The actual terrain cross sections, however, are not plotted.

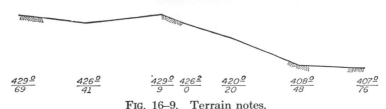

$$\frac{429^{\underline{0}}}{69} \qquad \frac{426^{\underline{0}}}{41} \qquad \frac{429^{\underline{0}}}{9} \ \frac{426^{\underline{2}}}{0} \quad \frac{420^{\underline{0}}}{20} \qquad \frac{408^{\underline{0}}}{48} \qquad \frac{407^{\underline{0}}}{76}$$

FIG. 16–9. Terrain notes.

A grade line that is established by the design engineer is super-imposed on a profile of the line plotted from elevations obtained from the design map. The lengths of the vertical curves are established, and the elevations of the stations on the vertical curves are computed. The grade elevation at each center-line station and plus is thus obtained.

Roadbed notes are prepared for each station and plus, taking into account the roadbed width, ditches in cuts, side slopes, roadbed crown, and superelevation on curves. The roadbed notes for a section coinciding with the section of Fig. 16-9 are given in Fig. 16-10, the roadbed itself being shown graphically. The actual roadbed cross sections, however, are not plotted. Point a is at the center line. Points b and c are known as hinge points, because the roadbed cross section breaks at these points when the section is in cut. Points e and f are at the edges of the shoulder in cut or in fill.

The configuration of the roadbed will remain constant as long as the highway is on a tangent. Since the notes will be used in subsequent computations, the values of the elevations at points b, e, f, and c can be tabulated as vertical distances from the center-line elevation, as shown in the lower notes of Fig. 16-10. Thus, as long as the configuration of the roadbed does not change, the numerators of the lower set of fractions will not change, except for that representing the grade elevation at the center line. This elevation is shown as 412.56 in Fig. 16-10. In the process of computation, these offset distances will be converted to elevations. The roadbed notes will vary on curves because of superelevation, and will vary in different materials because of changes in the side slopes.

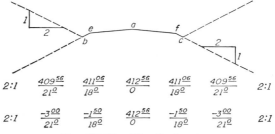

FIG. 16–10. Roadbed notes.

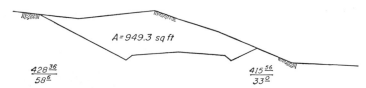

FIG. 16–11.   Terrain and roadbed notes combined.

The notes for the terrain cross section and the roadbed notes are key-punched for input into a high-speed electronic computer, and are brought together by a prepared computer program, the details of which are outside the scope of this book. The computer determines the distances to and the elevations of the catch points at each station, and the area of each cross section bounded by the roadbed, the side slopes, and the terrain. The distance to the catch point (on a final line) is used in the field to locate the position of each slope stake. A graphical portrayal of the solution of Fig. 16-9 and Fig. 16-10 in the computer is shown in Fig. 16-11. The distances to the left and right slope stakes are, respectively, 58.6 and 33.0 ft. The area of the cross section is computed as that of a closed traverse in the computer, and the result is 949.3 sq ft.

Using the average-end-area method, the computer determines the volumes between successive cross sections from the computed areas and the spacing of the cross sections in stations and plusses. These values are part of the data recorded by the computer and furnished to the design engineer.

When computations are to be made for a second trial line, the terrain notes need not be changed, provided that they were taken from the map at sufficient distances from the center line. The roadbed notes need not be changed if the grade line has not been changed. However, the amount of line shift at each station must be introduced into the computer. For example, if the section of Fig. 16-11 is shifted to the right by 20 ft, this is portrayed in graphical form in Fig. 16-12. The resulting distances to the left and right slope stakes determined by the computer are, respectively, 55.6 and 23.0 ft. The area of the cross section is 667.6 sq ft.

If a grade change is to be made, the elevation of the roadbed

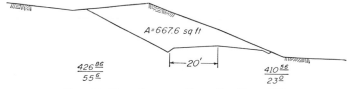

FIG. 16–12.   Cross section after line shift.

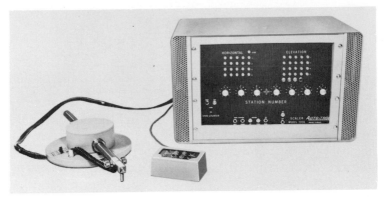

FIG. 16-13.   Automatic-recording scaler. (Courtesy
of Autotrol Corp.)

center line at each section must be changed correspondingly before
the data are introduced into the computer.

A device used to automatically scale distances and record elevations along terrain cross sections is shown in Fig. 16-13. The round
base plate is oriented on the topographic map in such fashion that
the cylindrical movable arm is caused to move along a line perpendicular to the center line of a trial line. With the pointing device,
located at the end of the arm, set at the center line, the elevation
counter is set to read the ground elevation at the center line, as
interpolated between the contour lines on the map. The vertical
counter is then set for the contour interval. As the arm is moved, say,
to the left of the center line, the pointer is set on the first contour
line encountered, and the operator depresses the register button. This
operation records or card-punches the distance to the left of the
center line and the contour elevation of the point. When the movement of the arm is continued to the next contour line, the vertical
counter automatically adds or subtracts the contour interval while
the movement of the arm measures the distance, and the values are
again registered. When the terrain cross section to the left has been
completed, the pointer is again indexed on the center line. The
measurements are then taken from the center line to the right. Information pertinent to the terrain cross section, such as the station
number, is set into the control console shown in Fig. 16-13 to be
registered automatically with the cross-section data.

The operator must depress a plus-minus button when going
across ascending or descending contour lines in order that the elevation counter will register the correct value of the contour line. If the
elevation of a point between contour lines is to be recorded, the

operator interpolates between the contour lines to obtain the value of the intermediate elevation. By depressing a button on the small control unit seen in Fig. 16-13, the small increments of elevation are added to or subtracted from the elevation counter until the intermediate elevation is registered on the console display. This value can be obtained by the operator, without having to observe the console display, simply by counting audible signals emitted by the counter. The register is then depressed to record or punch this intermediate elevation, together with the corresponding distance from the center line.

The automatic scaling device is accurate to about 0.001 in. over the travel of the arm. It is certainly far more accurate than are the locations of the map features and the contour lines. The scaler eliminates mistakes and scaling errors. The scaling is much easier and far more efficient than that done by means of an ordinary engineer's scale. By automatically punching out the data necessary for machine computation, the scaler eliminates not only the data-recording time but also the card-punching operation, which is always subject to mistakes.

The foregoing method of determining earthwork quantities in highway location entirely eliminates the field surveys for determining preliminary and final cross sections. Furthermore, the planning can be conducted well in advance of all but the initial control survey, and time is provided for purchasing the necessary right of way without too much danger of unscrupulous land speculation. The success of the entire method, of course, depends on the accuracy and reliability of the design map.

16-14. Earthwork Data from Photogrammetric Model. The compilation of a design map by photogrammetric methods requires that a pair of overlapping aerial photographs be oriented in a stereoscopic plotting instrument and then that the resulting spatial model be oriented to control which has been plotted on the map sheet. When these conditions are satisfied, the operator of the stereoplotter then proceeds to compile the planimetric and topographic features, using the measuring mark of the tracing table to guide him. This process is discussed in Sec. 15-11. The resulting topographic map is a graphical representation of the more complete and more detailed spatial model from which it was derived. In order to increase the accuracy of earthwork quantities, it would be logical to measure the spatial model directly, thus eliminating the inaccuracy and the incompleteness of the map.

FIG. 16-14.   Automatic scaler used to measure cross sections
directly in stereoscopic model. (Courtesy of Autotrol Corp.)

In Fig. 16-14 is shown the scaling device discussed in Sec. 16-13
in which the pointer has been replaced by the pencil holder of the
tracing table of a Kelsh plotter. The topographic map which was
compiled from the aerial photography has been used to study possible
trial center-line locations for a highway facility. After a trial center
line has been drawn on the map, the map in turn is re-oriented under
the stereoscopic model (see Fig. 15-25).

The base of the scaler is now oriented so that the tracing table
is constrained to move perpendicular to the center line drawn on the
map. This condition is readily apparent from a study of Fig. 16-14.
The stereoplotter operator then sets the tracing-table pencil on the
center line at a desired station, sets the measuring mark on the surface of the stereo model, and indexes the elevation and distance
counters. The elevation counter is actuated by the vertical movement
of the tracing table, being sensed by an encoder, and it displays the
elevation of the tracing table at all times.

After registering the center line elevation, the operator then
moves the tracing table, say, to the left of the center line until a

significant break in the terrain appears in the stereoscopic model. After setting the measuring mark in apparent contact with the surface of the model at this point, he then depresses the register button, causing the elevation of the point and its distance from the center line to be automatically recorded or punched out. A repetition of this procedure thus provides terrain cross-section notes which can be used to compute earthwork quantities along this trial line.

16-15. Earthwork Quantities by Grading Contours. A grading contour is a line of constant elevation which is plotted on a topographic map to represent a true contour line after the proposed grading has been performed. Because grading operations produce smooth surfaces with regular slopes, grading contours are either a series of straight, equally spaced lines or a series of curved lines that are equally spaced. Simple landscape grading is shown in Fig. 16-15. The original contour lines are shown as solid lines with a contour interval of 1 ft. The grading contours are drawn on the map as straight dashed lines. The irregular dashed lines have been drawn through the grade points to show the areas of cut and fill. The area marked I is enclosed by the original 879-ft contour line and the 879-ft grading contour. It is a horizontal surface at elevation 879 ft. Similarly the area marked

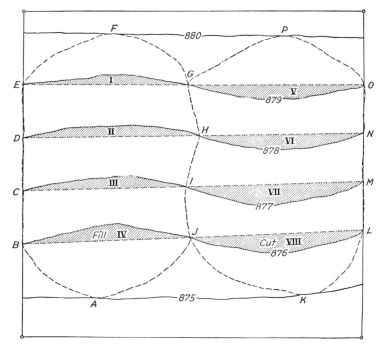

Fig. 16–15. Landscape grading.

II is a horizontal surface at elevation 878 ft. The volume of fill necessary between these two surfaces is obtained by planimetering each area, determining the average of the two areas and multiplying the average by the vertical separation or the contour interval which, in this instance, is 1 ft. Similarly, the volume between areas II and III and the volume between areas III and IV are obtained. The solid defined by the embankment between point F and area I is pyramidal in shape, as is also the solid defined by the embankment between point A and area IV. Each of these two volumes should be taken as ⅓ bh, where b is the shaded area representing the base of the solid and h is the contour interval, or 1 ft. The volume of excavation between K and P may be determined in the same manner.

In Fig. 16-16, the location of a highway roadbed is plotted to scale on a design map on which the contour interval is 5 ft. The line is stationed by scaling 100-ft distances. The grade elevation at station 55 + 00 is to be 465.00 ft and that at station 58 + 33 is to be 462.00 ft. The side slopes are 2:1 in cut and are 3:1 in fill. The grade line along the center line intersects the ground surface at stations 53 + 62 and 58 + 64. These grade points are located by finding where the grade elevations coincide with the ground elevations determined by interpolation between contour lines.

The road is in cut between stations 53 + 62 and 58 + 64. Since the side slopes in cut are 2:1, a distance 10 ft out from either edge at station 55 + 00 will be at elevation 470 ft after the slopes have been formed. Similarly, a point 16 ft out from an edge at station 58 + 33 will also be at elevation 470 after the slopes have been formed.

A straight line shown dashed in the figure on either side of the road, as a line joining two points at elevation 470, is a grading-contour line. The 470-ft grading contours intersect the 470-ft contour lines on the ground at points a and b. Grading contours at elevation 475 will lie 10 ft farther out; those at 480, another 10 ft farther out, and so on. In Fig. 16-16, these points are plotted along lines normal to the center line at stations 55 + 00 and 58 + 33, and the elevations of the grading contours are shown at these stations. The top of the cut runs out at elevation 513 ft on one side of the road and at 497 ft on the other side.

A line joining the intersections of the grading contours with the corresponding ground contours represents the edge of the cut or the intersection of the ground by the side slopes. Any point on this line represents a slope-stake position. For example, the slope stakes at station 57 + 00 would be located at points c and d.

In Fig. 16-17 (a) is shown the prismoid lying between the 475-ft and 480-ft contour lines in Fig. 16-16. To determine its volume, the area A_{475}, enclosed by the 475-ft ground contour and the 475-ft grad-

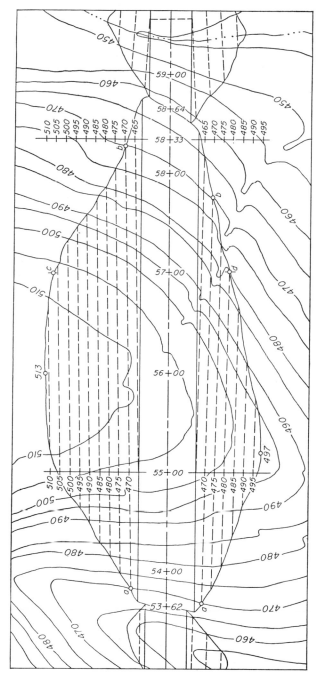

Fig. 16-16. Design map showing grading contours for roadbed in cut.

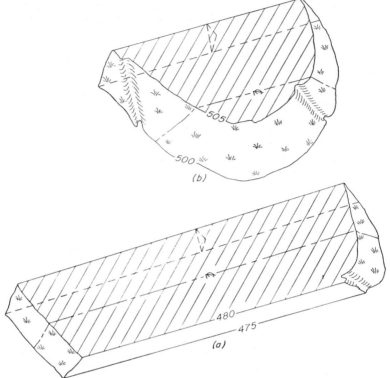

FIG. 16–17.   Volumes between successive contour surfaces.

ing contour on the map, is measured by using a planimeter. The area
A_{480}, enclosed by the 480-ft contour lines is also measured. The volume found by the average-end-area method is

$$V_{475-480} = 5 \times \frac{A_{475} + A_{480}}{2}$$

where the volume is in cubic feet and the areas are in square feet, since
the vertical distance between the two areas is in feet.

In Fig. 16-17 (b) is shown the prismoid between the 500-ft and
505-ft contour lines in Fig. 16-16, and its volume is determined in the
same manner.

The volume in Fig. 16-16 lying between the 510-ft contour and
the point at elevation 513 ft is computed by treating the earthwork as
a pyramid. This volume is

$$V_{510-513} = \tfrac{1}{3} \times 3 \times A_{510}$$

Similarly the volume lying between the 495-ft contour and the point
at elevation 497 ft is

$$V_{495-497} = \tfrac{1}{3} \times 2 \times A_{495}$$

The method of procedure to be used in determining earthwork volumes from a topographic map by means of grading contours is summarized as follows:

1. Plot the proposed facility, such as a building, highway, or dam, to scale in the desired position. This can be done by referencing the facility to the horizontal control shown on the map, or by using coordinates. (A design map must always show coordinate grid lines or grid ticks.)

2. Establish all grade points from the grade elevations shown on the plans of the facility by interpolating between existing contour lines. Locating these points allows a visualization of areas of cut and fill.

3. From known grade elevations at certain points and the side-slope ratios given on the plans, plot the positions of points which will lie on the grading contours.

4. Draw the grading contours in their proper positions, and terminate them where they join the existing ground contour lines.

5. Measure the areas enclosed by successive contours, and record the areas in a tabular form.

6. Compute the volumes lying between the successive contour surfaces by using the average-end-area method. Apply the pyramidal formula where the cut or fill runs out. In some instances, the prismoidal formula may be applied. In these instances, the vertical separation between surfaces will be twice the contour interval, since the area enclosed by the middle one of three consecutive contour lines will be the area M of the middle section.

The method of determining earthwork quantities by the grading-contour technique presupposes a reliable topographic map of reasonably large scale. The accuracy obtainable is equivalent to that obtained by field cross-sectioning methods and the work is performed more rapidly. The method is advantageously applied where the facility involves complicated warped grading surfaces, the dimensions of which are difficult to compute. Such would be the case in computing earthwork volumes at proposed highway interchanges.

16-16. Reservoir Volumes from Contour Maps. Two general methods are used in determining reservoir volumes from contour maps. One method is to planimeter the area enclosed by each contour. The volume is then computed by the average-end-area method, A_0

and A_1 being the planimetered areas of two adjacent contours, and L the contour interval. The prismoidal formula can also be used where there is an odd number of contours, alternate contours being considered as middle sections and L as twice the contour interval.

A second method, which can be used when the reservoir is regular in shape, is to scale the dimensions of vertical cross sections from the contour map. The volume is then calculated from the cross-sectional areas, as in the case of a route survey.

16-17. Mass Diagram. Many of the problems connected with the handling of earthwork on highway and railroad construction can be solved by means of a mass diagram. The earthwork mass-diagram is similar to those used in stream discharge studies. It is usually plotted directly below the profile of the route, the ordinate at any station representing the algebraic sum of the volumes of cut and fill up to that station. From the diagram the most economical distribution of materials can be determined.

There are two common types of grading contracts. In one, the contractor bids a lump sum for the work, handling the materials as he sees fit. The mass diagram is of great value to him in determining the most economical manner of doing the work. In the other form of contract, payment is on the basis of the number of cubic yards of material handled. In this contract the successful bidder is paid a specified price per cubic yard for excavation. Embankment is taken care of by a clause stating that the excavation shall be deposited as directed by the engineer, who naturally directs that the excavated material be placed in embankments.

Since it would be unfair to expect the contractor to haul the materials taken from the excavations unlimited distances in forming the embankments, the contract will state the distance—500, 1000, or 1500 ft—that the excavation must be hauled without increased compensation. As soon as the contract limit has been exceeded, an additional sum per cubic yard is paid for each 100 ft of excess distance. The specified distance is the *limit of free haul*, and any excess is *overhaul*. The volumes and lengths involved in the calculation of overhaul payments can be taken from the mass diagram.

16-18. Shrinkage. Material taken from an excavation may occupy a greater or less volume when deposited in an embankment. As the material is first excavated and placed in a truck or other conveyance, it usually will occupy a greater volume than in its original position. Solid rock that must be broken up for handling may occupy about twice as much space as it did before being excavated. When earth is placed in an embankment, it will be compacted and may occupy less space, especially if it has been removed from the surface of a cultivated field and deposited at the bottom of a 15- or 20-ft embankment. The weight of a high fill may cause the original ground surface to settle or subside. When the fill is across marshy ground, this subsidence may be considerable. As the material is transported from excavation to embankment, some of it is generally lost in transit. Hence, for embankments composed of anything but rock, a volume somewhat greater than the calculated volume of the embankment will be required to make the actual embankment. An allowance is usually made for this shrinkage. The amount allowed may vary from 5 to 15 per cent, the actual allowance depending on the character of the material handled and the condition of the ground on which the embankment is placed.

16-19. Computation of Mass Diagram. In studies which are made to decide upon the best line location and grade line, earthwork quantities are determined from preliminary cross sections taken in the field or from topographic maps. If the mass diagram is to be used in computing overhaul payments, the volumes used are usually taken from the final cross sections unless the contract specifies the use of large-scale maps for this purpose. In the latter event, the quantities computed for the final line discussed in Sec. 16-13 are used to compute the mass diagram.

Points beyond which it is not feasible to haul material define the limits of a mass diagram. A limit point may be the beginning of a project, the end of a project, a bank of a river, or an edge of a deep ravine.

The ordinates to the mass diagram are computed by adding the volumes between successive stations to the previous volumes, thus obtaining the accumulated volume up to any station. The volumes, and thus the ordinates, are in cubic yards. The abscissas are in stations. Excavation volumes are considered plus, and embankment volumes are minus. Before embankment volumes are used to compute ordinates, they must be increased to allow for shrinkage. This allowance is usually expressed as a per cent shrinkage or as a shrinkage factor. In the tabulation on page 550, the shrinkage factor is 10 per cent.

The initial ordinate in the tabulation is arbitrarily set at 10,000 cu yd, so that all ordinates are positive. Between stations 7 and 9, stations 19 and 22, stations 33 and 35, stations 41 and 45, and stations 50 and 52, both excavation and embankment occur. These are portions of the route similar to that shown in Fig. 16-8. Since excavation will be carried from one side of the roadway to the other during grad-

Calculation of Ordinates to Mass Diagram

Sta.	Cut Vol. (cu yd)	Fill Vol. + 10 per cent	Mass Diag.	Sta.	Cut Vol. (cu yd)	Fill Vol. + 10 per cent	Mass Diag.
0			10,000.0	28			6,040.4
		183.5				1,611.2	
1			9,816.5	29			4,429.2
		622.2				1,338.2	
2			9,194.3	30			3,091.0
		1,034.7				1,002.9	
3			8,159.6	31			2,088.1
		1,268.2				652.7	
4			6,891.4	32			1,435.4
		1,231.5				357.2	
5			5,659.9	33			1,078.2
		919.1			39.2	150.0	
6			4,740.8	34			967.4
		502.8			235.8	51.8	
7			4,238.0	35			1,151.4
	20.6	163.6			465.2		
8			4,095.0	36			1,616.6
	190.2	12.0			711.5		
9			4,273.2	37			2,328.1
	615.7				904.4		
10			4,888.9	38			3,232.5
	941.5				904.4		
11			5,830.4	39			4,136.9
	1,150.0				757.0		
12			6,980.4	40			4,893.9
	1,500.0				516.5		
13			8,480.4	41			5,410.4
	1,772.7				280.2	90.4	
14			10,253.1	42			5,600.2
	1,754.6				126.7	316.1	
15			12,007.7	43			5,410.8
	1,540.4				98.4	640.0	
16			13,548.1	44			4,869.2
	1,262.3				20.0	770.6	
17			14,810.4	45			4,118.6
	931.8					789.0	
18			15,742.2	46			3,329.6
	546.5					728.0	
19			16,288.7	47			2,601.6
	203.1	30.6				577.2	
20			16,461.2	48			2,024.4
	101.0	278.5				355.7	
21			16,283.7	49			1,668.7
	18.0	586.2				115.9	
22			15,715.5	50			1,552.8
		1,005.3			407.0	100.0	
23			14,710.2	51			1,859.8
		1,377.4			735.5	26.6	
24			13,332.8	52			2,568.7
		1,676.0			983.3		
25			11,656.8	53			3,552.0
		1,860.3			1,285.9		
26			9,796.5	54			4,837.9
		1,917.1			1,522.4		
27			7,879.4	55			6,360.3
		1,839.0					

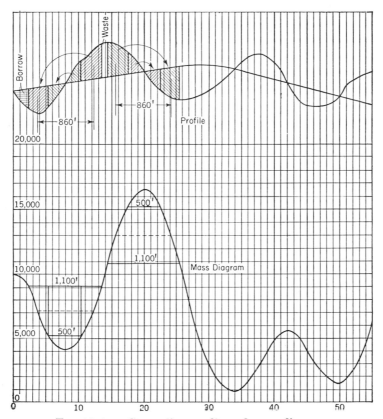

Fig. 16–18.   Center-line profile and mass diagram.

ing, only the net amount of cut or fill is used to compute the mass-diagram ordinate. In Fig. 16-18 the mass diagram is shown plotted below the center-line profile.

An inspection of the mass diagram will show that a rising curve indicates excavation; a descending curve, embankment. Maximum and minimum points on the mass diagram occur at grade points on the profile. If a horizontal line is drawn to intersect the diagram at two points, excavation and embankment (adjusted for shrinkage) will be equal between the two stations represented by the points of intersection. Such a horizontal line is called a balance line because the excavation balances the embankment between the two points at its ends.

Since the ordinates to the diagram represent the algebraic sums of the volumes of excavation and embankment referred to the initial ordinate, the total volumes of excavation and embankment will be equal where the final ordinate equals the initial ordinate. If the final ordinate is greater than the initial ordinate, there is an excess of excavation; if it is less than the initial ordinate, the volume of embankment is the greater and additional material must be obtained to complete the embankments.

In deciding upon the grade line to be adopted, reasonable rates of grade should not be exceeded and an attempt should be made to balance the volumes of cut and fill over moderately short stretches of the line. If this is not done, some of the material may have to be hauled excessively long distances. Where it is impossible to avoid long hauls, it is often cheaper to waste material in one place and obtain the volumes necessary to complete the embankments from borrow pits located along the right of way.

16-20. Calculation of Overhaul. When the contract prices are known, the economical limit of haul can be determined. This limit is reached when the cost of haul equals the cost of excavation. For longer distances it will be cheaper to waste in one place and borrow in another. As an example, the economical limit of haul will be 1100 ft if the cost of excavation and hauling 500 ft or less is 24 cents per cubic yard, and if the cost of hauling each additional 100 ft is 4 cents. At this distance, the cost for 1 cu yd will be 24 cents for excavation and hauling 500 ft, plus $6 \times 4 = 24$ cents for overhaul. For longer distances, the cost of excavating and hauling will be greater than 48 cents, or the cost of excavating twice, and it will be cheaper to borrow and waste. For distances under 1100 ft, the cost of excavating and hauling will be less than 48 cents, and hauling will be the cheaper method. These figures are on the assumption that fill material is available within the limits of the right of way. If additional land for borrow pits must be purchased, the economical limit of haul would be greater.

To determine the cost of the grading shown in Fig. 16-18, two horizontal lines are drawn. The length of one is 500 ft, the limit of free haul, and the length of the other is 1100 ft, the assumed economical limit of haul. Although excavation and embankment balance between station $0 + 00$ and station $14 + 00$, it would not be economical to haul material that distance. It will be cheaper to borrow 900 cu yd needed to make the fill from station $0 + 00$ to station $2 + 30$. The cost of this fill will be $900 \times \$0.24 = \$216.00$.

The 500-ft line intersects the mass diagram at station $5 + 40$ and at station $10 + 40$. When the excavation between the grade point at station $8 + 00$ and station $10 + 40$ is moved backward along the line, it will complete the fill from station $5 + 40$ to station $8 + 00$. The volume, as scaled from the diagram, is 1200 cu yd. Since no part of it is hauled more than 500 ft, the cost of this grading will be $1200 \times \$0.24 = \$288.00$.

A horizontal line 1100 ft long extends from station 2 + 30 to station 13 + 30. The volume from station 10 + 40 to station 13 + 30 is 3800 cu yd. This is the volume needed to complete the fill between station 2 + 30 and station 5 + 40. All of this material is hauled more than 500 ft. The positions of the centers of gravity of the masses of excavation and embankment can be found by drawing a horizontal line midway—vertically—between the 1100-ft and 500-ft horizontal lines. This line intersects the mass diagram at station 3 + 70, the center of gravity of the embankment, and at station 12 + 30, the center of gravity of the excavation. The average haul is the difference between these two stations, or 860 ft. Since the charge for overhaul is only for the distance in excess of 500 ft, the average overhaul distance is 860 − 500 = 360 ft. The cost of excavating and moving the material between station 10 + 40 and station 13 + 30 will be:

Excavation and 500-ft haul .... 3800 × $0.24 = $ 912.00
Overhaul—3.6 stations .... 3800 × 3.6 × 0.04 = 547.20
Total cost ...... = $1459.20

16-21. Economical Handling of Material. When there are frequent grade points on the profile, some study may be necessary to decide whether a given excavation should be moved forward or back along the line, or perhaps wasted. The mass diagram facilitates the choice of the plan requiring the least amount of work. Since the areas between horizontal lines and the mass diagram are the graphical products of volumes and distances, they are indicative of the amount of work involved in the grading. The smaller the areas, the less will be the work, and the cheaper the cost. Where the work may be done in two or more ways, the most economical way will be the one for which the areas between the mass diagram and the horizontal lines are a minimum.

These facts will be apparent from an investigation of the profile and mass diagram shown in Fig. 16-19. Although excavation and embankment balance between station 40 + 00 and station 70 + 00, there must be some waste and borrow if the economical limit of haul is not to be exceeded. If the horizontal line ab is lowered, some material would be hauled more than 2500 ft. Consequently, the line cannot be below ab. With the line in this position, there will be a volume of waste represented by the ordinate Aa. However, the total amount of waste will not be increased if the line ab is raised, since there is to be additional waste beyond b and any increase to the left of a will be compensated for by an equal decrease beyond b. The most economical position for the line will be efg, where ef = fg. With the line in this

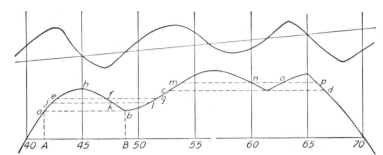

Fɪɢ. 16–19.   Economical handling of materials.

position, there is no increase in the total amount of waste, but the labor involved is a minimum. The area $ehf + fgb$ is a measure of the work required to make the corresponding excavations and embankments. Should the line be lowered to the position jkl, the corresponding area is $jhk + klb$. This area is greater than the former since the approximate trapezoid which has been added, or $efkj$, is greater than the one taken away, or $fglk$.

Similarly, if the line efg is raised, the area taken away from ehf will be less than the area added to fgb, and the resulting area will be greater. Consequently, the labor involved will be a minimum when $ef = fg$.

Beyond station 50 + 00, the horizontal line cannot be below cd without exceeding the economical limit of haul. For this line the most economical position is $mnop$, where $mn + op - no$ equals the economical limit of haul. By projecting these points onto the profile, it will be evident which parts of the excavations are to be moved forward and which backward in making the embankments.

PROBLEMS

16-1. Plot the following preliminary cross-section notes to a scale of 1 in. = 10 ft.

653.9	657.0	657.7	652.5	654.2	660.6	660.5	658.4
39.6	30.2	22.0	6.3	0	17.8	23.3	31.0

Assume a 32-ft roadbed at a grade elevation of 644.00 ft and side slopes of $1\frac{1}{2}$: 1. The roadbed center line coincides with the preliminary center line at this station. Plot the roadbed cross section, and scale the distances from the center line to the catch points and their elevations. Compute the cross-sectional area by the method of coordinates.

16-2. Change the grade elevation in Problem 16-1 to 649.00 ft and shift the roadbed 10 ft to the left. Then recompute the cross-sectional area.

Station	Ground Elevation	Grade Elevation	Cross Section		
			L	C	R
48 + 00	561.2	567.32	F 9.3 / 24.0	F 6.1 / 0	F 4.8 / 17.2
47 + 00	565.9	568.32	F 4.8 / 17.2	F 2.4 / 0	F 2.0 / 13.0
46 + 68	567.7	568.64	F 2.9 / 14.5	F 0.9 / 0	F 0.0 / 10.0
46 + 00	569.3	569.32	F 1.8 / 12.7	C 0.0 / 0	C 2.7 / 14.7
45 + 82	571.5	569.50	C 0.0 / 12.0	C 2.0 / 0	C 4.1 / 16.1
45 + 00	573.8	570.32	C 2.2 / 14.2	C 3.5 / 0	C 6.2 / 18.2
44 + 50	576.0	570.82	C 4.0 / 16.0	C 5.2 / 0	C 8.0 / 20.0
44 + 00	576.6	571.32	C 3.5 / 15.5	C 5.3 / 0	C 7.8 / 19.8
43 + 40	579.7	571.92	C 5.6 / 17.6	C 7.8 / 0	C 9.0 / 21.0
43 + 00	580.4	572.32	C 5.8 / 17.8	C 8.1 / 0	C 11.6 / 23.6

16-3. From the accompanying final cross-section notes, compute the total volume of cut and the total volume of fill between station 43 + 00 and station 48 + 00 by the average-end-area method. The roadbed width is 24 ft in cut and 20 ft in fill; and the side slopes are 1 : 1 in cut and 1½ : 1 in fill.

16-4. Compute the volume in cubic yards between stations 47 and 48 in Problem 16-3 by the prismoidal formula.

16-5. Compute the prismoidal correction in cubic yards to be applied to the average-end-area volume between stations 47 and 48 in Problem 16-3.

16-6. Assuming the unit prices used in Sec. 16-20, compute the cost of grading in Fig. 16-18.

16-7. Using the prismoidal formula, derive the expressions for the volume of a cone and the volume of a sphere.

16-8. In Fig. 14-7, the area bounded by points *C-1, C-6, F-6, F-4, H-4,* and *H-1* is to be brought to a level grade of 693.00 ft. The sides of the squares are 50 ft. Assuming vertical faces for all sides of the excavation, compute the volume to be removed in cubic yards by Eq. 16-13.

17

United States Public Land Surveys

17-1. Historical. The United States rectangular surveying system was devised with the object of marking on the ground and fixing for all time legal subdivisions for the purposes of description and disposal of the public domain under the general land laws of the United States. This system has been used in 30 states including Alaska. It has not been used in the older states along the Atlantic seaboard and in a few others where the lands were in private hands before the federal government came into being.

The rectangular system of survey of the public lands was inaugurated by a committee appointed by the Continental Congress. In 1784 this committee reported "An ordinance for ascertaining the mode of locating and disposing of lands in the western territory, and for other purposes therein mentioned." The ordinance, as finally passed on May 20, 1785, provided for townships 6 miles square, containing 36 sections 1 mile square. The first public surveys were made under the direction of the Geographer of the United States. The area surveyed now forms a part of the state of Ohio. In these initial surveys only the exterior lines of the townships were surveyed, but the plats were marked by subdivisions into sections 1 mile square, and mile corners were established on the township lines. The sections were numbered from 1 to 36, commencing with number one in the southeast corner of the township and closing with number thirty-six on the northwest corner thereof. By this method number six was in the northeast corner, and number seven was west of, and adjacent to, number one.

The act of congress approved May 18, 1796, provided for the appointment of a surveyor general and directed the survey of the lands northwest of the Ohio River and above the mouth of the Kentucky River. Under this law it was provided that "the sections shall be numbered, respectively, beginning with number one in the northeast section and proceeding west and east alternately through the township, with progressive numbers, till the thirty-sixth be completed." This method of numbering sections, shown in Fig. 17-1, is still in use.

Since that time the laws relating to the survey of the public lands have been amended several times. Until quite recently, it was the practice of the government to award contracts for the survey of certain portions of the public lands. These awards were frequently made, in payment of political obligations, to persons wholly unfit to be entrusted with such work. As a result, much of the work has been carelessly done. Fraudulent returns have been made to the advantage of speculators in timber and mineral lands. In more than one instance the government has been furnished with the field notes of a survey executed in the comparative comfort of a tent rather than upon the ground. In 1910, after most of the damage had been done, Congress abolished this contract system and authorized the interior department to employ a permanent body of surveyors, known as United States surveyors.

6	5	4	3	2	1
7	8	9	10	11	12
18	17	16	15	14	13
19	20	21	22	23	24
30	29	28	27	26	25
31	32	33	34	35	36

FIG. 17-1.   Method of numbering sections.

The interest of the present-day engineer or surveyor in the rectangular system is in the retracement of old lines and in the subdivision of the section into smaller units. For this reason, it is imperative that he be familiar with the methods used in the original survey.

17-2. Manual of Surveying Instructions. Various regions of the United States have been surveyed under different sets of instructions issued at periods ranging from 1785 to the present time. The earliest instructions were issued to surveyors in manuscript or in printed circulars. Regulations more in detail, improving the system for greater accuracy, permanency, and uniformity, were issued in book form in editions of 1855, 1881, 1890, 1894, 1902, 1919, 1930, and 1947. The methods outlined in the following articles are taken from the latest edition of the *Manual of Instructions for the Survey of the Public Lands of the United States*, prepared and published under the direction of the Director of the Bureau of Land Management, and printed by the Government Printing Office.

While the methods have, in general, been the same on all surveys, there have been important variations in detail. The local engineer or surveyor, before beginning the retracement of old land lines, should familiarize himself with the exact methods in use at the time the original survey was made.

17-3. General Procedure. The first step in the survey of an area is to divide it into tracts approximately 24 miles square by means of meridians and parallels of latitude. These 24-mile tracts are then divided into 16 townships, which are approximately 6 miles on a side. The last step, so far as the federal government is concerned, is to divide the township into 36 sections, each approximately 1 mile square. The subdivision of the sections into smaller units is the task of the local engineer and surveyor.

17-4. Initial Point. The place of beginning of the survey of any given region is called the initial point. Through this point is run a meridian, called the *principal meridian*, and a parallel of latitude, called the *base line*. The initial point is selected with a view to its control of extensive agricultural areas within reasonable geographical limitations. Upon the establishment of an initial point, the position of the point in latitude and longitude is determined by accurate field astronomical methods.

Since surveys in widely separated sections of the country have been in progress simultaneously, a large number of initial points have been established. The positions of these points and the areas governed by them are given in Table 17-1. Since many of the points were established before present-day facilities for accurate field astronomical determinations were available, some of the values shown are only approximately correct. Present instructions call for the establishment of the initial point in such a manner as to make it as nearly permanent as possible.

17-5. Principal Meridian. The principal meridian is a true meridian that is astronomically determined and is extended from the initial point, either north or south, or in both directions, as the conditions may require, to the limits of the area being subdivided. Monuments are placed on this line at intervals of 40 chains (½ mile), and at its intersection with navigable bodies of water, streams 3 chains or more in width, and lakes of an area of 25 acres or more.

Two independent sets of measurements of this line are made. Should the difference between the two sets exceed 20 links (13.2 ft) per 80 chains, it is required that the line be remeasured to reduce the difference. If tests for alignment show the line to have deviated more than 3 minutes from the true cardinal course, the alignment must be corrected.

TABLE 17-1

Meridians and Base Lines of the United States Rectangular Surveys

Meridian	Governing Surveys (Wholly or in Part) in the States of—	Longitude of Principal Meridian West from Greenwich			Latitude of Base Line North from Equator		
		°	′	″	°	′	″
Black Hills	South Dakota	104	03	16	43	59	44
Boise	Idaho	116	23	35	43	22	21
Chicasaw	Mississippi	89	14	47	35	01	58
Choctaw	Mississippi	90	14	41	31	52	32
Cimarron	Oklahoma	103	00	07	36	30	05
Copper River	Alaska	145	18	13	61	49	21
Fairbanks	Alaska	147	38	26	64	51	50
Fifth Principal	Arkansas, Iowa, Minnesota, Missouri, North Dakota, and South Dakota	91	03	07	34	38	45
First Principal	Ohio and Indiana	84	48	11	40	59	22
Fourth Principal	Illinois	90	27	11	40	00	50
Fourth Principal	Minnesota and Wisconsin	90	25	37	42	30	27
Gila and Salt River	Arizona	112	18	19	33	22	38
Humboldt	California	124	07	10	40	25	02
Huntsville	Alabama and Mississippi	86	34	16	34	59	27
Indian	Oklahoma	97	14	49	34	29	32
Louisiana	Louisiana	92	24	55	31	00	31
Michigan	Michigan and Ohio	84	21	53	42	25	28
Mount Diablo	California and Nevada	121	54	47	37	52	54
Navajo	Arizona	108	31	59	35	44	56
New Mexico Principal	Colorado and New Mexico	106	53	12	34	15	35
Principal	Montana	111	39	33	45	47	13
Salt Lake	Utah	111	53	27	40	46	11
San Bernardino	California	116	55	17	34	07	20
Second Principal	Illinois and Indiana	86	27	21	38	28	14
Seward	Alaska	149	21	24	60	07	36
Sixth Principal	Colorado, Kansas, Nebraska, South Dakota, and Wyoming	97	22	08	40	00	07
St. Helena	Lousiana	91	09	36	30	59	56
St. Stephens	Alabama and Mississippi	88	01	20	30	59	51
Tallahassee	Florida and Alabama	84	16	38	30	26	03
Third Principal	Illinois	89	08	54	38	28	27
Uintah	Utah	109	56	06	40	25	59
Ute	Colorado	108	31	59	39	06	23
Washington	Mississippi	91	09	36	30	59	56
Willamette	Oregon and Washington	122	44	34	45	31	11
Wind River	Wyoming	108	48	49	43	00	41

It should be borne in mind that the only equipment available for most of the early surveys was a compass and a chain. Therefore, discrepancies far in excess of these limits will be found in rerunning many old lines. In other cases the agreement will be surprisingly close, when one considers that much of the country was often heavily wooded at the time the surveys were made.

17-6. Base Line. From the initial point the base line is extended east and west on a true parallel of latitude to the limits of the area being surveyed. Monuments are placed on this line at intervals of 40

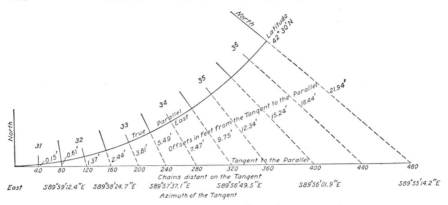

Fig. 17-2.   Base line by offsets from tangent.

chains and at its intersection with all meanderable bodies of water. The manner of making the measurement of the base line and the accuracy of both the alignment and the measurement must be the same as that required in the survey of the principal meridian.

Because of the convergence of meridians, a line making an angle of 90° with the principal meridian will, theoretically, be an east-and-west line for only an infinitesimal distance from the meridian. If extended, the resulting line is an arc of a great circle, and gradually departs southerly from the true parallel, which is a small circle. On this account, the base line, being a parallel of latitude, is run as a curve with chords 40 chains in length. Three methods are employed in running the base line, namely, the solar method, the tangent method, and the secant method.

The solar method is based on the fact that a line making a right angle with the meridian does not differ appreciably from the theoretical parallel of latitude in a distance of 40 chains. If a transit, equipped with a solar attachment (see Sec. 12-21) and in good adjustment, is employed, the true meridian may be determined by observation at the end of each half-mile interval. At each point an angle of 90° is turned from the new meridian, and this line is extended 40 chains to a point at which another meridian is determined. Thus, the direction of the line beyond each half-mile monument is determined by turning off a right angle from the meridian at that monument.

17-7. Base Line by Tangent Method. In the tangent method of locating a parallel of latitude, the direction of the tangent is determined by turning off a horizontal angle of 90° to the east or the west from the meridian. Points on the true parallel are established at half-mile intervals by offsets to the north from this tangent. The establishment of a base line in latitude 42° 30′ N is illustrated in Fig. 17-2.

TABLE 17-2
Offsets, in Feet, From Tangent to Parallel

Latitude	1 Mile	2 Miles	3 Miles	4 Miles	5 Miles	6 Miles
30°	0.38	1.54	3.46	6.15	9.61	13.83
31°	0.40	1.60	3.60	6.40	10.00	14.40
32°	0.42	1.66	3.74	6.65	10.40	14.97
33°	0.43	1.73	3.89	6.91	10.80	15.56
34°	0.45	1.80	4.04	7.18	11.22	16.16
35°	0.47	1.86	4.19	7.45	11.65	16.77
36°	0.48	1.93	4.35	7.73	12.09	17.40
37°	0.50	2.01	4.51	8.02	12.53	18.05
38°	0.52	2.08	4.68	8.32	12.99	18.71
39°	0.54	2.15	4.85	8.62	13.47	19.39
40°	0.56	2.23	5.02	8.93	13.95	20.09
41°	0.58	2.31	5.20	9.25	14.46	20.82
42°	0.60	2.40	5.39	9.58	14.97	21.56
43°	0.62	2.48	5.58	9.92	15.50	22.33
44°	0.64	2.57	5.78	10.28	16.06	23.12
45°	0.66	2.66	5.98	10.64	16.62	23.94
46°	0.69	2.75	6.20	11.02	17.21	24.79
47°	0.71	2.85	6.42	11.41	17.83	25.67
48°	0.74	2.95	6.65	11.81	18.46	26.58
49°	0.76	3.06	6.88	12.24	19.12	27.53
50°	0.79	3.17	7.13	12.68	19.81	28.52

TABLE 17-3
Azimuths of the Tangent to the Parallel

Latitude	1 Mile	2 Miles	3 Miles	4 Miles	5 Miles	6 Miles
	° ′ ″	° ′ ″	° ′ ″	° ′ ″	° ′ ″	° ′ ″
30°	89 59 30.0	89 59 00.0	89 58 29.9	89 57 59.9	89 57 29.9	89 56 59.9
31°	59 28.8	58 57.5	58 26.3	57 55.0	57 23.8	56 52.6
32°	59 27.5	58 55.0	58 22.5	57 50.0	57 17.5	56 45.1
33°	59 26.2	58 52.5	58 18.7	57 45.0	57 11.2	56 37.4
34°	59 24.9	58 49.9	58 14.8	57 39.7	57 04.6	56 29.6
35°	59 23.6	58 47.2	58 10.8	57 34.4	56 58.0	56 21.6
36°	59 22.2	58 44.5	58 06.7	57 28.9	56 51.1	56 13.4
37°	59 20.8	58 41.7	58 02.5	57 23.3	56 44.1	56 05.0
38°	59 19.4	58 38.8	57 58.2	57 17.6	56 36.9	55 56.3
39°	59 17.9	58 35.8	57 53.7	57 11.6	56 29.5	55 47.5
40°	59 16.4	58 32.8	57 49.2	57 05.6	56 21.9	55 38.3
41°	59 14.8	58 29.6	57 44.5	56 59.3	56 14.1	55 28.9
42°	59 13.2	58 26.4	57 39.6	56 52.8	56 06.0	55 19.3
43°	59 11.5	58 23.1	57 34.6	56 46.2	55 57.7	55 09.2
44°	59 09.8	58 19.6	57 29.5	56 39.3	55 49.1	54 58.9
45°	59 08.0	58 16.1	57 24.1	56 32.2	55 40.2	54 48.2
46°	59 06.2	58 12.4	57 18.6	56 24.7	55 31.0	54 37.2
47°	59 04.3	58 08.6	57 12.9	56 17.2	55 21.4	54 25.7
48°	59 02.3	58 04.6	57 06.9	56 09.2	55 11.5	54 13.9
49°	59 00.2	58 00.5	57 00.7	56 01.0	55 01.2	54 01.4
50°	58 58.1	57 56.2	56 54.3	55 52.4	54 50.5	53 48.6

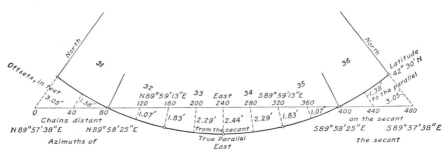

Fig. 17–3. Base line by offsets from secant.

The values of the offsets, which depend on the latitude and are proportional to the squares of the distances from the starting meridian, are shown in Table 17-2. Also the values of the azimuth of the tangent from the south point at the end of each mile are shown in Table 17-3.

As the field instructions require the location of all landmarks with respect to measurements along the true line and also require the blazing of trees along the true line, this method is not so convenient as the secant method, particularly when the country is so heavily wooded as to require the clearing of two lines, one for the tangent and another for the parallel.

17-8. Base Line by Secant Method. As shown in Fig. 17-3, the secant used in locating a parallel of latitude is the one passing through the 1- and 5-mile points on the parallel. The secant is located by offsetting to the south from the initial point and turning off a known angle from the meridian at the offset point. The secant is extended 6 miles, points on the parallel being located at half-mile intervals by offsets from the secant. The offsets at the ½- and 5½-mile points are to the north. The 1- and 5-mile points are on the secant, and the remaining points are south of the secant. The offsets and the values of the azimuth of the secant from the north at half-mile intervals up to 3 miles are shown in Table 17-4. For the other 3 miles the offsets are the same as for points at corresponding distances from the 3-mile point; and the azimuths are numerically equal to those at corresponding distances from the 3-mile point but are measured from the south.

The advantage of the secant method lies in the fact that the offsets are much smaller than those for the tangent method. By clearing a line of moderate width, both the secant and the parallel will be contained in the same clearing. Measurements to landmarks will be substantially the same along both the secant and the parallel.

TABLE 17-4

Azimuths of the Secant, and Offsets, in Feet, to the Parallel

Lati-tude	0 Miles	½ Mile	1 Mile	1½ Miles	2 Miles	2½ Miles	3 Miles
30°	89° 58′ 30″ 1.92 N	89° 58′ 45″ 0.86 N	89° 59′ 00″ 0.00	89° 59′ 15″ 0.68 S	89° 59′ 30″ 1.16 S	89° 59′ 45″ 1.44 S	90° (E or W) 1.54 S
31°	89° 58′ 26″ 2.00 N	89° 58′ 42″ 0.90 N	89° 58′ 58″ 0.00	89° 59′ 13″ 0.70 S	89° 59′ 29″ 1.20 S	89° 59′ 44″ 1.50 S	90° (E or W) 1.60 S
32°	89° 58′ 23″ 2.08 N	89° 58′ 39″ 0.94 N	89° 58′ 55″ 0.00	89° 59′ 11″ 0.72 S	89° 59′ 28″ 1.24 S	89° 59′ 44″ 1.56 S	90° (E or W) 1.66 S
33°	89° 58′ 19″ 2.16 N	89° 58′ 36″ 0.97 N	89° 58′ 53″ 0.00	89° 59′ 09″ 0.76 S	89° 59′ 26″ 1.30 S	89° 59′ 43″ 1.62 S	90° (E or W) 1.73 S
34°	89° 58′ 15″ 2.24 N	89° 58′ 32″ 1.01 N	89° 58′ 50″ 0.00	89° 59′ 07″ 0.79 S	89° 59′ 25″ 1.35 S	89° 59′ 42″ 1.69 S	90° (E or W) 1.80 S
35°	89° 58′ 11″ 2.32 N	89° 58′ 29″ 1.05 N	89° 58′ 47″ 0.00	89° 59′ 05″ 0.81 S	89° 59′ 24″ 1.39 S	89° 59′ 42″ 1.74 S	90° (E or W) 1.86 S
36°	89° 58′ 07″ 2.42 N	89° 58′ 26″ 1.09 N	89° 58′ 45″ 0.00	89° 59′ 03″ 0.84 S	89° 59′ 22″ 1.45 S	89° 59′ 41″ 1.81 S	90° (E or W) 1.93 S
37°	89° 58′ 03″ 2.50 N	89° 58′ 22″ 1.13 N	89° 58′ 42″ 0.00	89° 59′ 01″ 0.88 S	89° 59′ 21″ 1.51 S	89° 59′ 40″ 1.88 S	90° (E or W) 2.01 S
38°	89° 57′ 58″ 2.60 N	89° 58′ 19″ 1.17 N	89° 58′ 39″ 0.00	89° 58′ 59″ 0.91 S	89° 59′ 19″ 1.56 S	89° 59′ 40″ 1.95 S	90° (E or W) 2.08 S
39°	89° 57′ 54″ 2.70 N	89° 58′ 15″ 1.21 N	89° 58′ 36″ 0.00	89° 58′ 57″ 0.94 S	89° 59′ 18″ 1.61 S	89° 59′ 39″ 2.02 S	90° (E or W) 2.15 S
40°	89° 57′ 49″ 2.79 N	89° 58′ 11″ 1.26 N	89° 58′ 33″ 0.00	89° 58′ 55″ 0.97 S	89° 59′ 16″ 1.67 S	89° 59′ 38″ 2.09 S	90° (E or W) 2.23 S
41°	89° 57′ 45″ 2.89 N	89° 58′ 07″ 1.30 N	89° 58′ 30″ 0.00	89° 58′ 52″ 1.01 S	89° 59′ 15″ 1.73 S	89° 59′ 37″ 2.17 S	90° (E or W) 2.31 S
42°	89° 57′ 40″ 2.99 N	89° 58′ 03″ 1.35 N	89° 58′ 26″ 0.00	89° 58′ 50″ 1.05 S	89° 59′ 13″ 1.80 S	89° 59′ 37″ 2.25 S	90° (E or W) 2.40 S
43°	89° 57′ 35″ 3.10 N	89° 57′ 59″ 1.40 N	89° 58′ 23″ 0.00	89° 58′ 47″ 1.08 S	89° 59′ 12″ 1.86 S	89° 59′ 36″ 2.32 S	90° (E or W) 2.48 S
44°	89° 57′ 30″ 3.21 N	89° 57′ 55″ 1.45 N	89° 58′ 20″ 0.00	89° 58′ 45″ 1.12 S	89° 59′ 10″ 1.93 S	89° 59′ 35″ 2.41 S	90° (E or W) 2.57 S
45°	89° 57′ 24″ 3.32 N	89° 57′ 50″ 1.50 N	89° 58′ 16″ 0.00	89° 58′ 42″ 1.16 S	89° 59′ 08″ 2.00 S	89° 59′ 34″ 2.49 S	90° (E or W) 2.66 S
46°	89° 57′ 19″ 3.45 N	89° 57′ 46″ 1.55 N	89° 58′ 12″ 0.00	89° 58′ 39″ 1.20 S	89° 59′ 06″ 2.06 S	89° 59′ 33″ 2.58 S	90° (E or W) 2.75 S
47°	89° 57′ 13″ 3.57 N	89° 57′ 41″ 1.61 N	89° 58′ 09″ 0.00	89° 58′ 36″ 1.24 S	89° 59′ 04″ 2.14 S	89° 59′ 32″ 2.67 S	90° (E or W) 2.85 S
48°	89° 57′ 07″ 3.70 N	89° 57′ 36″ 1.66 N	89° 58′ 05″ 0.00	89° 58′ 33″ 1.29 S	89° 59′ 02″ 2.21 S	89° 59′ 31″ 2.77 S	90° (E or W) 2.95 S
49°	89° 57′ 01″ 3.82 N	89° 57′ 31″ 1.72 N	89° 58′ 01″ 0.00	89° 58′ 30″ 1.34 S	89° 59′ 00″ 2.30 S	89° 59′ 30″ 2.87 S	90° (E or W) 3.06 S
50°	89° 56′ 54″ 3.96 N	89° 57′ 25″ 1.79 N	89° 57′ 56″ 0.00	89° 58′ 27″ 1.38 S	89° 58′ 58″ 2.38 S	89° 59′ 29″ 2.97 S	90° (E or W) 3.17 S

17-9. Standard Parallels. The next step in the subdivision of the district being surveyed is to run the *standard parallels* or *correction lines*. These lines are parallels of latitude that are established in exactly the same manner as the base line. They are located at intervals of 24 miles north and south of the base line, and extend to the limits of the district being surveyed. These standard parallels are numbered,

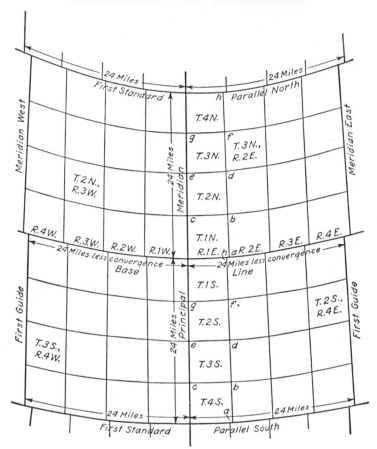

Fig. 17–4. Standard parallels and guide meridians.

as shown in Fig. 17-4, as the First (Second, Third, and so on) Standard Parallel North (or South). In the earlier surveys, standard parallels have been placed at intervals of 30 or 36 miles north and south of the base line. In connecting new work with old work, it has been necessary to establish intermediate correction lines which have been given local names, as "Fifth Auxiliary Standard Parallel North" or "Cedar Creek Correction Line."

17-10. Guide Meridians. The survey district is next divided into tracts approximately 24 miles square by means of guide meridians. These lines are true meridians which start at points on the base line or standard parallels at intervals of 24 miles east and west of the principal meridian, and extend north to their intersection with the next standard parallel, as shown in Fig. 17-4. Because of the convergence of the meridians, the distance between these lines will be 24 miles only at the starting points. At all other points the distance between them will be less than 24 miles. Guide meridians are designated by number, as the First (Second, Third, and so on) Guide Meridian East (or West). As they extend from one standard parallel to the next, their lengths are limited to 24 miles (30 or 36 miles on older work). At their intersection with the standard parallel to the north a new monument is established. On the standard parallels, two sets of monuments are thus to be found. The monuments that were established as the parallel was first located are called standard corners and apply to the area north of the parallel. The second set, found at the intersection of the parallel with the meridians from the south, are called closing corners, and govern the area to the south of the parallel. The distance between the closing corner and the nearest standard corner should be measured and recorded in the field notes.

The guide meridians are located with the same care for securing accuracy of alignment and measurement as is the principal meridian. The monuments are placed at half-mile intervals, except that all discrepancies in measurement are thrown into the last half-mile. For this reason the distance from the closing corner to the first monument south of the standard parallel may be more or less than 40 chains.

17-11. Township Exteriors. The regular order of establishing the township exteriors can be followed by reference to Fig. 17-4. Beginning at a, on the base line (or standard parallel) and 6 miles east of the principal meridian (or guide meridian), a line is run due north for 6 miles, monuments being established at intervals of 40 chains. From the township corner b, a random line is run to the west to intersect the principal meridian (or a guide meridian) at c. As this line is run, temporary monuments are set at intervals of 40 chains. From the amount by which the random line fails to strike c, the direction of the true line between c and b can be calculated. The line is then run on this calculated course from c back to b and the temporary monuments are replaced by permanent ones in proper position. The true line is blazed through timber, and distances to important items of topography are adjusted to the correct true-line measurements.

On account of the convergence of meridians and errors in field work, the northern boundary of the township will not be exactly 6 miles in length. All discrepancies due to convergence and to errors in measurement or alignment are thrown into the most westerly half-mile, all other distances being made exactly 40 chains. While every attempt is made to keep lines within 0° 14′ of the true courses, the boundaries of a township are not considered defective unless the error exceeds $0° \ 21'$. If the random north boundary fails to close on the corner previously set by more than 3 chains for line or by more than 3 chains, minus the theoretical convergence, for distance, it is evident that the $0° \ 21'$ limit has been exceeded, and the lines are retraced and the error is corrected.

The eastern boundary of the next township to the north is next run by extending the meridian from b to d, a distance of 6 miles, and locating permanent monuments at intervals of 40 chains. A random is then run westerly from d toward e and corrected back as the true line with monuments at intervals of 40 chains, measured from d, any discrepancy being thrown into the most westerly half-mile. The next step is to run the line df, a random from f to g, and the true line from g to f. From f the meridian is extended to its intersection h with the base line (or standard parallel), and a closing corner is established at the intersection. The distance from the closing corner to the nearest standard corner is measured and recorded in the field notes. Because of errors in measurement, the last half-mile on the meridian may be more or less than 40 chains in length.

The two other meridians of the 24-mile block are run in a similar manner, random lines being run to the west at the township corners to connect with the corners previously set. From the township corners on the third meridian of the block, randoms are also run to the east to connect with the township corners on the guide meridian. As these lines are corrected back to the west, monuments are established at intervals of 40 chains, measured from the guide meridian, and the discrepancy is thus thrown into the most westerly half-mile of the township, as before.

The instructions relative to the establishment of township exteriors in the case of irregular and partial surveys, as given in the Manual, are as follows: "As the remaining unsurveyed public lands are found to contain less and less extensive areas surveyable under the law, it becomes necessary to depart from the ideal procedure in order more directly to reach the areas authorized for survey. The many possible combinations are entirely too numerous to state in detail, but where an irregular order appears to be necessary such departure from the ideal order of survey will be specifically outlined in the written special instructions. Such departure should always be based on the principle of accomplishing, by whatever plan, the same relation of one township boundary to another as would have resulted from regular establishment under ideal conditions.

"In authorizing surveys to be executed it will not usually be provided that exteriors are to be carried forward until the township is to be subdivided; thus, where causes operate to prevent the establishment of the boundaries in full, it is not imperative that the survey of the exterior lines be completed; under such conditions it may be found necessary to run section lines as offsets to township exteriors and such section lines will be run either on cardinal courses or parallel to the governing boundaries of such townships, or even established when subdividing, as existing conditions may require."

17-12. Numbering Townships. The townships of a survey district are numbered meridionally into ranges and latitudinally into tiers with respect to the principal meridian and the base line of the district. As illustrated in Fig. 17-4, the third township south of the base line is in tier 3 south. Instead of tier, the word township is more frequently used; thus, any township in this particular tier is designated as township 3 south. The fourth township west of the principal meridian is in range 4 west. By this method of numbering, any township is located if its tier, range, and principal meridian are given, as Township 3 south, Range 4 west, of the Fifth Principal Meridian. This is abbreviated T. 3 S., R. 4 W., 5th P.M.

17-13. Convergence of Meridians. The angular convergence between two meridians is dependent on the distance between the meridians, the latitude, and the dimensions of the earth. The convergence θ, in seconds of arc, can be expressed by the equation

$$\theta = \frac{s \sqrt{1 - e^2 \sin^2 \phi} \tan \phi}{a \text{ arc } 1''} \tag{17-1}$$

where s = distance between the meridians;
e = eccentricity of the spheroid;
a = semimajor axis of the spheroid;
ϕ = latitude.

When tables for computing geographic positions are available, the equation may be written as follows:

$$\theta = sA \tan \phi \tag{17-2}$$

where $A = \sqrt{1 - e^2 \sin^2 \phi} / a$ arc $1''$. The value of log A, for s in meters, may be taken from the tables.

The linear convergence on the parallel, for two meridians of length l and at a distance s apart, is given by the equation

$$c = sl A \tan \phi \sin 1'' \tag{17-3}$$

The values of the convergence for two meridians 6 miles long and 6 miles apart, for latitudes between 30° and 51°, are given in Table 17-5.

TABLE 17-5

CONVERGENCE OF MERIDIANS 6 MILES LONG AND 6 MILES APART

| LATITUDE | CONVERGENCE | | LATITUDE | CONVERGENCE | |
	On the Parallel Feet	Angle ′ ″		On the Parallel Feet	Angle ′ ″
30°	27.67	03 00.1	41°	41.63	04 31.0
31°	28.79	03 07.5	42°	43.12	04 40.7
32°	29.94	03 14.9	43°	44.65	04 50.7
33°	31.11	03 22.6	44°	46.24	05 01.1
34°	32.32	03 30.4	45°	47.88	05 11.7
35°	33.55	03 38.4	46°	49.58	05 22.8
36°	34.80	03 46.6	47°	51.34	05 34.3
37°	36.10	03 55.0	48°	53.17	05 46.2
38°	37.42	04 03.7	49°	55.07	05 58.5
39°	38.79	04 12.5	50°	57.04	06 11.4
40°	40.19	04 21.7	51°	59.11	06 24.8

17-14. Subdivision of Township. In the work previously described, the exterior lines of the township are generally marked by monuments at half-mile intervals. However, because of errors in field work and the convergence of meridians, the most westerly and the most northerly half-miles of certain townships may be more or less than 40 chains in length. In subdividing the township into sections, the aim is to secure as many sections as possible which will be 1 mile on a side. To accomplish this, the error due to convergence of meridians is thrown as far to the west as possible by running lines parallel to the east boundary of the township, rather than running them as true meridians. The earlier practice has been to run these lines as true meridians. Errors in linear measurements are thrown as far to the north as possible by locating monuments at intervals of 40 chains along the lines parallel to the east boundary of the township. Thus, all the accumulated error falls in the most northerly half-mile, which may be more or less than 40 chains in length.

The order in which the lines are run to subdivide the township into sections is indicated by the numbers on the lines of the township shown in Fig. 17-5. The instructions for monumenting these lines, as given in the Manual, are: "The subdivisional survey will be commenced at the corner of sections 35 and 36, on the south boundary of the township, and the line between sections 35 and 36 will be run parallel to the east boundary of the township, or to the mean course thereof, if it is imperfect in alignment, but within limits, establishing the quarter-section corner at 40 chains, and at 80 chains, the corner of sections 25, 26, 35, and 36. From the last-named corner, a random

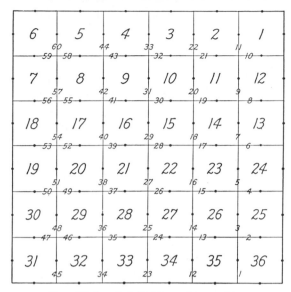

Fig. 17–5.   Subdivision of township.

line will be run eastward, without blazing, parallel to the south boundary of section 36, to its intersection with the east boundary of the township, placing at 40 chains from the point of beginning, a post for temporary quarter-section corner. If the random line intersects said township boundary exactly at the corner of sections 25 and 36, it will be blazed back and established as the true line, the permanent quarter-section corner being established thereon, midway between the initial and terminal section corners. If the random intersects said township boundary to the north or south of said corner, the falling will be carefully measured, and from the data thus obtained, the true return course will be calculated, and the true line blazed and established, and the position of the quarter-section corner determined, as directed above. The meridional section line will be continued on the same plan, likewise the successive latitudinal section lines except that each random will be run parallel to the true south boundary of the section to which it belongs. After having established the west and north boundaries of section 12, the line between sections 1 and 2 will be projected northward, on a random line, parallel to the east boundary of the township, or to its mean course, as the case may be, setting a post for temporary quarter-section corner at 40 chains, to its intersection with the north boundary of the township. If the random intersects said north boundary exactly at the corner of sections 1 and 2, it will be blazed back and established as the true line, the quarter-section corner being established permanently in its original temporary position, and the fractional measurement thrown into that portion of the line between the permanent quarter-section corner and the north boundary of the township. If, however, said random intersects the north boundary of the township to the east or west of the corner of sections 1 and 2, the falling will be carefully measured, and from the data thus obtained the true return course will be calculated and the true line established, the permanent quarter-section corner being placed upon the same at 40 chains from the initial corner of the random line, thereby throwing the fractional measurement in that portion lying between the quarter-section corner and the north boundary of the township. When the north boundary of a township is a base line or standard parallel, the line between sections 1 and 2 will be run as a true line parallel to the east boundary of the township, or to its mean course, as the case may be; the quarter-section corner will be placed at 40 chains, and a closing corner will be established at the point of intersection with such base or standard line; and in such case, the distance from said closing corner, to the nearest standard corner on such base or standard line, will be carefully measured and noted.

"The successive ranges of sections proceeding from east to west will be surveyed in the same manner; then after having established the west and north boundaries of section 32, a random line will be initiated at the corner of sections 29, 30, 31, and 32, which will be projected westward parallel to the south boundary of the township, setting a temporary quarter-section corner at 40 chains, to an intersection with the west boundary of the township, where the falling will be measured and the bearing of the true line calculated, whereupon the line between sections 30 and 31 will be permanently marked between the section corners, and the quarter-section corner thereon will be established at 40 chains from the east, thereby placing the fractional measurement in the west half mile as required by law. The survey of the west two ranges of sections will be continued on the same plan, and the random line between sections 6 and 7 will be run westward parallel to the true line between sections 7 and 18; the random will be corrected to a true line and the fractional measurement placed in the west half mile; finally the random line between sections 5 and 6 will be run northward parallel to the true line between sections 4 and 5; the random will be corrected to the true line and the fractional measurement placed in the north half mile."

In this manner the section lines are marked by monuments at half-mile intervals. The monuments on the east and west boundaries of a section are 40 chains apart, except for the fractional measurement placed in the most northerly half-mile of the township. As the east and west boundaries are not exactly parallel and as there may be errors in chaining, the north and south boundaries of the section may not be exactly 80 chains. If the error does not exceed 50 links, the lines are allowed to stand and the quarter-section corner is located midway between the two section corners, except for the west range of sections, where the quarter-section corner is placed at a distance of 40 chains from the northeast corner of the section.

In addition to the section and quarter-section corners, meander corners are established at the intersection of the section lines with all navigable streams, with all streams 3 or more chains in width, and with lakes of the area of 25 acres and upward.

As noted in Sec. 17-2, some of the details of subdivision have been changed from time to time. According to the present instructions, double sets of corners are found only when the north boundary of the township is a base line or a standard parallel. In some of the earlier surveys, closing corners are to be found on all four sides of a township. The first set of corners was established when the exterior boundaries of the township were located. Those monuments on the north boundary belong to sections lying to the north of the line. Those on the west boundary of the township belong to sections lying to the west of that line. The other set of corners was established at the time the township was subdivided. For instance, lines numbered 11, 22, 33, 44, and 60 in Fig. 17-5 were run to an intersection with the north boundary of the township, and closing corners were established at the intersections. In a similar manner, lines numbered 47, 50, 53, 56, and 59 were extended to an intersection with the west line of the township, and a closing corner was established at each intersection. The local surveyor should acquaint himself with the regulations in effect at the time any particular survey was made.

17-15. Meandering. The purpose of meandering is to locate the mean high-water line of all important rivers and lakes, in order to determine the areas of land which may be sold for agricultural purposes. The United States Supreme Court has given the principles governing the use and purpose of meandering shores in its decision in a noted case (R. R. Co. vs. Schurmcir, 7 Wallace, 286-287) as follows: "Meander lines are run in surveying fractional portions of the public lands bordering on navigable rivers, not as boundaries of the tract, but for the purpose of defining the sinuosities of the banks of the stream, and as the means of ascertaining the quantity of land in the fraction subject to sale, which is to be paid for by the purchaser. In preparing the official plat from the field notes, the meander line is represented as the border line of the stream, and shows to a demonstration that the water-course, and not the meander line as actually run on the land, is the boundary."

Meander corners are set at every point where standard, township, or section lines intersect the bank of a navigable stream, any river 3 or more chains in width, and any lake with an area of 25 or more acres. The meander corners are connected by traverses, which follow the bank or shore line. The true bearings and the lengths of the sides of the traverse are measured. Since the meander lines are not strict boundaries, the work is simplified by adjusting the locations of the stations on the meander line to give bearings to the exact quarter-degree and lengths of whole chains, or multiples of 10 links, with odd links only in the final course.

The latitudes and departures of the meander courses should be computed before leaving the vicinity, and if misclosure is found, indicating an error in the field measurements, the lines should be rerun.

In the case of lakes that are entirely within the boundaries of a section, a quarter-section line is run, if one crosses the lake, to the margin of the lake, where a *special meander corner* will be established. If the lake is entirely within a quarter section, an *auxiliary meander corner* will be established at some suitable point on its margin and connected with a regular corner on the section boundary.

17-16. Marking Lines Between Corners. The marking of the survey lines on the ground was supposed to be done in such a manner as to perpetuate the lines. This was done by monumenting the regular corners, by recording in the field notes all natural topographic features, and, whenever living timber was encountered, by means of blazing and hack marks on the trees.

A *blaze* is an axe mark which is made upon a tree trunk at about breast height, so that a flat scar is left upon the tree surface. The bark and a small amount of the live wood tissue are removed, and the smooth surface that is exposed forever brands the tree. A sufficient number of trees standing within 50 links of the line, on either side of it, are blazed on two sides quartering toward the line, in order to render the line conspicuous and readily traceable in either direction. The blazes are placed opposite each other and so that they coincide in direction with the line where the trees stand very near it, but approach nearer to each other and toward the line the farther the line passes from the blazed trees.

A *hack* is also an axe mark which is made upon a tree trunk at about breast height, but in this case a horizontal notch is cut into the surface of the tree. The notch is made V-shaped. Two hacks are cut to distinguish those made in the survey from accidental marks resulting from other causes. All trees intersected by the line will have two hacks or notches resembling a double-V $(\leqq)$ cut on each of the sides facing the line.

Unfortunately for the present-day surveyor, the monuments used on the early surveys were not permanent in character and forest fires and settlers have destroyed most of the timber, so that the retracing of the old lines is often difficult and in many instances impossible.

17-17. Objects Noted in the Survey. The field notes and plat of a survey furnish not only a technical record of the procedure, but also a report on the character of the land, soil, and timber traversed by the survey, and a detailed schedule of the topographical features along every line. It is necessary to include, in addition, accurate connections showing the relation of the rectangular surveys to other surveys, to natural objects, and to improvements. This information is often of considerable value in relocating obliterated lines.

According to the Manual, the information which should appear in the field notes is as follows:

1) The precise course and length of every line run, noting all necessary offsets therefrom, with the reason for making them, and the method employed.

2) The kind and diameter of all bearing trees, with the course and distance of the same from their respective corners, and the markings; all bearing objects and marks thereon, if any; and the precise relative position of witness corners to the true corners.

3) The kind of material of which the corners are constructed, their dimensions and markings, depth set in the ground, and their accessories.

4) Trees on line. The name, diameter, and distance on line to all trees which it intersects, and their markings.

5) Intersections by line of land objects. The distance at which the line intersects the boundary lines of every reservation, townsite, or private claim, noting the exact bearing of such boundary lines, and the precise distance to the nearest boundary corner; the center line of every railroad, canal, ditch, electric transmission line, or other right-of-way across public lands, noting the width of the right-of-way and the precise bearing of the center line; the change from one character of land to another, with the approximate bearing of the line of demarcation, and the estimated height in feet of the ascents and descents over the principal slopes typifying the topography of the country traversed, with the direction of said slopes; the distance to and the direction of the principal ridges, spurs, divides, rim rock, precipitous cliffs, etc.; the distance to where the line enters or leaves heavy or scattering timber, with the approximate bearing of the margin of all heavy timber, and the distance to where the line enters or leaves dense undergrowth.

6) Intersections by line of water objects. All unmeandered rivers, creeks, and smaller water-courses which the line crosses; the distance measured on the true line to the center of the same in the case of the smaller streams, and to both banks in the case of the larger streams, the course downstream at points of intersection, and their widths on line, if only the center is noted. All intermittent water-courses, such as ravines, gulches, arroyos, draws, dry-drains, etc.

7) The land's surface; whether level, rolling, broken, hilly or mountainous.

8) The soil; whether rocky, stony, gravelly, sandy, loam, clay, etc., and also whether first, second, third or fourth rate.

9) Timber; the several kinds of timber and undergrowth, in the order in which they predominate.

10) Bottom lands to be described as upland or swamp and over-flowed, and the depth of overflow at seasonal periods to be noted. The segregation of lands fit for cultivation without artificial drainage, from the swamp and overflowed lands.

11) Springs of water, whether fresh, saline, or mineral, with the course of the stream flowing therefrom. The location of all streams, springs, or water-holes, which because of their environment may be deemed to be of value in connection with the utilization of public grazing lands.

12) Lakes and ponds, describing their banks, tributaries and outlet, and whether the water is pure or stagnant, deep or shallow.

13) Improvements; towns and villages; post offices; Indian occupancy; houses or cabins, fields, or other improvements, with owner's name; mineral claims; mill sites; United States mineral monuments, and all other official monuments not belonging to the system of rectangular surveys will be located by bearing and distance or by intersecting bearings from given points.

14) Coal banks or beds, all ore bodies, with particular description of the same as to quality and extent; all mining surface improvements and underground workings; and salt licks.

15) Roads and trails, with their directions, whence and whither.

16) Rapids, cataracts, cascades, or falls of water, in their approximate position and estimated height of their fall in feet.

17) Stone quarries and ledges of rocks, with the kind of stone they afford.

18) Natural curiosities, petrifactions, fossils, organic remains, etc., also all archaeological remains, such as cliff dwellings, mounds, fortifications, or objects of like nature.

19) The general average of the magnetic declination in the township, with the maximum known range of local attraction and other

Chains	
	Beginning the subdivisional survey at the cor. of secs. 1, 2, 35 and 36, on the S. bdy. of the Tp., which is monumented with a sandstone, 8 × 6 × 5 ins. above ground, firmly set, marked and witnessed as described in the official record.
	N. 0° 01′ W., bet. secs. 35 and 36.
	Over level bottom land.
20.00	Enter scattering timber.
29.30	S. E. cor. of field; leave scattering timber.
31.50	A cabin bears West, 6.00 chs. dist.
39.50	Enter State Highway No. 25, bears N. along section line, and E.
40.00	Point for the ¼ sec. cor. of secs. 35 and 36.
	Bury a granite stone, 12 × 12 × 12 ins., mkd. X, 2 ft. underground, from which
	An iron post, 30 ins. long, 2 ins. diam., set 24 ins. in the ground, for a reference monument, with brass cap mkd. with an arrow pointing to the cor. and ¼ S 36 RM, bears East 46 lks. dist.
	An iron post 30 ins. long, 2 ins. diam., set 24 ins. in the ground, for a reference monument with brass cap mkd. with an arrow pointing to the cor. and ¼ S 35 RM, bears West 46 lks. dist.
50.50	N. E. cor. of field.
51.50	Highway turns to N. 70° W.
57.50	Enter heavy timber and dense undergrowth, edge bears N. 54° E. and S. 54° W.
72.00	Leave undergrowth.
80.00	Point for the cor. of secs. 25, 26, 35, and 36.
	Set an iron post, 30 ins. long, 2 ins. diam., 24 ins. in the ground with brass cap mkd.

T 15 N	R 20 E
S 26	S 25
S 35	S 36

1945

from which

A green ash, 13 ins. diam., bears N. 22° E., 26 lks. dist. mkd. T 15 N   R 20 E   S 25 BT.

A green ash, 23 ins. diam., bears S. 71¼° E., 37 lks. dist. mkd. T 15 N   R 20 E   S 36 BT.

A green ash, 17 ins. diam., bears S. 64° W., 41 lks. dist. mkd. T 15 N   R 20 E   S 35 BT.

A cottonwood, 13 ins. diam., bears N. 21¼° W., 36 lks. dist. mkd. T 15 N   R 20 E   S 26 BT.

Land, level bottom; northern 20 chs. subject to overflow.

Soil, alluvial, silt and loam.

Timber, green ash and cottonwood; undergrowth, willow.

variations, will be stated in the general description, and the general average for the township, subject to local attraction, will be shown upon the plat.

In addition to the field notes the surveyors are required to prepare, as the work progresses, an outline diagram showing the course and length of all established lines with connections, and a topographical sketch embracing all features usually shown upon the completed official township plat. These maps will be made to scale, and will be kept up with the progress of the field work. The interiors of the sections will be fully completed, and the topographical features will be sketched with care while in the view of the surveyor. These maps will then form the basis of the official plat, the ultimate purpose of which is a true and complete graphic representation of the public lands surveyed.

17-18. Specimen Field Notes. To give some idea of the manner in which the field notes are recorded, the notes on page 575 for one mile of the subdivision of T. 15 N., R. 20 E. of the Principal Base and Meridian of Montana have been taken from the Manual of 1947. That portion of the notes covering the adjustment of the transit, and a comparison of the chain with the one used in the survey of the township exterior, has been omitted.

17-19. Corner Monuments. The law provides that the original corners established during the progress of the survey shall forever remain fixed in position, and that even evident errors in the execution of the survey must be disregarded where these errors were undetected prior to the sale of the lands. The original monuments thus assume extreme importance in the location of land boundaries. Unfortunately, most of the public lands were surveyed before the present regulations relative to the character of monuments went into effect, and, as a consequence, most of the monuments used were of a very perishable nature. Their disappearance or destruction has rendered the relocation of old lines a very difficult task.

The present regulations call for the use of iron-pipe monuments, from 1 to 3 in. in diameter and about 3 ft long. One end of the pipe is split for a distance of about 4 or 5 in. and the two halves are spread to form flanges or foot plates. A brass cap is securely riveted to the opposite end of the pipe, and finally the pipe is filled with concrete. The 3-in. monuments are used for township corners, the 2-in. ones for section corners, and the 1-in. ones for quarter-section corners. The caps of the iron posts are suitably and plainly marked with steel dies at the time the posts are used. The posts are set with about three-fourths of their length in the ground, and earth and stone, if the latter is at hand, is tamped into the excavation to give the post a solid anchorage.

When the procedure has been duly authorized, the use of durable native stone may be substituted for the iron post. No stone can be used which is less than 20 in. in length, or less than 6 in. in either of its minor dimensions, or less than 1000 cu in. in volume. The stone is marked by letters chiseled on the faces. To aid in the identification of the sections to which it refers, grooves or notches are cut in the faces or edges. The number of these grooves or notches is a measure of the number of miles to the township line in that direction. Thus, the corner common to sections 10, 11, 14, and 15 would have two notches on the east edge and four notches on the south edge.

Where a corner point falls upon solid surface rock, and excavation is prevented, a cross (**X**) is cut at the exact corner point; and, if feasible, the monument is erected in the same position and is supported by a large stone mound of broad base, which is so well constructed that the monument will possess thorough stability.

Where the corner point falls exactly at the position occupied by a sound living tree, which is too large to be removed, the tree should be appropriately marked for the corner.

According to the earlier instructions, a corner monument could be a wooden post, or a mound of earth under which was buried a charred stake or a quart of charcoal, or some other fairly permanent and distinguishable mark, when nothing more permanent was available.

17·20. Witnesses. The corner monuments are witnessed by measuring the bearing and distance to natural or artificial objects in the immediate vicinity. Bearing trees, or other natural objects, are selected for marking, when they are available within 5 chains of the corner monument. One tree, or object, is marked in each section cornering at the monument, when available, and the true course and horizontal distance from the exact corner point to the center of the tree at its root crown, or to the cross (**X**) upon a marked object, are carefully determined and recorded with the description of the tree, or object, and its marks.

Trees that are used as witnesses are blazed, and the blazes are scribed with letters and figures which aid in identifying the location. Thus, a tree used as a witness for a section corner might bear the inscription, T 20 N R 12 E S 24 BT; this indicates that the tree stands in Sec. 24, T 20 N., R. 12 E., BT standing for bearing tree. A tree used as a witness for a quarter-section corner is marked ¼ S 32 BT, when the tree is in Sec. 32.

A cross (**X**) and the letters "BO" and the section number are chiseled into a bearing object, if it is of rock formation, and the record is made sufficiently complete to enable another surveyor to determine where the marks will be found.

Where stone is available, and the surface of the ground is favorable, a mound of stone is employed as a witness when a full quota of trees or other bearing objects are not available. The mound consists of not less than five stones and has a base not less than 2 ft wide and a minimum height of 1½ ft. In stony ground the size of the mound is sufficiently increased to make it conspicuous. The nearest point on the base is about 6 in. distant from the monument, and the size and position of the mound are recorded in the notes.

On open prairies where no trees, rock, or other natural objects are available, the corners may be witnessed by digging pits 18 in. square and 12 in. deep, with the nearest side 3 ft distant from the corner monument. The pits are oriented with a square side (and not a corner) toward the monument. The field notes should contain a description of the pits, including the size and position, as the regulations relative to this form of witness have been changed from those set forth in the earlier editions of the Manual.

When it is impossible to utilize any of the types of witnesses just mentioned, a suitable memorial will be deposited at the base of the monument. A memorial may consist of any durable article which will serve to identify the location of the corner in case the monument is destroyed. Such articles as glassware, stoneware, a stone marked with a cross (**X**), a charred stake, a quart of charcoal, or pieces of metal constitute a suitable memorial. A full description of such articles is embodied in the field notes wherever they are so employed.

17-21. Filing of Field Notes and Plats. Copies of the field notes, and of the township plats, are on record at the office of the Director of the Bureau of Land Management at Washington, D. C. When the survey of the public lands in a state has been completed, the original records are then turned over to some state officer. The custodians of these records in the various states are as follows:

Alabama: Secretary of State, Montgomery.
Alaska: Public Survey Office, Juneau.
Arizona: Public Survey Office, Phoenix.
Arkansas: Commissioner of State Lands, Little Rock.
California: Regional Survey Office, Sacramento.
Colorado: Public Survey Office, Denver.
Florida: Commissioner of Agriculture, Tallahassee.
Idaho: Public Survey Office, Boise.
Illinois: Auditor of State, Springfield.
Indiana: Auditor of State, Indianapolis.
Iowa: Secretary of State, Des Moines.
Kansas: Auditor of State and Register of State Lands, Topeka.

Louisiana: Register of State Lands, Baton Rouge.
Michigan: Department of Conservation, Lansing.
Minnesota: Secretary of State, St. Paul.
Mississippi: Commissioner of State Lands, Jackson.
Missouri: Secretary of State, Jefferson City.
Montana: Public Survey Office, Helena.
Nebraska: Commissioner of Public Lands and Buildings, Lincoln.
Nevada: Public Survey Office, Reno.
New Mexico: Public Survey Office, Santa Fe.
North Dakota: State Engineer, Bismarck.
Ohio: Auditor of State, Columbus.
Oklahoma: Bureau of Land Management, Washington, D. C.
Oregon: Regional Land Office, Portland.
South Dakota: Commissioner of School and Public Lands, Pierre.
Utah: Regional Survey Office, Salt Lake City.
Washington: Public Survey Office, Olympia.
Wisconsin: Commissioners of Public Lands, Madison.
Wyoming: Public Survey Office, Cheyenne.

Copies of the field notes can be obtained either from these officers or from the Director of the Bureau of Land Management at Washington, D. C. In many instances copies of those notes pertaining to a county have been obtained and made a part of the county records, being in the custody of the register of deeds, county surveyor, or other similar county official. Copies of the official township plats can be obtained from the Bureau of Land Management at Washington.

17-22. Subdivision of Sections. The function of the United States surveyor ends with the establishment of monuments at half-mile intervals on the external lines of the sections, and the filing of the detailed field notes and a plat. No monuments are set by him within the section, except in the case of a meanderable lake entirely within a section. As the rectangular system provides for the disposal of the public lands in units of quarter-quarter sections of 40 acres, the function of the local surveyor begins when he is employed as an expert to identify the lands which have passed into private ownership. This may be a simple task or a most complicated one, the difficulty depending on the condition of the original monuments. The work of the local surveyor usually includes the subdivision of the section into the smaller units shown on the official plat. It is apparent that he cannot properly serve his client unless he is familiar with the legal requirements concerning the subdivision of sections. If any of the original monuments are missing, it is necessary for him to know not only the methods used in the original survey, but also the principles which have been adopted by the courts, in order to be able to restore the missing corners legally.

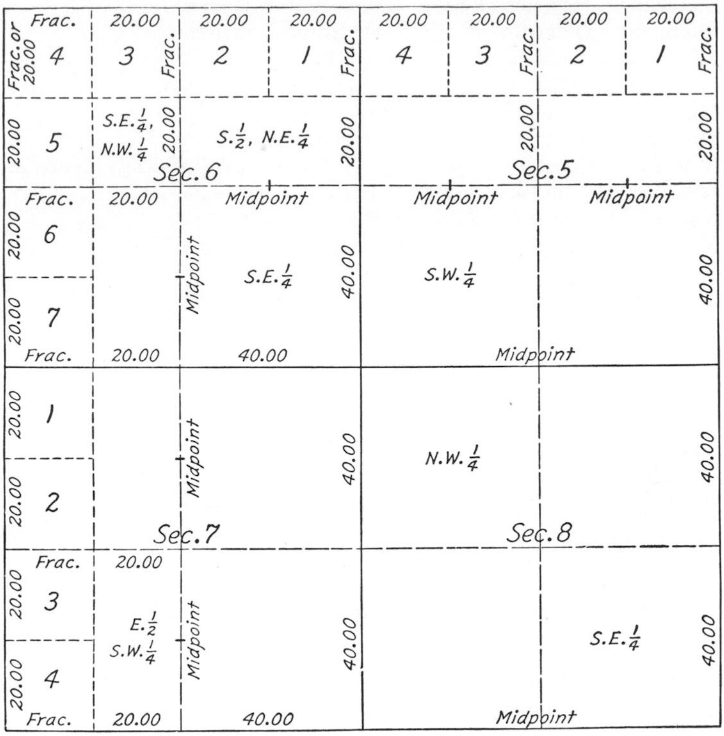

FIG. 17–6. Subdivision of sections.

After all the original monuments have been found or any missing ones have been replaced, the first step in the subdivision is the location of the center of the section. Regardless of the location of the section within the township, this point is always at the intersection of the line joining the east and west quarter-section corners (called the east-and-west quarter line) with the line joining the north and south quarter-section corners (called the north-and-south quarter line). By locating these lines on the ground, the section is divided into quarter-sections containing approximately 160 acres each.

The method of dividing these quarter-sections into the 40-acre parcels depends on the position of the section within the township. For any section except those along the north and west sides of the township, the subdivision is accomplished by bisecting each side of the quarter-section and connecting the opposite points by straight lines. The intersection of these lines is the center of the quarter-section.

The aim in subdividing the sections along the north and west sides of the township is to secure as many regular parcels as possible and to throw all irregularities caused by convergence or field work as far west and north as possible. The method of subdividing these sections is shown in Fig. 17-6. The corners on the north-and-south section lines are set at intervals of 20.00 chains, measured from the south, the discrepancy being thrown into the most northerly quarter-mile. Similarly, the monuments on the east-and-west lines are set at intervals of 20.00 chains, measured from the east, the fractional measurement being thrown into the most westerly quarter-mile. The fractional lots formed are numbered in a regular series progressively from east to west or from north to south, in each section. As section 6 borders on both the north and the west boundaries of the township, the fractional lots are numbered commencing with No. 1 in the northeast, thence progressively west to No. 4 in the northwest, and south to No. 7 in the southwest fractional quarter-quarter section.

It is the duty of the local surveyor to set these corners in the same positions they would have occupied had they been set in the original survey. For this reason, distances shown as 20.00 chains indicate distances of 20 chains according to the chain used by the original surveyor, and not 1320.00 ft according to the tape of the local surveyor. It is therefore necessary to establish these points by proportionate measurement, the local surveyor determining the length of the chain, in terms of his tape, by measuring the distance between the two existing monuments. Thus, if the measured distance from the north quarter-section corner of Sec. 6 to the northwest corner is 2637.24 ft, and if the field notes show this distance to be 39.82 chains, the local surveyor will measure $20.00 \times 2637.24/39.82 = 1324.58$ ft westward from the quarter-section corner in establishing the quarter-quarter-section corner.

Where some corners fall within meanderable bodies of water, every effort is made to run the necessary division lines in the same positions they would occupy in a regular section. Thus, when a quarter-section corner for an interior section could not be set, the quarter-section line is run from the opposite existing corner on a bearing which is the mean of the bearings of the two adjacent section lines. This same principle holds in the establishment of quarter-quarter-section lines.

17-23. Legal Descriptions. The rectangular system of subdivision provides a very convenient method of describing a piece of land which is to be conveyed by deed from one person to another. If the description is for a 40-acre parcel, the particular quarter of the quarter-section is first given, then the quarter-section in which the parcel is located, then the section number, followed by the township, range, and principal meridian. Thus, the parcel of land adjacent to lots 3, 4, and 5 in Sec. 6, Fig. 17-6, can be described as the S. E. ¼, N. W. ¼, Sec. 6, T. 8 N., R. 12 E. of the Third Principal Meridian. Lot 1 in Sec. 7 may also be described as the N. W. ¼, N. W. ¼, Sec. 7, T. 8 N., R. 12 E. of the Third Principal Meridian. The legal descriptions of the larger parcels appear in Fig. 17-6.

17-24. Relocating Lost Corners. Nothing in the practice of surveying calls for more skill, persistence, and good judgment on the part of the surveyor than the relocation of a missing corner. In the original survey it was presumed that permanent monuments were being carefully established and witnessed, so that long lines of monuments would be perfect guides to the place of any one that chanced to be missing. Unfortunately, the "monuments" were often nothing but green sticks driven into the ground, lines were carelessly run, monuments were inaccurately placed, witnesses were wanting in permanence, and recorded courses and lengths were incorrect. As the early settlers made little effort to perpetuate either the corner monuments or the witnesses, the task of the present-day surveyor in reconciling much conflicting evidence (or in even finding any kind of evidence) is often an extremely difficult task.

A *lost corner* is a point of a survey whose position cannot be determined, beyond reasonable doubt, either from original traces or from other reliable evidence relating to the position of the original monument, and whose restoration on the earth's surface can be accomplished only by means of a suitable surveying process with reference to interdependent existent corners.

A thorough search will often show that an apparently lost corner is really not lost. Where wooden stakes were used, a careful slicing of the earth may disclose a discoloration in the soil caused by the decaying of the stake. Roots or depressions in the soil may give an indication of the locations of the original witness trees. Fence lines, the testimony of nearby residents, and the field notes of adjacent surveys may be of value in ascertaining the location of the corner. It must be remembered that no matter how erroneously the original work is done, lines and monuments which can be identified still govern the land boundaries. The surveyor has no power to "establish" corners. In any case of disputed lines, unless the parties concerned settle the controversy by agreement, the determination of the line is necessarily a judicial act, and it must proceed upon evidence. The surveyor serves as an expert witness in the court proceedings, presenting all evidence he has been able to discover relative to the proper location of the corner in question. As a disinterested surveyor of proper training should be much more competent than any court to decide upon the proper location of any questionable line or corner, the surveyor should exert all his influence toward effecting a settlement by agreement, and thus save his client the expense of court proceedings. If this is impossible, he should insist that proper monuments, which are consistent with the court decree, be established, and if possible, be made a part of the decree.

When it is certain that a corner is lost, it is replaced in a manner which is in accord with the methods used in its original location. Lost

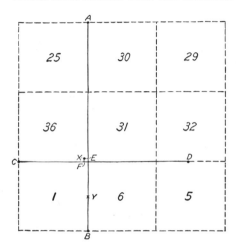

corners are established by either single or double proportionate measurement. The method of double proportionate measurement is generally applicable to the restoration of lost corners of four townships and of lost interior corners of four sections. Its application is illustrated in Fig. 17-7. In the lower enlarged sketch, E represents the location of the corner if only the existing corners A and B are considered, the point being determined by proportionate measurement. If the known points C and D are used, a second location F is found. The restored corner is placed at X, the intersection of a west line through E with a north line through F. In this manner, the distances from the replaced corner to the existing corners are consistent with the original field notes.

As a quarter-section corner was supposedly located on the straight line between the adjacent section corners, if there is no evidence on the ground to the contrary, a missing quarter-section corner is located on the straight line connecting the adjacent section corners. The distances from the section corners are determined by proportion, by comparing the present-day measurement between

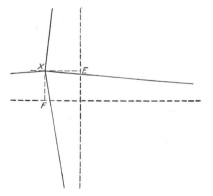

Fig. 17–7.   Restoring lost corner by double proportionate measurement.

existing corners with the same distance as recorded in the field notes. Thus, in Fig. 17-7 the quarter-section corner Y between Secs. 1 and 6 would be located on the line between B and X by a single proportionate measurement.

Before attempting work of this sort, the student should carefully examine the detailed rules and examples shown in the Manual, from which much of the material in this chapter has been taken.

BIBLIOGRAPHY

BROWN, C. M. *Boundary Control and Legal Principles*. New York: John Wiley and Sons, 1957.

BROWN, C. M., and W. H. ELDRIDGE. *Evidence and Procedures for Boundary Location*. New York: John Wiley and Sons, 1962.

GRIMES, J. S. *Clark on Surveying and Boundaries*. Indianapolis: Bobbs-Merril Co., 1959.

"MANUAL OF INSTRUCTIONS FOR THE SURVEY OF THE PUBLIC LANDS OF THE UNITED STATES," Bureau of Land Management, Government Printing Office, 1947.

"RESTORATION OF LOST OR OBLITERATED CORNERS AND SUBDIVISION OF SECTIONS," Bureau of Land Management, Government Printing Office, 1955.

SKELTON, R. H. *Boundaries and Adjacent Properties*. Indianapolis: Bobbs-Merril Co.

WATTLES, W. C. *Land Survey Descriptions*. Los Angeles: Title Insurance and Trust Co., 1956.

18

Municipal Surveys

18-1. Control Monuments and Maps. The value of a comprehensive city survey cannot be overestimated. All public agencies, utilities, land developers, engineers, and architects and others make constant use of the information furnished by city surveys. The money saved by the users of the information in planning, developing, engineering, and construction far exceeds the cost of the surveys.

Information furnished by well-planned and well-executed city surveys consists of horizontal-control and vertical-control monuments, together with their coordinates or elevations or both, large-scale base maps, topographic maps, property maps, and over-all city maps to smaller scale. Horizontal-control monuments are established by triangulation and traverse of first-, second-, and third-order accuracy. Vertical-control monuments, or bench marks, are established by first-, second-, and third-order lines of differential levels.

Base maps are compiled for a multiplicity of uses. In general, they are used to form a common basis for topographic maps, property maps, subdivision maps, and maps showing the positions of utility lines. For the compilation of base maps, scales of 1 in. = 50 ft, 1 in. = 100 ft, and 1 in. = 200 ft are most satisfactory, the choice depending on the intensity of land use. Topographic maps should be published at a scale of 1 in. = 200 ft; property maps, at a scale of 1 in. = 50 ft; and the over-all city map, at a scale no smaller than 1 in. = 2000 ft.

18-2. Steps in a City Survey. Where it is possible to make a complete survey, the first step is to establish a network of triangulation control. The triangulation should be of first-order accuracy, should be tied to existing U. S. Coast and Geodetic Survey triangulation stations, and should provide one control point for every 1 to 3 square miles throughout the metropolitan area. The next step is to run traverses connecting the triangulation stations. These traverses should furnish the equivalent of second-order control for the base maps and property surveys, and of third-order control for the topographic work. Leveling of the same three orders should follow the lines of horizontal control.

From this basic control, base maps are prepared as described in Sec. 18-6, and topographic maps are compiled either by photogrammetric methods or by plane-table methods, additional control being provided for the latter by plane-table traversing and plane-table leveling. Much of the information obtained in the topographic survey forms the basis of the property surveys that are made to locate the monuments and boundaries of all public property, supplementary information being obtained by a search of all public records and by additional field work.

18-3. Triangulation for City Surveys. Although the principles governing the triangulation survey for a city are the same as those given in Chapter 10, the work is modified somewhat because of the shorter lengths of the sides and because of the special conditions encountered. In planning the network, the tops of hills and of prominent buildings are utilized for stations, as far as possible, in order to keep the cost at a minimum. Towers are erected only when unavoidable. A line of sight which passes close to the ground along a hillside or bluff, or close to a building or chimney giving off heated air, is likely to produce uncertain results because of lateral refraction of the line of sight. Where such a sight is necessary, the observations should be made when the wind is blowing toward the object.

The triangulation net should be made up of either quadrilaterals or central-point figures, no single triangles being used. The diagram in Fig. 18-1 shows the main scheme first-order and second-order triangulation covering the city of Oakland, California, and including neighboring smaller cities. This is an excellent example of a strong triangulation network, which serves to control all subsequent municipal surveys in the area. The network is integrated directly into the triangulation network of the U. S. Coast and Geodetic Survey, and the positions of all the stations are given in state plane coordinates.

To maintain high precision, strong figures are necessary. The value of R_1 for any of the basic figures should seldom exceed 5. The value of R_1 between adjacent bases should be kept less than 20, if possible, and should seldom be allowed to exceed 25. The lengths of these bases should approximate the average length of the sides of the triangles.

In order to keep temperature effects to a minimum, and to control calibration errors, two or more standardized invar tapes are used in measuring the bases. If steel tapes must be used, the measurements should be made at night when the air temperature most truly indicates

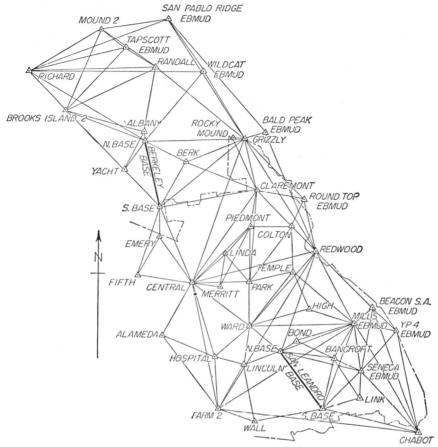

Fig. 18–1.   Triangulation diagram of the city of Oakland, California.
(Courtesy of city of Oakland.)

the actual temperature of the tape. The use of steel tripods, called taping bucks, for supporting the tape during measurement will be advantageous. These should weigh at least 15 pounds, and be from 15 to 30 in. high. The tape graduations are transferred to metal plates on top of the tripods by means of a pencil or steel awl.

A leveling party is necessary when measuring the base line in order to run levels over the tripod heads. The levels furnish the differences of elevation between successive tripods needed to compute the individual slope corrections to the tape lengths. The probable error of the bases should be no larger than 1:1,000,000. After a least-squares adjustment of the network, the discrepancy between the measured and computed lengths of the bases should average no greater than 1:100,000.

The angles are measured with either a 1-second direction instrument or a 10-second repeating instrument. The average triangle closure should not exceed 1 second, and the maximum allowable error should be about 3 seconds. To attain this precision, 8, 12, or 16 positions with the direction instrument (the number depending on the accuracy of the instrument and the conditions surrounding the measurements), or 6 sets of 6 direct and 6 reversed readings with the repeating instrument, will generally be required. Because of the relatively short lengths of the sides, the signals and the instrument must be centered within 0.1 in. All angles should be measured at night, any one of a variety of triangulation signal lights being used. The instrument should be shielded from the wind during the observation period by means of a canvas enclosure or other device. Except when the net is connected with the first-order control of the U. S. Coast and Geodetic Survey, astronomical observations for azimuths should be made at a few selected stations in the network.

The monuments should be of permanent character and carefully referenced. An iron pipe that is provided with a bronze cap and is set in a concrete post at least 12 in. in diameter makes a suitable monument if it extends below frost line and is so located as to minimize the chances of destruction by public or private construction. By using a bronze cap with a spherical top, the monument will serve also as a bench mark. The exact station mark can be designated by a small drill hole or an etched cross in the top of the cap. When the monument is set several inches below the surface of the ground, a small cast-iron box of the manhole type makes the monument more accessible.

In order to make the triangulation stations usable to a maximum number of people, the triangulation computations should be carried out on the state plane coordinate system. The least-squares adjustment is most easily made by the method of variation of plane coordinates described in *Special Publication No. 193* of the U. S. Coast and Geodetic Survey.

For the use of local surveyors and engineers, an index map showing the locations of all triangulation stations should be published. This map should be accompanied by a list of descriptions of the stations and their references, a tabulated list of coordinates, and the azimuths and lengths of the sides.

18-4. Traverse for Control of City Surveys. The use of first-order traverse as the principal horizontal control in a city survey, independent of triangulation, is advisable only for small areas where triangulation is unduly expensive because of topographic conditions. The principal use of first-order traverse is in establishing additional control points for originating second-order traverses, which control property surveys, and third-order traverses, which control the topographic surveys.

A first-order traverse begins at one triangulation station and closes on another triangulation station. This practice tends to eliminate the effects of unknown systematic errors in measuring the traverse sides. The traverse lines are marked at intervals not greater than a mile by pairs of permanent intervisible monuments, 500 to 1000 ft apart. These marked lines provide positions for subsequent traversing of lower order. Set in pairs, the monuments provide beginning azimuths for subsequent traverses. Intermediate stations are semipermanent, are marked by iron pins or by lead or copper hubs in pavements or sidewalks, and are referenced for future recovery. The stations should be so located as to provide long clear sights free from horizontal refraction. Where a series of short sights is necessary, azimuths should be carried by means of cut-off lines discussed in Sec. 8-8 in order to maintain accuracy in the directions of the lines. Long narrow circuits should be avoided, for connections subsequently made across the narrow dimension may show unallowable discrepancies, despite satisfactory closures obtained in the original circuit.

The average angular error, in seconds, should not exceed $2\sqrt{N}$, where N is the number of sides or angles in the traverse, and the maximum error should not exceed $4\sqrt{N}$. The angles may be measured with a 10-second repeating instrument, one set of 6 direct and 6 reversed readings being taken for both the angle and its explement. Or the angles may be measured by 4, 6, or 8 positions of a 1-second direction instrument, the number depending on the conditions surrounding the measurements. Triangulation lights or specially designed traverse lights may be used for signals in both day and night operations.

The linear measurements are performed in the same manner as the base-line measurements, but only a single measurement is usually made. The use of taping tripods for carrying the measurements forward will be found advantageous, as much of the measuring will be through or across city streets. A leveling party is necessary, as in baseline measurement, in order to furnish the information needed to compute slope corrections for the lines. After the azimuth errors are distributed, the average position closure should not exceed 1:35,000, and the maximum closure should not exceed 1:25,000.

The second-order traverse is used to furnish coordinates, bearings, and distances for street property monuments. The stations should coincide with the street monuments wherever possible. The angles can be read with either a 10- or 20-second repeating instrument. When the 10-second instrument is used, one set of 3 direct and

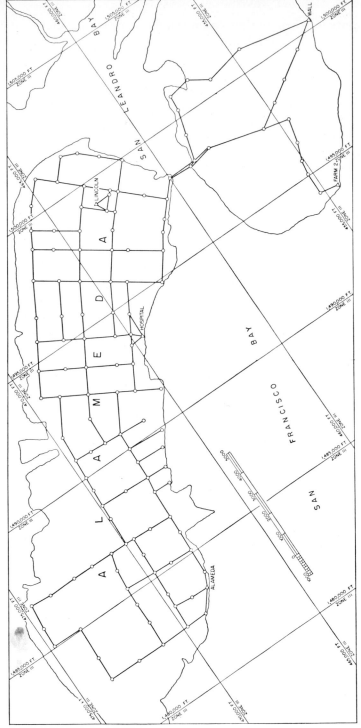

Fig. 18–2. Traverse diagram of the city of Alameda, California.
(Courtesy of city of Alameda.)

3 reversed readings of the angle and its explement is sufficient. When the 20-second instrument is used, one set of 6 direct and 6 reversed readings will give the required accuracy. When a 1-second direction instrument is used, 2 or 4 positions will suffice. The average angular closure, in seconds, should not exceed 10 $\sqrt{N}$, and the maximum closure should not exceed 15 $\sqrt{N}$. After the angular error is distributed, the average position closure should be 1:15,000 or better.

The diagram in Fig. 18-2 shows the traverse network covering the City of Alameda, California. The entire network is tied to five triangulation stations which appear in the lower left-hand part of Fig. 18-1. Nearly all the traverse lines are along the city streets (eliminated from the drawing for clarity), and the monuments are located at street corners. This is a flat-lying area of limited extent, and the traverse network is entirely adequate to control all subsequent surveys. The positions of the traverse stations are given by state plane coordinates.

The third-order traverse furnishes control for the topographic survey. Such a traverse should begin at a station of higher order and close on another station of higher order. Semipermanent monuments are used, since they can be replaced easily from the references or by retracing the survey. The average angular closure should not exceed 15 seconds per station. The angles can be measured with a 30-second or 1-minute engineer's transit, each angle being measured once direct and once reversed. After the angular error is distributed, the position closure should not exceed 1:7500. The distances, which should be checked by stadia readings, are measured with a steel tape (a hand level and spring balance being used), and the field measurements are adjusted for incorrect tape length, temperature, and sag.

The published data for the traverse stations should be the same as for the triangulation system, the order of the various stations being indicated. All rectangular coordinates should be referenced to the state plane coordinate system.

18-5. Leveling for City Surveys. One of the difficulties facing engineers, surveyors, and others who use city bench marks to control their operations is the multiplicity of vertical datums in existence in one given city. This is troublesome when trying to tie a line of levels to two networks on different datums. A city should endeavor to establish the elevations of all bench marks with respect to a common level datum at the earliest possible time. This datum should preferably be the Sea-Level Datum of 1929 based on leveling operations of the U. S. Coast and Geodetic Survey.

A first-order level net should be laid out along major streets and railroad lines if such a net has not already been established by the U. S. Coast and Geodetic Survey. Traverse monuments should be incorporated into the net where possible. Additional bench marks are set on bridge abutments or piers, masonry retaining walls, and masonry walls of buildings. These marks should be bronze tablets, and should be carefully described and referenced for future use. The levels are run according to the methods described in Sec. 3-42, and precise rods graduated in feet, yards, or meters are used. For speed and accuracy, a tilting level is desirable. The levels are run in both directions over a section. The resulting differences of elevation, in feet, should agree within $0.017 \sqrt{M}$, where M is the length of the section in miles.

The second-order levels are run in closed circuits that begin and end on the same first-order bench mark, or are run from one such bench mark to another. These lines of levels follow the lines of second-order traverse, the traverse stations serving as bench marks. Additional bench marks are established in such places as on fire hydrants, curb catch-basins, and crosses chiseled in concrete sidewalks. They are referenced by steel-tape measurements. The maximum closure, in feet, of any line or circuit should not exceed $0.035 \sqrt{M}$, where M is the length of the line or circuit in miles. Three-wire leveling should be used in conjunction with invar-strip leveling rods. A tilting level equipped with an optical micrometer can be used satisfactorily. In using such equipment, only one cross hair is read. Since a level-net adjustment is based on lengths of lines, these lengths must be determined. In single-wire leveling the distances may be paced, scaled from a map, or obtained directly from values for the traverse which the line happens to follow.

The final elevations, adopted after a least-squares adjustment of the level net, should be published for the use of local engineers and surveyors. The order of each bench mark should be indicated, together with its complete description and references and the vertical datum with respect to which its elevation is established.

18-6. Base Maps. As previously stated, a base map is prepared to provide a common basis for other types of maps. It should show a maximum amount of basic information regarding horizontal and vertical control, city property, street center lines, boundary lines, and related features. Base maps are most useful at scales of 50, 100, and 200 ft to the inch. They should be indexed in series by means of the state plane coordinates of the lower left-hand corner of each sheet. A series at a scale of 1 in. = 50 ft with a working area of 20 in. in the north-south direction, and 30 in. in the east-west direction will have index x-coordinates in multiples of 1500 ft and index y-coordinates in multiples of 1000 ft. A series at a scale of 1 in. = 200 ft on the same size sheet will have index coordinates in multiples of 6000 and 4000 ft in the x-direction and y-direction, respectively.

The base-map manuscript should be prepared in pencil on dimensionally stable translucent material. The manuscript should contain grid lines for state plane coordinates at 10-in. intervals. Triangulation and traverse stations are plotted by coordinates, and their names and coordinate values are shown directly on the map. The positions of bench marks, together with their elevations, should be indicated. The map should contain all construction-line notes, dimensions, and references; right-of-way lines; street center lines with bearings; every P.C., P.T., and P.I. along the center lines; and curve radii and central angles. The corners of streets and angle points should be clearly defined. Any information which cannot otherwise be made clear at the map scale should be shown in enlarged detail on the margin of the sheet. Streets should be plotted and their widths noted on the map.

The information shown on the base map should be reliable and complete, so that it will not be necessary to consult original records. The manuscripts should be kept up to date as more survey information is obtained. Results of survey activities conducted by state, federal, and private agencies, as well as by public utilities, should be shown on the base maps when the reliability of such information is established.

Reproductions of the base maps should be made available to surveyors and engineers operating in the city, so that all activities are coordinated on one common base.

18-7. Topographic Map of City. The topographic map should cover the built-up areas of the city and the development areas surrounding it. The map, to a scale of 1 in. = 200 ft and with a contour interval of 2 or 5 ft, should conform to the size of the base-map sheets. If the maps are to be published in color, the published sheets should show the topography by means of contours in brown. The drainage, comprising such features as streams, ponds, and lakes, is portrayed in blue. Black ink is used for the following features: structures, such as railroads, bridges, culverts, and curbs; bench marks and other monuments; property lines, including street lines; boundaries of public property and political subdivisions; boundaries of recorded subdivisions; street names; names of parks, subdivisions, streets, and lakes; names of buildings; property dimensions; the height and character of buildings; grid lines or grid ticks; and lot numbers. Wooded areas and public property are shown in green.

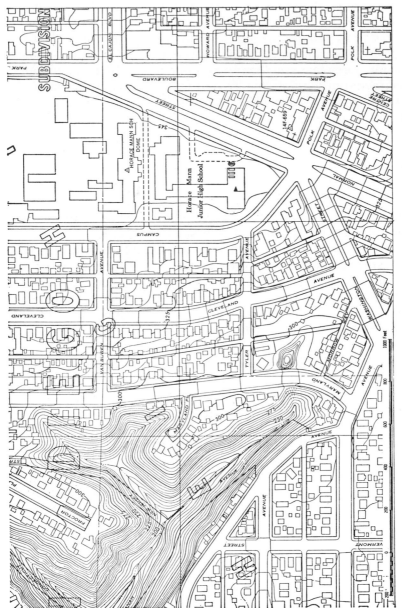

FIG. 18–3.   Portion of Sheet G-18 of the topographic map series covering the city of San Diego, California. Original scale is 1 in. = 200 ft. (Courtesy of city of San Diego.)

The compilation of city topographic maps by means of aerial photogrammetry is recommended as superior to any other method of topographic mapping in accuracy, time, and cost. The control is obtained by third-order traverse and levels, supplemented by transit-stadia or plane-table traverse and levels, or by existing base maps. Photogrammetric compilation is supplemented by plane-table mapping in areas where more information is necessary than can be obtained photogrammetrically.

In Fig. 18-3 is shown a portion of Sheet G-18 of the Metropolitan Topographic Survey of the City of San Diego, California. The published scale is 1 in. = 200 ft, and the contour interval is 5 ft. Elevations are based on the City of San Diego Vertical Datum. Grid lines of the California Coordinate System, Zone VI, are shown at 5-in. intervals. This series of maps was produced by aerial photogrammetry supplemented by field-completion and field-editing surveys.

A final topographic map is judged to be sufficiently accurate if elevations determined from the contours on the map are correct within one-half the contour interval. The horizontal position of any well-defined point should be correct within 0.02 in. at the published scale. Errors in excess of these limits should not occur in more than 10 per cent of the number of points tested. The mapping should be tested by running profile levels along traverse lines selected at random, and comparing these profiles with those obtained from the contours on the map.

Property lines located on the map are checked by assembling all available recorded plats of subdivisions. Distances between identified points and lines, such as monuments, fences, street lines, and block corners, are scaled from the manuscript sheets and compared with the corresponding distances shown on the recorded plats. Where there are many discrepancies, the manuscript sheet is checked in the field. When all identified lines have been checked, these lines are used as a basis for plotting the recorded information pertaining to the remaining lines and corners. The completed map should show street and alley lines, boundaries of recorded subdivisions, boundaries of public property, parks, playgrounds, schools, and other important areas.

18-8. City Property Survey. The city property survey marks by suitable monuments all corner, angle, and curve points of the street lines, and establishes coordinate values for these and other critical points. When this is done, property monuments which become lost or obliterated may be conveniently and precisely reestablished from their known mathematical relations with other marked points. Thus, each monument serves as a witness for every other monument.

The first aim of the property survey is the adequate location and recording of all street lines, which constitute the boundaries of the public's property. The property survey tends to stabilize the boundaries of private property by furnishing an adequate control for the use of those engaged in property surveying. It is usually desirable to complete the work of establishing authoritative dimensions for public property as rapidly as time and opportunity permit, especially in the older sections of a city, where original surveys are often very faulty. The work in the newer sections is usually of a better grade, having been controlled through plat laws.

The work is begun by assembling all the available recorded information and the records of earlier surveys. When little or no information is available, this fact should furnish one of the strongest arguments for immediate action. The next step is the field location of all street intersection, angle, and curve points. Locating such points involves skill and judgment that is acquired only by years of experience with this class of work. The experienced man is familiar with the more important court decisions and realizes the weight that must be given to occupation lines. As soon as the location of a point has been definitely determined, a monument should be set either directly at the point or at a standard offset distance from it. Because of present-day traffic conditions, the use of standard offset monuments is usually preferable. These monuments should be located from the second-order traverse with a precision of 1:15,000, or with such precision that any point whose location is dependent on that of the monument can be located within ¼ in. of its true position.

The property maps should be drawn to a scale of 1 in. = 50 ft, and the layout of the sheets should conform with that used for the topographic map. The original sheets should be of the best quality paper, and from them tracings should be made on the best quality linen. The maps should show the bearings and lengths of street lines, alley lines, and boundaries of public property; the street widths and intersections; the coordinates of all intersection, angle, and curve points; and the locations of traverse stations. In addition there should appear all existing monuments or other witness markers; public, industrial, and commercially important buildings; private buildings in sparsely settled areas; and such features as railroads and bridges. The lettering should include street names; names of parks, subdivisions, streams, and lakes; names of public or semipublic buildings; and the numbers of bench marks and other monuments.

18-9. Underground Map. The purpose of the underground map is to show the locations of all sewers, water pipes, gas mains, electrical conduits, heating lines, subways, and tunnels, including their elevations at critical points. Much of the information to appear on such a map can be taken from the original construction plans and the records of public-service companies, this information being supplemented by such field surveys as may be required to complete the map.

The property maps can be used as a base for the underground map, many of the property dimensions being omitted to prevent overcrowding. The final maps, made on the best quality tracing linen, should show street, alley, and easement lines, plotted to scale, with the various widths in figures; existing monuments and bench marks; and surface structures, such as sidewalks, curbs, pavements, street railroads, transmission-line poles, and trees in parking areas. The underground structures should be differentiated by suitable symbols, and the sizes of the pipes, the per cents of grade on gravity lines, and the elevations at critical points should be indicated. The leveling should be of second-order precision, or at least sufficiently accurate to permit the preparation of plans for new construction without fear of interference with existing structures. The horizontal locations should be shown with respect to the street and alley lines. As such a map soon becomes obsolete, some provision should be made for keeping it up to date.

18-10. City Wall Map. The wall map of the entire city and its immediate environs should be prepared to a scale not smaller than 1 in. = 2000 ft. Where this scale produces a map too large for desk use and for commercial distribution, a photographic reduction can be made for those uses. The wall map can usually be made from the topographic sheets by photographic reduction. The completed map should show, in black, all public property lines, streets, roads, alleys, political boundary lines and boundary lines of public property, private property lines of large undeveloped or industrial tracts, railroad lines and rights of way, public and semipublic buildings, industrially and commercially important buildings, bridges, viaducts, cemeteries and parks, harbor lines, docks, and piers. The drainage, as rivers, streams, lakes, ocean shore-lines, and marshes, should be shown in blue. The contours, drawn to an interval consistent with the scale of the map, should appear in brown. Green is used for the wooded areas. The map should be made sufficiently large to provide for future expansion without redrafting the original. The streets should be indexed by marginal letters and numbers.

18-11. Surveys for Public Improvements. Surveys for public improvements, such as sewers and water lines, involve no new principles. Before a sewer system can be intelligently designed, a topographic map of the area to be served, and preferably of the entire city, should be prepared. After the general plan has been adopted, detailed surveys, consisting of profiles of the lines to be traversed by the proposed sewers, are made for use in preparing the detailed plans.

18-12. Town, City, and Village Plats. A building lot which is to be conveyed by deed can be described either with respect to existing land lines or by reference to a plat. In the first method, the bearing and length of each side are given, and the description as a whole is tied to some section line or other well-defined property line. As the distance from the section line increases, the description becomes more and more complicated, particularly when curved boundaries are encountered and when the tie to the section line is a traverse of many sides. In the second method, the description is greatly simplified, consisting merely of the lot number and the name of the recorded plat of which it is a part.

Most states have laws which govern the platting or subdividing of land into city or town lots. While some of the details may differ, the main requirements in the various states are essentially the same. The first requirement is usually a well-defined boundary of the tract to be platted, with the corners marked by permanent monuments, to which reference is made on the plat. The tract is divided into streets and blocks by placing permanent monuments at all intersections of two streets, of two alleys, of a street and an alley, and of a street or alley with a boundary of the plat. The lot corners are marked by semipermanent monuments, preferably iron pipe.

The survey is then platted on paper, the plat showing all blocks, lots, streets, alleys, parks, and monuments; the sizes of all lots, the lot numbers, and the names or numbers of all streets with their widths and courses; the directions and lengths of the boundaries of the tract, and all other information that will enable surveyors to retrace the lines accurately. The plat contains a written or printed description, which should be so complete that from it, without reference to the plat, the starting point of the tract can be determined and the outlines can be run. The starting point should be located with reference to some well-defined point, such as some certain point in the section when the land platted is in a state where the rectangular system of subdivision has been in effect.

The owners of the land sign a certificate on the plat, acknowledging that they have caused the plat to be made, and dedicating all streets, alleys, and parks to the use of the public. The surveyor certifies that the plat is a correct one and that the monuments described in it have been placed as shown on the plat.

Before a plat can be recorded, it must be approved by certain public officials or boards. In this manner, the locations and widths of the streets, the sizes of the lots, and the proper grading of the streets can be controlled by the municipality or other interested public boards. When the plat has been finally approved, one copy is placed on record in the office of the register of deeds or similar official. Additional copies may be required for city and state records.

18-13. Survey for Plat. The first step in the subdivision of a tract into blocks and lots is an accurate survey of the boundaries of the parcel. The next step, if the ground is irregular, is a topographic survey of the area. The blocks and lots are then laid out on paper. Where zoning or planning boards are in existence, it is usually necessary to locate the principal streets in conformity with the general layout of the district adopted by such boards. In such cases, the widths of the streets are also specified by the board.

Rectangular blocks with streets at right angles to one another should not be adopted when the topography is such that curved streets and irregular-shaped lots would be more advantageous. By fitting the locations of the streets to the topography of the ground, the rates of grade will be comparatively low. Less grading will then be required for the streets, and the location of storm and sanitary sewers will generally be simplified. Some of the older portions of San Francisco can be pointed out as a horrible example of the adoption of a rectangular layout to topography that is utterly unsuited to such a plan. The result has been that the grades on some streets are so excessive as to render them practically worthless as thoroughfares.

After the paper layout has been completed, the field location is made. Street lines or block corners are first located from points on the boundaries of the tract, and the individual lot corners are then established. As these lines are to serve as property boundaries, extreme care should be taken to insure their accuracy. The work should be so conducted as to insure a precision of about 1:10,000. The monuments marking important points should be as permanent as possible and referenced whenever possible. Some state plat laws now require for all important monuments the use of iron pipe that is at least 1 in. in diameter and at least 15 in. long, and is set in a concrete base at least 4 in. in diameter and 48 in. in depth.

18-14. Lot Survey. The survey of a lot that is described with reference to a certain plat may be simple or complicated, the requirements depending on the shape of the block and on the monuments that may be available. In Fig. 18-4 is illustrated an example of the simpler sort, where the monuments which were placed at the block

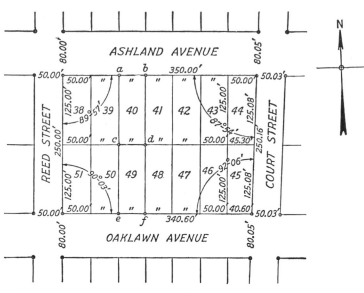

FIG. 18–4. Lot survey.

corners can be found and identified. In locating the corners of Lot No. 40, the method of proportionate measurements must be used. Although the widths of the lots fronting on Ashland Avenue are shown on the plat as 50.00 ft, it is also evident that the total frontage has been equally divided among the seven lots. Consequently, if there is any excess or deficiency in the frontage, it should be equally distributed. For this reason, the corners *a* and *b* are set at distances from the northwest corner of the block equal, respectively, to 2/7 and 3/7 times the total block frontage. Temporary marks are set at *e* and *f* by measuring the south side of the block and locating these points by proportionate measurements. The other two lot corners, *c* and *d*, are located at the mid-points of the lines *ae* and *bf*.

If corners set on the original survey can be found and identified, such points are usually held to be the true corners, even though they have been erroneously located. When land has been held by an owner for a certain period of time, ordinarily 20 years, and adjacent owners are unable to reach an agreement on the boundary lines and bring the case into court, the occupation lines are usually held by the court to be the property lines. As pointed out in Sec. 17-24, the surveyor has no power to "establish" property lines. In the majority of cases, particularly where there is no serious disagreement, his findings will be accepted as final by the adjacent property owners. He should at all times so conduct his work as to be reasonably certain that his opinions will be supported if the question of location is brought before a court for final decision.

When many of the monuments are missing and when errors have been made in the original survey, the problem will be much more difficult than in the example shown in Fig. 18-4. Considerable skill and judgment will be required to weigh properly the conflicting evidence that may be disclosed as the survey progresses.

Some of the more important legal decisions relative to property surveys are cited in the books listed in the Bibliography at the end of Chapter 17.

18-15. Metes and Bounds. The survey of a piece of ground by metes and bounds is the oldest type of land surveying. It consists of determining the length and direction of each side of the parcel and planting permanent monuments at the corners of the property. The lands in the thirteen original states were surveyed in this manner, but in many instances the descriptions are so vague and incomplete as to make the rerunning of the lines an impossibility. The following description, taken from the Hartford, Connecticut, Probate Court records for 1812 will illustrate what is often encountered.

"147 acres, 3 rods, and 19 rods after deducting whatever swamp, water, rock and road areas there may be included therein and all other lands of little or no value, the same being part of said deceased's 1280 acre colony grant, and the portion hereby set off being known as near to and on the other side of Black Oak Ridge, bounded and described more in particular as follows, to wit:—Commencing at a heap of stone, about a stone's throw from a certain small clump of alders, near a brook running down off from a rather high part of said ridge; thence, by a straight line to a certain marked white birch tree, about two or three times as far from a jog in a fence going around a ledge nearby; thence, by another straight line in a different direction, around said ledge and the Great Swamp, so called; thence, in line of said lot in part and in part by another piece of fence which joins on to said line, and by an extension of the general run of said fence to a heap of stone near a surface rock; thence, as aforesaid, to the 'Horn,' so called, and passing around the same as aforesaid, as far as the 'Great Bend,' so called, and from thence to a squarish sort of a jog in another fence, and so on to a marked black oak tree with stones piled around it; thence, by another straight line in about a contrary direction and somewhere about parallel with the line around by the ledge and the Great Swamp, to a stake and stone bounds not far off from the old Indian trail; thence, by another straight line on a course diagonally parallel, or nearly so, with 'Fox Hollow Run,' so called, to a certain marked red cedar tree out on a sandy sort of a plain; thence, by another straight line, in a different direction, to a certain marked yellow oak tree on the off side of a knoll with a flat stone laid against it; thence, after turning around in another direction, and by a sloping straight line to a certain heap of stone which is, by pacing, just 18 rods and about one half a rod more from the stump of the big hemlock tree where Philo Blake killed the bear; thence, to the corner begun at by two straight lines of about equal length, which are to be run by some skilled and competent surveyor, so as to include the area and acreage as herein before set forth."

For purposes of rerunning, a more favorable description would contain the length and bearing of each side and would include references to permanent objects which are still in existence. If the surveyor can find and identify the two ends of any one line, his work is greatly simplified, since that line affords him a comparison between his tape and the chain used in the original survey and makes unnecessary any consideration of magnetic declinations. The interior angles of the tract can be calculated from the given bearings and these computed angles turned off from the identified corners when searching for the remaining ones.

If only one of the original corners can be found, it will be necessary to know whether the bearings given in the description are magnetic or true ones. If they are magnetic, the surveyor must ascertain the value of the declination at the time the survey was made and what it is at present, if he is to use a compass in determining the approximate directions of the lines from that corner. What has been said in Sec. 17-24 relative to the relocation of lost corners applies also to the resurvey of a tract described by metes and bounds.

In many of the thirteen original states, extensive resurveys have been necessary to define property boundaries. Massachusetts has an active geodetic-survey organization which has extended the triangulation of the U. S. Coast and Geodetic Survey and has computed statewide plane coordinates for use in land surveys. Both land titles and land boundaries are adjudicated by a specially organized land court.

19

The Adjustment of Instruments

19-1. Remarks. No matter how perfectly an instrument may be adjusted when it leaves the instrument maker, it seldom remains in that condition for any considerable length of time, particularly when in daily use, subjected to rough handling, and transported by car or truck over all kinds of roads. While the field operations can be conducted so as to eliminate errors due to imperfect adjustment, more time is required when the work is done in this manner. For this reason, every engineer and surveyor should be able to determine whether or not his instruments are in proper adjustment and, if they are not, to adjust them.

Nearly all the adjustments of the transit and the level depend on the principle of reversion. By reversing the position of the instrument, the effect of the error is doubled. The adjustments are made by turning the capstan-headed screws or nuts which control the positions of the cross hairs and the bubble tubes. The beginner should be very careful not to put too much tension on these screws, as otherwise the threads may be stripped or the screw broken. The adjusting pins should be of the proper size to prevent damaging the holes in the screws and nuts.

When an instrument is badly out of adjustment, it may be necessary to repeat the adjustments several times. Time will usually be saved in such cases by not attempting to perfect each adjustment the first time, since the adjustment of the other parts of the instrument may affect the earlier adjustments.

19-2. Cross Hairs of Wye Level. The principal lines of the wye level, both in and out of adjustment, are shown in Fig. 19-1. When the instrument is in proper adjustment and carefully leveled, the horizontal cross hair should be truly horizontal and the intersection of the cross hairs should be a point on the optical axis of the telescope, as in view (*a*). When out of adjustment, the cross hairs may occupy the positions shown in exaggerated form in view (*b*).

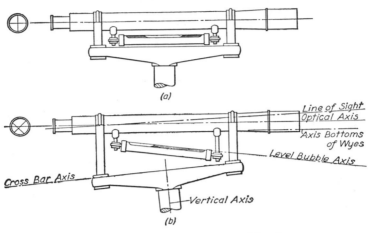

(a)

(b)

FIG. 19–1. Adjustments of level.

To test the inclination of the horizontal cross hair, some well-defined point is found near one end of the hair. The telescope is then turned on its vertical axis to determine whether or not the cross hair appears to remain on the point. If it moves off the point, an adjustment is necessary. On some levels the position of the stop against which the telescope is turned in the wyes can be changed. In other instruments two adjacent capstan screws, which hold the cross hair reticule in position, are loosened, and the cross hair ring is turned until the horizontal hair will remain on a point as the telescope is slowly turned in azimuth.

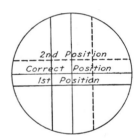

FIG. 19–2. Adjustments of cross hairs of level.

To make the line of sight parallel with the axis of the bottoms of the wyes, the clips that hold the telescope in the wyes are loosened and the intersection of the cross hairs is made to coincide with some well-defined point. The horizontal motion of the telescope is clamped and the telescope is rotated 180° in the wyes. If the cross hairs are out of adjustment, the intersection will not remain on the point but may take the position shown in Fig. 19-2. Each hair is adjusted by bringing it half-way back to the original position by loosening and tightening opposite screws which control the cross-hair ring. When properly adjusted, the intersection should remain on the point as the telescope is rotated 180° in the wyes. It is not necessary that the instrument be leveled for these two adjustments.

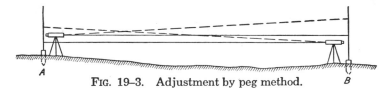

FIG. 19-3.   Adjustment by peg method.

19-3. Bubble Tube of Wye Level. When properly adjusted, the axis of the bubble of the wye level should be in the same plane, and parallel, with the line of sight. With the bubble in the center of the tube, the telescope is rotated a few degrees in the wyes. If the bubble moves from the center, it is brought back by means of the adjusting screws which control the lateral position of the tube. When the tube is in adjustment, the bubble will remain in the center of the tube as the telescope is rotated a few degrees in the wyes in either direction.

Two methods may be used to make the line of sight parallel with the axis of the bubble tube, namely, the *indirect method* and the *direct*, or *peg*, *method*. In the indirect method, the bubble is brought to the center of the tube, and the telescope is then carefully lifted from the wyes, turned end for end, and replaced in the wyes. If the bubble remains in the center, no adjustment is necessary. If it moves from the center, the tube is adjusted by bringing the bubble half-way back to the center by means of the vertical adjustment and the remaining distance by the leveling screws. When the collars of the level are worn, the adjustment cannot be made by this method.

In the direct, or peg, method, the difference in elevation between two fixed points is determined by reciprocal leveling, as shown in Fig. 19-3. The level is first set up so close to point *A* that the eyepiece barely clears a leveling rod held on the point. By sighting through the wrong end of the telescope, the reading of a rod held on *A* can be obtained. The reading of a rod held on *B* is obtained in the usual way. If the level is in adjustment, the difference between these two readings will be the true difference in elevation. The level is next set up very close to *B* and readings are taken of rods held on *B* and *A*. If the difference in elevation obtained from this position of the level does not agree with the value obtained with the level near *A*, the instrument is out of adjustment. The true difference in elevation will be the mean of the two differences. From this value and from the rod reading on *B*, the correct rod reading on *A* can be calculated. The cross hair is brought to this calculated reading by means of the leveling screws. The line of sight is now horizontal but the bubble is not centered. It is brought back to the center of the tube by means of the vertical adjustment at the end of the tube.

Various modifications of this method are in common use. One modification is to obtain the true difference in elevation by setting the level exactly midway between A and B. The level is then moved a little beyond either A or B and, the rod having been read on the near point, the correct reading for the distant point can be calculated. By setting A and B at the same elevation, the correct reading on the distant rod will be identical with the reading obtained on the near point.

19-4. Wyes. The object of adjusting the wyes is to make the axis of the bubble tube perpendicular to the vertical axis of the instrument, or parallel with the cross bar. With the instrument leveled up, the telescope is rotated 180° on the vertical axis. If the bubble moves from the center of the tube, it is brought half-way back by means of the large capstan-headed nuts at the ends of the cross bar. It is then brought back to the center by means of the leveling screws. When properly adjusted, the bubble should remain in the center of the tube as the telescope is turned in any direction on the vertical axis. Although this adjustment does not affect the precision of the work done with the level, it is a convenience in that it eliminates the necessity for recentering the bubble as the telescope is turned from one position to another.

19-5. Cross Hair of Dumpy Level. The first adjustment of the dumpy level is to make the horizontal cross hair truly horizontal when the instrument is leveled. The test is the same as for the wye level. A point is found which coincides with one end of the cross hair. If, as the telescope is slowly turned, the point does not remain on the hair, the adjustment is made by rotating the cross-hair ring. When the adjustment is completed, the horizontal cross hair will remain on the point as the telescope is slowly turned in azimuth.

19-6. Bubble Tube of Dumpy Level. The second adjustment of the dumpy level is the same as the final adjustment of the wye level, that is, to make the axis of the bubble tube perpendicular to the vertical axis. If the bubble moves from the center as the telescope is turned 180° in azimuth, an adjustment is necessary. As the position of the telescope with respect to the cross bar cannot be changed, as in the case of the wye level, the adjustment is made by raising or lowering one end of the bubble tube by means of the capstan-headed nuts provided for that purpose. The bubble is brought half-way back by raising or lowering the end of the bubble tube, and the remaining distance with the leveling screws. When the adjustment has been properly made, the bubble should remain in the center of the tube as the telescope is turned from one position to another.

19-7. Line of Sight of Dumpy Level. The final adjustment of the dumpy level is to make the line of sight parallel to the axis of the bubble tube, or to make the line of sight horizontal when the bubble is in the center of the tube. The direct, or peg, method, described in Sec. 19-3, is used in making this adjustment. Instead of adjusting the level bubble, as is done in the adjustment of the wye level, the horizontal cross hair is adjusted. When the rod reading that will give a horizontal line of sight has been calculated, the horizontal cross hair is brought to this reading by means of the capstan-headed screws which control the position of the cross-hair ring.

19-8. Cross Hair of Tilting Dumpy Level. The first adjustment of the tilting dumpy level is to make the horizontal cross hair truly horizontal when the bulls-eye bubble is centered. The test is the same as for the wye and dumpy level. A point is chosen which coincides with one end of the cross hair. If the point does not remain on the hair as the telescope is slowly turned about its vertical axis, the adjustment is made by loosening two adjacent capstan screws and rotating the cross-hair ring.

19-9. Bulls-Eye Bubble of Tilting Dumpy Level. The second adjustment of the tilting level is that of making the circular bubble stay in the center as the telescope is rotated about the vertical axis. If the bubble moves off center when the telescope is turned 180° in azimuth, it is brought half-way back to center in both directions by raising or lowering the bubble mount by means of either capstan screws or spring screws, the method depending on the make of level, and the remaining distance with the leveling screws. This adjustment is not critical because of the tilting feature of the level.

19-10. Bubble Tube of Sensitive Level of Tilting Level. This adjustment gives a horizontal line of sight when the main sensitive bubble is centered. If the level bubble is of the coincidence type, the coincidence of the two ends of the bubble indicates centering. The direct method, described in Sec. 19-3, is used to make this adjustment. When the rod reading that will give a horizontal line of sight has been calculated, the telescope is tilted up or down by means of the tilting knob until the horizontal cross hair is on the correct reading. The main bubble is brought to center (or to coincidence) by raising or lowering one end of the bubble vial.

19-11. Plate Bubbles of Transit. The first adjustment of the transit is to make the axes of the plate levels perpendicular to the vertical axis of the instrument. The transit is set up and each bubble is brought to the center of its tube by means of the leveling screws.

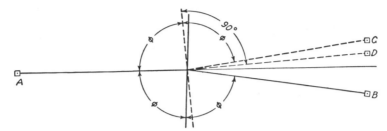

FIG. 19–4.   Second adjustment of vertical cross hair.

The instrument is then revolved on its vertical axis through 180°. If either bubble moves toward one end of the tube, it is brought halfway back by means of the capstan-headed screw at the end of the tube, and the remaining distance by means of the leveling screws. This operation is repeated until both bubbles remain in the centers of the tubes as the telescope is turned in azimuth.

19-12. Cross Hairs of Transit. The first adjustment of the cross hairs of a transit is to make the vertical cross hair perpendicular to the horizontal axis of the telescope, so that, when the other adjustments have been made, it will be truly vertical. This adjustment is made in a manner similar to the one used in making the horizontal cross hair in a level truly horizontal. One end of the vertical hair is brought to some well-defined point, and the telescope is revolved on its transverse axis, so that the point appears to move along the hair. If it does not remain on the hair throughout the motion, two adjacent screws which control the cross-hair ring are loosened, and the ring is rotated.

The purpose of the second adjustment of the vertical cross hair is to make the line of sight perpendicular to the horizontal axis. Whether or not an adjustment is necessary can be determined by prolonging a straight line by the method of double-centering, as described in Sec. 7-6. If, as shown in Fig. 19-4, the two points B and C do not coincide, the cross-hair ring should be shifted laterally until the vertical cross hair appears to strike D, which is at one-fourth of the distance from the second point C to the first point B. Since a double reversing is involved, the apparent error CB is four times the real error.

The third adjustment of the cross hairs is necessary when the transit is used as a level, or when it is used in measuring vertical angles. The purpose of the adjustment is to bring the horizontal hair into the plane of motion of the optical center of the object glass, so that the line of sight will be horizontal when the telescope bubble is

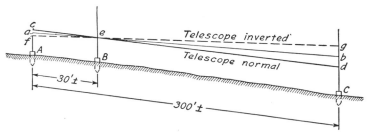

FIG. 19–5.   Adjustment of horizontal cross hair.

in adjustment and the bubble is centered. In making the adjustment, the transit is set up at A, Fig. 19-5, and two stakes are driven at B and C, on the same straight line and at distances of about 30 and 300 ft from A. With the telescope clamped in the normal position and the line of sight represented by cd, rod readings Be and Cd are obtained by holding leveling rods on the two stakes. The telescope is then plunged and the line of sight fg is brought to the former rod reading Be. If the rod reading on C agrees with the reading previously obtained, no adjustment is necessary. If the two readings do not agree, the target is set at Cb, which is the mean of the two readings Cd and Cg, and the horizontal cross hair is brought to the position a, where it appears to bisect the target, by shifting the cross-hair ring vertically by means of the capstan-headed screws on the top and bottom of the telescope. If the instrument is badly out of adjustment, the reading Be will be changed perceptibly as the cross-hair ring is shifted, and the adjustment may have to be repeated several times.

19-13. Standards. If the standards of the transit are in adjustment, the horizontal axis of the telescope is perpendicular to the vertical axis of the instrument. When the plates are leveled, the horizontal axis is truly horizontal, and the line of sight moves in a vertical plane as the telescope is raised and lowered. The test of the standards is made by sighting, with the telescope normal, to some well-defined point on a high object, such as a flagpole or church spire. In Fig. 19-6, A is such a high point. With the horizontal motion clamped, the telescope is depressed and a point B is set

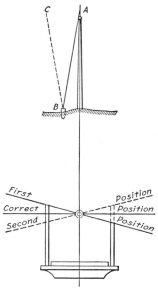

FIG. 19–6.   Adjustment of standards.

on the ground in the line of sight. The telescope is then plunged, the lower clamp is released, and a sight is taken on B. With the lower clamp tight, the telescope is again elevated. If the line of sight strikes the high point A, no adjustment is necessary. If, as in Fig. 19-6, the line of sight now strikes at C, one end of the horizontal axis must be raised or lowered to bring the line of sight midway between C and A. This is done by loosening the upper screws which hold the horizontal axis in place and then turning the small capstan-headed screw that controls the position of the block on which the horizontal axis rests. In the example shown in the figure, the left-hand side should be raised or the right-hand side lowered when the telescope is in the reversed position. When the axis has been properly adjusted, the upper screws are tightened just sufficiently to prevent looseness of the bearing. If the line of sight is now lowered, it should strike point B.

19-14. Telescope Bubble. The purpose of the adjustment of the telescope bubble is to make the axis of its tube parallel to the line of sight. This adjustment is necessary whenever the transit is to be used as a level. When the direction of a horizontal line of sight has been determined by the peg method, described in Sec. 19-3, the line of sight is brought to the correct reading by raising or lowering the telescope with the vertical tangent screw. The bubble tube is then adjusted to bring the bubble to the center of the tube.

19-15. Vertical-Circle Vernier. The vertical circle should preferably read $0°$ when the telescope is horizontal. With the instrument carefully leveled and the telescope bubble in the center of the tube, the screws holding the vernier in place are loosened slightly, and the zeros are made to coincide by tapping the vernier lightly.

19-16. Objective Slide in Telescope. As the telescope is focused for near and distant points, the objective slide should move parallel to the line of sight. On some instruments no provision is made for adjusting the slide; on others a set of screws between the objective and the cross hairs holds in place the ring through which the end of the objective moves. On a well-constructed instrument the adjustment of the objective slide will probably be unnecessary unless the instrument has been damaged. In testing the objective slide on a transit, the line of sight is first tested by the method described in Sec. 19-12, points several hundred feet away from the instrument being used. In the case of the wye level, the adjustment of the cross hairs is tested by rotating the telescope in the wyes, the sight being taken on a distant point. The same tests are then repeated, but points very close to the instrument are used, in order that the objective will be moved out in focusing. If the cross hairs now appear to be out of adjustment, it is because the objective slide has not been moving parallel to the line of sight. When an adjustment can be made, it is accomplished by turning the screws of the objective slide so as to move the slide up or down or laterally a distance equal to one-fourth of the error.

19-17. Centering the Eyepiece. If the intersection of the cross hairs appears to be out of the center of the field of view when the instrument is otherwise in adjustment, the end of the eyepiece must be out of position. Erecting eyepieces are usually held in place by a ring, similar to the cross-hair ring, which is controlled by a set of adjusting screws between the eyepiece and the cross-hair ring. By moving this ring, the intersection of the cross hairs can be brought to the center of the field. As the inverting eyepiece is very short, its inner end needs no support.

19-18. Plane-Table Alidade. The adjustments of the plane-table alidade are very similar to the corresponding adjustments of the transit and the wye level. As small errors in adjustment will have no appreciable effect on the accuracy of the plane-table map, it is unnecessary to make the adjustments with the same refinement that is required for the transit and the level. The methods of adjustment vary somewhat with the type of alidade. The telescope level on some alidades is rigidly attached to the telescope; on others it is a striding level which can be easily removed and turned end for end. On the latter type of alidade, the telescope is of the tube-in-sleeve type, and can be rotated in the same manner as the telescope of a wye level. Most alidades are provided with a vernier level. The board may be leveled by means of a circular level or two levels (similar to the plate levels on the transit) attached to the straightedge; with other alidades the board is leveled with the declinator.

19-19. Levels on Straightedge. The levels attached to the straightedge are adjusted by leveling the board and then lifting the alidade from the board and turning it end for end. The adjustment is made, when necessary, by bringing the bubble half-way back to the center by means of the adjusting screws. Since the board may be warped, the first position of the alidade must be carefully marked so that the alidade will occupy exactly the same position when it is turned end for end on the board.

19-20. Vertical Cross Hair of Alidade. The vertical cross hair of an alidade is adjusted according to the method described for the transit in Sec. 19-12, that is, by noting whether or not the cross hair remains on a fixed point as the telescope is raised or lowered. If an adjustment is necessary, two adjacent screws which hold the cross-hair ring are loosened, and the ring is then turned until the hair will remain on a point as the telescope is rotated.

19-21. Fixed Telescope Level. The adjustment of a level tube that is rigidly attached to the telescope is made by the peg method, exactly as described in Sec. 19-14 for the level on a transit telescope.

19-22. Striding Level. The striding level is attached to the tele-scope, and the bubble is brought to the center of the tube by means of the vertical tangent screw. It is then removed from the telescope and is turned end for end. If the bubble leaves the center of the tube, it is brought half-way back by means of the adjusting screw.

19-23. Line of Sight for Telescope of Tube-in-Sleeve Type. As described for the wye level in Sec. 19-2, the intersection of the cross hairs is brought to some well-defined point and the telescope is ro-tated 180° in the sleeve. If the intersection of the cross hairs leaves the point, each hair is brought half-way back by shifting the cross-hair ring.

19-24. Vernier. The adjustment of the alidade vernier is the same as the corresponding adjustment of the transit. The telescope is leveled by either the striding level or the fixed telescope level, and the zero of the vernier is shifted so as to coincide with the zero of the vertical circle.

19-25. Vernier Level. The telescope is leveled by means of the striding level, or by the peg method. The vernier is then set at zero and the vernier bubble is centered by means of the adjusting screw.

19-26. Index Glass of Sextant. The object of adjusting the index glass of a sextant is to make its plane perpendicular to the plane of the limb. In testing the adjustment, the index bar is placed near the middle of the limb. With his eye near the plane of the limb, the ob-server then notes whether the limb as seen directly and its image as reflected in the index glass form a smooth continuous curve. If they do, the glass is perpendicular to the plane of the limb and the adjust-ment is correct. If the reflected limb appears to be above that part of the limb seen directly, the glass leans forward. If the reflected limb appears to be below, the glass leans backward. In either case, the glass is made perpendicular to the plane of the limb by means of the adjusting screws at its base.

19-27. Horizon Glass. To make the plane of the horizon glass perpendicular to the plane of the limb, a sight is taken through the telescope and horizon glass toward a star or other well-defined distant object, and the index bar is moved slowly until the reflected image passes over the image seen directly. If these images coincide, the horizon glass is perpendicular to the plane of the limb. If they do not coincide, the horizon glass is adjusted by a screw placed under, behind, or beside the glass, according to the construction of the sextant.

19-28. Telescope of Sextant. To make the line of collimation of the telescope of a sextant parallel to the plane of the limb, the sextant is placed in a horizontal position on a table or other support, and the line of sight through the telescope is directed to some well-defined point or mark about 20 ft away. Two small blocks of equal height are placed on the limb, one near each extremity. These blocks should be of exactly equal height, so that a line of sight over their tops will be parallel to the plane of the limb, and should be at the same height above the limb as the center of the telescope. Some sextants are provided with two small brass sights that can be placed on the limb for this purpose. A sight is taken over the tops of the two blocks, or through the sights, as the case may be, in the direction of the point or mark sighted through the telescope. If the line of sight does not intersect the mark, but falls above or below it, the telescope is not parallel to the limb. The telescope can be made parallel by means of the screws in the collar that holds the telescope. This adjustment, however, is not usually made, unless the error is considerable, since a slight lack of parallelism between the line of sight and the plane of the limb does not appreciably affect the angular measurements on the limb.

19-29. Index Error. To make the planes of the mirrors of a sextant parallel when the index reading is zero, the vernier is set at zero, a sight is taken through the telescope toward a star or other distant object, and it is noted whether the direct and reflected images coincide. If they coincide, there is no index error. If they do not coincide, the index bar is moved until they do, and is clamped in this position. The vernier reading when in this position is the index error. The error can be corrected by means of screws at the back of the index glass, which cause it to revolve about an axis perpendicular to the plane of the limb. To make the correction, the vernier is set at zero and, by turning the screws, the index glass is revolved until the two images exactly coincide. This adjustment will usually disturb the previous adjustment of the index glass. As a rule, this adjustment is not made unless the index error is considerable.

19-30. Protection and Cleaning of Instruments. The instrumentman can do much to render unnecessary the frequent adjustment of any surveying instrument. The workmanship on a high-grade transit or level is comparable with that of the finest watch, and the instrument should be handled accordingly. When it is carried from point to point on the shoulder, the clamps should be tight enough to prevent needless wear, yet loose enough to yield if the parts are accidentally bumped. While the transit is not in use or is being carried, the needle should be raised. As the instrument is taken from the shoulder, it should be carefully set down. Otherwise, a cross hair may be broken or the instrument thrown out of adjustment. When being transported by car or truck, it should be held in the lap, if possible. When being transported long distances, it should be packed in its box, crumpled newspapers being used to hold it securely in place. The instrument box should then be packed in a box enough larger to permit the use of several inches of excelsior padding on all sides.

It should be remembered that repairs to a damaged instrument are costly. In addition, it is almost impossible to restore a badly damaged instrument to its original condition. For these reasons, a transit, level, or plane table should not be left unguarded, especially when a set-up on a sidewalk or pavement is unavoidable. The tripod legs should be spread and pushed into the ground sufficiently to prevent its being blown or knocked over.

The instrument should be protected from the rain by a waterproof cover. If such a cover is not at hand, the dust cap should be placed on the objective, and the object glass turned upward. When brought in wet from the field, the instrument should be thoroughly dried before it is replaced in the instrument box. The lenses should be wiped with a piece of the softest chamois skin, silk, or linen. If objects appear blurred or indistinct, the cause probably is a dirty eyepiece. Any dust should be removed with a fine camel's-hair brush. If very dirty, the eyepiece may be cleaned with alcohol and wiped with a clean soft cloth. The lenses should not be cleaned too frequently, as there is danger of their being scratched.

Extreme care should be used in wiping the vertical circle and vernier. The edges should not be rubbed, and the hands should be kept off the vertical circle to prevent tarnishing. If any of the graduated circles become tarnished, the dust should first be removed with a camel's-hair brush. A thin film of watch oil is then spread on the tarnished spots. The oil is allowed to remain for a few hours, and is then wiped off with a soft piece of linen.

While an instrument should not be taken apart unnecessarily, any part which does not work freely should not be forced, but cleaned. Old oil and accumulated dirt should be thoroughly removed with alcohol, or, in the case of screws and screw holes, by the use of soap and water. No oil should be used on the exposed parts, as it soon accumulates enough dust to prevent the part from working freely. On interior bearings, only the finest grade of watch oil should be used, and this very sparingly, since it tends to collect dust and in cold weather may become stiff and prevent the free movement of the part. Usually, enough oil will remain if the oiled part is wiped dry with a soft cloth before it is replaced in the instrument.

19-31. Replacing Broken Cross Hairs. The cross hairs in most American-made instruments are either very fine platinum wires or spider webs. The best type of spider web is taken from the inside of yellowish-brown cocoons found about old stumps and buildings. To replace a broken cross hair, the eyepiece and the two horizontal capstan screws which hold the cross-hair ring in place are removed. If the reticule is now turned 90°, a pointed stick can be screwed into one of the capstan-screw holes. The other two capstan screws are then removed and the reticule is withdrawn from the telescope tube.

The cross hairs are held in place by drops of shellac, their positions being indicated by very fine scratches placed on the reticule by the instrument maker. The old shellac should be removed before the new hairs are placed.

If the new hair is to be satisfactory, it should be clean, opaque, very fine, and stretched almost to the breaking point. Otherwise, it is likely to sag in wet weather. The two ends of the web are fastened with a little shellac to the ends of a partially split stick, and the web is stretched by spreading the ends of the stick with a small wedge. The web can be cleaned, and it will stretch better if it is placed in water for a few minutes before it is given the final stretching. When properly stretched, the web is carefully laid in the fine scratches on the reticule and the ends are fastened with drops of shellac. When dry, the ends are cut and the reticule is replaced in the telescope by means of the pointed stick. The cross hairs must, of course, be adjusted before the instrument is used.

The replacement of a cross hair may prove a very tedious operation. Great difficulty may be encountered in stretching the web sufficiently without breaking it, and also in placing the hair in its correct position without cutting it on the edges of the cross-hair ring.

Appendix

Adjustment of Elementary Surveying Measurements by the Method of Least Squares

A-1. General. Whenever the engineer or surveyor conducts a field survey, no matter how simple or complex, he invariably makes more measurements than are absolutely necessary to locate the points in the survey. A line taped in two directions introduces one measurement more than is necessary to establish the length of the line. Measuring all three angles of a triangle also introduces one superfluous measurement. Closing a line of levels on a fixed bench mark introduces more measurements than are necessary to determine the elevations of the unknown set bench marks. A closed traverse has more than enough measurements necessary to fix the positions of the intermediate traverse stations. These extra measurements are termed redundant measurements. They immediately impose conditions which must be satisfied in order to resolve disagreements or inconsistencies in the measurements.

The redundant measurements are made for the purpose of checking other measurements, uncovering mistakes, adjusting the measurements, and evaluating the magnitudes of the random errors. The mean of several measurements, for example, is the adjusted value of the measured quantity. The residuals resulting from subtracting the mean from the measured values furnish the data necessary to evaluate the random errors by determining the standard error of the set and of the mean value. The adjusted values of intermediate bench marks in a level net are obtained by first determining the closure on a known bench mark, and then distributing this closing error back through the line. This is the same procedure used for the adjustment of a traverse run between two fixed points.

In Chapter 4, procedures for adjusting some of the more elementary surveying measurements were discussed. These simple adjustments were based on one of the following principles of least squares: 1) In a set of measurements all of which are made with the same reliability, that is, all of which have equal weight, the most probable values which can be derived from the set are those which make the sum of the squares of the residuals or corrections a minimum. 2) In a set of measurements having unequal weights, the most probable values are those which make the sum of the products of the weights and the squares of the corrections a minimum. These principles may be stated briefly as follows: For equal-weight measurements,

$$\Sigma v^2 = \text{minimum}$$

For unequal-weight measurements,

$$\Sigma (pv^2) = \text{minimum}$$

The adjustment of measurements by the method of least squares accomplishes the double purpose of satisfying the above conditions and resolving discrepancies or closure errors of the measurements. The least-squares adjustment can be accomplished by either of two general methods. The first method makes use of the formation of *observation equations* in which the corrections are stated as functions of indirectly determined values or parameters of the measurements. By way of example, the mean of the series of measurements in Sec. 4-3 was shown to be most probable value by the formation of the following series of equations:

$$v_1 = M_1 - M$$
$$v_2 = M_2 - M$$
$$\vdots$$
$$v_n = M_n - M$$

These are observation equations. The corrections, or v's, appear on the left-hand side. These are expressed as functions of the measurements themselves and the mean, which is an indirectly determined value. Then, the condition of least squares was applied to the corrections by getting the sum of the squares of the corrections, differentiating with respect to the mean (the indirectly determined parameter), and setting the result equal to zero. The result of these operations is an equation of the form

$$\frac{d(\Sigma v^2)}{dM} = M_1 - M + M_2 - M + \cdots + M_n - M$$
$$= M_1 + M_2 + \cdots + M_n - nM = 0$$

Such an equation is known as a *normal equation*. The solution of this normal equation gives the value of the indirectly determined parameter, M. The residuals are then found by solving the observation equations for the v's. This least-squares adjustment is so simple that we do not bother to form observation equations, differentiate to get the normal equation, and then solve the normal equation to arrive at the mean value. We simply add up all the measured values and divide by the number of measurements.

For a more complex series of measurements, the observation equations must be formed, normalized, and solved, in order to arrive at the best set of parameters which will make Σv^2 a minimum. However, certain systematic procedures tend to simplify these operations, as will be shown later.

The second method for adjustment by least squares takes advantage of *a priori* conditions which must be imposed on the residuals. Such an *a priori* condition is the prior knowledge that the sum of three angles in a plane triangle must be 180°. Also, in a traverse between two fixed points, the sum of the latitudes must equal the difference between the Y-coordinates of the two fixed points. This second method is the method of *condition equations*. For example, if three angles A_0, B_0, and C_0 of a triangle are observed and $A_0 + B_0 + C_0 = 179° \ 59' \ 56.7''$, then we may state the condition by the equation

$$v_A + v_B + v_C = 3.3'' \text{ or } v_A + v_B + v_C - 3.3'' = 0$$

in which v_A, v_B, and v_C are the corrections to be applied to the measured angles. The solution of this condition equation, after the condition of least squares is imposed, is $v_A = + 1.1''$; $v_B = + 1.1''$; $v_C = + 1.1''$. This simple adjustment was discussed in Sec. 4-9.

When forming condition equations, we must include only as many corrections as there are independent measurements. Thus, in the preceding example, if A_0 and B_0 are considered independent, then C_0 must be considered dependent for the following reason: If there were no redundant measurements, then C would equal $180° - (A_0 + B_0)$. Therefore, if the corrections v_A and v_B to A_0 and B_0 are independent, then $v_C = + 3.3'' - (v_A + v_B)$. In other words,

$$v_A = v_A$$

$$v_B = v_B$$

$$v_C = + 3.3'' - (v_A + v_B)$$

These are connecting equations, relating all the v's in terms of only the number of v's which are independent. On squaring, we get

$$v_A{}^2 = v_A{}^2$$

$$v_B{}^2 = v_B{}^2$$

$$v_C{}^2 = [3.3'' - (v_A + v_B)]^2$$

Then
$$\Sigma v^2 = 2v_A{}^2 + 2v_B{}^2 + 3.3^2 - 6.6v_A - 6.6v_B + 2v_A v_B$$

In order to satisfy the condition of least squares, the partial derivative of Σv^2 with respect to each of the independent quantities v_A and

v_B must be made zero. Thus, we get the following normal equations:

$$\frac{\partial(\Sigma\,v^2)}{\partial\,v_A} = 0$$

$$\frac{\partial(\Sigma\,v^2)}{\partial\,v_B} = 0$$

When the differentiations are performed, the results are

$$4v_A - 6.6 + 2v_B = 0$$
$$4v_B - 6.6 + 2v_A = 0$$

By solving these equations, we get $v_A = +\,1.1''$ and $v_B = +\,1.1''$. Substitution of these values of v_A and v_B in the connecting equation $v_C = +\,3.3'' - (v_A + v_B)$ gives $v_C = +\,1.1''$.

When adjusting the three angles of a triangle, we do not bother to form condition equations, connecting equations, and normal equations, but we simply subtract $180°$ from the sum of the three measured angles, divide the discrepancy by 3, and apply a correction of opposite sign to each angle. However, if a quadrilateral or some other net is to be adjusted, many conditions must be satisfied simultaneously. Therefore, the equations must be formed in an orderly fashion in order that they may be solved simultaneously.

If the observations to be adjusted have different weights, then the weights must be incorporated into the adjustment procedure. Let us consider three measurements of the length of a line designated as M_1, M_2, and M_3, with corresponding weights p_1, p_2, and p_3. Also, let the most probable value be designated as $\overline{M}$. Then, by forming observation equations, squaring, and multiplying by the weights, we get

$$v_1 = M_1 - \overline{M}\ ;\ v_1{}^2 = (M_1 - \overline{M})^2\ ;\ p_1\,v_1{}^2 = p_1\,(M_1 - \overline{M})^2$$
$$v_2 = M_2 - \overline{M}\ ;\ v_2{}^2 = (M_2 - \overline{M})^2\ ;\ p_2\,v_2{}^2 = p_2\,(M_2 - \overline{M})^2$$
$$v_3 = M_3 - \overline{M}\ ;\ v_3{}^2 = (M_3 - \overline{M})^2\ ;\ p_3\,v_3{}^2 = p_3\,(M_3 - \overline{M})^2$$

In order to satisfy the condition that $\Sigma\,(pv^2) = $ a minimum, it is necessary to differentiate $\Sigma\,(pv^2)$ with respect to $\overline{M}$ and to set the derivative equal to zero. Thus,

$$\frac{d\Sigma(pv^2)}{d\overline{M}} = -\,2p_1\,(M_1 - \overline{M}) - 2p_2\,(M_2 - \overline{M}) - 2p_3\,(M_3 - \overline{M}) = 0$$

and

$$\overline{M} = \frac{p_1\,M_1 + p_2\,M_2 + p_3\,M_3}{p_1 + p_2 + p_3} = \frac{\Sigma(pM)}{\Sigma p}$$

This result is the weighted mean given by Eq. 4-17.

In the case of three angles of a triangle having different weights, the adjustment by condition equations is as follows: Let us assume that $A_0 + B_0 + C_0 = 179° \ 59' \ 30''$ and that $p_A = 6$, $p_B = 3$, and $p_C = 1$. The condition equation is

$$v_A + v_B + v_C - 30'' = 0$$

Since $v_C = 30'' - (v_A + v_B)$, the connecting equations are

$$v_A = v_A$$
$$v_B = v_B$$
$$v_C = 30'' - (v_A + v_B)$$

Squaring the v's and multiplying by the weights gives

$$v_A{}^2 = v_A{}^2 \qquad\qquad ; \ 6v_A{}^2 = 6v_A{}^2$$
$$v_B{}^2 = v_B{}^2 \qquad\qquad ; \ 3v_B{}^2 = 3v_B{}^2$$
$$v_C{}^2 = [30'' - (v_A + v_B)]^2 \ ; \ 1v_C{}^2 = 1 \ [30'' - (v_A + v_B)]^2$$

In order to satisfy the condition of least squares, the partial derivative of $\Sigma \ (pv^2)$ with respect to each of the independent quantities v_A v_B must be equated to zero. Thus,

$$\frac{\partial \Sigma (pv^2)}{\partial \ v_A} = 0$$

$$\frac{\partial \Sigma (pv^2)}{\partial \ v_R} = 0$$

$$\Sigma(pv^2) = 6v_A{}^2 + 3v_B{}^2 + [30'' - (v_A + v_B)]^2$$

By differentiating and setting the derivatives equal to zero, we get

$$14v_A + 2v_B - 60 = 0$$
$$2v_A + 8v_B - 60 = 0$$

The results obtained by solving these simultaneous equations are $v_A = + 3.3''$ and $v_B = + 6.7''$. Substituting these values in the connecting equation $v_C = 30'' - (v_A + v_B)$ gives $v_C = + 20.0''$. Compare these results with those of the example given in Sec. 4-10.

A-2. Adjustment of a Level Net by Observation Equations. The problem of adjusting a level net involves the tying of the net to previously established bench marks, and the adjustment of the differences in elevations (D.E.'s) between various junction points in the net so that, no matter what route is taken to a point, the same elevation will be obtained. Furthermore, in order to satisfy the condition of least squares, the corrections to the observed D.E.'s must be such that the sum of the weighted squares of the corrections will be a minimum. The weights of the D.E.'s between points are inversely proportional to the lengths of the routes along which the D.E.'s are obtained. For instance, if the D.E. between A and B is determined along two routes, the first one being 3 miles long and the second being 4 miles long, the weight of the first D.E. is $\frac{1}{3}$ and that of the second is $\frac{1}{4}$; or the first has weight 1, while the second has weight 0.75. Weights may also be assumed to be inversely proportional to the number of set-ups of the instrument between two points.

In the level net shown in Fig. A-1, there are eleven independent

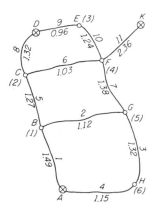

FIG. A-1. Level net.

lines, along which the differences in elevation have been obtained as a result of three-wire leveling. The values shown in the accompanying tabulation have been corrected for the C-factor discussed in Sec. 3-43.

Line	Length in miles	From To	Observed D.E.	Corr. to D.E.
1	1.49	$A-B$	$-\ 3.278$	v_1
2	1.12	$B-G$	$-\ 1.467$	v_2
3	1.32	$G-H$	$+\ 9.756$	v_3
4	1.15	$H-A$	$-\ 4.975$	v_4
5	1.27	$B-C$	$+\ 8.429$	v_5
6	1.03	$C-F$	$-\ 6.528$	v_6
7	1.38	$F-G$	$-\ 3.352$	v_7
8	1.32	$C-D$	$+16.724$	v_8
9	0.96	$D-E$	-12.563	v_9
10	1.24	$E-F$	-10.721	v_{10}
11	2.36	$F-K$	$+12.249$	v_{11}

The subscripts for the v's correspond to the numbers assigned to the lines in Fig. A-1. The elevations of the three bench marks A, D, and K are fixed, as follows: $A = 856.425$ ft; $D = 878.337$ ft; $K = 867.\ 271$ ft.

First, an approximate elevation is computed for each junction point by adding the D.E. of a line from a known elevation to the junction point. Thus,

Approx. Elev. $B = $ Elev. $A + $ D.E.$_{AB}$
Approx. Elev. $B = 856.425 - 3.278 = 853.147$ ft
Approx. Elev. $C = $ Approx. Elev. $B + $ D.E.$_{BC}$
Approx. Elev. $C = 853.147 + 8.429 = 861.576$ ft

Similarly, the approximate elevations of the other junction points are obtained as follows:

Point	From Line	Approx. Elev.
B	AB	853.147
C	BC	861.576
E	CF and FE	865.769
F	CF	855.048
G	BG	851.680
H	GH	861.436

These approximate elevations must be adjusted by adding corrections, which will be designated by x's with subscripts that correspond to the numbers of the junction points shown in parentheses in Fig. A-1. Thus, the adjusted elevations may be represented as follows:

Point	Adjusted Elevation
B......................	$853.147 + x_1$
C......................	$861.576 + x_2$
E......................	$865.769 + x_3$
F......................	$855.048 + x_4$
G......................	$851.680 + x_5$
H......................	$861.436 + x_6$

We can now derive observation equations by applying the following general relationship:

(Observed D.E.$_{1-2}$) + (corr. to D.E.$_{1-2}$) =
(Adjusted Elev. of 2) − (Adjusted Elev. of 1)

For example, between A and B,

$$- 3.278 + v_1 = (853.147 + x_1) - 856.425$$

Between B and G,

$$- 1.467 + v_2 = (851.680 + x_5) - (853.147 + x_1)$$

Between G and H,

$$+ 9.756 + v_3 = (861.436 + x_6) - (851.680 + x_5)$$

Between H and A,

$$- 4.975 + v_4 = (856.425) - (861.436 + x_6)$$

Between B and C,

$$+ 8.429 + v_5 = (861.576 + x_2) - (853.147 + x_1)$$

By writing an observation equation for each D.E. and combining numbers, we obtain eleven equations which express the v's, or the corrections to the D.E.'s, in terms of the x's, or the corrections to the elevations of the points. The results are:

$$v_1 = x_1 + 0$$
$$v_2 = - x_1 + x_5 + 0$$
$$v_3 = - x_5 + x_6 + 0$$
$$v_4 = - x_6 - 0.036$$
$$v_5 = - x_1 + x_2 + 0$$
$$v_6 = - x_2 + x_4 + 0$$
$$v_7 = - x_4 + x_5 - 0.016$$
$$v_8 = - x_2 + 0.037$$
$$v_9 = x_3 - 0.005$$
$$v_{10} = - x_3 + x_4 + 0$$
$$v_{11} = - x_4 - 0.026$$

If each D.E. had equal or unit weight, the condition to be satisfied would be that $\Sigma v^2 = $ minimum, or

$$v_1{}^2 + v_2{}^2 + v_3{}^2 + \cdots + v_{11}{}^2 = \text{minimum}$$

However, since each D.E. is obtained either through a different distance or by a different number of set-ups (the distance is used in this example), each D.E. has a weight which is inversely proportional to the distance involved. Consequently, the condition to be satisfied is $\Sigma \, (pv^2) = $ minimum, or

$$p_1 v_1{}^2 + p_2 v_2{}^2 + \cdots + p_{11} v_{11}{}^2 = \text{minimum}$$

The weights determined by taking the reciprocals of the lengths of the lines are tabulated as shown. It is usually desirable to adjust each weight by a factor in order to make the average weight equal to unity. In this example, it would be necessary to have the weights add up to 11. Since the sum of the tabulated weights is 8.676, each such weight would have to be multiplied by 11/8.676. However, it would be an unnecessary refinement to make the average weight equal to unity in the present example. When the square of each value of v is multiplied by the tabulated weight, the results are as follows:

$$0.672 v_1{}^2 = 0.672 \, (+ x_1 + 0)^2$$
$$0.893 v_2{}^2 = 0.893 \, (- x_1 + x_5 + 0)^2$$
$$0.758 v_3{}^2 = 0.758 \, (- x_5 + x_6 + 0)^2$$

$$0.870v_4{}^2 = 0.870\,(-\,x_6 - 0.036)^2$$

$$0.787v_5{}^2 = 0.787\,(-\,x_1 + x_2 + 0)^2$$

$$0.971v_6{}^2 = 0.971\,(-\,x_2 + x_4 + 0)^2$$

$$0.725v_7{}^2 = 0.725\,(-\,x_4 + x_5 - 0.016)^2$$

$$0.758v_8{}^2 = 0.758\,(-\,x_2 + 0.037)^2$$

$$1.043v_9{}^2 = 1.043\,(+\,x_3 - 0.005)^2$$

$$0.775v_{10}{}^2 = 0.775\,(-\,x_3 + x_4 + 0)^2$$

$$0.424v_{11}{}^2 = 0.424\,(-\,x_4 - 0.026)^2$$

Six normal equations can be formed by adding the right-hand sides of the above equations to get $\Sigma\,(pv^2)$ and then taking the

Line	From To	Length (Miles)	(Weight)
1	A–B	1.49	0.672
2	B–G	1.12	0.893
3	G–H	1.32	0.758
4	H–A	1.15	0.870
5	B–C	1.27	0.787
6	C–F	1.03	0.971
7	F–G	1.38	0.725
8	C–D	1.32	0.758
9	D–E	0.96	1.043
10	E–F	1.24	0.775
11	F–K	2.36	0.424

partial derivative of $\Sigma\,(pv^2)$ with respect to each of the x's and setting each partial derivative equal to zero. Thus,

$$\frac{\partial\Sigma(pv^2)}{\partial x_1} = 0\;;\quad \frac{\partial\Sigma(pv^2)}{\partial x_2} = 0\;;\;\cdots\;;\quad \frac{\partial\Sigma(pv^2)}{\partial x_6} = 0$$

The solution of these equations would give the values of the six parameters (the x's) which would satisfy the condition of least squares.

The formation of the normal equations can be made quite mechanical by realizing that they take the following form:

$[paa]x_1 + [pab]x_2 + [pac]x_3 + [pad]x_4 + [pae]x_5 + [paf]x_6 + [pak] = 0$
$[pba]x_1 + [pbb]x_2 + [pbc]x_3 + [pbd]x_4 + [pbe]x_5 + [pbf]x_6 + [pbk] = 0$
$[pca]x_1 + [pcb]x_2 + [pcc]x_3 + [pcd]x_4 + [pce]x_5 + [pcf]x_6 + [pck] = 0$
$[pda]x_1 + [pdb]x_2 + [pdc]x_3 + [pdd]x_4 + [pde]x_5 + [pdf]x_6 + [pdk] = 0$
$[pea]x_1 + [peb]x_2 + [pec]x_3 + [ped]x_4 + [pee]x_5 + [pef]x_6 + [pek] = 0$
$[pfa]x_1 + [pfb]x_2 + [pfc]x_3 + [pfd]x_4 + [pfe]x_5 + [pff]x_6 + [pfk] = 0$

In these equations the p's are the weights, the a's are the coefficients of the x_1's in the observation equations, the b's are the coefficients of the x_2's, and so on, and the k's are the constant terms of the observation equations. The quantity $[pbd]$, for example, is the sum of six products, or $p_1b_1d_1 + p_2b_2d_2 + p_3b_3d_3 + p_4b_4d_4 + p_5b_5d_5 + p_6b_6d_6$.

Arranging the observation equations in tabular form as shown simplifies the formation of the normal equations. The values under x_1

TABULATED OBSERVATION EQUATIONS

v	p	x_1	x_2	x_3	x_4	x_5	x_6	k
1	0.672	+ 1						0
2	0.893	− 1				+ 1		0
3	0.758					− 1	+ 1	0
4	0.870						− 1	− 0.036
5	0.787	− 1	+ 1					0
6	0.971		− 1		+ 1			0
7	0.725				− 1	+ 1		− 0.016
8	0.758		− 1					+ 0.037
9	1.043			+ 1				− 0.005
10	0.775			− 1	+ 1			0
11	0.424				− 1			− 0.026

are the a's, those under x_2 are the b's, and so on. The normal equations, which are formed as indicated, can also be tabulated as shown.

TABULATED NORMAL EQUATIONS

x_1	x_2	x_3	x_4	x_5	x_6	k	
+ 2.352	− 0.787			− 0.893		0	= 0
− 0.787	+ 2.516		− 0.971			− 0.02805	= 0
		+ 1.818	− 0.775			− 0.00521	= 0
	− 0.971	− 0.775	+ 2.895	− 0.725		+ 0.02262	= 0
− 0.893			− 0.725	+ 2.376	− 0.758	− 0.01160	= 0
				− 0.758	+ 1.628	+ 0.03132	= 0

Because $[pab] = [pba]$, $[pac] = [pca]$, and so on, the coefficients of the x's in the table are symmetrical about the diagonal running through the coefficients $[paa]$, $[pbb]$, ..., $[pff]$. Thus, the coefficients in the row i are equal to the coefficients in the column i. Being familiar with this symmetry obviously permits a great saving of time in forming the normal equations.

There are a number of ways of solving a set of normal equations, but the explanations of the procedures are considered outside the scope of this Appendix. You should refer to a textbook on least-squares adjustment for a thorough treatment of the subject.

The solution of the preceding set of six normal equations gives the values of the corrections to be added to the approximate elevations of the junction points to get their adjusted values. Solving the original observation equations for the v's gives the quantities needed to determine the standard errors of the measured values. The standard error of unit weight is

$$\sigma_0 = \sqrt{\frac{\Sigma v^2}{n - u}}$$

in which n is the number of lines and u is the number of junction points. The quantity $(n - u)$ is the number of redundant measurements or the number of degrees of freedom (see Sec. 4-4). In the case at hand, $n = 11$ and $u = 6$. Thus,

$$\sigma_0 = \sqrt{\frac{\Sigma v^2}{5}}$$

The standard error of each line is then obtained by Eq. 4-19.

After the approximate elevations of the junction points have been adjusted, the corrected values are considered as fixed elevations. The elevations of any intermediate bench marks established along the various lines are then adjusted between two fixed junction points by the method discussed in Sec. 4-11.

A-3. Adjustment of a Quadrilateral by Condition Equations. The conditions to be satisfied in a completed quadrilateral are as follows: 1) The angles in three of the four triangles must add up to 180°, and 2) the length of the closing side of the quadrilateral must be the same, no matter which way it is computed. Thus, there are three angle conditions and one side condition in a completed quadrilateral. To amplify the above conditions, consider the quadrilateral shown in Fig. A-2. On the left is shown the complete quadrilateral. The middle diagram shows C located from A and B by the lines AC and BC. These lines introduce an angle condition, but do not create a condition relating to the lengths of the sides. The right-hand diagram shows D located from C and A by the lines CD and AD. These two lines introduce a second angle condition because they complete the second triangle, but there is still no condition relating

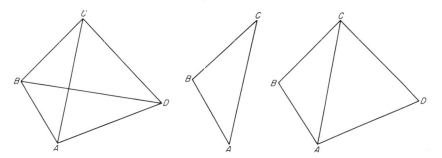

FIG. A-2. Conditions in a quadrilateral.

to the lengths of the sides. Now, consider the effect of adding the line BD. This line forms two additional triangles, and the angles of each must add up to 180°. However, if the angles of one of the two triangles sum up correctly, and the first two angle conditions are satisfied, the angle condition in the other triangle will be satisfied. Therefore, the addition of the line BD adds one more angle condition, making three in all. The addition of BD permits the development of a single side condition which is based on the following requirement: Beginning with side AB, four different routes may be taken through the triangles to calculate side CD, each of which must give the same value to the computed length of CD.

Following is a list of directions measured at the four stations shown in Fig. A-3.

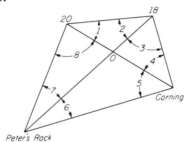

FIG. A-3. Observed quadrilateral.

Instrument at 20		Instrument at Corning	
18	0° 00′ 00.0″	Peters Rock	0° 00′ 00.0″
Corning	40° 08′ 17.9″	20	61° 29′ 34.3″
Peters Rock	112° 04′ 06.9″	18	103° 20′ 44.2″

Instrument at 18		Instrument at Peters Rock	
Corning	0° 00′ 00.0″	20	0° 00′ 00.0″
Peters Rock	53° 11′ 23.7″	18	23° 06′ 37.3″
20	98° 00′ 38.4″	Corning	46° 34′ 28.5″

The resulting angles including the corrections are:

1. $40° 08′ 17.9″ + v_1$ 5. $61° 29′ 34.3″ + v_5$
2. $44° 49′ 14.7″ + v_2$ 6. $23° 27′ 51.2″ + v_6$
3. $53° 11′ 23.7″ + v_3$ 7. $23° 06′ 37.3″ + v_7$
4. $41° 51′ 09.9″ + v_4$ 8. $71° 55′ 49.0″ + v_8$

When the angles in three of the four triangles are considered, the results are as follows:

Corning	$41° 51′ 09.9″ + v_4$
20	$40° 08′ 17.9″ + v_1$
18	$98° 00′ 38.4″ + v_2 + v_3$

$$180° 00′ 06.2″ + v_1 + v_2 + v_3 + v_4 = 180° 00′ 00.0″$$

Peters Rock	$23°\ 06'\ 37.3'' + v_7$
20	$112°\ 04'\ 06.9'' + v_1 + v_8$
18	$44°\ 49'\ 14.7'' + v_2$

$$179°\ 59'\ 58.9'' + v_1 + v_2 + v_7 + v_8 = 180°\ 00'\ 00.0''$$

Corning	$61°\ 29'\ 34.3'' + v_5$
Peters Rock	$46°\ 34'\ 28.5'' + v_6 + v_7$
20	$71°\ 55'\ 49.0'' + v_8$

$$179°\ 59'\ 51.8'' + v_5 + v_6 + v_7 + v_8 = 180°\ 00'\ 00.0''$$

These relationships give rise to the following three angle-condition equations:

$$v_1 + v_2 + v_3 + v_4 + 06.2'' = 0$$
$$v_1 + v_2 + v_7 + v_8 - \ \ 1.1'' = 0$$
$$v_5 + v_6 + v_7 + v_8 - \ \ 8.2'' = 0$$

The one side-condition equation can be arrived at by starting with any one of the four sides of the quadrilateral. The necessary relationships for each are as follows:

(a)
$$\frac{\text{Peters Rock–18}}{\text{Peters Rock–20}} = \frac{\sin (1 + 8)}{\sin 2}$$

$$\frac{\text{Peters Rock–Corning}}{\text{Peters Rock–18}} = \frac{\sin 3}{\sin (4 + 5)}$$

$$\frac{\text{Peters Rock–20}}{\text{Peters Rock–Corning}} - \frac{\sin 5}{\sin 8}$$

Here, angles 6 and 7 are omitted.

(b)
$$\frac{\text{20–Corning}}{\text{20–18}} = \frac{\sin (2 + 3)}{\sin 4}$$

$$\frac{\text{20–Peters Rock}}{\text{20–Corning}} = \frac{\sin 5}{\sin (6 + 7)}$$

$$\frac{\text{20–18}}{\text{20–Peters Rock}} = \frac{\sin 7}{\sin 2}$$

Here, angles 1 and 8 are omitted.

(c)
$$\frac{\text{18–Peters Rock}}{\text{18–Corning}} = \frac{\sin (4 + 5)}{\sin 6}$$

$$\frac{\text{18–20}}{\text{18–Peters Rock}} = \frac{\sin 7}{\sin (1 + 8)}$$

$$\frac{18\text{--Corning}}{18\text{--}20} = \frac{\sin 1}{\sin 4}$$

Here, angles 2 and 3 are omitted.

(d)
$$\frac{\text{Corning--}20}{\text{Corning--Peters Rock}} = \frac{\sin (6 + 7)}{\sin 8}$$

$$\frac{\text{Corning--}18}{\text{Corning--}20} = \frac{\sin 1}{\sin (2 + 3)}$$

$$\frac{\text{Corning--Peters Rock}}{\text{Corning--}18} = \frac{\sin 3}{\sin 6}$$

Here, angles 4 and 5 are omitted.

It is also possible to develop a side-condition equation by considering the point O in Fig. A-3 in the following manner:

(e)
$$\frac{O\text{--}20}{O\text{--Peters Rock}} = \frac{\sin 7}{\sin 8}$$

$$\frac{O\text{--}18}{O\text{--}20} = \frac{\sin 1}{\sin 2}$$

$$\frac{O\text{--Corning}}{O\text{--}18} = \frac{\sin 3}{\sin 4}$$

$$\frac{O\text{--Peters Rock}}{O\text{--Corning}} = \frac{\sin 5}{\sin 6}$$

In this case, all the measured angles are included.

The selection of some one of the five sets of triangles depends on the size of the angles involved. In order to make the constant term in the side-condition equation as large as possible, the smallest angles are selected. If all the angles involved are of the same general magnitude, then set (e) is selected because it involves all the angles. We will select set (b), since the sum of angles 1 and 8 is larger than the sum of the two angles at any other station.

Using the three equations in (b), we multiply the left-hand members, multiply the right-hand members, and equate the products. The result is:

$$\frac{(20\text{--Corning})}{(20\text{--}18)} \cdot \frac{(20\text{--Peters Rock})}{(20\text{--Corning})} \cdot \frac{(20\text{--}18)}{(20\text{--Peters Rock})}$$

$$= \frac{\sin (2 + 3)}{\sin 4} \cdot \frac{\sin 5}{\sin (6 + 7)} \cdot \frac{\sin 7}{\sin 2}$$

or

$$1 = \frac{\sin{(2+3)}}{\sin 4} \cdot \frac{\sin 5}{\sin{(6+7)}} \cdot \frac{\sin 7}{\sin 2}$$

Clearing fractions gives

$$\sin 4 \cdot \sin{(6+7)} \cdot \sin 2 = \sin{(2+3)} \cdot \sin 5 \cdot \sin 7$$

It is difficult to handle this trigonometric equation. We therefore make a linear equation by taking the logarithms of both sides, as follows:

$$\log \sin 4 + \log \sin{(6+7)} + \log \sin 2$$
$$= \log \sin{(2+3)} + \log \sin 5 + \log \sin 7$$

In order to make a condition equation, we include the corrections to the angles. Thus,

$$\log \sin{(4+v_4)} + \log \sin{(6+7+v_6+v_7)} + \log \sin{(2+v_2)}$$
$$= \log \sin{(2+3+v_2+v_3)} + \log \sin{(5+v_5)} + \log \sin{(7+v_7)}$$

If the v's are corrections in seconds, we can express each logarithm in a more convenient form. For example, the function for angle 4 would be

$$\log \sin{(4+v_4)}$$
$$= \log \sin 4 + (\text{change in value of log sin 4 per second})v_4$$

As in practically all adjustments of angles, the value of the difference in the logarithmic sine of an angle for one second is used with the decimal point after the 6th place. The side-condition equation is laid out as follows:

$$
\begin{aligned}
\text{l sin } 4 \quad &= 9.824\ 2681 + 2.35v_4 \\
\text{l sin } (6+7) &= 9.861\ 0980 + 2.00v_6 + 2.00v_7 \\
\text{l sin } 2 \quad &= 9.848\ 1221 + 2.12v_2 \\
\hline
&\ 9.533\ 4882 + 2.35v_4 + 2.00v_6 + 2.00v_7 + 2.12v_2
\end{aligned}
$$

$$
\begin{aligned}
\text{l sin } (2+3) &= 9.995\ 7414 - 0.30v_2 - 0.30v_3 \\
\text{l sin } 5 \quad &= 9.943\ 8691 + 1.14v_5 \\
\text{l sin } 7 \quad &= 9.593\ 8435 + 4.93v_7 \\
\hline
&= 9.533\ 4540 - 0.30v_2 - 0.30v_3 + 1.14v_5 + 4.93v_7
\end{aligned}
$$

Transposing all terms to the left, we have

$$9.5334882 - 9.5334540 + 2.35v_4 + 2.00v_6 + 2.00v_7$$
$$+ 2.12v_2 + 0.30v_2 + 0.30v_3 - 1.14v_5 - 4.93v_7 = 0$$

Collecting terms, simplifying, and arranging the v's in order, we get

$$+ 2.42v_2 + 0.30v_3 + 2.35v_4 - 1.14v_5$$
$$+ 2.00v_6 - 2.93v_7 + 34.2 = 0 \qquad (4)$$

The constant term 34.2 is the difference between the sums of the logarithms on both sides, with the decimal point after the 6th place. The form for adding the logarithms on both sides shown above is not strictly a tabular form with column headings. The work is shown in that manner to indicate better what the actual tabular form means. This is given as follows:

Angle	log sin (+)	Diff. 1″	Angle	log sin (−)	Diff. 1″
4	9.824 2681	+ 2.35	2 + 3	9.995 7414	− 0.30
6 + 7	9.861 0980	+ 2.00	5	9.943 8691	+ 1.14
2	9.848 1221	+ 2.12	7	9.593 8435	+ 4.93
	9.533 4882			9.533 4540	
	− 540				
	342				

The four condition equations are:

$$v_1 + v_2 + v_3 + v_4 + 6.2 = 0$$
$$v_1 + v_2 + v_7 + v_8 - 1.1 = 0$$
$$v_5 + v_6 + v_7 + v_8 - 8.2 = 0$$
$$2.42v_2 + 0.30v_3 + 2.35v_4 - 1.14v_5 + 2.00v_6 - 2.93v_7 + 34.2 = 0$$

If it is assumed that all the angles have been measured with the same degree of precision, then the weight of each measurement is unity. Consequently, Σv^2 must be a minimum in order to arrive at the most probable values for the angles in the solution. That is,

$$v_1^2 + v_2^2 + v_3^2 + v_4^2 + v_5^2 + v_6^2 + v_7^2 + v_8^2 = \text{minimum}$$

Since the four condition equations contain eight unknowns, there is no unique solution as they stand. Also, there are only four independent v's in these equations. However, the condition of least squares allows us to find a set of v's which satisfy the four condition equations, while at the same time forcing Σv^2 to be a minimum. Differentiation of the condition equations gives the following relationships:

$$dv_1 + dv_2 + dv_3 + dv_4 = 0 \qquad \text{(a-1)}$$
$$dv_1 + dv_2 + dv_7 + dv_8 = 0 \qquad \text{(a-2)}$$
$$dv_5 + dv_6 + dv_7 + dv_8 = 0 \qquad \text{(a-3)}$$
$$2.42dv_2 + 0.30dv_3 + 2.35dv_4$$
$$- 1.14dv_5 + 2.00dv_6 - 2.93dv_7 = 0 \qquad \text{(a-4)}$$

Also, by setting the derivative of Σv^2 equal to zero, because $\Sigma v^2 = $ minimum we get

$$v_1 dv_1 + v_2 dv_2 + v_3 dv_3 + v_4 dv_4 + v_5 dv_5 + v_6 dv_6 + v_7 dv_7 + v_8 dv_8 = 0$$
$$(\text{a-5})$$

Thus, the sum of the left-hand sides of Eqs. a-1, a-2, a-3, and a-4 must equal the left-hand side of Eq. a-5, since each is equal to zero. In order to find out which set of v's will satisfy both the group from a-1 to a-4 and also a-5, multiply each equation of the group of four by an arbitrary constant, as follows:

$$C_1 \left[dv_1 + dv_2 + dv_3 + dv_4 \right] = 0$$
$$C_2 \left[dv_1 + dv_2 + dv_7 + dv_8 \right] = 0$$
$$C_3 \left[dv_5 + dv_6 + dv_7 + dv_8 \right] = 0$$
$$C_4 \left[2.42 dv_2 + 0.30 dv_3 + 2.35 dv_4 - 1.14 dv_5 + 2.00 dv_6 - 2.93 dv_7 \right] = 0$$

Then,

$$C_1 dv_1 + C_1 dv_2 + C_1 dv_3 + C_1 dv_4 + C_2 dv_1 + C_2 dv_2 + C_2 dv_7$$
$$+ C_2 dv_8 + C_3 dv_5 + C_3 dv_6 + C_3 dv_7 + C_3 dv_8 + 2.42 C_4 dv_2$$
$$+ 0.30 C_4 dv_3 + 2.35 C_4 dv_4 - 1.14 C_4 dv_5 + 2.00 C_4 dv_6 - 2.93 C_4 dv_7 = 0$$

Collecting coefficients, we get

$$(C_1 + C_2)\, dv_1 + (C_1 + C_2 + 2.42 C_4)\, dv_2 + (C_1 + 0.30 C_4)\, dv_3$$
$$+ (C_1 + 2.35 C_4)\, dv_4 + (C_3 - 1.14 C_4)\, dv_5 + (C_3 + 2.00 C_4)\, dv_6$$
$$+ (C_2 + C_3 - 2.93 C_4)\, dv_7 + (C_2 + C_3)\, dv_8 = 0 \qquad (\text{a-6})$$

Comparison of Eq. a-5 with Eq. a-6 gives the following relationships:

$$v_1 = C_1 + C_2$$
$$v_2 = C_1 + C_2 \qquad\quad + 2.42 C_4$$
$$v_3 = C_1 \qquad\qquad\quad + 0.30 C_4$$
$$v_4 = C_1 \qquad\qquad\quad + 2.35 C_4$$
$$v_5 = \qquad\qquad C_3 - 1.14 C_4$$
$$v_6 = \qquad\qquad C_3 + 2.00 C_4$$
$$v_7 = \qquad C_2 + C_3 - 2.93 C_4$$
$$v_8 = \qquad C_2 + C_3$$

These are known as *correlate equations* and serve the same function as the connecting equations discussed in Sec. A-1. Note that there are only four variables on the right-hand sides of the equations expressing the values of the v's. Substitution of these values in the condition equations gives:

$$(C_1 + C_2) + (C_1 + C_2 + 2.42 C_4)$$
$$+ (C_1 + 0.30 C_4) + (C_1 + 2.35 C_4) + 6.2 = 0$$

$$(C_1 + C_2) + (C_1 + C_2 + 2.42 C_4)$$
$$+ (C_2 + C_3 - 2.93 C_4) + (C_2 + C_3) - 1.1 = 0$$

$$(C_3 - 1.14C_4) + (C_3 + 2.00C_4)$$
$$+ (C_2 + C_3 - 2.93C_4) + (C_2 + C_3) - 8.2 = 0$$

$$2.42\,(C_1 + C_2 + 2.42C_4) + 0.30\,(C_1 + 0.30C_4)$$
$$+ 2.35\,(C_1 + 2.35C_4) - 1.14\,(C_3 - 1.14C_4)$$
$$+ 2.00\,(C_3 + 2.00C_4) - 2.93\,(C_2 + C_3 - 2.93C_4) + 34.2 = 0$$

When the last four equations are reduced to their simplest forms, they become

$$4C_1 + \quad 2C_2 \qquad\qquad + \quad 5.07C_4 + \quad 6.2 = 0 \qquad \text{(a-7)}$$
$$2C_1 + \quad 4C_2 + \quad 2C_3 - \quad 0.51C_4 - \quad 1.1 = 0 \qquad \text{(a-8)}$$
$$+ \quad 2C_2 + \quad 4C_3 - \quad 2.07C_4 - \quad 8.2 = 0 \qquad \text{(a-9)}$$
$$5.07C_1 - 0.51C_2 - 2.07C_3 + 25.30C_4 + 34.2 = 0 \qquad \text{(a-10)}$$

Equations a-7, a-8, a-9, and a-10 are the normal equations derived from the original condition equations through the correlate equations.

When the C's are determined, they are substituted in the correlate equations to obtain the v's. The v's are then applied to the observed angles to obtain the adjusted angles.

To make the preceding operations more systematic, the condition equations are first tabulated as shown. Then the rows of co-

TABULATED CONDITION EQUATIONS

v_1	v_2	v_3	v_4	v_5	v_6	v_7	v_8	K
1	1	1	1					+ 6.2
1	1					1	1	− 1.1
				1	1	1	1	− 8.2
	2.42	0.30	2.35	− 1.14	2.00	− 2.93		+ 34.2

efficients of the condition equations are arranged as columns. The tabulated values represent the coefficients of the C's in the correlate equations, as indicated.

TABULATED CORRELATE EQUATIONS

	C_1	C_2	C_3	C_4
$v_1 =$	1	1		
$v_2 =$	1	1		2.42
$v_3 =$	1			0.30
$v_4 =$	1			2.35
$v_5 =$			1	− 1.14
$v_6 =$			1	2.00
$v_7 =$		1	1	− 2.93
$v_8 =$		1	1	

From the tabular arrangement for the correlate equations, the normal equations are formed by a cyclic and repetitive process. Let the coefficients of the C's be a, b, c, and d, respectively. Then the normal equations would be represented as follows:

$$[aa] C_1 + [ab] C_2 + [ac] C_3 + [ad] C_4 + K_1 = 0$$
$$[ba] C_1 + [bb] C_2 + [bc] C_3 + [bd] C_4 + K_2 = 0$$
$$[ca] C_1 + [cb] C_2 + [cc] C_3 + [cd] C_4 + K_3 = 0$$
$$[da] C_1 + [db] C_2 + [dc] C_3 + [dd] C_4 + K_4 = 0$$

in which
$$[aa] = a_1 a_1 + a_2 a_2 + a_3 a_3 + a_4 a_4$$
$$[ab] = a_1 b_1 + a_2 b_2 + a_3 b_3 + a_4 b_4$$
$$\text{and so on}$$

Also, K_1, K_2, K_3 and K_4 are the same as the constant terms of the condition equations.

Note that the coefficients of the C's about the diagonal terms are symmetrical. Thus, the coefficients in row i are the same as the coefficients in column i. The normal equations could be shown in tabular form as follows:

TABULATED NORMAL EQUATIONS

C_1	C_2	C_3	C_4	K	
$[aa]$	$[ab]$	$[ac]$	$[ad]$	K_1	$= 0$
$[ba]$	$[bb]$	$[bc]$	$[bd]$	K_2	$= 0$
$[ca]$	$[cb]$	$[cc]$	$[cd]$	K_3	$= 0$
$[da]$	$[db]$	$[dc]$	$[dd]$	K_4	$= 0$

In the assumed example, the tabulated normal equations would be as follows:

TABULATED NORMAL EQUATIONS

C_1	C_2	C_3	C_4	K	
4	2	0	5.07	$+\ 6.2$	$= 0$
2	4	2	$-\ 0.51$	$-\ 1.1$	$= 0$
0	2	4	$-\ 2.07$	$-\ 8.2$	$= 0$
5.07	$-\ 0.51$	$-\ 2.07$	$+\ 25.30$	$+\ 34.2$	$= 0$

The four normal equations are now solved simultaneously. Then the values of the C's are substituted in the correlate equations, from which the v's are obtained. A check on the calculations can be made by substituting the v's in the condition equations to see whether all four condition equations are satisfied. When the normal equations in the assumed example are solved, the results are:

$$C_1 = + 0.89; C_2 = - 1.35; C_3 = + 2.01; C_4 - = 1.39$$

Substitution in the correlate equations gives:

$$v_1 = -0.46'' \qquad v_5 = +3.59''$$
$$v_2 = -3.82'' \qquad v_6 = -0.77''$$
$$v_3 = +0.47'' \qquad v_7 = +4.73''$$
$$v_4 = -2.38'' \qquad v_8 = +0.66''$$

When this set of v's is substituted in the condition equations, all four of them are satisfied. Also, we are assured that Σv^2 is a minimum.

Since each angle is assumed to have unit weight, the standard error of the measured angles can be determined from the v's by Eq. A-1. Thus,

$$\sigma_0 = \sqrt{\frac{\Sigma v^2}{n - u}}$$

In this case, n is the number of angles and u is the number of conditions. The quantity $n - u$ again is the number of redundant observations, or the number of degrees of freedom. For a fully observed quadrilateral such as that in Fig. A-3, $n = 8$ and $u = 4$. Hence,

$$\sigma_0 = \sqrt{\frac{\Sigma v^2}{4}}$$

A-4. Adjustment of a Traverse Net by Observation Equations. In Sec. A-2, a level net was adjusted by assuming an initial set of junction-point elevations and then letting these values be changed by small amounts in order to cause the sum of the products of the weights of the lines of levels and the squares of the corrections to the measured D.E.'s of these lines to be a minimum. A traverse net consisting of several lines joined at junction points can be adjusted in a similar manner. In theory, however, there is one important difference. The corrections which we refer to as v's are supposed to be applied to quantities that are measured directly. In the level-net adjustment, we consider the D.E.'s to be measured directly, since they represent a series of additions and subtractions of directly observed readings of the leveling rod. The corrections which will be referred to in this section as v_x's and v_y's are applied to derived quantities, and not to direct observations.

The basis for the adjustment of a traverse net by the method of observation equations as set forth in this section is the compass rule discussed in Sec. 8-16. This rule states that the correction to the latitude or departure of a line is directly proportional to the length of that line. Let us consider a series of traverse lines joining two points A and B, as shown in Fig. A-4. Such a series of lines is referred to as a section. A traverse net is composed of several sections, each of

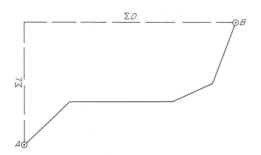

FIG. A-4. Traverse section.

which joins either two junction points or a junction point and a fixed point, as indicated in Fig. A-5. For each section, we compute the sum of the latitudes, called ΣL, and the sum of the departures, called ΣD. Each sum is analogous to the D.E. of a level line. The corrections to these two derived quantities are the v_y's and the v_x's, respectively. The quantities ΣL and ΣD are derived, since they are products of measured distances and functions of angles which have been obtained from measured angles, as explained in Chapter 8 (see also Sec. 4-7).

In Fig. A-5, traverse sections have been run from each of the four control points A, B, C, and D to each of the other three through the junction points E, F, and G. The fixed coordinates of the four control points in feet are as follows:

Point	Y	X
A	28,696.58	51,582.20
B	28,878.62	56,454.81
C	25,647.32	56,890.80
D	25,256.32	52,064.40

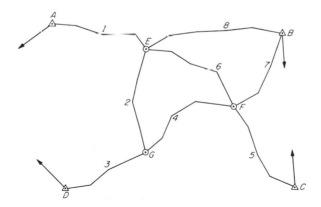

FIG. A-5. Traverse net.

The lines with the arrowheads at the four control points indicate azimuth backsights. A traverse can be carried, for example, by backsighting at A, running in succession to E, to F, and to C, and then closing in azimuth at C. When all the traversing shown in Fig. A-5 has been executed, the angular closures may be adjusted to give adjusted azimuths, or the computed azimuths may be used as unadjusted azimuths. The latter procedure is perhaps more valid. The latitudes and departures of all the lines are next computed by applying Eqs. 8-1 and 8-2 or Eqs. 8-3 and 8-4. The values of ΣL and ΣD for the sections are then determined and listed in tabular form.

Sec-tion	Length 1000 Feet	From To	ΣL	ΣD	Corr. to ΣL	Corr. to ΣD	p
1	2.24	A–E	− 357.30	+ 2076.02	v_{y_1}	v_{x_1}	1.04
2	2.20	E–G	− 2196.62	+ 96.08	v_{y_2}	v_{x_2}	1.06
3	1.88	G–D	− 886.02	− 1689.68	v_{y_3}	v_{x_3}	1.24
4	2.74	G–F	+ 1113.50	+ 1725.88	v_{y_4}	v_{x_4}	0.85
5	2.44	F–C	− 1609.23	+ 1410.42	v_{y_5}	v_{x_5}	0.96
6	2.51	E–F	− 1082.82	+ 1822.00	v_{y_6}	v_{x_6}	0.93
7	2.00	F–B	+ 1622.48	+ 974.60	v_{y_7}	v_{x_7}	1.17
8	3.02	B–E	− 539.59	− 2796.74	v_{y_8}	v_{x_8}	0.77

The measured and computed values for the traverse in Fig. A-5 are shown in the accompanying tabulation. The weights of the sections are assumed to be inversely proportional to their lengths, which is the basis of the compass rule. These weights have been modified so that their average is unity.

An approximate set of values for the coordinates of the junction points are now computed by adding the proper values of ΣL to known Y-coordinates and adding the proper values of ΣD to known X-coordinates. Thus, for point E,

$$Y_E = Y_A + \Sigma L_{AE} = 28{,}696.58 - 357.30 = 28{,}339.28$$
$$X_E = X_A + \Sigma D_{AE} = 51{,}582.20 + 2076.02 = 53{,}658.22$$

The values of the approximate coordinates of E, F, and G are as follows:

Point	From Section	Approximate Y	Approximate X
E	AE	28,339.28	53,658.22
F	BF	27,256.14	55,480.21
G	DG	26,142.34	53,754.08

We obtain the adjusted coordinates of each junction point by adding an as-yet unknown correction ΔY to the approximate Y-coordinate and a correction ΔX to the approximate X-coordinate. The adjusted coordinates may therefore be represented as follows:

Point	Adjusted Y	Adjusted X
E	$28{,}339.28 + \Delta Y_E$	$53{,}658.22 + \Delta X_E$
F	$27{,}256.14 + \Delta Y_F$	$55{,}480.21 + \Delta X_F$
G	$26{,}142.34 + \Delta Y_G$	$53{,}754.08 + \Delta X_G$

We can now derive an observation equation in Y and in X for each section. For example, for the section between A and E,

$$\Sigma L_{AE} + v_{y_1} = \text{Adjusted } Y_E - Y_A$$

or

$$-357.30 + v_{y_1} = 28{,}339.28 + \Delta Y_E - 28{,}696.58$$

Hence,

$$v_{y_1} = +\Delta Y_E + 0$$

Also,

$$\Sigma D_{AE} + v_{x_1} = \text{Adjusted } X_E - X_A$$

or

$$+2076.02 + v_{x_1} = 53{,}658.22 + \Delta X_E - 51{,}582.20$$

Hence,

$$v_{x_1} = +\Delta X_E + 0$$

The complete set of observation equations is as follows:

$$v_{y_1} = +\Delta Y_E + 0 \qquad\qquad v_{x_1} = +\Delta X_E + 0$$

$$v_{y_2} = -\Delta Y_E + \Delta Y_G - 0.32 \qquad\qquad v_{x_2} = -\Delta X_E + \Delta X_G - 0.22$$

$$v_{y_3} = -\Delta Y_G + 0 \qquad\qquad v_{x_3} = -\Delta X_G + 0$$

$$v_{y_4} = +\Delta Y_F - \Delta Y_G + 0.30 \qquad\qquad v_{x_4} = +\Delta X_F - \Delta X_G + 0.25$$

$$v_{y_5} = -\Delta Y_F + 0.41 \qquad\qquad v_{x_5} = -\Delta X_F + 0.17$$

$$v_{y_6} = -\Delta Y_E + \Delta Y_F - 0.32 \qquad\qquad v_{x_6} = -\Delta X_E + \Delta X_F - 0.01$$

$$v_{y_7} = -\Delta Y_F + 0 \qquad\qquad v_{x_7} = -\Delta X_F + 0$$

$$v_{y_8} = +\Delta Y_E + 0.25 \qquad\qquad v_{x_8} = +\Delta X_E + 0.15$$

Two sets of normal equations are formed, one in Y and one in X. The procedure for the formation of the normal equations is that described in Sec. A-2. The coefficients in both sets of equations will be identical. The constant terms, however, will be different. The values used in the solution of both sets of normal equations can be placed side by side, because of the equality of the coefficients.

The proper values of ΔY are added to the approximate Y-coordinates of the junction points, while the proper values of ΔX are added to the approximate X-coordinates. These results are the adjusted coordinates. The standard errors of the ΣL's and ΣD's are determined as discussed in Sec. A-2 for determining the standard errors of the D.E.'s.

After the adjusted coordinates of the junction points have been determined, the coordinates of the intermediate traverse stations in each section are made to be consistant with those of the junction points. This adjustment is an application of the compass rule, as outlined in Sec. 8-16 and as illustrated by the example in Sec. 8-22.

Tables

STADIA REDUCTIONS

Minutes	0° Hor. Dist.	0° Vert. Dist.	1° Hor. Dist.	1° Vert. Dist.	2° Hor. Dist.	2° Vert. Dist.	3° Hor. Dist.	3° Vert. Dist.
0	100.00	.00	99.97	1.74	99.88	3.49	99.73	5.23
2	100.00	.06	99.97	1.80	99.87	3.55	99.72	5.28
4	100.00	.12	99.97	1.86	99.87	3.60	99.71	5.34
6	100.00	.17	99.96	1.92	99.87	3.66	99.71	5.40
8	100.00	.23	99.96	1.98	99.86	3.72	99.70	5.46
10	100.00	.29	99.96	2.04	99.86	3.78	99.69	5.52
12	100.00	.35	99.96	2.09	99.85	3.84	99.69	5.57
14	100.00	.41	99.95	2.15	99.85	3.89	99.68	5.63
16	100.00	.47	99.95	2.21	99.84	3.95	99.68	5.69
18	100.00	.52	99.95	2.27	99.84	4.01	99.67	5.75
20	100.00	.58	99.95	2.33	99.83	4.07	99.66	5.80
22	100.00	.64	99.94	2.38	99.83	4.13	99.66	5.86
24	100.00	.70	99.94	2.44	99.82	4.18	99.65	5.92
26	99.99	.76	99.94	2.50	99.82	4.24	99.64	5.98
28	99.99	.81	99.93	2.56	99.81	4.30	99.63	6.04
30	99.99	.87	99.93	2.62	99.81	4.36	99.63	6.09
32	99.99	.93	99.93	2.67	99.80	4.42	99.62	6.15
34	99.99	.99	99.93	2.73	99.80	4.47	99.61	6.21
36	99.99	1.05	99.92	2.79	99.79	4.53	99.61	6.27
38	99.99	1.11	99.92	2.85	99.79	4.59	99.60	6.32
40	99.99	1.16	99.92	2.91	99.78	4.65	99.59	6.38
42	99.99	1.22	99.91	2.97	99.78	4.71	99.58	6.44
44	99.98	1.28	99.91	3.02	99.77	4.76	99.58	6.50
46	99.98	1.34	99.90	3.08	99.77	4.82	99.57	6.56
48	99.98	1.40	99.90	3.14	99.76	4.88	99.56	6.61
50	99.98	1.45	99.90	3.20	99.76	4.94	99.55	6.67
52	99.98	1.51	99.89	3.26	99.75	4.99	99.55	6.73
54	99.98	1.57	99.89	3.31	99.74	5.05	99.54	6.79
56	99.97	1.63	99.89	3.37	99.74	5.11	99.53	6.84
58	99.97	1.69	99.88	3.43	99.73	5.17	99.52	6.90
60	99.97	1.74	99.88	3.49	99.73	5.23	99.51	6.96
$C = .75$	.75	.01	.75	.02	.75	.03	.75	.05
$C = 1.00$	1.00	.01	1.00	.03	1.00	.04	1.00	.06
$C = 1.25$	1.25	.02	1.25	.03	1.25	.05	1.25	.08

TABLE A

STADIA REDUCTIONS

Minutes	4°		5°		6°		7°	
	Hor. Dist.	Vert. Dist.	Hor. Dist.	Vert. Dist.	Hor. Dist.	Vert. Dist.	Hor. Dist.	Vert. Dist.
0	99.51	6.96	99.24	8.68	98.91	10.40	98.51	12.10
2	99.51	7.02	99.23	8.74	98.90	10.45	98.50	12.15
4	99.50	7.07	99.22	8.80	98.88	10.51	98.49	12.21
6	99.49	7.13	99.21	8.85	98.87	10.57	98.47	12.27
8	99.48	7.19	99.20	8.91	98.86	10.62	98.46	12.32
10	99.47	7.25	99.19	8.97	98.85	10.68	98.44	12.38
12	99.46	7.30	99.18	9.03	98.83	10.74	98.43	12.43
14	99.46	7.36	99.17	9.08	98.82	10.79	98.41	12.49
16	99.45	7.42	99.16	9.14	98.81	10.85	98.40	12.55
18	99.44	7.48	99.15	9.20	98.80	10.91	98.39	12.60
20	99.43	7.53	99.14	9.25	98.78	10.96	98.37	12.66
22	99.42	7.59	99.13	9.31	98.77	11.02	98.36	12.72
24	99.41	7.65	99.11	9.37	98.76	11.08	98.34	12.77
26	99.40	7.71	99.10	9.43	98.74	11.13	98.33	12.83
28	99.39	7.76	99.09	9.48	98.73	11.19	98.31	12.88
30	99.38	7.82	99.08	9.54	98.72	11.25	98.30	12.94
32	99.38	7.88	99.07	9.60	98.71	11.30	98.28	13.00
34	99.37	7.94	99.06	9.65	98.69	11.36	98.27	13.05
36	99.36	7.99	99.05	9.71	98.68	11.42	98.25	13.11
38	99.35	8.05	99.04	9.77	98.67	11.47	98.24	13.17
40	99.34	8.11	99.03	9.83	98.65	11.53	98.22	13.22
42	99.33	8.17	99.01	9.88	98.64	11.59	98.20	13.28
44	99.32	8.22	99.00	9.94	98.63	11.64	98.19	13.33
46	99.31	8.28	98.99	10.00	98.61	11.70	98.17	13.39
48	99.30	8.34	98.98	10.05	98.60	11.76	98.16	13.45
50	99.29	8.40	98.97	10.11	98.58	11.81	98.14	13.50
52	99.28	8.45	98.96	10.17	98.57	11.87	98.13	13.56
54	99.27	8.51	98.94	10.22	98.56	11.93	98.11	13.61
56	99.26	8.57	98.93	10.28	98.54	11.98	98.10	13.67
58	99.25	8.63	98.92	10.34	98.53	12.04	98.08	13.73
60	99.24	8.68	98.91	10.40	98.51	12.10	98.06	13.78
C = .75	.75	.06	.75	.07	.75	.08	.74	.10
C = 1.00	1.00	.08	1.00	.10	.99	.11	.99	.13
C = 1.25	1.25	.10	1.24	.12	1.24	.14	1.24	.16

STADIA REDUCTIONS

Minutes	8°		9°		10°		11°	
	Hor. Dist.	Vert. Dist.	Hor. Dist.	Vert. Dist.	Hor. Dist.	Vert. Dist.	Hor. Dist.	Vert. Dist.
0	98.06	13.78	97.55	15.45	96.98	17.10	96.36	18.73
2	98.05	13.84	97.53	15.51	96.96	17.16	96.34	18.78
4	98.03	13.89	97.52	15.56	96.94	17.21	96.32	18.84
6	98.01	13.95	97.50	15.62	96.92	17.26	96.29	18.89
8	98.00	14.01	97.48	15.67	96.90	17.32	96.27	18.95
10	97.98	14.06	97.46	15.73	96.88	17.37	96.25	19.00
12	97.97	14.12	97.44	15.78	96.86	17.43	96.23	19.05
14	97.95	14.17	97.43	15.84	96.84	17.48	96.21	19.11
16	97.93	14.23	97.41	15.89	96.82	17.54	96.18	19.16
18	97.92	14.28	97.39	15.95	96.80	17.59	96.16	19.21
20	97.90	14.34	97.37	16.00	96.78	17.65	96.14	19.27
22	97.88	14.40	97.35	16.06	96.76	17.70	96.12	19.32
24	97.87	14.45	97.33	16.11	96.74	17.76	96.09	19.38
26	97.85	14.51	97.31	16.17	96.72	17.81	96.07	19.43
28	97.83	14.56	97.29	16.22	96.70	17.86	96.05	19.48
30	97.82	14.62	97.28	16.28	96.68	17.92	96.03	19.54
32	97.80	14.67	97.26	16.33	96.66	17.97	96.00	19.59
34	97.78	14.73	97.24	16.39	96.64	18.03	95.98	19.64
36	97.76	14.79	97.22	16.44	96.62	18.08	95.96	19.70
38	97.75	14.84	97.20	16.50	96.60	18.14	95.93	19.75
40	97.73	14.90	97.18	16.55	96.57	18.19	95.91	19.80
42	97.71	14.95	97.16	16.61	96.55	18.24	95.89	19.86
44	97.69	15.01	97.14	16.66	96.53	18.30	95.86	19.91
46	97.68	15.06	97.12	16.72	96.51	18.35	95.84	19.96
48	97.66	15.12	97.10	16.77	96.49	18.41	95.82	20.02
50	97.64	15.17	97.08	16.83	96.47	18.46	95.79	20.07
52	97.62	15.23	97.06	16.88	96.45	18.51	95.77	20.12
54	97.61	15.28	97.04	16.94	96.42	18.57	95.75	20.18
56	97.59	15.34	97.02	16.99	96.40	18.62	95.72	20.23
58	97.57	15.40	97.00	17.05	96.38	18.68	95.70	20.28
60	97.55	15.45	96.98	17.10	96.36	18.73	95.68	20.34
C = .75	.74	.11	.74	.12	.74	.14	.73	.15
C = 1.00	.99	.15	.99	.17	.98	.18	.98	.20
C = 1.25	1.24	.18	1.23	.21	1.23	.23	1.22	.25

TABLE A

STADIA REDUCTIONS

Minutes	12°		13°		14°		15°	
	Hor. Dist.	Vert. Dist.	Hor. Dist.	Vert. Dist.	Hor. Dist.	Vert. Dist.	Hor. Dist.	Vert. Dist.
0	95.68	20.34	94.94	21.92	94.15	23.47	93.30	25.00
2	95.65	20.39	94.91	21.97	94.12	23.52	93.27	25.05
4	95.63	20.44	94.89	22.02	94.09	23.58	93.24	25.10
6	95.61	20.50	94.86	22.08	94.07	23.63	93.21	25.15
8	95.58	20.55	94.84	22.13	94.04	23.68	93.18	25.20
10	95.56	20.60	94.81	22.18	94.01	23.73	93.16	25.25
12	95.53	20.66	94.79	22.23	93.98	23.78	93.13	25.30
14	95.51	20.71	94.76	22.28	93.95	23.83	93.10	25.35
16	95.49	20.76	94.73	22.34	93.93	23.88	93.07	25.40
18	95.46	20.81	94.71	22.39	93.90	23.93	93.04	25.45
20	95.44	20.87	94.68	22.44	93.87	23.99	93.01	25.50
22	95.41	20.92	94.66	22.49	93.84	24.04	92.98	25.55
24	95.39	20.97	94.63	22.54	93.82	24.09	92.95	25.60
26	95.36	21.03	94.60	22.60	93.79	24.14	92.92	25.65
28	95.34	21.08	94.58	22.65	93.76	24.19	92.89	25.70
30	95.32	21.13	94.55	22.70	93.73	24.24	92.86	25.75
32	95.29	21.18	94.52	22.75	93.70	24.29	92.83	25.80
34	95.27	21.24	94.50	22.80	93.67	24.34	92.80	25.85
36	95.24	21.29	94.47	22.85	93.65	24.39	92.77	25.90
38	95.22	21.34	94.44	22.91	93.62	24.44	92.74	25.95
40	95.19	21.39	94.42	22.96	93.59	24.49	92.71	26.00
42	95.17	21.45	94.39	23.01	93.56	24.55	92.68	26.05
44	95.14	21.50	94.36	23.06	93.53	24.60	92.65	26.10
46	95.12	21.55	94.34	23.11	93.50	24.65	92.62	26.15
48	95.09	21.60	94.31	23.16	93.47	24.70	92.59	26.20
50	95.07	21.66	94.28	23.22	93.45	24.75	92.56	26.25
52	95.04	21.71	94.26	23.27	93.42	24.80	92.53	26.30
54	95.02	21.76	94.23	23.32	93.39	24.85	92.49	26.35
56	94.99	21.81	94.20	23.37	93.36	24.90	92.46	26.40
58	94.97	21.87	94.17	23.42	93.33	24.95	92.43	26.45
60	94.94	21.92	94.15	23.47	93.30	25.00	92.40	26.50
$C = .75$	.73	.16	.73	.18	.73	.19	.72	.20
$C = 1.00$	.98	.22	.97	.23	.97	.25	.96	.27
$C = 1.25$	1.22	.27	1.22	.29	1.21	.31	1.20	.33

STADIA REDUCTIONS

Minutes	16°		17°		18°		19°	
	Hor. Dist.	Vert. Dist.	Hor. Dist.	Vert. Dist.	Hor. Dist.	Vert. Dist.	Hor. Dist.	Vert. Dist.
0	92.40	26.50	91.45	27.96	90.45	29.39	89.40	30.78
2	92.37	26.55	91.42	28.01	90.42	29.44	89.36	30.83
4	92.34	26.59	91.39	28.06	90.38	29.48	89.33	30.87
6	92.31	26.64	91.35	28.10	90.35	29.53	89.29	30.92
8	92.28	26.69	91.32	28.15	90.31	29.58	89.26	30.97
10	92.25	26.74	91.29	28.20	90.28	29.62	89.22	31.01
12	92.22	26.79	91.26	28.25	90.24	29.67	89.18	31.06
14	92.19	26.84	91.22	28.30	90.21	29.72	89.15	31.10
16	92.15	26.89	91.19	28.34	90.18	29.76	89.11	31.15
18	92.12	26.94	91.16	28.39	90.14	29.81	89.08	31.19
20	92.09	26.99	91.12	28.44	90.11	29.86	89.04	31.24
22	92.06	27.04	91.09	28.49	90.07	29.90	89.00	31.28
24	92.03	27.09	91.06	28.54	90.04	29.95	88.97	31.33
26	92.00	27.13	91.02	28.58	90.00	30.00	88.93	31.38
28	91.97	27.18	90.99	28.63	89.97	30.04	88.89	31.42
30	91.93	27.23	90.96	28.68	89.93	30.09	88.86	31.47
32	91.90	27.28	90.92	28.73	89.90	30.14	88.82	31.51
34	91.87	27.33	90.89	28.77	89.86	30.18	88.78	31.56
36	91.84	27.38	90.86	28.82	89.83	30.23	88.75	31.60
38	91.81	27.43	90.82	28.87	89.79	30.28	88.71	31.65
40	91.77	27.48	90.79	28.92	89.76	30.32	88.67	31.69
42	91.74	27.52	90.76	28.96	89.72	30.37	88.64	31.74
44	91.71	27.57	90.72	29.01	89.69	30.41	88.60	31.78
46	91.68	27.62	90.69	29.06	89.65	30.46	88.56	31.83
48	91.65	27.67	90.66	29.11	89.61	30.51	88.53	31.87
50	91.61	27.72	90.62	29.15	89.58	30.55	88.49	31.92
52	91.58	27.77	90.59	29.20	89.54	30.60	88.45	31.96
54	91.55	27.81	90.55	29.25	89.51	30.65	88.41	32.01
56	91.52	27.86	90.52	29.30	89.47	30.69	88.38	32.05
58	91.48	27.91	90.49	29.34	89.44	30.74	88.34	32.09
60	91.45	27.96	90.45	29.39	89.40	30.78	88.30	32.14
$C = .75$	.72	.21	.72	.23	.71	.24	.71	.25
$C = 1.00$	.96	.28	.95	.30	.95	.32	.94	.33
$C = 1.25$	1.20	.36	1.19	.38	1.19	.40	1.18	.42

TABLE A

Stadia Reductions

Minutes	20°		21°		22°		23°	
	Hor. Dist.	Vert. Dist.	Hor. Dist.	Vert. Dist.	Hor. Dist.	Vert. Dist.	Hor. Dist.	Vert. Dist.
0	88.30	32.14	87.16	33.46	85.97	34.73	84.73	35.97
2	88.26	32.18	87.12	33.50	85.93	34.77	84.69	36.01
4	88.23	32.23	87.08	33.54	85.89	34.82	84.65	36.05
6	88.19	32.27	87.04	33.59	85.85	34.86	84.6:	36.09
8	88.15	32.32	87.00	33.63	85.80	34.90	84.57	36.13
10	88.11	32.36	86.96	33.67	85.76	34.94	84.52	36.17
12	88.08	32.41	86.92	33.72	85.72	34.98	84.48	36.21
14	88.04	32.45	86.88	33.76	85.68	35.02	84.44	36.25
16	88.00	32.49	86.84	33.80	85.64	35.07	84.40	36.29
18	87.96	32.54	86.80	33.84	85.60	35.11	84.35	36.33
20	87.93	32.58	86.77	33.89	85.56	35.15	84.31	36.37
22	87.89	32.63	86.73	33.93	85.52	35.19	84.27	36.41
24	87.85	32.67	86.69	33.97	85.48	35.23	84.23	36.45
26	87.81	32.72	86.65	34.01	85.44	35.27	84.18	36.49
28	87.77	32.76	86.61	34.06	85.40	35.31	84.14	36.53
30	87.74	32.80	86.57	34.10	85.36	35.36	84.10	36.57
32	87.70	32.85	86.53	34.14	85.31	35.40	84.06	36.61
34	87.66	32.89	86.49	34.18	85.27	35.44	84.01	36.65
36	87.62	32.93	86.45	34.23	85.23	35.48	83.97	36.69
38	87.58	32.98	86.41	34.27	85.19	35.52	83.93	36.73
40	87.54	33.02	86.37	34.31	85.15	35.56	83.89	36.77
42	87.51	33.07	86.33	34.35	85.11	35.60	83.84	36.80
44	87.47	33.11	86.29	34.40	85.07	35.64	83.80	36.84
46	87.43	33.15	86.25	34.44	85.02	35.68	83.76	36.88
48	87.39	33.20	86.21	34.48	84.98	35.72	83.72	36.92
50	87.35	33.24	86.17	34.52	84.94	35.76	83.67	36.96
52	87.31	33.28	86.13	34.57	84.90	35.80	83.63	37.00
54	87.27	33.33	86.09	34.61	84.86	35.85	83.59	37.04
56	87.24	33.37	86.05	34.65	84.82	35.89	83.54	37.08
58	87.20	33.41	86.01	34.69	84.77	35.93	83.50	37.12
60	87.16	33.46	85.97	34.73	84.73	35.97	83.46	37.16
$C=$ .75	.70	.26	.70	.27	.69	.29	.69	.30
$C=$ 1.00	.94	.35	.93	.37	.92	.38	.92	.40
$C=$ 1.25	1.17	.44	1.16	.46	1.15	.48	1.15	.50

STADIA REDUCTIONS

Minutes	24°		25°		26°		27°	
	Hor. Dist.	Vert. Dist.	Hor. Dist.	Vert. Dist.	Hor. Dist.	Vert. Dist.	Hor. Dist.	Vert. Dist.
0	83.46	37.16	82.14	38.30	80.78	39.40	79.39	40.45
2	83.41	37.20	82.09	38.34	80.74	39.44	79.34	40.49
4	83.37	37.23	82.05	38.38	80.69	39.47	79.30	40.52
6	83.33	37.27	82.01	38.41	80.65	39.51	79.25	40.55
8	83.28	37.31	81.96	38.45	80.60	39.54	79.20	40.59
10	83.24	37.35	81.92	38.49	80.55	39.58	79.15	40.62
12	83.20	37.39	81.87	38.53	80.51	39.61	79.11	40.66
14	83.15	37.43	81.83	38.56	80.46	39.65	79.06	40.69
16	83.11	37.47	81.78	38.60	80.41	39.69	79.01	40.72
18	83.07	37.51	81.74	38.64	80.37	39.72	78.96	40.76
20	83.02	37.54	81.69	38.67	80.32	39.76	78.92	40.79
22	82.98	37.58	81.65	38.71	80.28	39.79	78.87	40.82
24	82.93	37.62	81.60	38.75	80.23	39.83	78.82	40.86
26	82.89	37.66	81.56	38.78	80.18	39.86	78.77	40.89
28	82.85	37.70	81.51	38.82	80.14	39.90	78.73	40.92
30	82.80	37.74	81.47	38.86	80.09	39.93	78.68	40.96
32	82.76	37.77	81.42	38.89	80.04	39.97	78.63	40.99
34	82.72	37.81	81.38	38.93	80.00	40.00	78.58	41.02
36	82.67	37.85	81.33	38.97	79.95	40.04	78.54	41.06
38	82.63	37.89	81.28	39.00	79.90	40.07	78.49	41.09
40	82.58	37.93	81.24	39.04	79.86	40.11	78.44	41.12
42	82.54	37.96	81.19	39.08	79.81	40.14	78.39	41.16
44	82.49	38.00	81.15	39.11	79.76	40.18	78.34	41.19
46	82.45	38.04	81.10	39.15	79.72	40.21	78.30	41.22
48	82.41	38.08	81.06	39.18	79.67	40.24	78.25	41.26
50	82.36	38.11	81.01	39.22	79.62	40.28	78.20	41.29
52	82.32	38.15	80.97	39.26	79.58	40.31	78.15	41.32
54	82.27	38.19	80.92	39.29	79.53	40.35	78.10	41.35
56	82.23	38.23	80.87	39.33	79.48	40.38	78.06	41.39
58	82.18	38.26	80.83	39.36	79.44	40.42	78.01	41.42
60	82.14	38.30	80.78	39.40	79.39	40.45	77.96	41.45
C = .75	.68	.31	.68	.32	.67	.33	.67	.35
C = 1.00	.91	.41	.90	.43	.89	.45	.89	.46
C = 1.25	1.14	.52	1.13	.54	1.12	.56	1.11	.58

TABLE A

STADIA REDUCTIONS

Minutes	28°		29°		30°	
	Hor. Dist.	Vert. Dist.	Hor. Dist.	Vert. Dist.	Hor. Dist.	Vert. Dist.
0	77.96	41.45	76.50	42.40	75.00	43.30
2	77.91	41.48	76.45	42.43	74.95	43.33
4	77.86	41.52	76.40	42.46	74.90	43.36
6	77.81	41.55	76 35	42.49	74.85	43.39
8	77.77	41.58	76.30	42.53	74.80	43.42
10	77.72	41.61	76.25	42.56	74.75	43.45
12	77.67	41.65	76.20	42.59	74.70	43.47
14	77.62	41.68	76.15	42.62	74.65	43.50
16	77.57	41.71	76.10	42.65	74.60	43.53
18	77.52	41.74	76.05	42.68	74.55	43.56
20	77.48	41.77	76.00	42.71	74.49	43.59
22	77.42	41.81	75.95	42.74	74.44	43.62
24	77.38	41.84	75.90	42.77	74.39	43.65
26	77.33	41.87	75.85	42.80	74.34	43.67
28	77.28	41.90	75.80	42.83	74.29	43.70
30	77.23	41.93	75.75	42.86	74.24	43.73
32	77.18	41.97	75.70	42.89	74.19	43.76
34	77.13	42.00	75.65	42.92	74.14	43.79
36	77.09	42.03	75.60	42.95	74.09	43.82
38	77.04	42.06	75.55	42.98	74.04	43.84
40	76.99	42.09	75.50	43.01	73.99	43.87
42	76.94	42.12	75.45	43.04	73.93	43.90
44	76.89	42.15	75.40	43.07	73.88	43.93
46	76.84	42.19	75.35	43.10	73.83	43.95
48	76.79	42.22	75.30	43.13	73.78	43.98
50	76.74	42.25	75.25	43.16	73.73	44.01
52	76.69	42.28	75.20	43.18	73.68	44.04
54	76.64	42.31	75.15	43.21	73.63	44.07
56	76.59	42.34	75.10	43.24	73.58	44.09
58	76.55	42.37	75.05	43.27	73.52	44.12
60	76.50	42.40	75.00	43.30	73.47	44.15
$C = .75$	.66	.36	.65	.37	.65	.38
$C = 1.00$	.88	.48	.87	.49	.86	.51
$C = 1.25$	1.10	.60	1.09	.62	1.08	.63

LOGARITHMS OF NUMBERS

No. 100—Log. 000   No. 109—Log. 040

N.	0	1	2	3	4	5	6	7	8	9	Diff.
100	000000	0434	0868	1301	1734	2166	2598	3029	3461	3891	432
101	4321	4751	5181	5609	6038	6466	6894	7321	7748	8174	428
102	8600	9026	9451	9876	*0300	*0724	*1147	*1570	*1993	*2415	424
103	012837	3259	3680	4100	4521	4940	5360	5779	6197	6616	420
104	7033	7451	7868	8284	8700	9116	9532	9947	*0361	*0775	416
105	021189	1603	2016	2428	2841	3252	3664	4075	4486	4896	412
106	5306	5715	6125	6533	6942	7350	7757	8164	8571	8978	408
107	9384	9789	*0195	*0600	*1004	*1408	*1812	*2216	*2619	*3021	404
108	033424	3826	4227	4628	5029	5430	5830	6230	6629	7028	400
109	7426	7825	8223	8620	9017	9414	9811	*0207	*0602	*0998	397

PROPORTIONAL PARTS

Diff.	1	2	3	4	5	6	7	8	9	Diff.
434	43	87	130	174	217	260	304	347	391	434
433	43	87	130	173	217	260	303	346	390	433
432	43	86	130	173	216	259	302	346	389	432
431	43	86	129	172	216	259	302	345	388	431
430	43	86	129	172	215	258	301	344	387	430
429	43	86	129	172	215	257	300	343	386	429
428	43	86	128	171	214	257	300	342	385	428
427	43	85	128	171	214	256	299	342	384	427
426	43	85	128	170	213	256	298	341	383	426
425	43	85	128	170	213	255	298	340	383	425
424	42	85	127	170	212	254	297	339	382	424
423	42	85	127	169	212	254	296	338	381	423
422	42	84	127	169	211	253	295	338	380	422
421	42	84	126	168	211	253	295	337	379	421
420	42	84	126	168	210	252	294	336	378	420
419	42	84	126	168	210	251	293	335	377	419
418	42	84	125	167	209	251	293	334	376	418
417	42	83	125	167	209	250	292	334	375	417
416	42	83	125	166	208	250	291	333	374	416
415	42	83	125	166	208	249	291	332	374	415
414	41	83	124	166	207	248	290	331	373	414
413	41	83	124	165	207	248	289	330	372	413
412	41	82	124	165	206	247	288	330	371	412
411	41	82	123	164	206	247	288	329	370	411
410	41	82	123	164	205	246	287	328	369	410
409	41	82	123	164	205	245	286	327	368	409
408	41	82	122	163	204	245	286	326	367	408
407	41	81	122	163	204	244	285	326	366	407
406	41	81	122	162	203	244	284	325	365	406
405	11	81	122	162	203	243	284	324	365	405
404	40	81	121	162	202	242	283	323	364	404
403	40	81	121	161	202	242	282	322	363	403
402	40	80	121	161	201	241	281	322	362	402
401	40	80	120	160	201	241	281	321	361	401
400	40	80	120	160	200	240	280	320	360	400
399	40	80	120	160	200	239	279	319	359	399
398	40	80	119	159	199	239	279	318	358	398
397	40	79	119	159	199	238	278	318	357	397
396	40	79	119	158	198	238	277	317	356	396
395	40	79	119	158	198	237	277	316	356	395
394	39	79	118	158	197	236	276	315	355	394
393	39	79	118	157	197	236	275	314	354	393
392	39	78	118	157	196	235	274	314	353	392
391	39	78	117	156	196	235	274	313	352	391
390	39	78	117	156	195	234	273	312	351	390
389	39	78	117	156	195	233	272	311	350	389
388	39	78	116	155	194	233	272	310	349	388

TABLE B

LOGARITHMS OF NUMBERS

No. 110—Log. 041   No. 124—Log. 096

N.	0	1	2	3	4	5	6	7	8	9	Diff.
110	041393	1787	2182	2576	2969	3362	3755	4148	4540	4932	393
111	5323	5714	6105	6495	6885	7275	7664	8053	8442	8830	390
112	9218	9606	9993	*0380	*0766	*1153	*1538	*1924	*2309	*2694	386
113	053078	3463	3846	4230	4613	4996	5378	5760	6142	6524	383
114	6905	7286	7666	8046	8426	8805	9185	9563	9942	*0320	379
115	060698	1075	1452	1829	2206	2582	2958	3333	3709	4083	376
116	4458	4832	5206	5580	5953	6326	6699	7071	7443	7815	373
117	8186	8557	8928	9298	9668	*0038	*0407	*0776	*1145	*1514	370
118	071882	2250	2617	2985	3352	3718	4085	4451	4816	5182	366
119	5547	5912	6276	6640	7004	7368	7731	8094	8457	8819	363
120	079181	9543	9904	*0266	*0626	*0987	*1347	*1707	*2067	*2426	360
121	082785	3144	3503	3861	4219	4576	4934	5291	5647	6004	357
122	6360	6716	7071	7426	7781	8136	8490	8845	9198	9552	355
123	9905	*0258	*0611	*0963	*1315	*1667	*2018	*2370	*2721	*3071	352
124	093422	3772	4122	4471	4820	5169	5518	5866	6215	6562	349

PROPORTIONAL PARTS

Diff.	1	2	3	4	5	6	7	8	9	Diff.
387	39	77	116	155	194	232	271	310	348	387
386	39	77	116	154	193	232	270	309	347	386
385	39	77	116	154	193	231	270	308	347	385
384	38	77	115	154	192	230	269	307	346	384
383	38	77	115	153	192	230	268	306	345	383
382	38	76	115	153	191	229	267	306	344	382
381	38	76	114	152	191	229	267	305	343	381
380	38	76	114	152	190	228	266	304	342	380
379	38	76	114	152	190	227	265	303	341	379
378	38	76	113	151	189	227	265	302	340	378
377	38	75	113	151	189	226	264	302	339	377
376	38	75	113	150	188	226	263	301	338	376
375	38	75	113	150	188	225	263	300	338	375
374	37	75	112	150	187	224	262	299	337	374
373	37	75	112	149	187	224	261	298	336	373
372	37	74	112	149	186	223	260	298	335	372
371	37	74	111	148	186	223	260	297	334	371
370	37	74	111	148	185	222	259	296	333	370
369	37	74	111	148	185	221	258	295	332	369
368	37	74	110	147	184	221	258	294	331	368
367	37	73	110	147	184	220	257	294	330	367
366	37	73	110	146	183	220	256	293	329	366
365	37	73	110	146	183	219	256	292	329	365
364	36	73	109	146	182	218	255	291	328	364
363	36	73	109	145	182	218	254	290	327	363
362	36	72	109	145	181	217	253	290	326	362
361	36	72	108	144	181	217	253	289	325	361
360	36	72	108	144	180	216	252	288	324	360
359	36	72	108	144	180	215	251	287	323	359
358	36	72	107	143	179	215	251	286	322	358
357	36	71	107	143	179	214	250	286	321	357
356	36	71	107	142	178	214	249	285	320	356
355	36	71	107	142	178	213	249	284	320	355
354	35	71	106	142	177	212	248	283	319	354
353	35	71	106	141	177	212	247	282	318	353
352	35	70	106	141	176	211	246	282	317	352
351	35	70	105	140	176	211	246	281	316	351
350	35	70	105	140	175	210	245	280	315	350
349	35	70	105	140	175	209	244	279	314	349
348	35	70	104	139	174	209	244	278	313	348
347	35	69	104	139	174	208	243	278	312	347

LOGARITHMS OF NUMBERS

No. 125—Log. 097   No. 139—Log. 145

N.	0	1	2	3	4	5	6	7	8	9	Diff.
125	096910	7257	7604	7951	8298	8644	8990	9335	9681	*0026	346
126	100371	0715	1059	1403	1747	2091	2434	2777	3119	3462	343
127	3804	4146	4487	4828	5169	5510	5851	6191	6531	6871	341
128	7210	7549	7888	8227	8565	8903	9241	9579	9916	*0253	338
129	110590	0926	1263	1599	1934	2270	2605	2940	3275	3609	335
130	113943	4277	4611	4944	5278	5611	5943	6276	6608	6940	333
131	7271	7603	7934	8265	8595	8926	9256	9586	9915	*0245	330
132	120574	0903	1231	1560	1888	2216	2544	2871	3198	3525	328
133	3852	4178	4504	4830	5156	5481	5806	6131	6456	6781	325
134	7105	7429	7753	8076	8399	8722	9045	9368	9690	*0012	323
135	130334	0655	0977	1298	1619	1939	2260	2580	2900	3219	321
136	3539	3858	4177	4496	4814	5133	5451	5769	6086	6403	318
137	6721	7037	7354	7671	7987	8303	8618	8934	9249	9564	316
138	9879	*0194	*0508	*0822	*1136	*1450	*1763	*2076	*2389	*2702	314
139	143015	3327	3639	3951	4263	4574	4885	5196	5507	5818	311

PROPORTIONAL PARTS

Diff.	1	2	3	4	5	6	7	8	9	Diff.
347	35	69	104	139	174	208	243	278	312	347
346	35	69	104	138	173	208	242	277	311	346
345	35	69	104	138	173	207	242	276	311	345
344	34	69	103	138	172	206	241	275	310	344
343	34	69	103	137	172	206	240	274	309	343
342	34	68	103	137	171	205	239	274	308	342
341	34	68	102	136	171	205	239	273	307	341
340	34	68	102	136	170	204	238	272	306	340
339	34	68	102	136	170	203	237	271	305	339
338	34	68	101	135	169	203	237	270	304	338
337	34	67	101	135	169	202	236	270	303	337
336	34	67	101	134	168	202	235	269	302	336
335	34	67	101	134	168	201	235	268	302	335
334	33	67	100	134	167	200	234	267	301	334
333	33	67	100	133	167	200	233	266	300	333
332	33	66	100	133	166	199	232	266	299	332
331	33	66	99	132	166	199	232	265	298	331
330	33	66	99	132	165	198	231	264	297	330
329	33	66	99	132	165	197	230	263	296	329
328	33	66	98	131	164	197	230	262	295	328
327	33	65	98	131	164	196	229	262	294	327
326	33	65	98	130	163	196	228	261	293	326
325	33	65	98	130	163	195	228	260	293	325
324	32	65	97	130	162	194	227	259	292	324
323	32	65	97	129	162	194	226	258	291	323
322	32	64	97	129	161	193	225	258	290	322
321	32	64	96	128	161	193	225	257	289	321
320	32	64	96	128	160	192	224	256	288	320
319	32	64	96	128	160	191	223	255	287	319
318	32	64	95	127	159	191	223	254	286	318
317	32	63	95	127	159	190	222	254	285	317
316	32	63	95	126	158	190	221	253	284	316
315	32	63	95	126	158	189	221	252	284	315
314	31	63	94	126	157	188	220	251	283	314
313	31	63	94	125	157	188	219	250	282	313
312	31	62	94	125	156	187	218	250	281	312
311	31	62	93	124	156	187	218	249	280	311
310	31	62	93	124	155	186	217	248	279	310
309	31	62	93	124	155	185	216	247	278	309
308	31	62	92	123	154	185	216	246	277	308
307	31	61	92	123	154	184	215	246	276	307

TABLE B

LOGARITHMS OF NUMBERS

No. 140—Log. 146   No. 159—Log. 203

N.	0	1	2	3	4	5	6	7	8	9	Diff.
140	146128	6438	6748	7058	7367	7676	7985	8294	8603	8911	309
141	9219	9527	9835	*0142	*0449	*0756	*1063	*1370	*1676	*1982	307
142	152288	2594	2900	3205	3510	3815	4120	4424	4728	5032	305
143	5336	5640	5943	6246	6549	6852	7154	7457	7759	8061	303
144	8362	8664	8965	9266	9567	9868	*0168	*0469	*0769	*1068	301
145	161368	1667	1967	2266	2564	2863	3161	3460	3758	4055	299
146	4353	4650	4947	5244	5541	5838	6134	6430	6726	7022	297
147	7317	7613	7908	8203	8497	8792	9086	9380	9674	9968	295
148	170262	0555	0848	1141	1434	1726	2019	2311	2603	2895	293
149	3186	3478	3769	4060	4351	4641	4932	5222	5512	5802	291
150	176091	6381	6670	6959	7248	7536	7825	8113	8401	8689	289
151	8977	9264	9552	9839	*0126	*0413	*0699	*0986	*1272	*1558	287
152	181844	2129	2415	2700	2985	3270	3555	3839	4123	4407	285
153	4691	4975	5259	5542	5825	6108	6391	6674	6956	7239	283
154	7521	7803	8084	8366	8647	8928	9209	9490	9771	*0051	281
155	190332	0612	0892	1171	1451	1730	2010	2289	2567	2846	279
156	3125	3403	3681	3959	4237	4514	4792	5069	5346	5623	278
157	5900	6176	6453	6729	7005	7281	7556	7832	8107	8382	276
158	8657	8932	9206	9481	9755	*0029	*0303	*0577	*0850	*1124	274
159	201397	1670	1943	2216	2488	2761	3033	3305	3577	3848	272

PROPORTIONAL PARTS

Diff.	1	2	3	4	5	6	7	8	9	Diff.
306	31	61	92	122	153	184	214	245	275	306
305	31	61	92	122	153	183	214	244	275	305
304	30	61	91	122	152	182	213	243	274	304
303	30	61	91	121	152	182	212	242	273	303
302	30	60	91	121	151	181	211	242	272	302
301	30	60	90	120	151	181	211	241	271	301
300	30	60	90	120	150	180	210	240	270	300
299	30	60	90	120	150	179	209	239	269	299
298	30	60	89	119	149	179	209	238	268	298
297	30	59	89	119	149	178	208	238	267	297
296	30	59	89	118	148	178	207	237	266	296
295	30	59	89	118	148	177	207	236	266	295
294	29	59	88	118	147	176	206	235	265	294
293	29	59	88	117	147	176	205	234	264	293
292	29	58	88	117	146	175	204	234	263	292
291	29	58	87	116	146	175	204	233	262	291
290	29	58	87	116	145	174	203	232	261	290
289	29	58	87	116	145	173	202	231	260	289
288	29	58	86	115	144	173	202	230	259	288
287	29	57	86	115	144	172	201	230	258	287
286	29	57	86	114	143	172	200	229	257	286
285	29	57	86	114	143	171	200	228	257	285
284	28	57	85	114	142	170	199	227	256	284
283	28	57	85	113	142	170	198	226	255	283
282	28	56	85	113	141	169	197	226	254	282
281	28	56	84	112	141	169	197	225	253	281
280	28	56	84	112	140	168	196	224	252	280
279	28	56	84	112	140	167	195	223	251	279
278	28	56	83	111	139	167	195	222	250	278
277	28	55	83	111	139	166	194	222	249	277
276	28	55	83	110	138	166	193	221	248	276
275	28	55	83	110	138	165	193	220	248	275
274	27	55	82	110	137	164	192	219	247	274
273	27	55	82	109	137	164	191	218	246	273
272	27	54	82	109	136	163	190	218	245	272
271	27	54	81	108	136	163	190	217	244	271

LOGARITHMS OF NUMBERS

No. 160—Log. 204   No. 179—Log. 255

N.	0	1	2	3	4	5	6	7	8	9	Diff.
160	204120	4391	4663	4934	5204	5475	5746	6016	6286	6556	271
161	6826	7096	7365	7634	7904	8173	8441	8710	8979	9247	269
162	9515	9783	*0051	*0319	*0586	*0853	*1121	*1388	*1654	*1921	267
163	212188	2454	2720	2986	3252	3518	3783	4049	4314	4579	266
164	4844	5109	5373	5638	5902	6166	6430	6694	6957	7221	264
165	217484	7747	8010	8273	8536	8798	9060	9323	9585	9846	262
166	220108	0370	0631	0892	1153	1414	1675	1936	2196	2456	261
167	2716	2976	3236	3496	3755	4015	4274	4533	4792	5051	259
168	5309	5568	5826	6084	6342	6600	6858	7115	7372	7630	258
169	7887	8144	8400	8657	8913	9170	9426	9682	9938	*0193	256
170	230449	0704	0960	1215	1470	1724	1979	2234	2488	2742	255
171	2996	3250	3504	3757	4011	4264	4517	4770	5023	5276	253
172	5528	5781	6033	6285	6537	6789	7041	7292	7544	7795	252
173	8046	8297	8548	8799	9049	9299	9550	9800	*0050	*0300	250
174	240549	0799	1048	1297	1546	1795	2044	2293	2541	2790	249
175	243038	3286	3534	3782	4030	4277	4525	4772	5019	5266	248
176	5513	5759	6006	6252	6499	6745	6991	7237	7482	7728	246
177	7973	8219	8464	8709	8954	9198	9443	9687	9932	*0176	245
178	250420	0664	0908	1151	1395	1638	1881	2125	2368	2610	243
179	2853	3096	3338	3580	3822	4064	4306	4548	4790	5031	242

PROPORTIONAL PARTS

Diff.	1	2	3	4	5	6	7	8	9	Diff.
272	27	54	82	109	136	163	190	218	245	272
271	27	54	81	108	136	163	190	217	244	271
270	27	54	81	108	135	162	189	216	243	270
269	27	54	81	108	135	161	188	215	242	269
268	27	54	80	107	134	161	188	214	241	268
267	27	53	80	107	134	160	187	214	240	267
266	27	53	80	106	133	160	186	213	239	266
265	27	53	80	106	133	159	186	212	239	265
264	26	53	79	106	132	158	185	211	238	264
263	26	53	79	105	132	158	184	210	237	263
262	26	52	79	105	131	157	183	210	236	262
261	26	52	78	104	131	157	183	209	235	261
260	26	52	78	104	130	156	182	208	234	260
259	26	52	78	104	130	155	181	207	233	259
258	26	52	77	103	129	155	181	206	232	258
257	26	51	77	103	129	154	180	206	231	257
256	26	51	77	102	128	154	179	205	230	256
255	26	51	77	102	128	153	179	204	230	255
254	25	51	76	102	127	152	178	203	229	254
253	25	51	76	101	127	152	177	202	228	253
252	25	50	76	101	126	151	176	202	227	252
251	25	50	75	100	126	151	176	201	226	251
250	25	50	75	100	125	150	175	200	225	250
249	25	50	75	100	125	149	174	199	224	249
248	25	50	74	99	124	149	174	198	223	248
247	25	49	74	99	124	148	173	198	222	247
246	25	49	74	98	123	148	172	197	221	246
245	25	49	74	98	123	147	172	196	221	245
244	24	49	73	98	122	146	171	195	220	244
243	24	49	73	97	122	146	170	194	219	243
242	24	48	73	97	121	145	169	194	218	242
241	24	48	72	96	121	145	169	193	217	241
240	24	48	72	96	120	144	168	192	216	240

TABLE B

LOGARITHMS OF NUMBERS

No. 180—Log. 255   No. 204—Log. 311

N.	0	1	2	3	4	5	6	7	8	9	Diff.
180	255273	5514	5755	5996	6237	6477	6718	6958	7198	7439	241
181	7679	7918	8158	8398	8637	8877	9116	9355	9594	9833	239
182	260071	0310	0548	0787	1025	1263	1501	1739	1976	2214	238
183	2451	2688	2925	3162	3399	3636	3873	4109	4346	4582	237
184	4818	5054	5290	5525	5761	5996	6232	6467	6702	6937	235
185	267172	7406	7641	7875	8110	8344	8578	8812	9046	9279	234
186	9513	9746	9980	*0213	*0446	*0679	*0912	*1144	*1377	*1609	233
187	271842	2074	2306	2538	2770	3001	3233	3464	3696	3927	232
188	4158	4389	4620	4850	5081	5311	5542	5772	6002	6232	230
189	6462	6692	6921	7151	7380	7609	7838	8067	8296	8525	229
190	278754	8982	9211	9439	9667	9895	*0123	*0351	*0578	*0806	228
191	281033	1261	1488	1715	1942	2169	2396	2622	2849	3075	227
192	3301	3527	3753	3979	4205	4431	4656	4882	5107	5332	226
193	5557	5782	6007	6232	6456	6681	6905	7130	7354	7578	225
194	7802	8026	8249	8473	8696	8920	9143	9366	9589	9812	223
195	290035	0257	0480	0702	0925	1147	1369	1591	1813	2034	222
196	2256	2478	2699	2920	3141	3363	3584	3804	4025	4246	221
197	4466	4687	4907	5127	5347	5567	5787	6007	6226	6446	220
198	6665	6884	7104	7323	7542	7761	7979	8198	8416	8635	219
199	8853	9071	9289	9507	9725	9943	*0161	*0378	*0595	*0813	218
200	301030	1247	1464	1681	1898	2114	2331	2547	2764	2980	217
201	3196	3412	3628	3844	4059	4275	4491	4706	4921	5136	216
202	5351	5566	5781	5996	6211	6425	6639	6854	7068	7282	215
203	7496	7710	7924	8137	8351	8564	8778	8991	9204	9417	213
204	9630	9843	*0056	*0268	*0481	*0693	*0906	*1118	*1330	*1542	212

PROPORTIONAL PARTS

Diff.	1	2	3	4	5	6	7	8	9	Diff.
239	24	48	72	96	120	143	167	191	215	239
238	24	48	71	95	119	143	167	190	214	238
237	24	47	71	95	119	142	166	190	213	237
236	24	47	71	94	118	142	165	189	212	236
235	24	47	71	94	118	141	165	188	212	235
234	23	47	70	94	117	140	164	187	211	234
233	23	47	70	93	117	140	163	186	210	233
232	23	46	70	93	116	139	162	186	209	232
231	23	46	69	92	116	139	162	185	208	231
230	23	46	69	92	115	138	161	184	207	230
229	23	46	69	92	115	137	160	183	206	229
228	23	46	68	91	114	137	160	182	205	228
227	23	45	68	91	114	136	159	182	204	227
226	23	45	68	90	113	136	158	181	203	226
225	23	45	68	90	113	135	158	180	203	225
224	22	45	67	90	112	134	157	179	202	224
223	22	45	67	89	112	134	156	178	201	223
222	22	44	67	89	111	133	155	178	200	222
221	22	44	66	88	111	133	155	177	199	221
220	22	44	66	88	110	132	154	176	198	220
219	22	44	66	88	110	131	153	175	197	219
218	22	44	65	87	109	131	153	174	196	218
217	22	43	65	87	109	130	152	174	195	217
216	22	43	65	86	108	130	151	173	194	216
215	22	43	65	86	108	129	151	172	194	215
214	21	43	64	86	107	128	150	171	193	214
213	21	43	64	85	107	128	149	170	192	213
212	21	42	64	85	106	127	148	170	191	212

LOGARITHMS OF NUMBERS

No. 205—Log. 311   **No. 234—Log. 370**

N.	0	1	2	3	4	5	6	7	8	9	Diff.
205	311754	1966	2177	2389	2600	2812	3023	3234	3445	3656	211
206	3867	4078	4289	4499	4710	4920	5130	5340	5551	5760	210
207	5970	6180	6390	6599	6809	7018	7227	7436	7646	7854	209
208	8063	8272	8481	8689	8898	9106	9314	9522	9730	9938	208
209	320146	0354	0562	0769	0977	1184	1391	1598	1805	2012	207
210	322219	2426	2633	2839	3046	3252	3458	3665	3871	4077	206
211	4282	4488	4694	4899	5105	5310	5516	5721	5926	6131	205
212	6336	6541	6745	6950	7155	7359	7563	7767	7972	8176	204
213	8380	8583	8787	8991	9194	9398	9601	9805	*0008	*0211	203
214	330414	0617	0819	1022	1225	1427	1630	1832	2034	2236	202
215	332438	2640	2842	3044	3246	3447	3649	3850	4051	4253	202
216	4454	4655	4856	5057	5257	5458	5658	5859	6059	6260	201
217	6460	6660	6860	7060	7260	7459	7659	7858	8058	8257	200
218	8456	8656	8855	9054	9253	9451	9650	9849	*0047	*0246	199
219	340444	0642	0841	1039	1237	1435	1632	1830	2028	2225	198
220	342423	2620	2817	3014	3212	3409	3606	3802	3999	4196	197
221	4392	4589	4785	4981	5178	5374	5570	5766	5962	6157	196
222	6353	6549	6744	6939	7135	7330	7525	7720	7915	8110	195
223	8305	8500	8694	8889	9083	9278	9472	9666	9860	*0054	194
224	350248	0442	0636	0829	1023	1216	1410	1603	1796	1989	193
225	352183	2375	2568	2761	2954	3147	3339	3532	3724	3916	193
226	4108	4301	4493	4685	4876	5068	5260	5452	5643	5834	192
227	6026	6217	6408	6599	6790	6981	7172	7363	7554	7744	191
228	7935	8125	8316	8506	8696	8886	9076	9266	9456	9646	190
229	9835	*0025	*0215	*0404	*0593	*0783	*0972	*1161	*1350	*1539	189
230	361728	1917	2105	2294	2482	2671	2859	3048	3236	3424	188
231	3612	3800	3988	4176	4363	4551	4739	4926	5113	5301	188
232	5488	5675	5862	6049	6236	6423	6610	6796	6983	7169	187
233	7356	7542	7729	7915	8101	8287	8473	8659	8845	9030	186
234	9216	9401	9587	9772	9958	*0143	*0328	*0513	*0698	*0883	185

PROPORTIONAL PARTS

Diff.	1	2	3	4	5	6	7	8	9	Diff.
212	21	42	64	85	106	127	148	170	191	212
211	21	42	63	84	106	127	148	169	190	211
210	21	42	63	84	105	126	147	168	189	210
209	21	42	63	84	105	125	146	167	188	209
208	21	42	62	83	104	125	146	166	187	208
207	21	41	62	83	104	124	145	166	186	207
206	21	41	62	82	103	124	144	165	185	206
205	21	41	62	82	103	123	144	164	185	205
204	20	41	61	82	102	122	143	163	184	204
203	20	41	61	81	102	122	142	162	183	203
202	20	40	61	81	101	121	141	162	182	202
201	20	40	60	80	101	121	141	161	181	201
200	20	40	60	80	100	120	140	160	180	200
199	20	40	60	80	100	119	139	159	179	199
198	20	40	59	79	99	119	139	158	178	198
197	20	39	59	79	99	118	138	158	177	197
196	20	39	59	78	98	118	137	157	176	196
195	20	39	59	78	98	117	137	156	176	195
194	19	39	58	78	97	116	136	155	175	194
193	19	39	58	77	97	116	135	154	174	193
192	19	38	58	77	96	115	134	154	173	192
191	19	38	57	76	96	115	134	153	172	191
190	19	38	57	76	95	114	133	152	171	190
189	19	38	57	76	95	113	132	151	170	189
188	19	38	56	75	94	113	132	150	169	188

TABLE B

Logarithms of Numbers

No. 235—Log. 371   . No. 264—Log. 423

N.	0	1	2	3	4	5	6	7	8	9	Diff.
235	371068	1253	1437	1622	1806	1991	2175	2360	2544	2728	184
236	2912	3096	3280	3464	3647	3831	4015	4198	4382	4565	184
237	4748	4932	5115	5298	5481	5664	5846	6029	6212	6394	183
238	6577	6759	6942	7124	7306	7488	7670	7852	8034	8216	182
239	8398	8580	8761	8943	9124	9306	9487	9668	9849	*0030	181
240	380211	0392	0573	0754	0934	1115	1296	1476	1656	1837	181
241	2017	2197	2377	2557	2737	2917	3097	3277	3456	3636	180
242	3815	3995	4174	4353	4533	4712	4891	5070	5249	5428	179
243	5606	5785	5964	6142	6321	6499	6677	6856	7034	7212	178
244	7390	7568	7746	7923	8101	8279	8456	8634	8811	*0759	178
245	389166	9343	9520	9698	9875	*0051	*0228	*0405	*0582	*0759	177
246	390935	1112	1288	1464	1641	1817	1993	2169	2345	2521	176
247	2697	2873	3048	3224	3400	3575	3751	3926	4101	4277	176
248	4452	4627	4802	4977	5152	5326	5501	5676	5850	6025	175
249	6199	6374	6548	6722	6896	7071	7245	7419	7592	7766	174
250	397940	8114	8287	8461	8634	8808	8981	9154	9328	9501	173
251	9674	9847	*0020	*0192	*0365	*0538	*0711	*0883	*1056	*1228	173
252	401401	1573	1745	1917	2089	2261	2433	2605	2777	2949	172
253	3121	3292	3464	3635	3807	3978	4149	4320	4492	4663	171
254	4834	5005	5176	5346	5517	5688	5858	6029	6199	6370	171
255	406540	6710	6881	7051	7221	7391	7561	7731	7901	8070	170
256	8240	8410	8579	8749	8918	9087	9257	9426	9595	9764	169
257	9933	*0102	*0271	*0440	*0609	*0777	*0946	*1114	*1283	*1451	169
258	411620	1788	1956	2124	2293	2461	2629	2796	2964	3132	168
259	3300	3467	3635	3803	3970	4137	4305	4472	4639	4806	167
260	414973	5140	5307	5474	5641	5808	5974	6141	6308	6474	167
261	6641	6807	6973	7139	7306	7472	7638	7804	7970	8135	166
262	8301	8467	8633	8798	8964	9129	9295	9460	9625	9791	165
263	9956	*0121	*0286	*0451	*0616	*0781	*0945	*1110	*1275	*1439	165
264	421604	1768	1933	2097	2261	2426	2590	2754	2918	3082	164

PROPORTIONAL PARTS

Diff.	1	2	3	4	5	6	7	8	9	Diff.
187	19	37	56	75	94	112	131	150	168	187
186	19	37	56	74	93	112	130	149	167	186
185	19	37	56	74	93	111	130	148	167	185
184	18	37	55	74	92	110	129	147	166	184
183	18	37	55	73	92	110	128	146	165	183
182	18	36	55	73	91	109	127	146	164	182
181	18	36	54	72	91	109	127	145	163	181
180	18	36	54	72	90	108	126	144	162	180
179	18	36	54	72	90	107	125	143	161	179
178	18	36	53	71	89	107	125	142	160	178
177	18	35	53	71	89	106	124	142	159	177
176	18	35	53	70	88	106	123	141	158	176
175	18	35	53	70	88	105	123	140	158	175
174	17	35	52	70	87	104	122	139	157	174
173	17	35	52	69	87	104	121	138	156	173
172	17	34	52	69	86	103	120	138	155	172
171	17	34	51	68	86	103	120	137	154	171
170	17	34	51	68	85	102	119	136	153	170
169	17	34	51	68	85	101	118	135	152	169
168	17	34	50	67	84	101	118	134	151	168
167	17	33	50	67	84	100	117	134	150	167
166	17	33	50	66	83	100	116	133	149	166
165	17	33	50	66	83	99	116	132	149	165
164	16	33	49	66	82	98	115	131	148	164

LOGARITHMS OF NUMBERS

No. 265—Log. 423   No. 299—Log. 476

N.	0	1	2	3	4	5	6	7	8	9	Diff.
265	423246	3410	3574	3737	3901	4065	4228	4392	4555	4718	164
266	4882	5045	5208	5371	5534	5697	5860	6023	6186	6349	163
267	6511	6674	6836	6999	7161	7324	7486	7648	7811	7973	162
268	8135	8297	8459	8621	8783	8944	9106	9268	9429	9591	162
269	9752	9914	*0075	*0236	*0398	*0559	*0720	*0881	*1042	*1203	161
270	431364	1525	1685	1846	2007	2167	2328	2488	2649	2809	161
271	2969	3130	3290	3450	3610	3770	3930	4090	4249	4409	160
272	4569	4729	4888	5048	5207	5367	5526	5685	5844	6004	159
273	6163	6322	6481	6640	6799	6957	7116	7275	7433	7592	159
274	7751	7909	8067	8226	8384	8542	8701	8859	9017	9175	158
275	439333	9491	9648	9806	9964	*0122	*0279	*0437	*0594	*0752	158
276	440909	1066	1224	1381	1538	1695	1852	2009	2166	2323	157
277	2480	2637	2793	2950	3106	3263	3419	3576	3732	3889	157
278	4045	4201	4357	4513	4669	4825	4981	5137	5293	5449	156
279	5604	5760	5915	6071	6226	6382	6537	6692	6848	7003	155
280	447158	7313	7468	7623	7778	7933	8088	8242	8397	8552	155
281	8706	8861	9015	9170	9324	9478	9633	9787	9941	*0095	154
282	450249	0403	0557	0711	0865	1018	1172	1326	1479	1633	154
283	1786	1940	2093	2247	2400	2553	2706	2859	3012	3165	153
284	3318	3471	3624	3777	3930	4082	4235	4387	4540	4692	153
285	454845	4997	5150	5302	5454	5606	5758	5910	6062	6214	152
286	6366	6518	6670	6821	6973	7125	7276	7428	7579	7731	152
287	7882	8033	8184	8336	8487	8638	8789	8940	9091	9242	151
288	9392	9543	9694	9845	9995	*0146	*0296	*0447	*0597	*0748	151
289	460898	1048	1198	1348	1499	1649	1799	1948	2098	2248	150
290	462398	2548	2697	2847	2997	3146	3296	3445	3594	3744	150
291	3893	4042	4191	4340	4490	4639	4788	4936	5085	5234	149
292	5383	5532	5680	5829	5977	6126	6274	6423	6571	6719	149
293	6868	7016	7164	7312	7460	7608	7756	7904	8052	8200	148
294	8347	8495	8643	8790	8938	9085	9233	9380	9527	9675	148
295	469822	9969	*0116	*0263	*0410	*0557	*0704	*0851	*0998	*1145	147
296	471292	1438	1585	1732	1878	2025	2171	2318	2464	2610	146
297	2756	2903	3049	3195	3341	3487	3633	3779	3925	4071	146
298	4216	4362	4508	4653	4799	4944	5090	5235	5381	5526	146
299	5671	5816	5962	6107	6252	6397	6542	6687	6832	6976	145

PROPORTIONAL PARTS

Diff.	1	2	3	4	5	6	7	8	9	Diff.
164	16	33	49	66	82	98	115	131	148	164
163	16	33	49	65	82	98	114	130	147	163
162	16	32	49	65	81	97	113	130	146	162
161	16	32	48	64	81	97	113	129	145	161
160	16	32	48	64	80	96	112	128	144	160
159	16	32	48	64	80	95	111	127	143	159
158	16	32	47	63	79	95	111	126	142	158
157	16	31	47	63	79	94	110	126	141	157
156	16	31	47	62	78	94	109	125	140	156
155	16	31	47	62	78	93	109	124	140	155
154	15	31	46	62	77	92	108	123	139	154
153	15	31	46	61	77	92	107	122	138	153
152	15	30	46	61	76	91	106	122	137	152
151	15	30	45	60	76	91	106	121	136	151
150	15	30	45	60	75	90	105	120	135	150
149	15	30	45	60	75	89	104	119	134	149
148	15	30	44	59	74	89	104	118	133	148
147	15	29	44	59	74	88	103	118	132	147
146	15	29	44	58	73	88	102	117	131	146
145	15	29	44	58	73	87	102	116	131	145
144	14	29	43	58	72	86	101	115	130	144
143	14	29	43	57	72	86	100	114	129	143

TABLE B

LOGARITHMS OF NUMBERS

No. 300—Log. 477   **No. 339—Log. 531**

N.	0	1	2	3	4	5	6	7	8	9	Diff.
300	477121	7266	7411	7555	7700	7844	7989	8133	8278	8422	145
301	8566	8711	8855	8999	9143	9287	9431	9575	9719	9863	144
302	480007	0151	0294	0438	0582	0725	0869	1012	1156	1299	144
303	1443	1586	1729	1872	2016	2159	2302	2445	2588	2731	143
304	2874	3016	3159	3302	3445	3587	3730	3872	4015	4157	143
305	484300	4442	4585	4727	4869	5011	5153	5295	5437	5579	142
306	5721	5863	6005	6147	6289	6430	6572	6714	6855	6997	142
307	7138	7280	7421	7563	7704	7845	7986	8127	8269	8410	141
308	8551	8692	8833	8974	9114	9255	9396	9537	9677	9818	141
309	9958	*0099	*0239	*0380	*0520	*0661	*0801	*0941	*1081	*1222	140
310	491362	1502	1642	1782	1922	2062	2201	2341	2481	2621	140
311	2760	2900	3040	3179	3319	3458	3597	3737	3876	4015	139
312	4155	4294	4433	4572	4711	4850	4989	5128	5267	5406	139
313	5544	5683	5822	5960	6099	6238	6376	6515	6653	6791	139
314	6930	7068	7206	7344	7483	7621	7759	7897	8035	8173	138
315	498311	8448	8586	8724	8862	8999	9137	9275	9412	9550	138
316	9687	9824	9962	*0099	*0236	*0374	*0511	*0648	*0785	*0922	137
317	501059	1196	1333	1470	1607	1744	1880	2017	2154	2291	137
318	2427	2564	2700	2837	2973	3109	3246	3382	3518	3655	136
319	3791	3927	4063	4199	4335	4471	4607	4743	4878	5014	136
320	505150	5286	5421	5557	5693	5828	5964	6099	6234	6370	136
321	6505	6640	6776	6911	7046	7181	7316	7451	7586	7721	135
322	7856	7991	8126	8260	8395	8530	8664	8799	8934	9068	135
323	9203	9337	9471	9606	9740	9874	*0009	*0143	*0277	*0411	134
324	510545	0679	0813	0947	1081	1215	1349	1482	1616	1750	134
325	511883	2017	2151	2284	2418	2551	2684	2818	2951	3084	133
326	3218	3351	3484	3617	3750	3883	4016	4149	4282	4415	133
327	4548	4681	4813	4946	5079	5211	5344	5476	5609	5741	133
328	5874	6006	6139	6271	6403	6535	6668	6800	6932	7064	132
329	7196	7328	7460	7592	7724	7855	7987	8119	8251	8382	132
330	518514	8646	8777	8909	9040	9171	9303	9434	9566	9697	131
331	9828	9959	*0090	*0221	*0353	*0484	*0615	*0745	*0876	*1007	131
332	521138	1269	1400	1530	1661	1792	1922	2053	2183	2314	131
333	2444	2575	2705	2835	2966	3096	3226	3356	3486	3616	130
334	3746	3876	4006	4136	4266	4396	4526	4656	4785	4915	130
335	525045	5174	5304	5434	5563	5693	5822	5951	6081	6210	129
336	6339	6469	6598	6727	6856	6985	7114	7243	7372	7501	129
337	7630	7759	7888	8016	8145	8274	8402	8531	8660	8788	129
338	8917	9045	9174	9302	9430	9559	9687	9815	9943	*0072	128
339	530200	0328	0456	0584	0712	0840	0968	1096	1223	1351	128

PROPORTIONAL PARTS

Diff.	1	2	3	4	5	6	7	8	9	Diff.
142	14	28	43	57	71	85	99	114	128	142
141	14	28	42	56	71	85	99	113	127	141
140	14	28	42	56	70	84	98	112	126	140
139	14	28	42	56	70	83	97	111	125	139
138	14	28	41	55	69	83	97	110	124	138
137	14	27	41	55	69	82	96	110	123	137
136	14	27	41	54	68	82	95	109	122	136
135	14	27	41	54	68	81	95	108	122	135
134	13	27	40	54	67	80	94	107	121	134
133	13	27	40	53	67	80	93	106	120	133
132	13	26	40	53	66	79	92	106	119	132
131	13	26	39	52	66	79	92	105	118	131
130	13	26	39	52	65	78	91	104	117	130
129	13	26	39	52	65	77	90	103	116	129
128	13	26	38	51	64	77	90	102	115	128
127	13	25	38	51	64	76	89	102	114	127

LOGARITHMS OF NUMBERS

No. 340—Log. 531   No. 379—Log. 579

N.	0	1	2	3	4	5	6	7	8	9	Diff.
340	531479	1607	1734	1862	1990	2117	2245	2372	2500	2627	128
341	2754	2882	3009	3136	3264	3391	3518	3645	3772	3899	127
342	4026	4153	4280	4407	4534	4661	4787	4914	5041	5167	127
343	5294	5421	5547	5674	5800	5927	6053	6180	6306	6432	126
344	6558	6685	6811	6937	7063	7189	7315	7441	7567	7693	126
345	537819	7945	8071	8197	8322	8448	8574	8699	8825	8951	126
346	9076	9202	9327	9452	9578	9703	9829	9954	*0079	*0204	125
347	540329	0455	0580	0705	0830	0955	1080	1205	1330	1454	125
348	1579	1704	1829	1953	2078	2203	2327	2452	2576	2701	125
349	2825	2950	3074	3199	3323	3447	3571	3696	3820	3944	124
350	544068	4192	4316	4440	4564	4688	4812	4936	5060	5183	124
351	5307	5431	5555	5678	5802	5925	6049	6172	6296	6419	124
352	6543	6666	6789	6913	7036	7159	7282	7405	7529	7652	123
353	7775	7898	8021	8144	8267	8389	8512	8635	8758	8881	123
354	9003	9126	9249	9371	9494	9616	9739	9861	9984	*0106	123
355	550228	0351	0473	0595	0717	0840	0962	1084	1206	1328	122
356	1450	1572	1694	1816	1938	2060	2181	2303	2425	2547	122
357	2668	2790	2911	3033	3155	3276	3398	3519	3640	3762	121
358	3883	4004	4126	4247	4368	4489	4610	4731	4852	4973	121
359	5094	5215	5336	5457	5578	5699	5820	5940	6061	6182	121
360	556303	6423	6544	6664	6785	6905	7026	7146	7267	7387	120
361	7507	7627	7748	7868	7988	8108	8228	8349	8469	8589	120
362	8709	8829	8948	9068	9188	9308	9428	9548	9667	9787	120
363	9907	*0026	*0146	*0265	*0385	*0504	*0624	*0743	*0863	*0982	119
364	561101	1221	1340	1459	1578	1698	1817	1936	2055	2174	119
365	562293	2412	2531	2650	2769	2887	3006	3125	3244	3362	119
366	3481	3600	3718	3837	3955	4074	4192	4311	4429	4548	119
367	4666	4784	4903	5021	5139	5257	5376	5494	5612	5730	118
368	5848	5966	6084	6202	6320	6437	6555	6673	6791	6909	118
369	7026	7144	7262	7379	7497	7614	7732	7849	7967	8084	118
370	568202	8319	8436	8554	8671	8788	8905	9023	9140	9257	117
371	9374	9491	9608	9725	9842	9959	*0076	*0193	*0309	*0426	117
372	570543	0660	0776	0893	1010	1126	1243	1359	1476	1592	117
373	1709	1825	1942	2058	2174	2291	2407	2523	2639	2755	116
374	2872	2988	3104	3220	3336	3452	3568	3684	3800	3915	116
375	574031	4147	4263	4379	4494	4610	4726	4841	4957	5072	116
376	5188	5303	5419	5534	5650	5765	5880	5996	6111	6226	115
377	6341	6457	6572	6687	6802	6917	7032	7147	7262	7377	115
378	7492	7607	7722	7836	7951	8066	8181	8295	8410	8525	115
379	8639	8754	8868	8983	9097	9212	9326	9441	9555	9669	114

PROPORTIONAL PARTS

Diff.	1	2	3	4	5	6	7	8	9	Diff.
128	13	26	38	51	64	77	90	102	115	128
127	13	25	38	51	64	76	89	102	114	127
126	13	25	38	50	63	76	88	101	113	126
125	13	25	38	50	63	75	88	100	113	125
124	12	25	37	50	62	74	87	99	112	124
123	12	25	37	49	62	74	86	98	111	123
122	12	24	37	49	61	73	85	98	110	122
121	12	24	36	48	61	73	85	97	109	121
120	12	24	36	48	60	72	84	96	108	120
119	12	24	36	48	60	71	83	95	107	119
118	12	24	35	47	59	71	83	94	106	118
117	12	23	35	47	59	70	82	94	105	117
116	12	23	35	46	58	70	81	93	104	116

TABLE B

Logarithms of Numbers

N.	0	1	2	3	4	5	6	7	8	9	Diff.
380	579784	9898	*0012	*0126	*0241	*0355	*0469	*0583	*0697	*0811	114
381	580925	1039	1153	1267	1381	1495	1608	1722	1836	1950	114
382	2063	2177	2291	2404	2518	2631	2745	2858	2972	3085	114
383	3199	3312	3426	3539	3652	3765	3879	3992	4105	4218	113
384	4331	4444	4557	4670	4783	4896	5009	5122	5235	5348	113
385	585461	5574	5686	5799	5912	6024	6137	6250	6362	6475	113
386	6587	6700	6812	6925	7037	7149	7262	7374	7486	7599	112
387	7711	7823	7935	8047	8160	8272	8384	8496	8608	8720	112
388	8832	8944	9056	9167	9279	9391	9503	9615	9726	9838	112
389	9950	*0061	*0173	*0284	*0396	*0507	*0619	*0730	*0842	*0953	112
390	591065	1176	1287	1399	1510	1621	1732	1843	1955	2066	111
391	2177	2288	2399	2510	2621	2732	2843	2954	3064	3175	111
392	3286	3397	3508	3618	3729	3840	3950	4061	4171	4282	111
393	4393	4503	4614	4724	4834	4945	5055	5165	5276	5386	110
394	5496	5606	5717	5827	5937	6047	6157	6267	6377	6487	110
395	596597	6707	6817	6927	7037	7146	7256	7366	7476	7586	110
396	7695	7805	7914	8024	8134	8243	8353	8462	8572	8681	110
397	8791	8900	9009	9119	9228	9337	9446	9556	9665	9774	109
398	9883	9992	*0101	*0210	*0319	*0428	*0537	*0646	*0755	*0864	109
399	600973	1082	1191	1299	1408	1517	1625	1734	1843	1951	109
400	602060	2169	2277	2386	2494	2603	2711	2819	2928	3036	108
401	3144	3253	3361	3469	3577	3686	3794	3902	4010	4118	108
402	4226	4334	4442	4550	4658	4766	4874	4982	5089	5197	108
403	5305	5413	5521	5628	5736	5844	5951	6059	6166	6274	108
404	6381	6489	6596	6704	6811	6919	7026	7133	7241	7348	107
405	607455	7562	7669	7777	7884	7991	8098	8205	8312	8419	107
406	8526	8633	8740	8847	8954	9061	9167	9274	9381	9488	107
407	9594	9701	9808	9914	*0021	*0128	*0234	*0341	*0447	*0554	107
408	610660	0767	0873	0979	1086	1192	1298	1405	1511	1617	106
409	1723	1829	1936	2042	2148	2254	2360	2466	2572	2678	106
410	612784	2890	2996	3102	3207	3313	3419	3525	3630	3736	106
411	3842	3947	4053	4159	4264	4370	4475	4581	4686	4792	106
412	4897	5003	5108	5213	5319	5424	5529	5634	5740	5845	105
413	5950	6055	6160	6265	6370	6476	6581	6686	6790	6895	105
414	7000	7105	7210	7315	7420	7525	7629	7734	7839	7943	105
415	618048	8153	8257	8362	8466	8571	8676	8780	8884	8989	105
416	9093	9198	9302	9406	9511	9615	9719	9824	9928	*0032	104
417	620136	0240	0344	0448	0552	0656	0760	0864	0968	1072	104
418	1176	1280	1384	1488	1592	1695	1799	1903	2007	2110	104
419	2214	2318	2421	2525	2628	2732	2835	2939	3042	3146	104

PROPORTIONAL PARTS

Diff.	1	2	3	4	5	6	7	8	9	Diff.
115	12	23	35	46	58	69	81	92	104	115
114	11	23	34	46	57	68	80	91	103	114
113	11	23	34	45	57	68	79	90	102	113
112	11	22	34	45	56	67	78	90	101	112
111	11	22	33	44	56	67	78	89	100	111
110	11	22	33	44	55	66	77	88	99	110
109	11	22	33	44	55	65	76	87	98	109
108	11	22	32	43	54	65	76	86	97	108
107	11	21	32	43	54	64	75	86	96	107
106	11	21	32	42	53	64	74	85	95	106
105	11	21	32	42	53	63	74	84	95	105
104	10	21	31	42	52	62	73	83	94	104
103	10	21	31	41	52	62	72	82	93	103

LOGARITHMS OF NUMBERS

No. 420—Log. 623   No. 464—Log. 667

N.	0	1	2	3	4	5	6	7	8	9	Diff.
420	623249	3353	3456	3559	3663	3766	3869	3973	4076	4179	103
421	4282	4385	4488	4591	4695	4798	4901	5004	5107	5210	103
422	5312	5415	5518	5621	5724	5827	5929	6032	6135	6238	103
423	6340	6443	6546	6648	6751	6853	6956	7058	7161	7263	103
424	7366	7468	7571	7673	7775	7878	7980	8082	8185	8287	102
425	628389	8491	8593	8695	8797	8900	9002	9104	9206	9308	102
426	9410	9512	9613	9715	9817	9919	*0021	*0123	*0224	*0326	102
427	630428	0530	0631	0733	0835	0936	1038	1139	1241	1342	102
428	1444	1545	1647	1748	1849	1951	2052	2153	2255	2356	101
429	2457	2559	2660	2761	2862	2963	3064	3165	3266	3367	101
430	633468	3569	3670	3771	3872	3973	4074	4175	4276	4376	101
431	4477	4578	4679	4779	4880	4981	5081	5182	5283	5383	101
432	5484	5584	5685	5785	5886	5986	6087	6187	6287	6388	100
433	6488	6588	6688	6789	6889	6989	7089	7189	7290	7390	100
434	7490	7590	7690	7790	7890	7990	8090	8190	8290	8389	100
435	638489	8589	8689	8789	8888	8988	9088	9188	9287	9387	100
436	9486	9586	9686	9785	9885	9984	*0084	*0183	*0283	*0382	99
437	640481	0581	0680	0779	0879	0978	1077	1177	1276	1375	99
438	1474	1573	1672	1771	1871	1970	2069	2168	2267	2366	99
439	2465	2563	2662	2761	2860	2959	3058	3156	3255	3354	99
440	643453	3551	3650	3749	3847	3946	4044	4143	4242	4340	98
441	4439	4537	4636	4734	4832	4931	5029	5127	5226	5324	98
442	5422	5521	5619	5717	5815	5913	6011	6110	6208	6306	98
443	6404	6502	6600	6698	6796	6894	6992	7089	7187	7285	98
444	7383	7481	7579	7676	7774	7872	7969	8067	8165	8262	98
445	648360	8458	8555	8653	8750	8848	8945	9043	9140	9237	97
446	9335	9432	9530	9627	9724	9821	9919	*0016	*0113	*0210	97
447	650308	0405	0502	0599	0696	0793	0890	0987	1084	1181	97
448	1278	1375	1472	1569	1666	1762	1859	1956	2053	2150	97
449	2246	2343	2440	2536	2633	2730	2826	2923	3019	3116	97
450	653213	3309	3405	3502	3598	3695	3791	3888	3984	4080	96
451	4177	4273	4369	4465	4562	4658	4754	4850	4946	5042	96
452	5138	5235	5331	5427	5523	5619	5715	5810	5906	6002	96
453	6098	6194	6290	6386	6482	6577	6673	6769	6864	6960	96
454	7056	7152	7247	7343	7438	7534	7629	7725	7820	7916	96
455	658011	8107	8202	8298	8393	8488	8584	8679	8774	8870	95
456	8965	9060	9155	9250	9346	9441	9536	9631	9726	9821	95
457	9916	*0011	*0106	*0201	*0296	*0391	*0486	*0581	*0676	*0771	95
458	660865	0960	1055	1150	1245	1339	1434	1529	1623	1718	95
459	1813	1907	2002	2096	2191	2286	2380	2475	2569	2663	95
460	662758	2852	2947	3041	3135	3230	3324	3418	3512	3607	94
461	3701	3795	3889	3983	4078	4172	4266	4360	4454	4548	94
462	4642	4736	4830	4924	5018	5112	5206	5299	5393	5487	94
463	5581	5675	5769	5862	5956	6050	6143	6237	6331	6424	94
464	6518	6612	6705	6799	6892	6986	7079	7173	7266	7360	94

PROPORTIONAL PARTS

Diff.	1	2	3	4	5	6	7	8	9	Diff.
104	10	21	31	42	52	62	73	83	94	104
103	10	21	31	41	52	62	72	82	93	103
102	10	20	31	41	51	61	71	82	92	102
101	10	20	30	40	51	61	71	81	91	101
100	10	20	30	40	50	60	70	80	90	100
99	10	20	30	40	50	59	69	79	89	99
98	10	20	29	39	49	59	69	78	88	98
97	10	19	29	39	49	58	68	78	87	97
96	10	19	29	38	48	58	67	77	86	96
95	10	19	29	38	48	57	67	76	86	95

TABLE B

LOGARITHMS OF NUMBERS

N.	0	1	2	3	4	5	6	7	8	9	Diff.
465	667453	7546	7640	7733	7826	7920	8013	8106	8199	8293	93
466	8386	8479	8572	8665	8759	8852	8945	9038	9131	9224	93
467	9317	9410	9503	9596	9689	9782	9875	9967	*0060	*0153	93
468	670246	0339	0431	0524	0617	0710	0802	0895	0988	1080	93
469	1173	1265	1358	1451	1543	1636	1728	1821	1913	2005	93
470	672098	2190	2283	2375	2467	2560	2652	2744	2836	2929	92
471	3021	3113	3205	3297	3390	3482	3574	3666	3758	3850	92
472	3942	4034	4126	4218	4310	4402	4494	4586	4677	4769	92
473	4861	4953	5045	5137	5228	5320	5412	5503	5595	5687	92
474	5778	5870	5962	6053	6145	6236	6328	6419	6511	6602	92
475	676694	6785	6876	6968	7059	7151	7242	7333	7424	7516	91
476	7607	7698	7789	7881	7972	8063	8154	8245	8336	8427	91
477	8518	8609	8700	8791	8882	8973	9064	9155	9246	9337	91
478	9428	9519	9610	9700	9791	9882	9973	*0063	*0154	*0245	91
479	680336	0426	0517	0607	0698	0789	0879	0970	1060	1151	91
480	681241	1332	1422	1513	1603	1693	1784	1874	1964	2055	90
481	2145	2235	2326	2416	2506	2596	2686	2777	2867	2957	90
482	3047	3137	3227	3317	3407	3497	3587	3677	3767	3857	90
483	3947	4037	4127	4217	4307	4396	4486	4576	4666	4756	90
484	4845	4935	5025	5114	5204	5294	5383	5473	5563	5652	90
485	685742	5831	5921	6010	6100	6189	6279	6368	6458	6547	89
486	6636	6726	6815	6904	6994	7083	7172	7261	7351	7440	89
487	7529	7618	7707	7796	7886	7975	8064	8153	8242	8331	89
488	8420	8509	8598	8687	8776	8865	8953	9042	9131	9220	89
489	9309	9398	9486	9575	9664	9753	9841	9930	*0019	*0107	89
490	690196	0285	0373	0462	0550	0639	0728	0816	0905	0993	89
491	1081	1170	1258	1347	1435	1524	1612	1700	1789	1877	88
492	1965	2053	2142	2230	2318	2406	2494	2583	2671	2759	88
493	2847	2935	3023	3111	3199	3287	3375	3463	3551	3639	88
494	3727	3815	3903	3991	4078	4166	4254	4342	4430	4517	88
495	694605	4693	4781	4868	4956	5044	5131	5219	5307	5394	88
496	5482	5569	5657	5744	5832	5919	6007	6094	6182	6269	87
497	6356	6444	6531	6618	6706	6793	6880	6968	7055	7142	87
498	7229	7317	7404	7491	7578	7665	7752	7839	7926	8014	87
499	8101	8188	8275	8362	8449	8535	8622	8709	8796	8883	87
500	698970	9057	9144	9231	9317	9404	9491	9578	9664	9751	87
501	9838	9924	*0011	*0098	*0184	*0271	*0358	*0444	*0531	*0617	87
502	700704	0790	0877	0963	1050	1136	1222	1309	1395	1482	86
503	1568	1654	1741	1827	1913	1999	2086	2172	2258	2344	86
504	2431	2517	2603	2689	2775	2861	2947	3033	3119	3205	86
505	703291	3377	3463	3549	3635	3721	3807	3893	3979	4065	86
506	4151	4236	4322	4408	4494	4579	4665	4751	4837	4922	86
507	5008	5094	5179	5265	5350	5436	5522	5607	5693	5778	86
508	5864	5949	6035	6120	6206	6291	6376	6462	6547	6632	85
509	6718	6803	6888	6974	7059	7144	7229	7315	7400	7485	85

PROPORTIONAL PARTS

Diff.	1	2	3	4	5	6	7	8	9	Diff.
94	9	19	28	38	47	56	66	75	85	94
93	9	19	28	37	47	56	65	74	84	93
92	9	18	28	37	46	55	64	74	83	92
91	9	18	27	36	46	55	64	73	82	91
90	9	18	27	36	45	54	63	72	81	90
89	9	18	27	36	45	53	62	71	80	89
88	9	18	26	35	44	53	62	70	79	88
87	9	17	26	35	44	52	61	70	78	87
86	9	17	26	34	43	52	60	69	77	86
85	9	17	26	34	43	51	60	68	77	85

TABLE B

Logarithms of Numbers

No. 510—Log. 707   No. 554—Log. 744

N.	0	1	2	3	4	5	6	7	8	9	Diff
510	707570	7655	7740	7826	7911	7996	8081	8166	8251	8336	85
511	8421	8506	8591	8676	8761	8846	8931	9015	9100	9185	85
512	9270	9355	9440	9524	9609	9694	9779	9863	9948	*0033	85
513	710117	0202	0287	0371	0456	0540	0625	0710	0794	0879	85
514	0963	1048	1132	1217	1301	1385	1470	1554	1639	1723	84
515	711807	1892	1976	2060	2144	2229	2313	2397	2481	2566	84
516	2650	2734	2818	2902	2986	3070	3154	3238	3323	3407	84
517	3491	3575	3659	3742	3826	3910	3994	4078	4162	4246	84
518	4330	4414	4497	4581	4665	4749	4833	4916	5000	5084	84
519	5167	5251	5335	5418	5502	5586	5669	5753	5836	5920	84
520	716003	6087	6170	6254	6337	6421	6504	6588	6671	6754	83
521	6838	6921	7004	7088	7171	7254	7338	7421	7504	7587	83
522	7671	7754	7837	7920	8003	8086	8169	8253	8336	8419	83
523	8502	8585	8668	8751	8834	8917	9000	9083	9165	9248	83
524	9331	9414	9497	9580	9663	9745	9828	9911	9994	*0077	83
525	720159	0242	0325	0407	0490	0573	0655	0738	0821	0903	83
526	0986	1068	1151	1233	1316	1398	1481	1563	1646	1728	82
527	1811	1893	1975	2058	2140	2222	2305	2387	2469	2552	82
528	2634	2716	2798	2881	2963	3045	3127	3209	3291	3374	82
529	3456	3538	3620	3702	3784	3866	3948	4030	4112	4194	82
530	724276	4358	4440	4522	4604	4685	4767	4849	4931	5013	82
531	5095	5176	5258	5340	5422	5503	5585	5667	5748	5830	82
532	5912	5993	6075	6156	6238	6320	6401	6483	6564	6646	82
533	6727	6809	6890	6972	7053	7134	7216	7297	7379	7460	81
534	7541	7623	7704	7785	7866	7948	8029	8110	8191	8273	81
535	728354	8435	8516	8597	8678	8759	8841	8922	9003	9084	81
536	9165	9246	9327	9408	9489	9570	9651	9732	9813	9893	81
537	9974	*0055	*0136	*0217	*0298	*0378	*0459	*0540	*0621	*0702	81
538	730782	0863	0944	1024	1105	1186	1266	1347	1428	1508	81
539	1589	1669	1750	1830	1911	1991	2072	2152	2233	2313	81
540	732394	2474	2555	2635	2715	2796	2876	2956	3037	3117	80
541	3197	3278	3358	3438	3518	3598	3679	3759	3839	3919	80
542	3999	4079	4160	4240	4320	4400	4480	4560	4640	4720	80
543	4800	4880	4960	5040	5120	5200	5279	5359	5439	5519	80
544	5599	5679	5759	5838	5918	5998	6078	6157	6237	6317	80
545	736397	6476	6556	6635	6715	6795	6874	6954	7034	7113	80
546	7193	7272	7352	7431	7511	7590	7670	7749	7829	7908	79
547	7987	8067	8146	8225	8305	8384	8463	8543	8622	8701	79
548	8781	8860	8939	9018	9097	9177	9256	9335	9414	9493	79
549	9572	9651	9731	9810	9889	9968	*0047	*0126	*0205	*0284	79
550	740363	0442	0521	0600	0678	0757	0836	0915	0994	1073	79
551	1152	1230	1309	1388	1467	1546	1624	1703	1782	1860	79
552	1939	2018	2096	2175	2254	2332	2411	2489	2568	2647	79
553	2725	2804	2882	2961	3039	3118	3196	3275	3353	3431	78
554	3510	3588	3667	3745	3823	3902	3980	4058	4136	4215	78

PROPORTIONAL PARTS

Diff.	1	2	3	4	5	6	7	8	9	Diff.
86	9	17	26	34	43	52	60	69	77	86
85	9	17	26	34	43	51	60	68	77	85
84	8	17	25	34	42	50	59	67	76	84
83	8	17	25	33	42	50	58	66	75	83
82	8	16	25	33	41	49	57	66	74	82
81	8	16	24	32	41	49	57	65	73	81
80	8	16	24	32	40	48	56	64	72	80
79	8	16	24	32	40	47	55	63	71	79

TABLE B

Logarithms of Numbers

No. 555—Log. 744   No. 599—Log. 778

N.	0	1	2	3	4	5	6	7	8	9	Diff.
555	744293	4371	4449	4528	4606	4684	4762	4840	4919	4997	78
556	5075	5153	5231	5309	5387	5465	5543	5621	5699	5777	78
557	5855	5933	6011	6089	6167	6245	6323	6401	6479	6556	78
558	6634	6712	6790	6868	6945	7023	7101	7179	7256	7334	78
559	7412	7489	7567	7645	7722	7800	7878	7955	8033	8110	78
560	748188	8266	8343	8421	8498	8576	8653	8731	8808	8885	77
561	8963	9040	9118	9195	9272	9350	9427	9504	9582	9659	77
562	9736	9814	9891	9968	*0045	*0123	*0200	*0277	*0354	*0431	77
563	750508	0586	0663	0740	0817	0894	0971	1048	1125	1202	77
564	1279	1356	1433	1510	1587	1664	1741	1818	1895	1972	77
565	752048	2125	2202	2279	2356	2433	2509	2586	2663	2740	77
566	2816	2893	2970	3047	3123	3200	3277	3353	3430	3506	77
567	3583	3660	3736	3813	3889	3966	4042	4119	4195	4272	77
568	4348	4425	4501	4578	4654	4730	4807	4883	4960	5036	76
569	5112	5189	5265	5341	5417	5494	5570	5646	5722	5799	76
570	755875	5951	6027	6103	6180	6256	6332	6408	6484	6560	76
571	6636	6712	6788	6864	6940	7016	7092	7168	7244	7320	76
572	7396	7472	7548	7624	7700	7775	7851	7927	8003	8079	76
573	8155	8230	8306	8382	8458	8533	8609	8685	8761	8836	76
574	8912	8988	9063	9139	9214	9290	9366	9441	9517	9592	76
575	759668	9743	9819	9894	9970	*0045	*0121	*0196	*0272	*0347	75
576	760422	0498	0573	0649	0724	0799	0875	0950	1025	1101	75
577	1176	1251	1326	1402	1477	1552	1627	1702	1778	1853	75
578	1928	2003	2078	2153	2228	2303	2378	2453	2529	2604	75
579	2679	2754	2829	2904	2978	3053	3128	3203	3278	3353	75
580	763428	3503	3578	3653	3727	3802	3877	3952	4027	4101	75
581	4176	4251	4326	4400	4475	4550	4624	4699	4774	4848	75
582	4923	4998	5072	5147	5221	5296	5370	5445	5520	5594	75
583	5669	5743	5818	5892	5966	6041	6115	6190	6264	6338	74
584	6413	6487	6562	6636	6710	6785	6859	6933	7007	7082	74
585	767156	7230	7304	7379	7453	7527	7601	7675	7749	7823	74
586	7898	7972	8046	8120	8194	8268	8342	8416	8490	8564	74
587	8638	8712	8786	8860	8934	9008	9082	9156	9230	9303	74
588	9377	9451	9525	9599	9673	9746	9820	9894	9968	*0042	74
589	770115	0189	0263	0336	0410	0484	0557	0631	0705	0778	74
590	770852	0926	0999	1073	1146	1220	1293	1367	1440	1514	74
591	1587	1661	1734	1808	1881	1955	2028	2102	2175	2248	73
592	2322	2395	2468	2542	2615	2688	2762	2835	2908	2981	73
593	3055	3128	3201	3274	3348	3421	3494	3567	3640	3713	73
594	3786	3860	3933	4006	4079	4152	4225	4298	4371	4444	73
595	774517	4590	4663	4736	4809	4882	4955	5028	5100	5173	73
596	5246	5319	5392	5465	5538	5610	5683	5756	5829	5902	73
597	5974	6047	6120	6193	6265	6338	6411	6483	6556	6629	73
598	6701	6774	6846	6919	6992	7064	7137	7209	7282	7354	73
599	7427	7499	7572	7644	7717	7789	7862	7934	8006	8079	72

PROPORTIONAL PARTS

Diff.	1	2	3	4	5	6	7	8	9	Diff.
78	8	16	23	31	39	47	55	62	70	78
77	8	15	23	31	39	46	54	62	69	77
76	8	15	23	30	38	46	53	61	68	76
75	8	15	23	30	38	45	53	60	68	75
74	7	15	22	30	37	44	52	59	67	74
73	7	15	22	29	37	44	51	58	66	73
72	7	14	22	29	36	43	50	58	65	72

LOGARITHMS OF NUMBERS

No. 600—Log. 778   **No. 649--Log. 812**

N.	0	1	2	3	4	5	6	7	8	9	Diff.
600	778151	8224	8296	8368	8441	8513	8585	8658	8730	8802	72
601	8874	8947	9019	9091	9163	9236	9308	9380	9452	9524	72'
602	9596	9669	9741	9813	9885	9957	*0029	*0101	*0173	*0245	72
603	780317	0389	0461	0533	0605	0677	0749	0821	0893	0965	72
604	1037	1109	1181	1253	1324	1396	1468	1540	1612	1684	72
605	781755	1827	1899	1971	2042	2114	2186	2258	2329	2401	72
606	2473	2544	2616	2688	2759	2831	2902	2974	3046	3117	72
607	3189	3260	3332	3403	3475	3546	3618	3689	3761	3832	71
608	3904	3975	4046	4118	4189	4261	4332	4403	4475	4546	71
609	4617	4689	4760	4831	4902	4974	5045	5116	5187	5259	71
610	785330	5401	5472	5543	5615	5686	5757	5828	5899	5970	71
611	6041	6112	6183	6254	6325	6396	6467	6538	6609	6680	71
612	6751	6822	6893	6964	7035	7106	7177	7248	7319	7390	71
613	7460	7531	7602	7673	7744	7815	7885	7956	8027	8098	71
614	8168	8239	8310	8381	8451	8522	8593	8663	8734	8804	71
615	788875	8946	9016	9087	9157	9228	9299	9369	9440	9510	71
616	9581	9651	9722	9792	9863	9933	*0004	*0074	*0144	*0215	70
617	790285	0356	0426	0496	0567	0637	0707	0778	0848	0918	70
618	0988	1059	1129	1199	1269	1340	1410	1480	1550	1620	70
619	1691	1761	1831	1901	1971	2041	2111	2181	2252	2322	70
620	792392	2462	2532	2602	2672	2742	2812	2882	2952	3022	70
621	3092	3162	3231	3301	3371	3441	3511	3581	3651	3721	70
622	3790	3860	3930	4000	4070	4139	4209	4279	4349	4418	70
623	4488	4558	4627	4697	4767	4836	4906	4976	5045	5115	70
624	5185	5254	5324	5393	5463	5532	5602	5672	5741	5811	70
625	795880	5949	6019	6088	6158	6227	6297	6366	6436	6505	69
626	6574	6644	6713	6782	6852	6921	6990	7060	7129	7198	69
627	7268	7337	7406	7475	7545	7614	7683	7752	7821	7890	69
628	7960	8029	8098	8167	8236	8305	8374	8443	8513	8582	69
629	8651	8720	8789	8858	8927	8996	9065	9134	9203	9272	69
630	799341	9409	9478	9547	9616	9685	9754	9823	9892	9961	69
631	800029	0098	0167	0236	0305	0373	0442	0511	0580	0648	69
632	0717	0786	0854	0923	0992	1061	1129	1198	1266	1335	69
633	1404	1472	1541	1609	1678	1747	1815	1884	1952	2021	69
634	2089	2158	2226	2295	2363	2432	2500	2568	2637	2705	68
635	802774	2842	2910	2979	3047	3116	3184	3252	3321	3389	68
636	3457	3525	3594	3662	3730	3798	3867	3935	4003	4071	68
637	4139	4208	4276	4344	4412	4480	4548	4616	4685	4753	68
638	4821	4889	4957	5025	5093	5161	5229	5297	5365	5433	68
639	5501	5569	5637	5705	5773	5841	5908	5976	6044	6112	68
640	806180	6248	6316	6384	6451	6519	6587	6655	6723	6790	68
641	6858	6926	6994	7061	7129	7197	7264	7332	7400	7467	68
642	7535	7603	7670	7738	7806	7873	7941	8008	8076	8143	68
643	8211	8279	8346	8414	8481	8549	8616	8684	8751	8818	67
644	8886	8953	9021	9088	9156	9223	9290	9358	9425	9492	67
645	809560	9627	9694	9762	9829	9896	9964	*0031	*0098	*0165	67
646	810233	0300	0367	0434	0501	0569	0636	0703	0770	0837	67
647	0904	0971	1039	1106	1173	1240	1307	1374	1441	1508	67
648	1575	1642	1709	1776	1843	1910	1977	2044	2111	2178	67
649	2245	2312	2379	2445	2512	2579	2646	2713	2780	2847	67

PROPORTIONAL PARTS

Diff.	1	2	3	4	5	6	7	8	9	Diff.
73	7	15	22	29	37	44	51	58	66	73
72	7	14	22	29	36	43	50	58	65	72
71	7	14	21	28	36	43	50	57	64	71
70	7	14	21	28	35	42	49	56	63	70
69	7	14	21	28	35	41	48	55	62	69
68	7	14	20	27	34	41	48	54	61	68

TABLE B

LOGARITHMS OF NUMBERS

No. 650—Log. 812   No. 699—Log. 845

N.	0	1	2	3	4	5	6	7	8	9	Diff.
650	812913	2980	3047	3114	3181	3247	3314	3381	3448	3514	67
651	3581	3648	3714	3781	3848	3914	3981	4048	4114	4181	67
652	4248	4314	4381	4447	4514	4581	4647	4714	4780	4847	67
653	4913	4980	5046	5113	5179	5246	5312	5378	5445	5511	66
654	5578	5644	5711	5777	5843	5910	5976	6042	6109	6175	66
655	816241	6308	6374	6440	6506	6573	6639	6705	6771	6838	66
656	6904	6970	7036	7102	7169	7235	7301	7367	7433	7499	66
657	7565	7631	7698	7764	7830	7896	7962	8028	8094	8160	66
658	8226	8292	8358	8424	8490	8556	8622	8688	8754	8820	66
659	8885	8951	9017	9083	9149	9215	9281	9346	9412	9478	66
660	819544	9610	9676	9741	9807	9873	9939	*0004	*0070	*0136	66
661	820201	0267	0333	0399	0464	0530	0595	0661	0727	0792	66
662	0858	0924	0989	1055	1120	1186	1251	1317	1382	1448	66
663	1514	1579	1645	1710	1775	1841	1906	1972	2037	2103	65
664	2168	2233	2299	2364	2430	2495	2560	2626	2691	2756	65
665	822822	2887	2952	3018	3083	3148	3213	3279	3344	3409	65
666	3474	3539	3605	3670	3735	3800	3865	3930	3996	4061	65
667	4126	4191	4256	4321	4386	4451	4516	4581	4646	4711	65
668	4776	4841	4906	4971	5036	5101	5166	5231	5296	5361	65
669	5426	5491	5556	5621	5686	5751	5815	5880	5945	6010	65
670	826075	6140	6204	6269	6334	6399	6464	6528	6593	6658	65
671	6723	6787	6852	6917	6981	7046	7111	7175	7240	7305	65
672	7369	7434	7499	7563	7628	7692	7757	7821	7886	7951	65
673	8015	8080	8144	8209	8273	8338	8402	8467	8531	8595	64
674	8660	8724	8789	8853	8918	8982	9046	9111	9175	9239	64
675	829304	9368	9432	9497	9561	9625	9690	9754	9818	9882	64
676	9947	*0011	*0075	*0139	*0204	*0268	*0332	*0396	*0460	*0525	64
677	830589	0653	0717	0781	0845	0909	0973	1037	1102	1166	64
678	1230	1294	1358	1422	1486	1550	1614	1678	1742	1806	64
679	1870	1934	1998	2062	2126	2189	2253	2317	2381	2445	64
680	832509	2573	2637	2700	2764	2828	2892	2956	3020	3083	64
681	3147	3211	3275	3338	3402	3466	3530	3593	3657	3721	64
682	3784	3848	3912	3975	4039	4103	4166	4230	4294	4357	64
683	4421	4484	4548	4611	4675	4739	4802	4866	4929	4993	64
684	5056	5120	5183	5247	5310	5373	5437	5500	5564	5627	63
685	835691	5754	5817	5881	5944	6007	6071	6134	6197	6261	63
686	6324	6387	6451	6514	6577	6641	6704	6767	6830	6894	63
687	6957	7020	7083	7146	7210	7273	7336	7399	7462	7525	63
688	7588	7652	7715	7778	7841	7904	7967	8030	8093	8156	63
689	8219	8282	8345	8408	8471	8534	8597	8660	8723	8786	63
690	838849	8912	8975	9038	9101	9164	9227	9289	9352	9415	63
691	9478	9541	9604	9667	9729	9792	9855	9918	9981	*0043	63
692	840106	0169	0232	0294	0357	0420	0482	0545	0608	0671	63
693	0733	0796	0859	0921	0984	1046	1109	1172	1234	1297	63
694	1359	1422	1485	1547	1610	1672	1735	1797	1860	1922	63
695	841985	2047	2110	2172	2235	2297	2360	2422	2484	2547	62
696	2609	2672	2734	2796	2859	2921	2983	3046	3108	3170	62
697	3233	3295	3357	3420	3482	3544	3606	3669	3731	3793	62
698	3855	3918	3980	4042	4104	4166	4229	4291	4353	4415	62
699	4477	4539	4601	4664	4726	4788	4850	4912	4974	5036	62

PROPORTIONAL PARTS

Diff.	1	2	3	4	5	6	7	8	9	Diff.
67	7	13	20	27	34	40	47	54	60	67
66	7	13	20	26	33	40	46	53	59	66
65	7	13	20	26	33	39	46	52	59	65
64	6	13	19	26	32	38	45	51	58	64
63	6	13	19	25	32	38	44	50	57	63
62	6	12	19	25	31	37	43	50	56	62

LOGARITHMS OF NUMBERS

No. 700—Log. 845   **No. 749—Log. 875**

N.	0	1	2	3	4	5	6	7	8	9	Diff.
700	845098	5160	5222	5284	5346	5408	5470	5532	5594	5656	62
701	5718	5780	5842	5904	5966	6028	6090	6151	6213	6275	62
702	6337	6399	6461	6523	6585	6646	6708	6770	6832	6894	62
703	6955	7017	7079	7141	7202	7264	7326	7388	7449	7511	62
704	7573	7634	7696	7758	7819	7881	7943	8004	8066	8128	62
705	848189	8251	8312	8374	8435	8497	8559	8620	8682	8743	62
706	8805	8866	8928	8989	9051	9112	9174	9235	9297	9358	61
707	9419	9481	9542	9604	9665	9726	9788	9849	9911	9972	61
708	850033	0095	0156	0217	0279	0340	0401	0462	0524	0585	61
709	0646	0707	0769	0830	0891	0952	1014	1075	1136	1197	61
710	851258	1320	1381	1442	1503	1564	1625	1686	1747	1809	61
711	1870	1931	1992	2053	2114	2175	2236	2297	2358	2419	61
712	2480	2541	2602	2663	2724	2785	2846	2907	2968	3029	61
713	3090	3150	3211	3272	3333	3394	3455	3516	3577	3637	61
714	3698	3759	3820	3881	3941	4002	4063	4124	4185	4245	61
715	854306	4367	4428	4488	4549	4610	4670	4731	4792	4852	61
716	4913	4974	5034	5095	5156	5216	5277	5337	5398	5459	61
717	5519	5580	5640	5701	5761	5822	5882	5943	6003	6064	61
718	6124	6185	6245	6306	6366	6427	6487	6548	6608	6668	60
719	6729	6789	6850	6910	6970	7031	7091	7152	7212	7272	60
720	857332	7393	7453	7513	7574	7634	7694	7755	7815	7875	60
721	7935	7995	8056	8116	8176	8236	8297	8357	8417	8477	60
722	8537	8597	8657	8718	8778	8838	8898	8958	9018	9078	60
723	9138	9198	9258	9318	9379	9439	9499	9559	9619	9679	60
724	9739	9799	9859	9918	9978	*0038	*0098	*0158	*0218	*0278	60
725	860338	0398	0458	0518	0578	0637	0697	0757	0817	0877	60
726	0937	0996	1056	1116	1176	1236	1295	1355	1415	1475	60
727	1534	1594	1654	1714	1773	1833	1893	1952	2012	2072	60
728	2131	2191	2251	2310	2370	2430	2489	2549	2608	2668	60
729	2728	2787	2847	2906	2966	3025	3085	3144	3204	3263	60
730	863323	3382	3442	3501	3561	3620	3680	3739	3799	3858	59
731	3917	3977	4036	4096	4155	4214	4274	4333	4392	4452	59
732	4511	4570	4630	4689	4748	4808	4867	4926	4985	5045	59
733	5104	5163	5222	5282	5341	5400	5459	5519	5578	5637	59
734	5696	5755	5814	5874	5933	5992	6051	6110	6169	6228	59
735	866287	6346	6405	6465	6524	6583	6642	6701	6760	6819	59
736	6878	6937	6996	7055	7114	7173	7232	7291	7350	7409	59
737	7467	7526	7585	7644	7703	7762	7821	7880	7939	7998	59
738	8056	8115	8174	8233	8292	8350	8409	8468	8527	8586	59
739	8644	8703	8762	8821	8879	8938	8997	9056	9114	9173	59
740	869232	9290	9349	9408	9466	9525	9584	9642	9701	9760	59
741	9818	9877	9935	9994	*0053	*0111	*0170	*0228	*0287	*0345	59
742	870404	0462	0521	0579	0638	0696	0755	0813	0872	0930	58
743	0989	1047	1106	1164	1223	1281	1339	1398	1456	1515	58
744	1573	1631	1690	1748	1806	1865	1923	1981	2040	2098	58
745	872156	2215	2273	2331	2389	2448	2506	2564	2622	2681	58
746	2739	2797	2855	2913	2972	3030	3088	3146	3204	3262	58
747	3321	3379	3437	3495	3553	3611	3669	3727	3785	3844	58
748	3902	3960	4018	4076	4134	4192	4250	4308	4366	4424	58
749	4482	4540	4598	4656	4714	4772	4830	4888	4945	5003	58

PROPORTIONAL PARTS

Diff.	1	2	3	4	5	6	7	8	9	Diff.
62	6	12	19	25	31	37	43	50	56	62
61	6	12	18	24	31	37	43	49	55	61
60	6	12	18	24	30	36	42	48	54	60
59	6	12	18	24	30	35	41	47	53	59
58	6	12	17	23	29	35	41	46	52	58

TABLE B

LOGARITHMS OF NUMBERS

No. 750—Log. 875   **No. 799—Log. 903**

N.	0	1	2	3	4	5	6	7	8	9	Diff.
750	875061	5119	5177	5235	5293	5351	5409	5466	5524	5582	58
751	5640	5698	5756	5813	5871	5929	5987	6045	6102	6160	58
752	6218	6276	6333	6391	6449	6507	6564	6622	6680	6737	58
753	6795	6853	6910	6968	7026	7083	7141	7199	7256	7314	58
754	7371	7429	7487	7544	7602	7659	7717	7774	7832	7889	58
755	877947	8004	8062	8119	8177	8234	8292	8349	8407	8464	57
756	8522	8579	8637	8694	8752	8809	8866	8924	8981	9039	57
757	9096	9153	9211	9268	9325	9383	9440	9497	9555	9612	57
758	9669	9726	9784	9841	9898	9956	*0013	*0070	*0127	*0185	57
759	880242	0299	0356	0413	0471	0528	0585	0642	0699	0756	57
760	880814	0871	0928	0985	1042	1099	1156	1213	1271	1328	57
761	1385	1442	1499	1556	1613	1670	1727	1784	1841	1898	57
762	1955	2012	2069	2126	2183	2240	2297	2354	2411	2468	57
763	2525	2581	2638	2695	2752	2809	2866	2923	2980	3037	57
764	3093	3150	3207	3264	3321	3377	3434	3491	3548	3605	57
765	883661	3718	3775	3832	3888	3945	4002	4059	4115	4172	57
766	4229	4285	4342	4399	4455	4512	4569	4625	4682	4739	57
767	4795	4852	4909	4965	5022	5078	5135	5192	5248	5305	57
768	5361	5418	5474	5531	5587	5644	5700	5757	5813	5870	57
769	5926	5983	6039	6096	6152	6209	6265	6321	6378	6434	56
770	886491	6547	6604	6660	6716	6773	6829	6885	6942	6998	56
771	7054	7111	7167	7223	7280	7336	7392	7449	7505	7561	56
772	7617	7674	7730	7786	7842	7898	7955	8011	8067	8123	56
773	8179	8236	8292	8348	8404	8460	8516	8573	8629	8685	56
774	8741	8797	8853	8909	8965	9021	9077	9134	9190	9246	56
775	889302	9358	9414	9470	9526	9582	9638	9694	9750	9806	56
776	9862	9918	9974	*0030	*0086	*0141	*0197	*0253	*0309	*0365	56
777	890421	0477	0533	0589	0645	0700	0756	0812	0868	0924	56
778	0980	1035	1091	1147	1203	1259	1314	1370	1426	1482	56
779	1537	1593	1649	1705	1760	1816	1872	1928	1983	2039	56
780	892095	2150	2206	2262	2317	2373	2429	2484	2540	2595	56
781	2651	2707	2762	2818	2873	2929	2985	3040	3096	3151	56
782	3207	3262	3318	3373	3429	3484	3540	3595	3651	3706	56
783	3762	3817	3873	3928	3984	4039	4094	4150	4205	4261	55
784	4316	4371	4427	4482	4538	4593	4648	4704	4759	4814	55
785	894870	4925	4980	5036	5091	5146	5201	5257	5312	5367	55
786	5423	5478	5533	5588	5644	5699	5754	5809	5864	5920	55
787	5975	6030	6085	6140	6195	6251	6306	6361	6416	6471	55
788	6526	6581	6636	6692	6747	6802	6857	6912	6967	7022	55
789	7077	7132	7187	7242	7297	7352	7407	7462	7517	7572	55
790	897627	7682	7737	7792	7847	7902	7957	8012	8067	8122	55
791	8176	8231	8286	8341	8396	8451	8506	8561	8615	8670	55
792	8725	8780	8835	8890	8944	8999	9054	9109	9164	9218	55
793	9273	9328	9383	9437	9492	9547	9602	9656	9711	9766	55
794	9821	9875	9930	9985	*0039	*0094	*0149	*0203	*0258	*0312	55
795	900367	0422	0476	0531	0586	0640	0695	0749	0804	0859	55
796	0913	0968	1022	1077	1131	1186	1240	1295	1349	1404	55
797	1458	1513	1567	1622	1676	1731	1785	1840	1894	1948	54
798	2003	2057	2112	2166	2221	2275	2329	2384	2438	2492	54
799	2547	2601	2655	2710	2764	2818	2873	2927	2981	3036	54

PROPORTIONAL PARTS

Diff.	1	2	3	4	5	6	7	8	9	Diff.
57	6	11	17	23	29	34	40	46	51	57
56	6	11	17	22	28	34	39	45	50	56
55	6	11	17	22	28	33	39	44	50	55
54	5	11	16	22	27	32	38	43	49	54

LOGARITHMS OF NUMBERS

No. 800—Log. 903   **No. 849—Log. 929**

N.	0	1	2	3	4	5	6	7	8	9	Diff.
800	903090	3144	3199	3253	3307	3361	3416	3470	3524	3578	54
801	3633	3687	3741	3795	3849	3904	3958	4012	4066	4120	54
802	4174	4229	4283	4337	4391	4445	4499	4553	4607	4661	54
803	4716	4770	4824	4878	4932	4986	5040	5094	5148	5202	54
804	5256	5310	5364	5418	5472	5526	5580	5634	5688	5742	54
805	905796	5850	5904	5958	6012	6066	6119	6173	6227	6281	54
806	6335	6389	6443	6497	6551	6604	6658	6712	6766	6820	54
807	6874	6927	6981	7035	7089	7143	7196	7250	7304	7358	54
808	7411	7465	7519	7573	7626	7680	7734	7787	7841	7895	54
809	7949	8002	8056	8110	8163	8217	8270	8324	8378	8431	54
810	908485	8539	8592	8646	8699	8753	8807	8860	8914	8967	54
811	9021	9074	9128	9181	9235	9289	9342	9396	9449	9503	54
812	9556	9610	9663	9716	9770	9823	9877	9930	9984	*0037	53
813	910091	0144	0197	0251	0304	0358	0411	0464	0518	0571	53
814	0624	0678	0731	0784	0838	0891	0944	0998	1051	1104	53
815	911158	1211	1264	1317	1371	1424	1477	1530	1584	1637	53
816	1690	1743	1797	1850	1903	1956	2009	2063	2116	2169	53
817	2222	2275	2328	2381	2435	2488	2541	2594	2647	2700	53
818	2753	2806	2859	2913	2966	3019	3072	3125	3178	3231	53
819	3284	3337	3390	3443	3496	3549	3602	3655	3708	3761	53
820	913814	3867	3920	3973	4026	4079	4132	4184	4237	4290	53
821	4343	4396	4449	4502	4555	4608	4660	4713	4766	4819	53
822	4872	4925	4977	5030	5083	5136	5189	5241	5294	5347	53
823	5400	5453	5505	5558	5611	5664	5716	5769	5822	5875	53
824	5927	5980	6033	6085	6138	6191	6243	6296	6349	6401	53
825	916454	6507	6559	6612	6664	6717	6770	6822	6875	6927	53
826	6980	7033	7085	7138	7190	7243	7295	7348	7400	7453	53
827	7506	7558	7611	7663	7716	7768	7820	7873	7925	7978	52
828	8030	8083	8135	8188	8240	8293	8345	8397	8450	8502	52
829	8555	8607	8659	8712	8764	8816	8869	8921	8973	9026	52
830	919078	9130	9183	9235	9287	9340	9392	9444	9496	9549	52
831	9601	9653	9706	9758	9810	9862	9914	9967	*0019	*0071	52
832	920123	0176	0228	0280	0332	0384	0436	0489	0541	0593	52
833	0645	0697	0749	0801	0853	0906	0958	1010	1002	1114	52
834	1166	1218	1270	1322	1374	1426	1478	1530	1582	1634	52
835	921686	1738	1790	1842	1894	1946	1998	2050	2102	2154	52
836	2206	2258	2310	2362	2414	2466	2518	2570	2622	2674	52
837	2725	2777	2829	2881	2933	2985	3037	3089	3140	3192	52
838	3244	3296	3348	3399	3451	3503	3555	3607	3658	3710	52
839	3762	3814	3865	3917	3969	4021	4072	4124	4176	4228	52
840	924279	4331	4383	4434	4486	4538	4589	4641	4693	4744	52
841	4796	4848	4899	4951	5003	5054	5106	5157	5209	5261	52
842	5312	5364	5415	5467	5518	5570	5621	5673	5725	5776	52
843	5828	5879	5931	5982	6034	6085	6137	6188	6240	6291	51
844	6342	6394	6445	6497	6548	6600	6651	6702	6754	6805	51
845	926857	6908	6959	7011	7062	7114	7165	7216	7268	7310	51
846	7370	7422	7473	7524	7576	7627	7678	7730	7781	7832	51
847	7883	7935	7986	8037	8088	8140	8191	8242	8293	8345	51
848	8396	8447	8498	8549	8601	8652	8703	8754	8805	8857	51
849	8908	8959	9010	9061	9112	9163	9215	9266	9317	9368	51

PROPORTIONAL PARTS

Diff.	1	2	3	4	5	6	7	8	9	Diff.
55	6	11	17	22	28	33	39	44	50	55
54	5	11	16	22	27	32	38	43	49	54
53	5	11	16	21	27	32	37	42	48	53
52	5	10	16	21	26	31	36	42	47	52

TABLE B

Logarithms of Numbers

N.	0	1	2	3	4	5	6	7	8	9	Diff.
850	929419	9470	9521	9572	9623	9674	9725	9776	9827	9879	51
851	9930	9981	*0032	*0083	*0134	*0185	*0236	*0287	*0338	*0389	51
852	930440	0491	0542	0592	0643	0694	0745	0796	0847	0898	51
853	0949	1000	1051	1102	1153	1204	1254	1305	1356	1407	51
854	1458	1509	1560	1610	1661	1712	1763	1814	1865	1915	51
855	931966	2017	2068	2118	2169	2220	2271	2322	2372	2423	51
856	2474	2524	2575	2626	2677	2727	2778	2829	2879	2930	51
857	2981	3031	3082	3133	3183	3234	3285	3335	3386	3437	51
858	3487	3538	3589	3639	3690	3740	3791	3841	3892	3943	51
859	3993	4044	4094	4145	4195	4246	4296	4347	4397	4448	51
860	934498	4549	4599	4650	4700	4751	4801	4852	4902	4953	50
861	5003	5054	5104	5154	5205	5255	5306	5356	5406	5457	50
862	5507	5558	5608	5658	5709	5759	5809	5860	5910	5960	50
863	6011	6061	6111	6162	6212	6262	6313	6363	6413	6463	50
864	6514	6564	6614	6665	6715	6765	6815	6865	6916	6966	50
865	937016	7066	7117	7167	7217	7267	7317	7367	7418	7468	50
866	7518	7568	7618	7668	7718	7769	7819	7869	7919	7969	50
867	8019	8069	8119	8169	8219	8269	8320	8370	8420	8470	50
868	8520	8570	8620	8670	8720	8770	8820	8870	8920	8970	50
869	9020	9070	9120	9170	9220	9270	9320	9369	9419	9469	50
870	939519	9569	9619	9669	9719	9769	9819	9869	9918	9968	50
871	940018	0068	0118	0168	0218	0267	0317	0367	0417	0467	50
872	0516	0566	0616	0666	0716	0765	0815	0865	0915	0964	50
873	1014	1064	1114	1163	1213	1263	1313	1362	1412	1462	50
874	1511	1561	1611	1660	1710	1760	1809	1859	1909	1958	50
875	942008	2058	2107	2157	2207	2256	2306	2355	2405	2455	50
876	2504	2554	2603	2653	2702	2752	2801	2851	2901	2950	50
877	3000	3049	3099	3148	3198	3247	3297	3346	3396	3445	49
878	3495	3544	3593	3643	3692	3742	3791	3841	3890	3939	49
879	3989	4038	4088	4137	4186	4236	4285	4335	4384	4433	49
880	944483	4532	4581	4631	4680	4729	4779	4828	4877	4927	49
881	4976	5025	5074	5124	5173	5222	5272	5321	5370	5419	49
882	5469	5518	5567	5616	5665	5715	5764	5813	5862	5912	49
883	5961	6010	6059	6108	6157	6207	6256	6305	6354	6403	49
884	6452	6501	6551	6600	6649	6698	6747	6796	6845	6894	49
885	946943	6992	7041	7090	7140	7189	7238	7287	7336	7385	49
886	7434	7483	7532	7581	7630	7679	7728	7777	7826	7875	49
887	7924	7973	8022	8070	8119	8168	8217	8266	8315	8364	49
888	8413	8462	8511	8560	8609	8657	8706	8755	8804	8853	49
889	8902	8951	8999	9048	9097	9146	9195	9244	9292	9341	49
890	949390	9439	9488	9536	9585	9634	9683	9731	9780	9829	49
891	9878	9926	9975	*0024	*0073	*0121	*0170	*0219	*0267	*0316	49
892	950365	0414	0462	0511	0560	0608	0657	0706	0754	0803	49
893	0851	0900	0949	0997	1046	1095	1143	1192	1240	1289	49
894	1338	1386	1435	1483	1532	1580	1629	1677	1726	1775	49
895	951823	1872	1920	1969	2017	2066	2114	2163	2211	2260	48
896	2308	2356	2405	2453	2502	2550	2599	2647	2696	2744	48
897	2792	2841	2889	2938	2986	3034	3083	3131	3180	3228	48
898	3276	3325	3373	3421	3470	3518	3566	3615	3663	3711	48
899	3760	3808	3856	3905	3953	4001	4049	4098	4146	4194	48

PROPORTIONAL PARTS

Diff.	1	2	3	4	5	6	7	8	9	Diff.
51	5	10	15	20	26	31	36	41	46	51
50	5	10	15	20	25	30	35	40	45	50
49	5	10	15	20	25	29	34	39	44	49
48	5	10	14	19	24	29	34	38	43	48

LOGARITHMS OF NUMBERS

No. 900—Log. 954   No. 949—Log. 977

N.	0	1	2	3	4	5	6	7	8	9	Diff.
900	954243	4291	4339	4387	4435	4484	4532	4580	4628	4677	48
901	4725	4773	4821	4869	4918	4966	5014	5062	5110	5158	48
902	5207	5255	5303	5351	5399	5447	5495	5543	5592	5640	48
903	5688	5736	5784	5832	5880	5928	5976	6024	6072	6120	48
904	6168	6216	6265	6313	6361	6409	6457	6505	6553	6601	48
905	956649	6697	6745	6793	6840	6888	6936	6984	7032	7080	48
906	7128	7176	7224	7272	7320	7368	7416	7464	7512	7559	48
907	7607	7655	7703	7751	7799	7847	7894	7942	7990	8038	48
908	8086	8134	8181	8229	8277	8325	8373	8421	8468	8516	48
909	8564	8612	8659	8707	8755	8803	8850	8898	8946	8994	48
910	959041	9089	9137	9185	9232	9280	9328	9375	9423	9471	48
911	9518	9566	9614	9661	9709	9757	9804	9852	9900	9947	48
912	9995	*0042	*0090	*0138	*0185	*0233	*0280	*0328	*0376	*0423	48
913	960471	0518	0566	0613	0661	0709	0756	0804	0851	0899	48
914	0946	0994	1041	1089	1136	1184	1231	1279	1326	1374	48
915	961421	1469	1516	1563	1611	1658	1706	1753	1801	1848	47
916	1895	1943	1990	2038	2085	2132	2180	2227	2275	2322	47
917	2369	2417	2464	2511	2559	2606	2653	2701	2748	2795	47
918	2843	2890	2937	2985	3032	3079	3126	3174	3221	3268	47
919	3316	3363	3410	3457	3504	3552	3599	3646	3693	3741	47
920	963788	3835	3882	3929	3977	4024	4071	4118	4165	4212	47
921	4260	4307	4354	4401	4448	4495	4542	4590	4637	4684	47
922	4731	4778	4825	4872	4919	4966	5013	5061	5108	5155	47
923	5202	5249	5296	5343	5390	5437	5484	5531	5578	5625	47
924	5672	5719	5766	5813	5860	5907	5954	6001	6048	6095	47
925	966142	6189	6236	6283	6329	6376	6423	6470	6517	6564	47
926	6611	6658	6705	6752	6799	6845	6892	6939	6986	7033	47
927	7080	7127	7173	7220	7267	7314	7361	7408	7454	7501	47
928	7548	7595	7642	7688	7735	7782	7829	7875	7922	7969	47
929	8016	8062	8109	8156	8203	8249	8296	8343	8390	8436	47
930	968483	8530	8576	8623	8670	8716	8763	8810	8856	8903	47
931	8950	8996	9043	9090	9136	9183	9229	9276	9323	9369	47
932	9416	9463	9509	9556	9602	9649	9695	9742	9789	9835	47
933	9882	9928	9975	*0021	*0068	*0114	*0161	*0207	*0254	*0300	47
934	970347	0393	0440	0486	0533	0579	0626	0672	0719	0765	46
935	970812	0858	0904	0951	0997	1044	1090	1137	1183	1229	46
936	1276	1322	1369	1415	1461	1508	1554	1601	1647	1693	46
937	1740	1786	1832	1879	1925	1971	2018	2064	2110	2157	46
938	2203	2249	2295	2342	2388	2434	2481	2527	2573	2619	46
939	2666	2712	2758	2804	2851	2897	2943	2989	3035	3082	46
940	973128	3174	3220	3266	3313	3359	3405	3451	3497	3543	46
941	3590	3636	3682	3728	3774	3820	3866	3913	3959	4005	46
942	4051	4097	4143	4189	4235	4281	4327	4374	4420	4466	46
943	4512	4558	4604	4650	4696	4742	4788	4834	4880	4926	46
944	4972	5018	5064	5110	5156	5202	5248	5294	5340	5386	46
945	975432	5478	5524	5570	5616	5662	5707	5753	5799	5845	46
946	5891	5937	5983	6029	6075	6121	6167	6212	6258	6304	46
947	6350	6396	6442	6488	6533	6579	6625	6671	6717	6763	46
948	6808	6854	6900	6946	6992	7037	7083	7129	7175	7220	46
949	7266	7312	7358	7403	7449	7495	7541	7586	7632	7678	46

PROPORTIONAL PARTS

Diff.	1	2	3	4	5	6	7	8	9	Diff.
49	5	10	15	20	25	29	34	39	44	49
48	5	10	14	19	24	29	34	38	43	48
47	5	9	14	19	24	28	33	38	42	47
46	5	9	14	18	23	28	32	37	41	46

TABLE B

LOGARITHMS OF NUMBERS

No. 950—Log. 977   No. 999—Log. 999

N.	0	1	2	3	4	5	6	7	8	9	Diff.
950	977724	7769	7815	7861	7906	7952	7998	8043	8089	8135	46
951	8181	8226	8272	8317	8363	8409	8454	8500	8546	8591	46
952	8637	8683	8728	8774	8819	8865	8911	8956	9002	9047	46
953	9093	9138	9184	9230	9275	9321	9366	9412	9457	9503	46
954	9548	9594	9639	9685	9730	9776	9821	9867	9912	9958	46
955	980003	0049	0094	0140	0185	0231	0276	0322	0367	0412	45
956	0458	0503	0549	0594	0640	0685	0730	0776	0821	0867	45
957	0912	0957	1003	1048	1093	1139	1184	1229	1275	1320	45
958	1366	1411	1456	1501	1547	1592	1637	1683	1728	1773	45
959	1819	1864	1909	1954	2000	2045	2090	2135	2181	2226	45
960	982271	2316	2362	2407	2452	2497	2543	2588	2633	2678	45
961	2723	2769	2814	2859	2904	2949	2994	3040	3085	3130	45
962	3175	3220	3265	3310	3356	3401	3446	3491	3536	3581	45
963	3626	3671	3716	3762	3807	3852	3897	3942	3987	4032	45
964	4077	4122	4167	4212	4257	4302	4347	4392	4437	4482	45
965	984527	4572	4617	4662	4707	4752	4797	4842	4887	4932	45
966	4977	5022	5067	5112	5157	5202	5247	5292	5337	5382	45
967	5426	5471	5516	5561	5606	5651	5696	5741	5786	5830	45
968	5875	5920	5965	6010	6055	6100	6144	6189	6234	6279	45
969	6324	6369	6413	6458	6503	6548	6593	6637	6682	6727	45
970	986772	6817	6861	6906	6951	6996	7040	7085	7130	7175	45
971	7219	7264	7309	7353	7398	7443	7488	7532	7577	7622	45
972	7666	7711	7756	7800	7845	7890	7934	7979	8024	8068	45
973	8113	8157	8202	8247	8291	8336	8381	8425	8470	8514	45
974	8559	8604	8648	8693	8737	8782	8826	8871	8916	8960	45
975	989005	9049	9094	9138	9183	9227	9272	9316	9361	9405	45
976	9450	9494	9539	9583	9628	9672	9717	9761	9806	9850	44
977	9895	9939	9983	*0028	*0072	*0117	*0161	*0206	*0250	*0294	44
978	990339	0383	0428	0472	0516	0561	0605	0650	0694	0738	44
979	0783	0827	0871	0916	0960	1004	1049	1093	1137	1182	44
980	991226	1270	1315	1359	1403	1448	1492	1536	1580	1625	44
981	1669	1713	1758	1802	1846	1890	1935	1979	2023	2067	44
982	2111	2156	2200	2244	2288	2333	2377	2421	2465	2509	44
983	2554	2598	2642	2686	2730	2774	2819	2863	2907	2951	44
984	2995	3039	3083	3127	3172	3216	3260	3304	3348	3392	44
985	993436	3480	3524	3568	3613	3657	3701	3745	3789	3833	44
986	3877	3921	3965	4009	4053	4097	4141	4185	4229	4273	44
987	4317	4361	4405	4449	4493	4537	4581	4625	4669	4713	44
988	4757	4801	4845	4889	4933	4977	5021	5065	5108	5152	44
989	5196	5240	5284	5328	5372	5416	5460	5504	5547	5591	44
990	995635	5679	5723	5767	5811	5854	5898	5942	5986	6030	44
991	6074	6117	6161	6205	6249	6293	6337	6380	6424	6468	44
992	6512	6555	6599	6643	6687	6731	6774	6818	6862	6906	44
993	6949	6993	7037	7080	7124	7168	7212	7255	7299	7343	44
994	7386	7430	7474	7517	7561	7605	7648	7692	7736	7779	44
995	997823	7867	7910	7954	7998	8041	8085	8129	8172	8216	44
996	8259	8303	8347	8390	8434	8477	8521	8564	8608	8652	44
997	8695	8739	8782	8826	8869	8913	8956	9000	9043	9087	44
998	9131	9174	9218	9261	9305	9348	9392	9435	9479	9522	44
999	9565	9609	9652	9696	9739	9783	9826	9870	9913	9957	43

PROPORTIONAL PARTS

Diff.	1	2	3	4	5	6	7	8	9	Diff.
46	5	9	14	18	23	28	32	37	41	46
45	5	9	14	18	23	27	32	36	41	45
44	4	9	13	18	22	26	31	35	40	44
43	4	9	13	17	22	26	30	34	39	43

TABLE C 675

LOGARITHMIC SINES, COSINES, TANGENTS, AND COTANGENTS

0°   **179°**

M.	Sin.	D. 1".	Cos.	D. 1".	Tan.	D. 1".	Cot.	
0	− Inf.		10.000000	.00	− Inf.		+ Inf.	60
1	6.463726	5017.17	.000000	.00	6.463726	5017.17	3.536274	59
2	.764756	2934.85	.000000	.00	.764756	2934.85	.235244	58
3	.940847	2082.32	.000000	.00	.940847	2082.32	.059153	57
4	7.065786	1615.17	.000000	.00	7.065786	1615.17	2.934214	56
5	7.162696	1319.68	10.000000	.02	7.162696	1319.70	2.837304	55
6	.241877	1115.78	9.999999	.00	.241878	1115.78	.758122	54
7	.308824	966.53	.999999	.00	.308825	966.53	.691175	53
8	.366816	852.53	.999999	.00	.366817	852.55	.633183	52
9	.417968	762.63	.999999	.02	.417970	762.62	.582030	51
10	7.463726	689.87	9.999998	.00	7.463727	689.88	2.536273	50
11	.505118	629.80	.999998	.02	.505120	629.82	.494880	49
12	.542906	579.37	.999997	.00	.542909	579.38	.457091	48
13	.577668	536.42	.999997	.02	.577672	536.42	.422328	47
14	.609853	499.38	.999996	.00	.609857	499.38	.390143	46
15	7.639816	467.15	9.999996	.02	7.639820	467.15	2.360180	45
16	.667845	438.80	.999995	.00	.667849	438.83	.332151	44
17	.694173	413.73	.999995	.02	.694179	413.73	.305821	43
18	.718997	391.35	.999994	.02	.719003	391.35	.280997	42
19	.742478	371.27	.999993	.00	.742484	371.28	.257516	41
20	7.764754	353.15	9.999993	.02	7.764761	353.17	2.235239	40
21	.785943	336.72	.999992	.02	.785951	336.73	.214049	39
22	.806146	321.75	.999991	.02	.806155	321.75	.193845	38
23	.825451	308.05	.999990	.02	.825460	308.07	.174540	37
24	.843934	295.47	.999989	.00	.843944	295.50	.156056	36
25	7.861662	283.88	9.999989	.02	7.861674	283.90	2.138326	35
26	.878695	273.17	.999988	.02	.878708	273.18	.121292	34
27	.895085	263.23	.999987	.02	.895099	263.25	.104901	33
28	.910879	254.00	.999986	.02	.910894	254.00	.089106	32
29	.926119	245.38	.999985	.03	.926134	245.40	.073866	31
30	7.940842	237.33	9.999983	.02	7.940858	237.37	2.059142	30
31	.955082	220.80	.999982	.02	.955100	229.82	.044900	29
32	.968870	222.72	.999981	.02	.968889	222.73	.031111	28
33	.982233	216.08	.999980	.02	.982253	216.10	.017747	27
34	.995198	209.82	.999979	.03	.995219	209.83	.004781	26
35	8.007787	203.90	9.999977	.02	8.007809	203.92	1.992191	25
36	.020021	198.30	.999976	.02	.020011	198.35	.979956	24
37	.031919	193.03	.999975	.03	.031945	193.03	.968055	23
38	.043501	188.00	.999973	.02	.043527	188.03	.956473	22
39	.054781	183.25	.999972	.02	.054809	183.28	.945191	21
40	8.065776	178.73	9.999971	.03	8.065806	178.75	1.934194	20
41	.076500	174.42	.999969	.02	.076531	174.43	.923469	19
42	.086965	170.30	.999968	.03	.086997	170.33	.913003	18
43	.097183	166.40	.999966	.03	.097217	166.43	.902783	17
44	.107167	162.65	.999964	.02	.107203	162.67	.892797	16
45	8.116926	159.08	9.999963	.03	8.116963	159.12	1.883037	15
46	.126471	155.65	.999961	.03	.126510	155.68	.873490	14
47	.135810	152.38	.999959	.02	.135851	152.42	.864149	13
48	.144953	149.23	.999958	.03	.144996	149.27	.855004	12
49	.153907	146.23	.999956	.03	.153052	146.25	.846048	11
50	8.162681	143.32	9.999954	.03	8.162727	143.35	1.837273	10
51	.171280	140.55	.999952	.03	.171328	140.58	.828672	9
52	.179713	137.87	.999950	.03	.179763	137.88	.820237	8
53	.187985	135.28	.999948	.03	.188036	135.33	.811964	7
54	.196102	132.80	.999946	.03	.196156	132.83	.803844	6
55	8.204070	130.42	9.999944	.03	8.204126	130.45	1.795874	5
56	.211895	128.10	.999942	.03	.211953	128.13	.788047	4
57	.219581	125.88	.999940	.03	.219641	125.90	.780359	3
58	.227134	123.72	.999938	.03	.227195	123.77	.772805	2
59	.234557	121.63	.999936	.03	.234621	121.67	.765379	1
60	8.241855		9.999934		8.241921		1.758079	0
	Cos.	D. 1".	Sin.	D. 1".	Cot.	D. 1".	Tan.	M.

TABLE C

Logarithmic Sines, Cosines, Tangents, and Cotangents

1° 　　　　　　　　　　　　　　　　　　　　　　　　　　　　　　　**178°**

M.	Sin.	D. 1".	Cos.	D. 1".	Tan.	D. 1"	Cot.	
0	8.241855	119.63	9.999934	.03	8.241921	119.68	1.758079	60
1	.249033	117.68	.999932	.05	.249102	117.72	.750898	59
2	.256094	115.80	.999929	.03	.256165	115.83	.743835	58
3	.263042	113.98	.999927	.03	.263115	114.02	.736885	57
4	.269881	112.22	.999925	.05	.269956	112.25	.730044	56
5	8.276614	110.48	9.999922	.03	8.276691	110.53	1.723309	55
6	.283243	108.83	.999920	.03	.283323	108.88	.716677	54
7	.289773	107.23	.999918	.05	.289856	107.27	.710144	53
8	.296207	105.65	.999915	.03	.296292	105.70	.703708	52
9	.302546	104.13	.999913	.05	.302634	104.17	.697366	51
10	8.308794	102.67	9.999910	.05	8.308884	102.70	1.691116	50
11	.314954	101.22	.999907	.03	.315046	101.27	.684954	49
12	.321027	99.82	.999905	.05	.321122	99.87	.678878	48
13	.327016	98.47	.999902	.05	.327114	98.52	.672886	47
14	.332924	97.15	.999899	.03	.333025	97.18	.666975	46
15	8.338753	95.85	9.999897	.05	8.338856	95.90	1.661144	45
16	.344504	94.62	.999894	.05	.344610	94.65	.655390	44
17	.350181	93.37	.999891	.05	.350289	93.43	.649711	43
18	.355783	92.20	.999888	.05	.355895	92.25	.644105	42
19	.361315	91.03	.999885	.05	.361430	91.08	.638570	41
20	8.366777	89.90	9.999882	.05	8.366895	89.95	1.633105	40
21	.372171	88.80	.999879	.05	.372292	88.83	.627708	39
22	.377499	87.72	.999876	.05	.377622	87.78	.622378	38
23	.382762	86.67	.999873	.05	.382889	86.72	.617111	37
24	.387962	85.65	.999870	.05	.388092	85.70	.611908	36
25	8.393101	84.63	9.999867	.05	8.393234	84.68	1.606766	35
26	.398179	83.67	.999864	.05	.398315	83.72	.601685	34
27	.403199	82.70	.999861	.05	.403338	82.77	.596662	33
28	.408161	81.78	.999858	.07	.408304	81.82	.591696	32
29	.413068	80.85	.999854	.05	.413213	80.92	.586787	31
30	8.417919	79.97	9.999851	.05	8.418068	80.02	1.581932	30
31	.422717	79.08	.999848	.07	.422869	79.15	.577131	29
32	.427462	78.23	.999844	.05	.427618	78.28	.572382	28
33	.432156	77.40	.999841	.05	.432315	77.45	.567685	27
34	.436800	76.57	.999838	.07	.436962	76.63	.563038	26
35	8.441394	75.78	9.999834	.05	8.441560	75.83	1.558440	25
36	.445941	74.98	.999831	.07	.446110	75.05	.553890	24
37	.450440	74.22	.999827	.05	.450613	74.28	.549387	23
38	.454893	73.47	.999824	.07	.455070	73.52	.544930	22
39	.459301	72.73	.999820	.07	.459481	72.80	.540519	21
40	8.463665	72.00	9.999816	.05	8.463849	72.05	1.536151	20
41	.467985	71.30	.999813	.07	.468172	71.37	.531828	19
42	.472263	70.58	.999809	.07	.472454	70.65	.527546	18
43	.476498	69.92	.999805	.07	.476693	69.98	.523307	17
44	.480693	69.25	.999801	.07	.480892	69.30	.519108	16
45	8.484848	68.58	9.999797	.05	8.485050	68.67	1.514950	15
46	.488963	67.95	.999794	.07	.489170	68.00	.510830	14
47	.493040	67.30	.999790	.07	.493250	67.38	.506750	13
48	.497078	66.70	.999786	.07	.497293	66.75	.502707	12
49	.501080	66.08	.999782	.07	.501298	66.15	.498702	11
50	8.505045	65.48	9.999778	.07	8.505267	65.55	1.494733	10
51	.508974	64.88	.999774	.08	.509200	64.97	.490800	9
52	.512867	64.32	.999769	.07	.513098	64.38	.486902	8
53	.516726	63.75	.999765	.07	.516961	63.82	.483039	7
54	.520551	63.20	.999761	.07	.520790	63.27	.479210	6
55	8.524343	62.65	9.999757	.07	8.524586	62.72	1.475414	5
56	.528102	62.10	.999753	.08	.528349	62.18	.471651	4
57	.531828	61.58	.999748	.07	.532080	61.65	.467920	3
58	.535523	61.05	.999744	.07	.535779	61.13	.464221	2
59	.539186	60.55	.999740	.08	.539447	60.62	.460553	1
60	8.542819		9.999735		8.543084		1.456916	0
	Cos.	D. 1".	Sin.	D. 1".	Cot.	D. 1".	Tan.	M.

91° 　　　　　　　　　　　　　　　　　　　　　　　　　　　　　　　**88°**

TABLE C   677

LOGARITHMIC SINES, COSINES, TANGENTS, AND COTANGENTS

2°   177°

M.	Sin.	D. 1″.	Cos.	D. 1″.	Tan.	D. 1″.	Cot.	
0	8.542819	60.05	9.999735	.07	8.543084	60.12	1.456916	60
1	.546422	59.55	.999731	.08	.546691	59.62	.453309	59
2	.549995	59.07	.999726	.07	.550268	59.15	.449732	58
3	.553539	58.58	.999722	.08	.553817	58.65	.446183	57
4	.557054	58.10	.999717	.07	.557336	58.20	.442664	56
5	8.560540	57.65	9.999713	.08	8.560828	57.72	1.439172	55
6	.563999	57.20	.999708	.07	.564291	57.27	.435709	54
7	.567431	56.75	.999704	.08	.567727	56.83	.432273	53
8	.570836	56.30	.999699	.08	.571137	56.38	.428863	52
9	.574214	55.87	.999694		.574520	55.95	.425480	51
10	8.577566	55.43	9.999689	.07	8.577877	55.52	1.422123	50
11	.580892	55.02	.999685	.08	.581208	55.10	.418792	49
12	.584193	54.60	.999680	.08	.584514	54.68	.415486	48
13	.587469	54.20	.999675	.08	.587795	54.27	.412205	47
14	.590721	53.78	.999670	.08	.591051	53.87	.408949	46
15	8.593948	53.40	9.999665	.08	8.594283	53.48	1.405717	45
16	.597152	53.00	.999660	.08	.597492	53.08	.402508	44
17	.600332	52.62	.999655	.08	.600677	52.70	.399323	43
18	.603489	52.23	.999650	.08	.603839	52.32	.396161	42
19	.606623	51.85	.999645	.08	.606978	51.93	.393022	41
20	8.609734	51.48	9.999640	.08	8.610094	51.58	1.389906	40
21	.612823	51.13	.999635	.10	.613189	51.22	.386811	39
22	.615891	50.77	.999629	.08	.616262	50.85	.383738	38
23	.618937	50.42	.999624	.08	.619313	50.50	.380687	37
24	.621962	50.05	.999619	.08	.622343	50.15	.377657	36
25	8.624965	49.72	9.999614	.10	8.625352	49.80	1.374648	35
26	.627948	49.38	.999608	.08	.628340	49.47	.371660	34
27	.630911	49.05	.999603	.10	.631308	49.13	.368692	33
28	.633854	48.70	.999597	.08	.634256	48.80	.365744	32
29	.636776	48.40	.999592	.10	.637184	48.48	.362816	31
30	8.639680	48.05	9.999586	.08	8.640093	48.15	1.359907	30
31	.642563	47.75	.999581	.10	.642982	47.85	.357018	29
32	.645428	47.43	.000575	.08	.645853	47.52	.354147	28
33	.648274	47.13	.999570	.10	.648704	47.22	.351296	27
34	.651102	46.82	.999564	.10	.651537	46.92	.348463	26
35	8.653911	46.52	9.999558	.08	8.654352	46.62	1.345648	25
36	.656702	46.22	.999553	.10	.657149	46.32	.342851	24
37	.659475	45.92	.999547	.10	.659928	46.02	.340072	23
38	.662230	45.63	.999541	.10	.662689	45.73	.337311	22
39	.664968	45.35	.999535	.10	.665433	45.45	.334567	21
40	8.667689	45.07	9.999529	.08	8.668160	45.17	1.331840	20
41	.670393	44.78	.999524	.10	.670870	44.88	.329130	19
42	.673080	44.52	.999518	.10	.673563	44.60	.326437	18
43	.675751	44.23	.999512	.10	.676239	44.35	.323761	17
44	.678405	43.97	.999506	.10	.678900	44.07	.321100	16
45	8.681043	43.70	9.999500	.12	8.681544	43.80	1.318456	15
46	.683665	43.45	.999493	.10	.684172	43.53	.315828	14
47	.686272	43.18	.999487	.10	.686784	43.28	.313216	13
48	.688863	42.92	.999481	.10	.689381	43.03	.310619	12
49	.691438	42.67	.999475	.10	.691963	42.77	.308037	11
50	8.693998	42.42	9.999469	.10	8.694529	42.53	1.305471	10
51	.696543	42.17	.999463	.12	.697081	42.27	.302919	9
52	.699073	41.93	.999456	.10	.699617	42.03	.300383	8
53	.701589	41.68	.999450	.12	.702139	41.78	.297861	7
54	.704090	41.45	.999443	.10	.704646	41.57	.295354	6
55	8.706577	41.20	9.999437	.10	8.707140	41.30	1.292860	5
56	.709049	40.97	.999431	.12	.709618	41.08	.290382	4
57	.711507	40.75	.999424	.10	.712083	40.85	.287917	3
58	.713952	40.52	.999418	.12	.714534	40.63	.285466	2
59	.716383	40.28	.999411	.12	.716972	40.40	.283028	1
60	8.718800		9.999404		8.719396		1.280604	0
	Cos.	D. 1″.	Sin.	D. 1″.	Cot.	D. 1″.	Tan.	M.

TABLE C

LOGARITHMIC SINES, COSINES, TANGENTS, AND COTANGENTS

3°   176°

M.	Sin.	D. 1″.	Cos.	D. 1″.	Tan.	D. 1″.	Cot.	
0	8.718800	40.07	9.999404	.10	8.719396	40.17	1.280604	60
1	.721204	39.85	.999398	.12	.721806	39.97	.278194	59
2	.723595	39.62	.999391	.12	.724204	39.73	.275793	58
3	.725972	39.42	.999384	.10	.726588	39.52	.273412	57
4	.728337	39.18	.999378	.12	.728959	39.30	.271041	56
5	8.730688	38.98	9.999371	.12	8.731317	39.10	1.268683	55
6	.733027	38.78	.999364	.12	.733663	38.88	.266337	54
7	.735354	38.55	.999357	.12	.735996	38.68	.264004	53
8	.737667	38.37	.999350	.12	.738317	38.48	.261683	52
9	.739969	38.17	.999343	.12	.740626	38.27	.259374	51
10	8.742259	37.95	9.999336	.12	8.742922	38.08	1.257078	50
11	.744536	37.77	.999329	.12	.745207	37.87	.254793	49
12	.746802	37.55	.999322	.12	.747479	37.68	.252521	48
13	.749055	37.37	.999315	.12	.749740	37.48	.250260	47
14	.751297	37.18	.999308	.12	.751989	37.30	.248011	46
15	8.753528	36.98	9.999301	.12	8.754227	37.10	1.245773	45
16	.755747	36.80	.999294	.12	.756453	36.92	.243547	44
17	.757955	36.60	.999287	.13	.758668	36.73	.241332	43
18	.760151	36.43	.999279	.12	.760872	36.55	.239128	42
19	.762337	36.23	.999272	.12	.763065	36.35	.236935	41
20	8.764511	36.07	9.999265	.13	8.765246	36.18	1.234754	40
21	.766675	35.88	.999257	.12	.767417	36.02	.232583	39
22	.768828	35.70	.999250	.13	.769578	35.82	.230422	38
23	.770970	35.52	.999242	.12	.771727	35.65	.228273	37
24	.773101	35.37	.999235	.13	.773866	35.48	.226134	36
25	8.775223	35.17	9.999227	.12	8.775995	35.32	1.224005	35
26	.777333	35.02	.999220	.13	.778114	35.13	.221886	34
27	.779434	34.83	.999212	.12	.780222	34.97	.219778	33
28	.781524	34.68	.999205	.13	.782320	34.80	.217680	32
29	.783605	34.50	.999197	.13	.784408	34.63	.215592	31
30	8.785675	34.35	9.999189	.13	8.786486	34.47	1.213514	30
31	.787736	34.18	.999181	.12	.788554	34.32	.211446	29
32	.789787	34.02	.999174	.13	.790613	34.15	.209387	28
33	.791828	33.85	.999166	.13	.792662	33.98	.207338	27
34	.793859	33.70	.999158	.13	.794701	33.83	.205299	26
35	8.795881	33.55	9.999150	.13	8.796731	33.68	1.203269	25
36	.797894	33.38	.999142	.13	.798752	33.52	.201248	24
37	.799897	33.25	.999134	.13	.800763	33.37	.199237	23
38	.801892	33.07	.999126	.13	.802765	33.22	.197235	22
39	.803876	32.93	.999118	.13	.804758	33.07	.195242	21
40	8.805852	32.78	9.999110	.13	8.806742	32.92	1.193258	20
41	.807819	32.63	.999102	.13	.808717	32.77	.191283	19
42	.809777	32.48	.999094	.13	.810683	32.63	.189317	18
43	.811726	32.35	.999086	.15	.812641	32.47	.187359	17
44	.813667	32.20	.999077	.13	.814589	32.33	.185411	16
45	8.815599	32.05	9.999069	.13	8.816529	32.20	1.183471	15
46	.817522	31.90	.999061	.15	.818461	32.05	.181539	14
47	.819436	31.78	.999053	.13	.820384	31.90	.179616	13
48	.821343	31.62	.999044	.15	.822298	31.78	.177702	12
49	.823240	31.50	.999036	.13	.824205	31.63	.175795	11
50	8.825130	31.35	9.999027	.15	8.826103	31.48	1.173897	10
51	.827011	31.22	.999019	.13	.827992	31.37	.172008	9
52	.828884	31.08	.999010	.15	.829874	31.23	.170126	8
53	.830749	30.97	.999002	.15	.831748	31.08	.168252	7
54	.832607	30.82	.998993	.15	.833613	30.97	.166387	6
55	8.834456	30.68	9.998984	.13	8.835471	30.83	1.164529	5
56	.836297	30.55	.998976	.15	.837321	30.70	.162679	4
57	.838130	30.43	.998967	.15	.839163	30.58	.160837	3
58	.839956	30.30	.998958	.13	.840998	30.45	.159002	2
59	.841774	30.18	.998950	.15	.842825	30.32	.157175	1
60	8.843585		9.998941		8.844644		1.155356	0
	Cos.	D. 1″.	Sin.	D. 1″.	Cot.	D. 1″.	Tan.	M.

93°   86°

TABLE C 679

LOGARITHMIC SINES, COSINES, TANGENTS, AND COTANGENTS

4° 175°

M.	Sin.	D. 1″.	Cos.	D. 1″.	Tan.	D. 1″.	Cot.	
0	8.843585	30.03	9.998941	.15	8.844644	30.18	1.155356	60
1	.845387	29.93	.998932	.15	.846455	30.08	.153545	59
2	.847183	29.80	.998923	.15	.848260	29.95	.151740	58
3	.848971	29.67	.998914	.15	.850057	29.82	.149943	57
4	.850751	29.57	.998905	.15	.851846	29.70	.148154	56
5	8.852525	29.43	9.998896	.15	8.853628	29.58	1.146372	55
6	.854291	29.30	.998887	.15	.855403	29.47	.144597	54
7	.856049	29.20	.998878	.15	.857171	29.35	.142829	53
8	.857801	29.08	.998869	.15	.858932	29.23	.141068	52
9	.859546	28.95	.998860	.15	.860686	29.12	.139314	51
10	8.861283	28.85	9.998851	.17	8.862433	29.00	1.137567	50
11	.863014	28.73	.998841	.15	.864173	28.88	.135827	49
12	.864738	28.62	.998832	.15	.865906	28.77	.134094	48
13	.866455	28.50	.998823	.17	.867632	28.65	.132368	47
14	.868165	28.38	.998813	.15	.869351	28.55	.130649	46
15	8.869868	28.28	9.998804	.15	8.871064	28.43	1.128936	45
16	.871565	28.17	.998795	.17	.872770	28.32	.127230	44
17	.873255	28.05	.998785	.15	.874469	28.22	.125531	43
18	.874938	27.95	.998776	.17	.876162	28.12	.123838	42
19	.876615	27.83	.998766	.15	.877849	28.00	.122151	41
20	8.878285	27.73	9.998757	.17	8.879529	27.88	1.120471	40
21	.879949	27.63	.998747	.15	.881202	27.78	.118798	39
22	.881607	27.52	.998738	.17	.882869	27.68	.117131	38
23	.883258	27.42	.998728	.17	.884530	27.58	.115470	37
24	.884903	27.32	.998718	.17	.886185	27.47	.113815	36
25	8.886542	27.20	9.998708	.15	8.887833	27.38	1.112167	35
26	.888174	27.12	.998699	.17	.889476	27.27	.110524	34
27	.889801	27.00	.998689	.17	.891112	27.17	.108888	33
28	.891421	26.90	.998679	.17	.892742	27.07	.107258	32
29	.893035	26.80	.998669	.17	.894366	26.97	.105634	31
30	8.894643	26.72	9.998659	.17	8.895984	26.87	1.104016	30
31	.896246	26.60	.998649	.17	.897596	26.78	.102404	29
32	.897842	26.50	.998639	.17	.899203	26.67	.100797	28
33	.899432	26.42	.998629	.17	.900803	26.58	.099197	27
34	.901017	26.32	.998619	.17	.902398	26.48	.097602	26
35	8.902596	26.22	9.998609	.17	8.903987	26.38	1.096013	25
36	.904169	26.12	.998599	.17	.905570	26.28	.094430	24
37	.905736	26.02	.998589	.18	.907147	26.20	.092853	23
38	.907297	25.93	.998578	.17	.908719	26.10	.091281	22
39	.908853	25.85	.998568	.17	.910285	26.02	.089715	21
40	8.910404	25.75	9.998558	.17	8.911846	25.92	1.088154	20
41	.911949	25.65	.998548	.18	.913401	25.83	.086599	19
42	.913488	25.57	.998537	.17	.914951	25.73	.085049	18
43	.915022	25.47	.998527	.18	.916495	25.65	.083505	17
44	.916550	25.38	.998516	.17	.918034	25.57	.081966	16
45	8.918073	25.30	9.998506	.18	8.919568	25.47	1.080432	15
46	.919591	25.20	.998495	.17	.921096	25.38	.078904	14
47	.921103	25.12	.998485	.18	.922619	25.28	.077381	13
48	.922610	25.03	.998474	.17	.924136	25.22	.075864	12
49	.924112	24.95	.998464	.18	.925649	25.12	.074351	11
50	8.925609	24.85	9.998453	.18	8.927156	25.03	1.072844	10
51	.927100	24.78	.998442	.18	.928658	24.95	.071342	9
52	.928587	24.68	.998431	.17	.930155	24.87	.069845	8
53	.930068	24.60	.998421	.18	.931647	24.78	.068353	7
54	.931544	24.52	.998410	.18	.933134	24.70	.066866	6
55	8.933015	24.43	9.998399	.18	8.934616	24.62	1.065384	5
56	.934481	24.35	.998388	.18	.936093	24.53	.063907	4
57	.935942	24.27	.998377	.18	.937565	24.45	.062435	3
58	.937398	24.20	.998366	.18	.939032	24.37	.060968	2
59	.938850	24.10	.998355	.18	.940494	24.30	.059506	1
60	8.940296		9.998344		8.941952		1.058048	0
	Cos.	D. 1″.	Sin.	D. 1″.	Cot.	D. 1″.	Tan.	M.

94° 85°

TABLE C

Logarithmic Sines, Cosines, Tangents, and Cotangents

5° 174°

M.	Sin.	D. 1″.	Cos.	D. 1″.	Tan.	D. 1″.	Cot.	
0	8.940296	24.03	9.998344	.18	8.941952	24.20	1.058048	60
1	.941738	23.93	.998333	.18	.943404	24.13	.056596	59
2	.943174	23.87	.998322	.18	.944852	24.05	.055148	58
3	.944606	23.80	.998311	.18	.946295	23.98	.053705	57
4	.946034	23.70	.998300	.18	.947734	23.90	.052266	56
5	8.947456	23.63	9.998289	.20	8.949168	23.82	1.050832	55
6	.948874	23.55	.998277	.18	.950597	23.73	.049403	54
7	.950287	23.48	.998266	.18	.952021	23.67	.047979	53
8	.951696	23.40	.998255	.20	.953441	23.58	.046559	52
9	.953100	23.32	.998243	.18	.954856	23.52	.045144	51
10	8.954499	23.25	9.998232	.20	8.956267	23.45	1.043733	50
11	.955894	23.17	.998220	.18	.957674	23.35	.042326	49
12	.957284	23.10	.998209	.20	.959075	23.30	.040925	48
13	.958670	23.03	.998197	.18	.960473	23.22	.039527	47
14	.960052	22.95	.998186	.20	.961866	23.15	.038134	46
15	8.961429	22.87	9.998174	.18	8.963255	23.07	1.036745	45
16	.962801	22.82	.998163	.20	.964639	23.00	.035361	44
17	.964170	22.73	.998151	.20	.966019	22.92	.033981	43
18	.965534	22.65	.998139	.20	.967394	22.87	.032606	42
19	.966893	22.60	.998128	.18	.968766	22.78	.031234	41
20	8.968249	22.52	9.998116	.20	8.970133	22.72	1.029867	40
21	.969600	22.45	.998104	.20	.971496	22.65	.028504	39
22	.970947	22.37	.998092	.20	.972855	22.57	.027145	38
23	.972289	22.32	.998080	.20	.974209	22.52	.025791	37
24	.973628	22.23	.998068	.20	.975560	22.43	.024440	36
25	8.974962	22.18	9.998056	.20	8.976906	22.37	1.023094	35
26	.976293	22.10	.998044	.20	.978248	22.30	.021752	34
27	.977619	22.03	.998032	.20	.979586	22.25	.020414	33
28	.978941	21.97	.998020	.20	.980921	22.17	.019079	32
29	.980259	21.90	.998008	.20	.982251	22.10	.017749	31
30	8.981573	21.83	9.997996	.20	8.983577	22.03	1.016423	30
31	.982883	21.77	.997984	.20	.984899	21.97	.015101	29
32	.984189	21.70	.997972	.22	.986217	21.92	.013783	28
33	.985491	21.63	.997959	.20	.987532	21.83	.012468	27
34	.986789	21.57	.997947	.20	.988842	21.78	.011158	26
35	8.988083	21.52	9.997935	.22	8.990149	21.70	1.009851	25
36	.989374	21.43	.997922	.20	.991451	21.65	.008549	24
37	.990660	21.38	.997910	.22	.992750	21.58	.007250	23
38	.991943	21.32	.997897	.20	.994045	21.52	.005955	22
39	.993222	21.25	.997885	.22	.995337	21.45	.004663	21
40	8.994497	21.18	9.997872	.20	8.996624	21.40	1.003376	20
41	.995768	21.13	.997860	.22	.997908	21.33	.002092	19
42	.997036	21.05	.997847	.20	.999188	21.28	.000812	18
43	.998299	21.02	.997835	.22	9.000465	21.22	0.999535	17
44	.999560	20.93	.997822	.22	.001738	21.15	.998262	16
45	9.000816	20.88	9.997809	.20	9.003007	21.08	0.996993	15
46	.002069	20.82	.997797	.22	.004272	21.03	.995728	14
47	.003318	20.75	.997784	.22	.005534	20.97	.994466	13
48	.004563	20.70	.997771	.22	.006792	20.92	.993208	12
49	.005805	20.65	.997758	.22	.008047	20.85	.991953	11
50	9.007044	20.57	9.997745	.22	9.009298	20.80	0.990702	10
51	.008278	20.53	.997732	.22	.010546	20.73	.989454	9
52	.009510	20.45	.997719	.22	.011790	20.68	.988210	8
53	.010737	20.42	.997706	.22	.013031	20.62	.986969	7
54	.011962	20.33	.997693	.22	.014268	20.57	.985732	6
55	9.013182	20.30	9.997680	.22	9.015502	20.50	0.984498	5
56	.014400	20.22	.997667	.22	.016732	20.45	.983268	4
57	.015613	20.18	.997654	.22	.017959	20.40	.982041	3
58	.016824	20.12	.997641	.22	.019183	20.33	.980817	2
59	.018031	20.07	.997628	.23	.020403	20.28	.979597	1
60	9.019235		9.997614		9.021620		0.978380	0
	Cos.	D. 1″.	Sin.	D. 1″.	Cot.	D. 1″.	Tan.	M.

95° 84°

TABLE C   681

LOGARITHMIC SINES, COSINES, TANGENTS, AND COTANGENTS

M.	Sin.	D. 1″.	Cos.	D. 1″.	Tan.	D. 1″.	Cot.	
0	9.019235	20.00	9.997614	.22	9.021620	20.23	0.978380	60
1	.020435	19.95	.997601	.22	.022834	20.17	.977166	59
2	.021632	19.83	.997588	.23	.024044	20.12	.975956	58
3	.022825	19.85	.997574	.22	.025251	20.07	.974749	57
4	.024016	19.78	.997561	.23	.026455	20.00	.973545	56
5	9.025203	19.72	9.997547	.22	9.027655	19.95	0.972345	55
6	.026386	19.68	.997534	.23	.028852	19.90	.971148	54
7	.027567	19.62	.997520	.22	.030046	19.85	.969954	53
8	.028744	19.57	.997507	.23	.031237	19.80	.968763	52
9	.029918	19.52	.997493	.22	.032425	19.73	.967575	51
10	9.031089	19.47	9.997480	.23	9.033609	19.70	0.966391	50
11	.032257	19.40	.997466	.23	.034791	19.63	.965209	49
12	.033421	19.35	.997452	.22	.035969	19.58	.964031	48
13	.034582	19.32	.997439	.23	.037144	19.53	.962856	47
14	.035741	19.25	.997425	.23	.038316	19.48	.961684	46
15	9.036896	19.20	9.997411	.23	9.039485	19.43	0.960515	45
16	.038048	19.15	.997397	.23	.040651	19.37	.959349	44
17	.039197	19.08	.997383	.23	.041813	19.33	.958187	43
18	.040342	19.05	.997369	.23	.042973	19.28	.957027	42
19	.041485	19.00	.997355	.23	.044130	19.23	.955870	41
20	9.042625	18.95	9.997341	.23	9.045284	19.17	0.954716	40
21	.043762	18.88	.997327	.23	.046434	19.13	.953566	39
22	.044895	18.85	.997313	.23	.047582	19.08	.952418	38
23	.046026	18.80	.997299	.23	.048727	19.03	.951273	37
24	.047154	18.75	.997285	.23	.049869	18.98	.950131	36
25	9.048279	18.68	9.997271	.23	9.051008	18.93	0.948992	35
26	.049400	18.65	.997257	.25	.052144	18.88	.947856	34
27	.050519	18.60	.997242	.23	.053277	18.83	.946723	33
28	.051635	18.57	.997228	.23	.054407	18.80	.945593	32
29	.052749	18.50	.997214	.25	.055535	18.73	.944465	31
30	9.053859	18.45	9.997199	.23	9.056659	18.70	0.943341	30
31	.054966	18.42	.997185	.25	.057781	18.65	.942219	29
32	.056071	18.35	.997170	.23	.058900	18.60	.941100	28
33	.057172	18.32	.997156	.25	.060016	18.57	.939984	27
34	.058271	18.27	.997141	.23	.061130	18.50	.938870	26
35	9.059367	18.22	9.997127	.25	9.062240	18.47	0.937760	25
36	.060460	18.18	.997112	.23	.063348	18.42	.936652	24
37	.061551	18.13	.997098	.25	.064453	18.38	.935547	23
38	.062639	18.08	.997083	.25	.065556	18.32	.934444	22
39	.063724	18.03	.997068	.25	.066655	18.28	.933345	21
40	9.064806	17.98	9.997053	.23	9.067752	18.23	0.932248	20
41	.065885	17.95	.997039	.25	.068846	18.20	.931154	19
42	.066962	17.90	.997024	.25	.069938	18.15	.930062	18
43	.068036	17.85	.997009	.25	.071027	18.10	.928973	17
44	.069107	17.82	.996994	.25	.072113	18.07	.927887	16
45	9.070176	17.77	9.996979	.25	9.073197	18.02	0.926803	15
46	.071242	17.73	.996964	.25	.074278	17.97	.925722	14
47	.072306	17.67	.996949	.25	.075356	17.93	.924644	13
48	.073366	17.63	.996934	.25	.076432	17.88	.923568	12
49	.074424	17.60	.996919	.25	.077505	17.85	.922495	11
50	9.075480	17.55	9.996904	.25	9.078576	17.80	0.921424	10
51	.076533	17.50	.996889	.25	.079644	17.77	.920356	9
52	.077583	17.47	.996874	.27	.080710	17.72	.919290	8
53	.078631	17.42	.996858	.25	.081773	17.67	.918227	7
54	.079676	17.38	.996843	.25	.082833	17.63	.917167	6
55	9.080719	17.33	9.996828	.27	9.083891	17.60	0.916109	5
56	.081759	17.30	.996812	.25	.084947	17.55	.915053	4
57	.082797	17.25	.996797	.25	.086000	17.50	.914000	3
58	.083832	17.20	.996782	.27	.087050	17.47	.912950	2
59	.084864	17.17	.996766	.25	.088098	17.43	.911902	1
60	9.085894		9.996751		9.089144		0.910856	0
	Cos.	D. 1″.	Sin.	D. 1″.	Cot.	D. 1″.	Tan.	M.

TABLE C

Logarithmic Sines, Cosines, Tangents, and Cotangents

7°   172°

M.	Sin.	D. 1″.	Cos.	D. 1″.	Tan.	D. 1″.	Cot.	
0	9.085894	17.13	9.996751	.27	9.089144	17.38	0.910856	60
1	.086922	17.08	.996735	.25	.090187	17.35	.909813	59
2	.087947	17.05	.996720	.27	.091228	17.30	.908772	58
3	.088970	17.00	.996704	.27	.092266	17.27	.907734	57
4	.089990	16.97	.996688	.25	.093302	17.23	.906698	56
5	9.091008	16.93	9.996673	.27	9.094336	17.18	0.905664	55
6	.092024	16.88	.996657	.27	.095367	17.13	.904633	54
7	.093037	16.83	.996641	.27	.096395	17 12	.903605	53
8	.094047	16.82	.996625	.25	.097422	17.07	.902578	52
9	.095056	16.77	.996610	.27	.098446	17.03	.901554	51
10	9.096062	16.72	9.996594	.27	9.099468	16.98	0.900532	50
11	.097065	16.68	.996578	.27	.100487	16.95	.899513	49
12	.098066	16.65	.996562	.27	.101504	16.92	.898496	48
13	.099065	16.62	.996546	.27	.102519	16.88	.897481	47
14	.100062	16.57	.996530	.27	.103532	16.83	.896468	46
15	9.101056	16.53	9.996514	.27	9.104542	16.80	0.895458	45
16	.102048	16.48	.996498	.27	.105550	16.77	.894450	44
17	.103037	16.47	.996482	.28	.106556	16.72	.893444	43
18	.104025	16.42	.996465	.27	.107559	16.68	.892441	42
19	.105010	16.37	.996449	.27	.108560	16.65	.891440	41
20	9.105992	16.35	9.996433	.27	9.109559	16.62	0.890441	40
21	.106973	16.30	.996417	.28	.110556	16.58	.889444	39
22	.107951	16.27	.996400	.27	.111551	16.53	.888449	38
23	.108927	16.23	.996384	.27	.112543	16.50	.887457	37
24	.109901	16.20	.996368	.28	.113533	16.47	.886467	36
25	9.110873	16.15	9.996351	.27	9.114521	16.43	0.885479	35
26	.111842	16.12	.996335	.28	.115507	16.40	.884493	34
27	.112809	16.08	.996318	.27	.116491	16.35	.883509	33
28	.113774	16.05	.996302	.28	.117472	16.33	.882528	32
29	.114737	16.02	.996285	.27	.118452	16.28	.881548	31
30	9.115698	15.97	9.996269	.28	9.119429	16.25	0.880571	30
31	.116656	15.95	.996252	.28	.120404	16.22	.879596	29
32	.117613	15.90	.996235	.27	.121377	16.18	.878623	28
33	.118567	15.87	.996219	.28	.122348	16.15	.877652	27
34	.119519	15.83	.996202	.28	.123317	16.12	.876683	26
35	9.120469	15.80	9.996185	.28	9.124284	16.08	0.875716	25
36	.121417	15.75	.996168	.28	.125249	16.03	.874751	24
37	.122362	15.73	.996151	.28	.126211	16.02	.873789	23
38	.123306	15.70	.996134	.28	.127172	15.97	.872828	22
39	.124248	15.65	.996117	.28	.128130	15.95	.871870	21
40	9.125187	15.63	9.996100	.28	9.129087	15.90	0.870913	20
41	.126125	15.58	.996083	.28	.130041	15.88	.869959	19
42	.127060	15.55	.996066	.28	.130994	15.83	.869006	18
43	.127993	15.53	.996049	.28	.131944	15.82	.868056	17
44	.128925	15.48	.996032	.28	.132893	15.77	.867107	16
45	9.129854	15.45	9.996015	.28	9.133839	15.75	0.866161	15
46	.130781	15.42	.995998	.30	.134784	15.70	.865216	14
47	.131706	15.40	.995980	.28	.135726	15.68	.864274	13
48	.132630	15.35	.995963	.28	.136667	15.63	.863333	12
49	.133551	15.32	.995946	.30	.137605	15.62	.862395	11
50	9.134470	15.28	9.995928	.28	9.138542	15.57	0.861458	10
51	.135387	15.27	.995911	.28	.139476	15.55	.860524	9
52	.136303	15.22	.995894	.30	.140409	15.52	.859591	8
53	.137216	15.20	.995876	.28	.141340	15.48	.858660	7
54	.138128	15.15	.995859	.30	.142269	15.45	.857731	6
55	9.139037	15.12	9.995841	.30	9.143196	15.42	0.856804	5
56	.139944	15.10	.995823	.28	.144121	15.38	.855879	4
57	.140850	15.07	.995806	.30	.145044	15.37	.854956	3
58	.141754	15.02	.995788	.28	.145966	15.32	.854034	2
59	.142655	15.00	.995771	.30	.146885	15.30	.853115	1
60	9.143555		9.995753		9.147803		0.852197	0
	Cos.	D. 1″.	Sin.	D. 1″.	Cot.	D. 1″.	Tan.	M.

97°   82°

TABLE C

683

Logarithmic Sines, Cosines, Tangents, and Cotangents

8°   171°

M.	Sin.	D. 1″	Cos.	D. 1″.	Tan.	D. 1″.	Cot.	
0	9.143555	14.97	9.995753	.30	9.147803	15.25	0.852197	60
1	.144453	14.93	.995735	.30	.148718	15.23	.851282	59
2	.145349	14.90	.995717	.30	.149632	15.20	.850368	58
3	.146243	14.88	.995699	.30	.150544	15.17	.849456	57
4	.147136	14.83	.995681	.30	.151454	15.15	.848546	56
5	9.148026	14.82	9.995664	.28	9.152363	15.10	0.847637	55
6	.148915	14.78	.995646	.30	.153269	15.08	846731	54
7	.149802	14.73	.995628	.30	.154174	15.05	.845826	53
8	.150686	14.72	.995610	.30	.155077	15.02	.844923	52
9	.151569	14.70	.995591	.32	.155978	14.98	.844022	51
10	9.152451	14.65	9.995573	.30	9.156877	14.97	0.843123	50
11	.153330	14.63	.995555	.30	.157775	14.93	.842225	49
12	.154208	14.58	.995537	.30	.158671	14.90	.841329	48
13	.155083	14.57	.995519	.30	.159565	14.87	.840435	47
14	.155957	14.55	.995501	.30	.160457	14.83	.839543	46
15	9.156830	14.50	9.995482	.32	9.161347	14.82	0.838653	45
16	.157700	14.48	.995464	.30	.162236	14.78	.837764	44
17	.158569	14.43	.995446	.30	.163123	14.75	.836877	43
18	.159435	14.43	.995427	.32	.164008	14.73	.835992	42
19	.160301	14.38	.995409	.30	.164892	14.70	.835108	41
20	9.161164	14.35	9.995390	.32	9.165774	14.67	0.834226	40
21	.162025	14.33	.995372	.30	.166654	14.63	.833346	39
22	.162885	14.30	.995353	.32	.167532	14.62	.832468	38
23	.163743	14.28	.995334	.32	.168409	14.58	.831591	37
24	.164600	14.23	.995316	.30	.169284	14.55	.830716	36
25	9.165454	14.22	9.995297	.32	9.170157	14.53	0.829843	35
26	.166307	14.20	.995278	.32	.171029	14.50	.828971	34
27	.167159	14.15	.995260	.30	.171899	14.47	.828101	33
28	.168008	14.13	.995241	.32	.172767	14.45	.827233	32
29	.168856	14.10	.995222	.32	.173634	14.42	.826366	31
30	9.169702	14.08	9.995203	.32	9.174499	14.38	0.825501	30
31	.170547	14.03	.995184	.32	.175362	14.37	.824638	29
32	.171389	14.02	.995165	.32	.176224	14.33	.823776	28
33	.172230	14.00	.995146	.32	.177084	14.30	.822916	27
34	.173070	13.97	.995127	.32	.177942	14.28	.822058	26
35	9.173908	13.93	9.995108	.32	9.178799	14.27	0.821201	25
36	.174744	13.90	.995089	.32	.179655	14.22	.820345	24
37	.175578	13.88	.995070	.32	.180508	14.20	.819492	23
38	.176411	13.85	.995051	.32	.181360	14.18	.818640	22
39	.177242	13.83	.995032	.32	.182211	14.13	.817789	21
40	9.178072	13.80	9.995013	.33	9.183059	14.13	0.816941	20
41	.178900	13.77	.994993	.32	.183907	14.08	.816093	19
42	.179726	13.75	.994974	.32	.184752	14.08	.815248	18
43	.180551	13.72	.994955	.33	.185597	14.03	.814403	17
44	.181374	13.70	.994935	.32	.186439	14.02	.813561	16
45	9.182196	13.67	9.994916	.33	9.187280	14.00	0.812720	15
46	.183016	13.63	.994896	.32	.188120	13.97	.811880	14
47	.183834	13.62	.994877	.33	.188958	13.93	.811042	13
48	.184651	13.58	.994857	.32	.189794	13.92	.810206	12
49	.185466	13.57	.994838	.33	.190629	13.88	.809371	11
50	9.186280	13.53	9.994818	.33	9.191462	13.87	0.808538	10
51	.187092	13.52	.994798	.32	.192294	13.83	.807706	9
52	.187903	13.48	.994779	.33	.193124	13.82	.806876	8
53	.188712	13.45	.994759	.33	.193953	13.78	.806047	7
54	.189519	13.43	.994739	.32	.194780	13.77	.805220	6
55	9.190325	13.42	9.994720	.33	9.195606	13.73	0.804394	5
56	.191130	13.38	.994700	.33	.196430	13.72	.803570	4
57	.191933	13.35	.994680	.33	.197253	13.68	.802747	3
58	.192734	13.33	.994660	.33	.198074	13.67	.801926	2
59	.193534	13.30	.994640	.33	.198894	13.65	.801106	1
60	9.194332		9.994620		9.199713		0.800287	0
	Cos.	D. 1″.	Sin.	D. 1″.	Cot.	D. 1″.	Tan.	M.

TABLE C

LOGARITHMIC SINES, COSINES, TANGENTS, AND COTANGENTS

9°   170°

M.	Sin.	D. 1″.	Cos.	D. 1″.	Tan.	D. 1″.	Cot.	
0	9.194332	13.28	9.994620	.33	9.199713	13.60	0.800287	60
1	.195129	13.27	.994600	.33	.200529	13.60	.799471	59
2	.195925	13.23	.994580	.33	.201345	13.57	.798655	58
3	.196719	13.20	.994560	.33	.202159	13.53	.797841	57
4	.197511	13.18	.994540	.35	.202971	13.52	.797029	56
5	9.198302	13.15	9.994519	.33	9.203782	13.50	0.796218	55
6	.199091	13.13	.994499	.33	.204592	13.47	.795408	54
7	.199879	13.12	.994479	.33	.205400	13.45	.794600	53
8	.200666	13.08	.994459	.35	.206207	13.43	.793793	52
9	.201451	13.05	.994438	.33	.207013	13.40	.792987	51
10	9.202234	13.05	9.994418	.33	9.207817	13.37	0.792183	50
11	.203017	13.00	.994398	.35	.208619	13.35	.791381	49
12	.203797	13.00	.994377	.33	.209420	13.33	.790580	48
13	.204577	12.95	.994357	.35	.210220	13.30	.789780	47
14	.205354	12.95	.994336	.33	.211018	13.28	.788982	46
15	9.206131	12.92	9.994316	.35	9.211815	13.27	0.788185	45
16	.206906	12.88	.994295	.35	.212611	13.23	.787389	44
17	.207679	12.88	.994274	.33	.213405	13.22	.786595	43
18	.208452	12.83	.994254	.35	.214198	13.18	.785802	42
19	.209222	12.83	.994233	.35	.214989	13.18	.785011	41
20	9.209992	12.80	9.994212	.35	9.215780	13.13	0.784220	40
21	.210760	12.77	.994191	.33	.216568	13.13	.783432	39
22	.211526	12.75	.994171	.35	.217356	13.10	.782644	38
23	.212291	12.73	.994150	.35	.218142	13.07	.781858	37
24	.213055	12.72	.994129	.35	.218926	13.07	.781074	36
25	9.213818	12.68	9.994108	.35	9.219710	13.03	0.780290	35
26	.214579	12.65	.994087	.35	.220492	13.00	.779508	34
27	.215338	12.65	.994066	.35	.221272	13.00	.778728	33
28	.216097	12.62	.994045	.35	.222052	12.97	.777948	32
29	.216854	12.58	.994024	.35	.222830	12.95	.777170	31
30	9.217609	12.57	9.994003	.35	9.223607	12.92	0.776393	30
31	.218363	12.55	.993982	.37	.224382	12.90	.775618	29
32	.219116	12.53	.993960	.35	.225156	12.88	.774844	28
33	.219868	12.50	.993939	.35	.225929	12.85	.774071	27
34	.220618	12.48	.993918	.35	.226700	12.85	.773300	26
35	9.221367	12.47	9.993897	.37	9.227471	12.80	0.772529	25
36	.222115	12.43	.993875	.35	.228239	12.80	.771761	24
37	.222861	12.42	.993854	.37	.229007	12.77	.770993	23
38	.223606	12.38	.993832	.35	.229773	12.77	.770227	22
39	.224349	12.38	.993811	.37	.230539	12.72	.769461	21
40	9.225092	12.35	9.993789	.35	9.231302	12.72	0.768698	20
41	.225833	12.33	.993768	.37	.232065	12.68	.767935	19
42	.226573	12.30	.993746	.35	.232826	12.67	.767174	18
43	.227311	12.28	.993725	.37	.233586	12.65	.766414	17
44	.228048	12.27	.993703	.37	.234345	12.63	.765655	16
45	9.228784	12.23	9.993681	.35	9.235103	12.60	0.764897	15
46	.229518	12.23	.993660	.37	.235859	12.58	.764141	14
47	.230252	12.20	.993638	.37	.236614	12.57	.763386	13
48	.230984	12.18	.993616	.37	.237368	12.53	.762632	12
49	.231715	12.15	.993594	.37	.238120	12.53	.761880	11
50	9.232444	12.13	9.993572	.37	9.238872	12.50	0.761128	10
51	.233172	12.12	.993550	.37	.239622	12.48	.760378	9
52	.233899	12.10	.993528	.37	.240371	12.45	.759629	8
53	.234625	12.07	.993506	.37	.241118	12.45	.758882	7
54	.235349	12.07	.993484	.37	.241865	12.42	.758135	6
55	9.236073	12.03	9.993462	.37	9.242610	12.40	0.757390	5
56	.236795	12.00	.993440	.37	.243354	12.38	.756646	4
57	.237515	12.00	.993418	.37	.244097	12.37	.755903	3
58	.238235	11.97	.993396	.37	.244839	12.33	.755161	2
59	.238953	11.95	.993374	.38	.245579	12.33	.754421	1
60	9.239670		9.993351		9.246319		0.753681	0
	Cos.	D. 1″.	Sin.	D. 1″.	Cot.	D. 1″.	Tan.	M.

99°   80°

TABLE C 685

LOGARITHMIC SINES, COSINES, TANGENTS, AND COTANGENTS

10° 169°

M.	Sin.	D. 1".	Cos.	D. 1".	Tan.	D. 1".	Cot.	
0	9.239670	11.93	9.993351	.37	9.246319	12.30	0.753681	60
1	.240386	11.92	.993329	.37	.247057	12.28	.752943	59
2	.241101	11.88	.993307	.37	.247794	12.27	.752206	58
3	.241814	11.87	.993284	.38	.248530	12.23	.751470	57
4	.242526	11.85	.993262	.37	.249264	12.23	.750736	56
5	9.243237	11.83	9.993240	.37	9.249998	12.20	0.750002	55
6	.243947	11.82	.993217	.38	.250730	12.18	.749270	54
7	.244656	11.78	.993195	.37	.251461	12.17	.748539	53
8	.245363	11.77	.993172	.38	.252191	12.15	.747809	52
9	.246069	11.77	.993149	.38	.252920	12.13	.747080	51
10	9.246775	11.72	9.993127	.37	9.253648	12.10	0.746352	50
11	.247478	11.72	.993104	.38	.254374	12.10	.745626	49
12	.248181	11.70	.993081	.38	.255100	12.07	.744900	48
13	.248883	11.67	.993059	.37	.255824	12.05	.744176	47
14	.249583	11.65	.993036	.38	.256547	12.03	.743453	46
15	9.250282	11.63	9.993013	.38	9.257269	12.02	0.742731	45
16	.250980	11.62	.992990	.38	.257990	12.00	.742010	44
17	.251677	11.60	.992967	.38	.258710	11.98	.741290	43
18	.252373	11.57	.992944	.38	.259429	11.95	.740571	42
19	.253067	11.57	.992921	.38	.260146	11.95	.739854	41
20	9.253761	11.53	9.992898	.38	9.260863	11.92	0.739137	40
21	.254453	11.52	.992875	.38	.261578	11.90	.738422	39
22	.255144	11.50	.992852	.38	.262292	11.88	.737708	38
23	.255834	11.48	.992829	.38	.263005	11.87	.736995	37
24	.256523	11.47	.992806	.38	.263717	11.85	.736283	36
25	9.257211	11.45	9.992783	.38	9.264428	11.83	0.735572	35
26	.257898	11.42	.992759	.40	.265138	11.82	.734862	34
27	.258583	11.42	.992736	.38	.265847	11.80	.734153	33
28	.259268	11.38	.992713	.38	.266555	11.77	.733445	32
29	.259951	11.37	.992690	.38	.267261	11.77	.732739	31
30	9.260633	11.35	9.992666	.40	9.267967	11.73	0.732033	30
31	.261314	11.33	.992643	.38	.268671	11.73	.731329	29
32	.261994	11.32	.992619	.40	.269375	11.70	.730025	28
33	.262673	11.30	.992596	.38	.270077	11.70	.729923	27
34	.263351	11.27	.992572	.40	.270779	11.67	.729221	26
35	9.264027	11.27	9.992549	.38	9.271479	11.65	0.728521	25
36	.264703	11.23	.992525	.40	.272178	11.63	.727822	24
37	.265377	11.23	.992501	.40	.272876	11.62	.727124	23
38	.266051	11.20	.992478	.38	.273573	11.60	.726427	22
39	.266723	11.20	.992454	.40	.274269	11.58	.725731	21
40	9.267395	11.17	9.992430	.40	9.274964	11.57	0.725036	20
41	.268065	11.15	.992406	.40	.275658	11.55	.724342	19
42	.268734	11.13	.992382	.40	.276351	11.53	.723649	18
43	.269402	11.12	.992359	.38	.277043	11.52	.722957	17
44	.270069	11.10	.992335	.40	.277734	11.50	.722266	16
45	9.270735	11.08	9.992311	.40	9.278424	11.48	0.721576	15
46	.271400	11.07	.992287	.40	.279113	11.47	.720887	14
47	.272064	11.03	.992263	.40	.279801	11.45	.720199	13
48	.272726	11.03	.992239	.42	.280488	11.43	.719512	12
49	.273388	11.02	.992214	.40	.281174	11.40	.718826	11
50	9.274049	10.98	9.992190	.40	9.281858	11.40	0.718142	10
51	.274708	10.98	.992166	.40	.282542	11.38	.717458	9
52	.275367	10.97	.992142	.40	.283225	11.37	.716775	8
53	.276025	10.93	.992118	.42	.283907	11.35	.716093	7
54	.276681	10.93	.992093	.40	.284588	11.33	.715412	6
55	9.277337	10.90	9.992069	.42	9.285268	11.32	0.714732	5
56	.277991	10.90	.992044	.40	.285947	11.28	.714053	4
57	.278645	10.87	.992020	.40	.286624	11.28	.713376	3
58	.279297	10.85	.991996	.42	.287301	11.27	.712699	2
59	.279948	10.85	.991971	.40	.287977	11.25	.712023	1
60	9.280599		9.991947		9.288652		0.711348	0
	Cos.	D. 1".	Sin.	D. 1".	Cot.	D. 1".	Tan.	M.

100° 79°

LOGARITHMIC SINES, COSINES, TANGENTS, AND COTANGENTS

M.	Sin.	D. 1".	Cos.	D. 1".	Tan.	D. 1".	Cot.	
0	9.280599	10.82	9.991947	.42	9.288652	11.23	0.711348	60
1	.281248	10.82	.991922	.42	.289326	11.22	.710674	59
2	.281897	10.78	.991897	.40	.289999	11.20	.710001	58
3	.282544	10.77	.991873	.42	.290671	11.18	.709329	57
4	.283190	10.77	.991848	.42	.291342	11.18	.708658	56
5	9.283836	10.73	9.991823	.40	9.292013	11.15	0.707987	55
6	.284480	10.73	.991799	.42	.292682	11.13	.707318	54
7	.285124	10.70	.991774	.42	.293350	11.13	.706650	53
8	.285766	10.70	.991749	.42	.294017	11.12	.705983	52
9	.286408	10.67	.991724	.42	.294684	11.12	.705316	51
10	9.287048	10.67	9.991699	.42	9.295349	11.08	0.704651	50
11	.287688	10.63	.991674	.42	.296013	11.07	.703987	49
12	.288326	10.63	.991649	.42	.296677	11.07	.703323	48
13	.288964	10.60	.991624	.42	.297339	11.03	.702661	47
14	.289600	10.60	.991599	.42	.298001	11.03	.701999	46
15	9.290236	10.57	9.991574	.42	9.298662	11.02	0.701338	45
16	.290870	10.57	.991549	.42	.299322	11.00	.700678	44
17	.291504	10.55	.991524	.42	.299980	10.97	.700020	43
18	.292137	10.52	.991498	.43	.300638	10.97	.699362	42
19	.292768	10.52	.991473	.42	.301295	10.95	.698705	41
20	9.293399	10.50	9.991448	.42	9.301951	10.93	0.698049	40
21	.294029	10.48	.991422	.43	.302607	10.93	.697393	39
22	.294658	10.47	.991397	.42	.303261	10.90	.696739	38
23	.295286	10.45	.991372	.42	.303914	10.88	.696086	37
24	.295913	10.43	.991346	.43	.304567	10.88	.695433	36
25	9.296539	10.42	9.991321	.42	9.305218	10.85	0.694782	35
26	.297164	10.40	.991295	.43	.305869	10.85	.694131	34
27	.297788	10.40	.991270	.42	.306519	10.83	.693481	33
28	.298412	10.37	.991244	.43	.307168	10.82	.692832	32
29	.299034	10.35	.991218	.43	.307816	10.80	.692184	31
30	9.299655	10.35	9.991193	.42	9.308463	10.78	0.691537	30
31	.300276	10.32	.991167	.43	.309109	10.77	.690891	29
32	.300895	10.32	.991141	.43	.309754	10.75	.690246	28
33	.301514	10.30	.991115	.43	.310399	10.75	.689601	27
34	.302132	10.27	.991090	.42	.311042	10.72	.688958	26
35	9.302748	10.27	9.991064	.43	9.311685	10.72	0.688315	25
36	.303364	10.25	.991038	.43	.312327	10.70	.687673	24
37	.303979	10.23	.991012	.43	.312968	10.68	.687032	23
38	.304593	10.23	.990986	.43	.313608	10.67	.686392	22
39	.305207	10.20	.990960	.43	.314247	10.65	.685753	21
40	9.305819	10.18	9.990934	.43	9.314885	10.63	0.685115	20
41	.306430	10.18	.990908	.43	.315523	10.63	.684477	19
42	.307041	10.15	.990882	.43	.316159	10.60	.683841	18
43	.307650	10.15	.990855	.45	.316795	10.60	.683205	17
44	.308259	10.13	.990829	.43	.317430	10.58	.682570	16
45	9.308867	10.12	9.990803	.43	9.318064	10.57	0.681936	15
46	.309474	10.10	.990777	.43	.318697	10.55	.681303	14
47	.310080	10.08	.990750	.45	.319330	10.55	.680670	13
48	.310685	10.07	.990724	.43	.319961	10.52	.680039	12
49	.311289	10.07	.990697	.45	.320592	10.52	.679408	11
50	9.311893	10.03	9.990671	.43	9.321222	10.50	0.678778	10
51	.312495	10.03	.990645	.43	.321851	10.48	.678149	9
52	.313097	10.02	.990618	.45	.322479	10.47	.677521	8
53	.313698	9.98	.990591	.45	.323106	10.45	.676894	7
54	.314297	10.00	.990565	.43	.323733	10.45	.676267	6
55	9.314897	9.97	9.990538	.45	9.324358	10.42	0.675642	5
56	.315495	9.95	.990511	.45	.324983	10.42	.675017	4
57	.316092	9.95	.990485	.43	.325607	10.40	.674393	3
58	.316689	9.92	.990458	.45	.326231	10.40	.673769	2
59	.317284	9.92	.990431	.45	.326853	10.37	.673147	1
60	9.317879		9.990404	.45	9.327475	10.37	0.672525	0
	Cos.	D. 1".	Sin.	D. 1".	Cot.	D. 1".	Tan.	M.

TABLE C
687

LOGARITHMIC SINES, COSINES, TANGENTS, AND COTANGENTS

12°   **167°**

M.	Sin.	D. 1″.	Cos.	D. 1″.	Tan.	D. 1″.	Cot.	
0	9.317879	9.90	9.990404	.43	9.327475	10.33	0.672525	60
1	.318473	9.88	.990378	.45	.328095	10.33	.671905	59
2	.319066	9.87	.990351	.45	.328715	10.32	.671285	58
3	.319658	9.85	.990324	.45	.329334	10.32	.670666	57
4	.320249	9.85	.990297	.45	.329953	10.28	.670047	56
5	9.320840	9.83	9.990270	.45	9.330570	10.28	0.669430	55
6	.321430	9.82	.990243	.47	.331187	10.27	.668813	54
7	.322019	9.80	.990215	.45	.331803	10.25	.668197	53
8	.322607	9.78	.990188	.45	.332418	10.25	.667582	52
9	.323194	9.77	.990161	.45	.333033	10.22	.666967	51
10	9.323780	9.77	9.990134	.45	9.333646	10.22	0.666354	50
11	.324366	9.73	.990107	.47	.334259	10.20	.665741	49
12	.324950	9.73	.990079	.45	.334871	10.18	.665129	48
13	.325534	9.72	.990052	.45	.335482	10.18	.664518	47
14	.326117	9.72	.990025	.47	.336093	10.15	.663907	46
15	9.326700	9.68	9.989997	.45	9.336702	10.15	0.663298	45
16	.327281	9.68	.989970	.47	.337311	10.13	.662689	44
17	.327862	9.67	.989942	.45	.337919	10.13	.662081	43
18	.328442	9.65	.989915	.47	.338527	10.10	.661473	42
19	.329021	9.63	.989887	.45	.339133	10.10	.660867	41
20	9.329599	9.62	9.989860	.47	9.339739	10.08	0.660261	40
21	.330176	9.62	.989832	.47	.340344	10.07	.659656	39
22	.330753	9.60	.989804	.45	.340948	10.07	.659052	38
23	.331329	9.57	.989777	.47	.341552	10.05	.658448	37
24	.331903	9.58	.989749	.47	.342155	10.03	.657845	36
25	9.332478	9.55	9.989721	.47	9.342757	10.02	0.657243	35
26	.333051	9.55	.989693	.47	.343358	10.00	.656642	34
27	.333624	9.52	.989665	.47	.343958	10.00	.656042	33
28	.334195	9.53	.989637	.45	.344558	9.98	.655442	32
29	.334767	9.50	.989610	.47	.345157	9.97	.654843	31
30	9.335337	9.48	9.989582	.48	9.345755	9.97	0.654245	30
31	.335906	9.48	.989553	.47	.346353	9.93	.653047	29
32	.336475	9.47	.989525	.47	.346949	9.93	.653051	28
33	.337043	9.45	.989497	.47	.347545	9.93	.652455	27
34	.337610	9.43	.989469	.47	.348141	9.90	.651859	26
35	9.338176	9.43	9.989441	.47	9.348735	9.90	0.651265	25
36	.338742	9.42	.989413	.47	.349329	9.88	.650671	24
37	.339307	9.40	.989385	.47	.349922	9.87	.650078	23
38	.339871	9.38	.989356	.48	.350514	9.87	.649486	22
39	.340434	9.37	.989328	.47	.351106	9.85	.648894	21
40	9.340996	9.37	9.989300	.48	9.351697	9.83	0.648303	20
41	.341558	9.35	.989271	.47	.352287	9.82	.647713	19
42	.342119	9.33	.989243	.48	.352876	9.82	.647124	18
43	.342679	9.33	.989214	.47	.353465	9.80	.646535	17
44	.343239	9.30	.989186	.48	.354053	9.78	.645947	16
45	9.343797	9.30	9.989157	.48	9.354640	9.78	0.645360	15
46	.344355	9.28	.989128	.47	.355227	9.77	.644773	14
47	.344912	9.28	.989100	.48	.355813	9.75	.644187	13
48	.345469	9.25	.989071	.48	.356398	9.73	.643602	12
49	.346024	9.25	.989042	.47	.356982	9.73	.643018	11
50	9.346579	9.25	9.989014	.48	9.357566	9.72	0.642434	10
51	.347134	9.22	.988985	.48	.358149	9.70	.641851	9
52	.347687	9.22	.988956	.48	.358731	9.70	.641269	8
53	.348240	9.20	.988927	.48	.359313	9.67	.640687	7
54	.348792	9.18	.988898	.48	.359893	9.68	.640107	6
55	9.349343	9.17	9.988869	.48	9.360474	9.65	0.639526	5
56	.349893	9.17	.988840	.48	.361053	9.65	.638947	4
57	.350443	9.15	.988811	.48	.361632	9.63	.638368	3
58	.350992	9.13	.988782	.48	.362210	9.62	.637790	2
59	.351540	9.13	.988753	.48	.362787	9.62	.637213	1
60	9.352088		9.988724		9.363364		0.636636	0
	Cos.	D. 1″.	Sin.	D. 1″.	Cot.	D. 1″.	Tan.	M.

TABLE C

LOGARITHMIC SINES, COSINES, TANGENTS, AND COTANGENTS

13°   **166°**

M.	Sin.	D. 1″.	Cos.	D. 1″.	Tan.	D. 1″.	Cot.	
0	9.352088		9.988724		9.363364		0.636636	60
1	.352635	9.12	.988695	.48	.363940	9.60	.636060	59
2	.353181	9.10	.988666	.48	.364515	9.58	.635485	58
3	.353726	9.08	.988636	.50	.365090	9.58	.634910	57
4	.354271	9.08	.988607	.48	.365664	9.57	.634336	56
5	9.354815	9.07	9.988578	.48	9.366237	9.55	0.633763	55
6	.355358	9.05	.988548	.50	.366810	9.55	.633190	54
7	.355901	9.05	.988519	.48	.367382	9.53	.632618	53
8	.356443	9.03	.988489	.50	.367953	9.52	.632047	52
9	.356984	9.02	.988460	.48	.368524	9.52	.631476	51
10	9.357524	9.00	9.988430	.50	9.369094	9.50	0.630906	50
11	.358064	9.00	.988401	.48	.369663	9.48	.630337	49
12	.358603	8.98	.988371	.50	.370232	9.48	.629768	48
13	.359141	8.97	.988342	.48	.370799	9.45	.629201	47
14	.359678	8.95	.988312	.50	.371367	9.47	.628633	46
15	9.360215	8.95	9.988282	.50	9.371933	9.43	0.628067	45
16	.360752	8.95	.988252	.50	.372499	9.43	.627501	44
17	.361287	8.92	.988223	.48	.373064	9.42	.626936	43
18	.361822	8.92	.988193	.50	.373629	9.42	.626371	42
19	.362356	8.90	.988163	.50	.374193	9.40	.625807	41
20	9.362889	8.88	9.988133	.50	9.374756	9.38	0.625244	40
21	.363422	8.88	.988103	.50	.375319	9.38	.624681	39
22	.363954	8.87	.988073	.50	.375881	9.37	.624119	38
23	.364485	8.85	.988043	.50	.376442	9.35	.623558	37
24	.365016	8.85	.988013	.50	.377003	9.35	.622997	36
25	9.365546	8.83	9.987983	.50	9.377563	9.33	0.622437	35
26	.366075	8.82	.987953	.50	.378122	9.32	.621878	34
27	.366604	8.82	.987922	.52	.378681	9.32	.621319	33
28	.367131	8.78	.987892	.50	.379239	9.30	.620761	32
29	.367659	8.80	.987862	.50	.379797	9.30	.620203	31
30	9.368185	8.77	9.987832	.52	9.380354	9.28	0.619646	30
31	.368711	8.77	.987801	.50	.380910	9.27	.619090	29
32	.369236	8.75	.987771	.52	.381466	9.27	.618534	28
33	.369761	8.75	.987740	.50	.382020	9.23	.617980	27
34	.370285	8.73	.987710	.52	.382575	9.25	.617425	26
35	9.370808	8.72	9.987679	.50	9.383129	9.23	0.616871	25
36	.371330	8.70	.987649	.52	.383682	9.22	.616318	24
37	.371852	8.70	.987618	.50	.384234	9.20	.615766	23
38	.372373	8.68	.987588	.52	.384786	9.20	.615214	22
39	.372894	8.68	.987557	.52	.385337	9.18	.614663	21
40	9.373414	8.67	9.987526	.50	9.385888	9.18	0.614112	20
41	.373933	8.65	.987496	.52	.386438	9.17	.613562	19
42	.374452	8.65	.987465	.52	.386987	9.15	.613013	18
43	.374970	8.63	.987434	.52	.387536	9.15	.612464	17
44	.375487	8.62	.987403	.52	.388084	9.13	.611916	16
45	9.376003	8.60	9.987372	.52	9.388631	9.12	0.611369	15
46	.376519	8.60	.987341	.52	.389178	9.12	.610822	14
47	.377035	8.60	.987310	.52	.389724	9.10	.610276	13
48	.377549	8.57	.987279	.52	.390270	9.10	.609730	12
49	.378063	8.57	.987248	.52	.390815	9.08	.609185	11
50	9.378577	8.57	9.987217	.52	9.391360	9.08	0.608640	10
51	.379089	8.53	.987186	.52	.391903	9.05	.608097	9
52	.379601	8.53	.987155	.52	.392447	9.07	.607553	8
53	.380113	8.53	.987124	.53	.392989	9.03	.607011	7
54	.380624	8.52	.987092	.52	.393531	9.03	.606469	6
55	9.381134	8.50	9.987061	.52	9.394073	9.03	0.605927	5
56	.381643	8.48	.987030	.53	.394614	9.02	.605386	4
57	.382152	8.48	.986998	.52	.395154	9.00	.604846	3
58	.382661	8.48	.986967	.52	.395694	9.00	.604306	2
59	.383168	8.45	.986936	.53	.396233	8.98	.603767	1
60	9.383675	8.45	9.986904		9.396771	8.97	0.603229	0
	Cos.	D. 1″.	Sin.	D. 1″.	Cot.	D. 1″.	Tan.	M.

103°   **76°**

TABLE C   689

LOGARITHMIC SINES, COSINES, TANGENTS, AND COTANGENTS

14°   **165°**

M.	Sin.	D. 1″.	Cos.	D. 1″.	Tan.	D. 1″.	Cot.	
0	9.383675	8.45	9.986904	.52	9.396771	8.97	0.603229	60
1	.384182	8.42	.986873	.53	.397309	8.95	.602691	59
2	.384687	8.42	.986841	.53	.397846	8.95	.602154	58
3	.385192	8.42	.986809	.52	.398383	8.93	.601617	57
4	.385697	8.40	.986778	.53	.398919	8.93	.601081	56
5	9.386201	8.38	9.986746	.53	9.399455	8.92	0.600545	55
6	.386704	8.38	.986714	.52	.399990	8.90	.600010	54
7	.387207	8.37	.986683	.53	.400524	8.90	.599476	53
8	.387709	8.35	.986651	.53	.401058	8.88	.598942	52
9	.388210	8.35	.986619	.53	.401591	8.88	.598409	51
10	9.388711	8.33	9.986587	.53	9.402124	8.87	0.597876	50
11	.389211	8.33	.986555	.53	.402656	8.85	.597344	49
12	.389711	8.32	.986523	.53	.403187	8.85	.596813	48
13	.390210	8.30	.986491	.53	.403718	8.85	.596282	47
14	.390708	8.30	.986459	.53	.404249	8.82	.595751	46
15	9.391206	8.28	9.986427	.53	9.404778	8.83	0.595222	45
16	.391703	8.27	.986395	.53	.405308	8.80	.594692	44
17	.392199	8.27	.986363	.53	.405836	8.80	.594164	43
18	.392695	8.27	.986331	.53	.406364	8.80	.593636	42
19	.393191	8.23	.986299	.55	.406892	8.78	.593108	41
20	9.393685	8.23	9.986266	.53	9.407419	8.77	0.592581	40
21	.394179	8.23	.986234	.53	.407945	8.77	.592055	39
22	.394673	8.22	.986202	.55	.408471	8.75	.591529	38
23	.395166	8.20	.986169	.53	.408996	8.75	.591004	37
24	.395658	8.20	.986137	.55	.409521	8.73	.590479	36
25	9.396150	8.18	9.986104	.53	9.410045	8.73	0.589955	35
26	.396641	8.18	.986072	.55	.410569	8.72	.589431	34
27	.397132	8.15	.986039	.53	.411092	8.72	.588908	33
28	.397621	8.17	.986007	.55	.411615	8.70	.588385	32
29	.398111	8.15	.985974	.53	.412137	8.68	.587863	31
30	9.398600	8.13	9.985942	.55	9.412658	8.68	0.587342	30
31	.399088	8.12	.985909	.55	.413179	8.67	.586821	29
32	.399575	8.12	.985876	.55	.413699	8.67	.586301	28
33	.400062	8.12	.985843	.53	.414219	8.65	.585781	27
34	.400549	8.10	.985811	.55	.414738	8.65	.585262	26
35	9.401035	8.08	9.985778	.55	9.415257	8.63	0.584743	25
36	.401520	8.08	.985745	.55	.415775	8.63	.584225	24
37	.402005	8.07	.985712	.55	.416293	8.62	.583707	23
38	.402489	8.05	.985679	.55	.416810	8.60	.583190	22
39	.402972	8.05	.985646	.55	.417326	8.60	.582674	21
40	9.403455	8.05	9.985613	.55	9.417842	8.60	0.582158	20
41	.403938	8.03	.985580	.55	.418358	8.58	.581642	19
42	.404420	8.02	.985547	.55	.418873	8.57	.581127	18
43	.404901	8.02	.985514	.57	.419387	8.57	.580613	17
44	.405382	8.00	.985480	.55	.419901	8.57	.580099	16
45	9.405862	7.98	9.985447	.55	9.420415	8.53	0.579585	15
46	.406341	7.98	.985414	.55	.420927	8.55	.579073	14
47	.406820	7.98	.985381	.57	.421440	8.53	.578560	13
48	.407299	7.97	.985347	.55	.421952	8.52	.578048	12
49	.407777	7.95	.985314	.57	.422463	8.52	.577537	11
50	9.408254	7.95	9.985280	.55	9.422974	8.50	0.577026	10
51	.408731	7.93	.985247	.57	.423484	8.48	.576516	9
52	.409207	7.92	.985213	.55	.423993	8.50	.576007	8
53	.409682	7.92	.985180	.57	.424503	8.47	.575497	7
54	.410157	7.92	.985146	.55	.425011	8.47	.574989	6
55	9.410632	7.90	9.985113	.57	9.425519	8.47	0.574481	5
56	.411106	7.88	.985079	.57	.426027	8.45	.573973	4
57	.411579	7.88	.985045	.57	.426534	8.45	.573466	3
58	.412052	7.87	.985011	.55	.427041	8.43	.572959	2
59	.412524	7.87	.984978	.57	.427547	8.42	.572453	1
60	9.412996		9.984944		9.428052		0.571948	0
	Cos.	D. 1″.	Sin.	D. 1.″	Cot.	D. 1″.	Tan.	M.

104°   **75°**

TABLE C

LOGARITHMIC SINES, COSINES, TANGENTS, AND COTANGENTS

15°   **164°**

M.	Sin.	D. 1″.	Cos.	D. 1″.	Tan.	D. 1″.	Cot.	
0	9.412996	7.85	9.984944	.57	9.428052	8.43	0.571948	60
1	.413467	7.85	.984910	.57	.428558	8.40	.571442	59
2	.413938	7.83	.984876	.57	.429062	8.40	.570938	58
3	.414408	7.83	.984842	.57	.429566	8.40	.570434	57
4	.414878	7.82	.984808	.57	.430070	8.38	.569930	56
5	9.415347	7.80	9.984774	.57	9.430573	8.37	0.569427	55
6	.415815	7.80	.984740	.57	.431075	8.37	.568925	54
7	.416283	7.80	.984706	.57	.431577	8.37	.568423	53
8	.416751	7.77	.984672	.57	.432079	8.35	.567921	52
9	.417217	7.78	.984638	.58	.432580	8.33	.567420	51
10	9.417684	7.77	9.984603	.57	9.433080	8.33	0.566920	50
11	.418150	7.75	.984569	.57	.433580	8.33	.566420	49
12	.418615	7.73	.984535	.58	.434080	8.32	.565920	48
13	.419079	7.75	.984500	.57	.434579	8.32	.565421	47
14	.419544	7.72	.984466	.57	.435078	8.30	.564922	46
15	9.420007	7.72	9.984432	.58	9.435576	8.28	0.564424	45
16	.420470	7.72	.984397	.57	.436073	8.28	.563927	44
17	.420933	7.70	.984363	.58	.436570	8.28	.563430	43
18	.421395	7.70	.984328	.57	.437067	8.27	.562933	42
19	.421857	7.68	.984294	.58	.437563	8.27	.562437	41
20	9.422318	7.67	9.984259	.58	9.438059	8.25	0.561941	40
21	.422778	7.67	.984224	.57	.438554	8.23	.561446	39
22	.423238	7.65	.984190	.58	.439048	8.25	.560952	38
23	.423697	7.65	.984155	.58	.439543	8.22	.560457	37
24	.424156	7.65	.984120	.58	.440036	8.22	.559964	36
25	9.424615	7.63	9.984085	.58	9.440529	8.22	0.559471	35
26	.425073	7.62	.984050	.58	.441022	8.20	.558978	34
27	.425530	7.62	.984015	.57	.441514	8.20	.558486	33
28	.425987	7.60	.983981	.58	.442006	8.18	.557994	32
29	.426443	7.60	.983946	.58	.442497	8.18	.557503	31
30	9.426899	7.58	9.983911	.60	9.442988	8.18	0.557012	30
31	.427354	7.58	.983875	.58	.443479	8.15	.556521	29
32	.427809	7.57	.983840	.58	.443968	8.17	.556032	28
33	.428263	7.57	.983805	.58	.444458	8.15	.555542	27
34	.428717	7.55	.983770	.58	.444947	8.13	.555053	26
35	9.429170	7.55	9.983735	.58	9.445435	8.13	0.554565	25
36	.429623	7.53	.983700	.60	.445923	8.13	.554077	24
37	.430075	7.53	.983664	.58	.446411	8.12	.553589	23
38	.430527	7.52	.983629	.58	.446898	8.10	.553102	22
39	.430978	7.52	.983594	.60	.447384	8.10	.552616	21
40	9.431429	7.50	9.983558	.58	9.447870	8.10	0.552130	20
41	.431879	7.50	.983523	.60	.448356	8.08	.551644	19
42	.432329	7.48	.983487	.58	.448841	8.08	.551159	18
43	.432778	7.47	.983452	.60	.449326	8.07	.550674	17
44	.433226	7.48	.983416	.58	.449810	8.07	.550190	16
45	9.433675	7.45	9.983381	.60	9.450294	8.05	0.549706	15
46	.434122	7.45	.983345	.60	.450777	8.05	.549223	14
47	.434569	7.45	.983309	.60	.451260	8.05	.548740	13
48	.435016	7.43	.983273	.60	.451743	8.03	.548257	12
49	.435462	7.43	.983238	.58	.452225	8.02	.547775	11
50	9.435908	7.42	9.983202	.60	9.452706	8.02	0.547294	10
51	.436353	7.42	.983166	.60	.453187	8.02	.546813	9
52	.436798	7.40	.983130	.60	.453668	8.00	.546332	8
53	.437242	7.40	.983094	.60	.454148	8.00	.545852	7
54	.437686	7.38	.983058	.60	.454628	7.98	.545372	6
55	9.438129	7.38	9.983022	.60	9.455107	7.98	0.544893	5
56	.438572	7.37	.982986	.60	.455586	7.97	.544414	4
57	.439014	7.37	.982950	.60	.456064	7.97	.543936	3
58	.439456	7.35	.982914	.60	.456542	7.95	.543458	2
59	.439897	7.35	.982878	.60	.457019	7.95	.542981	1
60	9.440338		9.982842		9.457496		0.542504	0
	Cos.	D. 1″.	Sin.	D. 1″.	Cot.	D. 1″.	Tan.	M.

105°   **74°**

TABLE C

691

LOGARITHMIC SINES, COSINES, TANGENTS, AND COTANGENTS

16°   163°

M.	Sin.	D. 1″.	Cos.	D. 1″.	Tan.	D. 1″.	Cot.	
0	9.440338	7.33	9.982842	.62	9.457496	7.95	0.542504	60
1	.440778	7.33	.982805	.60	.457973	7.93	.542027	59
2	.441218	7.33	.982769	.60	.458449	7.93	.541551	58
3	.441658	7.30	.982733	.62	.458925	7.92	.541075	57
4	.442096	7.32	.982696	.60	.459400	7.92	.540600	56
5	9.442535	7.30	9.982660	.60	9.459875	7.90	0.540125	55
6	.442973	7.28	.982624	.62	.460349	7.90	.539651	54
7	.443410	7.28	.982587	.60	.460823	7.90	.539177	53
8	.443847	7.28	.982551	.62	.461297	7.88	.538703	52
9	.444284	7.27	.982514	.62	.461770	7.87	.538230	51
10	9.444720	7.25	9.982477	.60	9.462242	7.88	0.537758	50
11	.445155	7.25	.982441	.62	.462715	7.85	.537285	49
12	.445590	7.25	.982404	.62	.463186	7.87	.536814	48
13	.446025	7.23	.982367	.60	.463658	7.83	.536342	47
14	.446459	7.23	.982331	.62	.464128	7.85	.535872	46
15	9.446893	7.22	9.982294	.62	9.464599	7.83	0.535401	45
16	.447326	7.22	.982257	.62	.465069	7.83	.534931	44
17	.447759	7.20	.982220	.62	.465539	7.82	.534461	43
18	.448191	7.20	.982183	.62	.466008	7.82	.533992	42
19	.448623	7.18	.982146	.62	.466477	7.80	.533523	41
20	9.449054	7.18	9.982109	.62	9.466945	7.80	0.533055	40
21	.449485	7.17	.982072	.62	.467413	7.78	.532587	39
22	.449915	7.17	.982035	.62	.467880	7.78	.532120	38
23	.450345	7.17	.981998	.62	.468347	7.78	.531653	37
24	.450775	7.15	.981961	.62	.468814	7.77	.531186	36
25	9.451204	7.13	9.981924	.63	9.469280	7.77	0.530720	35
26	.451632	7.13	.981886	.62	.469746	7.75	.530254	34
27	.452060	7.13	.981849	.62	.470211	7.75	.529789	33
28	.452488	7.12	.981812	.63	.470676	7.75	.529324	32
29	.452915	7.12	.981774	.62	.471141	7.73	.528859	31
30	9.453342	7.10	9.981737	.62	9.471605	7.73	0.528395	30
31	.453768	7.10	.981700	.63	.472069	7.72	.527931	29
32	.454194	7.08	.981662	.62	.472532	7.72	.527468	28
33	.454619	7.08	.981625	.63	.472995	7.70	.527005	27
34	.455044	7.08	.981587	.63	.473457	7.70	.526543	26
35	9.455469	7.07	9.981549	.62	9.473919	7.70	0.526081	25
36	.455893	7.05	.981512	.63	.474381	7.68	.525619	24
37	.456316	7.05	.981474	.63	.474842	7.68	.525158	23
38	.456739	7.05	.981436	.63	.475303	7.67	.524697	22
39	.457162	7.03	.981399	.62	.475763	7.67	.524237	21
40	9.457584	7.03	9.981361	.63	9.476223	7.67	0.523777	20
41	.458006	7.02	.981323	.63	.476683	7.65	.523317	19
42	.458427	7.02	.981285	.63	.477142	7.65	.522858	18
43	.458848	7.00	.981247	.63	.477601	7.63	.522399	17
44	.459268	7.00	.981209	.63	.478059	7.63	.521941	16
45	9.459688	7.00	9.981171	.63	9.478517	7.63	0.521483	15
46	.460108	6.98	.981133	.63	.478975	7.62	.521025	14
47	.460527	6.98	.981095	.63	.479432	7.62	.520568	13
48	.460946	6.97	.981057	.63	.479889	7.60	.520111	12
49	.461364	6.97	.981019	.63	.480345	7.60	.519655	11
50	9.461782	6.95	9.980981	.65	9.480801	7.60	0.519199	10
51	.462199	6.95	.980942	.63	.481257	7.58	.518743	9
52	.462616	6.93	.980904	.63	.481712	7.58	.518288	8
53	.463032	6.93	.980866	.65	.482167	7.57	.517833	7
54	.463448	6.93	.980827	.63	.482621	7.57	.517379	6
55	9.463864	6.92	9.980789	.65	9.483075	7.57	0.516925	5
56	.464279	6.92	.980750	.63	.483529	7.55	.516471	4
57	.464694	6.90	.980712	.65	.483982	7.55	.516018	3
58	.465108	6.90	.980673	.63	.484435	7.53	.515565	2
59	.465522	6.88	.980635	.65	.484887	7.53	.515113	1
60	9.465935		9.980596		9.485339		0.514661	0
	Cos.	D. 1″.	Sin.	D. 1″.	Cot.	D. 1″.	Tan.	M.

TABLE C

LOGARITHMIC SINES, COSINES, TANGENTS, AND COTANGENTS

M.	Sin.	D. 1″.	Cos.	D. 1″.	Tan.	D. 1″.	Cot.	
0	9.465935	6.88	9.980596	.63	9.485339	7.53	0.514661	60
1	.466348	6.88	.980558	.65	.485791	7.52	.514209	59
2	.466761	6.87	.980519	.65	.486242	7.52	.513758	58
3	.467173	6.87	.980480	.63	.486693	7.50	.513307	57
4	.467585	6.85	.980442	.65	.487143	7.50	.512857	56
5	9.467996	6.85	9.980403	.65	9.487593	7.50	0.512407	55
6	.468407	6.83	.980364	.65	.488043	7.48	.511957	54
7	.468817	6.83	.980325	.65	.488492	7.48	.511508	53
8	.469227	6.83	.980286	.65	.488941	7.48	.511059	52
9	.469637	6.82	.980247	.65	.489390	7.47	.510610	51
10	9.470046	6.82	9.980208	.65	9.489838	7.47	0.510162	50
11	.470455	6.80	.980169	.65	.490286	7.45	.509714	49
12	.470863	6.80	.980130	.65	.490733	7.45	.509267	48
13	.471271	6.80	.980091	.65	.491180	7.45	.508820	47
14	.471679	6.78	.980052	.67	.491627	7.43	.508373	46
15	9.472086	6.77	9.980012	.65	9.492073	7.43	0.507927	45
16	.472492	6.77	.979973	.65	.492519	7.43	.507481	44
17	.472898	6.77	.979934	.65	.492965	7.42	.507035	43
18	.473304	6.77	.979895	.67	.493410	7.40	.506590	42
19	.473710	6.75	.979855	.65	.493854	7.42	.506146	41
20	9.474115	6.73	9.979816	.67	9.494299	7.40	0.505701	40
21	.474519	6.73	.979776	.65	.494743	7.38	.505257	39
22	.474923	6.73	.979737	.67	.495186	7.40	.504814	38
23	.475327	6.72	.979697	.65	.495630	7.38	.504370	37
24	.475730	6.72	.979658	.67	.496073	7.37	.503927	36
25	9.476133	6.72	9.979618	.65	9.496515	7.37	0.503485	35
26	.476536	6.70	.979579	.67	.496957	7.37	.503043	34
27	.476938	6.70	.979539	.67	.497399	7.37	.502601	33
28	.477340	6.68	.979499	.67	.497841	7.35	.502159	32
29	.477741	6.68	979459	.65	.498282	7.33	.501718	31
30	9.478142	6.67	9.979420	.67	9.498722	7.35	0.501278	30
31	.478542	6.67	.979380	.67	.499163	7.33	.500837	29
32	.478942	6.67	.979340	.67	.499603	7.32	.500397	28
33	.479342	6.65	.979300	.67	.500042	7.32	.499958	27
34	.479741	6.65	.979260	.67	.500481	7.32	.499519	26
35	9.480140	6.65	9.979220	.67	9.500920	7.32	0.499080	25
36	.480539	6.63	.979180	.67	.501359	7.30	.498641	24
37	.480937	6.62	.979140	.67	.501797	7.30	.498203	23
38	.481334	6.62	.979100	.68	.502235	7.28	.497765	22
39	.481731	6.62	.979059	.67	.502672	7.28	.497328	21
40	9.482128	6.62	9.979019	.67	9.503109	7.28	0.496891	20
41	.482525	6.60	.978979	.67	.503546	7.27	.496454	19
42	.482921	6.58	.978939	.68	.503982	7.27	.496018	18
43	.483316	6.60	.978898	.67	.504418	7.27	.495582	17
44	.483712	6.58	.978858	.68	.504854	7.25	.495146	16
45	9.484107	6.57	9.978817	.67	9.505289	7.25	0.494711	15
46	.484501	6.57	.978777	.67	.505724	7.25	.494276	14
47	.484895	6.57	.978737	.68	.506159	7.23	.493841	13
48	.485289	6.55	.978696	.68	.506593	7.23	.493407	12
49	.485682	6.55	.978655	.67	.507027	7.22	.492973	11
50	9.486075	6.53	9.978615	.68	9.507460	7.22	0.492540	10
51	.486467	6.55	.978574	.68	.507893	7.22	.492107	9
52	.486860	6.52	.978533	.67	.508326	7.22	.491674	8
53	.487251	6.53	.978493	.68	.508759	7.20	.491241	7
54	.487643	6.52	.978452	.68	.509191	7.18	.490809	6
55	9.488034	6.50	9.978411	.68	9.509622	7.20	0.490378	5
56	.488424	6.50	.978370	.68	.510054	7.18	.489946	4
57	.488814	6.50	.978329	.68	.510485	7.18	.489515	3
58	.489204	6.48	.978288	.68	.510916	7.18	.489084	2
59	.489593	6.48	.978247	.68	.511346	7.17	.488654	1
60	9.489982		9.978206		9.511776	7.17	0.488224	0
	Cos.	D. 1″.	Sin.	D. 1″.	Cot.	D. 1″.	Tan.	M.

TABLE C 693

LOGARITHMIC SINES, COSINES, TANGENTS, AND COTANGENTS

18°   **161°**

M.	Sin.	D. 1″.	Cos.	D. 1″.	Tan.	D. 1″.	Cot.	
0	9.489982	6.48	9.978206	.68	9.511776	7.17	0.488224	60
1	.490371	6.47	.978165	.68	.512206	7.15	.487794	59
2	.490759	6.47	.978124	.68	.512635	7.15	.487365	58
3	.491147	6.47	.978083	.68	.513064	7.15	.486936	57
4	.491535	6.45	.978042	.68	.513493	7.13	.486507	56
5	9.491922	6.43	9.978001	.70	9.513921	7.13	0.486079	55
6	.492308	6.45	.977959	.68	.514349	7.13	.485651	54
7	.492695	6.43	.977918	.68	.514777	7.13	.485223	53
8	.493081	6.42	.977877	.68	.515204	7.12	.484796	52
9	.493466	6.42	.977835	.70	.515631	7.10	.484369	51
10	9.493851	6.42	9.977794	.68	9.516057	7.12	0.483943	50
11	.494236	6.42	.977752	.70	.516484	7.10	.483516	49
12	.494621	6.40	.977711	.68	.516910	7.08	.483090	48
13	.495005	6.38	.977669	.70	.517335	7.10	.482665	47
14	.495388	6.40	.977628	.68	.517761	7.08	.482239	46
15	9.495772	6.37	9.977586	.70	9.518186	7.07	0.481814	45
16	.496154	6.38	.977544	.70	.518610	7.07	.481390	44
17	.496537	6.37	.977503	.68	.519034	7.07	.480966	43
18	.496919	6.37	.977461	.70	.519458	7.07	.480542	42
19	.497301	6.35	.977419	.70	.519882	7.05	.480118	41
20	9.497682	6.37	9.977377	.70	9.520305	7.05	0.479695	40
21	.498064	6.33	.977335	.70	.520728	7.05	.479272	39
22	.498444	6.35	.977293	.70	.521151	7.03	.478849	38
23	.498825	6.32	.977251	.70	.521573	7.03	.478427	37
24	.499204	6.33	.977209	.70	.521995	7.03	.478005	36
25	9.499584	6.32	9.977167	.70	9.522417	7.02	0.477583	35
26	.499963	6.32	.977125	.70	.522838	7.02	.477162	34
27	.500342	6.32	.977083	.70	.523259	7.02	.476741	33
28	.500721	6.30	.977041	.70	.523680	7.00	.476320	32
29	.501099	6.28	.976999	.70	.524100	7.00	.475900	31
30	9.501476	6.30	9.976957	.72	9.524520	7.00	0.475480	30
31	.501854	6.28	.976914	.70	.524940	6.98	.475060	29
32	.502231	6.27	.976872	.70	.525359	6.98	.474641	28
33	.502607	6.28	.976830	.72	.525778	6.98	.474222	27
34	.502984	6.27	.976787	.70	.526197	6.97	.473803	26
35	9.503360	6.25	9.976745	.72	9.526615	6.97	0.473385	25
36	.503735	6.25	.976702	.70	.527033	6.97	.472907	24
37	.504110	6.25	.976660	.72	.527451	6.95	.472549	23
38	.504485	6.25	.976617	.72	.527868	6.95	.472132	22
39	.504860	6.23	.976574	.70	.528285	6.95	.471715	21
40	9.505234	6.23	9.976532	.72	9.528702	6.95	0.471298	20
41	.505608	6.22	.976489	.72	.529119	6.93	.470881	19
42	.505981	6.22	.976446	.70	.529535	6.93	.470465	18
43	.506354	6.22	.976404	.72	.529951	6.92	.470049	17
44	.506727	6.20	.976361	.72	.530366	6.92	.469634	16
45	9.507099	6.20	9.976318	.72	9.530781	6.92	0.469219	15
46	.507471	6.20	.976275	.72	.531196	6.92	.468804	14
47	.507843	6.18	.976232	.72	.531611	6.90	.468389	13
48	.508214	6.18	.976189	.72	.532025	6.90	.467975	12
49	.508585	6.18	.976146	.72	.532439	6.90	.467561	11
50	9.508956	6.17	9.976103	.72	9.532853	6.88	0.467147	10
51	.509326	6.17	.976060	.72	.533266	6.88	.466734	9
52	.509696	6.15	.976017	.72	.533679	6.88	.466321	8
53	.510065	6.15	.975974	.72	.534092	6.87	.465908	7
54	.510434	6.15	.975930	.73	.534504	6.87	.465496	6
55	9.510803	6.15	9.975887	.72	9.534916	6.87	0.465084	5
56	.511172	6.13	.975844	.72	.535328	6.87	.464672	4
57	.511540	6.12	.975800	.73	.535739	6.85	.464261	3
58	.511907	6.13	.975757	.72	.536150	6.85	.463850	2
59	.512275	6.12	.975714	.72	.536561	6.85	.463439	1
60	9.512642		9.975670	.73	9.536972	6.85	0.463028	0
	Cos.	D. 1″.	Sin.	D. 1″.	Cot.	D. 1″.	Tan.	M.

TABLE C

LOGARITHMIC SINES, COSINES, TANGENTS, AND COTANGENTS

19°   **160°**

M.	Sin.	D. 1″.	Cos.	D. 1″.	Tan.	D. 1″.	Cot.	
0	9.512642	6.12	9.975670	.72	9.536972	6.83	0.463028	60
1	.513009	6.10	.975627	.73	.537382	6.83	.462618	59
2	.513375	6.10	.975583	.73	.537792	6.83	.462208	58
3	.513741	6.10	.975539	.72	.538202	6.82	.461798	57
4	.514107	6.08	.975496	.73	.538611	6.82	.461389	56
5	9.514472	6.08	9.975452	.73	9.539020	6.82	0.460980	55
6	.514837	6.08	.975408	.72	.539429	6.80	.460571	54
7	.515202	6.07	.975365	.73	.539837	6.80	.460163	53
8	.515566	6.07	.975321	.73	.540245	6.80	.459755	52
9	.515930	6.07	.975277	.73	.540653	6.80	.459347	51
10	9.516294	6.05	9.975233	.73	9.541061	6.78	0.458939	50
11	.516657	6.05	.975189	.73	.541468	6.78	.458532	49
12	.517020	6.03	.975145	.73	.541875	6.77	.458125	48
13	.517382	6.05	.975101	.73	.542281	6.78	.457719	47
14	.517745	6.03	.975057	.73	.542688	6.77	.457312	46
15	9.518107	6.02	9.975013	.73	9.543094	6.75	0.456906	45
16	.518468	6.02	.974969	.73	.543499	6.77	.456501	44
17	.518829	6.02	.974925	.75	.543905	6.75	.456095	43
18	.519190	6.02	.974880	.73	.544310	6.75	.455690	42
19	.519551	6.00	.974836	.73	.544715	6.73	.455285	41
20	9.519911	6.00	9.974792	.73	9.545119	6.75	0.454881	40
21	.520271	6.00	.974748	.75	.545524	6.73	.454476	39
22	.520631	5.98	.974703	.73	.545928	6.72	.454072	38
23	.520990	5.98	.974659	.75	.546331	6.73	.453669	37
24	.521349	5.97	.974614	.73	.546735	6.72	.453265	36
25	9.521707	5.98	9.974570	.75	9.547138	6.70	0.452862	35
26	.522066	5.97	.974525	.73	.547540	6.72	.452460	34
27	.522424	5.95	.974481	.75	.547943	6.70	.452057	33
28	.522781	5.95	.974436	.75	.548345	6.70	.451655	32
29	.523138	5.95	.974391	.73	.548747	6.70	.451253	31
30	9.523495	5.95	9.974347	.75	9.549149	6.68	0.450851	30
31	.523852	5.93	.974302	.75	.549550	6.68	.450450	29
32	.524208	5.93	.974257	.75	.549951	6.68	.450049	28
33	.524564	5.93	.974212	.75	.550352	6.67	.449648	27
34	.524920	5.92	.974167	.75	.550752	6.68	.449248	26
35	9.525275	5.92	9.974122	.75	9.551153	6.65	0.448847	25
36	.525630	5.30	.974077	.75	.551552	6.67	.448448	24
37	.525984	5.92	.974032	.75	.551952	6.65	.448048	23
38	.526339	5.90	.973987	.75	.552351	6.65	.447649	22
39	.526693	5.88	.973942	.75	.552750	6.65	.447250	21
40	9.527046	5.90	9.973897	.75	9.553149	6.65	0.446851	20
41	.527400	5.88	.973852	.75	.553548	6.63	.446452	19
42	.527753	5.87	.973807	.77	.553946	6.63	.446054	18
43	.528105	5.88	.973761	.75	.554344	6.62	.445656	17
44	.528458	5.87	.973716	.75	.554741	6.63	.445259	16
45	9.528810	5.85	9.973671	.77	9.555139	6.62	0.444861	15
46	.529161	5.87	.973625	.75	.555536	6.62	.444464	14
47	.529513	5.85	.973580	.75	.555933	6.60	.444067	13
48	.529864	5.85	.973535	.77	.556329	6.60	.443671	12
49	.530215	5.83	.973489	.75	.556725	6.60	.443275	11
50	9.530565	5.83	9.973444	.77	9.557121	6.60	0.442879	10
51	.530915	5.83	.973398	.77	.557517	6.60	.442483	9
52	.531265	5.82	.973352	.75	.557913	6.58	.442087	8
53	.531614	5.82	.973307	.77	.558308	6.58	.441692	7
54	.531963	5.82	.973261	.77	.558703	6.57	.441297	6
55	9.532312	5.82	9.973215	.77	9.559097	6.57	0.440903	5
56	.532661	5.80	.973169	.75	.559491	6.57	.440509	4
57	.533009	5.80	.973124	.77	.559885	6.57	.440115	3
58	.533357	5.78	.973078	.77	.560279	6.57	.439721	2
59	.533704	5.80	.973032	.77	.560673	6.55	.439327	1
60	9.534052		9.972986		9.561066		0.438934	0
	Cos.	D. 1″.	Sin.	D. 1″.	Cot.	D. 1″.	Tan.	M.

TABLE C 695

LOGARITHMIC SINES, COSINES, TANGENTS, AND COTANGENTS

M.	Sin.	D. 1″.	Cos.	D. 1″.	Tan.	D. 1″.	Cot.	
0	9.534052	5.78	9.972986	.77	9.561066	6.55	0.438934	60
1	.534399	5.77	.972940	.77	.561459	6.53	.438541	59
2	.534745	5.78	.972894	.77	.561851	6.55	.438149	58
3	.535092	5.77	.972848	.77	.562244	6.53	.437756	57
4	.535438	5.75	.972802	.78	.562636	6.53	.437364	56
5	9.535783	5.77	9.972755	.77	9.563028	6.52	0.436972	55
6	.536129	5.75	.972709	.77	.563419	6.53	.436581	54
7	.536474	5.73	.972663	.77	.563811	6.52	.436189	53
8	.536818	5.75	.972617	.78	.564202	6.52	.435798	52
9	.537163	5.73	.972570	.77	.564593	6.50	.435407	51
10	9.537507	5.73	9.972524	.77	9.564983	6.50	0.435017	50
11	.537851	5.72	.972478	.78	.565373	6.50	.434627	49
12	.538194	5.73	.972431	.77	.565763	6.50	.434237	48
13	.538538	5.70	.972385	.78	.566153	6.48	.433847	47
14	.538880	5.72	.972338	.78	.566542	6.50	.433458	46
15	9.539223	5.70	9.972291	.77	9.566932	6.47	0.433068	45
16	.539565	5.70	.972245	.78	.567320	6.48	.432680	44
17	.539907	5.70	.972198	.78	.567709	6.48	.432291	43
18	.540249	5.68	.972151	.77	.568098	6.47	.431902	42
19	.540590	5.68	.972105	.78	.568486	6.45	.431514	41
20	9.540931	5.68	9.972058	.78	9.568873	6.47	0.431127	40
21	.541272	5.68	.972011	.78	.569261	6.45	.430739	39
22	.541613	5.67	.971964	.78	.569648	6.45	.430352	38
23	.541953	5.67	.971917	.78	.570035	6.45	.429965	37
24	.542293	5.65	.971870	.78	.570422	6.45	.429578	36
25	9.542632	5.65	9.971823	.78	9.570809	6.43	0.429191	35
26	.542971	5.65	.971776	.78	.571195	6.43	.428805	34
27	.543310	5.65	.971729	.78	.571581	6.43	.428419	33
28	.543649	5.63	.971682	.78	.571967	6.42	.428033	32
29	.543987	5.63	.971635	.78	.572352	6.43	.427648	31
30	9.544325	5.63	9.971588	.80	9.572738	6.42	0.427262	30
31	.544663	5.62	.971540	.78	.573123	6.40	.426877	29
32	.545000	5.63	.971493	.78	.573507	6.42	.426493	28
33	.545338	5.60	.971446	.80	.573892	6.40	.426108	27
34	.545674	5.62	.971398	.78	.574276	6.40	.425724	26
35	9.546011	5.60	9.971351	.80	9.574660	6.40	0.425340	25
36	.546347	5.60	.971303	.78	.575044	6.38	.424956	24
37	.546683	5.60	.971256	.80	.575427	6.38	.424573	23
38	.547019	5.58	.971208	.80	.575810	6.38	.424190	22
39	.547354	5.58	.971161	.80	.576193	6.38	.423807	21
40	9.547689	5.58	9.971113	.78	9.576576	6.38	0.423424	20
41	.548024	5.58	.971066	.80	.576959	6.37	.423041	19
42	.548359	5.57	.971018	.80	.577341	6.37	.422659	18
43	.548693	5.57	.970970	.80	.577723	6.35	.422277	17
44	.549027	5.55	.970922	.80	.578104	6.37	.421896	16
45	9.549360	5.55	9.970874	.78	9.578486	6.35	0.421514	15
46	.549693	5.55	.970827	.80	.578867	6.35	.421133	14
47	.550026	5.55	.970779	.80	.579248	6.35	.420752	13
48	.550359	5.55	.970731	.80	.579629	6.33	.420371	12
49	.550692	5.53	.970683	.80	.580009	6.33	.419991	11
50	9.551024	5.53	9.970635	.82	9.580389	6.33	0.419611	10
51	.551356	5.52	.970586	.80	.580769	6.33	.419231	9
52	.551687	5.52	.970538	.80	.581149	6.32	.418851	8
53	.552018	5.52	.970490	.80	.581528	6.32	.418472	7
54	.552349	5.52	.970442	.80	.581907	6.32	.418093	6
55	9.552680	5.50	9.970394	.82	9.582286	6.32	0.417714	5
56	.553010	5.52	.970345	.80	.582665	6.32	.417335	4
57	.553341	5.48	.970297	.80	.583044	6.30	.416956	3
58	.553670	5.50	.970249	.82	.583422	6.30	.416578	2
59	.554000	5.48	.970200	.80	.583800	6.28	.416200	1
60	9.554329		9.970152		9.584177		0.415823	0
	Cos.	D. 1″.	Sin.	D. 1″.	Cot.	D. 1″.	Tan.	M.

TABLE C

LOGARITHMIC SINES, COSINES, TANGENTS, AND COTANGENTS

21° 158°

M.	Sin.	D. 1″.	Cos.	D. 1″.	Tan.	D. 1″.	Cot.	
0	9.554329	5.48	9.970152	.82	9.584177	6.30	0.415823	60
1	.554658	5.48	.970103	.80	.584555	6.28	.415445	59
2	.554987	5.47	.970055	.82	.584932	6.28	.415068	58
3	.555315	5.47	.970006	.82	.585309	6.28	.414691	57
4	.555643	5.47	.969957	.80	.585686	6.27	.414314	56
5	9.555971	5.47	9.969909	.82	9.586062	6.28	0.413938	55
6	.556299	5.45	.969860	.82	.586439	6.27	.413561	54
7	.556626	5.45	.969811	.82	.586815	6.25	.413185	53
8	.556953	5.45	.969762	.80	.587190	6.27	.412810	52
9	.557280	5.43	.969714	.82	.587566	6.25	.412434	51
10	9.557606	5.43	9.969665	.82	9.587941	6.25	0.412059	50
11	.557932	5.43	.969616	.82	.588316	6.25	.411684	49
12	.558258	5.42	.969567	.82	.588691	6.25	.411309	48
13	.558583	5.43	.969518	.82	.589066	6.23	.410934	47
14	.558909	5.42	.969469	.82	.589440	6.23	.410560	46
15	9.559234	5.40	9.969420	.83	9.589814	6.23	0.410186	45
16	.559558	5.42	.969370	.82	.590188	6.23	.409812	44
17	.559883	5.40	.969321	.82	.590562	6.22	.409438	43
18	.560207	5.40	.969272	.82	.590935	6.22	.409065	42
19	.560531	5.40	.969223	.83	.591308	6.22	.408692	41
20	9.560855	5.38	9.969173	.82	9.591681	6.22	0.408319	40
21	.561178	5.38	.969124	.82	.592054	6.20	.407946	39
22	.561501	5.38	.969075	.83	.592426	6.22	.407574	38
23	.561824	5.37	.969025	.82	.592799	6.20	.407201	37
24	.562146	5.37	.968976	.83	.593171	6.18	.406829	36
25	9.562468	5.37	9.968926	.82	9.593542	6.20	0.406458	35
26	.562790	5.37	.968877	.83	.593914	6.18	.406086	34
27	.563112	5.35	.968827	.83	.594285	6.18	.405715	33
28	.563433	5.37	.968777	.82	.594656	6.18	.405344	32
29	.563755	5.33	.968728	.83	.595027	6.18	.404973	31
30	9.564075	5.35	9.968678	.83	9.595398	6.17	0.404602	30
31	.564396	5.33	.968628	.83	.595768	6.17	.404232	29
32	.564716	5.33	.968578	.83	.596138	6.17	.403862	28
33	.565036	5.33	.968528	.82	.596508	6.17	.403492	27
34	.565356	5.33	.968479	.83	.596878	6.15	.403122	26
35	9.565676	5.32	9.968429	.83	9.597247	6.15	0.402753	25
36	.565995	5.32	.968379	.83	.597616	6.15	.402384	24
37	.566314	5.30	.968329	.85	.597985	6.15	.402015	23
38	.566632	5.32	.968278	.83	.598354	6.13	.401646	22
39	.566951	5.30	.968228	.83	.598722	6.15	.401278	21
40	9.567269	5.30	9.968178	.83	9.599091	6.13	0.400909	20
41	.567587	5.28	.968128	.83	.599459	6.13	.400541	19
42	.567904	5.30	.968078	.85	.599827	6.12	.400173	18
43	.568222	5.28	.968027	.83	.600194	6.13	.399806	17
44	.568539	5.28	.967977	.83	.600562	6.12	.399438	16
45	9.568856	5.27	9.967927	.85	9.600929	6.12	0.399071	15
46	.569172	5.27	.967876	.83	.601296	6.12	.398704	14
47	.569488	5.27	.967826	.85	.601663	6.10	.398337	13
48	.569804	5.27	.967775	.83	.602029	6.10	.397971	12
49	.570120	5.25	.967725	.85	.602395	6.10	.397605	11
50	9.570435	5.27	9.967674	.83	9.602761	6.10	0.397239	10
51	.570751	5.25	.967624	.85	.603127	6.10	.396873	9
52	.571066	5.23	.967573	.85	.603493	6.08	.396507	8
53	.571380	5.25	.967522	.85	.603858	6.08	.396142	7
54	.571695	5.23	.967471	.83	.604223	6.08	.395777	6
55	9.572009	5.23	9.967421	.85	9.604588	6.08	0.395412	5
56	.572323	5.22	.967370	.85	.604953	6.07	.395047	4
57	.572636	5.23	.967319	.85	.605317	6.08	.394683	3
58	.572950	5.22	.967268	.85	.605682	6.07	.394318	2
59	.573263	5.20	.967217	.85	.606046	6.07	.393954	1
60	9.573575		9.967166		9.606410		0.393590	0
	Cos.	D. 1″.	Sin.	D. 1″.	Cot.	D. 1″.	Tan.	M.

111° 68°

TABLE C 697

LOGARITHMIC SINES, COSINES, TANGENTS, AND COTANGENTS

22°   **157°**

M.	Sin.	D. 1″.	Cos.	D. 1″.	Tan.	D. 1″.	Cot.	
0	9.573575	5.22	9.967166	.85	9.606410	6.05	0.393590	60
1	.573888	5.20	.967115	.85	.606773	6.07	.393227	59
2	.574200	5.20	.967064	.85	.607137	6.05	.392863	58
3	.574512	5.20	.967013	.87	.607500	6.05	.392500	57
4	.574824	5.20	.966961	.85	.607863	6.03	.392137	56
5	9.575136	5.18	9.966910	.85	9.608225	6.05	0.391775	55
6	.575447	5.18	.966859	.87	.608588	6.03	.391412	54
7	.575758	5.18	.966808	.85	.608950	6.03	.391050	53
8	.576069	5.17	.966756	.87	.609312	6.03	.390688	52
9	.576379	5.17	.966705	.85	.609674	6.03	.390326	51
10	9.576689	5.17	9.966653	.87	9.610036	6.02	0.389964	50
11	.576999	5.17	.966602	.85	.610397	6.03	.389603	49
12	.577309	5.15	.966550	.87	.610759	6.02	.389241	48
13	.577618	5.15	.966499	.85	.611120	6.00	.388880	47
14	.577927	5.15	.966447	.87	.611480	6.02	.388520	46
15	9.578236	5.15	9.966395	.87	9.611841	6.00	0.388159	45
16	.578545	5.13	.966344	.85	.612201	6.00	.387799	44
17	.578853	5.15	.966292	.87	.612561	6.00	.387439	43
18	.579162	5.13	.966240	.87	.612921	6.00	.387079	42
19	.579470	5.12	.966188	.87	.613281	6.00	.386719	41
20	9.579777	5.13	9.966136	.87	9.613641	5.98	0.386359	40
21	.580085	5.12	.966085	.85	.614000	5.98	.386000	39
22	.580392	5.12	.966033	.87	.614359	5.98	.385641	38
23	.580699	5.10	.965981	.87	.614718	5.98	.385282	37
24	.581005	5.12	.965929	.87	.615077	5.97	.384923	36
25	9.581312	5.10	9.965876	.88	9.615435	5.97	0.384565	35
26	.581618	5.10	.965924	.87	.615793	5.97	.384207	34
27	.581924	5.10	.965772	.87	.616151	5.97	.383849	33
28	.582229	5.08	.965720	.87	.616509	5.97	.383491	32
29	.582535	5.08	.965668	.87	.616867	5.95	.383133	31
30	9.582840	5.08	9.965615	.88	9.617224	5.97	0.382776	30
31	.583145	5.07	.965563	.87	.617582	5.95	.382418	29
32	.583449	5.08	.965511	.87	.617939	5.93	.382061	28
33	.583754	5.07	.965458	.88	.618295	5.95	.381705	27
34	.584058	5.05	.965406	.87	.618652	5.93	.381348	26
35	9.584361	5.07	9.965353	.88	9.619008	5.93	0.380992	25
36	.584665	5.05	.965301	.87	.619364	5.93	.380636	24
37	.584968	5.07	.965248	.88	.619720	5.93	.380280	23
38	.585272	5.03	.965195	.88	.620076	5.93	.379924	22
39	.585574	5.05	.965143	.87	.620432	5.93	.379568	21
40	9.585877	5.03	9.965090	.88	9.620787	5.92	0.379213	20
41	.586179	5.05	.965037	.88	.621142	5.92	.378858	19
42	.586482	5.02	.964984	.88	.621497	5.92	.378503	18
43	.586783	5.03	.964931	.88	.621852	5.92	.378148	17
44	.587085	5.02	.964879	.87	.622207	5.92	.377793	16
45	9.587386	5.03	9.964826	.88	9.622561	5.90	0.377439	15
46	.587688	5.02	.964773	.88	.622915	5.90	.377085	14
47	.587989	5.00	.964720	.88	.623269	5.90	.376731	13
48	.588289	5.02	.964666	.90	.623623	5.88	.376377	12
49	.588590	5.00	.964613	.88	.623976	5.90	.376024	11
50	9.588890	5.00	9.964560	.88	9.624330	5.88	0.375670	10
51	.589190	4.98	.964507	.88	.624683	5.88	.375317	9
52	.589489	5.00	.964454	.90	.625036	5.87	.374964	8
53	.589789	4.98	.964400	.88	.625388	5.88	.374612	7
54	.590088	4.98	.964347	.88	.625741	5.87	.374259	6
55	9.590387	4.98	9.964294	.90	9.626093	5.87	0.373907	5
56	.590686	4.97	.964240	.88	.626445	5.87	.373555	4
57	.590984	4.97	.964187	.90	.626797	5.87	.373203	3
58	.591282	4.97	.964133	.88	.627149	5.87	.372851	2
59	.591580	4.97	.964080	.90	.627501	5.85	.372499	1
60	9.591878		9.964026		9.627852		0.372148	0
	Cos.	D. 1″.	Sin.	D. 1″.	Cot.	D. 1″.	Tan.	M.

TABLE C

LOGARITHMIC SINES, COSINES, TANGENTS, AND COTANGENTS

23° **156°**

M.	Sin.	D. 1″.	Cos.	D. 1″.	Tan.	D. 1″.	Cot.	
0	9.591878		9.964026		9.627852		0.372148	60
1	.592176	4.97	.963972	.90	.628203	5.85	.371797	59
2	.592473	4.95	.963919	.88	.628554	5.85	.371446	58
3	.592770	4.95	.963865	.90	.628905	5.85	.371095	57
4	.593067	4.95	.963811	.90	.629255	5.83	.370745	56
5	9.593363	4.93	9.963757	.90	9.629606	5.85	0.370394	55
6	.593659	4.93	.963704	.88	.629956	5.83	.370044	54
7	.593955	4.93	.963650	.90	.630306	5.83	.369694	53
8	.594251	4.93	.963596	.90	.630656	5.83	.369344	52
9	.594547	4.93	.963542	.90	.631005	5.82	.368995	51
		4.92		.90		5.83		
10	9.594842	4.92	9.963488	.90	9.631355	5.82	0.368645	50
11	.595137	4.92	.963434	.92	.631704	5.82	.368296	49
12	.595432	4.92	.963379	.90	.632053	5.82	.367947	48
13	.595727	4.90	.963325	.90	.632402	5.80	.367598	47
14	.596021	4.90	.963271	.90	.632750	5.82	.367250	46
15	9.596315	4.90	9.963217	.90	9.633099	5.80	0.366901	45
16	.596609	4.90	.963163	.92	.633447	5.80	.366553	44
17	.596903	4.90	.963108	.90	.633795	5.80	.366205	43
18	.597196	4.88	.963054	.92	.634143	5.78	.365857	42
19	.597490	4.90	.962999	.90	.634490	5.80	.365510	41
		4.88						
20	9.597783	4.87	9.962945	.92	9.634838	5.78	0.365162	40
21	.598075	4.88	.962890	.90	.635185	5.78	.364815	39
22	.598368	4.87	.962836	.92	.635532	5.78	.364468	38
23	.598660	4.87	.962781	.90	.635879	5.78	.364121	37
24	.598952	4.87	.962727	.92	.636226	5.77	.363774	36
25	9.599244	4.87	9.962672	.92	9.636572	5.78	0.363428	35
26	.599536	4.85	.962617	.92	.636919	5.77	.363081	34
27	.599827	4.85	.962562	.90	.637265	5.77	.362735	33
28	.600118	4.85	.962508	.92	.637611	5.75	.362389	32
29	.600409	4.85	.962453	.92	.637956	5.77	.362044	31
30	9.600700	4.83	9.962398	.92	9.638302	5.75	0.361698	30
31	.600990	4.83	.962343	.92	.638647	5.75	.361353	29
32	.601280	4.83	.962288	.92	.638992	5.75	.361008	28
33	.601570	4.83	.962233	.92	.639337	5.75	.360663	27
34	.601860	4.83	.962178	.92	.639682	5.75	.360318	26
35	9.602150	4.82	9.962123	.93	9.640027	5.73	0.359973	25
36	.602439	4.82	.962067	.92	.640371	5.75	.359629	24
37	.602728	4.82	.962012	.92	.640716	5.73	.359284	23
38	.603017	4.80	.961957	.92	.641060	5.73	.358940	22
39	.603305	4.82	.961902	.93	.641404	5.72	.358596	21
40	9.603594	4.80	9.961846	.92	9.641747	5.73	0.358253	20
41	.603882	4.80	.961791	.93	.642091	5.72	.357909	19
42	.604170	4.78	.961735	.92	.642434	5.72	.357566	18
43	.604457	4.80	.961680	.93	.642777	5.72	.357223	17
44	.604745	4.78	.961624	.92	.643120	5.72	.356880	16
45	9.605032	4.78	9.961569	.93	9.643463	5.72	0.356537	15
46	.605319	4.78	.961513	.92	.643806	5.70	.356194	14
47	.605606	4.77	.961458	.93	.644148	5.70	.355852	13
48	.605892	4.78	.961402	.93	.644490	5.70	.355510	12
49	.606179	4.77	.961346	.93	.644832	5.70	.355168	11
50	9.606465	4.77	9.961290	.92	9.645174	5.70	0.354826	10
51	.606751	4.75	.961235	.93	.645516	5.68	.354484	9
52	.607036	4.77	.961179	.93	.645857	5.70	.354143	8
53	.607322	4.75	.961123	.93	.646199	5.68	.353801	7
54	.607607	4.75	.961067	.93	.646540	5.68	.353460	6
55	9.607892	4.75	9.961011	.93	9.646881	5.68	0.353119	5
56	.608177	4.73	.960955	.93	.647222	5.67	.352778	4
57	.608461	4.73	.960899	.93	.647562	5.68	.352438	3
58	.608745	4.73	.960843	.95	.647903	5.67	.352097	2
59	.609029	4.73	.960786	.93	.648243	5.67	.351757	1
60	9.609313		9.960730		9.648583		0.351417	0
	Cos.	D. 1″.	Sin.	D. 1″.	Cot.	D. 1″.	Tan.	M.

113° **66°**

TABLE C

699

LOGARITHMIC SINES, COSINES, TANGENTS, AND COTANGENTS

24°   **155°**

M.	Sin.	D. 1″.	Cos.	D. 1″.	Tan.	D. 1″.	Cot.	
0	9.609313	4.73	9.960730	.93	9.648583	5.67	0.351417	60
1	.609597	4.72	.960674	.93	.648923	5.67	.351077	59
2	.609880	4.73	.960618	.95	.649263	5.65	.350737	58
3	.610164	4.72	.960561	.93	.649602	5.67	.350398	57
4	.610447	4.70	.960505	.95	.649942	5.65	.350058	56
5	9.610729	4.72	9.960448	.93	9.650281	5.65	0.349719	55
6	.611012	4.70	.960392	.95	.650620	5.65	.349380	54
7	.611294	4.70	.960335	.93	.650959	5.63	.349041	53
8	.611576	4.70	.960279	.95	.651297	5.65	.348703	52
9	.611858	4.70	.960222	.95	.651636	5.63	.348364	51
10	9.612140	4.68	9.960165	.93	9.651974	5.63	0.348026	50
11	.612421	4.68	.960109	.95	.652312	5.63	.347688	49
12	.612702	4.68	.960052	.95	.652650	5.63	.347350	48
13	.612983	4.68	.959995	.95	.652988	5.63	.347012	47
14	.613264	4.68	.959938	.93	.653326	5.62	.346674	46
15	9.613545	4.67	9.959882	.95	9.653663	5.62	0.346337	45
16	.613825	4.67	.959825	.95	.654000	5.62	.346000	44
17	.614105	4.67	.959768	.95	.654337	5.62	.345663	43
18	.614385	4.67	.959711	.95	.654674	5.62	.345326	42
19	.614665	4.65	.959654	.97	.655011	5.62	.344989	41
20	9.614944	4.65	9.959596	.95	9.655348	5.60	0.344652	40
21	.615223	4.65	.959539	.95	.655684	5.60	.344316	39
22	.615502	4.65	.959482	.95	.656020	5.60	.343980	38
23	.615781	4.65	.959425	.95	.656356	5.60	.343644	37
24	.616060	4.63	.959368	.97	.656692	5.60	.343308	36
25	9.616338	4.63	9.959310	.95	9.657028	5.60	0.342972	35
26	.616616	4.63	.959253	.97	.657364	5.58	.342636	34
27	.616894	4.63	.959195	.95	.657699	5.58	.342301	33
28	.617172	4.63	.959138	.97	.658034	5.58	.341966	32
29	.617450	4.62	.959080	.95	.658369	5.58	.341631	31
30	9.617727	4.62	9.959023	.97	9.658704	5.58	0.341296	30
31	.618004	4.62	.058965	.95	.650030	5.57	.340961	29
32	.618281	4.62	.958908	.97	.659373	5.58	.340627	28
33	.618558	4.60	.958850	.97	.659708	5.57	.340292	27
34	.618834	4.60	.958792	.97	.660042	5.57	.339958	26
35	9.619110	4.60	9.958734	.05	9.660376	5.57	0.339624	25
36	.619386	4.60	.958677	.97	.660710	5.55	.339290	24
37	.619662	4.60	.958619	.97	.661043	5.57	.338957	23
38	.619938	4.58	.958561	.97	.661377	5.55	.338623	22
39	.620213	4.58	.958503	.97	.661710	5.55	.338290	21
40	9.620488	4.58	9.958445	.97	9.662043	5.55	0.337957	20
41	.620763	4.58	.958387	.97	.662376	5.55	.337624	19
42	.621038	4.58	.958329	.97	.662709	5.55	.337291	18
43	.621313	4.57	.958271	.97	.663042	5.55	.336958	17
44	.621587	4.57	.958213	.98	.663375	5.53	.336625	16
45	9.621861	4.57	9.958154	.97	9.663707	5.53	0.336293	15
46	.622135	4.57	.958096	.97	.664039	5.53	.335961	14
47	.622409	4.55	.958038	.98	.664371	5.53	.335629	13
48	.622682	4.57	.957979	.07	.664703	5.53	.335297	12
49	.622956	4.55	.957921	.97	.665035	5.52	.334965	11
50	9.623229	4.55	9.957863	.98	9.665396	5.53	0.334634	10
51	.623502	4.53	.957804	.97	.665698	5.52	.334302	9
52	.623774	4.55	.957746	.98	.666029	5.52	.333971	8
53	.624047	4.53	.957687	.98	.666360	5.52	.333640	7
54	.624319	4.53	.957628	.97	.666691	5.52	.333309	6
55	9.624591	4.53	9.957570	.98	9.667021	5.50	0.332979	5
56	.624863	4.53	.957511	.98	.667352	5.52	.332648	4
57	.625135	4.52	.957452	.98	.667682	5.52	.332318	3
58	.625406	4.52	.957393	.98	.668013	5.50	.331987	2
59	.625677	4.52	.957335	.97	.668343	5.50	.331657	1
60	9.625948		9.957276	.98	9.668673		0.331327	0
	Cos.	D. 1″.	Sin.	D. 1″.	Cot.	D. 1″.	Tan.	M.

114°   **65°**

TABLE C

Logarithmic Sines, Cosines, Tangents, and Cotangents

25°   154°

M.	Sin.	D. 1".	Cos.	D. 1."	Tan.	D. 1".	Cot.	
0	9.625948	4.52	9.957276	.98	9.668673	5.48	0.331327	60
1	.626219	4.52	.957217	.98	.669002	5.50	.330998	59
2	.626490	4.50	.957158	.98	.669332	5.48	.330668	58
3	.626760	4.50	.957099	.98	.669661	5.50	.330339	57
4	.627030	4.50	.957040	.98	.669991	5.48	.330009	56
5	9.627300	4.50	9.956981	1.00	9.670320	5.48	0.329680	55
6	.627570	4.50	.956921	.98	.670649	5.48	.329351	54
7	.627840	4.48	.956862	.98	.670977	5.47	.329023	53
8	.628109	4.48	.956803	.98	.671306	5.48	.328694	52
9	.628378	4.48	.956744	1.00	.671635	5.48	.328365	51
10	9.628647	4.48	9.956684	.98	9.671963	5.47	0.328037	50
11	.628916	4.48	.956625	.98	.672291	5.47	.327709	49
12	.629185	4.47	.956566	1.00	.672619	5.47	.327381	48
13	.629453	4.47	.956506	.98	.672947	5.47	.327053	47
14	.629721	4.47	.956447	1.00	.673274	5.45	.326726	46
15	9.629989	4.47	9.956387	1.00	9.673602	5.47	0.326398	45
16	.630257	4.45	.956327	.98	.673929	5.45	.326071	44
17	.630524	4.47	.956268	1.00	.674257	5.47	.325743	43
18	.630792	4.45	.956208	1.00	.674584	5.45	.325416	42
19	.631059	4.45	.956148	.98	.674911	5.45	.325089	41
20	9.631326	4.45	9.956089	1.00	9.675237	5.43	0.324763	40
21	.631593	4.43	.956029	1.00	.675564	5.45	.324436	39
22	.631859	4.43	.955969	1.00	.675890	5.43	.324110	38
23	.632125	4.45	.955909	1.00	.676217	5.45	.323783	37
24	.632392	4.43	.955849	1.00	.676543	5.43	.323457	36
25	9.632658	4.42	9.955789	1.00	9.676869	5.43	0.323131	35
26	.632923	4.43	.955729	1.00	.677194	5.42	.322806	34
27	.633189	4.42	.955669	1.00	.677520	5.43	.322480	33
28	.633454	4.42	.955609	1.02	.677846	5.43	.322154	32
29	.633719	4.42	.955548	1.00	.678171	5.42	.321829	31
30	9.633984	4.42	9.955488	1.00	9.678496	5.42	0.321504	30
31	.634249	4.42	.955428	1.00	.678821	5.42	.321179	29
32	.634514	4.40	.955368	1.02	.679146	5.42	.320854	28
33	.634778	4.40	.955307	1.00	.679471	5.42	.320529	27
34	.635042	4.40	.955247	1.02	.679795	5.40	.320205	26
35	9.635306	4.40	9.955186	1.00	9.680120	5.42	0.319880	25
36	.635570	4.40	.955126	1.02	.680444	5.40	.319556	24
37	.635834	4.38	.955065	1.00	.680768	5.40	.319232	23
38	.636097	4.38	.955005	1.02	.681092	5.40	.318908	22
39	.636360	4.38	.954944	1.02	.681416	5.40	.318584	21
40	9.636623	4.38	9.954883	1.00	9.681740	5.38	0.318260	20
41	.636886	4.37	.954823	1.02	.682063	5.40	.317937	19
42	.637148	4.38	.954762	1.02	.682387	5.38	.317613	18
43	.637411	4.37	.954701	1.02	.682710	5.38	.317290	17
44	.637673	4.37	.954640	1.02	.683033	5.38	.316967	16
45	9.637935	4.37	9.954579	1.02	9.683356	5.38	0.316644	15
46	.638197	4.35	.954518	1.02	.683679	5.37	.316321	14
47	.638458	4.37	.954457	1.02	.684001	5.38	.315999	13
48	.638720	4.35	.954396	1.02	.684324	5.37	.315676	12
49	.638981	4.35	.954335	1.02	.684646	5.37	.315354	11
50	9.639242	4.35	9.954274	1.02	9.684968	5.37	0.315032	10
51	.639503	4.35	.954213	1.02	.685290	5.37	.314710	9
52	.639764	4.33	.954152	1.03	.685612	5.37	.314388	8
53	.640024	4.33	.954090	1.02	.685934	5.35	.314066	7
54	.640284	4.33	.954029	1.02	.686255	5.37	.313745	6
55	9.640544	4.33	9.953968	1.03	9.686577	5.35	0.313423	5
56	.640804	4.33	.953906	1.02	.686898	5.35	.313102	4
57	.641064	4.33	.953845	1.03	.687219	5.35	.312781	3
58	.641324	4.32	.953783	1.02	.687540	5.35	.312460	2
59	.641583	4.32	.953722	1.03	.687861	5.35	.312139	1
60	9.641842		9.953660		9.688182		0.311818	0
	Cos.	D. 1".	Sin.	D. 1".	Cot.	D. 1".	Tan.	M.

115°   64°

TABLE C   701

LOGARITHMIC SINES, COSINES, TANGENTS, AND COTANGENTS

26°   153°

M.	Sin.	D. 1″.	Cos.	D. 1″.	Tan.	D. 1″.	Cot.	
0	9.641842	4.32	9.953660	1.02	9.688182	5.33	0.311818	60
1	.642101	4.32	.953599	1.03	.688502	5.35	.311498	59
2	.642360	4.30	.953537	1.03	.688823	5.33	.311177	58
3	.642618	4.32	.953475	1.03	.689143	5.33	.310857	57
4	.642877	4.30	.953413	1.02	.689463	5.33	.310537	56
5	9.643135	4.30	9.953352	1.03	9.689783	5.33	0.310217	55
6	.643393	4.30	.953290	1.03	.690103	5.33	.309897	54
7	.643650	4.28	.953228	1.03	.690423	5.33	.309577	53
8	.643908	4.30	.953166	1.03	.690742	5.32	.309258	52
9	.644165	4.28	.953104	1.03	.691062	5.33	.308938	51
10	9.644423	4.30	9.953042	1.03	9.691381	5.32	0.308619	50
11	.644680	4.28	.952980	1.03	.691700	5.32	.308300	49
12	.644936	4.27	.952918	1.05	692019	5.32	.307981	48
13	.645193	4.28	.952855	1.03	.692338	5.32	.307662	47
14	.645450	4.28	.952793	1.03	.692656	5.30	.307344	46
15	9.645706	4.27	9.952731	1.03	9.692975	5.32	0.307025	45
16	.645962	4.27	.952669	1.05	.693293	5.30	.306707	44
17	.646218	4.27	.952606	1.03	.693612	5.32	.306388	43
18	.646474	4.27	.952544	1.05	.693930	5.30	.306070	42
19	.646729	4.25	.952481	1.03	.694248	5.30	.305752	41
20	9.646984	4.25	9.952419	1.05	9.694566	5.30	0.305434	40
21	.647240	4.27	.952356	1.03	.694883	5.28	.305117	39
22	.647494	4.23	.952294	1.05	.695201	5.30	.304799	38
23	.647749	4.25	.952231	1.05	.695518	5.28	.304482	37
24	.648004	4.25	.952168	1.03	.695836	5.30	.304164	36
25	9.648258	4.23	9.952106	1.05	9.696153	5.28	0.303847	35
26	.648512	4.23	.952043	1.05	.696470	5.28	.303530	34
27	.648766	4.23	.951980	1.05	.696787	5.28	.303213	33
28	.649020	4.23	.951917	1.05	.697103	5.27	.302897	32
29	.649274	4.23	.951854	1.05	.697420	5.28	.302580	31
30	9.649527	4.22	9.951791	1.05	9.697736	5.27	0.302264	30
31	.649781	4.23	.951728	1.05	.698053	5.28	.301947	29
32	.650034	4.22	.951665	1.05	.698369	5.27	.301631	28
33	.650287	4.22	.951602	1.05	.698685	5.27	.301315	27
34	.650539	4.20	.951539	1.05	.699001	5.27	.300999	26
35	9.650792	4.22	9.951476	1.07	9.699316	5.25	0.300684	25
36	.651044	4.20	.951412	1.05	.699632	5.27	.300368	24
37	.651297	4.22	.951349	1.05	.699947	5.25	.300053	23
38	.651549	4.20	.951286	1.07	.700263	5.27	.299737	22
39	.651800	4.18	.951222	1.05	.700578	5.25	.299422	21
40	9.652052	4.20	9.951159	1.05	9.700893	5.25	0.299107	20
41	.652304	4.20	.951096	1.07	.701208	5.25	.298792	19
42	.652555	4.18	.951032	1.07	.701523	5.23	.298477	18
43	.652806	4.18	.950968	1.05	.701837	5.25	.298163	17
44	.653057	4.18	.950905	1.07	.702152	5.23	.297848	16
45	9.653308	4.18	9.950841	1.05	9.702466	5.25	0.297534	15
46	.653558	4.17	.950778	1.07	.702781	5.23	.297219	14
47	.653808	4.17	.950714	1.07	.703095	5.23	.296905	13
48	.654059	4.18	.950650	1.07	.703409	5.22	.296591	12
49	.654309	4.17	.950586	1.07	.703722	5.23	.296278	11
50	9.654558	4.15	9.950522	1.07	9.704036	5.23	0.295964	10
51	.654808	4.17	.950458	1.07	.704350	5.22	.295650	9
52	.655058	4.17	.950394	1.07	.704663	5.22	.295337	8
53	.655307	4.15	.950330	1.07	.704976	5.23	.295024	7
54	.655556	4.15	.950266	1.07	.705290	5.22	.294710	6
55	9.655805	4.15	9.950202	1.07	9.705603	5.22	0.294397	5
56	.656054	4.15	.950138	1.07	.705916	5.20	.294084	4
57	.656302	4.13	.950074	1.07	.706228	5.22	.293772	3
58	.656551	4.15	.950010	1.08	.706541	5.22	.293459	2
59	.656799	4.13	.949945	1.07	.706854	5.20	.293146	1
60	9.657047	4.13	9.949881		9.707166		0.292834	0
	Cos.	D. 1″.	Sin.	D. 1″.	Cot.	D. 1″.	Tan.	M.

116°   63°

TABLE C

Logarithmic Sines, Cosines, Tangents, and Cotangents

M.	Sin.	D. 1".	Cos.	D. 1".	Tan.	D. 1".	Cot.	
0	9.657047	4.13	9.949881	1.08	9.707166	5.20	0.292834	60
1	.657295	4.12	.949816	1.07	.707478	5.20	.292522	59
2	.657542	4.13	.949752	1.07	.707790	5.20	.292210	58
3	.657790	4.12	.949688	1.08	.708102	5.20	.291898	57
4	.658037	4.12	.949623	1.08	.708414	5.20	.291586	56
5	9.658284	4.12	9.949558	1.07	9.708726	5.18	0.291274	55
6	.658531	4.12	.949494	1.08	.709037	5.20	.290963	54
7	.658778	4.12	.949429	1.08	.709349	5.18	.290651	53
8	.659025	4.10	.949364	1.07	.709660	5.18	.290340	52
9	.659271	4.10	.949300	1.08	.709971	5.18	.290029	51
10	9.659517	4.10	9.949235	1.08	9.710282	5.18	0.289718	50
11	.659763	4.10	.949170	1.08	.710593	5.18	.289407	49
12	.660009	4.10	.949105	1.08	.710904	5.18	.289096	48
13	.660255	4.10	.949040	1.08	.711215	5.17	.288785	47
14	.66υ501	4.08	.948975	1.08	.711525	5.18	.288475	46
15	9.660746	4.08	9.948910	1.08	9.711836	5.17	0.288164	45
16	.660991	4.08	.948845	1.08	.712146	5.17	.287854	44
17	.661236	4.08	.948780	1.08	.712456	5.17	.287544	43
18	.661481	4.08	.948715	1.08	.712766	5.17	.287234	42
19	.661726	4.07	.948650	1.10	.713076	5.17	.286924	41
20	9.661970	4.07	9.948584	1.08	9.713386	5.17	0.286614	40
21	.662214	4.08	.948519	1.08	.713696	5.15	.286304	39
22	.662459	4.07	.948454	1.10	.714005	5.15	.285995	38
23	.662703	4.05	.948388	1.08	.714314	5.17	.285686	37
24	.662946	4.07	.948323	1.10	.714624	5.15	.285376	36
25	9.663190	4.05	9.948257	1.08	9.714933	5.15	0.285067	35
26	.663433	4.07	.948192	1.10	.715242	5.15	.284758	34
27	.663677	4.05	.948126	1.10	.715551	5.15	.284449	33
28	.663920	4.05	.948060	1.08	.715860	5.13	.284140	32
29	.664163	4.05	.947995	1.10	.716168	5.15	.283832	31
30	9.664406	4.03	9.947929	1.10	9.716477	5.13	0.283523	30
31	.664648	4.05	.947863	1.10	.716785	5.13	.283215	29
32	.664891	4.03	.947797	1.10	.717093	5.13	.282907	28
33	.665133	4.03	.947731	1.10	.717401	5.13	.282599	27
34	.665375	4.03	.947665	1.08	.717709	5.13	.282291	26
35	9.665617	4.03	9.947600	1.12	9.718017	5.13	0.281983	25
36	.665859	4.02	.947533	1.10	.718325	5.13	.281675	24
37	.666100	4.03	.947467	1.10	.718633	5.12	.281367	23
38	.666342	4.02	.947401	1.10	.718940	5.13	.281060	22
39	.666583	4.02	.947335	1.10	.719248	5.12	.280752	21
40	9.666824	4.02	9.947269	1.10	9.719555	5.12	0.280445	20
41	.667065	4.00	.947203	1.12	.719862	5.12	.280138	19
42	.667305	4.02	.947136	1.10	.720169	5.12	.279831	18
43	.667546	4.00	.947070	1.10	.720476	5.12	.279524	17
44	.667786	4.02	.947004	1.12	.720783	5.10	.279217	16
45	9.668027	4.00	9.946937	1.10	9.721089	5.12	0.278911	15
46	.668267	3.98	.946871	1.12	.721396	5.10	.278604	14
47	.668506	4.00	.946804	1.10	.721702	5.12	.278298	13
48	.668746	4.00	.946738	1.12	.722009	5.10	.277991	12
49	.668986	3.98	.946671	1.12	.722315	5.10	.277685	11
50	9.669225	3.98	9.946604	1.10	9.722621	5.10	0.277379	10
51	.669464	3.98	.946538	1.12	.722927	5.08	.277073	9
52	.669703	3.98	.946471	1.12	.723232	5.10	.276768	8
53	.669942	3.98	.946404	1.12	.723538	5.10	.276462	7
54	.670181	3.97	.946337	1.12	.723844	5.08	.276156	6
55	9.670419	3.98	9.946270	1.12	9.724149	5.08	0.275851	5
56	.670658	3.97	.946203	1.12	.724454	5.10	.275546	4
57	.670896	3.97	.946136	1.12	.724760	5.08	.275240	3
58	.671134	3.97	.946069	1.12	.725065	5.08	.274935	2
59	.671372	3.95	.946002	1.12	.725370	5.07	.274630	1
60	9.671609		9.945935		9.725674		0.274326	0
	Cos.	D. 1".	Sin.	D. 1".	Cot.	D. 1".	Tan.	M.

TABLE C

703

Logarithmic Sines, Cosines, Tangents, and Cotangents

M.	Sin.	D. 1″.	Cos.	D. 1″.	Tan.	D. 1″.	Cot.	
0	9.671609		9.945935		9.725674		0.274326	60
1	.671847	3.97	.945868	1.12	.725979	5.08	.274021	59
2	.672084	3.95	.945800	1.13	.726284	5.08	.273716	58
3	.672321	3.95	.945733	1.12	.726588	5.07	.273412	57
4	.672558	3.95	.945666	1.12	.726892	5.07	.273108	56
5	9.672795	3.95	9.945598	1.13	9.727197	5.08	0.272803	55
6	.673032	3.95	.945531	1.12	.727501	5.07	.272499	54
7	.673268	3.93	.945464	1.12	.727805	5.07	.272195	53
8	.673505	3.95	.945396	1.13	.728109	5.07	.271891	52
9	.673741	3.93	.945328	1.13	.728412	5.05	.271588	51
10	9.673977	3.93	9.945261	1.12	9.728716	5.07	0.271284	50
11	.674213	3.93	.945193	1.13	.729020	5.07	.270980	49
12	.674448	3.92	.945125	1.13	.729323	5.05	.270677	48
13	.674684	3.93	.945058	1.13	.729626	5.05	.270374	47
14	.674919	3.92	.944990	1.12	.729929	5.05	.270071	46
15	9.675155	3.93	9.944922	1.13	9.730233	5.07	0.269767	45
16	.675390	3.92	.944854	1.13	.730535	5.03	.269465	44
17	.675624	3.90	.944786	1.13	.730838	5.05	.269162	43
18	.675859	3.92	.944718	1.13	.731141	5.05	.268859	42
19	.676094	3.92	.944650	1.13	.731444	5.05	.268556	41
20	9.676328	3.90	9.944582	1.13	9.731746	5.03	0.268254	40
21	.676562	3.90	.944514	1.13	.732048	5.05	.267952	39
22	.676796	3.90	.944446	1.13	.732351	5.05	.267649	38
23	.677030	3.90	.944377	1.15	.732653	5.03	.267347	37
24	.677264	3.90	.944309	1.13	.732955	5.03	.267045	36
25	9.677498	3.90	9.944241	1.13	9.733257	5.03	0.266743	35
26	.677731	3.88	.944172	1.15	.733558	5.02	.266442	34
27	.677964	3.88	.944104	1.13	.733860	5.03	.266140	33
28	.678197	3.88	.944036	1.13	.734162	5.03	.265838	32
29	.678430	3.88	.943967	1.15	.734463	5.02	.265537	31
30	9.678663	3.88	9.943899	1.13	9.734764	5.02	0.265236	30
31	.678895	3.87	.943830	1.15	.735066	5.03	.264934	29
32	.679128	3.88	.943761	1.15	.735367	5.02	.264633	28
33	.679360	3.87	.943693	1.13	.735668	5.02	.264332	27
34	.679592	3.87	.943624	1.15	.735969	5.02	.264031	26
35	9.679824	3.87	9.943555	1.15	9.736269	5.00	0.263731	25
36	.680056	3.87	.943486	1.15	.736570	5.02	.263430	24
37	.680288	3.87	.943417	1.15	.736870	5.00	.263130	23
38	.680519	3.85	.943348	1.15	.737171	5.02	.262829	22
39	.680750	3.85	.943279	1.15	.737471	5.00	.262529	21
40	9.680982	3.87	9.943210	1.15	9.737771	5.00	0.262229	20
41	.681213	3.85	.943141	1.15	.738071	5.00	.261929	19
42	.681443	2.85	.943072	1.15	.738371	5.00	.261629	18
43	.681674	3.85	.943003	1.15	.738671	5.00	.261329	17
44	.681905	3.83	.942934	1.15	.738971	5.00	.261029	16
45	9.682135	3.83	9.942864	1.17	9.739271	5.00	0.260729	15
46	.682365	3.83	.942795	1.15	.739570	4.98	.260430	14
47	.682595	3.83	.942726	1.15	.739870	5.00	.260130	13
48	.682825	3.83	.942656	1.17	.740169	4.98	.259831	12
49	.683055	3.82	.942587	1.15	.740468	4.98	.259532	11
50	9.683284	3.83	9.942517	1.17	9.740767	4.98	0.259233	10
51	.683514	3.82	.942448	1.15	.741066	4.98	.258934	9
52	.683743	3.82	.942378	1.17	.741365	4.98	.258635	8
53	.683972	3.82	.942308	1.17	.741664	4.98	.258336	7
54	.684201	3.82	.942239	1.15	.741962	4.97	.258038	6
55	9.684430	3.80	9.942169	1.17	9.742261	4.98	0.257739	5
56	.684658	3.82	.942099	1.17	.742559	4.97	.257441	4
57	.684887	3.80	.942029	1.17	.742858	4.98	.257142	3
58	.685115	3.80	.941959	1.17	.743156	4.97	.256844	2
59	.685343	3.80	.941889	1.17	.743454	4.97	.256546	1
60	9.685571	3.80	9.941819	1.17	9.743752	4.97	0.256248	0
	Cos.	D. 1″.	Sin.	D. 1″.	Cot.	D. 1″.	Tan.	M.

TABLE C

LOGARITHMIC SINES, COSINES, TANGENTS, AND COTANGENTS

29°   **150⁰**

M.	Sin.	D. 1″.	Cos.	D. 1″.	Tan.	D. 1″.	Cot.	
0	9.685571	3.80	9.941819	1.17	9.743752	4.97	0.256248	60
1	.685799	3.80	.941749	1.17	.744050	4.97	.255950	59
2	.686027	3.78	.941679	1.17	.744348	4.95	.255652	58
3	.686254	3.80	.941609	1.17	.744645	4.97	.255355	57
4	.686482	3.78	.941539	1.17	.744943	4.95	.255057	56
5	9.686709	3.78	9.941469	1.18	9.745240	4.97	0.254760	55
6	.686936	3.78	.941398	1.17	.745538	4.95	.254462	54
7	.687163	3.77	.941328	1.17	.745835	4.95	.254165	53
8	.687389	3.78	.941258	1.18	.746132	4.95	.253868	52
9	.687616	3.78	.941187	1.17	.746429	4.95	.253571	51
10	9.687843	3.77	9.941117	1.18	9.746726	4.95	0.253274	50
11	.688069	3.77	.941046	1.18	.747023	4.93	.252977	49
12	.688295	3.77	.940975	1.17	.747319	4.95	.252681	48
13	.688521	3.77	.940905	1.18	.747616	4.95	.252384	47
14	.688747	3.75	.940834	1.18	.747913	4.93	.252087	46
15	9.688972	3.77	9.940763	1.17	9.748209	4.93	0.251791	45
16	.689198	3.75	.940693	1.18	.748505	4.93	.251495	44
17	.689423	3.75	.940622	1.18	.748801	4.93	.251199	43
18	.689648	3.75	.940551	1.18	.749097	4.93	.250903	42
19	.689873	3.75	.940480	1.18	.749393	4.93	.250607	41
20	9.690098	3.75	9.940409	1.18	9.749689	4.93	0.250311	40
21	.690323	3.75	.940338	1.18	.749985	4.93	.250015	39
22	.690548	3.73	.940267	1.18	.750281	4.93	.249719	38
23	.690772	3.73	.940196	1.18	.750576	4.92	.249424	37
24	.690996	3.73	.940125	1.18	.750872	4.93	.249128	36
25	9.691220	3.73	9.940054	1.20	9.751167	4.92	0.248833	35
26	.691444	3.73	.939982	1.18	.751462	4.92	.248538	34
27	.691668	3.73	.939911	1.18	.751757	4.92	.248243	33
28	.691892	3.72	.939840	1.20	.752052	4.92	.247948	32
29	.692115	3.73	.939768	1.18	.752347	4.92	.247653	31
30	9.692339	3.72	9.939697	1.20	9.752642	4.92	0.247358	30
31	.692562	3.72	.939625	1.18	.752937	4.90	.247063	29
32	.692785	3.72	.939554	1.20	.753231	4.92	.246769	28
33	.693008	5.72	.939482	1.20	.753526	4.90	.246474	27
34	.693231	3.70	.939410	1.18	.753820	4.92	.246180	26
35	9.693453	3.72	9.939339	1.20	9.754115	4.90	0.245885	25
36	.693676	3.70	.939267	1.20	.754409	4.90	.245591	24
37	.693898	3.70	.939195	1.20	.754703	4.90	.245297	23
38	.694120	3.70	.939123	1.18	.754997	4.90	.245003	22
39	.694342	3.70	.939052	1.20	.755291	4.90	.244709	21
40	9.694564	3.70	9.938980	1.20	9.755585	4.88	0.244415	20
41	.694786	3.68	.938908	1.20	.755878	4.90	.244122	19
42	.695007	3.70	.938836	1.22	.756172	4.88	.243828	18
43	.695229	3.68	.938763	1.20	.756465	4.90	.243535	17
44	.695450	3.68	.938691	1.20	.756759	4.88	.243241	16
45	9.695671	3.68	9.938619	1.20	9.757052	4.88	0.242948	15
46	.695892	3.68	.938547	1.20	.757345	4.88	.242655	14
47	.696113	3.68	.938475	1.22	.757638	4.88	.242362	13
48	.696334	3.67	.938402	1.20	.757931	4.88	.242069	12
49	.696554	3.68	.938330	1.20	.758224	4.88	.241776	11
50	9.696775	3.67	9.938258	1.22	9.758517	4.88	0.241483	10
51	.696995	3.67	.938185	1.20	.758810	4.87	.241190	9
52	.697215	3.67	.938113	1.22	.759102	4.88	.240898	8
53	.697435	3.65	.938040	1.22	.759395	4.87	.240605	7
54	.697654	3.67	.937967	1.22	.759687	4.87	.240313	6
55	9.697874	3.67	9.937895	1.20	9.759979	4.88	0.240021	5
56	.698094	3.65	.937822	1.22	.760272	4.87	.239728	4
57	.698313	3.65	.937749	1.22	.760564	4.87	.239436	3
58	.698532	3.65	.937676	1.22	.760856	4.87	239144	2
59	.698751	3.65	.937604	1.20	.761148	4.85	.238852	1
60	9.698970		9.937531	1.22	9.761439		0.238561	0
	Cos.	D. 1″.	Sin.	D. 1″.	Cot.	D. 1″.	Tan.	M.

119°   **60°**

TABLE C   705

LOGARITHMIC SINES, COSINES, TANGENTS, AND COTANGENTS

30°   149°

M.	Sin.	D. 1″.	Cos.	D. 1″.	Tan.	D. 1″.	Cot.	
0	9.698970	3.65	9.937531	1.22	9.761439	4.87	0.238561	60
1	.699189	3.63	.937458	1.22	.761731	4.87	.238269	59
2	.699407	3.65	.937385	1.22	.762023	4.85	.237977	58
3	.699626	3.63	.937312	1.23	.762314	4.87	.237686	57
4	.699844	3.63	.937238	1.22	.762606	4.85	.237394	56
5	9.700062	3.63	9.937165	1.22	9.762897	4.85	0.237103	55
6	.700280	3.63	.937092	1.22	.763188	4.85	.236812	54
7	.700498	3.63	.937019	1.22	.763479	4.85	.236521	53
8	.700716	3.63	.936946	1.23	.763770	4.85	.236230	52
9	.700933	3.62	.936872	1.22	.764061	4.85	.235939	51
10	9.701151	3.63	9.936799	1.23	9.764352	4.85	0.235648	50
11	.701368	3.62	.936725	1.22	.764643	4.83	.235357	49
12	.701585	3.62	.936652	1.23	.764933	4.85	.235067	48
13	.701802	3.62	.936578	1.22	.765224	4.83	.234776	47
14	.702019	3.62	.936505	1.23	.765514	4.85	.234486	46
15	9.702236	3.62	9.936431	1.23	9.765805	4.83	0.234195	45
16	.702452	3.60	.936357	1.22	.766095	4.83	.233905	44
17	.702669	3.62	.936284	1.23	.766385	4.83	.233615	43
18	.702885	3.60	.936210	1.23	.766675	4.83	.233325	42
19	.703101	3.60	.936136	1.23	.766965	4.83	.233035	41
20	9.703317	3.60	9.936062	1.23	9.767255	4.83	0.232745	40
21	.703533	3.60	.935988	1.23	.767545	4.82	.232455	39
22	.703749	3.58	.935914	1.23	.767834	4.83	.232166	38
23	.703964	3.58	.935840	1.23	.768124	4.83	.231876	37
24	.704179	3.60	.935766	1.23	.768414	4.82	.231586	36
25	9.704395	3.58	9.935692	1.23	9.768703	4.82	0.231297	35
26	.704610	3.58	.935618	1.25	.768992	4.82	.231008	34
27	.704825	3.58	.935543	1.23	.769281	4.83	.230719	33
28	.705040	3.57	.935469	1.23	.769571	4.82	.230429	32
29	.705254	3.58	.935395	1.25	.769860	4.80	.230140	31
30	9.705469	3.57	9.935320	1.23	9.770148	4.82	0.229852	30
31	.705683	3.58	.935246	1.25	.770437	4.82	.229563	29
32	.705898	3.57	.935171	1.23	.770726	4.82	.229274	28
33	.706112	3.57	.935097	1.25	.771015	4.80	.228985	27
34	.706326	3.55	.935022	1.23	.771303	4.82	.228697	26
35	9.706539	3.57	9.934948	1.25	9.771592	4.80	0.228408	25
36	.706753	3.57	.934873	1.25	.771880	4.80	.228120	24
37	.706967	3.55	.934798	1.25	.772168	4.82	.227832	23
38	.707180	3.55	.934723	1.23	.772457	4.80	.227543	22
39	.707393	3.55	.934649	1.25	.772745	4.80	.227255	21
40	9.707606	3.55	9.934574	1.25	9.773033	4.80	0.226967	20
41	.707819	3.55	.934499	1.25	.773321	4.78	.226679	19
42	.708032	3.55	.934424	1.25	.773608	4.80	.226392	18
43	.708245	3.55	.934349	1.25	.773896	4.80	.226104	17
44	.708458	3.53	.934274	1.25	.774184	4.78	.225816	16
45	9.708670	3.53	9.934199	1.27	9.774471	4.80	0.225529	15
46	.708882	3.53	.934123	1.25	.774759	4.78	.225241	14
47	.709094	3.53	.934048	1.25	.775046	4.78	.224954	13
48	.709306	3.53	.933973	1.25	.775333	4.80	.224667	12
49	.709518	3.53	.933898	1.27	.775621	4.78	.224379	11
50	9.709730	3.52	9.933822	1.25	9.775908	4.78	0.224092	10
51	.709941	3.53	.933747	1.27	.776195	4.78	.223805	9
52	.710153	3.52	.933671	1.25	.776482	4.77	.223518	8
53	.710364	3.52	.933596	1.27	.776768	4.78	.223232	7
54	.710575	3.52	.933520	1.25	.777055	4.78	.222945	6
55	9.710786	3.52	9.933445	1.27	9.777342	4.77	0.222658	5
56	.710997	3.52	.933369	1.27	.777628	4.78	.222372	4
57	.711208	3.52	.933293	1.27	.777915	4.78	.222085	3
58	.711419	3.50	.933217	1.27	.778201	4.77	.221799	2
59	.711629	3.50	.933141	1.25	.778488	4.78	.221512	1
60	9.711839		9.933066		9.778774	4.77	0.221226	0
	Cos.	D.1″.	Sin.	D. 1″.	Cot.	D. 1″.	Tan.	M.

120°   59°

TABLE C

LOGARITHMIC SINES, COSINES, TANGENTS, AND COTANGENTS

M.	Sin.	D. 1″.	Cos.	D. 1″.	Tan.	D. 1″.	Cot.	
0	9.711839	3.52	9.933066	1.27	9.778774	4.77	0.221226	60
1	.712050	3.50	.932990	1.27	.779060	4.77	.220940	59
2	.712260	3.48	.932914	1.27	.779346	4.77	.220654	58
3	.712469	3.50	.932838	1.27	.779632	4.77	.220368	57
4	.712679	3.50	.932762	1.28	.779918	4.75	.220082	56
5	9.712889	3.48	9.932685	1.27	9.780203	4.77	0.219797	55
6	.713098	3.50	.932609	1.27	.780489	4.77	.219511	54
7	.713308	3.48	.932533	1.27	.780775	4.75	.219225	53
8	.713517	3.48	.932457	1.28	.781060	4.77	.218940	52
9	.713726	3.48	.932380	1.27	.781346	4.75	.218654	51
10	9.713935	3.48	9.932304	1.27	9.781631	4.75	0.218369	50
11	.714144	3.47	.932228	1.28	.781916	4.75	.218084	49
12	.714352	3.48	.932151	1.27	.782201	4.75	.217799	48
13	.714561	3.47	.932075	1.28	.782486	4.75	.217514	47
14	.714769	3.48	.931998	1.28	.782771	4.75	.217229	46
15	9.714978	3.47	9.931921	1.27	9.783056	4.75	0.216944	45
16	.715186	3.47	.931845	1.28	.783341	4.75	.216659	44
17	.715394	3.47	.931768	1.28	.783626	4.73	.216374	43
18	.715602	3.45	.931691	1.28	.783910	4.75	.216090	42
19	.715809	3.47	.931614	1.28	.784195	4.73	.215805	41
20	9.716017	3.45	9.931537	1.28	9.784479	4.75	0.215521	40
21	.716224	3.47	.931460	1.28	.784764	4.73	.215236	39
22	.716432	3.45	.931383	1.28	.785048	4.73	.214952	38
23	.716639	3.45	.931306	1.28	.785332	4.73	.214668	37
24	.716846	3.45	.931229	1.28	.785616	4.73	.214384	36
25	9.717053	3.43	9.931152	1.28	9.785900	4.73	0.214100	35
26	.717259	3.45	.931075	1.28	.786184	4.73	.213816	34
27	.717466	3.45	.930998	1.28	.786468	4.73	.213532	33
28	.717673	3.43	.930921	1.30	.786752	4.73	.213248	32
29	.717879	3.43	.930843	1.28	.787036	4.72	.212964	31
30	9.718085	3.43	9.930766	1.30	9.787319	4.73	0.212681	30
31	.718291	3.43	.930688	1.28	.787603	4.72	.212397	29
32	.718497	3.43	.930611	1.30	.787886	4.73	.212114	28
33	.718703	3.43	.930533	1.28	.788170	4.72	.211830	27
34	.718909	3.42	.930456	1.30	.788453	4.72	.211547	26
35	9.719114	3.43	9.930378	1.30	9.788736	4.72	0.211264	25
36	.719320	3.42	.930300	1.30	.789019	4.72	.210981	24
37	.719525	3.42	.930223	1.28	.789302	4.72	.210698	23
38	.719730	3.42	.930145	1.30	.789585	4.72	.210415	22
39	.719935	3.42	.930067	1.30	.789868	4.72	.210132	21
40	9.720140	3.42	9.929989	1.30	9.790151	4.72	0.209849	20
41	.720345	3.40	.929911	1.30	.790434	4.70	.209566	19
42	.720549	3.42	.929833	1.30	.790716	4.72	.209284	18
43	.720754	3.40	.929755	1.30	.790999	4.70	.209001	17
44	.720958	3.40	.929677	1.30	.791281	4.70	.208719	16
45	9.721162	3.40	9.929599	1.30	9.791563	4.72	0.208437	15
46	.721366	3.40	.929521	1.32	.791846	4.70	.208154	14
47	.721570	3.40	.929442	1.30	.792128	4.70	.207872	13
48	.721774	3.40	.929364	1.30	.792410	4.70	.207590	12
49	.721978	3.38	.929286	1.32	.792692	4.70	.207308	11
50	9.722181	3.40	9.929207	1.30	9.792974	4.70	0.207026	10
51	.722385	3.38	.929129	1.32	.793256	4.70	.206744	9
52	.722588	3.38	.929050	1.30	.793538	4.68	.206462	8
53	.722791	3.38	.928972	1.32	.793819	4.70	.206181	7
54	.722994	3.38	.928893	1.30	.794101	4.70	.205899	6
55	9.723197	3.38	9.928815	1.32	9.794383	4.68	0.205617	5
56	.723400	3.38	.928736	1.32	.794664	4.70	.205336	4
57	.723603	3.37	.928657	1.32	.794946	4.68	.205054	3
58	.723805	3.37	.928578	1.32	.795227	4.68	.204773	2
59	.724007	3.38	.928499	1.32	.795508	4.68	.204492	1
60	9.724210		9.928420		9.795789		0.204211	0
	Cos.	D. 1″.	Sin.	D. 1″.	Cot.	D. 1″.	Tan.	M.

TABLE C 707

LOGARITHMIC SINES, COSINES, TANGENTS, AND COTANGENTS

32° **147°**

M.	Sin.	D. 1″.	Cos.	D. 1″.	Tan.	D. 1″.	Cot.	
0	9.724210	3.37	9.928420	1.30	9.795789	4.68	0.204211	60
1	.724412	3.37	.928342	1.32	.796070	4.68	.203930	59
2	.724614	3.37	.928263	1.33	.796351	4.68	.203649	58
3	.724816	3.35	.928183	1.32	.796632	4.68	.203368	57
4	.725017	3.37	.928104	1.32	.796913	4.68	.203087	56
5	9.725219	3.35	9.928025	1.32	9.797194	4.67	0.202806	55
6	.725420	3.37	.927946	1.32	.797474	4.68	.202526	54
7	.725622	3.35	.927867	1.33	.797755	4.68	.202245	53
8	.725823	3.35	.927787	1.32	.798036	4.67	.201964	52
9	.726024	3.35	.927708	1.32	.798316	4.67	.201684	51
10	9.726225	3.35	9.927629	1.33	9.798596	4.68	0.201404	50
11	.726426	3.33	.927549	1.32	.798877	4.67	.201123	49
12	.726626	3.35	.927470	1.33	.799157	4.67	.200843	48
13	.726827	3.33	.927390	1.33	.799437	4.67	.200563	47
14	.727027	3.35	.927310	1.33	.799717	4.67	.200283	46
15	9.727228	3.33	9.927231	1.32	9.799997	4.67	0.200003	45
16	.727428	3.33	.927151	1.33	.800277	4.67	.199723	44
17	.727628	3.33	.927071	1.33	.800557	4.65	.199443	43
18	.727828	3.32	.926991	1.33	.800836	4.67	.199164	42
19	.728027	3.33	.926911	1.33	.801116	4.67	.198884	41
20	9.728227	3.33	9.926831	1.33	9.801396	4.65	0.198604	40
21	.728427	3.32	.926751	1.33	.801675	4.67	.198325	39
22	.728626	3.32	.926671	1.33	.801955	4.65	.198045	38
23	.728825	3.32	.926591	1.33	.802234	4.65	.197766	37
24	.729024	3.32	.926511	1.33	.802513	4.65	.197487	36
25	9.729223	3.32	9.926431	1.33	9.802792	4.67	0.197208	35
26	.729422	3.32	.926351	1.35	.803072	4.65	.196928	34
27	.729621	3.32	.926270	1.33	.803351	4.65	.196649	33
28	.729820	3.30	.926190	1.33	.803630	4.65	.196370	32
29	.730018	3.32	.926110	1.35	.803909	4.63	.196091	31
30	9.730217	3.30	9.926029	1.33	9.804187	4.65	0.195813	30
31	.730415	3.30	.925949	1.35	.804466	4.65	.195534	29
32	.730613	3.30	.925868	1.33	.804745	4.63	.195255	28
33	.730811	3.30	.925788	1.35	.805023	4.65	.194977	27
34	.731009	3.28	.925707	1.35	.805302	4.63	.194698	26
35	9.731206	3.30	9.925626	1.35	9.805580	4.65	0.194420	25
36	.731404	3.30	.925545	1.33	.805859	4.63	.194141	24
37	.731602	3.28	.925465	1.35	.806137	4.63	.193863	23
38	.731799	3.28	.925384	1.35	.806415	4.63	.193585	22
39	.731996	3.28	.925303	1.35	.806693	4.63	.193307	21
40	9.732193	3.28	9.925222	1.35	9.806971	4.63	0.193029	20
41	.732390	3.28	.925141	1.35	.807249	4.63	.192751	19
42	.732587	3.28	.925060	1.35	.807527	4.63	.192473	18
43	.732784	3.27	.924979	1.37	.807805	4.63	.192195	17
44	.732980	3.28	.924897	1.35	.808083	4.63	.191917	16
45	9.733177	3.27	9.924816	1.35	9.808361	4.62	0.191639	15
46	.733373	3.27	.924735	1.35	.808638	4.63	.191362	14
47	.733569	3.27	.924654	1.37	.808916	4.62	.191084	13
48	.733765	3.27	.924572	1.35	.809193	4.63	.190807	12
49	.733961	3.27	.924491	1.37	.809471	4.62	.190529	11
50	9.734157	3.27	9.924409	1.35	9.809748	4.62	0.190252	10
51	.734353	3.27	.924328	1.37	.810025	4.62	.189975	9
52	.734549	3.25	.924246	1.37	.810302	4.63	.189698	8
53	.734744	3.25	.924164	1.35	.810580	4.62	.189420	7
54	.734939	3.27	.924083	1.37	.810857	4.62	.189143	6
55	9.735135	3.25	9.924001	1.37	9.811134	4.60	0.188866	5
56	.735330	3.25	.923919	1.37	.811410	4.62	.188590	4
57	.735525	3.23	.923837	1.37	.811687	4.62	.188313	3
58	.735719	3.25	.923755	1.37	.811964	4.62	.188036	2
59	.735914	3.25	.923673	1.37	.812241	4.60	.187759	1
60	9.736109		9.923591		9.812517		0.187483	0
	Cos.	D. 1″.	Sin.	D. 1″.	Cot.	D. 1″.	Tan.	M.

TABLE C

Logarithmic Sines, Cosines, Tangents, and Cotangents

33°   **146°**

M.	Sin.	D. 1″.	Cos.	D. 1″.	Tan.	D. 1″.	Cot.	
0	9.736109	3.23	9.923591	1.37	9.812517	4.62	0.187483	60
1	.736303	3.25	.923509	1.37	.812794	4.60	.187206	59
2	.736498	3.23	.923427	1.37	.813070	4.62	.186930	58
3	.736692	3.23	.923345	1.37	.813347	4.60	.186653	57
4	.736886	3.23	.923263	1.37	.813623	4.60	.186377	56
5	9.737080	3.23	9.923181	1.38	9.813899	4.62	0.186101	55
6	.737274	3.22	.923098	1.37	.814176	4.60	.185824	54
7	.737467	3.23	.923016	1.38	.814452	4.60	.185548	53
8	.737661	3.23	.922933	1.37	.814728	4.60	.185272	52
9	.737855	3.22	.922851	1.38	.815004	4.60	.184996	51
10	9.738048	3.22	9.922768	1.37	9.815280	4.58	0.184720	50
11	.738241	3.22	.922686	1.38	.815555	4.60	.184445	49
12	.738434	3.22	.922603	1.38	.815831	4.60	.184169	48
13	.738627	3.22	.922520	1.37	.816107	4.58	.183893	47
14	.738820	3.22	.922438	1.38	.816382	4.60	.183618	46
15	9.739013	3.22	9.922355	1.38	9.816658	4.58	0.183342	45
16	.739206	3.20	.922272	1.38	.816933	4.60	.183067	44
17	.739398	3.20	.922189	1.38	.817209	4.58	.182791	43
18	.739590	3.22	.922106	1.38	.817484	4.58	.182516	42
19	.739783	3.20	.922023	1.38	.817759	4.60	.182241	41
20	9.739975	3.20	9.921940	1.38	9.818035	4.58	0.181965	40
21	.740167	3.20	.921857	1.38	.818310	4.58	.181690	39
22	.740359	3.18	.921774	1.38	.818585	4.58	.181415	38
23	.740550	3.20	.921691	1.40	.818860	4.58	.181140	37
24	.740742	3.20	.921607	1.38	.819135	4.58	.180865	36
25	9.740934	3.18	9.921524	1.38	9.819410	4.57	0.180590	35
26	.741125	3.18	.921441	1.40	.819684	4.58	.180316	34
27	.741316	3.20	.921357	1.38	.819959	4.58	.180041	33
28	.741508	3.18	.921274	1.40	.820234	4.57	.179766	32
29	.741699	3.17	.921190	1.38	.820508	4.58	.179492	31
30	9.741889	3.18	9.921107	1.40	9.820783	4.57	0.179217	30
31	.742080	3.18	.921023	1.40	.821057	4.58	.178943	29
32	.742271	3.18	.920939	1.38	.821332	4.57	.178668	28
33	.742462	3.17	.920856	1.40	.821606	4.57	.178394	27
34	.742652	3.18	.920772	1.40	.821880	4.57	.178120	26
35	9.742842	3.17	9.920688	1.40	9.822154	4.58	0.177846	25
36	.743033	3.17	.920604	1.40	.822429	4.57	.177571	24
37	.743223	3.17	.920520	1.40	.822703	4.57	.177297	23
38	.743413	3.15	.920436	1.40	.822977	4.57	.177023	22
39	.743602	3.17	.920352	1.40	.823251	4.55	.176749	21
40	9.743792	3.17	9.920268	1.40	9.823524	4.57	0.176476	20
41	.743982	3.15	.920184	1.42	.823798	4.57	.176202	19
42	.744171	3.17	.920099	1.40	.824072	4.55	.175928	18
43	.744361	3.15	.920015	1.40	.824345	4.57	.175655	17
44	.744550	3.15	.919931	1.42	.824619	4.57	.175381	16
45	9.744739	3.15	9.919846	1.40	9.824893	4.55	0.175107	15
46	.744928	3.15	.919762	1.42	.825166	4.55	.174834	14
47	.745117	3.15	.919677	1.40	.825439	4.57	.174561	13
48	.745306	3.13	.919593	1.42	.825713	4.55	.174287	12
49	.745494	3.15	.919508	1.40	.825986	4.55	.174014	11
50	9.745683	3.13	9.919424	1.42	9.826259	4.55	0.173741	10
51	.745871	3.15	.919339	1.42	.826532	4.55	.173468	9
52	.746060	3.13	.919254	1.42	.826805	4.55	.173195	8
53	.746248	3.13	.919169	1.40	.827078	4.55	.172922	7
54	.746436	3.13	.919085	1.42	.827351	4.55	.172649	6
55	9.746624	3.13	9.919000	1.42	9.827624	4.55	0.172376	5
56	.746812	3.12	.918915	1.42	.827897	4.53	.172103	4
57	.746999	3.13	.918830	1.42	.828170	4.55	.171830	3
58	.747187	3.12	.918745	1.43	.828442	4.53	.171558	2
59	.747374	3.13	.918659	1.42	.828715		.171285	1
60	9.747562		9.918574		9.828987		0.171013	0
	Cos.	D. 1″.	Sin.	D. 1″.	Cot.	D. 1″.	Tan.	M.

123°   **56°**

TABLE C   709

LOGARITHMIC SINES, COSINES, TANGENTS, AND COTANGENTS

34°   **145°**

M.	Sin.	D. 1″.	Cos.	D. 1″.	Tan.	D. 1′.	Cot.	
0	9.747562	3.12	9.918574	1.42	9.828987	4.55	0.171013	60
1	.747749	3.12	.918489	1.42	.829260	4.53	.170740	59
2	.747936	3.12	.918404	1.43	.829532	4.55	.170468	58
3	.748123	3.12	.918318	1.42	.829805	4.53	.170195	57
4	.748310	3.12	.918233	1.43	.830077	4.53	.169923	56
5	9.748497	3.10	9.918147	1.42	9.830349	4.53	0.169651	55
6	.748683	3.12	.918062	1.43	.830621	4.53	.169379	54
7	.748870	3.10	.917976	1.42	.830893	4.53	.169107	53
8	.749056	3.12	.917891	1.43	.831165	4.53	.168835	52
9	.749243	3.10	.917805	1.43	.831437	4.53	.168563	51
10	9.749429	3.10	9.917719	1.42	9.831709	4.53	0.168291	50
11	.749615	3.10	.917634	1.43	.831981	4.53	.168019	49
12	.749801	3.10	.917548	1.43	.832253	4.53	.167747	48
13	.749987	3.08	.917462	1.43	.832525	4.52	.167475	47
14	.750172	3.10	.917376	1.43	.832796	4.53	.167204	46
15	9.750358	3.08	9.917290	1.43	9.833068	4.52	0.166932	45
16	.750543	3.10	.917204	1.43	.833339	4.53	.166661	44
17	.750729	3.08	.917118	1.43	.833611	4.52	.166389	43
18	.750914	3.08	.917032	1.43	.833882	4.53	.166118	42
19	.751099	3.08	.916946	1.45	.834154	4.52	.165846	41
20	9.751284	3.08	9.916859	1.43	9.834425	4.52	0.165575	40
21	.751469	3.08	.916773	1.43	.834696	4.52	.165304	39
22	.751654	3.08	.916687	1.45	.834967	4.52	.165033	38
23	.751839	3.07	.916600	1.43	.835238	4.52	.164762	37
24	.752023	3.08	.916514	1.45	.835509	4.52	.164491	36
25	9.752208	3.07	9.916427	1.43	9.835780	4.52	0.164220	35
26	.752392	3.07	.916341	1.45	.836051	4.52	.163949	34
27	.752576	3.07	.916254	1.45	.836322	4.52	.163678	33
28	.752760	3.07	.916167	1.43	.836593	4.52	.163407	32
29	.752944	3.07	.916081	1.45	.836864	4.50	.163136	31
30	9.753128	3.07	9.915994	1.45	9.837134	4.52	0.162866	30
31	.753312	3.05	.915907	1.45	.837405	4.50	.102595	29
32	.753495	3.07	.915820	1.45	.837675	4.52	.162325	28
33	.753679	3.05	.915733	1.45	.837946	4.50	.162054	27
34	.753862	3.07	.915646	1.45	.838216	4.52	.161784	26
35	9.754046	3.05	9.915559	1.45	9.838487	4.50	0.161513	25
36	.754229	3.05	.915472	1.45	.838757	4.50	.161243	24
37	.754412	3.05	.915385	1.47	.839027	4.50	.160973	23
38	.754595	3.05	.915297	1.45	.839297	4.52	.160703	22
39	.754778	3.03	.915210	1.45	.839568	4.50	.160432	21
40	9.754960	3.05	9.915123	1.47	9.839838	4.50	0.160162	20
41	.755143	3.05	.915035	1.45	.840108	4.50	.159892	19
42	.755326	3.03	.914948	1.47	.840378	4.50	.159622	18
43	.755508	3.03	.914860	1.45	.840648	4.50	.159352	17
44	.755690	3.03	.914773	1.47	.840917	4.48	.159083	16
45	9.755872	3.03	9.914685	1.45	9.841187	4.50	0.158813	15
46	.756054	3.03	.914598	1.47	.841457	4.50	.158543	14
47	.756236	3.03	.914510	1.47	.841727	4.48	.158273	13
48	.756418	3.03	.914422	1.47	.841996	4.50	.158004	12
49	.756600	3.03	.914334	1.47	.842266	4.48	.157734	11
50	9.756782	3.02	9.914246	1.47	9.842535	4.50	0.157465	10
51	.756963	3.02	.914158	1.47	.842805	4.48	.157195	9
52	.757144	3.03	.914070	1.47	.843074	4.48	.156926	8
53	.757326	3.02	.913982	1.47	.843343	4.48	.156657	7
54	.757507	3.02	.913894	1.47	.843612	4.50	.156388	6
55	9.757688	3.02	9.913806	1.47	9.843882	4.48	0.156118	5
56	.757869	3.02	.913718	1.47	.844151	4.48	.155849	4
57	.758050	3.00	.913630	1.48	.844420	4.48	.155580	3
58	.758230	3.02	.913541	1.47	.844689	4.48	.155311	2
59	.758411	3.00	.913453	1.47	.844958	4.48	.155042	1
60	9.758591		9.913365		9.845227		0.154773	0
	Cos.	D. 1″.	Sin.	D. 1″.	Cot.	D. 1″.	Tan.	M.

124°   **55°**

Logarithmic Sines, Cosines, Tangents, and Cotangents

M.	Sin.	D. 1".	Cos.	D. 1".	Tan.	D. 1".	Cot.	
0	9.758591	3.02	9.913365	1.48	9.845227	4.48	0.154773	60
1	.758772	3.00	.913276	1.48	.845496	4.47	.154504	59
2	.758952	3.00	.913187	1.47	.845764	4.48	.154236	58
3	.759132	3.00	.913099	1.48	.846033	4.48	.153967	57
4	.759312	3.00	.913010	1.47	.846302	4.47	.153698	56
5	9.759492	3.00	9.912922	1.48	9.846570	4.48	0.153430	55
6	.759672	3.00	.912833	1.48	.846839	4.48	.153161	54
7	.759852	2.98	.912744	1.48	.847108	4.47	.152892	53
8	.760031	3.00	.912655	1.48	.847376	4.47	.152624	52
9	.760211	2.98	.912566	1.48	.847644	4.48	.152356	51
10	9.760390	2.98	9.912477	1.48	9.847913	4.47	0.152087	50
11	.760569	2.98	.912388	1.48	.848181	4.47	.151819	49
12	.760748	2.98	.912299	1.48	.848449	4.47	.151551	48
13	.760927	2.98	.912210	1.48	.848717	4.48	.151283	47
14	.761106	2.98	.912121	1.48	.848986	4.47	.151014	46
15	9.761285	2.98	9.912031	1.50	9.849254	4.47	0.150746	45
16	.761464	2.97	.911942	1.48	.849522	4.47	.150478	44
17	.761642	2.98	.911853	1.48	.849790	4.45	.150210	43
18	.761821	2.97	.911763	1.50	.850057	4.47	.149943	42
19	.761999	2.97	.911674	1.48	.850325	4.47	.149675	41
20	9.762177	2.98	9.911584	1.50	9.850593	4.47	0.149407	40
21	.762356	2.97	.911495	1.48	.850861	4.47	.149139	39
22	.762534	2.97	.911405	1.50	.851129	4.45	.148871	38
23	.762712	2.95	.911315	1.50	.851396	4.47	.148604	37
24	.762889	2.97	.911226	1.48	.851664	4.45	.148336	36
25	9.763067	2.97	9.911136	1.50	9.851931	4.47	0.148069	35
26	.763245	2.95	.911046	1.50	.852199	4.45	.147801	34
27	.763422	2.97	.910956	1.50	.852466	4.45	.147534	33
28	.763600	2.95	.910866	1.50	.852733	4.47	.147267	32
29	.763777	2.95	.910776	1.50	.853001	4.45	.146999	31
30	9.763954	2.95	9.910686	1.50	9.853268	4.45	0.146732	30
31	.764131	2.95	.910596	1.50	.853535	4.45	.146465	29
32	.764308	2.95	.910506	1.52	.853802	4.45	.146198	28
33	.764485	2.95	.910415	1.50	.854069	4.45	.145931	27
34	.764662	2.93	.910325	1.50	.854336	4.45	.145664	26
35	9.764838	2.95	9.910235	1.52	9.854603	4.45	0.145397	25
36	.765015	2.93	.910144	1.50	.854870	4.45	.145130	24
37	.765191	2.93	.910054	1.52	.855137	4.45	.144863	23
38	.765367	2.95	.909963	1.50	.855404	4.45	.144596	22
39	.765544	2.93	.909873	1.52	.855671	4.45	.144329	21
40	9.765720	2.93	9.909782	1.52	9.855938	4.43	0.144062	20
41	.765896	2.93	.909691	1.50	.856204	4.45	.143796	19
42	.766072	2.92	.909601	1.52	.856471	4.43	.143529	18
43	.766247	2.93	.909510	1.52	.856737	4.45	.143263	17
44	.766423	2.92	.909419	1.52	.857004	4.43	.142996	16
45	9.766598	2.93	9.909328	1.52	9.857270	4.45	0.142730	15
46	.766774	2.92	.909237	1.52	.857537	4.43	.142463	14
47	.766949	2.92	.909146	1.52	.857803	4.43	.142197	13
48	.767124	2.93	.909055	1.52	.858069	4.45	.141931	12
49	.767300	2.92	.908964	1.52	.858336	4.43	.141664	11
50	9.767475	2.90	9.908873	1.53	9.858602	4.43	0.141398	10
51	.767649	2.92	.908781	1.52	.858868	4.43	.141132	9
52	.767824	2.92	.908690	1.52	.859134	4.43	.140866	8
53	.767999	2.90	.908599	1.53	.859400	4.43	.140600	7
54	.768173	2.92	.908507	1.52	.859666	4.43	.140334	6
55	9.768348	2.90	9.908416	1.53	9.859932	4.43	0.140068	5
56	.768522	2.92	.908324	1.52	.860198	4.43	.139802	4
57	.768697	2.90	.908233	1.53	.860464	4.43	.139536	3
58	.768871	2.90	.908141	1.53	.860730	4.42	.139270	2
59	.769045	2.90	.908049	1.52	.860995	4.43	.139005	1
60	9.769219		9.907958		9.861261		0.138739	0
	Cos.	D. 1".	Sin.	D. 1".	Cot.	D. 1".	Tan.	M.

TABLE C 711

LOGARITHMIC SINES, COSINES, TANGENTS, AND COTANGENTS

36° 143°

M.	Sin.	D. 1″.	Cos.	D. 1″.	Tan.	D. 1″.	Cot.	
0	9.769219	2.90	9.907958	1.53	9.861261	4.43	0.138739	60
1	.769393	2.88	.907866	1.53	.861527	4.42	.138473	59
2	.769566	2.90	.907774	1.53	.861792	4.43	.138208	58
3	.769740	2.88	.907682	1.53	.862058	4.42	.137942	57
4	.769913	2.90	.907590	1.53	.862323	4.43	.137677	56
5	9.770087	2.88	9.907498	1.53	9.862589	4.42	0.137411	55
6	.770260	2.88	.907406	1.53	.862854	4.42	.137146	54
7	.770433	2.88	.907314	1.53	.863119	4.43	.136881	53
8	.770606	2.88	.907222	1.55	.863385	4.42	.136615	52
9	.770779	2.88	.907129	1.53	.863650	4.42	.136350	51
10	9.770952	2.88	9.907037	1.53	9.863915	4.42	0.136085	50
11	.771125	2.88	.906945	1.55	.864180	4.42	.135820	49
12	.771298	2.87	.906852	1.53	.864445	4.42	.135555	48
13	.771470	2.88	.906760	1.55	.864710	4.42	.135290	47
14	.771643	2.87	.906667	1.53	.864975	4.42	.135025	46
15	9.771815	2.87	9.906575	1.53	9.865240	4.42	0.134760	45
16	.771987	2.87	.906482	1.55	.865505	4.42	.134495	44
17	.772159	2.87	.906389	1.55	.865770	4.42	.134230	43
18	.772331	2.87	.906296	1.53	.866035	4.42	.133965	42
19	.772503	2.87	.906204	1.55	.866300	4.40	.133700	41
20	9.772675	2.87	9.906111	1.55	9.866564	4.42	0.133436	40
21	.772847	2.85	.906018	1.55	.866829	4.42	.133171	39
22	.773018	2.87	.905925	1.55	.867094	4.40	.132906	38
23	.773190	2.85	.905832	1.55	.867358	4.42	.132642	37
24	.773361	2.87	.905739	1.57	.867625	4.42	.132377	36
25	9.773533	2.85	9.905645	1.55	9.867887	4.42	0.132113	35
26	.773704	2.85	.905552	1.55	.868152	4.40	.131848	34
27	.773875	2.85	.905459	1.55	.868416	4.40	.131584	33
28	.774046	2.85	.905366	1.57	.868680	4.42	.131320	32
29	.774217	2.85	.905272	1.55	.868945	4.40	.131055	31
30	9.774388	2.83	9.905179	1.57	9.869209	4.40	0.130791	30
31	.774558	2.85	.905085	1.55	.869473	4.40	.130527	29
32	.774729	2.83	.904992	1.57	.869737	4.40	.130263	28
33	.774899	2.85	.904898	1.57	.870001	4.40	.129999	27
34	.775070	2.83	.904804	1.57	.870265	4.40	.129735	26
35	9.775240	2.83	9.904711	1.55	9.870529	4.40	0.129471	25
36	.775410	2.83	.904617	1.57	.870790	4.40	.129207	24
37	.775580	2.83	.904523	1.57	.871057	4.40	.128943	23
38	.775750	2.83	.904429	1.57	.871321	4.40	.128679	22
39	.775920	2.83	.904335	1.57	.871585	4.40	.128415	21
40	9.776090	2.82	9.904241	1.57	9.871849	4.38	0.128151	20
41	.776259	2.83	.904147	1.57	.872112	4.40	.127888	19
42	.776429	2.82	.904053	1.57	.872376	4.40	.127624	18
43	.776598	2.83	.903959	1.58	.872640	4.38	.127360	17
44	.776768	2.82	.903864	1.57	.872903	4.40	.127097	16
45	9.776937	2.82	9.903770	1.57	9.873167	4.38	0.126833	15
46	.777106	2.82	.903676	1.58	.873430	4.40	.126570	14
47	.777275	2.82	.903581	1.57	.873694	4.38	.126306	13
48	.777444	2.82	.903487	1.58	.873957	4.38	.126043	12
49	.777613	2.80	.903302	1.57	.874220	4.40	.125780	11
50	9.777781	2.82	9.903298	1.58	9.874484	4.38	0.125516	10
51	.777950	2.82	.903203	1.58	.874747	4.38	.125253	9
52	.778119	2.80	.903108	1.57	.875010	4.38	.124990	8
53	.778287	2.80	.903014	1.58	.875273	4.40	.124727	7
54	.778455	2.82	.902919	1.58	.875537	4.38	.124463	6
55	9.778624	2.80	9.902824	1.58	9.875800	4.38	0.124200	5
56	.778792	2.80	.902729	1.58	.876063	4.38	.123937	4
57	.778960	2.80	.902634	1.58	.876326	4.38	.123674	3
58	.779128	2.78	.902539	1.58	.876589	4.38	.123411	2
59	.779295	2.80	.902444	1.58	.876852	4.37	.123148	1
60	9.779463		9.902349		9.877114		0.122886	0
	Cos.	D. 1″.	Sin.	D. 1″.	Cot.	D. 1″.	Tan.	M.

TABLE C

LOGARITHMIC SINES, COSINES, TANGENTS, AND COTANGENTS

37°   **142°**

M.	Sin.	D. 1″.	Cos.	D. 1″.	Tan.	D. 1″.	Cot.	
0	9.779463	2.89	9.902349	1.60	9.877114	4.38	0.122886	60
1	.779631	2.78	.902253	1.58	.877377	4.38	.122623	59
2	.779798	2.80	.902158	1.58	.877640	4.38	.122360	58
3	.779966	2.78	.902063	1.60	.877903	4.37	.122097	57
4	.780133	2.78	.901967	1.58	.878165	4.38	.121835	56
5	9.780300	2.78	9.901872	1.60	9.878428	4.38	0.121572	55
6	.780467	2.78	.901776	1.58	.878691	4.37	.121309	54
7	.780634	2.78	.901681	1.60	.878953	4.38	.121047	53
8	.780801	2.78	.901585	1.58	.879216	4.37	.120784	52
9	.780968	2.77	.901490	1.60	.879478	4.38	.120522	51
10	9.781134	2.78	9.901394	1.60	9.879741	4.37	0.120259	50
11	.781301	2.78	.901298	1.60	.880003	4.37	.119997	49
12	.781468	2.77	.901202	1.60	.880265	4.38	.119735	48
13	.781634	2.77	.901106	1.60	.880528	4.37	.119472	47
14	.781800	2.77	.901010	1.60	.880790	4.37	.119210	46
15	9.781966	2.77	9.900914	1.60	9.881052	4.37	0.118948	45
16	.782132	2.77	.900818	1.60	.881314	4.38	.118686	44
17	.782298	2.77	.900722	1.60	.881577	4.37	.118423	43
18	.782464	2.77	.900626	1.62	.881839	4.37	.118161	42
19	.782630	2.77	.900529	1.60	.882101	4.37	.117899	41
20	9.782796	2.75	9.900433	1.60	9.882363	4.37	0.117637	40
21	.782961	2.77	.900337	1.62	.882625	4.37	.117375	39
22	.783127	2.75	.900240	1.60	.882887	4.35	.117113	38
23	.783292	2.77	.900144	1.62	.883148	4.37	.116852	37
24	.783458	2.75	.900047	1.60	.883410	4.37	.116590	36
25	9.783623	2.75	9.899951	1.62	9.883672	4.37	0.116328	35
26	.783788	2.75	.899854	1.62	.883934	4.37	.116066	34
27	.783953	2.75	.899757	1.62	.884196	4.35	.115804	33
28	.784118	2.73	.899660	1.60	.884457	4.37	.115543	32
29	.784282	2.75	.899564	1.62	.884719	4.35	.115281	31
30	9.784447	2.75	9.899467	1.62	9.884980	4.37	0.115020	30
31	.784612	2.73	.899370	1.62	.885242	4.37	.114758	29
32	.784776	2.75	.899273	1.62	.885504	4.35	.114496	28
33	.784941	2.73	.899176	1.63	.885765	4.35	.114235	27
34	.785105	2.73	.899078	1.62	.886026	4.37	.113974	26
35	9.785269	2.73	9.898981	1.62	9.886288	4.35	0.113712	25
36	.785433	2.73	.898884	1.62	.886549	4.37	.113451	24
37	.785597	2.73	.898787	1.63	.886811	4.35	.113189	23
38	.785761	2.73	.898689	1.62	.887072	4.35	.112928	22
39	.785925	2.73	.898592	1.63	.887333	4.35	.112667	21
40	9.786089	2.72	9.898494	1.62	9.887594	4.35	0.112406	20
41	.786252	2.73	.898397	1.63	.887855	4.35	.112145	19
42	.786416	2.72	.898299	1.62	.888116	4.37	.111884	18
43	.786579	2.72	.898202	1.63	.888378	4.35	.111622	17
44	.786742	2.73	.898104	1.63	.888639	4.35	.111361	16
45	9.786906	2.72	9.898006	1.63	9.888900	4.35	0.111100	15
46	.787069	2.72	.897908	1.63	.889161	4.33	.110839	14
47	.787232	2.72	.897810	1.63	.889421	4.35	.110579	13
48	.787395	2.70	.897712	1.63	.889682	4.35	.110318	12
49	.787557	2.72	.897614	1.63	.889943	4.35	.110057	11
50	9.787720	2.72	9.897516	1.63	9.890204	4.35	0.109796	10
51	.787883	2.70	.897418	1.63	.890465	4.33	.109535	9
52	.788045	2.72	.897320	1.63	.890725	4.35	.109275	8
53	.788208	2.70	.897222	1.65	.890986	4.35	.109014	7
54	.788370	2.70	.897123	1.63	.891247	4.33	.108753	6
55	9.788532	2.70	9.897025	1.65	9.891507	4.35	0.108493	5
56	.788694	2.70	.896926	1.63	.891768	4.33	.108232	4
57	.788856	2.70	.896828	1.65	.892028	4.35	.107972	3
58	.789018	2.70	.896729	1.63	.892289	4.33	.107711	2
59	.789180	2.70	.896631	1.65	.892549	4.35	.107451	1
60	9.789342		9.896532		9.892810		0.107190	0
	Cos.	D. 1″.	Sin.	D. 1″.	Cot.	D. 1″.	Tan.	M.

TABLE C 713

Logarithmic Sines, Cosines, Tangents, and Cotangents

38° **141°**

M.	Sin.	D. 1″.	Cos.	D. 1″.	Tan.	D. 1″.	Cot.	
0	9.789342	2.70	9.896532	1.65	9.892810	4.33	0.107190	60
1	.789504	2.68	.896433	1.63	.893070	4.35	.106930	59
2	.789665	2.70	.896335	1.65	.893331	4.33	.106669	58
3	.789827	2.68	.896236	1.65	.893591	4.33	.106409	57
4	.789988	2.68	.896137	1.65	.893851	4.33	.106149	56
5	9.790149	2.68	9.896038	1.65	9.894111	4.35	0.105889	55
6	.790310	2.68	.895939	1.65	.894372	4.33	.105628	54
7	.790471	2.68	.895840	1.65	.894632	4.33	.105368	53
8	.790632	2.68	.895741	1.67	.894892	4.33	.105108	52
9	.790793	2.68	.895641	1.65	.895152	4.33	.104848	51
10	9.790954	2.68	9.895542	1.65	9.895412	4.33	0.104588	50
11	.791115	2.67	.895443	1.67	.895672	4.33	.104328	49
12	.791275	2.68	.895343	1.67	.895932	4.33	.104068	48
13	.791436	2.67	.895244	1.65	.896192	4.33	.103808	47
14	.791596	2.68	.895145	1.65	.896452	4.33	.103548	46
15	9.791757	2.67	9.895045	1.67	9.896712	4.32	0.103288	45
16	.791917	2.67	.894945	1.65	.896971	4.33	.103029	44
17	.792077	2.67	.894846	1.67	.897231	4.33	.102769	43
18	.792237	2.67	.894746	1.67	.897491	4.33	.102509	42
19	.792397	2.67	.894646	1.67	.897751	4.32	.102249	41
20	9.792557	2.65	9.894546	1.67	9.898010	4.33	0.101990	40
21	.792716	2.67	.894446	1.67	.898270	4.33	.101730	39
22	.792876	2.65	.894346	1.67	.898530	4.32	.101470	38
23	.793035	2.67	.894246	1.67	.898789	4.33	.101211	37
24	.793195	2.65	.894146	1.67	.899049	4.32	.100951	36
25	9.793354	2.67	9.894046	1.67	9.899308	4.33	0.100692	35
26	.793514	2.65	.893946	1.67	.899568	4.32	.100432	34
27	.793673	2.65	.893846	1.68	.899827	4.33	.100173	33
28	.793832	2.65	.893745	1.67	.900087	4.32	.099913	32
29	.793991	2.65	.893645	1.68	.900346	4.32	.099654	31
30	9.794150	2.63	9.893544	1.67	9.900605	4.32	0.099395	30
31	.794308	2.65	.893444	1.68	.900864	4.33	.099136	29
32	.794467	2.65	.893343	1.67	.901124	4.32	.098876	28
33	.794626	2.63	.893243	1.68	.901383	4.32	.098617	27
34	.794784	2.63	.893142	1.68	.901642	4.32	.098358	26
35	9.794942	2.65	9.893041	1.68	9.901901	4.32	0.098099	25
36	.795101	2.63	.892940	1.68	.902160	4.33	.097840	24
37	.795259	2.63	.892839	1.68	.902420	4.32	.097580	23
38	.795417	2.63	.892739	1.67	.902679	4.32	.097321	22
39	.795575	2.63	.892638	1.70	.902938	4.32	.097062	21
40	9.795733	2.63	9.892536	1.68	9.903197	4.32	0.096803	20
41	.795891	2.63	.892435	1.68	.903456	4.30	.096544	19
42	.796049	2.62	.892334	1.68	.903714	4.32	.096286	18
43	.796206	2.63	.892233	1.68	.903973	4.32	.096027	17
44	.796364	2.62	.892132	1.70	.904232	4.32	.095768	16
45	9.796521	2.63	9.892030	1.68	9.904491	4.32	0.095509	15
46	.796679	2.62	.891929	1.70	.904750	4.30	.095250	14
47	.796836	2.62	.891827	1.70	.905008	4.32	.094992	13
48	.796993	2.62	.891726	1.68	.905267	4.32	.094733	12
49	.797150	2.62	.891624	1.70	.905526	4.32	.094474	11
50	9.797307	2.62	9.891523	1.70	9.905785	4.30	0.094215	10
51	.797464	2.62	.891421	1.70	.906043	4.32	.093957	9
52	.797621	2.60	.891319	1.70	.906302	4.30	.093698	8
53	.797777	2.62	.891217	1.70	.906560	4.32	.093440	7
54	.797934	2.62	.891115	1.70	.906819	4.30	.093181	6
55	9.798091	2.60	9.891013	1.70	9.907077	4.32	0.092923	5
56	.798247	2.60	.890911	1.70	.907336	4.30	.092664	4
57	.798403	2.62	.890809	1.70	.907594	4.30	.092406	3
58	.798560	2.60	.890707	1.70	.907853	4.30	.092147	2
59	.798716	2.60	.890605	1.70	.908111	4.30	.091889	1
60	9.798872		9.890503		9.908369		0.091631	0
	Cos.	D. 1″.	Sin.	D. 1″.	Cot.	D. 1″.	Tan.	M.

TABLE C

LOGARITHMIC SINES, COSINES, TANGENTS, AND COTANGENTS

M.	Sin.	D. 1".	Cos.	D. 1".	Tan.	D. 1".	Cot.	
0	9.798872	2.60	9.890503	1.72	9.908369	4.32	0.091631	60
1	.799028	2.60	.890400	1.70	.908628	4.30	.091372	59
2	.799184	2.58	.890298	1.72	.908886	4.30	.091114	58
3	.799339	2.60	.890195	1.70	.909144	4.30	.090856	57
4	.799495	2.60	.890093	1.72	.909402	4.30	.090598	56
5	9.799651	2.58	9.889990	1.70	9.909660	4.30	0.090340	55
6	.799806	2.60	.889888	1.72	.909918	4.32	.090082	54
7	.799962	2.58	.889785	1.72	.910177	4.30	.089823	53
8	.800117	2.58	.889682	1.72	.910435	4.30	.089565	52
9	.800272	2.58	.889579	1.70	.910693	4.30	.089307	51
10	9.800427	2.58	9.889477	1.72	9.910951	4.30	0.089049	50
11	.800582	2.58	.889374	1.72	.911209	4.30	.088791	49
12	.800737	2.58	.889271	1.72	.911467	4.30	.088533	48
13	.800892	2.58	.889168	1.73	.911725	4.28	.088275	47
14	.801047	2.57	.889064	1.72	.911982	4.30	.088018	46
15	9.801201	2.58	9.888961	1.72	9.912240	4.30	0.087760	45
16	.801356	2.58	.888858	1.72	.912498	4.30	.087502	44
17	.801511	2.57	.888755	1.73	.912756	4.30	.087244	43
18	.801665	2.57	.888651	1.72	.913014	4.28	.086986	42
19	.801819	2.57	.888548	1.73	.913271	4.30	.086729	41
20	9.801973	2.58	9.888444	1.72	9.913529	4.30	0.086471	40
21	.802128	2.57	.888341	1.73	.913787	4.28	.086213	39
22	.802282	2.57	.888237	1.72	.914044	4.30	.085956	38
23	.802436	2.55	.888134	1.73	.914302	4.30	.085698	37
24	.802589	2.57	.888030	1.73	.914560	4.28	.085440	36
25	9.802743	2.57	9.887926	1.73	9.914817	4.30	0.085183	35
26	.802897	2.55	.887822	1.73	.915075	4.28	.084925	34
27	.803050	2.57	.887718	1.73	.915332	4.30	.084668	33
28	.803204	2.55	.887614	1.73	.915590	4.28	.084410	32
29	.803357	2.57	.887510	1.73	.915847	4.28	.084153	31
30	9.803511	2.55	9.887406	1.73	9.916104	4.30	0.083896	30
31	.803664	2.55	.887302	1.73	.916362	4.28	.083638	29
32	.803817	2.55	.887198	1.75	.916619	4.30	.083381	28
33	.803970	2.55	.887093	1.73	.916877	4.28	.083123	27
34	.804123	2.55	.886989	1.73	.917134	4.28	.082866	26
35	9.804276	2.53	9.886885	1.75	9.917391	4.28	0.082609	25
36	.804428	2.55	.886780	1.73	.917648	4.30	.082352	24
37	.804581	2.55	.886676	1.75	.917906	4.28	.082094	23
38	.804734	2.53	.886571	1.75	.918163	4.28	.081837	22
39	.804886	2.55	.886466	1.73	.918420	4.28	.081580	21
40	9.805039	2.53	9.886362	1.75	9.918677	4.28	0.081323	20
41	.805191	2.53	.886257	1.75	.918934	4.28	.081066	19
42	.805343	2.53	.886152	1.75	.919191	4.28	.080809	18
43	.805495	2.53	.886047	1.75	.919448	4.28	.080552	17
44	.805647	2.53	.885942	1.75	.919705	4.28	.080295	16
45	9.805799	2.53	9.885837	1.75	9.919962	4.28	0.080038	15
46	.805951	2.53	.885732	1.75	.920219	4.28	.079781	14
47	.806103	2.52	.885627	1.75	.920476	4.28	.079524	13
48	.806254	2.53	.885522	1.77	.920733	4.28	.079267	12
49	.806406	2.52	.885416	1.75	.920990	4.28	.079010	11
50	9.806557	2.53	9.885311	1.77	9.921247	4.27	0.078753	10
51	.806709	2.52	.885205	1.75	.921503	4.28	.078497	9
52	.806860	2.52	.885100	1.77	.921760	4.28	.078240	8
53	.807011	2.53	.884994	1.75	.922017	4.27	.077983	7
54	.807163	2.52	.884889	1.77	.922274	4.28	.077726	6
55	9.807314	2.52	9.884783	1.77	9.922530	4.28	0.077470	5
56	.807465	2.50	.884677	1.75	.922787	4.28	.077213	4
57	.807615	2.52	.884572	1.77	.923044	4.27	.076956	3
58	.807766	2.52	.884466	1.77	.923300	4.28	.076700	2
59	.807917	2.50	.884360	1.77	.923557	4.28	.076443	1
60	9.808067		9.884254	1.77	9.923814		0.076186	0
	Cos.	D. 1".	Sin.	D. 1".	Cot.	D. 1".	Tan.	M.

Logarithmic Sines, Cosines, Tangents, and Cotangents

40°   139°

M.	Sin.	D. 1″.	Cos.	D. 1″.	Tan.	D. 1″.	Cot.	
0	9.808067	2.52	9.884254	1.77	9.923814	4.27	0.076186	60
1	.808218	2.50	.884148	1.77	.924070	4.28	.075930	59
2	.808368	2.52	.884042	1.77	.924327	4.27	.075673	58
3	.808519	2.50	.883936	1.78	.924583	4.28	.075417	57
4	.808669	2.50	.883829	1.77	.924840	4.27	.075160	56
5	9.808819	2.50	9.883723	1.77	9.925096	4.27	0.074904	55
6	.808969	2.50	.883617	1.78	.925352	4.28	.074648	54
7	.809119	2.50	.883510	1.77	.925609	4.27	.074391	53
8	.809269	2.50	.883404	1.78	.925865	4.28	.074135	52
9	.809419	2.50	.883297	1.77	.926122	4.27	.073878	51
10	9.809569	2.48	9.883191	1.78	9.926378	4.27	0.073622	50
11	.809718	2.50	.883084	1.78	.926634	4.27	.073366	49
12	.809868	2.48	.882977	1.78	.926890	4.28	.073110	48
13	.810017	2.50	.882871	1.77	.927147	4.27	.072853	47
14	.810167	2.48	.882764	1.78	.927403	4.27	.072597	46
15	9.810316	2.48	9.882657	1.78	9.927659	4.27	0.072341	45
16	.810465	2.48	.882550	1.78	.927915	4.27	.072085	44
17	.810614	2.48	.882443	1.78	.928171	4.27	.071829	43
18	.810763	2.48	.882336	1.78	.928427	4.28	.071573	42
19	.810912	2.48	.882229	1.80	.928684	4.27	.071316	41
20	9.811061	2.48	9.882121	1.78	9.928940	4.27	0.071060	40
21	.811210	2.47	.882014	1.78	.929196	4.27	.070804	39
22	.811358	2.48	.881907	1.80	.929452	4.27	.070548	38
23	.811507	2.47	.881799	1.78	.929708	4.27	.070292	37
24	.811655	2.48	.881692	1.80	.929964	4.27	.070036	36
25	9.811804	2.47	9.881584	1.78	9.930220	4.25	0.069780	35
26	.811952	2.47	.881477	1.80	.930475	4.27	.069525	34
27	.812100	2.47	.881369	1.80	.930731	4.27	.069269	33
28	.812248	2.47	.881261	1.80	.930987	4.27	.069013	32
29	.812396	2.17	.881153	1.78	.931243	4.27	.068757	31
30	9.812544	2.47	9.881046	1.80	9.931499	4.27	0.068501	30
31	.812692	2.47	.880938	1.80	.931755	4.25	.068245	29
32	.812840	2.47	.880830	1.80	.932010	4.27	.067990	28
33	.812988	2.45	.880722	1.82	.932266	4.27	.067734	27
34	.813135	2.47	.880613	1.80	.932522	4.27	.067478	26
35	9.813283	2.45	9.880505	1.80	9.932778	4.25	0.067222	25
36	.813430	2.47	.880397	1.80	.933033	4.27	.066967	24
37	.813578	2.45	.880289	1.80	.933289	4.27	.066711	23
38	.813725	2.45	.880180	1.82	.933545	4.25	.066455	22
39	.813872	2.45	.880072	1.80	.933800	4.27	.066200	21
40	9.814019	2.45	9.879963	1.82	9.934056	4.25	0.065944	20
41	.814166	2.45	.879855	1.80	.934311	4.27	.065689	19
42	.814313	2.45	.879746	1.82	.934567	4.25	.065433	18
43	.814460	2.45	.879637	1.82	.934822	4.27	.065178	17
44	.814607	2.43	.879529	1.80	.935078	4.25	.064922	16
45	9.814753	2.45	9.879420	1.82	9.935333	4.27	0.064667	15
46	.814900	2.43	.879311	1.82	.935589	4.25	.064411	14
47	.815046	2.45	.879202	1.82	.935844	4.27	.064156	13
48	.815193	2.43	.879093	1.82	.936100	4.25	.063900	12
49	.815330	2.43	.878984	1.82	.936355	4.27	.063645	11
50	9.815485	2.45	9.878875	1.82	9.936611	4.25	0.063389	10
51	.815632	2.43	.878766	1.83	.936866	4.25	.063134	9
52	.815778	2.43	.878656	1.82	.937121	4.27	.062879	8
53	.815924	2.42	.878547	1.82	.937377	4.25	.062623	7
54	.816069	2.43	.878438	1.83	.937632	4.25	.062368	6
55	9.816215	2.43	9.878328	1.82	9.937887	4.25	0.062113	5
56	.816361	2.43	.878219	1.83	.938142	4.27	.061858	4
57	.816507	2.42	.878109	1.83	.938398	4.25	.061602	3
58	.816652	2.43	.877999	1.82	.938653	4.25	.061347	2
59	.816798	2.42	.877890	1.83	.938908	4.25	.061092	1
60	9.816943		9.877780		9.939163		0.060837	0
	Cos.	D. 1″.	Sin.	D. 1″.	Cot.	D. 1″.	Tan.	M.

TABLE C

LOGARITHMIC SINES, COSINES, TANGENTS, AND COTANGENTS

41°   138°

M.	Sin.	D. 1″.	Cos.	D. 1″.	Tan.	D. 1″.	Cot.	
0	9.816943	2.42	9.877780	1.83	9.939163	4.25	0.060837	60
1	.817088	2.42	.877670	1.83	.939418	4.25	.060582	59
2	.817233	2.43	.877560	1.83	.939673	4.25	.060327	58
3	.817379	2.42	.877450	1.83	.939928	4.25	.060072	57
4	.817524	2.40	.877340	1.83	.940183	4.27	.059817	56
5	9.817668	2.42	9.877230	1.83	9.940439	4.25	0.059561	55
6	.817813	2.42	.877120	1.83	.940694	4.25	.059306	54
7	.817958	2.42	.877010	1.85	.940949	4.25	.059051	53
8	.818103	2.42	.876899	1.83	.941204	4.25	.058796	52
9	.818247	2.40	.876789	1.85	.941459	4.23	.058541	51
10	9.818392	2.42	9.876678	1.83	9.941713	4.25	0.058287	50
11	.818536	2.40	.876568	1.85	.941968	4.25	.058032	49
12	.818681	2.42	.876457	1.83	.942223	4.25	.057777	48
13	.818825	2.40	.876347	1.85	.942478	4.25	.057522	47
14	.818969	2.40	.876236	1.85	.942733	4.25	.057267	46
15	9.819113	2.40	9.876125	1.85	9.942988	4.25	0.057012	45
16	.819257	2.40	.876014	1.83	.943243	4.25	.056757	44
17	.819401	2.40	.875904	1.85	.943498	4.23	.056502	43
18	.819545	2.40	.875793	1.85	.943752	4.25	.056248	42
19	.819689	2.38	.875682	1.85	.944007	4.25	.055993	41
20	9.819832	2.40	9.875571	1.87	9.944262	4.25	0.055738	40
21	.819976	2.40	.875459	1.85	.944517	4.23	.055483	39
22	.820120	2.38	.875348	1.85	.944771	4.25	.055229	38
23	.820263	2.38	.875237	1.85	.945026	4.25	.054974	37
24	.820406	2.40	.875126	1.87	.945281	4.23	.054719	36
25	9.820550	2.38	9.875014	1.85	9.945535	4.25	0.054465	35
26	.820693	2.38	.874903	1.87	.945790	4.25	.054210	34
27	.820836	2.38	.874791	1.85	.946045	4.23	.053955	33
28	.820979	2.38	.874680	1.87	.946299	4.25	.053701	32
29	.821122	2.38	.874568	1.87	.946554	4.23	.053446	31
30	9.821265	2.37	9.874456	1.87	9.946808	4.25	0.053192	30
31	.821407	2.38	.874344	1.87	.947063	4.25	.052937	29
32	.821550	2.38	.874232	1.85	.947318	4.23	.052682	28
33	.821693	2.37	.874121	1.87	.947572	4.25	.052428	27
34	.821835	2.37	.874009	1.88	.947827	4.23	.052173	26
35	9.821977	2.38	9.873896	1.87	9.948081	4.23	0.051919	25
36	.822120	2.37	.873784	1.87	.948335	4.25	.051665	24
37	.822262	2.37	.873672	1.87	.948590	4.23	.051410	23
38	.822404	2.37	.873560	1.87	.948844	4.25	.051156	22
39	.822546	2.37	.873448	1.88	.949099	4.23	.050901	21
40	9.822688	2.37	9.873335	1.87	9.949353	4.25	0.050647	20
41	.822830	2.37	.873223	1.88	.949608	4.23	.050392	19
42	.822972	2.37	.873110	1.87	.949862	4.23	.050138	18
43	.823114	2.35	.872998	1.88	.950116	4.25	.049884	17
44	.823255	2.37	.872885	1.88	.950371	4.23	.049629	16
45	9.823397	2.37	9.872772	1.88	9.950625	4.23	0.049375	15
46	.823539	2.35	.872659	1.87	.950879	4.23	.049121	14
47	.823680	2.35	.872547	1.88	.951133	4.25	.048867	13
48	.823821	2.37	.872434	1.88	.951388	4.23	.048612	12
49	.823963	2.35	.872321	1.88	.951642	4.23	.048358	11
50	9.824104	2.35	9.872208	1.88	9.951896	4.23	0.048104	10
51	.824245	2.35	.872095	1.90	.952150	4.25	.047850	9
52	.824386	2.35	.871981	1.88	.952405	4.23	.047595	8
53	.824527	2.35	.871868	1.88	.952659	4.23	.047341	7
54	.824668	2.33	.871755	1.90	.952913	4.23	.047087	6
55	9.824808	2.35	9.871641	1.88	9.953167	4.23	0.046833	5
56	.824949	2.35	.871528	1.90	.953421	4.23	.046579	4
57	.825090	2.33	.871414	1.88	.953675	4.23	.046325	3
58	.825230	2.35	.871301	1.90	.953929	4.23	.046071	2
59	.825371	2.33	.871187	1.90	.954183	4.23	.045817	1
60	9.825511		9.871073		9.954437		0.045563	0
	Cos.	D. 1″.	Sin.	D. 1″.	Cot.	D. 1″.	Tan.	M.

131°   48°

TABLE C   717

LOGARITHMIC SINES. COSINES, TANGENTS, AND COTANGENTS

42°   137°

M.	Sin.	D. 1″.	Cos.	D. 1″.	Tan.	D. 1″.	Cot.	
0	9.825511	2.33	9.871073	1.88	9.954437	4.23	0.045563	60
1	.825651	2.33	.870960	1.90	.954691	4.25	.045309	59
2	.825791	2.33	.870846	1.90	.954946	4.23	.045054	58
3	.825931	2.33	.870732	1.90	.955200	4.23	.044800	57
4	.826071	2.33	.870618	1.90	.955454	4.23	.044546	56
5	9.826211	2.33	9.870504	1.90	9.955708	4.22	0.044292	55
6	.826351	2.33	.870390	1.90	.955961	4.23	.044039	54
7	.826491	2.33	.870276	1.92	.956215	4.23	.043785	53
8	.826631	2.32	.870161	1.90	.956469	4.23	.043531	52
9	.826770	2.33	.870047	1.90	.956723	4.23	.043277	51
10	9.826910	2.32	9.869933	1.92	9.956977	4.23	0.013023	50
11	.827049	2.33	.869818	1.90	.957231	4.23	.042769	49
12	.827189	2.32	.869704	1.92	.957485	4.23	.042515	48
13	.827328	2.32	.869589	1.92	.957739	4.23	.042261	47
14	.827467	2.32	.869474	1.90	.957993	4.23	.042007	46
15	9.827606	2.32	9.869360	1.92	9.958247	4.22	0.041753	45
16	.827745	2.32	.869245	1.92	.958500	4.23	.041500	44
17	.827884	2.32	.869130	1.92	.958754	4.23	.041246	43
18	.828023	2.32	.869015	1.92	.959008	4.23	.040992	42
19	.828162	2.32	.868900	1.92	.959262	4.23	.040738	41
20	9.828301	2.30	9.868785	1.92	9.959516	4.22	0.040484	40
21	.828439	2.32	.868670	1.92	.959769	4.23	.040231	39
22	.828578	2.30	.868555	1.92	.960023	4.23	.039977	38
23	.828716	2.32	.868440	1.93	.960277	4.22	.039723	37
24	.828855	2.30	.868324	1.92	.960530	4.23	.039470	36
25	9.828993	2.30	9.868209	1.93	9.960784	4.23	0.039216	35
26	.829131	2.30	.868093	1.92	.961038	4.23	.038962	34
27	.829269	2.30	.867978	1.93	.961292	4.22	.038708	33
28	.829407	2.30	.867862	1.92	.961545	4.23	.038455	32
29	.829545	2.30	.867747	1.93	.961799	4.22	.038201	31
30	9.829683	2.30	9.867631	1.93	9.962052	4.23	0.037948	30
31	.829821	2.30	.867515	1.93	.962306	4.23	.037694	29
32	.829959	2.30	.867399	1.93	.962560	4.22	.037440	28
33	.830097	2.28	.867283	1.93	.962813	4.23	.037187	27
34	.830234	2.30	.867167	1.93	.963067	4.22	.036933	26
35	9.830372	2.28	9.867051	1.93	9.963320	4.23	0.036680	25
36	.830509	2.28	.866935	1.93	.963574	4.23	.036426	24
37	.830646	2.30	.866819	1.93	.963828	4.22	.036172	23
38	.830784	2.28	.866703	1.95	.964081	4.23	.035919	22
39	.830921	2.28	.866586	1.93	.964335	4.22	.035665	21
40	9.831058	2.28	9.866470	1.95	9.964588	4.23	0.035412	20
41	.831195	2.28	.866353	1.93	.964842	4.22	.035158	19
42	.831332	2.28	.866237	1.95	.965095	4.23	.034905	18
43	.831469	2.28	.866120	1.93	.965349	4.22	.034651	17
44	.831606	2.27	.866004	1.95	.965602	4.22	.034398	16
45	9.831742	2.28	9.865887	1.95	9.965855	4.23	0.034145	15
46	.831879	2.27	.865770	1.95	.966109	4.22	.033891	14
47	.832015	2.28	.865653	1.95	.966362	4.23	.033638	13
48	.832152	2.27	.865536	1.95	.966616	4.22	.033384	12
49	.832288	2.28	.865419	1.95	.966869	4.23	.033131	11
50	9.832425	2.27	9.865302	1.95	9.967123	4.22	0.032877	10
51	.832561	2.27	.865185	1.95	.967376	4.22	.032624	9
52	.832697	2.27	.865068	1.97	.967629	4.23	.032371	8
53	.832833	2.27	.864950	1.95	.967883	4.22	.032117	7
54	.832969	2.27	.864833	1.95	.968136	4.22	.031864	6
55	9.833105	2.27	9.864716	1.97	9.968389	4.23	0.031611	5
56	.833241	2.27	.864598	1.95	.968643	4.22	.031357	4
57	.833377	2.25	.864481	1.97	.968896	4.22	.031104	3
58	.833512	2.27	.864363	1.97	.969149	4.23	.030851	2
59	.833648	2.25	.864245	1.97	.969403	4.22	.030597	1
60	9.833783		9.864127		9.969656		0.030344	0
	Cos.	D. 1″.	Sin.	D. 1″.	Cot.	D. 1″.	Tan.	M.

718

TABLE C

LOGARITHMIC SINES, COSINES, TANGENTS, AND COTANGENTS

43°   136°

M.	Sin.	D. 1″.	Cos.	D. 1″.	Tan.	D. 1″.	Cot.	
0	9.833783	2.27	9.864127	1.95	9.969656	4.22	0.030344	60
1	.833919	2.25	.864010	1.97	.969909	4.22	.030091	59
2	.834054	2.25	.863892	1.97	.970162	4.23	.029838	58
3	.834189	2.27	.863774	1.97	.970416	4.22	.029584	57
4	.834325	2.25	.863656	1.97	.970669	4.22	.029331	56
5	9.834460	2.25	9.863538	1.98	9.970922	4.22	0.029078	55
6	.834595	2.25	.863419	1.97	.971175	4.23	.028825	54
7	.834730	2.25	.863301	1.97	.971429	4.22	.028571	53
8	.834865	2.23	.863183	1.98	.971682	4.22	.028318	52
9	.834999	2.25	.863064	1.97	.971935	4.22	.028065	51
10	9.835134	2.25	9.862946	1.98	9.972188	4.22	0.027812	50
11	.835269	2.23	.862827	1.97	.972441	4.23	.027559	49
12	.835403	2.25	.862709	1.98	.972695	4.22	.027305	48
13	.835538	2.23	.862590	1.98	.972948	4.22	.027052	47
14	.835672	2.25	.862471	1.97	.973201	4.22	.026799	46
15	9.835807	2.23	9.862353	1.98	9.973454	4.22	0.026546	45
16	.835941	2.23	.862234	1.98	.973707	4.22	.026293	44
17	.836075	2.23	.862115	1.98	.973960	4.22	.026040	43
18	.836209	2.23	.861996	1.98	.974213	4.22	.025787	42
19	.836343	2.23	.861877	1.98	.974466	4.23	.025534	41
20	9.836477	2.23	9.861758	2.00	9.974720	4.22	0.025280	40
21	.836611	2.23	.861638	1.98	.974973	4.22	.025027	39
22	.836745	2.22	.861519	1.98	.975226	4.22	.024774	38
23	.836878	2.23	.861400	2.00	.975479	4.22	.024521	37
24	.837012	2.23	.861280	1.98	.975732	4.22	.024268	36
25	9.837146	2.22	9.861161	2.00	9.975985	4.22	0.024015	35
26	.837279	2.22	.861041	2.00	.976238	4.22	.023762	34
27	.837412	2.23	.860922	1.98	.976491	4.22	.023509	33
28	.837546	2.22	.860802	2.00	.976744	4.22	.023256	32
29	.837679	2.22	.860682	2.00	.976997	4.22	.023003	31
30	9.837812	2.22	9.860562	2.00	9.977250	4.22	0.022750	30
31	.837945	2.22	.860442	2.00	.977503	4.22	.022497	29
32	.838078	2.22	.860322	2.00	.977756	4.22	.022244	28
33	.838211	2.22	.860202	2.00	.978009	4.22	.021991	27
34	.838344	2.22	.860082	2.00	.978262	4.22	.021738	26
35	9.838477	2.22	9.859962	2.00	9.978515	4.22	0.021485	25
36	.838610	2.20	.859842	2.00	.978768	4.22	.021232	24
37	.838742	2.22	.859721	2.02	.979021	4.22	.020979	23
38	.838875	2.20	.859601	2.00	.979274	4.22	.020726	22
39	.839007	2.22	.859480	2.02	.979527	4.22	.020473	21
40	9.839140	2.20	9.859360	2.00	9.979780	4.22	0.020220	20
41	.839272	2.20	.859239	2.02	.980033	4.22	.019967	19
42	.839404	2.20	.859119	2.00	.980286	4.20	.019714	18
43	.839536	2.20	.858998	2.02	.980538	4.22	.019462	17
44	.839668	2.20	.858877	2.02	.980791	4.22	.019209	16
45	9.839800	2.20	9.858756	2.02	9.981044	4.22	0.018956	15
46	.839932	2.20	.858635	2.02	.981297	4.22	.018703	14
47	.840064	2.20	.858514	2.02	.981550	4.22	.018450	13
48	.840196	2.20	.858393	2.02	.981803	4.22	.018197	12
49	.840328	2.18	.858272	2.02	.982056	4.22	.017944	11
50	9.840459	2.20	9.858151	2.03	9.982309	4.22	0.017691	10
51	.840591	2.18	.858029	2.02	.982562	4.20	.017438	9
52	.840722	2.20	.857908	2.03	.982814	4.22	.017186	8
53	.840854	2.18	.857786	2.02	.983067	4.22	.016933	7
54	.840985	2.18	.857665	2.03	.983320	4.22	.016680	6
55	9.841116	2.18	9.857543	2.02	9.983573	4.22	0.016427	5
56	.841247	2.18	.857422	2.03	.983826	4.22	.016174	4
57	.841378	2.18	.857300	2.03	.984079	4.22	.015921	3
58	.841509	2.18	.857178	2.03	.984332	4.20	.015668	2
59	.841640	2.18	.857056	2.03	.984584	4.22	.015416	1
60	9.841771		9.856934		9.984837		0.015163	0
	Cos.	D. 1″.	Sin.	D. 1″.	Cot.	D. 1″.	Tan.	M.

133°   46°

TABLE C 719

LOGARITHMIC SINES, COSINES, TANGENTS, AND COTANGENTS

44° 135°

M.	Sin.	D. 1″.	Cos.	D. 1″.	Tan.	D. 1″.	Cot.	
0	9.841771	2.18	9.856934	2.03	9.984837	4.22	0.015163	60
1	.841902	2.18	.856812	2.03	.985090	4.22	.014910	59
2	.842033	2.17	.856690	2.03	.985343	4.22	.014657	58
3	.842163	2.18	.856568	2.03	.985596	4.20	.014404	57
4	.842294	2.17	.856446	2.05	.985848	4.22	.014152	56
5	9.842424	2.18	9.856323	2.03	9.986101	4.22	0.013899	55
6	.842555	2.17	.856201	2.05	.986354	4.22	.013646	54
7	.842685	2.17	.856078	2.03	.986607	4.22	.013393	53
8	.842815	2.18	.855956	2.05	.986860	4.20	.013140	52
9	.842946	2.17	.855833	2.03	.987112	4.22	.012888	51
10	9.843076	2.17	9.855711	2.05	9.987365	4.22	0.012635	50
11	.843206	2.17	.855588	2.05	.987618	4.22	.012382	49
12	.843336	2.17	.855465	2.05	.987871	4.20	.012129	48
13	.843466	2.15	.855342	2.05	.988123	4.22	.011877	47
14	.843595	2.17	.855219	2.05	.988376	4.22	.011624	46
15	9.843725	2.17	9.855096	2.05	9.988629	4.22	0.011371	45
16	.843855	2.15	.854973	2.05	.988882	4.20	.011118	44
17	.843984	2.17	.854850	2.05	.989134	4.22	.010866	43
18	.844114	2.15	.854727	2.07	.989387	4.22	.010613	42
19	.844243	2.15	.854603	2.05	.989640	4.22	.010360	41
20	9.844372	2.17	9.854480	2.07	9.989893	4.20	0.010107	40
21	.844502	2.15	.854356	2.05	.990145	4.22	.009855	39
22	.844631	2.15	.854233	2.07	.990398	4.22	.009602	38
23	.844760	2.15	.854109	2.05	.990651	4.20	.009349	37
24	.844889	2.15	.853986	2.07	.990903	4.22	.009097	36
25	9.845018	2.15	9.853862	2.07	9.991156	4.22	0.008844	35
26	.845147	2.15	.853738	2.07	.991409	4.22	.008591	34
27	.845276	2.15	.853614	2.07	.991662	4.20	.008338	33
28	.845405	2.13	.853490	2.07	.991914	4.22	.008086	32
29	.845533	2.15	.853366	2.07	.992167	4.22	.007833	31
30	9.845662	2.13	9.853242	2.07	9.992420	4.20	0.007580	30
31	.845790	2.15	.853118	2.07	.992672	4.22	.007328	29
32	.845919	2.13	.852994	2.08	.992925	4.22	.007075	28
33	.846047	2.13	.852869	2.07	.993178	4.22	.006822	27
34	.846175	2.15	.852745	2.08	.993431	4.20	.006569	26
35	9.846304	2.13	9.852620	2.07	9.993683	4.22	0.006317	25
36	.846432	2.13	.852496	2.08	.993936	4.22	.006064	24
37	.846560	2.13	.852371	2.07	.994189	4.20	.005811	23
38	.846688	2.13	.852247	2.08	.994441	4.22	.005559	22
39	.846816	2.13	.852122	2.08	.994694	4.22	.005306	21
40	9.846944	2.12	9.851997	2.08	9.994947	4.20	0.005053	20
41	.847071	2.13	.851872	2.08	.995199	4.22	.004801	19
42	.847199	2.13	.851747	2.08	.995452	4.22	.004548	18
43	.847327	2.12	.851622	2.08	.995705	4.20	.004295	17
44	.847454	2.13	.851497	2.08	.995957	4.22	.004043	16
45	9.847582	2.12	9.851372	2.10	9.996210	4.22	0.003790	15
46	.847709	2.12	.851246	2.08	.996463	4.20	.003537	14
47	.847836	2.13	.851121	2.08	.996715	4.22	.003285	13
48	.847964	2.12	.850996	2.10	.996968	4.22	.003032	12
49	.848091	2.12	.850870	2.08	.997221	4.20	.002779	11
50	9.848218	2.12	9.850745	2.10	9.997473	4.22	0.002527	10
51	.848345	2.12	.850619	2.10	.997726	4.22	.002274	9
52	.848472	2.12	.850493	2.08	.997979	4.20	.002021	8
53	.848599	2.12	.850368	2.10	.998231	4.22	.001769	7
54	.848726	2.10	.850242	2.10	.998484	4.22	.001516	6
55	9.848852	2.12	9.850116	2.10	9.998737	4.20	0.001263	5
56	.848979	2.12	.849990	2.10	.998989	4.22	.001011	4
57	.849106	2.10	.849864	2.10	.999242	4.22	.000758	3
58	.849232	2.12	.849738	2.12	.999495	4.20	.000505	2
59	.849359	2.10	.849611	2.10	.999747	4.22	.000253	1
60	9.849485		9.849485		0.000000		0.000000	0
	Cos.	D. 1″.	Sin.	D. 1″.	Cot.	D. 1″.	Tan.	M.

134° 45°

TABLE D

Auxiliary Table for Logarithmic Sines and Tangents of Small Angles

M.	S.	Sin.	Tan.	S.	Sin.	Tan.	S.	Sin.	Tan.	M.
		0° 4.68			1° 4.68			2° 4.68		
0	0	5575	5575	3600	5553	5619	7200	5487	5751	0
1	60	5575	5575	3660	5552	5620	7260	5485	5754	1
2	120	5575	5575	3720	5551	5622	7320	5484	5757	2
3	180	5575	5575	3780	5551	5623	7380	5482	5760	3
4	240	5575	5575	3840	5550	5625	7440	5481	5763	4
5	300	5575	5575	3906	5549	5627	7500	5479	5766	5
6	360	5575	5575	3960	5548	5628	7560	5478	5769	6
7	420	5575	5575	4020	5547	5630	7620	5476	5773	7
8	480	5574	5576	4080	5547	5632	7680	5475	5776	8
9	540	5574	5576	4140	5546	5633	7740	5473	5779	9
10	600	5574	5576	4200	5545	5635	7800	5471	5782	10
11	660	5574	5576	4260	5544	5637	7860	5470	5785	11
12	720	5574	5577	4320	5543	5638	7920	5468	5788	12
13	780	5574	5577	4380	5542	5640	7980	5467	5792	13
14	840	5574	5577	4440	5541	5642	8040	5465	5795	14
15	900	5573	5578	4500	5540	5644	8100	5463	5798	15
16	960	5573	5578	4560	5539	5646	8160	5462	5802	16
17	1020	5573	5578	4620	5539	5648	8220	5460	5805	17
18	1080	5573	5579	4680	5538	5649	8280	5458	5808	18
19	1140	5573	5579	4740	5537	5651	8340	5457	5812	19
20	1200	5572	5580	4800	5536	5653	8400	5455	5815	20
21	1260	5572	5580	4860	5535	5655	8460	5453	5818	21
22	1320	5572	5581	4920	5534	5657	8520	5451	5822	22
23	1380	5572	5581	4980	5533	5659	8580	5450	5825	23
24	1440	5571	5582	5040	5532	5661	8640	5448	5829	24
25	1500	5571	5583	5100	5531	5663	8700	5446	5833	25
26	1560	5571	5583	5160	5530	5665	8760	5444	5836	26
27	1620	5570	5584	5220	5529	5668	8820	5443	5840	27
28	1680	5570	5584	5280	5527	5670	8880	5441	5843	28
29	1740	5570	5585	5340	5526	5672	8940	5439	5847	29
30	1800	5569	5586	5400	5525	5674	9000	5437	5851	30
31	1860	5569	5587	5460	5524	5676	9060	5435	5854	31
32	1920	5569	5587	5520	5523	5679	9120	5433	5858	32
33	1980	5568	5588	5580	5522	5681	9180	5431	5862	33
34	2040	5568	5589	5640	5521	5683	9210	5430	5866	34
35	2100	5567	5590	5700	5520	5685	9300	5428	5869	35
36	2160	5567	5591	5760	5518	5688	9360	5426	5873	36
37	2220	5566	5592	5820	5517	5690	9420	5424	5877	37
38	2280	5566	5593	5880	5516	5693	9480	5422	5881	38
39	2340	5566	5593	5940	5515	5695	9540	5420	5885	39
40	2400	5565	5594	6000	5514	5697	9600	5418	5889	40
41	2460	5565	5595	6060	5512	5700	9660	5416	5893	41
42	2520	5564	5596	6120	5511	5702	9720	5414	5897	42
43	2580	5564	5598	6180	5510	5705	9780	5412	5900	43
44	2640	5563	5599	6240	5509	5707	9810	5410	5905	44
45	2700	5562	5600	6300	5507	5710	9900	5408	5909	45
46	2760	5562	5601	6360	5506	5713	9960	5406	5913	46
47	2820	5561	5602	6420	5505	5715	10020	5404	5917	47
48	2880	5561	5603	6480	5503	5718	10080	5402	5921	48
49	2940	5560	5604	6540	5502	5720	10140	5400	5925	49
50	3000	5560	5605	6600	5501	5723	10200	5398	5929	50
51	3060	5559	5607	6660	5499	5726	10260	5396	5933	51
52	3120	5558	5608	6720	5498	5729	10320	5394	5937	52
53	3180	5558	5609	6780	5497	5731	10380	5392	5942	53
54	3240	5557	5611	6840	5495	5734	10440	5389	5946	54
55	3300	5556	5612	6900	5494	5737	10500	5387	5950	55
56	3360	5556	5613	6960	5492	5740	10560	5385	5955	56
57	3420	5555	5615	7020	5491	5743	10620	5383	5959	57
58	3480	5554	5616	7080	5490	5745	10680	5381	5963	58
59	3540	5554	5618	7140	5488	5748	10740	5379	5968	59
60	3600	5553	5619	7200	5487	5751	10800	5376	5972	60
M.	S.	Sin.	Tan.	S.	Sin.	Tan.	S.	Sin.	Tan.	M.

AUXILIARY TABLE FOR LOGARITHMIC SINES AND TANGENTS OF SMALL ANGLES

	3°			4°			5°			
M.	S.	Sin.	Tan.	S.	Sin.	Tan.	S.	Sin.	Tan.	M.
			4.68			4.68			4.68	
0	10800	5376	5972	14400	5222	6281	18000	5024	6679	0
1	10860	5374	5976	14460	5219	6287	18060	5020	6687	1
2	10920	5372	5981	14520	5216	6293	18120	5016	6694	2
3	10980	5370	5985	14580	5213	6299	18180	5012	6702	3
4	11040	5367	5990	14640	5210	6305	18240	5009	6709	4
5	11100	5365	5994	14700	5207	6311	18300	5005	6716	5
6	11160	5363	5999	14760	5204	6317	18360	5001	6724	6
7	11220	5361	6004	14820	5201	6323	18420	4997	6732	7
8	11280	5358	6008	14880	5198	6329	18480	4994	6739	8
9	11340	5356	6013	14940	5195	6335	18540	4990	6747	9
10	11400	5354	6017	15000	5192	6341	18600	4986	6754	10
11	11460	5351	6022	15060	5189	6348	18660	4982	6762	11
12	11520	5349	6027	15120	5186	6354	18720	4978	6770	12
13	11580	5347	6031	15180	5183	6360	18780	4975	6777	13
14	11640	5344	6036	15240	5180	6366	18840	4971	6785	14
15	11700	5342	6041	15300	5177	6372	18900	4967	6793	15
16	11760	5340	6046	15360	5173	6379	18960	4963	6800	16
17	11820	5337	6051	15420	5170	6385	19020	4959	6808	17
18	11880	5335	6055	15480	5167	6391	19080	4955	6816	18
19	11940	5332	6060	15540	5164	6398	19140	4951	6824	19
20	12000	5330	6065	15600	5161	6404	19200	4948	6832	20
21	12060	5327	6070	15660	5158	6410	19260	4944	6840	21
22	12120	5325	6075	15720	5154	6417	19320	4940	6848	22
23	12180	5322	6080	15780	5151	6423	19380	4936	6855	23
24	12240	5320	6085	15840	5148	6430	19440	4932	6863	24
25	12300	5317	6090	15900	5145	6436	19500	4928	6871	25
26	12360	5315	6095	15960	5141	6443	19560	4924	6879	26
27	12420	5312	6100	16020	5138	6449	19620	4920	6887	27
28	12480	5310	6105	16080	5135	6456	19680	4916	6896	28
29	12540	5307	6110	16140	5132	6463	19740	4912	6904	29
30	12600	5305	6116	16200	5128	6469	19800	4908	6912	30
31	12660	5302	6121	16260	5125	6470	19860	4904	6920	31
32	12720	5300	6126	16320	5122	6482	19920	4900	6928	32
33	12780	5297	6131	16380	5118	6489	19980	4895	6936	33
34	12840	5294	6136	16440	5115	6496	20040	4891	6944	34
35	12900	5292	6142	16500	5112	6503	20100	4887	6953	35
36	12960	5289	6147	16560	5108	6509	20160	4883	6961	36
37	13020	5286	6152	16620	5105	6516	20220	4880	6969	37
38	13080	5284	6158	16680	5101	6523	20280	4875	6977	38
39	13140	5281	6163	16740	5098	6530	20340	4871	6986	39
40	13200	5278	6168	16800	5095	6537	20400	4867	6994	40
41	13260	5276	6174	16860	5091	6544	20460	4862	7003	41
42	13320	5273	6179	16920	5088	6551	20520	4858	7011	42
43	13380	5270	6185	16980	5084	6557	20580	4854	7019	43
44	13440	5268	6190	17040	5081	6564	20640	4850	7028	44
45	13500	5265	6196	17100	5077	6571	20700	4846	7036	45
46	13560	5262	6201	17160	5074	6578	20760	4841	7045	46
47	13620	5259	6207	17220	5070	6585	20820	4837	7053	47
48	13680	5256	6212	17280	5067	6593	20880	4833	7062	48
49	13740	5254	6218	17340	5063	6600	20940	4829	7070	49
50	13800	5251	6224	17400	5060	6607	21000	4824	7079	50
51	13860	5248	6229	17460	5056	6614	21060	4820	7088	51
52	13920	5245	6235	17520	5053	6621	21120	4816	7096	52
53	13980	5242	6241	17580	5049	6628	21180	4811	7105	53
54	14040	5239	6246	17640	5045	6635	21240	4807	7114	54
55	14100	5237	6252	17700	5042	6643	21300	4803	7122	55
56	14160	5234	6258	17760	5038	6650	21360	4798	7131	56
57	14220	5231	6264	17820	5034	6657	21420	4794	7140	57
58	14280	5228	6269	17880	5031	6665	21480	4790	7149	58
59	14340	5225	6275	17940	5027	6672	21540	4785	7158	59
60	14400	5222	6281	18000	5024	6679	21600	4781	7166	60
M.	S.	Sin.	Tan.	S.	Sin.	Tan.	S.	Sin.	Tan.	M.

TABLE E

NATURAL SINES AND COSINES

′	5° Sine	5° Cosine	6° Sine	6° Cosine	7° Sine	7° Cosine	8° Sine	8° Cosine	9° Sine	9° Cosine	′
0	.08716	.99619	.10453	.99452	.12187	.99255	.13917	.99027	.15643	.98769	60
1	.08745	.99617	.10482	.99449	.12216	.99251	.13946	.99023	.15672	.98764	59
2	.08774	.99614	.10511	.99446	.12245	.99248	.13975	.99019	.15701	.98760	58
3	.08803	.99612	.10540	.99443	.12274	.99244	.14004	.99015	.15730	.98755	57
4	.08831	.99609	.10569	.99440	.12302	.99240	.14033	.99011	.15758	.98751	56
5	.08860	.99607	.10597	.99437	.12331	.99237	.14061	.99006	.15787	.98746	55
6	.08889	.99604	.10626	.99434	.12360	.99233	.14090	.99002	.15816	.98741	54
7	.08918	.99602	.10655	.99431	.12389	.99230	.14119	.98998	.15845	.98737	53
8	.08947	.99599	.10684	.99428	.12418	.99226	.14148	.98994	.15873	.98732	52
9	.08976	.99596	.10713	.99424	.12447	.99222	.14177	.98990	.15902	.98728	51
10	.09005	.99594	.10742	.99421	.12476	.99219	.14205	.98986	.15931	.98723	50
11	.09034	.99591	.10771	.99418	.12504	.99215	.14234	.98982	.15959	.98718	49
12	.09063	.99588	.10800	.99415	.12533	.99211	.14263	.98978	.15988	.98714	48
13	.09092	.99586	.10829	.99412	.12562	.99208	.14292	.98973	.16017	.98709	47
14	.09121	.99583	.10858	.99409	.12591	.99204	.14320	.98969	.16046	.98704	46
15	.09150	.99580	.10887	.99406	.12620	.99200	.14349	.98965	.16074	.98700	45
16	.09179	.99578	.10916	.99402	.12649	.99197	.14378	.98961	.16103	.98695	44
17	.09208	.99575	.10945	.99399	.12678	.99193	.14407	.98957	.16132	.98690	43
18	.09237	.99572	.10973	.99396	.12706	.99189	.14436	.98953	.16160	.98686	42
19	.09266	.99570	.11002	.99393	.12735	.99186	.14464	.98948	.16189	.98681	41
20	.09295	.99567	.11031	.99390	.12764	.99182	.14493	.98944	.16218	.98676	40
21	.09324	.99564	.11060	.99386	.12793	.99178	.14522	.98940	.16246	.98671	39
22	.09353	.99562	.11089	.99383	.12822	.99175	.14551	.98936	.16275	.98667	38
23	.09382	.99559	.11118	.99380	.12851	.99171	.14580	.98931	.16304	.98662	37
24	.09411	.99556	.11147	.99377	.12880	.99167	.14608	.98927	.16333	.98657	36
25	.09440	.99553	.11176	.99374	.12908	.99163	.14637	.98923	.16361	.98652	35
26	.09469	.99551	.11205	.99370	.12937	.99160	.14666	.98919	.16390	.98648	34
27	.09498	.99548	.11234	.99367	.12966	.99156	.14695	.98914	.16419	.98643	33
28	.09527	.99545	.11263	.99364	.12995	.99152	.14723	.98910	.16447	.98638	32
29	.09556	.99542	.11291	.99360	.13024	.99148	.14752	.98906	.16476	.98633	31
30	.09585	.99540	.11320	.99357	.13053	.99144	.14781	.98902	.16505	.98629	30
31	.09614	.99537	.11349	.99354	.13081	.99141	.14810	.98897	.16533	.98624	29
32	.09642	.99534	.11378	.99351	.13110	.99137	.14838	.98893	.16562	.98619	28
33	.09671	.99531	.11407	.99347	.13139	.99133	.14867	.98889	.16591	.98614	27
34	.09700	.99528	.11436	.99344	.13168	.99129	.14896	.98884	.16620	.98609	26
35	.09729	.99526	.11465	.99341	.13197	.99125	.14925	.98880	.16648	.98604	25
36	.09758	.99523	.11494	.99337	.13226	.99122	.14954	.98876	.16677	.98600	24
37	.09787	.99520	.11523	.99334	.13254	.99118	.14982	.98871	.16706	.98595	23
38	.09816	.99517	.11552	.99331	.13283	.99114	.15011	.98867	.16734	.98590	22
39	.09845	.99514	.11580	.99327	.13312	.99110	.15040	.98863	.16763	.98585	21
40	.09874	.99511	.11609	.99324	.13341	.99106	.15069	.98858	.16792	.98580	20
41	.09903	.99508	.11638	.99320	.13370	.99102	.15097	.98854	.16820	.98575	19
42	.09932	.99506	.11667	.99317	.13399	.99098	.15126	.98849	.16849	.98570	18
43	.09961	.99503	.11696	.99314	.13427	.99094	.15155	.98845	.16878	.98565	17
44	.09990	.99500	.11725	.99310	.13456	.99091	.15184	.98841	.16906	.98561	16
45	.10019	.99497	.11754	.99307	.13485	.99087	.15212	.98836	.16935	.98556	15
46	.10048	.99494	.11783	.99303	.13514	.99083	.15241	.98832	.16964	.98551	14
47	.10077	.99491	.11812	.99300	.13543	.99079	.15270	.98827	.16992	.98546	13
48	.10106	.99488	.11840	.99297	.13572	.99075	.15299	.98823	.17021	.98541	12
49	.10135	.99485	.11869	.99293	.13600	.99071	.15327	.98818	.17050	.98536	11
50	.10164	.99482	.11898	.99290	.13629	.99067	.15356	.98814	.17078	.98531	10
51	.10192	.99479	.11927	.99286	.13658	.99063	.15385	.98809	.17107	.98526	9
52	.10221	.99476	.11956	.99283	.13687	.99059	.15414	.98805	.17136	.98521	8
53	.10250	.99473	.11985	.99279	.13716	.99055	.15442	.98800	.17164	.98516	7
54	.10279	.99470	.12014	.99276	.13744	.99051	.15471	.98796	.17193	.98511	6
55	.10308	.99467	.12043	.99272	.13773	.99047	.15500	.98791	.17222	.98506	5
56	.10337	.99464	.12071	.99269	.13802	.99043	.15529	.98787	.17250	.98501	4
57	.10366	.99461	.12100	.99265	.13831	.99039	.15557	.98782	.17279	.98496	3
58	.10395	.99458	.12129	.99262	.13860	.99035	.15586	.98778	.17308	.98491	2
59	.10424	.99455	.12158	.99258	.13889	.99031	.15615	.98773	.17336	.98486	1
60	.10453	.99452	.12187	.99255	.13917	.99027	.15643	.98769	.17365	.98481	0
′	Cosine	Sine	Cosine	Sine	Cosine	Sine	Cosine	Sine	Cosine	Sine	′
	84°		83°		82°		81°		80°		

NATURAL SINES AND COSINES

′	10° Sine	10° Cosine	11° Sine	11° Cosine	12° Sine	12° Cosine	13° Sine	13° Cosine	14° Sine	14° Cosine	′
0	.17365	.98481	.19081	.98163	.20791	.97815	.22495	.97437	.24192	.97030	60
1	.17393	.98476	.19109	.98157	.20820	.97809	.22523	.97430	.24220	.97023	59
2	.17422	.98471	.19138	.98152	.20848	.97803	.22552	.97424	.24249	.97015	58
3	.17451	.98466	.19167	.98146	.20877	.97797	.22580	.97417	.24277	.97008	57
4	.17479	.98461	.19195	.98140	.20905	.97791	.22608	.97411	.24305	.97001	56
5	.17508	.98455	.19224	.98135	.20933	.97784	.22637	.97404	.24333	.96994	55
6	.17537	.98450	.19252	.98129	.20962	.97778	.22665	.97398	.24362	.96987	54
7	.17565	.98445	.19281	.98124	.20990	.97772	.22693	.97391	.24390	.96980	53
8	.17594	.98440	.19309	.98118	.21019	.97766	.22722	.97384	.24418	.96973	52
9	.17623	.98435	.19338	.98112	.21047	.97760	.22750	.97378	.24446	.96966	51
10	.17651	.98430	.19366	.98107	.21076	.97754	.22778	.97371	.24474	.96959	50
11	.17680	.98425	.19395	.98101	.21104	.97748	.22807	.97365	.24503	.96952	49
12	.17708	.98420	.19423	.98096	.21132	.97742	.22835	.97358	.24531	.96945	48
13	.17737	.98414	.19452	.98090	.21161	.97735	.22863	.97351	.24559	.96937	47
14	.17766	.98409	.19481	.98084	.21189	.97729	.22892	.97345	.24587	.96930	46
15	.17794	.98404	.19509	.98079	.21218	.97723	.22920	.97338	.24615	.96923	45
16	.17823	.98399	.19538	.98073	.21246	.97717	.22948	.97331	.24644	.96916	44
17	.17852	.98394	.19566	.98067	.21275	.97711	.22977	.97325	.24672	.96909	43
18	.17880	.98389	.19595	.98061	.21303	.97705	.23005	.97318	.24700	.96902	42
19	.17909	.98383	.19623	.98056	.21331	.97698	.23033	.97311	.24728	.96894	41
20	.17937	.98378	.19652	.98050	.21360	.97692	.23062	.97304	.24756	.96887	40
21	.17966	.98373	.19680	.98044	.21388	.97686	.23090	.97298	.24784	.96880	39
22	.17995	.98368	.19709	.98039	.21417	.97680	.23118	.97291	.24813	.96873	38
23	.18023	.98362	.19737	.98033	.21445	.97673	.23146	.97284	.24841	.96866	37
24	.18052	.98357	.19766	.98027	.21474	.97667	.23175	.97278	.24869	.96858	36
25	.18081	.98352	.19794	.98021	.21502	.97661	.23203	.97271	.24897	.96851	35
26	.18109	.98347	.19823	.98016	.21530	.97655	.23231	.97264	.24925	.96844	34
27	.18138	.98341	.19851	.98010	.21559	.97648	.23260	.97257	.24954	.96837	33
28	.18166	.98336	.19880	.98004	.21587	.97642	.23288	.97251	.24982	.96829	32
29	.18195	.98331	.19908	.97998	.21616	.97636	.23316	.97244	.25010	.96822	31
30	.18224	.98325	.19937	.97992	.21644	.97630	.23345	.97237	.25038	.96815	30
31	.18252	.98320	.19965	.97987	.21672	.97623	.23373	.97230	.25066	.96807	29
32	.18281	.98315	.19994	.97981	.21701	.97617	.23401	.97223	.25094	.96800	28
33	.18309	.98310	.20022	.97975	.21729	.97611	.23429	.97217	.25122	.96793	27
34	.18338	.98304	.20051	.97969	.21758	.97604	.23458	.97210	.25151	.96786	26
35	.18367	.98299	.20079	.97963	.21786	.97598	.23486	.97203	.25179	.96778	25
36	.18395	.98294	.20108	.97958	.21814	.97592	.23514	.97196	.25207	.96771	24
37	.18424	.98288	.20136	.97952	.21843	.97585	.23542	.97189	.25235	.96764	23
38	.18452	.98283	.20165	.97946	.21871	.97579	.23571	.97182	.25263	.96756	22
39	.18481	.98277	.20193	.97940	.21899	.97573	.23599	.97176	.25291	.96749	21
40	.18509	.98272	.20222	.97934	.21928	.97566	.23627	.97169	.25320	.96742	20
41	.18538	.98267	.20250	.97928	.21956	.97560	.23656	.97162	.25348	.96734	19
42	.18567	.98261	.20279	.97922	.21985	.97553	.23684	.97155	.25376	.96727	18
43	.18595	.98256	.20307	.97916	.22013	.97547	.23712	.97148	.25404	.96719	17
44	.18624	.98250	.20336	.97910	.22041	.97541	.23740	.97141	.25432	.96712	16
45	.18652	.98245	.20364	.97905	.22070	.97534	.23769	.97134	.25460	.96705	15
46	.18681	.98240	.20393	.97899	.22098	.97528	.23797	.97127	.25488	.96697	14
47	.18710	.98234	.20421	.97893	.22126	.97521	.23825	.97120	.25516	.96690	13
48	.18738	.98229	.20450	.97887	.22155	.97515	.23853	.97113	.25545	.96682	12
49	.18767	.98223	.20478	.97881	.22183	.97508	.23882	.97106	.25573	.96675	11
50	.18795	.98218	.20507	.97875	.22212	.97502	.23910	.97100	.25601	.96667	10
51	.18824	.98212	.20535	.97869	.22240	.97496	.23938	.97093	.25629	.96660	9
52	.18852	.98207	.20563	.97863	.22268	.97489	.23966	.97086	.25657	.96653	8
53	.18881	.98201	.20592	.97857	.22297	.97483	.23995	.97079	.25685	.96645	7
54	.18910	.98196	.20620	.97851	.22325	.97476	.24023	.97072	.25713	.96638	6
55	.18938	.98190	.20649	.97845	.22353	.97470	.24051	.97065	.25741	.96630	5
56	.18967	.98185	.20677	.97839	.22382	.97463	.24079	.97058	.25769	.96623	4
57	.18995	.98179	.20706	.97833	.22410	.97457	.24108	.97051	.25798	.96615	3
58	.19024	.98174	.20734	.97827	.22438	.97450	.24136	.97044	.25826	.96608	2
59	.19052	.98168	.20763	.97821	.22467	.97444	.24164	.97037	.25854	.96600	1
60	.19081	.98163	.20791	.97815	.22495	.97437	.24192	.97030	.25882	.96593	0

′	79° Cosine	79° Sine	78° Cosine	78° Sine	77° Cosine	77° Sine	76° Cosine	76° Sine	75° Cosine	75° Sine	′

TABLE E

NATURAL SINES AND COSINES

′	15° Sine	Cosine	16° Sine	Cosine	17° Sine	Cosine	18° Sine	Cosine	19° Sine	Cosine	′
0	.25882	.96593	.27564	.96126	.29237	.95630	.30902	.95106	.32557	.94552	60
1	.25910	.96585	.27592	.96118	.29265	.95622	.30929	.95097	.32584	.94542	59
2	.25938	.96578	.27620	.96110	.29293	.95613	.30957	.95088	.32612	.94533	58
3	.25966	.96570	.27648	.96102	.29321	.95605	.30985	.95079	.32639	.94523	57
4	.25994	.96562	.27676	.96094	.29348	.95596	.31012	.95070	.32667	.94514	56
5	.26022	.96555	.27704	.96086	.29376	.95588	.31040	.95061	.32694	.94504	55
6	.26050	.96547	.27731	.96078	.29404	.95579	.31068	.95052	.32722	.94495	54
7	.26079	.96540	.27759	.96070	.29432	.95571	.31095	.95043	.32749	.94485	53
8	.26107	.96532	.27787	.96062	.29460	.95562	.31123	.95033	.32777	.94476	52
9	.26135	.96524	.27815	.96054	.29487	.95554	.31151	.95024	.32804	.94466	51
10	.26163	.96517	.27843	.96046	.29515	.95545	.31178	.95015	.32832	.94457	50
11	.26191	.96509	.27871	.96037	.29543	.95536	.31206	.95006	.32859	.94447	49
12	.26219	.96502	.27899	.96029	.29571	.95528	.31233	.94997	.32887	.94438	48
13	.26247	.96494	.27927	.96021	.29599	.95519	.31261	.94988	.32914	.94428	47
14	.26275	.96486	.27955	.96013	.29626	.95511	.31289	.94979	.32942	.94418	46
15	.26303	.96479	.27983	.96005	.29654	.95502	.31316	.94970	.32969	.94409	45
16	.26331	.96471	.28011	.95997	.29682	.95493	.31344	.94961	.32997	.94399	44
17	.26359	.96463	.28039	.95989	.29710	.95485	.31372	.94952	.33024	.94390	43
18	.26387	.96456	.28067	.95981	.29737	.95476	.31399	.94943	.33051	.94380	42
19	.26415	.96448	.28095	.95972	.29765	.95467	.31427	.94933	.33079	.94370	41
20	.26443	.96440	.28123	.95964	.29793	.95459	.31454	.94924	.33106	.94361	40
21	.26471	.96433	.28150	.95956	.29821	.95450	.31482	.94915	.33134	.94351	39
22	.26500	.96425	.28178	.95948	.29849	.95441	.31510	.94906	.33161	.94342	38
23	.26528	.96417	.28206	.95940	.29876	.95433	.31537	.94897	.33189	.94332	37
24	.26556	.96410	.28234	.95931	.29904	.95424	.31565	.94888	.33216	.94322	36
25	.26584	.96402	.28262	.95923	.29932	.95415	.31593	.94878	.33244	.94313	35
26	.26612	.96394	.28290	.95915	.29960	.95407	.31620	.94869	.33271	.94303	34
27	.26640	.96386	.28318	.95907	.29987	.95398	.31648	.94860	.33298	.94293	33
28	.26668	.96379	.28346	.95898	.30015	.95389	.31675	.94851	.33326	.94284	32
29	.26696	.96371	.28374	.95890	.30043	.95380	.31703	.94842	.33353	.94274	31
30	.26724	.96363	.28402	.95882	.30071	.95372	.31730	.94832	.33381	.94264	30
31	.26752	.96355	.28429	.95874	.30098	.95363	.31758	.94823	.33408	.94254	29
32	.26780	.96347	.28457	.95865	.30126	.95354	.31786	.94814	.33436	.94245	28
33	.26808	.96340	.28485	.95857	.30154	.95345	.31813	.94805	.33463	.94235	27
34	.26836	.96332	.28513	.95849	.30182	.95337	.31841	.94795	.33490	.94225	26
35	.26864	.96324	.28541	.95841	.30209	.95328	.31868	.94786	.33518	.94215	25
36	.26892	.96316	.28569	.95832	.30237	.95319	.31896	.94777	.33545	.94206	24
37	.26920	.96308	.28597	.95824	.30265	.95310	.31923	.94768	.33573	.94196	23
38	.26948	.96301	.28625	.95816	.30292	.95301	.31951	.94758	.33600	.94186	22
39	.26976	.96293	.28652	.95807	.30320	.95293	.31979	.94749	.33627	.94176	21
40	.27004	.96285	.28680	.95799	.30348	.95284	.32006	.94740	.33655	.94167	20
41	.27032	.96277	.28708	.95791	.30376	.95275	.32034	.94730	.33682	.94157	19
42	.27060	.96269	.28736	.95782	.30403	.95266	.32061	.94721	.33710	.94147	18
43	.27088	.96261	.28764	.95774	.30431	.95257	.32089	.94712	.33737	.94137	17
44	.27116	.96253	.28792	.95766	.30459	.95248	.32116	.94702	.33764	.94127	16
45	.27144	.96246	.28820	.95757	.30486	.95240	.32144	.94693	.33792	.94118	15
46	.27172	.96238	.28847	.95749	.30514	.95231	.32171	.94684	.33819	.94108	14
47	.27200	.96230	.28875	.95740	.30542	.95222	.32199	.94674	.33846	.94098	13
48	.27228	.96222	.28903	.95732	.30570	.95213	.32227	.94665	.33874	.94088	12
49	.27256	.96214	.28931	.95724	.30597	.95204	.32254	.94656	.33901	.94078	11
50	.27284	.96206	.28959	.95715	.30625	.95195	.32282	.94646	.33929	.94068	10
51	.27312	.96198	.28987	.95707	.30653	.95186	.32309	.94637	.33956	.94058	9
52	.27340	.96190	.29015	.95698	.30680	.95177	.32337	.94627	.33983	.94049	8
53	.27368	.96182	.29042	.95690	.30708	.95168	.32364	.94618	.34011	.94039	7
54	.27396	.96174	.29070	.95681	.30736	.95159	.32392	.94609	.34038	.94029	6
55	.27424	.96166	.29098	.95673	.30763	.95150	.32419	.94599	.34065	.94019	5
56	.27452	.96158	.29126	.95664	.30791	.95142	.32447	.94590	.34093	.94009	4
57	.27480	.96150	.29154	.95656	.30819	.95133	.32474	.94580	.34120	.93999	3
58	.27508	.96142	.29182	.95647	.30846	.95124	.32502	.94571	.34147	.93989	2
59	.27536	.96134	.29209	.95639	.30874	.95115	.32529	.94561	.34175	.93979	1
60	.27564	.96126	.29237	.95630	.30902	.95106	.32557	.94552	.34202	.93969	0
′	Cosine	Sine	Cosine	Sine	Cosine	Sine	Cosine	Sine	Cosine	Sine	′
	74°		73°		72°		71°		70°		

Natural Sines and Cosines

/	20° Sine	20° Cosine	21° Sine	21° Cosine	22° Sine	22° Cosine	23° Sine	23° Cosine	24° Sine	24° Cosine	/
0	.34202	.93969	.35837	.93358	.37461	.92718	.39073	.92050	.40674	.91355	60
1	.34229	.93959	.35864	.93348	.37488	.92707	.39100	.92039	.40700	.91343	59
2	.34257	.93949	.35891	.93337	.37515	.92697	.39127	.92028	.40727	.91331	58
3	.34284	.93939	.35918	.93327	.37542	.92686	.39153	.92016	.40753	.91319	57
4	.34311	.93929	.35945	.93316	.37569	.92675	.39180	.92005	.40780	.91307	56
5	.34339	.93919	.35973	.93306	.37595	.92664	.39207	.91994	.40806	.91295	55
6	.34366	.93909	.36000	.93295	.37622	.92653	.39234	.91982	.40833	.91283	54
7	.34393	.93899	.36027	.93285	.37649	.92642	.39260	.91971	.40860	.91272	53
8	.34421	.93889	.36054	.93274	.37676	.92631	.39287	.91959	.40886	.91260	52
9	.34448	.93879	.36081	.93264	.37703	.92620	.39314	.91948	.40913	.91248	51
10	.34475	.93869	.36108	.93253	.37730	.92609	.39341	.91936	.40939	.91236	50
11	.34503	.93859	.36135	.93243	.37757	.92598	.39367	.91925	.40966	.91224	49
12	.34530	.93849	.36162	.93232	.37784	.92587	.39394	.91914	.40992	.91212	48
13	.34557	.93839	.36190	.93222	.37811	.92576	.39421	.91902	.41019	.91200	47
14	.34584	.93829	.36217	.93211	.37838	.92565	.39448	.91891	.41045	.91188	46
15	.34612	.93819	.36244	.93201	.37865	.92554	.39474	.91879	.41072	.91176	45
16	.34639	.93809	.36271	.93190	.37892	.92543	.39501	.91868	.41098	.91164	44
17	.34666	.93799	.36298	.93180	.37919	.92532	.39528	.91856	.41125	.91152	43
18	.34694	.93789	.36325	.93169	.37946	.92521	.39555	.91845	.41151	.91140	42
19	.34721	.93779	.36352	.93159	.37973	.92510	.39581	.91833	.41178	.91128	41
20	.34748	.93769	.36379	.93148	.37999	.92499	.39608	.91822	.41204	.91116	40
21	.34775	.93759	.36406	.93137	.38026	.92488	.39635	.91810	.41231	.91104	39
22	.34803	.93748	.36434	.93127	.38053	.92477	.39661	.91799	.41257	.91092	38
23	.34830	.93738	.36461	.93116	.38080	.92466	.39688	.91787	.41284	.91080	37
24	.34857	.93728	.36488	.93106	.38107	.92455	.39715	.91775	.41310	.91068	36
25	.34884	.93718	.36515	.93095	.38134	.92444	.39741	.91764	.41337	.91056	35
26	.34912	.93708	.36542	.93084	.38161	.92432	.39768	.91752	.41363	.91044	34
27	.34939	.93698	.36569	.93074	.38188	.92421	.39795	.91741	.41390	.91032	33
28	.34966	.93688	.36596	.93063	.38215	.92410	.39822	.91729	.41416	.91020	32
29	.34993	.93677	.36623	.93052	.38241	.92399	.39848	.91718	.41443	.91008	31
30	.35021	.93667	.36650	.93042	.38268	.92388	.39875	.91706	.41469	.90996	30
31	.35048	.93657	.36677	.93031	.38295	.92377	.39902	.91694	.41496	.90984	29
32	.35075	.93647	.36704	.93020	.38322	.92366	.39928	.91683	.41522	.90972	28
33	.35102	.93637	.36731	.93010	.38349	.92355	.39955	.91671	.41549	.90960	27
34	.35130	.93626	.36758	.92999	.38376	.92343	.39982	.91660	.41575	.90948	26
35	.35157	.93616	.36785	.92988	.38403	.92332	.40008	.91648	.41602	.90936	25
36	.35184	.93606	.36812	.92978	.38430	.92321	.40035	.91636	.41628	.90924	24
37	.35211	.93596	.36839	.92967	.38456	.92310	.40062	.91625	.41655	.90911	23
38	.35239	.93585	.36867	.92956	.38483	.92299	.40088	.91613	.41681	.90899	22
39	.35266	.93575	.36894	.92945	.38510	.92287	.40115	.91601	.41707	.90887	21
40	.35293	.93565	.36921	.92935	.38537	.92276	.40141	.91590	.41734	.90875	20
41	.35320	.93555	.36948	.92924	.38564	.92265	.40168	.91578	.41760	.90863	19
42	.35347	.93544	.36975	.92913	.38591	.92254	.40195	.91566	.41787	.90851	18
43	.35375	.93534	.37002	.92902	.38617	.92243	.40221	.91555	.41813	.90839	17
44	.35402	.93524	.37029	.92892	.38644	.92231	.40248	.91543	.41840	.90826	16
45	.35429	.93514	.37056	.92881	.38671	.92220	.40275	.91531	.41866	.90814	15
46	.35456	.93503	.37083	.92870	.38698	.92209	.40301	.91519	.41892	.90802	14
47	.35484	.93493	.37110	.92859	.38725	.92198	.40328	.91508	.41919	.90790	13
48	.35511	.93483	.37137	.92849	.38752	.92186	.40355	.91496	.41945	.90778	12
49	.35538	.93472	.37164	.92838	.38778	.92175	.40381	.91484	.41972	.90766	11
50	.35565	.93462	.37191	.92827	.38805	.92164	.40408	.91472	.41998	.90753	10
51	.35592	.93452	.37218	.92816	.38832	.92152	.40434	.91461	.42024	.90741	9
52	.35619	.93441	.37245	.92805	.38859	.92141	.40461	.91449	.42051	.90729	8
53	.35647	.93431	.37272	.92794	.38886	.92130	.40488	.91437	.42077	.90717	7
54	.35674	.93420	.37299	.92784	.38912	.92119	.40514	.91425	.42104	.90704	6
55	.35701	.93410	.37326	.92773	.38939	.92107	.40541	.91414	.42130	.90692	5
56	.35728	.93400	.37353	.92762	.38966	.92096	.40567	.91402	.42156	.90680	4
57	.35755	.93389	.37380	.92751	.38993	.92085	.40594	.91390	.42183	.90668	3
58	.35782	.93379	.37407	.92740	.39020	.92073	.40621	.91378	.42209	.90655	2
59	.35810	.93368	.37434	.92729	.39046	.92062	.40647	.91366	.42235	.90643	1
60	.35837	.93358	.37461	.92718	.39073	.92050	.40674	.91355	.42262	.90631	0
/	Cosine	Sine	Cosine	Sine	Cosine	Sine	Cosine	Sine	Cosine	Sine	/
	69°		68°		67°		66°		65°		

TABLE E

Natural Sines and Cosines

′	25° Sine	25° Cosine	26° Sine	26° Cosine	27° Sine	27° Cosine	28° Sine	28° Cosine	29° Sine	29° Cosine	′
0	.42262	.90631	.43837	.89879	.45399	.89101	.46947	.88295	.48481	.87462	60
1	.42288	.90618	.43863	.89867	.45425	.89087	.46973	.88281	.48506	.87448	59
2	.42315	.90606	.43889	.89854	.45451	.89074	.46999	.88267	.48532	.87434	58
3	.42341	.90594	.43916	.89841	.45477	.89061	.47024	.88254	.48557	.87420	57
4	.42367	.90582	.43942	.89828	.45503	.89048	.47050	.88240	.48583	.87406	56
5	.42394	.90569	.43968	.89816	.45529	.89035	.47076	.88226	.48608	.87391	55
6	.42420	.90557	.43994	.89803	.45554	.89021	.47101	.88213	.48634	.87377	54
7	.42446	.90545	.44020	.89790	.45580	.89008	.47127	.88199	.48659	.87363	53
8	.42473	.90532	.44046	.89777	.45606	.88995	.47153	.88185	.48684	.87349	52
9	.42499	.90520	.44072	.89764	.45632	.88981	.47178	.88172	.48710	.87335	51
10	.42525	.90507	.44098	.89752	.45658	.88968	.47204	.88158	.48735	.87321	50
11	.42552	.90495	.44124	.89739	.45684	.88955	.47229	.88144	.48761	.87306	49
12	.42578	.90483	.44151	.89726	.45710	.88942	.47255	.88130	.48786	.87292	48
13	.42604	.90470	.44177	.89713	.45736	.88928	.47281	.88117	.48811	.87278	47
14	.42631	.90458	.44203	.89700	.45762	.88915	.47306	.88103	.48837	.87264	46
15	.42657	.90446	.44229	.89687	.45787	.88902	.47332	.88089	.48862	.87250	45
16	.42683	.90433	.44255	.89674	.45813	.88888	.47358	.88075	.48888	.87235	44
17	.42709	.90421	.44281	.89662	.45839	.88875	.47383	.88062	.48913	.87221	43
18	.42736	.90408	.44307	.89649	.45865	.88862	.47409	.88048	.48938	.87207	42
19	.42762	.90396	.44333	.89636	.45891	.88848	.47434	.88034	.48964	.87193	41
20	.42788	.90383	.44359	.89623	.45917	.88835	.47460	.88020	.48989	.87178	40
21	.42815	.90371	.44385	.89610	.45942	.88822	.47486	.88006	.49014	.87164	39
22	.42841	.90358	.44411	.89597	.45968	.88808	.47511	.87993	.49040	.87150	38
23	.42867	.90346	.44437	.89584	.45994	.88795	.47537	.87979	.49065	.87136	37
24	.42894	.90334	.44464	.89571	.46020	.88782	.47562	.87965	.49090	.87121	36
25	.42920	.90321	.44490	.89558	.46046	.88768	.47588	.87951	.49116	.87107	35
26	.42946	.90309	.44516	.89545	.46072	.88755	.47614	.87937	.49141	.87093	34
27	.42972	.90296	.44542	.89532	.46097	.88741	.47639	.87923	.49166	.87079	33
28	.42999	.90284	.44568	.89519	.46123	.88728	.47665	.87909	.49192	.87064	32
29	.43025	.90271	.44594	.89506	.46149	.88715	.47690	.87896	.49217	.87050	31
30	.43051	.90259	.44620	.89493	.46175	.88701	.47716	.87882	.49242	.87036	30
31	.43077	.90246	.44646	.89480	.46201	.88688	.47741	.87868	.49268	.87021	29
32	.43104	.90233	.44672	.89467	.46226	.88674	.47767	.87854	.49293	.87007	28
33	.43130	.90221	.44698	.89454	.46252	.88661	.47793	.87840	.49318	.86993	27
34	.43156	.90208	.44724	.89441	.46278	.88647	.47818	.87826	.49344	.86978	26
35	.43182	.90196	.44750	.89428	.46304	.88634	.47844	.87812	.49369	.86964	25
36	.43209	.90183	.44776	.89415	.46330	.88620	.47869	.87798	.49394	.86949	24
37	.43235	.90171	.44802	.89402	.46355	.88607	.47895	.87784	.49419	.86935	23
38	.43261	.90158	.44828	.89389	.46381	.88593	.47920	.87770	.49445	.86921	22
39	.43287	.90146	.44854	.89376	.46407	.88580	.47946	.87756	.49470	.86906	21
40	.43313	.90133	.44880	.89363	.46433	.88566	.47971	.87743	.49495	.86892	20
41	.43340	.90120	.44906	.89350	.46458	.88553	.47997	.87729	.49521	.86878	19
42	.43366	.90108	.44932	.89337	.46484	.88539	.48022	.87715	.49546	.86863	18
43	.43392	.90095	.44958	.89324	.46510	.88526	.48048	.87701	.49571	.86849	17
44	.43418	.90082	.44984	.89311	.46536	.88512	.48073	.87687	.49596	.86834	16
45	.43445	.90070	.45010	.89298	.46561	.88499	.48099	.87673	.49622	.86820	15
46	.43471	.90057	.45036	.89285	.46587	.88485	.48124	.87659	.49647	.86805	14
47	.43497	.90045	.45062	.89272	.46613	.88472	.48150	.87645	.49672	.86791	13
48	.43523	.90032	.45088	.89259	.46639	.88458	.48175	.87631	.49697	.86777	12
49	.43549	.90019	.45114	.89245	.46664	.88445	.48201	.87617	.49723	.86762	11
50	.43575	.90007	.45140	.89232	.46690	.88431	.48226	.87603	.49748	.86748	10
51	.43602	.89994	.45166	.89219	.46716	.88417	.48252	.87589	.49773	.86733	9
52	.43628	.89981	.45192	.89206	.46742	.88404	.48277	.87575	.49798	.86719	8
53	.43654	.89968	.45218	.89193	.46767	.88390	.48303	.87561	.49824	.86704	7
54	.43680	.89956	.45243	.89180	.46793	.88377	.48328	.87546	.49849	.86690	6
55	.43706	.89943	.45269	.89167	.46819	.88363	.48354	.87532	.49874	.86675	5
56	.43733	.89930	.45295	.89153	.46844	.88349	.48379	.87518	.49899	.86661	4
57	.43759	.89918	.45321	.89140	.46870	.88336	.48405	.87504	.49924	.86646	3
58	.43785	.89905	.45347	.89127	.46896	.88322	.48430	.87490	.49950	.86632	2
59	.43811	.89892	.45373	.89114	.46921	.88308	.48456	.87476	.49975	.86617	1
60	.43837	.89879	.45399	.89101	.46947	.88295	.48481	.87462	.50000	.86603	0
′	Cosine	Sine	Cosine	Sine	Cosine	Sine	Cosine	Sine	Cosine	Sine	′
	64°		63°		62°		61°		60°		

Natural Sines and Cosines

′	30°		31°		32°		33°		34°		′
	Sine	Cosine	Sine	Cosine	Sine	Cosine	Sine	Cosine	Sine	Cosine	
0	.50000	.86603	.51504	.85717	.52992	.84805	.54464	.83867	.55919	.82904	60
1	.50025	.86588	.51529	.85702	.53017	.84789	.54488	.83851	.55943	.82887	59
2	.50050	.86573	.51554	.85687	.53041	.84774	.54513	.83835	.55968	.82871	58
3	.50076	.86559	.51579	.85672	.53066	.84759	.54537	.83819	.55992	.82855	57
4	.50101	.86544	.51604	.85657	.53091	.84743	.54561	.83804	.56016	.82839	56
5	.50126	.86530	.51628	.85642	.53115	.84728	.54586	.83788	.56040	.82822	55
6	.50151	.86515	.51653	.85627	.53140	.84712	.54610	.83772	.56064	.82806	54
7	.50176	.86501	.51678	.85612	.53164	.84697	.54635	.83756	.56088	.82790	53
8	.50201	.86486	.51703	.85597	.53189	.84681	.54659	.83740	.56112	.82773	52
9	.50227	.86471	.51728	.85582	.53214	.84666	.54683	.83724	.56136	.82757	51
10	.50252	.86457	.51753	.85567	.53238	.84650	.54708	.83708	.56160	.82741	50
11	.50277	.86442	.51778	.85551	.53263	.84635	.54732	.83692	.56184	.82724	49
12	.50302	.86427	.51803	.85536	.53288	.84619	.54756	.83676	.56208	.82708	48
13	.50327	.86413	.51828	.85521	.53312	.84604	.54781	.83660	.56232	.82692	47
14	.50352	.86398	.51852	.85506	.53337	.84588	.54805	.83645	.56256	.82675	46
15	.50377	.86384	.51877	.85491	.53361	.84573	.54829	.83629	.56280	.82659	45
16	.50403	.86369	.51902	.85476	.53386	.84557	.54854	.83613	.56305	.82643	44
17	.50428	.86354	.51927	.85461	.53411	.84542	.54878	.83597	.56329	.82626	43
18	.50453	.86340	.51952	.85446	.53435	.84526	.54902	.83581	.56353	.82610	42
19	.50478	.86325	.51977	.85431	.53460	.84511	.54927	.83565	.56377	.82593	41
20	.50503	.86310	.52002	.85416	.53484	.84495	.54951	.83549	.56401	.82577	40
21	.50528	.86295	.52026	.85401	.53509	.84480	.54975	.83533	.56425	.82561	39
22	.50553	.86281	.52051	.85385	.53534	.84464	.54999	.83517	.56449	.82544	38
23	.50578	.86266	.52076	.85370	.53558	.84448	.55024	.83501	.56473	.82528	37
24	.50603	.86251	.52101	.85355	.53583	.84433	.55048	.83485	.56497	.82511	36
25	.50628	.86237	.52126	.85340	.53607	.84417	.55072	.83469	.56521	.82495	35
26	.50654	.86222	.52151	.85325	.53632	.84402	.55097	.83453	.56545	.82478	34
27	.50679	.86207	.52175	.85310	.53656	.84386	.55121	.83437	.56569	.82462	33
28	.50704	.86192	.52200	.85294	.53681	.84370	.55145	.83421	.56593	.82446	32
29	.50729	.86178	.52225	.85279	.53705	.84355	.55169	.83405	.56617	.82429	31
30	.50754	.86163	.52250	.85264	.53730	.84339	.55194	.83389	.56641	.82413	30
31	.50779	.86148	.52275	.85249	.53754	.84324	.55218	.83373	.56665	.82396	29
32	.50804	.86133	.52299	.85234	.53779	.84308	.55242	.83356	.56689	.82380	28
33	.50829	.86119	.52324	.85218	.53804	.84292	.55266	.83340	.56713	.82363	27
34	.50854	.86104	.52349	.85203	.53828	.84277	.55291	.83324	.56736	.82347	26
35	.50879	.86089	.52374	.85188	.53853	.84261	.55315	.83308	.56760	.82330	25
36	.50904	.86074	.52399	.85173	.53877	.84245	.55339	.83292	.56784	.82314	24
37	.50929	.86059	.52423	.85157	.53902	.84230	.55363	.83276	.56808	.82297	23
38	.50954	.86045	.52448	.85142	.53926	.84214	.55388	.83260	.56832	.82281	22
39	.50979	.86030	.52473	.85127	.53951	.84198	.55412	.83244	.56856	.82264	21
40	.51004	.86015	.52498	.85112	.53975	.84182	.55436	.83228	.56880	.82248	20
41	.51029	.86000	.52522	.85096	.54000	.84167	.55460	.83212	.56904	.82231	19
42	.51054	.85985	.52547	.85081	.54024	.84151	.55484	.83195	.56928	.82214	18
43	.51079	.85970	.52572	.85066	.54049	.84135	.55509	.83179	.56952	.82198	17
44	.51104	.85956	.52597	.85051	.54073	.84120	.55533	.83163	.56976	.82181	16
45	.51129	.85941	.52621	.85035	.54097	.84104	.55557	.83147	.57000	.82165	15
46	.51154	.85926	.52646	.85020	.54122	.84088	.55581	.83131	.57024	.82148	14
47	.51179	.85911	.52671	.85005	.54146	.84072	.55605	.83115	.57047	.82132	13
48	.51204	.85896	.52696	.84989	.54171	.84057	.55630	.83098	.57071	.82115	12
49	.51229	.85881	.52720	.84974	.54195	.84041	.55654	.83082	.57095	.82098	11
50	.51254	.85866	.52745	.84959	.54220	.84025	.55678	.83066	.57119	.82082	10
51	.51279	.85851	.52770	.84943	.54244	.84009	.55702	.83050	.57143	.82065	9
52	.51304	.85836	.52794	.84928	.54269	.83994	.55726	.83034	.57167	.82048	8
53	.51329	.85821	.52819	.84913	.54293	.83978	.55750	.83017	.57191	.82032	7
54	.51354	.85806	.52844	.84897	.54317	.83962	.55775	.83001	.57215	.82015	6
55	.51379	.85792	.52869	.84882	.54342	.83946	.55799	.82985	.57238	.81999	5
56	.51404	.85777	.52893	.84866	.54366	.83930	.55823	.82969	.57262	.81982	4
57	.51429	.85762	.52918	.84851	.54391	.83915	.55847	.82953	.57286	.81965	3
58	.51454	.85747	.52943	.84836	.54415	.83899	.55871	.82936	.57310	.81949	2
59	.51479	.85732	.52967	.84820	.54440	.83883	.55895	.82920	.57334	.81932	1
60	.51504	.85717	.52992	.84805	.54464	.83867	.55919	.82904	.57358	.81915	0
′	Cosine	Sine	Cosine	Sine	Cosine	Sine	Cosine	Sine	Cosine	Sine	′
	59°		58°		57°		56°		55°		

TABLE E

Natural Sines and Cosines

′	35° Sine	35° Cosine	36° Sine	36° Cosine	37° Sine	37° Cosine	38° Sine	38° Cosine	39° Sine	39° Cosine	′
0	.57358	.81915	.58779	.80902	.60182	.79864	.61566	.78801	.62932	.77715	60
1	.57381	.81899	.58802	.80885	.60205	.79846	.61589	.78783	.62955	.77696	59
2	.57405	.81882	.58826	.80867	.60228	.79829	.61612	.78765	.62977	.77678	58
3	.57429	.81865	.58849	.80850	.60251	.79811	.61635	.78747	.63000	.77660	57
4	.57453	.81848	.58873	.80833	.60274	.79793	.61658	.78729	.63023	.77641	56
5	.57477	.81832	.58896	.80816	.60298	.79776	.61681	.78711	.63045	.77623	55
6	.57501	.81815	.58920	.80799	.60321	.79758	.61704	.78694	.63068	.77605	54
7	.57524	.81798	.58943	.80782	.60344	.79741	.61726	.78676	.63090	.77586	53
8	.57548	.81782	.58967	.80765	.60367	.79723	.61749	.78658	.63113	.77568	52
9	.57572	.81765	.58990	.80748	.60390	.79706	.61772	.78640	.63135	.77550	51
10	.57596	.81748	.59014	.80730	.60414	.79688	.61795	.78622	.63158	.77531	50
11	.57619	.81731	.59037	.80713	.60437	.79671	.61818	.78604	.63180	.77513	49
12	.57643	.81714	.59061	.80696	.60460	.79653	.61841	.78586	.63203	.77494	48
13	.57667	.81698	.59084	.80679	.60483	.79635	.61864	.78568	.63225	.77476	47
14	.57691	.81681	.59108	.80662	.60506	.79618	.61887	.78550	.63248	.77458	46
15	.57715	.81664	.59131	.80644	.60529	.79600	.61909	.78532	.63271	.77439	45
16	.57738	.81647	.59154	.80627	.60553	.79583	.61932	.78514	.63293	.77421	44
17	.57762	.81631	.59178	.80610	.60576	.79565	.61955	.78496	.63316	.77402	43
18	.57786	.81614	.59201	.80593	.60599	.79547	.61978	.78478	.63338	.77384	42
19	.57810	.81597	.59225	.80576	.60622	.79530	.62001	.78460	.63361	.77366	41
20	.57833	.81580	.59248	.80558	.60645	.79512	.62024	.78442	.63383	.77347	40
21	.57857	.81563	.59272	.80541	.60668	.79494	.62046	.78424	.63406	.77329	39
22	.57881	.81546	.59295	.80524	.60691	.79477	.62069	.78405	.63428	.77310	38
23	.57904	.81530	.59318	.80507	.60714	.79459	.62092	.78387	.63451	.77292	37
24	.57928	.81513	.59342	.80489	.60738	.79441	.62115	.78369	.63473	.77273	36
25	.57952	.81496	.59365	.80472	.60761	.79424	.62138	.78351	.63496	.77255	35
26	.57976	.81479	.59389	.80455	.60784	.79406	.62160	.78333	.63518	.77236	34
27	.57999	.81462	.59412	.80438	.60807	.79388	.62183	.78315	.63540	.77218	33
28	.58023	.81445	.59436	.80420	.60830	.79371	.62206	.78297	.63563	.77199	32
29	.58047	.81428	.59459	.80403	.60853	.79353	.62229	.78279	.63585	.77181	31
30	.58070	.81412	.59482	.80386	.60876	.79335	.62251	.78261	.63608	.77162	30
31	.58094	.81395	.59506	.80368	.60899	.79318	.62274	.78243	.63630	.77144	29
32	.58118	.81378	.59529	.80351	.60922	.79300	.62297	.78225	.63653	.77125	28
33	.58141	.81361	.59552	.80334	.60945	.79282	.62320	.78206	.63675	.77107	27
34	.58165	.81344	.59576	.80316	.60968	.79264	.62342	.78188	.63698	.77088	26
35	.58189	.81327	.59599	.80299	.60991	.79247	.62365	.78170	.63720	.77070	25
36	.58212	.81310	.59622	.80282	.61015	.79229	.62388	.78152	.63742	.77051	24
37	.58236	.81293	.59646	.80264	.61038	.79211	.62411	.78134	.63765	.77033	23
38	.58260	.81276	.59669	.80247	.61061	.79193	.62433	.78116	.63787	.77014	22
39	.58283	.81259	.59693	.80230	.61084	.79176	.62456	.78098	.63810	.76996	21
40	.58307	.81242	.59716	.80212	.61107	.79158	.62479	.78079	.63832	.76977	20
41	.58330	.81225	.59739	.80195	.61130	.79140	.62502	.78061	.63854	.76959	19
42	.58354	.81208	.59763	.80178	.61153	.79122	.62524	.78043	.63877	.76940	18
43	.58378	.81191	.59786	.80160	.61176	.79105	.62547	.78025	.63899	.76921	17
44	.58401	.81174	.59809	.80143	.61199	.79087	.62570	.78007	.63922	.76903	16
45	.58425	.81157	.59832	.80125	.61222	.79069	.62592	.77988	.63944	.76884	15
46	.58449	.81140	.59856	.80108	.61245	.79051	.62615	.77970	.63966	.76866	14
47	.58472	.81123	.59879	.80091	.61268	.79033	.62638	.77952	.63989	.76847	13
48	.58496	.81106	.59902	.80073	.61291	.79016	.62660	.77934	.64011	.76828	12
49	.58519	.81089	.59926	.80056	.61314	.78998	.62683	.77916	.64033	.76810	11
50	.58543	.81072	.59949	.80038	.61337	.78980	.62706	.77897	.64056	.76791	10
51	.58567	.81055	.59972	.80021	.61360	.78962	.62728	.77879	.64078	.76772	9
52	.58590	.81038	.59995	.80003	.61383	.78944	.62751	.77861	.64100	.76754	8
53	.58614	.81021	.60019	.79986	.61406	.78926	.62774	.77843	.64123	.76735	7
54	.58637	.81004	.60042	.79968	.61429	.78908	.62796	.77824	.64145	.76717	6
55	.58661	.80987	.60065	.79951	.61451	.78891	.62819	.77806	.64167	.76698	5
56	.58684	.80970	.60089	.79934	.61474	.78873	.62842	.77788	.64190	.76679	4
57	.58708	.80953	.60112	.79916	.61497	.78855	.62864	.77769	.64212	.76661	3
58	.58731	.80936	.60135	.79899	.61520	.78837	.62887	.77751	.64234	.76642	2
59	.58755	.80919	.60158	.79881	.61543	.78819	.62909	.77733	.64256	.76623	1
60	.58779	.80902	.60182	.79864	.61566	.78801	.62932	.77715	.64279	.76604	0
′	Cosine	Sine	Cosine	Sine	Cosine	Sine	Cosine	Sine	Cosine	Sine	′
	54°		53°		52°		51°		50°		

NATURAL SINES AND COSINES

′	40° Sine	40° Cosine	41° Sine	41° Cosine	42° Sine	42° Cosine	43° Sine	43° Cosine	44° Sine	44° Cosine	′
0	.64279	.76604	.65606	.75471	.66913	.74314	.68200	.73135	.69466	.71934	60
1	.64301	.76586	.65628	.75452	.66935	.74295	.68221	.73116	.69487	.71914	59
2	.64323	.76567	.65650	.75433	.66956	.74276	.68242	.73096	.69508	.71894	58
3	.64346	.76548	.65672	.75414	.66978	.74256	.68264	.73076	.69529	.71873	57
4	.64368	.76530	.65694	.75395	.66999	.74237	.68285	.73056	.69549	.71853	56
5	.64390	.76511	.65716	.75375	.67021	.74217	.68306	.73036	.69570	.71833	55
6	.64412	.76492	.65738	.75356	.67043	.74198	.68327	.73016	.69591	.71813	54
7	.64435	.76473	.65759	.75337	.67064	.74178	.68349	.72996	.69612	.71792	53
8	.64457	.76455	.65781	.75318	.67086	.74159	.68370	.72976	.69633	.71772	52
9	.64479	.76436	.65803	.75299	.67107	.74139	.68391	.72957	.69654	.71752	51
10	.64501	.76417	.65825	.75280	.67129	.74120	.68412	.72937	.69675	.71732	50
11	.64524	.76398	.65847	.75261	.67151	.74100	.68434	.72917	.69696	.71711	49
12	.64546	.76380	.65869	.75241	.67172	.74080	.68455	.72897	.69717	.71691	48
13	.64568	.76361	.65891	.75222	.67194	.74061	.68476	.72877	.69737	.71671	47
14	.64590	.76342	.65913	.75203	.67215	.74041	.68497	.72857	.69758	.71650	46
15	.64612	.76323	.65935	.75184	.67237	.74022	.68518	.72837	.69779	.71630	45
16	.64635	.76304	.65956	.75165	.67258	.74002	.68539	.72817	.69800	.71610	44
17	.64657	.76286	.65978	.75146	.67280	.73983	.68561	.72797	.69821	.71590	43
18	.64679	.76267	.66000	.75126	.67301	.73963	.68582	.72777	.69842	.71569	42
19	.64701	.76248	.66022	.75107	.67323	.73944	.68603	.72757	.69862	.71549	41
20	.64723	.76229	.66044	.75088	.67344	.73924	.68624	.72737	.69883	.71529	40
21	.64746	.76210	.66066	.75069	.67366	.73904	.68645	.72717	.69904	.71508	39
22	.64768	.76192	.66088	.75050	.67387	.73885	.68666	.72697	.69925	.71488	38
23	.64790	.76173	.66109	.75030	.67409	.73865	.68688	.72677	.69946	.71468	37
24	.64812	.76154	.66131	.75011	.67430	.73846	.68709	.72657	.69966	.71447	36
25	.64834	.76135	.66153	.74992	.67452	.73826	.68730	.72637	.69987	.71427	35
26	.64856	.76116	.66175	.74973	.67473	.73806	.68751	.72617	.70008	.71407	34
27	.64878	.76097	.66197	.74953	.67495	.73787	.68772	.72597	.70029	.71386	33
28	.64901	.76078	.66218	.74934	.67516	.73767	.68793	.72577	.70049	.71366	32
29	.64923	.76059	.66240	.74915	.67538	.73747	.68814	.72557	.70070	.71345	31
30	.64945	.76041	.66262	.74896	.67559	.73728	.68835	.72537	.70091	.71325	30
31	.64967	.76022	.66284	.74876	.67580	.73708	.68857	.72517	.70112	.71305	29
32	.64989	.76003	.66306	.74857	.67602	.73688	.68878	.72497	.70132	.71284	28
33	.65011	.75984	.66327	.74838	.67623	.73669	.68899	.72477	.70153	.71264	27
34	.65033	.75965	.66349	.74818	.67645	.73649	.68920	.72457	.70174	.71243	26
35	.65055	.75946	.66371	.74799	.67666	.73629	.68941	.72437	.70195	.71223	25
36	.65077	.75927	.66393	.74780	.67688	.73610	.68962	.72417	.70215	.71203	24
37	.65100	.75908	.66414	.74760	.67709	.73590	.68983	.72397	.70236	.71182	23
38	.65122	.75889	.66436	.74741	.67730	.73570	.69004	.72377	.70257	.71162	22
39	.65144	.75870	.66458	.74722	.67752	.73551	.69025	.72357	.70277	.71141	21
40	.65166	.75851	.66480	.74703	.67773	.73531	.69046	.72337	.70298	.71121	20
41	.65188	.75832	.66501	.74683	.67795	.73511	.69067	.72317	.70319	.71100	19
42	.65210	.75813	.66523	.74664	.67816	.73491	.69088	.72297	.70339	.71080	18
43	.65232	.75794	.66545	.74644	.67837	.73472	.69109	.72277	.70360	.71059	17
44	.65254	.75775	.66566	.74625	.67859	.73452	.69130	.72257	.70381	.71039	16
45	.65276	.75756	.66588	.74606	.67880	.73432	.69151	.72236	.70401	.71019	15
46	.65298	.75738	.66610	.74586	.67901	.73413	.69172	.72216	.70422	.70998	14
47	.65320	.75719	.66632	.74567	.67923	.73393	.69193	.72196	.70443	.70978	13
48	.65342	.75700	.66653	.74548	.67944	.73373	.69214	.72176	.70463	.70957	12
49	.65364	.75680	.66675	.74528	.67965	.73353	.69235	.72156	.70484	.70937	11
50	.65386	.75661	.66697	.74509	.67987	.73333	.69256	.72136	.70505	.70916	10
51	.65408	.75642	.66718	.74489	.68008	.73314	.69277	.72116	.70525	.70896	9
52	.65430	.75623	.66740	.74470	.68029	.73294	.69298	.72095	.70546	.70875	8
53	.65452	.75604	.66762	.74451	.68051	.73274	.69319	.72075	.70567	.70855	7
54	.65474	.75585	.66783	.74431	.68072	.73254	.69340	.72055	.70587	.70834	6
55	.65496	.75566	.66805	.74412	.68093	.73234	.69361	.72035	.70608	.70813	5
56	.65518	.75547	.66827	.74392	.68115	.73215	.69382	.72015	.70628	.70793	4
57	.65540	.75528	.66848	.74373	.68136	.73195	.69403	.71995	.70649	.70772	3
58	.65562	.75509	.66870	.74353	.68157	.73175	.69424	.71974	.70670	.70752	2
59	.65584	.75490	.66891	.74334	.68179	.73155	.69445	.71954	.70690	.70731	1
60	.65606	.75471	.66913	.74314	.68200	.73135	.69466	.71934	.70711	.70711	0

′	Cosine	Sine	Cosine	Sine	Cosine	Sine	Cosine	Sine	Cosine	Sine	′
	49°		48°		47°		46°		45°		

TABLE F

Natural Tangents and Cotangents

′	0°		1°		2°		3°		4°		′
	Tang	Cotang	Tang	Cotang	Tang	Cotang	Tang	Cotang	Tang	Cotang	
0	.00000	Infinite	.01746	57.2900	.03492	28.6363	.05241	19.0811	.06993	14.3007	60
1	.00029	3437.75	.01775	56.3506	.03521	28.3994	.05270	18.9755	.07022	14.2411	59
2	.00058	1718.87	.01804	55.4415	.03550	28.1664	.05299	18.8711	.07051	14.1821	58
3	.00087	1145.92	.01833	54.5613	.03579	27.9372	.05328	18.7678	.07080	14.1235	57
4	.00116	859.436	.01862	53.7086	.03609	27.7117	.05357	18.6656	.07110	14.0655	56
5	.00145	687.549	.01891	52.8821	.03638	27.4899	.05387	18.5645	.07139	14.0079	55
6	.00175	572.957	.01920	52.0807	.03667	27.2715	.05416	18.4645	.07168	13.9507	54
7	.00204	491.106	.01949	51.3032	.03696	27.0566	.05445	18.3655	.07197	13.8940	53
8	.00233	429.718	.01978	50.5485	.03725	26.8450	.05474	18.2677	.07227	13.8378	52
9	.00262	381.971	.02007	49.8157	.03754	26.6367	.05503	18.1708	.07256	13.7821	51
10	.00291	343.774	.02036	49.1039	.03783	26.4316	.05533	18.0750	.07285	13.7267	50
11	.00320	312.521	.02066	48.4121	.03812	26.2296	.05562	17.9802	.07314	13.6719	49
12	.00349	286.478	.02095	47.7395	.03842	26.0307	.05591	17.8863	.07344	13.6174	48
13	.00378	264.441	.02124	47.0853	.03871	25.8348	.05620	17.7934	.07373	13.5634	47
14	.00407	245.552	.02153	46.4489	.03900	25.6418	.05649	17.7015	.07402	13.5098	46
15	.00436	229.182	.02182	45.8294	.03929	25.4517	.05678	17.6106	.07431	13.4566	45
16	.00465	214.858	.02211	45.2261	.03958	25.2644	.05708	17.5205	.07461	13.4039	44
17	.00495	202.219	.02240	44.6386	.03987	25.0798	.05737	17.4314	.07490	13.3515	43
18	.00524	190.984	.02269	44.0661	.04016	24.8978	.05766	17.3432	.07519	13.2996	42
19	.00553	180.932	.02298	43.5081	.04046	24.7185	.05795	17.2558	.07548	13.2480	41
20	.00582	171.885	.02328	42.9641	.04075	24.5418	.05824	17.1693	.07578	13.1969	40
21	.00611	163.700	.02357	42.4335	.04104	24.3675	.05854	17.0837	.07607	13.1461	39
22	.00640	156.259	.02386	41.9158	.04133	24.1957	.05883	16.9990	.07636	13.0958	38
23	.00669	149.465	.02415	41.4106	.04162	24.0263	.05912	16.9150	.07665	13.0458	37
24	.00698	143.237	.02444	40.9174	.04191	23.8593	.05941	16.8319	.07695	12.9962	36
25	.00727	137.507	.02473	40.4358	.04220	23.6945	.05970	16.7496	.07724	12.9469	35
26	.00756	132.219	.02502	39.9655	.04250	23.5321	.05999	16.6681	.07753	12.8981	34
27	.00785	127.321	.02531	39.5059	.04279	23.3718	.06029	16.5874	.07782	12.8496	33
28	.00815	122.774	.02560	39.0568	.04308	23.2137	.06058	16.5075	.07812	12.8014	32
29	.00844	118.540	.02589	38.6177	.04337	23.0577	.06087	16.4283	.07841	12.7536	31
30	.00873	114.589	.02619	38.1885	.04366	22.9038	.06116	16.3499	.07870	12.7062	30
31	.00902	110.892	.02648	37.7686	.04395	22.7519	.06145	16.2722	.07899	12.6591	29
32	.00931	107.426	.02677	37.3579	.04424	22.6020	.06175	16.1952	.07929	12.6124	28
33	.00960	104.171	.02706	36.9560	.04454	22.4541	.06204	16.1190	.07958	12.5660	27
34	.00989	101.107	.02735	36.5627	.04483	22.3081	.06233	16.0435	.07987	12.5199	26
35	.01018	98.2179	.02764	36.1776	.04512	22.1640	.06262	15.9687	.08017	12.4742	25
36	.01047	95.4895	.02793	35.8006	.04541	22.0217	.06291	15.8945	.08046	12.4288	24
37	.01076	92.9085	.02822	35.4313	.04570	21.8813	.06321	15.8211	.08075	12.3838	23
38	.01105	90.4633	.02851	35.0695	.04599	21.7426	.06350	15.7483	.08104	12.3390	22
39	.01135	88.1436	.02881	34.7151	.04628	21.6056	.06379	15.6762	.08134	12.2946	21
40	.01164	85.9398	.02910	34.3678	.04658	21.4704	.06408	15.6048	.08163	12.2505	20
41	.01193	83.8435	.02939	34.0273	.04687	21.3369	.06437	15.5340	.08192	12.2067	19
42	.01222	81.8470	.02968	33.6935	.04716	21.2049	.06467	15.4638	.08221	12.1632	18
43	.01251	79.9434	.02997	33.3662	.04745	21.0747	.06496	15.3943	.08251	12.1201	17
44	.01280	78.1263	.03026	33.0452	.04774	20.9460	.06525	15.3254	.08280	12.0772	16
45	.01309	76.3900	.03055	32.7303	.04803	20.8188	.06554	15.2571	.08309	12.0346	15
46	.01338	74.7292	.03084	32.4213	.04833	20.6932	.06584	15.1893	.08339	11.9923	14
47	.01367	73.1390	.03114	32.1181	.04862	20.5691	.06613	15.1222	.08368	11.9504	13
48	.01396	71.6151	.03143	31.8205	.04891	20.4465	.06642	15.0557	.08397	11.9087	12
49	.01425	70.1533	.03172	31.5284	.04920	20.3253	.06671	14.9898	.08427	11.8673	11
50	.01455	68.7501	.03201	31.2416	.04949	20.2056	.06700	14.9244	.08456	11.8262	10
51	.01484	67.4019	.03230	30.9599	.04978	20.0872	.06730	14.8596	.08485	11.7853	9
52	.01513	66.1055	.03259	30.6833	.05007	19.9702	.06759	14.7954	.08514	11.7448	8
53	.01542	64.8580	.03288	30.4116	.05037	19.8546	.06788	14.7317	.08544	11.7045	7
54	.01571	63.6567	.03317	30.1446	.05066	19.7403	.06817	14.6685	.08573	11.6645	6
55	.01600	62.4992	.03346	29.8823	.05095	19.6273	.06847	14.6059	.08602	11.6248	5
56	.01629	61.3829	.03376	29.6245	.05124	19.5156	.06876	14.5438	.08632	11.5853	4
57	.01658	60.3058	.03405	29.3711	.05153	19.4051	.06905	14.4823	.08661	11.5461	3
58	.01687	59.2659	.03434	29.1220	.05182	19.2959	.06934	14.4212	.08690	11.5072	2
59	.01716	58.2612	.03463	28.8771	.05212	19.1879	.06963	14.3607	.08720	11.4685	1
60	.01746	57.2900	.03492	28.6363	.05241	19.0811	.06993	14.3007	.08749	11.4301	0
′	Cotang	Tang	Cotang	Tang	Cotang	Tang	Cotang	Tang	Cotang	Tang	′
	89°		88°		87°		86°		85°		

NATURAL TANGENTS AND COTANGENTS

′	5° Tang	5° Cotang	6° Tang	6° Cotang	7° Tang	7° Cotang	8° Tang	8° Cotang	9° Tang	9° Cotang	′
0	.08749	11.4301	.10510	9.51436	.12278	8.14435	.14054	7.11537	.15838	6.31375	60
1	.08778	11.3919	.10540	9.48781	.12308	8.12481	.14084	7.10038	.15868	6.30189	59
2	.08807	11.3540	.10569	9.46141	.12338	8.10536	.14113	7.08546	.15898	6.29007	58
3	.08837	11.3163	.10599	9.43515	.12367	8.08600	.14143	7.07059	.15928	6.27829	57
4	.08866	11.2789	.10628	9.40904	.12397	8.06674	.14173	7.05579	.15958	6.26655	56
5	.08895	11.2417	.10657	9.38307	.12426	8.04756	.14202	7.04105	.15988	6.25486	55
6	.08925	11.2048	.10687	9.35724	.12456	8.02848	.14232	7.02637	.16017	6.24321	54
7	.08954	11.1681	.10716	9.33155	.12485	8.00948	.14262	7.01174	.16047	6.23160	53
8	.08983	11.1316	.10746	9.30599	.12515	7.99058	.14291	6.99718	.16077	6.22003	52
9	.09013	11.0954	.10775	9.28058	.12544	7.97176	.14321	6.98268	.16107	6.20851	51
10	.09042	11.0594	.10805	9.25530	.12574	7.95302	.14351	6.96823	.16137	6.19703	50
11	.09071	11.0237	.10834	9.23016	.12603	7.93438	.14381	6.95385	.16167	6.18559	49
12	.09101	10.9882	.10863	9.20516	.12633	7.91582	.14410	6.93952	.16196	6.17419	48
13	.09130	10.9529	.10893	9.18028	.12662	7.89734	.14440	6.92525	.16226	6.16283	47
14	.09159	10.9178	.10922	9.15554	.12692	7.87895	.14470	6.91104	.16256	6.15151	46
15	.09189	10.8829	.10952	9.13093	.12722	7.86064	.14499	6.89683	.16286	6.14023	45
16	.09218	10.8483	.10981	9.10646	.12751	7.84242	.14529	6.88278	.16316	6.12899	44
17	.09247	10.8139	.11011	9.08211	.12781	7.82428	.14559	6.86874	.16346	6.11779	43
18	.09277	10.7797	.11040	9.05789	.12810	7.80622	.14588	6.85475	.16376	6.10664	42
19	.09306	10.7457	.11070	9.03379	.12840	7.78825	.14618	6.84082	.16405	6.09552	41
20	.09335	10.7119	.11099	9.00983	.12869	7.77035	.14648	6.82694	.16435	6.08444	40
21	.09365	10.6783	.11128	8.98598	.12899	7.75254	.14678	6.81312	.16465	6.07340	39
22	.09394	10.6450	.11158	8.96227	.12929	7.73480	.14707	6.79936	.16495	6.06240	38
23	.09423	10.6118	.11187	8.93867	.12958	7.71715	.14737	6.78564	.16525	6.05143	37
24	.09453	10.5789	.11217	8.91520	.12988	7.69957	.14767	6.77199	.16555	6.04051	36
25	.09482	10.5462	.11246	8.89185	.13017	7.68208	.14796	6.75838	.16585	6.02962	35
26	.09511	10.5136	.11276	8.86862	.13047	7.66466	.14826	6.74483	.16615	6.01878	34
27	.09541	10.4813	.11305	8.84551	.13076	7.64732	.14856	6.73133	.16645	6.00797	33
28	.09570	10.4491	.11335	8.82252	.13106	7.63005	.14886	6.71789	.16674	5.99720	32
29	.09600	10.4172	.11364	8.79964	.13136	7.61287	.14915	6.70450	.16704	5.98646	31
30	.09629	10.3854	.11394	8.77689	.13165	7.59575	.14945	6.69116	.16734	5.97576	30
31	.09658	10.3538	.11423	8.75425	.13195	7.57872	.14975	6.67787	.16764	5.96510	29
32	.09688	10.3224	.11452	8.73172	.13224	7.56176	.15005	6.66463	.16794	5.95448	28
33	.09717	10.2913	.11482	8.70931	.13254	7.54487	.15034	6.65144	.16824	5.94390	27
34	.09746	10.2602	.11511	8.68701	.13284	7.52806	.15064	6.63831	.16854	5.93335	26
35	.09776	10.2294	.11541	8.66482	.13313	7.51132	.15094	6.62523	.16884	5.92283	25
36	.09805	10.1988	.11570	8.64275	.13343	7.49465	.15124	6.61219	.16914	5.91236	24
37	.09834	10.1683	.11600	8.62078	.13372	7.47806	.15153	6.59921	.16944	5.90191	23
38	.09864	10.1381	.11629	8.59893	.13402	7.46154	.15183	6.58627	.16974	5.89151	22
39	.09893	10.1080	.11659	8.57718	.13432	7.44509	.15213	6.57339	.17004	5.88114	21
40	.09923	10.0780	.11688	8.55555	.13461	7.42871	.15243	6.56055	.17033	5.87080	20
41	.09952	10.0483	.11718	8.53402	.13491	7.41240	.15272	6.54777	.17063	5.86051	19
42	.09981	10.0187	.11747	8.51259	.13521	7.39616	.15302	6.53503	.17093	5.85024	18
43	.10011	9.98931	.11777	8.49128	.13550	7.37999	.15332	6.52234	.17123	5.84001	17
44	.10040	9.96007	.11806	8.47007	.13580	7.36389	.15362	6.50970	.17153	5.82982	16
45	.10069	9.93101	.11836	8.44896	.13609	7.34786	.15391	6.49710	.17183	5.81966	15
46	.10099	9.90211	.11865	8.42795	.13639	7.33190	.15421	6.48456	.17213	5.80953	14
47	.10128	9.87338	.11895	8.40705	.13669	7.31600	.15451	6.47206	.17243	5.79944	13
48	.10158	9.84482	.11924	8.38625	.13698	7.30018	.15481	6.45961	.17273	5.78938	12
49	.10187	9.81641	.11954	8.36555	.13728	7.28442	.15511	6.44720	.17303	5.77936	11
50	.10216	9.78817	.11983	8.34496	.13758	7.26873	.15540	6.43484	.17333	5.76937	10
51	.10246	9.76009	.12013	8.32446	.13787	7.25310	.15570	6.42253	.17363	5.75941	9
52	.10275	9.73217	.12042	8.30406	.13817	7.23754	.15600	6.41026	.17393	5.74949	8
53	.10305	9.70441	.12072	8.28376	.13846	7.22204	.15630	6.39804	.17423	5.73960	7
54	.10334	9.67680	.12101	8.26355	.13876	7.20661	.15660	6.38587	.17453	5.72974	6
55	.10363	9.64935	.12131	8.24345	.13906	7.19125	.15689	6.37374	.17483	5.71992	5
56	.10393	9.62205	.12160	8.22344	.13935	7.17594	.15719	6.36165	.17513	5.71013	4
57	.10422	9.59490	.12190	8.20352	.13965	7.16071	.15749	6.34961	.17543	5.70037	3
58	.10452	9.56791	.12219	8.18370	.13995	7.14553	.15779	6.33761	.17573	5.69064	2
59	.10481	9.54106	.12249	8.16398	.14024	7.13042	.15809	6.32566	.17603	5.68094	1
60	.10510	9.51436	.12278	8.14435	.14054	7.11537	.15838	6.31375	.17633	5.67128	0
′	Cotang	Tang	Cotang	Tang	Cotang	Tang	Cotang	Tang	Cotang	Tang	′
	84°		83°		82°		81°		80°		

TABLE F

Natural Tangents and Cotangents

′	10° Tang	10° Cotang	11° Tang	11° Cotang	12° Tang	12° Cotang	13° Tang	13° Cotang	14° Tang	14° Cotang	′
0	17633	5.67128	.19438	5.14455	.21256	4.70463	.23087	4.33148	.24933	4.01078	60
1	.17663	5.66165	.19468	5.13658	.21286	4.69791	.23117	4.32573	.24964	4.00582	59
2	.17693	5.65205	.19498	5.12862	.21316	4.69121	.23148	4.32001	.24995	4.00086	58
3	.17723	5.64248	.19529	5.12069	.21347	4.68452	.23179	4.31430	.25026	3.99592	57
4	.17753	5.63295	.19559	5.11279	.21377	4.67786	.23209	4.30860	.25056	3.99099	56
5	.17783	5.62344	.19589	5.10490	.21408	4.67121	.23240	4.30291	.25087	3.98607	55
6	.17813	5.61397	.19619	5.09704	.21438	4.66458	.23271	4.29724	.25118	3.98117	54
7	.17843	5.60452	.19649	5.08921	.21469	4.65797	.23301	4.29159	.25149	3.97627	53
8	.17873	5.59511	.19630	5.08139	.21499	4.65138	.23332	4.28595	.25180	3.97139	52
9	.17903	5.58573	.19710	5.07360	.21529	4.64480	.23363	4.28032	.25211	3.96651	51
10	.17933	5.57638	.19740	5.06584	.21560	4.63825	.23393	4.27471	.25242	3.96165	50
11	.17963	5.56706	.19770	5.05809	.21590	4.63171	.23424	4.26911	.25273	3.95680	49
12	.17993	5.55777	.19801	5.05037	.21621	4.62518	.23455	4.26352	.25304	3.95196	48
13	.18023	5.54851	.19831	5.04267	.21651	4.61868	.23485	4.25795	.25335	3.94713	47
14	.18053	5.53927	.19861	5.03499	.21682	4.61219	.23516	4.25239	.25366	3.94232	46
15	.18083	5.53007	.19891	5.02734	.21712	4.60572	.23547	4.24685	.25397	3.93751	45
16	.18113	5.52090	.19921	5.01971	.21743	4.59927	.23578	4.24132	.25428	3.93271	44
17	.18143	5.51176	.19952	5.01210	.21773	4.59283	.23608	4.23580	.25459	3.92793	43
18	.18173	5.50264	.19982	5.00451	.21804	4.58641	.23639	4.23030	.25490	3.92316	42
19	.18203	5.49356	.20012	4.99695	.21834	4.58001	.23670	4.22481	.25521	3.91839	41
20	.18233	5.48451	.20042	4.98940	.21864	4.57363	.23700	4.21933	.25552	3.91364	40
21	.18263	5.47548	.20073	4.98188	.21895	4.56726	.23731	4.21387	.25583	3.90890	39
22	.18293	5.46648	.20103	4.97438	.21925	4.56091	.23762	4.20842	.25614	3.90417	38
23	.18323	5.45751	.20133	4.96690	.21956	4.55458	.23793	4.20298	.25645	3.89945	37
24	.18353	5.44857	.20164	4.95945	.21986	4.54826	.23823	4.19756	.25676	3.89474	36
25	.18384	5.43966	.20194	4.95201	.22017	4.54196	.23854	4.19215	.25707	3.89004	35
26	.18414	5.43077	.20224	4.94460	.22047	4.53568	.23885	4.18675	.25738	3.88536	34
27	.18444	5.42192	.20254	4.93721	.22078	4.52941	.23916	4.18137	.25769	3.88068	33
28	.18474	5.41309	.20285	4.92984	.22108	4.52316	.23946	4.17600	.25800	3.87601	32
29	.18504	5.40429	.20315	4.92249	.22139	4.51693	.23977	4.17064	.25831	3.87136	31
30	.18534	5.39552	.20345	4.91516	.22169	4.51071	.24008	4.16530	.25862	3.86671	30
31	.18564	5.38677	.20376	4.90785	.22200	4.50451	.24039	4.15997	.25893	3.86208	29
32	.18594	5.37805	.20406	4.90056	.22231	4.49832	.24069	4.15465	.25924	3.85745	28
33	.18624	5.36936	.20436	4.89330	.22261	4.49215	.24100	4.14934	.25955	3.85284	27
34	.18654	5.36070	.20466	4.88605	.22292	4.48600	.24131	4.14405	.25986	3.84824	26
35	.18684	5.35206	.20497	4.87882	.22322	4.47986	.24162	4.13877	.26017	3.84364	25
36	.18714	5.34345	.20527	4.87162	.22353	4.47374	.24193	4.13350	.26048	3.83906	24
37	.18745	5.33487	.20557	4.86444	.22383	4.46764	.24223	4.12825	.26079	3.83449	23
38	.18775	5.32631	.20588	4.85727	.22414	4.46155	.24254	4.12301	.26110	3.82992	22
39	.18805	5.31778	.20618	4.85013	.22444	4.45543	.24285	4.11778	.26141	3.82537	21
40	.18835	5.30928	.20648	4.84300	.22475	4.44942	.24316	4.11256	.26172	3.82083	20
41	.18865	5.30080	.20679	4.83590	.22505	4.44338	.24347	4.10736	.26203	3.81630	19
42	.18895	5.29235	.20709	4.82882	.22536	4.43735	.24377	4.10216	.26235	3.81177	18
43	.18925	5.28393	.20739	4.82175	.22567	4.43134	.24408	4.09699	.26266	3.80726	17
44	.18955	5.27553	.20770	4.81471	.22597	4.42534	.24439	4.09182	.26297	3.80276	16
45	.18986	5.26715	.20800	4.80769	.22628	4.41936	.24470	4.08666	.26328	3.79827	15
46	.19016	5.25880	.20830	4.80068	.22658	4.41340	.24501	4.08152	.26359	3.79378	14
47	.19046	5.25048	.20861	4.79370	.22689	4.40745	.24532	4.07639	.26390	3.78931	13
48	.19076	5.24218	.20891	4.78673	.22719	4.40152	.24562	4.07127	.26421	3.78485	12
49	.19106	5.23391	.20921	4.77978	.22750	4.39560	.24593	4.06616	.26452	3.78040	11
50	.19136	5.22566	.20952	4.77286	.22781	4.38969	.24624	4.06107	.26483	3.77595	10
51	.19166	5.21744	.20982	4.76595	.22811	4.38381	.24655	4.05599	.26515	3.77152	9
52	.19197	5.20925	.21013	4.75906	.22842	4.37793	.24686	4.05092	.26546	3.76709	8
53	.19227	5.20107	.21043	4.75219	.22872	4.37207	.24717	4.04586	.26577	3.76268	7
54	.19257	5.19293	.21073	4.74534	.22903	4.36623	.24747	4.04081	.26608	3.75828	6
55	.19287	5.18480	.21104	4.73851	.22934	4.36040	.24778	4.03578	.26639	3.75388	5
56	.19317	5.17671	.21134	4.73170	.22964	4.35459	.24809	4.03076	.26670	3.74950	4
57	.19347	5.16863	.21164	4.72490	.22995	4.34879	.24840	4.02574	.26701	3.74512	3
58	.19378	5.16058	.21195	4.71813	.23026	4.34300	.24871	4.02074	.26733	3.74075	2
59	.19408	5.15256	.21225	4.71137	.23056	4.33723	.24902	4.01576	.26764	3.73640	1
60	.19438	5.14455	.21256	4.70463	.23087	4.33148	.24933	4.01078	.26795	3.73205	0
′	Cotang	Tang	Cotang	Tang	Cotang	Tang	Cotang	Tang	Cotang	Tang	′
	79°		78°		77°		76°		75°		

Natural Tangents and Cotangents

′	15° Tang	15° Cotang	16° Tang	16° Cotang	17° Tang	17° Cotang	18° Tang	18° Cotang	19° Tang	19° Cotang	′
0	.26795	3.73205	.28675	3.48741	.30573	3.27085	.32492	3.07768	.34433	2.90421	60
1	.26826	3.72771	.28706	3.48359	.30605	3.26745	.32524	3.07464	.34465	2.90147	59
2	.26857	3.72338	.28738	3.47977	.30637	3.26406	.32556	3.07160	.34498	2.89873	58
3	.26888	3.71907	.28769	3.47596	.30669	3.26067	.32588	3.06857	.34530	2.89600	57
4	.26920	3.71476	.28800	3.47216	.30700	3.25729	.32621	3.06554	.34563	2.89327	56
5	.26951	3.71046	.28832	3.46837	.30732	3.25392	.32653	3.06252	.34596	2.89055	55
6	.26982	3.70616	.28864	3.46453	.30764	3.25055	.32685	3.05950	.34628	2.88783	54
7	.27013	3.70188	.28895	3.46080	.30796	3.24719	.32717	3.05649	.34661	2.88511	53
8	.27044	3.69761	.28927	3.45703	.30828	3.24383	.32749	3.05349	.34693	2.88240	52
9	.27076	3.69335	.28958	3.45327	.30860	3.24049	.32782	3.05049	.34726	2.87970	51
10	.27107	3.68909	.28990	3.44951	.30891	3.23714	.32814	3.04749	.34758	2.87700	50
11	.27138	3.68485	.29021	3.44576	.30923	3.23381	.32846	3.04450	.34791	2.87430	49
12	.27169	3.68061	.29053	3.44202	.30955	3.23048	.32878	3.04152	.34824	2.87161	48
13	.27201	3.67638	.29084	3.43829	.30987	3.22715	.32911	3.03854	.34856	2.86892	47
14	.27232	3.67217	.29116	3.43456	.31019	3.22384	.32943	3.03556	.34889	2.86624	46
15	.27263	3.66796	.29147	3.43084	.31051	3.22053	.32975	3.03260	.34922	2.86356	45
16	.27294	3.66376	.29179	3.42713	.31083	3.21722	.33007	3.02963	.34954	2.86089	44
17	.27326	3.65957	.29210	3.42343	.31115	3.21392	.33040	3.02667	.34987	2.85822	43
18	.27357	3.65538	.29242	3.41973	.31147	3.21063	.33072	3.02372	.35020	2.85555	42
19	.27388	3.65121	.29274	3.41604	.31178	3.20734	.33104	3.02077	.35052	2.85289	41
20	.27419	3.64705	.29305	3.41236	.31210	3.20406	.33136	3.01783	.35085	2.85023	40
21	.27451	3.64289	.29337	3.40869	.31242	3.20079	.33169	3.01489	.35118	2.84758	39
22	.27482	3.63874	.29368	3.40502	.31274	3.19752	.33201	3.01196	.35150	2.84494	38
23	.27513	3.63461	.29400	3.40136	.31306	3.19426	.33233	3.00903	.35183	2.84229	37
24	.27545	3.63048	.29432	3.39771	.31338	3.19100	.33266	3.00611	.35216	2.83965	36
25	.27576	3.62636	.29463	3.39406	.31370	3.18775	.33298	3.00319	.35248	2.83702	35
26	.27607	3.62224	.29495	3.39042	.31402	3.18451	.33330	3.00028	.35281	2.83439	34
27	.27638	3.61814	.29526	3.38679	.31434	3.18127	.33363	2.99738	.35314	2.83176	33
28	.27670	3.61405	.29558	3.38317	.31466	3.17804	.33395	2.99447	.35346	2.82914	32
29	.27701	3.60996	.29590	3.37955	.31498	3.17481	.33427	2.99158	.25379	2.82653	31
30	.27732	3.60588	.29621	3.37594	.31530	3.17159	.33460	2.98868	.35412	2.82391	30
31	.27764	3.60181	.29653	3.37234	.31562	3.16838	.33492	2.98580	.35445	2.82130	29
32	.27795	3.59775	.29685	3.36875	.31594	3.16517	.33524	2.98292	.35477	2.81870	28
33	.17826	3.59370	.29716	3.36516	.31626	3.16197	.33557	2.98004	.35510	2.81610	27
34	.27858	3.58966	.29748	3.36158	.31658	3.15877	.33589	2.97717	.35543	2.81350	26
35	.27889	3.58562	.29780	3.35800	.31690	3.15558	.33621	2.97430	.35576	2.81091	25
36	.27921	3.58160	.29811	3.35443	.31722	3.15240	.33654	2.97144	.35608	2.80833	24
37	.27952	3.57758	.29843	3.35087	.31754	3.14922	.33686	2.96858	.35641	2.80574	23
38	.27983	3.57357	.29875	3.34732	.31786	3.14605	.33718	2.96573	.35674	2.80316	22
39	.28015	3.56957	.29906	3.34377	.31818	3.14288	.33751	2.96288	.35707	2.80059	21
40	.28046	3.56557	.29938	3.34023	.31850	3.13972	.33783	2.96004	.35740	2:79802	20
41	.28077	3.56159	.29970	3.33670	.31882	3.13656	.33816	2.95721	.35772	2.79545	19
42	.28109	3.55761	.30001	3.33317	.31914	3.13341	.33848	2.95437	.35805	2.79289	18
43	.28140	3.55364	.30033	3.32965	.31946	3.13027	.33881	2.95155	.35838	2.79033	17
44	.28172	3.54968	.30065	3.32614	.31978	3.12713	.33913	2.94872	.35871	2.78778	16
45	.28203	3.54573	.30097	3.32264	.32010	3.12400	.33945	2.94591	.35904	2.78523	15
46	.28234	3.54179	.30128	3.31914	.32042	3.12087	.33978	2.94309	.35937	2.78269	14
47	.28266	3.53785	.30160	3.31565	.32074	3.11775	.34010	2.94028	.35969	2.78014	13
48	.28297	3.53393	.30192	3.31216	.32106	3.11464	.34043	2.93748	.36002	2.77761	12
49	.28329	3.53001	.30224	3.30868	.32139	3.11153	.34075	2.93468	.36035	2.77507	11
50	.28360	3.52609	.30255	3.30521	.32171	3.10842	.34108	2.93189	.36068	2.77254	10
51	.28391	3.52219	.30287	3.30174	.32203	3.10532	.34140	2.92910	.36101	2.77002	9
52	.28423	3.51829	.30319	3.29829	.32235	3.10223	.34173	2.92632	.36134	2.76750	8
53	.28454	3.51441	.30351	3.29483	.32267	3.09914	.34205	2.92354	.36167	2.76498	7
54	.28486	3.51053	.30382	3.29139	.32299	3.09606	.34238	2.92076	.36199	2.76247	6
55	.28517	3.50666	.30414	3.28795	.32331	3.09298	.34270	2.91799	.36232	2.75996	5
56	.28549	3.50279	.30446	3.28452	.32363	3.08991	.34303	2.91523	.36265	2.75746	4
57	.28580	3.49894	.30478	3.28109	.32396	3.08685	.34335	2.91246	.36298	2.75496	3
58	.28612	3.49509	.30509	3.27767	.32428	3.08379	.34368	2.90971	.36331	2.75246	2
59	.28643	3.49125	.30541	3.27426	.32460	3.08073	.34400	2.90696	.36364	2.74997	1
60	.28675	3.48741	.30573	3.27085	.32492	3.07768	.34433	2.90421	.36397	2.74748	0
′	Cotang	Tang	Cotang	Tang	Cotang	Tang	Cotang	Tang	Cotang	Tang	′
	74°		73°		72°		71°		70°		

TABLE F

Natural Tangents and Cotangents

′	20°		21°		22°		23°		24°		′
	Tang	Cotang	Tang	Cotang	Tang	Cotang	Tang	Cotang	Tang	Cotang	
0	.36397	2.74748	.38386	2.60509	.40403	2.47509	.42447	2.35585	.44523	2.24604	60
1	.36430	2.74499	.38420	2.60283	.40436	2.47302	.42482	2.35395	.44558	2.24428	59
2	.36463	2.74251	.38453	2.60057	.40470	2.47095	.42516	2.35205	.44593	2.24252	58
3	.36496	2.74004	.38487	2.59831	.40504	2.46888	.42551	2.35015	.44627	2.24077	57
4	.36529	2.73756	.38520	2.59606	.40538	2.46682	.42585	2.34825	.44662	2.23902	56
5	.36562	2.73509	.38553	2.59381	.40572	2.46476	.42619	2.34636	.44697	2.23727	55
6	.36595	2.73263	.38587	2.59156	.40606	2.46270	.42654	2.34447	.44732	2.23553	54
7	.36628	2.73017	.38620	2.58932	.40640	2.46065	.42688	2.34258	.44767	2.23378	53
8	.36661	2.72771	.38654	2.58708	.40674	2.45860	.42722	2.34069	.44802	2.23204	52
9	.36694	2.72526	.38687	2.58484	.40707	2.45655	.42757	2.33881	.44837	2.23030	51
10	.36727	2.72281	.38721	2.58261	.40741	2.45451	.42791	2.33693	.44872	2.22857	50
11	.36760	2.72036	.38754	2.58038	.40775	2.45246	.42826	2.33505	.44907	2.22683	49
12	.36793	2.71792	.38787	2.57815	.40809	2.45043	.42860	2.33317	.44942	2.22510	48
13	.36826	2.71548	.38821	2.57593	.40843	2.44839	.42894	2.33130	.44977	2.22337	47
14	.36859	2.71305	.38854	2.57371	.40877	2.44636	.42929	2.32943	.45012	2.22164	46
15	.36892	2.71062	.38888	2.57150	.40911	2.44433	.42963	2.32756	.45047	2.21992	45
16	.36925	2.70819	.38921	2.56928	.40945	2.44230	.42998	2.32570	.45082	2.21819	44
17	.36958	2.70577	.38955	2.56707	.40979	2.44027	.43032	2.32383	.45117	2.21647	43
18	.36991	2.70335	.38988	2.56487	.41013	2.43825	.43067	2.32197	.45152	2.21475	42
19	.37024	2.70094	.39022	2.56266	.41047	2.43623	.43101	2.32012	.45187	2.21304	41
20	.37057	2.69853	.39055	2.56046	.41081	2.43422	.43136	2.31826	.45222	2.21132	40
21	.37090	2.69612	.39089	2.55827	.41115	2.43220	.43170	2.31641	.45257	2.20961	39
22	.37123	2.69371	.39122	2.55608	.41149	2.43019	.43205	2.31456	.45292	2.20790	38
23	.37157	2.69131	.39156	2.55389	.41183	2.42819	.43230	2.31271	.45327	2.20619	37
24	.37190	2.68892	.39190	2.55170	.41217	2.42618	.43274	2.31086	.45362	2.20449	36
25	.37223	2.68653	.39223	2.54952	.41251	2.42418	.43308	2.30902	.45397	2.20278	35
26	.37256	2.68414	.39257	2.54734	.41285	2.42218	.43343	2.30718	.45432	2.20108	34
27	.37289	2.68175	.39290	2.54516	.41319	2.42019	.43378	2.30534	.45467	2.19938	33
28	.37322	2.67937	.39324	2.54299	.41353	2.41819	.43412	2.30351	.45502	2.19769	32
29	.37355	2.67700	.39357	2.54082	.41387	2.41620	.43447	2.30167	.45538	2.19599	31
30	.37388	2.67462	.39391	2.53865	.41421	2.41421	.43481	2.29984	.45573	2.19430	30
31	.37422	2.67225	.39425	2.53648	.41455	2.41223	.43516	2.29801	.45608	2.19261	29
32	.37455	2.66989	.39458	2.53432	.41490	2.41025	.43550	2.29619	.45643	2.19092	28
33	.37488	2.66752	.39492	2.53217	.41524	2.40827	.43585	2.29437	.45678	2.18923	27
34	.37521	2.66516	.39526	2.53001	.41558	2.40629	.43620	2.29254	.45713	2.18755	26
35	.37554	2.66281	.39559	2.52786	.41592	2.40432	.43654	2.29073	.45748	2.18587	25
36	.37588	2.66046	.39593	2.52571	.41626	2.40235	.43689	2.28891	.45784	2.18419	24
37	.37621	2.65811	.39626	2.52357	.41660	2.40038	.43724	2.28710	.45819	2.18251	23
38	.37654	2.65576	.39660	2.52142	.41694	2.39841	.43758	2.28528	.45854	2.18084	22
39	.37687	2.65342	.39694	2.51929	.41728	2.39645	.43793	2.28348	.45889	2.17916	21
40	.37720	2.65109	.39727	2.51715	.41763	2.39449	.43828	2.28167	.45924	2.17749	20
41	.37754	2.64875	.39761	2.51502	.41797	2.39253	.43862	2.27987	.45960	2.17582	19
42	.37787	2.64642	.39795	2.51289	.41831	2.39058	.43897	2.27806	.45995	2.17416	18
43	.37820	2.64410	.39829	2.51076	.41865	2.38863	.43932	2.27626	.46030	2.17249	17
44	.37853	2.64177	.39862	2.50864	.41899	2.38668	.43966	2.27447	.46065	2.17083	16
45	.37887	2.63945	.39896	2.50652	.41933	2.38473	.44001	2.27267	.46101	2.16917	15
46	.37920	2.63714	.39930	2.50440	.41968	2.38279	.44036	2.27088	.46136	2.16751	14
47	.37953	2.63483	.39963	2.50229	.42002	2.38084	.44071	2.26909	.46171	2.16585	13
48	.37986	2.63252	.39997	2.50018	.42036	2.37891	.44105	2.26730	.46206	2.16420	12
49	.38020	2.63021	.40031	2.49807	.42070	2.37697	.44140	2.26552	.46242	2.16255	11
50	.38053	2.62791	.40065	2.49597	.42105	2.37504	.44175	2.26374	.46277	2.16090	10
51	.38086	2.62561	.40098	2.49386	.42139	2.37311	.44210	2.26196	.46312	2.15925	9
52	.38120	2.62332	.40132	2.49177	.42173	2.37118	.44244	2.26018	.46348	2.15760	8
53	.38153	2.62103	.40166	2.48967	.42207	2.36925	.44279	2.25840	.46383	2.15596	7
54	.38186	2.61874	.40200	2.48758	.42242	2.36733	.44314	2.25663	.46418	2.15432	6
55	.38220	2.61646	.40234	2.48549	.42276	2.36541	.44349	2.25486	.46454	2.15268	5
56	.38253	2.61418	.40267	2.48340	.42310	2.36349	.44384	2.25309	.46489	2.15104	4
57	.38286	2.61190	.40301	2.48132	.42345	2.36158	.44418	2.25132	.46525	2.14940	3
58	.38320	2.60963	.40335	2.47924	.42379	2.35967	.44453	2.24956	.46560	2.14777	2
59	.38353	2.60736	.40369	2.47716	.42413	2.35776	.44488	2.24780	.46595	2.14614	1
60	.38386	2.60509	.40403	2.47509	.42447	2.35585	.44523	2.24604	.46631	2.14451	0
′	Cotang	Tang	Cotang	Tang	Cotang	Tang	Cotang	Tang	Cotang	Tang	′
	69°		68°		67°		66°		65°		

NATURAL TANGENTS AND COTANGENTS

′	25° Tang	25° Cotang	26° Tang	26° Cotang	27° Tang	27° Cotang	28° Tang	28° Cotang	29° Tang	29° Cotang	′
0	.46631	2.14451	.48773	2.05030	.50953	1.96261	.53171	1.88073	.55431	1.80405	60
1	.46666	2.14288	.48809	2.04879	.50989	1.96120	.53208	1.87941	.55469	1.80281	59
2	.46702	2.14125	.48845	2.04728	.51026	1.95979	.53246	1.87809	.55507	1.80158	58
3	.46737	2.13963	.48881	2.04577	.51063	1.95838	.53283	1.87677	.55545	1.80034	57
4	.46772	2.13801	.48917	2.04426	.51099	1.95698	.53320	1.87546	.55583	1.79911	56
5	.46808	2.13639	.48953	2.04276	.51136	1.95557	.53358	1.87415	.55621	1.79788	55
6	.46843	2.13477	.48989	2.04125	.51173	1.95417	.53395	1.87283	.55659	1.79665	54
7	.46879	2.13316	.49026	2.03975	.51209	1.95277	.53432	1.87152	.55697	1.79542	53
8	.46914	2.13154	.49062	2.03825	.51246	1.95137	.53470	1.87021	.55736	1.79419	52
9	.46950	2.12993	.49098	2.03675	.51283	1.94997	.53507	1.86891	.55774	1.79296	51
10	.46985	2.12832	.49134	2.03526	.51319	1.94858	.53545	1.86760	.55812	1.79174	50
11	.47021	2.12671	.49170	2.03376	.51356	1.94718	.53582	1.86630	.55850	1.79051	49
12	.47056	2.12511	.49206	2.03227	.51393	1.94579	.53620	1.86499	.55888	1.78929	48
13	.47092	2.12350	.49242	2.03078	.51430	1.94440	.53657	1.86369	.55926	1.78807	47
14	.47128	2.12190	.49278	2.02929	.51467	1.94301	.53694	1.86239	.55964	1.78685	46
15	.47163	2.12030	.49315	2.02780	.51503	1.94162	.53732	1.86109	.56003	1.78563	45
16	.47199	2.11871	.49351	2.02631	.51540	1.94023	.53769	1.85979	.56041	1.78441	44
17	.47234	2.11711	.49387	2.02483	.51577	1.93885	.53807	1.85850	.56079	1.78319	43
18	.47270	2.11552	.49423	2.02335	.51614	1.93746	.53844	1.85720	.56117	1.78198	42
19	.47305	2.11392	.49459	2.02187	.51651	1.93608	.53882	1.85591	.56156	1.78077	41
20	.47341	2.11233	.49495	2.02039	.51688	1.93470	.53920	1.85462	.56194	1.77955	40
21	.47377	2.11075	.49532	2.01891	.51724	1.93332	.53957	1.85333	.56232	1.77834	39
22	.47412	2.10916	.49568	2.01743	.51761	1.93195	.53995	1.85204	.56270	1.77713	38
23	.47448	2.10758	.49604	2.01596	.51798	1.93057	.54032	1.85075	.56309	1.77592	37
24	.47483	2.10600	.49640	2.01449	.51835	1.92920	.54070	1.84946	.56347	1.77471	36
25	.47519	2.10442	.49677	2.01302	.51872	1.92782	.54107	1.84818	.56385	1.77351	35
26	.47555	2.10284	.49713	2.01155	.51909	1.92645	.54145	1.84689	.56424	1.77230	34
27	.47590	2.10126	.49749	2.01008	.51946	1.92508	.54183	1.84561	.56462	1.77110	33
28	.47626	2.09969	.49786	2.00862	.51983	1.92371	.54220	1.84433	.56501	1.76990	32
29	.47662	2.09811	.49822	2.00715	.52020	1.92235	.54258	1.84305	.56539	1.76869	31
30	.47698	2.09654	.49858	2.00569	.52057	1.92098	.54296	1.84177	.56577	1.76749	30
31	.47733	2.09498	.49894	2.00423	.52094	1.91962	.54333	1.84049	.56616	1.76629	29
32	.47769	2.09341	.49931	2.00277	.52131	1.91826	.54371	1.83922	.56654	1.76510	28
33	.47805	2.09184	.49967	2.00131	.52168	1.91690	.54409	1.83794	.56693	1.76390	27
34	.47840	2.09028	.50004	1.99986	.52205	1.91554	.54446	1.83667	.56731	1.76271	26
35	.47876	2.08872	.50040	1.99841	.52242	1.91418	.54484	1.83540	.56769	1.76151	25
36	.47912	2.08716	.50076	1.99695	.52279	1.91282	.54522	1.83413	.56808	1.76032	24
37	.47948	2.08560	.50113	1.99550	.52316	1.91147	.54560	1.83286	.56846	1.75913	23
38	.47984	2.08405	.50149	1.99406	.52353	1.91012	.54597	1.83159	.56885	1.75794	22
39	.48019	2.08250	.50185	1.99261	.52390	1.90876	.54635	1.83033	.56923	1.75675	21
40	.48055	2.08094	.50222	1.99116	.52427	1.90741	.54673	1.82906	.56962	1.75556	20
41	.48091	2.07939	.50258	1.98972	.52464	1.90607	.54711	1.82780	.57000	1.75437	19
42	.48127	2.07785	.50295	1.98828	.52501	1.90472	.54748	1.82654	.57039	1.75319	18
43	.48163	2.07630	.50331	1.98684	.52538	1.90337	.54786	1.82528	.57078	1.75200	17
44	.48198	2.07476	.50368	1.98540	.52575	1.90203	.54824	1.82402	.57116	1.75082	16
45	.48234	2.07321	.50404	1.98396	.52613	1.90069	.54862	1.82276	.57155	1.74964	15
46	.48270	2.07167	.50441	1.98253	.52650	1.89935	.54900	1.82150	.57193	1.74846	14
47	.48306	2.07014	.50477	1.98110	.52687	1.89801	.54938	1.82025	.57232	1.74728	13
48	.48342	2.06860	.50514	1.97966	.52724	1.89667	.54975	1.81899	.57271	1.74610	12
49	.48378	2.06706	.50550	1.97823	.52761	1.89533	.55013	1.81774	.57309	1.74492	11
50	.48414	2.06553	.50587	1.97681	.52798	1.89400	.55051	1.81649	.57348	1.74375	10
51	.48450	2.06400	.50623	1.97538	.52836	1.89266	.55089	1.81524	.57386	1.74257	9
52	.48486	2.06247	.50660	1.97395	.52873	1.89133	.55127	1.81399	.57425	1.74140	8
53	.48521	2.06094	.50696	1.97253	.52910	1.89000	.55165	1.81274	.57464	1.74022	7
54	.48557	2.05942	.50733	1.97111	.52947	1.88867	.55203	1.81150	.57503	1.73905	6
55	.48593	2.05790	.50769	1.96969	.52985	1.88734	.55241	1.81025	.57541	1.73788	5
56	.48629	2.05637	.50806	1.96827	.53022	1.88602	.55279	1.80901	.57580	1.73671	4
57	.48665	2.05485	.50843	1.96685	.53059	1.88469	.55317	1.80777	.57619	1.73555	3
58	.48701	2.05333	.50879	1.96544	.53096	1.88337	.55355	1.80653	.57657	1.73438	2
59	.48737	2.05182	.50916	1.96402	.53134	1.88205	.55393	1.80529	.57696	1.73321	1
60	.48773	2.05030	.50953	1.96261	.53171	1.88073	.55431	1.80405	.57735	1.73205	0
′	Cotang	Tang	Cotang	Tang	Cotang	Tang	Cotang	Tang	Cotang	Tang	′
	64°		63°		62°		61°		60°		

TABLE F

NATURAL TANGENTS AND COTANGENTS

′	30° Tang	30° Cotang	31° Tang	31° Cotang	32° Tang	32° Cotang	33° Tang	33° Cotang	34° Tang	34° Cotang	′
0	.57735	1.73205	.60086	1.66428	.62487	1.60033	.64941	1.53986	.67451	1.48256	60
1	.57774	1.73089	.60126	1.66318	.62527	1.59930	.64982	1.53888	.67493	1.48163	59
2	.57813	1.72973	.60165	1.66209	.62568	1.59826	.65024	1.53791	.67536	1.48070	58
3	.57851	1.72857	.60205	1.66099	.62608	1.59723	.65065	1.53693	.67578	1.47977	57
4	.57890	1.72741	.60245	1.65990	.62649	1.59620	.65106	1.53595	.67620	1.47885	56
5	.57929	1.72625	.60284	1.65881	.62689	1.59517	.65148	1.53497	.67663	1.47792	55
6	.57968	1.72509	.60324	1.65772	.62730	1.59414	.65189	1.53400	.67705	1.47699	54
7	.58007	1.72393	.60364	1.65663	.62770	1.59311	.65231	1.53302	.67748	1.47607	53
8	.58046	1.72278	.60403	1.65554	.62811	1.59208	.65272	1.53205	.67790	1.47514	52
9	.58085	1.72163	.60443	1.65445	.62852	1.59105	.65314	1.53107	.67832	1.47422	51
10	.58124	1.72047	.60483	1.65337	.62892	1.59002	.65355	1.53010	.67875	1.47330	50
11	.58162	1.71932	.60522	1.65228	.62933	1.58900	.65397	1.52913	.67917	1.47238	49
12	.58201	1.71817	.60562	1.65120	.62973	1.58797	.65438	1.52816	.67960	1.47146	48
13	.58240	1.71702	.60602	1.65011	.63014	1.58695	.65480	1.52719	.68002	1.47053	47
14	.58279	1.71588	.60642	1.64903	.63055	1.58593	.65521	1.52622	.68045	1.46962	46
15	.58318	1.71473	.60681	1.64795	.63095	1.58490	.65563	1.52525	.68088	1.46870	45
16	.58357	1.71358	.60721	1.64687	.63136	1.58388	.65604	1.52429	.68130	1.46778	44
17	.58396	1.71244	.60761	1.64579	.63177	1.58286	.65646	1.52332	.68173	1.46686	43
18	.58435	1.71129	.60801	1.64471	.63217	1.58184	.65688	1.52235	.68215	1.46595	42
19	.58474	1.71015	.60841	1.64363	.63258	1.58083	.65729	1.52139	.68258	1.46503	41
20	.58513	1.70901	.60881	1.64256	.63299	1.57981	.65771	1.52043	.68301	1.46411	40
21	.58552	1.70787	.60921	1.64148	.63340	1.57879	.65813	1.51946	.68343	1.46320	39
22	.58591	1.70673	.60960	1.64041	.63380	1.57778	.65854	1.51850	.68386	1.46229	38
23	.58631	1.70560	.61000	1.63934	.63421	1.57676	.65896	1.51754	.68429	1.46137	37
24	.58670	1.70446	.61040	1.63826	.63462	1.57575	.65938	1.51658	.68471	1.46046	36
25	.58709	1.70332	.61080	1.63719	.63503	1.57474	.65980	1.51562	.68514	1.45955	35
26	.58748	1.70219	.61120	1.63612	.63544	1.57372	.66021	1.51466	.68557	1.45864	34
27	.58787	1.70106	.61160	1.63505	.63584	1.57271	.66063	1.51370	.68600	1.45773	33
28	.58826	1.69992	.61200	1.63398	.63625	1.57170	.66105	1.51275	.68642	1.45682	32
29	.58865	1.69879	.61240	1.63292	.63666	1.57069	.66147	1.51179	.68685	1.45592	31
30	.58905	1.69766	.61280	1.63185	.63707	1.56969	.66189	1.51084	.68728	1.45501	30
31	.58944	1.69653	.61320	1.63079	.63748	1.56868	.66230	1.50988	.68771	1.45410	29
32	.58983	1.69541	.61360	1.62972	.63789	1.56767	.66272	1.50893	.68814	1.45320	28
33	.59022	1.69428	.61400	1.62866	.63830	1.56667	.66314	1.50797	.68857	1.45229	27
34	.59061	1.69316	.61440	1.62760	.63871	1.56566	.66356	1.50702	.68900	1.45139	26
35	.59101	1.69203	.61480	1.62654	.63912	1.56466	.66398	1.50607	.68942	1.45049	25
36	.59140	1.69091	.61520	1.62548	.63953	1.56366	.66440	1.50512	.68985	1.44958	24
37	.59179	1.68979	.61561	1.62442	.63994	1.56265	.66482	1.50417	.69028	1.44868	23
38	.59218	1.68866	.61601	1.62336	.64035	1.56165	.66524	1.50322	.69071	1.44778	22
39	.59258	1.68754	.61641	1.62230	.64076	1.56065	.66566	1.50228	.69114	1.44688	21
49	.59297	1.68643	.61681	1.62125	.64117	1.55966	.66608	1.50133	.69157	1.44598	20
41	.59336	1.68531	.61721	1.62019	.64158	1.55866	.66650	1.50038	.69200	1.44508	19
42	.59376	1.68419	.61761	1.61914	.64199	1.55766	.66692	1.49944	.69243	1.44418	18
43	.59415	1.68308	.61801	1.61808	.64240	1.55666	.66734	1.49849	.69286	1.44329	17
44	.59454	1.68196	.61842	1.61703	.64281	1.55567	.66776	1.49755	.69329	1.44239	16
45	.59494	1.68085	.61882	1.61598	.64322	1.55467	.66818	1.49661	.69372	1.44149	15
46	.59533	1.67974	.61922	1.61493	.64363	1.55368	.66860	1.49566	.69416	1.44060	14
47	.59573	1.67863	.61962	1.61388	.64404	1.55269	.66902	1.49472	.69459	1.43970	13
48	.59612	1.67752	.62003	1.61283	.64446	1.55170	.66944	1.49378	.69502	1.43881	12
49	.59651	1.67641	.62043	1.61179	.64487	1.55071	.66986	1.49284	.69545	1.43792	11
50	.59691	1.67530	.62083	1.61074	.64528	1.54972	.67028	1.49190	.69588	1.43703	10
51	.59730	1.67419	.62124	1.60970	.64569	1.54873	.67071	1.49097	.69631	1.43614	9
52	.59770	1.67309	.62164	1.60865	.64610	1.54774	.67113	1.49003	.69675	1.43525	8
53	.59809	1.67198	.62204	1.60761	.64652	1.54675	.67155	1.48909	.69718	1.43436	7
54	.59849	1.67088	.62245	1.60657	.64693	1.54576	.67197	1.48816	.69761	1.43347	6
55	.59888	1.66978	.62285	1.60553	.64734	1.54478	.67239	1.48722	.69804	1.43258	5
56	.59928	1.66867	.62325	1.60449	.64775	1.54379	.67282	1.48629	.69847	1.43169	4
57	.59967	1.66757	.62366	1.60345	.64817	1.54281	.67324	1.48536	.69891	1.43080	3
58	.60007	1.66647	.62406	1.60241	.64858	1.54183	.67366	1.48442	.69934	1.42992	2
59	.60046	1.66538	.62446	1.60137	.64899	1.54085	.67409	1.48349	.69977	1.42903	1
60	.60086	1.66428	.62487	1.60033	.64941	1.53986	.67451	1.48256	.70021	1.42815	0
′	Cotang	Tang	Cotang	Tang	Cotang	Tang	Cotang	Tang	Cotang	Tang	′
	59°		58°		57°		56°		55°		

Natural Tangents and Cotangents

′	35° Tang	35° Cotang	36° Tang	36° Cotang	37° Tang	37° Cotang	38° Tang	38° Cotang	39° Tang	39° Cotang	′
0	.70021	1.42815	.72654	1.37638	.75355	1.32704	.78129	1.27994	.80978	1.23490	60
1	.70064	1.42726	.72699	1.37554	.75401	1.32624	.78175	1.27917	.81027	1.23416	59
2	.70107	1.42638	.72743	1.37470	.75447	1.32544	.78222	1.27841	.81075	1.23343	58
3	.70151	1.42550	.72788	1.37386	.75492	1.32464	.78269	1.27764	.81123	1.23270	57
4	.70194	1.42462	.72832	1.37302	.75538	1.32384	.78316	1.27688	.81171	1.23196	56
5	.70238	1.42374	.72877	1.37218	.75584	1.32304	.78363	1.27611	.81220	1.23123	55
6	.70281	1.42286	.72921	1.37134	.75629	1.32224	.78410	1.27535	.81268	1.23050	54
7	.70325	1.42198	.72966	1.37050	.75675	1.32144	.78457	1.27458	.81316	1.22977	53
8	.70368	1.42110	.73010	1.36967	.75721	1.32064	.78504	1.27382	.81364	1.22904	52
9	.70412	1.42022	.73055	1.36883	.75767	1.31984	.78551	1.27306	.81413	1.22831	51
10	.70455	1.41934	.73100	1.36800	.75812	1.31904	.78598	1.27230	.81461	1.22758	50
11	.70499	1.41847	.73144	1.36716	.75858	1.31825	.78645	1.27153	.81510	1.22685	49
12	.70542	1.41759	.73189	1.36633	.75904	1.31745	.78692	1.27077	.81558	1.22612	48
13	.70586	1.41672	.73234	1.36549	.75950	1.31666	.78739	1.27001	.81606	1.22539	47
14	.70629	1.41584	.73278	1.36466	.75996	1.31586	.78786	1.26925	.81655	1.22467	46
15	.70673	1.41497	.73323	1.36383	.76042	1.31507	.78834	1.26849	.81703	1.22394	45
16	.70717	1.41409	.73368	1.36300	.76088	1.31427	.78881	1.26774	.81752	1.22321	44
17	.70760	1.41322	.73413	1.36217	.76134	1.31348	.78928	1.26698	.81800	1.22249	43
18	.70804	1.41235	.73457	1.36134	.76180	1.31269	.78975	1.26622	.81849	1.22176	42
19	.70848	1.41148	.73502	1.36051	.76226	1.31190	.79022	1.26546	.81898	1.22104	41
20	.70891	1.41061	.73547	1.35968	.76272	1.31110	.79070	1.26471	.81946	1.22031	40
21	.70935	1.40974	.73592	1.35885	.76318	1.31031	.79117	1.26395	.81995	1.21959	39
22	.70979	1.40887	.73637	1.35802	.76364	1.30952	.79164	1.26319	.82044	1.21886	38
23	.71023	1.40800	.73681	1.35719	.76410	1.30873	.79212	1.26244	.82092	1.21814	37
24	.71066	1.40714	.73726	1.35637	.76456	1.30795	.79259	1.26169	.82141	1.21742	36
25	.71110	1.40627	.73771	1.35554	.76502	1.30716	.79306	1.26093	.82190	1.21670	35
26	.71154	1.40540	.73816	1.35472	.76548	1.30637	.79354	1.26018	.82238	1.21598	34
27	.71198	1.40454	.73861	1.35389	.76594	1.30558	.79401	1.25943	.82287	1.21526	33
28	.71242	1.40367	.73906	1.35307	.76640	1.30480	.79449	1.25867	.82336	1.21454	32
29	.71285	1.40281	.73951	1.35224	.76686	1.30401	.79496	1.25792	.82385	1.21382	31
30	.71329	1.40195	.73996	1.35142	.76733	1.30323	.79544	1.25717	.82434	1.21310	30
31	.71373	1.40109	.74041	1.35060	.76779	1.30244	.79591	1.25642	.82483	1.21238	29
32	.71417	1.40022	.74086	1.34978	.76825	1.30166	.79639	1.25567	.82531	1.21166	28
33	.71461	1.39936	.74131	1.34896	.76871	1.30087	.79686	1.25492	.82580	1.21094	27
34	.71505	1.39850	.74176	1.34814	.76918	1.30009	.79734	1.25417	.82629	1.21023	26
35	.71549	1.39764	.74221	1.34732	.76964	1.29931	.79781	1.25343	.82678	1.20951	25
36	.71593	1.39679	.74267	1.34650	.77010	1.29853	.79829	1.25268	.82727	1.20879	24
37	.71637	1.39593	.74312	1.34568	.77057	1.29775	.79877	1.25193	.82776	1.20808	23
38	.71681	1.39507	.74357	1.34487	.77103	1.29696	.79924	1.25118	.82825	1.20736	22
39	.71725	1.39421	.74402	1.34405	.77149	1.29618	.79972	1.25044	.82874	1.20665	21
40	.71769	1.39336	.74447	1.34323	.77196	1.29541	.80020	1.24969	.82923	1.20593	20
41	.71813	1.39250	.74492	1.34242	.77242	1.29463	.80067	1.24895	.82972	1.20522	19
42	.71857	1.39165	.74538	1.34160	.77289	1.29385	.80115	1.24820	.83022	1.20451	18
43	.71901	1.39079	.74583	1.34079	.77335	1.29307	.80163	1.24746	.83071	1.20379	17
44	.71946	1.38994	.74628	1.33998	.77382	1.29229	.80211	1.24672	.83120	1.20308	16
45	.71990	1.38909	.74674	1.33916	.77428	1.29152	.80258	1.24597	.83169	1.20237	15
46	.72034	1.38824	.74719	1.33835	.77475	1.29074	.80306	1.24523	.83218	1.20166	14
47	.72078	1.38738	.74764	1.33754	.77521	1.28997	.80354	1.24449	.83268	1.20095	13
48	.72122	1.38653	.74810	1.33673	.77568	1.28919	.80402	1.24375	.83317	1.20024	12
49	.72167	1.38568	.74855	1.33592	.77615	1.28842	.80450	1.24301	.83366	1.19953	11
50	.72211	1.38484	.74900	1.33511	.77661	1.28764	.80498	1.24227	.83415	1.19882	10
51	.72255	1.38399	.74946	1.33430	.77708	1.28687	.80546	1.24153	.83465	1.19811	9
52	.72299	1.38314	.74991	1.33349	.77754	1.28610	.80594	1.24079	.83514	1.19740	8
53	.72344	1.38229	.75037	1.33268	.77801	1.28533	.80642	1.24005	.83564	1.19669	7
54	.72388	1.38145	.75082	1.33187	.77848	1.28456	.80690	1.23931	.83613	1.19599	6
55	.72432	1.38060	.75128	1.33107	.77895	1.28379	.80738	1.23858	.83662	1.19528	5
56	.72477	1.37976	.75173	1.33026	.77941	1.28302	.80786	1.23784	.83712	1.19457	4
57	.72521	1.37891	.75219	1.32946	.77988	1.28225	.80834	1.23710	.83761	1.19387	3
58	.72565	1.37807	.75264	1.32865	.78035	1.28148	.80882	1.23637	.83811	1.19316	2
59	.72610	1.37722	.75310	1.32785	.78082	1.28071	.80930	1.23563	.83860	1.19246	1
60	.72654	1.37638	.75355	1.32704	.78129	1.27994	.80978	1.23490	.83910	1.19175	0
′	Cotang	Tang	Cotang	Tang	Cotang	Tang	Cotang	Tang	Cotang	Tang	′
	54°		53°		52°		51°		50°		

TABLE F

NATURAL TANGENTS AND COTANGENTS

′	40°		41°		42°		43°		44°		′
	Tang	Cotang	Tang	Cotang	Tang	Cotang	Tang	Cotang	Tang	Cotang	
0	.83910	1.19175	.86929	1.15037	.90040	1.11061	.93252	1.07237	.96569	1.03553	60
1	.83960	1.19105	.86980	1.14969	.90093	1.10996	.93306	1.07174	.96625	1.03493	59
2	.84009	1.19035	.87031	1.14902	.90146	1.10931	.93360	1.07112	.96681	1.03433	58
3	.84059	1.18964	.87082	1.14834	.90199	1.10867	.93415	1.07049	.96738	1.03372	57
4	.84108	1.18894	.87133	1.14767	.90251	1.10802	.93469	1.06987	.96794	1.03312	56
5	.84158	1.18824	.87184	1.14699	.90304	1.10737	.93524	1.06925	.96850	1.03252	55
6	.84208	1.18754	.87236	1.14632	.90357	1.10672	.93578	1.06862	.96907	1.03192	54
7	.84258	1.18684	.87287	1.14565	.90410	1.10607	.93633	1.06800	.96963	1.03132	53
8	.84307	1.18614	.87338	1.14498	.90463	1.10543	.93688	1.06738	.97020	1.03072	52
9	.84357	1.18544	.87389	1.14430	.90516	1.10478	.93742	1.06676	.97076	1.03012	51
10	.84407	1.18474	.87441	1.14363	.90569	1.10414	.93797	1.06613	.97133	1.02952	50
11	.84457	1.18404	.87492	1.14296	.90621	1.10349	.93852	1.06551	.97189	1.02892	49
12	.84507	1.18334	.87543	1.14229	.90674	1.10285	.93906	1.06489	.97246	1.02832	48
13	.84556	1.18264	.87595	1.14162	.90727	1.10220	.93961	1.06427	.97302	1.02772	47
14	.84606	1.18194	.87646	1.14095	.90781	1.10156	.94016	1.06365	.97359	1.02713	46
15	.84656	1.18125	.87698	1.14028	.90834	1.10091	.94071	1.06303	.97416	1.02653	45
16	.84706	1.18055	.87749	1.13961	.90887	1.10027	.94125	1.06241	.97472	1.02593	44
17	.84756	1.17986	.87801	1.13894	.90940	1.09963	.94180	1.06179	.97529	1.02533	43
18	.84806	1.17916	.87852	1.13828	.90993	1.09899	.94235	1.06117	.97586	1.02474	42
19	.84856	1.17846	.87904	1.13761	.91046	1.09834	.94290	1.06056	.97643	1.02414	41
20	.84906	1.17777	.87955	1.13694	.91099	1.09770	.94345	1.05994	.97700	1.02355	40
21	.84956	1.17708	.88007	1.13627	.91153	1.09706	.94400	1.05932	.97756	1.02295	39
22	.85006	1.17638	.88059	1.13561	.91206	1.09642	.94455	1.05870	.97813	1.02236	38
23	.85057	1.17569	.88110	1.13494	.91259	1.09578	.94510	1.05809	.97870	1.02176	37
24	.85107	1.17500	.88162	1.13428	.91313	1.09514	.94565	1.05747	.97927	1.02117	36
25	.85157	1.17430	.88214	1.13361	.91366	1.09450	.94620	1.05685	.97984	1.02057	35
26	.85207	1.17361	.88265	1.13295	.91419	1.09386	.94676	1.05624	.98041	1.01998	34
27	.85257	1.17292	.88317	1.13228	.91473	1.09322	.94731	1.05562	.98098	1.01939	33
28	.85308	1.17223	.88369	1.13162	.91526	1.09258	.94786	1.05501	.98155	1.01879	32
29	.85358	1.17154	.88421	1.13096	.91580	1.09195	.94841	1.05439	.98213	1.01820	31
30	.85408	1.17085	.88473	1.13029	.91633	1.09131	.94896	1.05378	.98270	1.01761	30
31	.85458	1.17016	.88524	1.12963	.91687	1.09067	.94952	1.05317	.98327	1.01702	29
32	.85509	1.16947	.88576	1.12897	.91740	1.09003	.95007	1.05255	.98384	1.01642	28
33	.85559	1.16878	.88628	1.12831	.91794	1.08940	.95062	1.05194	.98441	1.01583	27
34	.85609	1.16809	.88680	1.12765	.91847	1.08876	.95118	1.05133	.98499	1.01524	26
35	.85660	1.16741	.88732	1.12699	.91901	1.08813	.95173	1.05072	.98556	1.01465	25
36	.85710	1.16672	.88784	1.12633	.91955	1.08749	.95229	1.05010	.98613	1.01406	24
37	.85761	1.16603	.88836	1.12567	.92008	1.08686	.95284	1.04949	.98671	1.01347	23
38	.85811	1.16535	.88888	1.12501	.92062	1.08622	.95340	1.04888	.98728	1.01288	22
39	.85862	1.16466	.88940	1.12435	.92116	1.08559	.95395	1.04827	.98786	1.01229	21
40	.85912	1.16398	.88992	1.12369	.92170	1.08496	.95451	1.04766	.98843	1.01170	20
41	.85963	1.16329	.89045	1.12303	.92224	1.08432	.95506	1.04705	.98901	1.01112	19
42	.86014	1.16261	.89097	1.12238	.92277	1.08369	.95562	1.04644	.98958	1.01053	18
43	.86064	1.16192	.89149	1.12172	.92331	1.08306	.95618	1.04583	.99016	1.00994	17
44	.86115	1.16124	.89201	1.12106	.92385	1.08243	.95673	1.04522	.99073	1.00935	16
45	.86166	1.16056	.89253	1.12041	.92439	1.08179	.95729	1.04461	.99131	1.00876	15
46	.86216	1.15987	.89306	1.11975	.92493	1.08116	.95785	1.04401	.99189	1.00818	14
47	.86267	1.15919	.89358	1.11909	.92547	1.08053	.95841	1.04340	.99247	1.00759	13
48	.86318	1.15851	.89410	1.11844	.92601	1.07990	.95897	1.04279	.99304	1.00701	12
49	.86368	1.15783	.89463	1.11778	.92655	1.07927	.95952	1.04218	.99362	1.00642	11
50	.86419	1.15715	.89515	1.11713	.92709	1.07864	.96008	1.04158	.99420	1.00583	10
51	.86470	1.15647	.89567	1.11648	.92763	1.07801	.96064	1.04097	.99478	1.00525	9
52	.86521	1.15579	.89620	1.11582	.92817	1.07738	.96120	1.04036	.99536	1.00467	8
53	.86572	1.15511	.89672	1.11517	.92872	1.07676	.96176	1.03976	.99594	1.00408	7
54	.86623	1.15443	.89725	1.11452	.92926	1.07613	.96232	1.03915	.99652	1.00350	6
55	.86674	1.15375	.89777	1.11387	.92980	1.07550	.96288	1.03855	.99710	1.00291	5
56	.86725	1.15308	.89830	1.11321	.93034	1.07487	.96344	1.03794	.99768	1.00233	4
57	.86776	1.15240	.89883	1.11256	.93088	1.07425	.96400	1.03734	.99826	1.00175	3
58	.86827	1.15172	.89935	1.11191	.93143	1.07362	.96457	1.03674	.99884	1.00116	2
59	.86878	1.15104	.89988	1.11126	.93197	1.07299	.96513	1.03613	.99942	1.00058	1
60	.86929	1.15037	.90040	1.11061	.93252	1.07237	.96569	1.03553	1.00000	1.00000	0
′	Cotang	Tang	Cotang	Tang	Cotang	Tang	Cotang	Tang	Cotang	Tang	′
	49°		48°		47°		46°		45°		

Lengths of Circular Arcs for Radius = 1

Deg.	Length	Deg.	Length	Min.	Length	Sec.	Length
1	0.017 45 329	61	1.064 65 084	1	.000 29 089	1	.000 00 485
2	.034 90 659	62	.082 10 414	2	0 58 178	2	00 970
3	.052 35 988	63	.099 55 743	3	0 87 266	3	01 454
4	.069 81 317	64	.117 01 072	4	1 16 355	4	01 939
5	0.087 26 646	65	1.134 46 401	5	.001 45 444	5	.000 02 424
6	.104 71 976	66	.151 91 731	6	1 74 533	6	02 909
7	.122 17 305	67	.169 37 060	7	2 03 622	7	03 394
8	.139 62 634	68	.186 82 389	8	2 32 711	8	03 879
9	.157 07 963	69	.204 27 718	9	2 61 799	9	04 363
10	0.174 53 293	70	1.221 73 048	10	.002 90 888	10	.000 04 848
11	.191 98 622	71	.239 18 377	11	3 19 977	11	05 333
12	.209 43 951	72	.256 63 706	12	3 49 066	12	05 818
13	.226 89 280	73	.274 09 035	13	3 78 155	13	06 303
14	.244 34 610	74	.291 54 365	14	4 07 243	14	06 787
15	0.261 79 939	75	1.308 99 694	15	.004 36 332	15	.000 07 272
16	.279 25 268	76	.326 45 023	16	4 65 421	16	07 757
17	.296 70 597	77	.343 90 352	17	4 94 510	17	08 242
18	.314 15 927	78	.361 35 682	18	5 23 599	18	08 727
19	.331 61 256	79	.378 81 011	19	5 52 688	19	09 211
20	0.349 06 585	80	1.396 26 340	20	.005 81 776	20	.000 09 696
21	.366 51 914	81	.413 71 669	21	6 10 865	21	10 181
22	.383 97 244	82	.431 16 999	22	6 39 954	22	10 666
23	.401 42 573	83	.448 62 328	23	6 69 043	23	11 151
24	.418 87 902	84	.466 07 657	24	6 98 132	24	11 636
25	0.436 33 231	85	1.483 52 986	25	.007 27 221	25	.000 12 120
26	.453 78 561	86	.500 98 316	26	7 56 309	26	12 605
27	.471 23 890	87	.518 43 645	27	7 85 398	27	13 090
28	.488 69 219	88	.535 88 974	28	8 14 487	28	13 575
29	.506 14 548	89	.553 34 303	29	8 43 576	29	14 060
30	0.523 59 878	90	1.570 79 633	30	.008 72 665	30	.000 14 544
31	.541 05 207	91	.588 24 962	31	9 01 753	31	15 029
32	.558 50 536	92	.605 70 291	32	9 30 842	32	15 514
33	.575 95 865	93	.623 15 620	33	9 59 931	33	15 999
34	.593 41 195	94	.640 60 950	34	9 89 020	34	16 484
35	0.610 86 524	95	1.658 06 279	35	.010 18 109	35	.000 16 969
36	.628 31 853	96	.675 51 608	36	10 47 198	36	17 453
37	.645 77 182	97	.692 96 937	37	10 76 286	37	17 938
38	.663 22 512	98	.710 42 267	38	11 05 375	38	18 423
39	.680 67 841	99	.727 87 596	39	11 34 464	39	18 908
40	0.698 13 170	100	1.745 32 925	40	.011 63 553	40	.000 19 393
41	.715 58 499	101	.762 78 254	41	11 92 642	41	19 877
42	.733 03 829	102	.780 23 584	42	12 21 730	42	20 362
43	.750 49 158	103	.797 68 913	43	12 50 819	43	20 847
44	.767 94 487	104	.815 14 242	44	12 79 908	44	21 332
45	0.785 39 816	105	1.832 59 571	45	.013 08 997	45	.000 21 817
46	.802 85 146	106	.850 04 901	46	13 38 086	46	22 301
47	.820 30 475	107	.867 50 230	47	13 67 175	47	22 786
48	.837 75 804	108	.884 95 559	48	13 96 263	48	23 271
49	.855 21 133	109	.902 40 888	49	14 25 352	49	23 756
50	0.872 66 463	110	1.919 86 218	50	.014 54 441	50	.000 24 241
51	.890 11 792	111	.937 31 547	51	14 83 530	51	24 726
52	.907 57 121	112	.954 76 876	52	15 12 619	52	25 210
53	.925 02 450	113	.972 22 205	53	15 41 708	53	25 695
54	.942 47 780	114	.989 67 535	54	15 70 796	54	26 180
55	0.959 93 109	115	2.007 12 864	55	.015 99 885	55	.000 26 665
56	.977 38 438	116	.024 58 193	56	16 28 974	56	27 150
57	0.994 83 767	117	.042 03 522	57	16 58 063	57	27 634
58	1.012 29 097	118	.059 48 852	58	16 87 152	58	28 119
59	1.029 74 426	119	.076 94 181	59	17 16 240	59	28 604
60	1.047 19 755	120	.094 39 510	60	17 45 329	60	29 089

Trigonometric Formulas for the Solution of Right Triangles

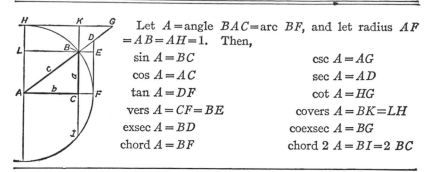

Let A = angle BAC = arc BF, and let radius AF = AB = AH = 1. Then,

$\sin A = BC$	$\csc A = AG$
$\cos A = AC$	$\sec A = AD$
$\tan A = DF$	$\cot A = HG$
$\text{vers } A = CF = BE$	$\text{covers } A = BK = LH$
$\text{exsec } A = BD$	$\text{coexsec } A = BG$
$\text{chord } A = BF$	$\text{chord } 2\,A = BI = 2\,BC$

In the right-angled triangle ABC, let $AB = c$, $BC = a$, $CA = b$. Then,

1. $\sin A = \dfrac{a}{c}$

2. $\cos A = \dfrac{b}{c}$

3. $\tan A = \dfrac{a}{b}$

4. $\cot A = \dfrac{b}{a}$

5. $\sec A = \dfrac{c}{b}$

6. $\csc A = \dfrac{c}{a}$

7. $\text{vers } A = 1 - \cos A = \dfrac{c-b}{c} = \text{covers } B$

8. $\text{exsec } A = \sec A - 1 = \dfrac{c-b}{b} = \text{coexsec } B$

9. $\text{covers } A = \dfrac{c-a}{c} = \text{vers } B$

10. $\text{coexsec } A = \dfrac{c-a}{a} = \text{exsec } B$

11. $a = c \sin A = b \tan A$

12. $b = c \cos A = a \cot A$

13. $c = \dfrac{a}{\sin A} = \dfrac{b}{\cos A}$

14. $a = c \cos B = b \cot B$

15. $b = c \sin B = a \tan B$

16. $c = \dfrac{a}{\cos B} = \dfrac{b}{\sin B}$

17. $a = \sqrt{c^2 - b^2} = \sqrt{(c-b)(c+b)}$

18. $b = \sqrt{c^2 - a^2} = \sqrt{(c-a)(c+a)}$

19. $c = \sqrt{a^2 + b^2}$

20. $C = 90° = A + B$

21. Area $= \frac{1}{2}ab$

TABLE I 743

TRIGONOMETRIC FORMULAS FOR THE SOLUTION OF OBLIQUE TRIANGLES

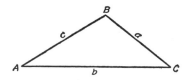

No.	Given	Sought	Formula
22	A, B, a	C, b, c	$C = 180° - (A+B)$
			$b = \dfrac{a}{\sin A} \times \sin B$
			$c = \dfrac{a}{\sin A} \times \sin(A+B) = \dfrac{a}{\sin A} \times \sin C$
		Area	$\text{Area} = \tfrac{1}{2}ab \sin C = \dfrac{a^2 \sin B \sin C}{2 \sin A}$
23	A, a, b	B, C, c	$\sin B = \dfrac{\sin A}{a} \times b$
			$C = 180° - (A+B)$
			$c = \dfrac{a}{\sin A} \times \sin C$
		Area	$\text{Area} = \tfrac{1}{2}ab \sin C$
24	$C, a, b,$	c	$c = \sqrt{a^2 + b^2 - 2ab \cos C}$
25		$\tfrac{1}{2}(A+B)$	$\tfrac{1}{2}(A+B) = 90° - \tfrac{1}{2}C$
26		$\tfrac{1}{2}(A-B)$	$\tan \tfrac{1}{2}(A-B) = \dfrac{a-b}{a+b} \times \tan \tfrac{1}{2}(A+B)$
27		A, B	$A = \tfrac{1}{2}(A+B) + \tfrac{1}{2}(A-B)$
			$B = \tfrac{1}{2}(A+B) - \tfrac{1}{2}(A-B)$
28		c	$c = (a+b) \times \dfrac{\cos \tfrac{1}{2}(A+B)}{\cos \tfrac{1}{2}(A-B)} = (a-b) \times \dfrac{\sin \tfrac{1}{2}(A+B)}{\sin \tfrac{1}{2}(A-B)}$
29		Area	$\text{Area} = \tfrac{1}{2}ab \sin C$
30	a, b, c	A	$\text{Let } s = \dfrac{a+b+c}{2}.$
31			$\sin \tfrac{1}{2}A = \sqrt{\dfrac{(s-b)(s-c)}{bc}}$
			$\cos \tfrac{1}{2}A = \sqrt{\dfrac{s(s-a)}{bc}}$
			$\tan \tfrac{1}{2}A = \sqrt{\dfrac{(s-b)(s-c)}{s(s-a)}}$
32			$\sin A = \dfrac{2\sqrt{s(s-a)(s-b)(s-c)}}{bc}$
			$\cos A = \dfrac{b^2 + c^2 - a^2}{2bc}$
33		Area	$\text{Area} = \sqrt{s(s-a)(s-b)(s-c)}$

Index